ANNUAL REVIEW OF PHYSIOLOGY

EDITORIAL COMMITTEE (1987)

Responsible for the organization of Volume 49
(Editorial Committee, 1985)

ANNUAL REVIEW OF PHYSIOLOGY

VOLUME 49, 1987

ROBERT M. BERNE, *Editor*

University of Virginia Medical School

JOSEPH F. HOFFMAN, *Associate Editor*

Yale University School of Medicine

ANNUAL REVIEWS INC.   4139 EL CAMINO WAY   P.O. BOX 10139   PALO ALTO, CALIFORNIA 94306

⅍ ANNUAL REVIEWS INC.
Palo Alto, California, USA

International Standard Serial Number: 0066–4278
International Standard Book Number: 0–8243–0349–0
Library of Congress Catalog Card Number: 39–15404

Typesetting by Kachina Typesetting Inc., Tempe, Arizona; John Olson, President
Typesetting coordinator, Janis Hoffman

PRINTED AND BOUND IN THE UNITED STATES OF AMERICA

Annual Review of Physiology
Volume 49, 1987

CONTENTS

PREFATORY CHAPTER

A Silver Spoon, *J. R. Pappenheimer*   1

GASTROINTESTINAL PHYSIOLOGY

Introduction, *John G. Forte, Section Editor*   17

Regulation of Intracellular pH in the Stomach, *Terry
E. Machen and Anthony M. Paradiso*   19

Role of H^+ and HCO_3^- in Salt Transport in Gallbladder
Epithelium, *Luis Reuss and James S. Stoddard*   35

Proton and Bicarbonate Transport Mechanisms in the
Intestine, *Ulrich Hopfer and Carole M. Liedtke*   51

Proton Transport by Hepatocyte Organelles and Isolated
Membrane Vesicles, *Bruce F. Scharschmidt and
Rebecca W. Van Dyke*   69

Role of Proton and Bicarbonate Transport in Pancreatic
Cell Function, *Gemma A. J. Kuijpers and Jan Joep
H. H. M. De Pont*   87

COMPARATIVE PHYSIOLOGY

Introduction, *Fred N. White, Section Editor*   105

Scaling Energetics of Homeothermic Vertebrates: An
Operational Allometry, *William A. Calder III*   107

What Does the Power Function Reveal About Structure and
Function in Animals of Different Size?, *A. A. Heusner*   121

Structural and Functional Limits to Oxidative Metabolism:
Insights from Scaling, *C. Richard Taylor*   135

Scaling of Structural and Functional Variables in the
Respiratory System, *Ewald R. Weibel*   147

(continued)   v

CELL AND MOLECULAR PHYSIOLOGY

Introduction, *Joseph F. Hoffman, Section Editor*   161

Lateral Diffusion of Proteins in Membranes, *Ken Jacobson, Akira Ishihara, and Richard Inman*   163

Red Cell Deformability and Its Relevance to Blood Flow, *Shu Chien*   177

Intracellular Lipid Transport in Eukaryotes, *Richard G. Sleight*   193

Erythrocyte Membrane Elasticity and Viscosity, *R. M. Hochmuth and R. E. Waugh*   209

Lipid Modulation of Transport Proteins in Vertebrate Cell Membranes, *B. Deuticke and C. W. M. Haest*   221

Red Cell Biochemical Anatomy and Membrane Properties, *Joel Anne Chasis and Stephen B. Shohet*   237

RENAL AND ELECTROLYTE PHYSIOLOGY

Introduction, *Carl W. Gottschalk, Section Editor*   249

The Tubuloglomerular Feedback Mechanism: Functional and Biochemical Aspects, *Josephine P. Briggs and Jurgen Schnermann*   251

Calcium as a Mediator of Tubuloglomerular Feedback, *P. Darwin Bell, Martha Franco, and L. G. Navar*   275

Altered Reactivity of Tubuloglomerular Feedback, *William J. Arendshorst*   295

ENDOCRINOLOGY

Introduction, *Jack L. Kostyo, Section Editor*   319

Thyroid Hormones and Brain Development, *Jean H. Dussault and Jean Ruel*   321

Insulin in the Brain, *Denis G. Baskin, Dianne P. Figlewicz, Stephen C. Woods, Daniel Porte, Jr., and Daniel M. Dorsa*   335

Sex Steroids and Afferent Input: Their Roles in Brain Sexual Differentiation, *Carlos Beyer and Harvey H. Feder*   349

Central Actions of Ovarian Steroids in the Feedback Regulation of Pulsatile Secretion of Luteinizing Hormone, *Fred J. Karsch*   365

Gastroenteropancreatic Peptides and the Central Nervous System, *Dianne P. Figlewicz, Francoise Lacour, Alfred Sipols, Daniel Porte, Jr., and Stephen C. Woods*   383

Adrenocortical Steroids and the Brain, *J. W. Funder and K. Sheppard*   397

Functions of Angiotensin in the Central Nervous System, *M. Ian Phillips*   413

CARDIOVASCULAR PHYSIOLOGY

Introduction, *Harvey V. Sparks, Jr., Section Editor*   437

Microcirculatory Adaptation to Skeletal Muscle Transplantation, *Harold W. Burton, Bruce M. Carlson, and John A. Faulkner*   439

Mechanisms of Angiogenesis, *Patricia A. D'Amore and Robert W. Thompson*   453

Cardiovascular Responses to Chronic Hypoxia, *Natalio Banchero*   465

Coronary Vascular Adaptations to Myocardial Hypertrophy, *William M. Chilian and Melvin L. Marcus*   477

Vascular Smooth Muscle Adaptation to Increased Load, *C. L. Seidel and L. A. Schildmeyer*   489

Cardiocyte Adaptation to Chronically Altered Load, *George Cooper, IV*   501

Cardiac Muscle Changes in Senescence, *Edward G. Lakatta*   519

Biochemical Mechanisms of Cardiac Hypertrophy, *H. E. Morgan, E. E. Gordon, Y. Kira, B. H. L. Chua, L. A. Russo, C. J. Peterson, P. J. McDermott, and P. A. Watson*   533

Chronic Adaptations in Contractile Proteins: Genetic Regulation, *Eugene Morkin*   545

RESPIRATORY PHYSIOLOGY

Introduction, *Robert E. Forster, II, Section Editor*   555

Polypeptide-Containing Neurons in Airway Smooth Muscle, *J. M. Lundberg and A. Saria*   557

Peripheral Airway Ganglia, *Ronald F. Coburn*   573

Innervation of Airway Smooth Muscle: Fine Structure, *Giorgio Gabella*   583

Organization of Central Control of Airways, *Madhu P. Kalia*   595

Nervous Receptors of the Tracheobronchial Tree, *Giuseppe Sant'Ambrogio*   611

SPECIAL TOPIC: MOLECULAR MECHANISM OF MUSCLE CONTRACTION

General Introduction, *Y. E. Goldman, Section Editor,
and B. Brenner*   629

Kinetics of the Actomyosin ATPase in Muscle Fibers,
Yale E. Goldman   637

Mechanical and Structural Approaches to Correlation of
Cross-Bridge Action in Muscle with Actomyosin
ATPase in Solution, *Bernhard Brenner*   655

Muscle Enthalpy Production and Its Relationship to
Actomyosin ATPase, *Earl Homsher*   673

Spectroscopic Probes of Muscle Cross-Bridge Rotation,
David D. Thomas   691

SPECIAL TOPIC: PHOTOTRANSDUCTION IN VERTEBRATES

General Introduction, *E. N. Pugh, Jr. and
William H. Miller, Section Editors*   711

The Nature and Identity of the Internal Excitational
Transmitter of Vertebrate Phototransduction,
E. N. Pugh, Jr.   715

Ionic Conductances in Rod Photoreceptors, *W.
Geoffrey Owen*   743

The Molecular Mechanism of Visual Excitation and
Its Relation to the Structure and Composition of
the Rod Outer Segment, *Paul A. Liebman, Kenton R.
Parker, and Edward A. Dratz*   765

Molecular Properties of the cGMP Cascade of Vertebrate
Photoreceptors, *James B. Hurley*   793

INDEXES

Subject Index   813

Cumulative Index of Contributing Authors, Volumes 45–49   829

Cumulative Index of Chapter Titles, Volumes 45–49   832

OTHER REVIEWS OF INTEREST TO PHYSIOLOGISTS

From the *Annual Review of Biochemistry*, Volume 56 (1987):

Inositol Trisphosphate and Diacylglycerol: Two Interacting Second Messangers,
M. J. Berridge
Intracellular Calcium Homeostasis, E. Carafoli
The Nucleus: Structure, Function, and Dynamics, J. W. Newport and D. J. Forbes
Interferons and Their Actions, S. Pestka, J. A. Langer, K. C. Zoon, and C. E.
Samuel
G Proteins: Transducers of Receptor-Generated Signals, A. G. Gilman
Receptors for Epidermal Growth Factor and Other Polypeptide Mitogens, G.
Carpenter

From the *Annual Review of Medicine*, Volume 38 (1987):

Platelet-Derived Growth Factor, R. Ross
The Biochemistry and Pathophysiology of the Prethrombotic State, R. D. Rosen-
berg
Endogenous Digitalis-Like Natriuretic Factors, S. W. Graves and G. H. Williams
Clinical Perspectives on Neuropeptides, D. A. Lewis and F. E. Bloom

From the *Annual Review of Neuroscience*, Volume 10 (1987):

*An Integrated View of the Molecular Toxinology of Sodium Channel Gating in
Excitable Cells,* G. Strichartz, T. Rando, and G.-K. Wang
Molecular Properties of the Muscarinic Acetylcholine Receptor, N. M. Nathanson
Calcium Action in Synaptic Transmitter Release, G. J. Augustine, M. P. Charlton,
and S. J Smith
Extrathalamic Modulation of Cortical Function, S. L. Foote and J. H. Morrison
*Visual Motion Processing and Sensory-Motor Intergration for Smooth Pursuit Eye
Movements,* S. G. Lisberger, E. J. Morris, and L. Tychsen
Visual Processing in Monkey Extrastriate Cortex, J. H. R. Maunsell and W. T.
Newsome
*The Analysis of Visual Motion: From Computational Theory to Neuronal Mech-
anisms,* E. C. Hildreth and C. Koch
The Organization and Function of the Vomeronasal System, M. Halpern
Gustatory Neural Processing in the Hindbrain, J. B. Travers, S. P. Travers, and R.
Norgren
Molecular Biology of Visual Pigments, J. Nathans

Developmental Regulation of Nicotinic Acetylcholine Receptors, S. M. Schuetze and L. W. Role

The Neurobiology of Fever: Thoughts on Recent Developments, K. E. Cooper

Molecular Mechanisms for Memory: Second-Messenger Induced Modifications of Protein Kinases in Neurons, J. H. Schwartz and S. M. Greenberg

From the *Annual Review of Pharmacology and Toxicology*, Volume 27 (1987):

Calcium Channel Ligands, D. J. Triggle and R. A. Janis

Acetylcholine and the Regulation of REM Sleep: Basic Mechanisms and Clinical Implications of Affective Illness and Narcolepsy, P. J. Shiromani, J. C. Gillin, and S. J. Henriksen

Cotransmission, G. Campbell

Inhibin, C. H. Li and K. Ramasharma

Purine Receptors in Mammalian Tissues: Pharmacology and Functional Significance, M. Williams

Statistical Methods and the Applications of Bioassay, E. M. Laska and M. J. Meisner

Metabolism of Alpha- and Beta-Adrenergic Receptors: In Vivo and In Vitro, L. C. Mahan, R. M. McKernan, and P. A. Insel

Platelet-Activating Factor Antagonists, R. N. Saunders and D. A. Handley

Prostaglandins, Leukotrienes, and Platelet-Activating Factor in Shock, G. Feuerstein and J. M. Hallenbeck

For the convenience of readers, a detachable order form/envelope is bound into the back of this volume.

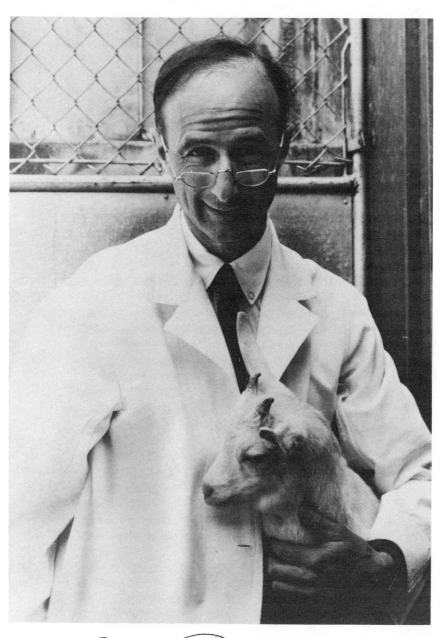

John Papenheimer

Ann. Rev. Physiol. 1987. 49:1–15

A SILVER SPOON

J. R. Pappenheimer

Department of Physiology and Biophysics, Harvard Medical School, 25 Shattuck Street, Boston, Massachusetts 02115

An invitation to write the prefatory chapter for the *Annual Review of Physiology* provokes mixed feelings. There is no question as to the honor it confers; a glance at the list of previous invitees attests to that. On the other hand, it signals the unwanted passage of time, and it implies that the invitee, after 50 years of physiology, should have profound and useful things to say about the past and future. Alas, I must confess at the outset that the pearls of wisdom within my shell have been slow to mature, and they are still too small to spread before the sophisticated readers of this *Annual Reviews* volume. I can only use them as decorations for a personal narrative.

PRELUDE

I was born in 1915 in New York City. My father, Alwin M. Pappenheimer, Sr., was Professor of Pathology at Columbia University and one of the leading experimental pathologists of his day. He came from a well-to-do family and had every opportunity to make use of his natural talents for both science and the art of living. The summers of his youth were spent travelling in Europe, and he spoke French and German fluently. He made many drawings, etchings, and paintings, and he played the violin and viola well enough to participate in most of the classical literature of chamber music. I grew up with the sound of string quartets in the living room. My mother had a similar background, and she too was proficient in languages and music. My elder brother, who later became Professor of Biology and Master of Dunster House at Harvard, already played the violin well at the time I was started on the cello in 1922. On several occasions my scientific career has been influenced indirectly, but importantly, by music.

1

0066-4278/87/0315-0001$02.00

My father loved his work, and the excitement of his research permeated our family life. Students and colleagues from many parts of the world came to visit, and as far back as I can remember our conversations at home included science. Sometimes I was taken to the lab to share the excitement firsthand and listen to scientific palaver over a sandwich lunch with my father's colleagues. Much of the vocabulary of biology was mine by the time I was twelve years old, and about this time, my father began taking me to meetings, including Harvey Lectures at the Academy and evening joint sessions of FASEB when they were in New York. We went to these lectures in the same spirit as we went to concerts. My father often complained ruefully that he did not know enough chemistry and physics to solve his research problems, and perhaps it was for this reason that I inclined towards physiology, which depends so heavily on the exact sciences.

On sabbatical years my father travelled extensively in Europe, Russia, and the Far East. I began my schooling at the École Alsacienne in Paris in 1921. Classes were from 8:30 to 4:30 with daily homework as well. The pace was faster than in America, and on returning home I skipped one and one-half grades at our local elementary school in Scarsdale. Later I was sent to the Lincoln School in New York City, one of the leading progressive schools of its period. I entered Harvard at 16, intellectually prepared but too young to enjoy fully the broad educational and social opportunities Harvard had to offer. My father was a devoted Harvard man, and it did not occur to any of his children to apply elsewhere. It was 1932 and we, the freshmen, were observers of the Great Depression, but few of us were a part of it. Harvard had yet to reach out for the best and brightest, and we took for granted a Certificate of Admission and full financial support from our parents. To paraphrase T. S. Eliot (3):

> We came this way, taking the route we were
>   most likely to take
> From the place we would most likely come from . . .
> Either we had no purpose or the purpose was
>   beyond the end we had figured and was
>   altered in fulfillment.

I concentrated heavily in science but did not do particularly well in formal courses and in the end failed to obtain honors. My tutor was Jeffries Wyman, Jr., who introduced me to quantitative biology in general and to the physical chemistry of proteins and amino acids in particular. In the parlance of the 1980s, Wyman would be considered a molecular biologist, and indeed, his contributions to the mechanism of the Bohr effect and the general theory of allosteric reactions of proteins are cornerstones in modern theory of protein function (27). I was in awe of his command of thermodynamics and mathematics. Our joint work on the surface tension of solutions of dipolar ions was published in the *Journal of the American Chemical Society* (23) in 1936. Jeffries (though of course I did not then address him so) wrote the first draft and gave it to me for criticism. I rewrote some of it, added a whole new section, and handed back the manuscript in fear and trepidation. He studied the changes and without hesitation or emotion said, "It is much improved, but now you must be the senior author." Not long ago I was flattered on two counts when a well-known biophysicist in England asked me whether my father had written this enduring paper.

In the summer of 1935 I took the Physiology course at Woods Hole under the direction of Laurence Irving. Our instructors included such distinguished biophysical chemists as Leonor Michaelis and Rudolf Höber; the latter taught me how to prefuse frog kidneys via the portal system and how to cannulate a frog's ureter. Later, the 1945 edition of Höber's *Physical Chemistry of Cells and Tissues* became one of the most well-worn books in my scientific library. At the end of the course, I was awarded the Collecting Net Prize ($50 was a lot in those days) to come back the next summer to work on the kinetics of CO_2 transport and carbamino formation in fish blood with J. K. W. Ferguson, who had just published important work with Roughton on carbamino hemoglobin in human blood. We did not find carbamino hemoglobin in fish bood, but we did find an anomalous distribution of HCO_3^- and Cl^- in elasmobranch red cells and duly published in the *Biological Bulletin* (5).

ROOTS IN ENGLAND

In the autumn of 1936 I sailed for England with a letter of introduction to Sir Joseph Barcroft from Jeffries Wyman. An aunt had left me a legacy of about $2000 a year, and this was more than sufficient to support a research student in pre-war England. What would I have done without it? I arrived in Cambridge not yet 21 but eager to begin work in the laboratory. I learned, however, that Sir Joseph was in the United States and would not return until October. I spent the next few weeks practicing the cello and reading old Norse poetry in the University library. When Sir Joseph returned, he was extremely kind to me, perhaps because he was fond of my brother-in-law, Will Forbes, who had worked with him ten years previously. He gave me a small research project on fetal red cells and arranged for me to take the Part II honors course in Physiology, an experience for which I am endlessly grateful. I was dreadfully self-conscious, and I admired Sir Joseph so much that I could scarcely speak in his presence. He seemed to sense this and made a point of sitting next to me at laboratory teas and trying to put me at ease by telling funny stories and anecdotes. There were eight Part II students, selected from some 300 who had taken Part I. Our instructors included E. D. Adrian, B. H. C. Matthews, F. R. Winton, E. B. Verney, W. A. H. Rushton, and F. J. W.

Roughton, and I developed life-long associations with all of them. Alan Hodgkin was a teaching assistant in the practical class; his job was to come in early in the morning to decerebrate cats for our class experiments. There were five lectures a week for three full terms, and each lecture involved analysis of significant papers in the field. We came to know the important literature in almost every aspect of physiology and in three languages. During the spring term I was introduced to F. R. Winton's experiments on isolated perfused mammalian kidneys, and this opened the door to a new world for me.

Winton was then Reader in Physiology at Cambridge and the author, with L. E. Bayliss, of a widely used elementary textbook of physiology. He had trained at University College, London, under Starling, W. M. Bayliss, Verney, Lovatt Evans, and A. V. Hill. Sir William Bayliss's "Principles of General Physiology" represented for me (and still does) the essence of all that is good in physiology, but I thought of Bayliss as someone who had lived long ago. It was amazing and thrilling for me to talk with someone who had been a close friend of both Starling and Bayliss. In Winton's hands the original Starling-Verney heart-lung preparation developed into a sophisticated technique for perfusing isolated organs from a pump-lung circulation; it was the forerunner of modern artificial heart and life-support systems. I was spellbound by the sight of an isolated dog kidney sitting on a glass plate and producing clear golden urine from thick red blood.

Winton was an expert with instrumentation, and he designed most of his own transducers, amplifiers, recording oscillographs, etc. The perfusion apparatus was itself a complex, inorganic organism—a maze of motors, plumbing, and electrical devices for measuring, recording, and controlling flows, pressures, temperatures, ion concentrations, and blood oxygen saturation. All of this appealed enormously to my scientific senses; it seemed to me to be the ideal compromise between in vitro research and the unsatisfying complexities of whole animal research. I was swayed, also, by the fact that Winton was a fine cellist and his wife, Bessie Rawlins, was one of the foremost concert violinists in England. They invited me home to play second cello in the great Schubert C major quintet (Opus 163), and this settled matters for me. I had been brought up with the Schubert but never had I played it with such accomplished musicians. Winton, together with Grace Eggleton (later to become Mrs. Leonard Bayliss), was about to start an investigation of renal oxygen consumption as a function of osmotic work of urine formation. He welcomed me as a graduate student, possibly because of my previous training in physical chemistry and blood-gas transport; or was it because of my interest in string quartets? Two foreign postdoctoral fellows were working with Winton at this time: Jim Shannon (later Director of NIH) was there to compare inulin with creatinine clearances in the isolated kidney, and Kurt Kramer from Göttingen was there to develop, with Winton and

Glenn Millikan, a spectrophotometric device for continuous recording of arteriovenous oxygen differences in flowing blood. It must be remembered that in 1936 solid-state photocells were in their infancy, and the success of this project depended on the spectral characteristics of a prototype selenium barrier cell made only in Germany. Five years later Kurt Kramer in Germany and Glenn Millikan and I in the United States used this experience to develop the ear oximeter (15). In the meantime, Winton, Eggleton, and I produced a series of papers on the mechanisms of urine formation in perfused kidneys. It was the start of a close personal relationship, which lasted until Frank Winton's death in 1985. Winton's ingenious techniques for estimating renal glomerular pressure (2, 26) provided the basis for my own first contributions to capillary physiology a decade later.

In this period, also, I came to enjoy student life in Cambridge. I played in the University Orchestra and took part in activities at Clare College. On a dark, cold winter's night we (the University Orchestra with soloists from London) performed Verdi's Requiem in King's Chapel, the most beautiful setting imaginable for this gorgeous music. William and Marjorie Rushton also played in the orchestra, and through them, I was invited to Music Camp in the Berkshire Downs. This, too, opened the way for life-long friendships. I was an avid skier and spent memorable winter holidays in the Alps and in the rugged Jotunheimen of central Norway. At Finse I raced in the downhill (Class C), coming in 89th in a field of 115 entrants. I was the only foreigner, as was duly noted by the Oslo and Bergen newspapers.

In 1938 Winton moved to the Chair of Pharmacology at University College, and he took me with him as research student on leave from Cambridge. Hermann Rein, one of the most prominent physiologists in Germany (and Kurt Kramer's chief), had just published a paper alleging that metabolism of resting muscle was regulated by the sympathetic nervous system. Winton suggested that I look into this in perfused hindlimb preparations, utilizing the methods for recording blood oxygen we had used for studies of renal metabolism. I was able to confirm Rein's surprising results, but I found a much simpler explanation for them that was based on sympathetic control of the microcirculation rather than on metabolism (17). This project gave me experience with the perfused hindlimb preparation, which I eventually used for studies of capillary permeability.

Of course we worked under the constant threat of war and with nagging inner voices telling us to stop everything worthwhile to prepare for it.

WAR YEARS

War came on September 2, 1939. I was on vacation at a music houseparty in Harvard, Massachusetts, and I intended to return to University College as

Demonstrator in Pharmacology. Passports were cancelled, along with my job. Winton became Dean of the Medical School, which was removed to Surrey before its buildings were destroyed during the Blitz of 1940. I sought help from A. N. Richards at the University of Pennsylvania. When I came for an interview, I launched into a detailed account of my work on perfused muscle, but he soon interrupted. "All I want to know," he said, "is whether you are a good experimenter." Torn between outward modesty and inner faith, I finally opted for the latter, and that was the end of the interview. He set me up with a temporary appointment in Bazett's Department of Physiology and an emergency research grant of $250, which enabled me to complete work begun in England and to send in two papers to the *Journal of Physiology*. At the same time, I joined forces with Glenn Millikan to help develop the ear oximeter. Glenn, like myself, had been cast adrift from his position in England, and he sought help from Detlev Bronk at the Johnson Foundation for Medical Physics. It seemed obvious that the US would soon be in the war, and all of us wanted to contribute what we could as scientists as soon as possible. For the next six years, Glenn and I worked closely together on oximetry, on oxygen demand valves, chemical oxygen generators, carbon monoxide poisoning in tanks and military aircraft, positive pressure breathing, and other problems in applied physiology for the military.

Let me digress for a moment to pay tribute to Glenn Millikan, who was killed in a mountain climbing accident in 1947. He was the son of Robert A. Millikan, President of the California Institute of Technology, who was famous for the oil drop experiment used to measure the charge of the electron. Glenn was known as "the little oil drop." He was probably the most well-known and charismatic young physiologist of his day in Europe and America. He exuded energy, curiosity, and *joie de vivre*. He found his way from Harvard to Cambridge, England, where he did highly original and important work on myoglobin, which culminated in a Physiological Review in 1939 (14). He was elected to a Fellowship at Trinity College, where he became a source of inspiration to students of physiology. He is still remembered with affection by colleagues in both Europe and America, and certainly his premature death deprived American physiology of one of its most promising young scientists.

In 1939, our Air Force was woefully lacking in equipment for high-altitude flying, and only a few physiologists had the knowledge and the vision to understand what was needed. Among these few were Bruce Dill, Detlev Bronk, and Walter Boothby. The Aeromedical Research Laboratory at Wright Field consisted of one altitude chamber and two or three poorly equipped laboratories staffed by a few junior medical officers and enlisted men. There was no formal provision or support for civilian research in this area, and during 1940 Glenn and I usually made the long trip out to Dayton in our own car. Operational aircraft seldom flew above 18,000 feet, and in most cases they were equipped with rudimentary oxygen equipment. Only three years later, the USAF sent more than 10,000 fighting men aloft daily in un-pressurized aircraft to operate for many hours at altitudes where conscious-ness would fail within a few seconds without supplementary oxygen. The enterprise as a whole required vast training programs in the use of oxygen, as well as continual work to improve the design and efficiency of oxygen equipment, which competed in weight with the load of gasoline and arma-ment.

Bronk saw the magnitude of these problems at an early stage, and he became a leader for both the military and civilian effort. Most of the time he worked directly out of the Air Surgeon's office in Washington, but he retained a small group at the Johnson Foundation to carry out applied research on oxygen equipment and on visual problems. Those of us who worked in his home laboratory as civilians had continual access to operational problems and to the flight testing facilities of the services and the aircraft industry. We spent hundreds of unhealthy hypoxic hours testing experimental equipment at sim-ulated altitudes of 40,000 feet or more and temperatures of $-40°$ in the altitude chamber in Philadelphia.

I also participated in experimental flights to extreme altitudes in stripped down B-17s and in the first prototype B-29 heavy bomber just prior to its disastrous loss with all hands aboard in December 1942. I did a survey of carbon monoxide from gunfire in tanks and aircraft, and the Navy asked me to test a chemical oxygen generator retrieved from a Japanese Zero shot down in the Pacific. I found 0.1% CO in the oxygen. The Navy broadcast this result to the Japanese, hoping it might shake the confidence of their pilots in their equipment; at the same time, my report was classified as secret in the US, so I could no longer read it or keep it in my files.

Most of the time, at least up to 1944, we worked long hours and with a sense of urgency. Bronk was tireless; he would often arrive from Washington late in the day, talk with us until midnight and then return to Washington. I, too, led a somewhat frenetic and heady life of travel to military establishments and aircraft factories all over the country, not to mention frequent trips to Washington. Nevertheless, I remained in touch with a saner world through playing in string quartets, mostly with Catherine Drinker Bowen and with Helen Rice, who later founded the Association of Amateur Chamber Music Players, an international organization which now has more than 6000 mem-bers.

I had been brought up in an academic world that emphasized distinctions between "pure" and "applied" science. I was surprised and excited by the rapidity with which knowledge, previously considered interesting but useless, could be transformed to practical use on a large scale. Conversely, exposure to practical problems often stimulated new questions in the realm of fundamental science. Certainly, this was true of respiratory physiology, which advanced rapidly in fundamental ways under the stimulus of applied research for the military. This was a lesson for my generation of academic scientists, a lesson which in its broader context was transformed into public policy after the War.

My own experience with applied research during the War was immensely enriched by close association with Detlev Bronk and the small group of biophysicists in his entourage, including Keffer Hartline, Frank Brink, Martin Larrabee, John Hervey, Glenn Millikan, and John Lilly. They were all experts in instrumentation, especially electronics. We were a close-knit family, and one would have to be very impermeable indeed not to learn by osmosis from daily association with such alert and knowledgeable minds.

By 1945, however, the War's end was in sight and all of us were "de-exhilarated" and eager to return to academic life. The project I was then working on, the storage of oxygen in the form of perchlorates, was already in pilot production in Pittsburgh, but it seemed unlikely to me that it would ever be used for its intended purpose as a source of emergency oxygen for aircraft or for portable welding apparatus. I was anxious to resume studies of the microcirculation, and after V-J Day it was natural for me to apply to E. M. Landis, an authority on capillary circulation who had just succeeded W. B. Cannon as the Higginson Professor of Physiology at Harvard. He had not yet made new appointments of faculty rank, and I had the good fortune to be selected as his right-hand man.

CAPILLARIES AND MEMBRANE PERMEABILITY (1946–1954)

I arrived in Boston in December 1945 to start a new life. There was a heavy load of teaching awaiting me. Gene Landis had organized a super course in mammalian physiology; all chapters of the fat textbooks of physiology were represented in both lecture and lab. It was a veritable *dinosaur* of a course, doomed to extinction as new branches of biology evolved to dominate the medical curriculum. For me it meant another period of intensive work and learning; I was frequently on deck at 6 AM to prepare live demonstrations or student labs prior to my 9 AM lecture.

It was not until June 1946 that I found time to resume experimental work. I had a vague plan for studying edema formation in isolated perfused muscle but without any clearly defined goal. NIH had not yet started large-scale support for university-based medical research, but even if it had, I don't think I could have written an acceptable request for a grant. Certainly I had no inkling that the project would lead rather swiftly to a logical sequence of enduring advances in the physiology of the microcirculation and the biophysics of membrane transport. After only a few experiments, I saw how to set the mean capillary pressure to known values, how to measure the effective osmotic pressure exerted by the plasma proteins across capillary walls, and how to relate these to rates of net filtration and absorption. In the following year, these preliminary experiments were verified and extended in detail with Armando Soto-Rivera; they were first presented at the 17th International Congress of Physiology held in Oxford in 1947. It was the first Congress after the War, and physiologists were happily reunited after many years of forced separation. It was a moving contrast to the grim Congress in Zurich which I had attended in 1938, just prior to the invasion of Czechoslovakia. August Krogh listened to my paper at Oxford; afterwards he came "backstage" to say nice things about it, and of course I was thrilled because his work in respiratory, comparative, and capillary physiology was (and still is) such a large part of our heritage. At the closing plenary session in the beautiful Sheldonian Theatre, Albert Szent-Gyorgi gave a speech of thanks in nine different languages.

The methods developed for measurement of capillary pressure and effective transcapillary protein osmotic pressure were soon extended to the analysis of transcapillary concentration gradients during diffusional exchange of hydrophilic solutes between blood and tissues. This, in turn, led to a general theoretical analysis of the relations between restricted diffusion, hydrodynamic flow, and molecular sieving—an analysis applicable to a wide variety of biological and artificial membranes. The theory and preliminary results were first presented (with E. M. Renkin and L. Borrero) at the 18th International Congress of Physiology in Copenhagen in 1950, under the title *Filtration and Molecular Diffusion from the Capillaries in Muscle, with Deductions Concerning the Number and Dimensions of Ultramicroscopic Openings in the Capillary Wall*. The complete paper subsequently appeared in the *American Journal of Physiology* (25). I recently wrote a history of this development and its relation to the parallel development of irreversible thermodynamics as applied to membrane transport (21). The American Physiological Society Handbook volumes on *Microcirculation* (edited by E. M. Renkin and C. C. Michel) provide full review of the many modifications and extensions of the original theory that have been made in the last 35 years.

In 1949 I married Hylie Palmer, a violinist at the Julliard School of Music and a pupil of Galamian. She has been first fiddle in my life ever since.

Alexander Forbes was still in the Department of Physiology at Harvard when I arrived in 1946, and it was a great privilege to come to know him. He was a pioneer in electrophysiology and one of its most distinguished leaders for more than 50 years (13). He was the first to use vacuum tube amplifiers in conjunction with the string galvanometer for recording nerve action potentials

(6), which set the stage for the classic work of Gasser and Erlanger on peripheral nerve and of Adrian, Bronk, Zotterman, Matthews, and others on single unit analysis in sensory systems (8). Alex was also a pioneer of oblique photogammetry from the air and an authority on off-shore navigation. In 1935 he mapped northern Laborador and Baffin Land from his own plane, thus charting the way for the northern air route to Europe during World War II (7). He was awarded the Charles Daly Medal of the Geographical Society, and his election to the National Academy of Sciences might equally well have been for his contributions to geographical science as to neurophysiology. He seemed to know every inch of the New England coast and how it had changed during the sixty years he sailed it. He was a marvelous raconteur. In the evening, after a long day's sail, he would relax over a "Chickatawbut" cocktail in the cabin of his ketch *Stormsvala* and draw on an endless repertoire of stories and anecdotes, which he always introduced by saying who had told it to him and when. There must have been dozens of young people, including my wife and me, who thought of him affectionately as Uncle Alex.

During the 1950s the American Heart Association established some fellowships designed to relieve young professors from administrative duties, and I was selected for one of these generous lifetime awards. This allowed me to continue laboratory work on a small scale in company with occasional graduate students and postdoctoral fellows. It also gave me the freedom to explore novel ideas without worrying about short-term success or failure. My first effort was indeed a failure. I had the idea that several puzzling features of the renal circulation might be explained by plasma skimming in the interlobular arteries and afferent arterioles. This idea turned out to be incorrect, at least in the renal cortex. Although my theory, which was presented as a Bowditch Lecture and elsewhere (22), failed to survive, it nevertheless stimulated lively discussion and experimentation for several years and I do not regret being wrong in this case.

GOATS

Beginning in 1957 I undertook development of techniques for perfusion of the ventricular system in unanesthetized animals. I was stimulated by the work of I. Leusen from Ghent, who had shown that perfusion of the ventricles with acid solutions caused hyperventilation in anesthetized animals even though the arterial blood became alkaline (11). Previous theories of chemical regulation of breathing were concerned solely with the composition of blood, and it seemed to me that Leusen's experiments had some exceptionally important implications for this field. No one had ever perfused the brain ventricular system in unanesthetized animals, and I had no experience with surgery for chronic experiments. My friends in the Neurosurgery Department were very skeptical about the feasibility of chronic cannulation of the cisterna magna. We found, however, that the size and shape of the skull in goats or sheep make possible the implantation of guide tubes through thick occipital bone pointing towards the atlanto-occipital membrane. The cistern could then be punctured at will through the guide tube without causing pain to the un-anesthetized animals. At the same time, Feldberg, in England, described techniques for chronic implantation of cannulae in cerebral ventricles (4); so the stage was set for ventriculo-cisternal perfusions in goats. Nevertheless, it took us almost five years to perfect the surgical techniques and to learn how to carry out perfusions of the brain for long periods in healthy, confident animals. Eventually, the project was productive in three disparate fields of physiology, as follows:

1. Exchange of materials between blood and cerebrospinal fluid (CSF), including the first measurements of CSF production and absorption by clearance techniques. The results were first presented in 1961 at the International Congress of Pharmacology in Stockholm and have since been described in reviews and textbooks.
2. Central chemical control of breathing [reviewed in a Harvey Lecture, 1967 (18)].
3. Investigation of sleep-inducing factors released into CSF during sleep deprivation [reviewed for *Scientific American,* 1976 (19) and in a Bayliss-Starling Lecture, 1982 (20)].

It would be difficult to initiate a project of this kind at a reputable medical school of the 1980s. My assistant, Jim Nicholl, never went to college, but he was a jack-of-all-trades who could do everything from metal spinning in the machine shop to milking goats. In fact, he became more adept than I at implanting cisternal guide tubes. Together we built a goat shed and fences amid the ventilators on the roof of the Medical School, and we did not even ask permission from Buildings and Grounds. We found farmers (within a radius of 100 miles) who would supply us with their "surplus" goats free of charge. We transported goats and hay in my station wagon. In summer the operated animals (with neckbands to protect their carotid loops and aluminum hats attached to their horns to protect ventricular guide tubes) travelled with us for vacations at our summer home in the Berkshires. Astonishment, laughter, and curiosity were plain to see in the faces of motorists who passed our station wagon with its cargo of capped goats and children. At about this time I began to serve on national committees in Washington and elsewhere, and the airplanes often passed over the Medical School, where I could look down to see my goats capering on the roof.

All of this would be illegal today, and the cost of purchase and care of more than a hundred goats in accredited facilities would be quite out of line with the potential of the project as it was viewed at the time.

SLEEP

It was my habit to spend Saturday mornings browsing amongst the journals of the week. That was how I stumbled on an article by Monnier and Hosli with the intriguing title *Humoral transmission of sleep and wakefulness; hemodialysis of a sleep-inducing humor during stimulation of the thalamic somnogenic area* (16). That article referred me to Pieron's early work on the sleep-inducing properties of CSF drawn from sleep-deprived animals. A copy of Pieron's 1913 monograph *Le problème physiologique du sommeil* was at hand in our departmental library. On several occasions I have been to the library to browse or to look up a specific reference and was led by chance to an unrelated paper that changed the course of my subsequent research. This sort of serendipity is something the computer cannot supply and I am reminded again of the quotation from T. S. Eliot's *Four Quartets* paraphrased in the prelude to this essay. In this case I realized at once that my colony of goats provided the means for collecting large quantities of CSF from sleep-deprived animals, and I resolved to "give it a fling." Jim Nicholl and I rigged up a system to keep the goats awake while Tracy Miller and Cecilie Goodrich implanted ventricular cannulae in cats to enable us to introduce CSF from the goats into the cats. To our surprise, the very first experiments corroborated the findings of Pieron: CSF from a sleep-deprived goat infused into the ventricles of a cat appeared to make the cat torporous for several hours, whereas normal fluid from the same goat had no effect. Of course we had no EEG to judge the nature of the induced sleep, but we all agreed about the behavioral effects in the three cats tested.

Our first publication in this field was in 1967 (24), and it was followed by 15 years of frustrating attempts to isolate and identify "the" sleep factor. Early in the project I was joined by Manfred Karnovsky, a distinguished biochemist who was (and still is) sympathetic to old-fashioned physiology and physiologists. Our starting material changed from CSF derived from sleep-deprived goats (six liters obtained laboriously from 25 goats over a three-year period), to the brains of 15,000 sleep-deprived rabbits, to 5000 liters of normal human urine. We had many collaborators, but much of the credit for the final isolation and identification of an active muramyl tetrapeptide from urine belongs to Dr. James Krueger (10, 12). The natural product and certain synthetic muramyl peptides have now been shown to induce high-amplitude, slow-wave sleep in rats, rabbits, cats, and squirrel monkeys. I am still not convinced, however, that the material isolated from urine is related to the sleep-inducing Factor S we originally found in the CSF of sleep-deprived animals. The latter is surely of importance to normal physiology, but there are reasons to believe that the muramyl peptides are involved in immunological reactions to bacterial infection, including fever as well as sleep. The history of this still controversial subject has been reviewed in several recent publications (1, 9, 10, 19, 20).

INTERNATIONAL

The romance of travel to international meetings has been badly tarnished by the jet. The up-and-coming young physiologist thinks nothing of waltzing off to Europe for three-day meetings several times a year, attaché case and 2 × 2 slides in hand. There is prestige value when the secretary can answer phone calls with "Dr. S. is out of the country until Thursday. Do you want him to call?" The airport at landing is the same as the one at take-off, and Hilton-Budapest is not much different from Hilton–San Diego or New Delhi.

It was not always so. Less than 40 years ago the triennial International Congresses of Physiology were about the *only* international meetings for biochemists, endocrinologists, nutritionists, and pharmacologists, as well as physiologists; and there was no such word as *neuroscience*. Biological scientists, young and old, saved their pennies for the triennial treat. It was unethical to use research funds for travel to meetings, even to local FASEB meetings. It took a week to cross the Atlantic (depending on the weather), and it did not make sense to embark on such a long trip without spending at least a month on the other side. How to compare the excitement of a midnight sailing, the sound of the bugle warning visitors off the ship, the rattle of chains as the gangplank is raised and the hawsers cast away, cutting one loose from home with no way of quick return even in emergency—how to compare this, I say, with the long line of tired, vetted passengers boarding Flight 6339, which might just as well be going to Kansas City as to Paris or Copenhagen?

The scientists I admired most, both in England and America, were internationally minded, and my generation of physiologists inherited a strong tradition of loyalty to *THE* International Congress of Physiology. I attended most of these Congresses from 1938 onwards. In 1964, when Wallace Fenn asked me to be Program Director for the 1968 Congress in Washington, D.C., I jumped at the chance. From then until 1983 I had the joy and privilege of working with Councils of the IUPS together with my counterparts from the USSR, Poland, Hungary, South America, India, Australia, and Japan, as well as those from Western Europe and Scandinavia whom I already knew well. One of my main concerns in this period was to maintain strong representation of "Neuroscience" within IUPS, in hopes that this most exciting part of physiology would not break away into a separate union. It seems to me that physiology in the United States has suffered greatly by the establishment of separate departments or divisions of neuroscience within universities, national societies, and academies. This has not occurred in other countries, where departments and societies have moved with the times to incorporate the enlarged scope of modern neurophysiology in which immunology, peptide chemistry, embryology, etc play such important roles. It may be that the size and success of developments in neuroscience within the United States made fission inevitable, but whatever the reason, it has adversely affected many departments of physiology across the land.

In addition to service with IUPS, I have had many other opportunities to participate in international meetings or projects, some in exotic places. In 1957, after a lecture tour of Swedish universities, I revisited Jotunheimen on skis to replay the adventures of 20 years previously. Björn Folkow from Göteborg accompanied me on this expedition, during which we skied to Storbreen glacier. There my old friend Per Scholander was extracting gas bubbles from the ice to estimate the composition of the atmosphere at the time the glacier ice was laid down. In 1942 Scholander and I almost lost our lives when we were caught for three days in a severe blizzard on the summit of Mt. Mansfield in sub-zero temperatures and high winds. Other memorable ex-peditions, all in the name of Physiology, were in Kashmir, in the foothills of the Himalayas; in the alps of Southern New Zealand; and in Valdivia, 16 hours by train south of Santiago, Chile.

On two occasions I returned to England for full years; first as Overseas Fellow of Churchill College, Cambridge, and subsequently as Eastman Pro-fessor and Supernumerary Fellow of Balliol College, Oxford. These were years for renewal of old friendships, cementing of new ones, and the sharing of both with my wife and children. Three of our children continued for five years or more in England to complete their schooling and university educa-tions. All of them chose art, music, or literature as a life work: not an easy way to earn a living, and I admire their courage and idealism. It seems unlikely that the Arts will ever receive even a small fraction of the support given to Science in the second half of the 20th century.

ACKNOWLEDGMENTS

Parts of this essay will also appear in *Men and Ideas in Membrane Transport*, an American Physiological Society Centennial volume (21). I thank the editors for their permission to use some of the same wording in each of these two publications.

Literature Cited

1. Borbely, A., Tobler, I. 1980. The search for an endogenous 'sleep-substance'. *Trends in Pharmacological Sciences* 1:357–59
2. Eggleton, M. G., Pappenheimer, J. R., Winton, F. R. 1940. The relation between ureter, venous and arterial pressures in the isolated kidney of the dog. *J. Physiol.* 99:135–52
3. Eliot, T. S. 1943. *Four Quartets: IV. Little Gidding.* New York: Harcourt Brace
4. Feldberg, W. 1963. *A Pharmacological Approach to the Brain from its Inner and Outer Surface.* Baltimore: Williams & Wilkins
5. Ferguson, J. K. W., Horvath, S. M., Pappenheimer, J. R. 1938. The transport of carbon dioxide by erythrocytes and plasma in dogfish blood. *Biol. Bull.* 75:381–88
6. Forbes, A., Thacher, C. 1920. Amplification of action currents with the electron tube in recording with the string galvanometer. *Amer. J. Physiol.* 52: 409–71
7. Forbes, A. 1953. *Quest for a Northern Air Route.* Cambridge, Mass.: Harvard Univ. Press
8. Hodgkin, A. L. 1979. *Baron Adrian of Cambridge, Biographical Memoirs of the Royal Society.* London: R. Soc.
9. Inoué, S., Borbely, A., eds. 1985. *Endogenous Sleep Substances and Sleep Regulation.* Utrecht, The Netherlands: VNU
10. Krueger, J. M., Walter, J., Levin, C. 1985. Endogenous sleep factors. In *Brain Mechanisms of Sleep,* ed. D. McGinty, pp. 253–75. New York: Raven
11. Leusen, I. R. 1954. Chemosensitivity of the respiratory center. Influence of CO_2 in the cerebral ventricles on respiration. *Amer. J. Physiol.* 176:39–44
12. Martin, S., Karnovsky, M. L., Krueger, J. M., Pappenheimer, J. R., Bieman, K. 1984. Peptidoglycans as promoters of slow wave sleep; structure of the sleep-promoting factor isolated from human urine. *J. Biol. Chem.* 259:12652–58
13. Memorial minute on the life of Alexander Forbes. *Harvard University Gazette LXI, No. 5* 1965.
14. Millikan, G. A. 1939. Muscle hemoglobin. *Physiol. Rev.* 19:503–23
15. Millikan, G. A., Pappenheimer, J. R., Rawson, A. J., Hervey, J. P. 1941. The continuous measurement of arterial saturation in man. *Amer. J. Physiol.* 133:390 (Abstr.)
16. Monnier, A., Hosli, L. 1965. Humoral transmission of sleep and wakefulness: II. Hemodialysis of a sleep-inducing humor during stimulation of the thalamic hypnogenic area. *Pflüg. Arch. Ges. Physiol.* 282:60–75
17. Pappenheimer, J. R. 1941. Vasoconstrictor nerves and oxygen consumption in the isolated perfused hindlimb muscles of the dog. *J. Physiol.* 99:182–200
18. Pappenheimer, J. R. 1967. The ionic composition of cerebral extracellular fluid and its relation to control of breathing. *Harvey Lecture Ser.* 61:71–94. New York: Academic
19. Pappenheimer, J. R. 1976. The sleep factor. *Sci. Amer.* 235:24–29
20. Pappenheimer, J. R. 1983. Induction of sleep by muramyl peptides. (Bayliss-Starling Memorial Lecture) *J. Physiol.* 336:1–11
21. Pappenheimer, J. R. Flow and diffusion through biological membranes. In *Men and Ideas in Membrane Transport,* ed. D. C. Tosteson. *Amer. Physiol. Soc.* 100: In press
22. Pappenheimer, J. R., Kinter, W. B. 1956. Hematocrit ratio of blood within the mammalian kidney and its significance for renal hemodynamics. *Amer. J. Physiol.* 185:377–90
23. Pappenheimer, J. R., Lepie, M. P., Wyman, J. Jr. 1936. The surface tension of aqueous solutions of dipolar ions. *J. Amer. Chem. Soc.* 58:1851–55
24. Pappenheimer, J. R., Miller, T. B., Goodrich, C. A. 1967. Sleep-promoting effects of cerebrospinal fluid from sleep-deprived goats. *Proc. Natl. Acad. Sci. USA* 58:513–17
25. Pappenheimer, J. R., Renkin, E. M., Borrero, L. M. 1951. Filtration, diffusion and molecular sieving through peripheral capillary membranes. *Amer. J. Physiol.* 167:13–46
26. Winton, F. R. 1931. The glomerular pressure in the isolated mammalian kidney. *J. Physiol.* 72:361–75
27. Wyman, J. Jr. 1964. Linked functions and reciprocal effects in proteins *Adv. Protein Chem.* 19:224–86

GASTROINTESTINAL PHYSIOLOGY

PROTON AND BICARBONATE TRANSPORT SYSTEMS IN GASTOINTESTINAL EPITHELIA

Introduction, John G. Forte, *Section Editor*

The operation of distinctive proton and bicarbonate transport mechanisms has long been recognized for the support of various functional activities of the gastrointestinal tract. Certainly, the voluminous acidic and alkaline secretions of digestive glands have received enormous attention for more than a century. It is now clear that specific membrane mechanisms for the transport of H^+, OH^-, and/or HCO_3^- are necessary to maintain intracellular pH, contribute to the acid-base balance of the body, and couple the movement of H^+ and HCO_3^- to the flow of other ions and water. In this volume, the section on gastrointestinal physiology reviews membrane mechanisms for the transport of H^+, OH^-, and/or HCO_3^-. A number of unique mechanisms have been identified, and the reader will find that for many systems the mechanistic details remain unclear. However, throughout the gastrointestinal tract there is a remarkable thematic repetition involving the operation of two electroneutral ion exchangers, a Na^+-H^+ exchanger and a Cl^--HCO_3^- exchanger. Differences in their activity and membrane localization (e.g. apical versus basolateral) provide a wide range of functional attributes for the ion exchangers.

In the first article, Machen & Paradiso examine the mechanisms available to parietal and other gastric cells for the maintenance of a stable intracellular pH. This is a significant problem since voluminous gastric acid output requires efficient means to deal with the equivalent cellular production of alkali, as well as any acid reflux that might occur under physiological conditions. A system of dual exchangers, one for Na^+-H^+ exchange and one for Cl^--HCO_3^- exchange, has been identified in basolateral membranes of

17

gastric epithelial cells. These ion exchangers are prominent participants in cellular pH homeostatis and gastric ion transport.

In their review of salt transport by the gallbladder epithelium, Reuss & Stoddard discuss the evidence to support an indirect coupling for the inward fluxes of Na^+ and Cl^- across the apical membrane. They point out the inadequacies of the earlier notion of a tightly coupled NaCl apical transport pathway, and demonstrate the operation of a double exchanger system (Na^+-H^+ and Cl^--HCO_3^-) modulated by intracellular pH. In addition, the authors suggest a role for cyclic AMP in modulating the activity of the apical ion exchangers and other membrane transport pathways as the basis for alterations in fluid absorption by the gallbladder.

Through its secretory and absorptive processes the intestinal mucosa regulates the pH of chyme and contributes to the overall acid-base balance. Hopfer & Liedtke review the various mechanisms for proton and bicarbonate transport in the intestine. They emphasize a system of Na^+-H^+ and Cl^--HCO_3^- double exchangers in the apical (brush border) membrane of mammalian small intestine, which accounts for so-called coupled NaCl transport. They further suggest that differences in the relative activities of the two types of exchangers may provide a basis for net proton or net bicarbonate secretion in different regions of the intestine, as well as to maintain constant intracellular pH.

Scharschmidt & Van Dyke review mechanisms for proton transport in hepatocyte membranes and their role in liver function. A Na^+-H^+ exchange system has been clearly localized to basolateral plasma membranes with possible suggested functions in intracellular pH regulation, canalicular bile formation, and hepatic regeneration. A Cl^--HCO_3^- exchanger has been identified in canalicular plasma membrane vesicles, but the functional significance of the anion exchanger remains unclear. The authors also provide extensive detail for the existence of another hepatic proton transport system, an electrogenic H^+-ATPase. Similarities in the characteristics of H^+ transport activity identified in several hepatocyte organelles and isolated membrane vesicles suggest an identical or closely related H^+-ATPase. This membrane H^+-ATPase may serve an important role in receptor-mediated endocytosis as well as other hepatic functions.

In addition to the release of digestive enzymes, the pancreas has a major function to secrete a HCO_3^--rich fluid that helps to neutralize gastric acid entering the duodenum. In the last article, Kuijpers & De Pont review the mechanisms of proton and bicarbonate transport in pancreatic ductular tissue. They conclude that transepithelial HCO_3^- secretion is coupled to Na^+ transport and energized by the Na^+ pump (Na^+ gradient) at the basolateral membrane. The exact nature of the coupling among Na^+, H^+, Cl^-, and HCO_3^- at the basolateral membrane is uncertain, at present, and various hypotheses are discussed.

Ann. Rev. Physiol. 1987. 49:19–33

REGULATION OF INTRACELLULAR pH IN THE STOMACH

Terry E. Machen and Anthony M. Paradiso

Physiology-Anatomy Department, University of California, Berkeley, California 94720

INTRODUCTION

The stomach is a single-layered and highly folded epithelium composed of two or three different cell types. In the mammal, acid secretion and enzyme secretion are accomplished by oxyntic cells (OC) and chief cells (CC), respectively, which are located deep within the tubular gastric glands (which are 300 μm long). Mucus-secreting surface epithelial cells (SEC) cover the areas of the stomach wall in direct contact with the lumen, and they extend part of the way down the openings of the gastric pits, which are the openings to the lumen of the gastric glands.

All living cells have an intracellular pH (pH_i) somewhere in the range of 6.9–7.5 (see 46 for review). A variety of different membrane mechanisms have been developed by different cells to maintain a constant pH_i despite the tendency to accumulate H^+ that results from metabolism and from the negative potential gradient of most cells (46). This tendency to acidify is particularly pronounced for gastric CC and SEC, which must withstand the very acidic (pH = 1) solution that flows over their luminal surface during every meal. The OC must also rid themselves of the excess OH^- (12) produced during the secretion of H^+ via the H,K-ATPase (26, 48) located at their apical membranes.

This review discusses the membrane mechanisms by which the OC, CC, and SEC maintain their pH_i in the range of 7.1–7.5. We cover only work on in vitro preparations, e.g. intact gastric mucosa, gastric glands, single cells, or isolated membrane vesicles. Because there appear to be important interactions between the mechanisms responsible for regulation of pH_i and the mech-

19

0066-4278/87/0315-0019$02.00

anisms responsible for active H^+, Cl^-, and HCO_3 transport, we also try to integrate the available information into a coherent picture of transepithelial ion transport by the different cells. Finally, we present a model to explain the barrier function of the stomach.

STUDIES ON INTACT GASTRIC MUCOSA

Hersey and his collaborators (21–23) were the first to use spectroscopy to measure pH_i in the gastric mucosa. Bromthymol blue (BTB) is a pH-sensitive indicator that permeates the cell membrane and becomes trapped in the epithelial cells. In principle, it is possible to obtain a quantitative estimate of pH_i by measuring the absorbance difference at wavelengths of 620–690 nm of BTB-treated gastric mucosa mounted in a dual beam spectrophotometer. In practice, the measurements must be adjusted to account for dye bound to intracellular sites (which changes the pK_a of BTB from 6.95 to 8.0) and for dye trapped in the extracellular space.

Using this technique Hersey (22) found that in resting tissues bathed in a NaCl Ringer's solution containing both CO_2 and HCO_3 pH_i was 7.43. Addition of histamine caused pH_i to increase slowly (over the course of 10 min) to 8.02, and there was a positive, linear relationship between pH_i and the rate of acid secretion. Acetazolamide (an inhibitor of carbonic anhydrase) caused pH_i to increase even further in stimulated tissues (23). Conversely, SCN^- decreased H^+ secretion to zero and caused pH_i to decrease to 7.13 (22).

pH_i has also been measured in the intact frog gastric mucosa by measuring the apparent equilibrium constant of the creatine kinase reaction during histamine stimulation of the OC (14). The reaction

$$MgATP + creatine \rightleftarrows MgADP + creatine\text{-}PO_4 + H^+$$

has an equilibrium constant (K') that is a sensitive function of pH (47); measurement of K' can thus yield pH_i. Ekblad (14) generated a "calibration curve" of K' versus pH_i in *resting* tissues (frozen gastric mucosa) by measuring concentrations of creatine-PO_4, creatine, ADP, and ATP at different values of pH_i, which was measured using the weak acid DMO (55). The pH_i of the resting tissues changed as the pH of the serosal solution was varied. The pH_i was a linear function of pH_o when pH_o was between 5 and 8 (also see 29, 35). Using the calibrated measurements of K', it was then found that pH_i increased from 7.51 to 7.93 during histamine-induced stimulation of H^+ secretion.

The studies cited above indicate the following: (a) pH_i increases in OC during stimulation with histamine; (b) SCN^- may block H^+ secretion by causing a back-diffusion of H^+ from the gland lumen into OC; (c) carbonic anhydrase may be important for catalyzing the reaction $OH^- + CO_2 \rightarrow HCO_3$, which neutralizes the OH^- generated during active H^+ secretion; (d) in the resting tissue, changes in the pH of the serosal solution have large effects on pH$_i$. These are important findings, but quantitative conclusions about changes in pH$_i$ cannot be obtained using the DMO, creatine kinase, or BTB techniques. For example, it is technically difficult to account for BTB or DMO trapped in the extracellular space. Further, both DMO and BTB are membrane-permeant, and they therefore yield a volume-weighted average of pH in the cytoplasm, mitochondria, tubulovesicles, and other membrane-bound compartments. Mitochondria are generally believed to be more alkaline than cytoplasm, and they tend to increase in alkalinity during increases in metabolic activity (53), while tubulovesicles may be more acidic than the cytoplasm (5). Finally, measurements of pH$_i$ in intact frog tissue must be viewed as an integrated value of all component cell types.

STUDIES ON ISOLATED GASTRIC GLANDS

Although most of the problems associated with the above techniques can be obviated by using pH microelectrodes, there has been only one published attempt to use them on the cells of isolated gastric glands (24). Separate potential-sensitive and pH-sensitive microelectrodes were used to show that in NaCl Ringer's solution the pH$_i$ was 7.11 and that average pH$_i$ decreased to 6.90 during histamine stimulation. In some penetrations, pH values as low as 3 were recorded. In such cases the microelectrode was probably in the glandular lumen and not inside the cell. In another set of experiments, Na^+-free Ringer's solution caused average pH$_i$ to decrease from 7.45 to 7.17.

These measurements must be viewed critically. Microelectrode impalements may generate leaks in these fragile cells. Such leaks may explain the small membrane potentials measured (average V_m = 6.1 mV) and the lack of change in V_m with large changes in solution $[K^+]$, $[Cl^-]$, or $[Na^+]$. Also, it was not possible to localize the microelectrode tip in either the OC or CC or, perhaps, even within the lumen of the gland. Finally, the technique assumes that all glandular cells have the same V_m; this may not be the case if OC and CC are not electrically coupled.

Another technique that has recently become popular is the use of 2',7'-bis(carboxyethyl)-5(6)-carboxyfluorescein (BCECF), which has been shown to be a useful probe for continuous measurements of pH$_i$ in a variety of cells (e.g. 19, 40, 45). Control experiments on gastric glands have shown that the dye is not incorporated into mitochondria and other membrane-bound compartments (39). Calibration of the fluorescence signal to yield pH$_i$ is most effectively done by permeablizing the cell membranes using nigercin (H^+-K^+ exchanger) in the presence of high [K^+] Ringer's solutions of different pH_o.

BCECF has been used to assess mechanisms of regulation in isolated gastric glands (39, 40). Because the gastric gland is made up of roughly 50% parietal cells and 50% chief cells, the results from such experiments have to be interpreted in terms of the activities of both cell types. One set of experiments was designed to test for Na^+-H^+ exchange. Cells were first acidified from a control pH_i of 7.11 down to a pH_i of 6.5–6.8 in Na^+-free solutions (46). When Na^+ or Li^+ was subsequently added, there was a monotonic realkalinization ($t_{1/2} = 0.2$ min); the recovery occurred somewhat faster in Cl^--free as compared with Cl^--containing solutions. Realkalinization was mostly, but not completely, blocked by 1-mM amiloride, which inhibits Na^+-H^+ exchange in other systems (4). Rates of Na^+-dependent recovery from acid loads were not affected by changing [K^+], or including valinomycin (the K^+ ionophore) in the external medium.

Na^+-free solutions caused pH_i to decrease from 7.11 to 6.82 (39). This acidification was increased if the glands were first treated with ouabain to increase cellular [Na^+] (40). The Na^+-free-induced acidication was largely, but not completely, blocked by amiloride. These studies concluded that glandular cells have a Na^+-H^+ exchanger that can operate in the absence of Cl^-. The activity of the exchanger is probably electrically neutral since maneuvers expected to change the membrane potential did not affect the rate of transport. The Na^+-H^+ exchanger can operate in reverse if there is an outward-directed gradient of [Na^+].

Cl^--HCO_3 exchange in glandular cells, which was originally proposed based on electrophysiological evidence (43), was demonstrated by changing extracellular Cl^-, [Cl^-]$_o$, and monitoring the resulting change in pH_i (39). The Cl^--HCO_3 exchanger was expected to couple transmembrane Cl^- movements (driven by [Cl^-] gradients) to HCO_3 movements, thereby causing changes in pH_i. When [Cl^-]$_o$ was changed from 150 mM to zero, pH_i increased rapidly from 7.1 to 7.3. If the glands were first treated with 0.2 mM 4,4'-diisothiocyanostilbene-2,2'-disulfonic acid (DIDS), which inhibits Cl^--HCO_3 exchange in red cells (28), Cl^--free treatment did not affect pH_i. DIDS also blocked the normal acidification (from pH_i 7.3 to 7.1) observed when Cl^- was added to a suspension of glands in Cl^--free solutions. The conclusion was that glands exhibit Cl^--HCO_3 exchange activity, though the Na^+ dependence of this exchange was not tested. All solutions were equilibrated with atmospheric air at pH_i=7.45. Under these conditions [HCO_3]$_o$ = 0.2 mM and [HCO_3]$_i$ is only somewhat larger (due to the cellular production of CO_2 and hydration to form HCO_3). Given these low [HCO_3], it is possible that Cl^- is exchanged for the OH^- ion alone.

STUDIES ON PARIETAL CELLS

Na^+-H^+ and Cl^--HCO_3 Exchange

Both intact OC (separated and purified to 75–90% homogeneity from rabbit stomachs) and basolateral membranes isolated from OC were used in a comprehensive study of some of the mechanisms involved in pH$_i$ regulation (37). pH$_i$ in OC was measured using the fluorescent, pH-sensitive dye dimethylcarboxyfluorescein, which has many properties in common with BCECF. Transmembrane gradients of pH were measured in isolated basolateral membrane vesicles using the fluorescent weak base, acridine orange (AO). This dye accumulates in acidic spaces, and as the dye concentration increases, its fluorescence (or, as in the present experiments, its absorbance) is quenched due to dye stacking (27). The experiments were designed to test for Na^+-H^+ and Cl^--HCO_3 exchange and also H^+ conductance.

When the basolateral membrane vesicles were incubated in a Cl^--free medium with a transmembrane gradient of $[Na^+]$ ($[Na^+]_o = 0$, $[Na^+]_i = 190$ mM), there was an amiloride-inhibitable quench of AO absorbance. The high concentration of amiloride required for inhibition ([amiloride] = 0.5 mM) was consistent with its blocking Na^+-H^+ exchange rather than Na^+ conductance channels, which are blocked by micromolar concentrations of amiloride (4). When transmembrane pH gradients were established (pH$_o$ = 7.5, pH$_i$ = 6.0), $^{22}Na^+$ uptake was largely, but not completely, blocked by amiloride. The isolated vesicles also exhibited properties consistent with the presence of a Cl^--HCO_3 exchanger with many characteristics similar to the red cell anion exchanger. When vesicles were loaded with solution containing Cl^- (and $^{36}Cl^-$) but no Na^+, the rate of Cl^- efflux into a Cl^--free solution increased manyfold upon addition of HCO_3 to the external bath.

Complementary studies were performed on isolated OC. When the cells were acidified by brief treatment with a low dose of nigericin, there was a monotonic, Na^+-dependent alkalinization with a recovery time of 5 min. This recovery was completely blocked by 1-mM amiloride and was not affected by high $[K^+]$ plus valinomycin. By monitoring pH$_i$ at different $[Na^+]$, the apparent K_m for the Na^+-dependent alkalinization was found to be 45.6 mM Na^+. Also, efflux of Cl^- was stimulated by increased $[Cl^-]_i$ or $[HCO_3]_o$, while Cl^- influx was stimulated by increased $[Cl^-]_o$ or $[HCO_3]_i$. The HCO_3-dependent Cl^- fluxes were blocked by 0.2-mM DIDS. By varying $[Cl^-]$ and $[HCO_3]$ inside and outside of the cells, the following estimates of K_m were obtained: HCO_{3in} = 2.5 mM, HCO_{3out} = 7.5 mM, Cl_{in} = 20 mM, Cl_{out} = 17.5 mM. Thus, the affinities for Cl^- were approximately the same on both sides of the serosal membrane, while there was a higher affinity for HCO_3 inside as compared with outside.

These experiments on isolated cells and membrane vesicles are generally consistent with there being both Na^+-H^+ and Cl^--HCO_3 exchangers present in the serosal membranes of OC. However, neither the isolated OC nor the isolated membrane vesicles were completely pure, so the exchangers may be located in other cell types or in the apical membrane. In addition, the cells in the intact epithelium may behave differently from cells and membranes that have been pulled from their normal *in vivo* orientation.

The recently developed microspectrofluorimetric technique for determining pH_i in single OC within isolated rabbit gastric glands has obviated these problems (41, 42). In this approach, pH_i in a single OC in an intact rabbit gastric gland is determined by using a fluorimeter attached to a microscope (54). This technique also allows measurements of pH_i in adjacent CC, which behave rather differently from OC (see below). It has been shown that OC exhibited Na^+-dependent and Cl^--dependent changes in pH_i that are similar, but not identical, to the changes measured in whole glands (compare 39, 40 and 41, 42).

When the solution bathing the glands was changed from one containing NaCl to a Na^+-free Ringer's solution, the pH_i of the OC decreased (reversibly) from 7.1 to 6.8; when it was changed from NaCl to Cl^--free Ringer's solution the pH_i increased to 7.4–7.7. The independence of the Na^+ and Cl^- effects was demonstrated most clearly in experiments in which the glands were first bathed with Na^+-free *and* Cl^--free Ringer's solution (*N*-methylglucamine gluconate, NMGglu). When an inward-directed gradient of Cl^- was created by replacing NMGglu with NMGCl, the OC acidified rapidly from a pH_i of 7.0–7.2 to 6.5–6.7. When an inward-directed Na^+ gradient was subsequently established by treatment with Na-gluconate, the cells alkalinized from a pH_i of 7.0–7.2 to 7.3–7.6. The Cl^--dependent change was blocked by 0.2-mM DIDS; the Na^+-dependent change was blocked by 1-mM amiloride. Measurements of rate coefficients showed that Cl^--dependent changes in pH_i occurred at least four times faster than did Na^+-dependent changes (42). Thus, microspectrofluorimetric measurements have confirmed the presence of Na^+-H^+ and Cl^--HCO_3 exchangers in OC. The anion exchanger has a higher activity than the cation exchanger.

It would be interesting to study pH_i regulation in intact epithelium under conditions in which the luminal and serosal solutions could be manipulated independently. This would provide useful information about the H^+ permeability and pH_i regulatory mechanisms in the apical and basolateral membranes. It will also be important to determine if these exchangers are the same as those in other cell types. For example, Muallem et al (37) performed their investigations of Na^+-H^+ exchange in OC under conditions ($pH_i = 7.5$, $pH_o = 6.0$) that would have completely blocked the activity of the Na^+-H^+ exchanger of other cell types (e.g. 2, 3, 19). The low sensitivity of the anion exchanger in OC to DIDS suggests that it is related, but not identical, to the anion exchanger of red cells. Finally, the fact that amiloride does not always completely block realkalinization of acidified cells may indicate that other pH$_i$ regulatory mechanisms, e.g. Na-H-Cl-HCO$_3$ transport (7, 52) or NaHCO$_3$ symport (6), may exist. This possibility should be investigated.

How Much Does pH$_i$ in OC Change During the Resting-Secreting Transition?

Experiments on frog gastric mucosa using spectroscopic (BTB) or biochemical (creatine kinase reaction) methods (14, 22) showed large increases in pH$_i$ (e.g. from pH$_i$ 7.1–7.4 to 8.0) during stimulation of H$^+$ secretion with histamine, which uses cyclic AMP as a second messenger (31). In contrast, experiments performed on isolated OC using DMO indicated that stimulation causes only small increases or no change in pH$_i$. For example, isolated canine OC suspended in a Ringer's solution (pH$_o$ = 7.30–7.45) have a DMO-derived pH$_i$ = 7.28 whether in a resting or histamine-stimulated state (9). In isolated frog OC (36) stimulation of resting OC (pH$_i$ = 7.19) with dibutyryl cyclic AMP caused pH$_i$ to increase by 0.12 pH units. Because of the technical problems associated with the DMO, BTB, and creatine kinase techniques, it is not possible to conclude whether pH$_i$ increases by a small ($\leq$ 0.1 pH unit) or large (0.4–1.0 pH unit) amount.

We recently completed a study in which pH$_i$ of OC was measured using microspectrofluorimetry of BCECF-loaded OC in intact rabbit gastric glands perfused with an NaCl Ringer's solution containing 10-mM HEPES and equilibrated with air [pH$_o$ = 7.45 (42)]. Under resting conditions, pH$_i$ was 7.11 and did not change in response to stimulation with histamine. Histamine plus isobutylmethylxanthine (IBMX, a potent phosphodiesterase inhibitor) caused pH$_i$ to increase in only 60% of the OC; the average increase in pH$_i$ in these cases was only 0.11 pH units. In the other 40% of the cases, pH$_i$ remained constant during treatment with histamine plus IBMX. Although it was not possible to measure actual H$^+$ secretion by the individual cells, the relatively large sample size ($>$ 30 cells) indicates that the pH$_i$ in OC is close to 7.1 in both resting and stimulated OC. Thus the Cl$^-$-HCO$_3$ exchanger in the serosal membrane of OC appears to be very good at eliminating excess base produced during H$^+$ secretion by the H,K-ATPase at the luminal membrane (for more details see below).

Is There a H$^+$ Conductance in the Basolateral Membrane of Oxyntic Cells?

Muallem et al (37) showed that *isolated* basolateral membranes had conductance pathways for K$^+$ and H$^+$ (but, interestingly, not for Cl$^-$). When an in $>$ out gradient of [K$^+$] was established (creating an inside negative potential), there was an uptake of AO that was inhibited by Ba^{2+}, which blocks K^+ channels. These studies imply that there was a potential-driven uptake of H^+ into the vesicles. However, this apparent H^+ conductance has not been observed in intact glands (39). When acidified glands (pH_i 6.6–6.7) were treated with high $[K^+]$ or high $[K^+]$ and valinomycin, pH_i did not change. pH_i changed only after tetrachlorosalicylanide (a potent protonophore) was added to the gland suspension. Similar results have also been obtained on isolated OC (37). The data indicate that isolated basolateral membranes demonstrate a H^+ conductance that the membranes of the intact cells do not exhibit.

Buffer Capacity of Oxyntic and Chief Cells

The buffer capacity (B_i) of a solution is defined as $\Delta[H^+]/\Delta pH$. The intrinsic B_i of OC was determined to be 51 mM/pH (37) by monitoring the immediate increase in pH_i after NH_4Cl was added to a suspension of cells. Intact gastric glands also have $B_i = 45$ mM/pH (39). These data indicate that B_i of CC must also be 45–50 mM/pH.

STUDIES ON CHIEF CELLS

Two recent studies (41, 42) have shown that CC exhibit both similarities to and differences from OC. When CC in isolated rabbit gastric glands were treated with Na^+-free Ringer's solution, pH_i decreased rapidly from 7.1 down to 6.50; OC acidify only to pH_i 6.8. When the glands were treated with Cl^--free solutions, pH_i of CC increased from 7.1 to 7.3; OC alkalinize to pH_i 7.4–7.7. As was true for the OC, when an in > out gradient of $[Na^+]$ was established in Cl^--free solutions, CC alkalinized; when an in > out gradient of $[Cl^-]$ was established in Na^+-free solutions, CC acidified.

STUDIES ON SURFACE CELLS

Regulation of pH_i in isolated SEC has been studied using the acridine orange (AO) technique (described above for work on isolated membrane vesicles). AO is distributed across all the cellular membrane compartments according to the established pH gradients, so it is impossible to obtain quantitative information about pH_i using this technique. However, Fromm and his colleagues have argued that qualitative information about mechanisms of pH_i regulation can be obtained (18, 38). Their general approach was to acidify isolated SEC using the ammonium-loading technique mentioned above; this treatment causes the AO signal to be quenched. The dissipation of this apparent acidification was then monitored under a variety of conditions.

When acid-loaded cells were resuspended in a NaCl Ringer's solution containing 5 mM K$^+$ (HEPES-buffered, [HCO$_3$] = 0.2 mM) there was an initial rapid dissipation of the pH gradient followed by a much slower rate of dissipation over the course of 30 min. The two phases of gradient dissipation were stimulated twofold if the Na$^+$-containing solutions were also made K$^+$-free; dissipation was blocked in Na$^+$-free solutions. The apparent K_m for the Na$^+$ effect was 56 mM. Li$^+$ alone had 40% of the effect of Na$^+$, but Li$^+$ added in the presence of Na$^+$ was inhibitory. In the presence of a 50-mM Na$^+$ solution with no K$^+$ outside, amiloride inhibited the rate of gradient dissipation with an ID$_{50}$ = 38 μM (38). Dibutyrylcyclic AMP inhibited the rate of Na$^+$-induced dissipation of the gradient, though these inhibitory effects were very small (18).

Much of these data for SEC (Na$^+$ dependence and inhibition by Li$^+$ and amiloride) are consistent with the presence of a Na$^+$-H$^+$ exchanger in SEC that is inhibited by cyclic AMP [much like that observed in *Necturus* gallbladder (44)]. However, the K$^+$ dependence of this apparent Na$^+$-H$^+$ exchanger is quite unusual. The Na$^+$-H$^+$ exchanger of OC (37) and gastric glands (39) is not affected by [K$^+$] between 5 and 150 mM. Also, the slow time course of gradient dissipation in SEC was very different from that observed in OC or gastric glands. It will be important to determine the origin of the K$^+$ dependence of apparent Na$^+$-H$^+$ exchange in SEC.

The same AO technique was utilized to assess HCO$_3$-induced dissipation of the apparent acidic pH gradient of SEC (18). When the isolated cells were suspended in a Na$^+$-free Ringer's solution, there was a HCO$_3$-dependent (or pH-dependent; pH was not held constant) dissipation of the pH gradient. This dissipation was unaffected by the presence of Cl$^-$, but it was inhibited 80% by 10 μM SITS (which blocks red cell anion exchange), 25% by 1-mM dbcAMP, 15% by 1-mM IBMX, and 50% by 1-μM prostaglandin E$_2$ (PGE$_2$). These data are consistent with the presence of a HCO$_3$ conductance in SEC that is inhibited by SITS, cAMP, and PGE$_2$.

pH$_i$ REGULATION, ION TRANSPORT, AND ULCERS

Cl$^-$-HCO$_3$ and Na$^+$-H$^+$ Exchange and H$^+$ and Cl$^-$ Transport by Gland Cells

The short-circuited gastric mucosa secretes more Cl$^-$ than H$^+$ in both resting and histamine-stimulated states, which creates a lumen-directed, negative short-circuit current (30). Recent experiments on *Necturus* gastric mucosa have shown that this electrogenic Cl$^-$ secretion occurs solely from the glands, which contain only OC (13).

In *resting* tissues (from which no H$^+$ is secreted) Cl$^-$ secretion may be generated by the same cation and anion exchangers involved in pH$_i$ regulation. For example, the simultaneous operation of Na$^+$-H$^+$ and Cl$^-$-HCO$_3$

exchangers in parallel at the serosal membrane of resting OC (and CC?) could lead to the accumulation of Cl^- above its electrochemical equilibrium, as observed at the serosal membranes of SEC (11, 33). In the short-circuited state, the presence of Cl^- conductance channels in the mucosal membrane (10, 57) would allow Cl^- to "leak" from the cell to the luminal solution. The following data are consistent with this parallel exchanger model: (a) Cl^- transport by resting gastric mucosa is critically dependent on the presence of both Na^+ (30) and HCO_3 (35, 51) in the serosal solution; (b) Cl^- transport is inhibited more than 60% by amiloride analogues, which are potent inhibitors of Na^+-H^+ exchange, and more than 80% by SITS (T. E. Machen et al, unpublished data).

In *stimulated* gastric mucosa both H^+ and Cl^- secretion increase compared to resting tissues; Cl^- secretion is greater than H^+ secretion. The rate of Cl^- secretion increases by a factor of at least two during stimulation of H^+ secretion in amphibian mucosae (T. E. Machen, unpublished results), and by a factor of three in the piglet (17). This increase in Cl^- transport serves both to rid the OC of HCO_3 and to accompany H^+ secreted into the gland lumen *via* the H,K-ATPase. Thus, the Cl^--HCO_3 exchanger at the serosal membrane of OC increases its turnover by at least a factor of two or three during the resting-stimulated transition. This increase in turnover could occur through any (or all) of three different mechanisms: (a) an increase in V_{max} (e.g. an increase in the number of exchangers); (b) a change in K_m for HCO_3 or Cl^- on the two sides of the membrane; or (c) a decrease in cellular $[Cl^-]$. This third possibility arises because pH_o, pH_i, and therefore $[HCO_3]_o$ and $[HCO_3]_i$, and $[Cl^-]_o$ all remain constant during stimulation. Alternatively, other mechanisms [e.g. Na-HCO_3 symport (6)] could be activated to operate in parallel with the Cl^--HCO_3 exchanger. The simplest possibility is that $[Cl^-]_i$ decreases (e.g. due to a large efflux from the cell into the glandular lumen), and this serves to increase the turnover of the anion exchanger. It will be important to determine which of these possibilities is correct and whether other agents known to affect gastric function can alter the activity of the pH_i regulatory mechanisms present in the various cell types.

Interactions Among pH_o, pH_i, Na^+ Absorption, and HCO_3 Secretion

SEC appear to fulfill two ion transport functions, Na^+ absorption (13) and HCO_3 secretion (15, 16, 51). Na^+ absorption probably occurs as described by the Koefoed-Johnsen-Ussing (25) leak-pump model: Na^+ leaks into the cell across the mucosal membrane through amiloride-sensitive Na^+ channels (13) and is pumped across the serosal membrane on the Na,K-ATPase (also see 32). The Na^+ entry step is markedly pH sensitive: Transport is completely blocked when the luminal pH is 2 (32) with an apparent pK of 4. Reducing luminal pH from 7.5 to 2 on *Necturus* antrum (which has no OC, only SEC) has no effect on BCECF-determined pH$_i$ (M. Townsley & T. E. Machen, unpublished results). This finding implies that blockage of Na$^+$ entry by low luminal pH is exerted at the outside surface of the membrane.

SEC also appear to secrete HCO$_3$ at low rates (1/10 to 1/20 of H$^+$ secretion) (15, 16, 51). HCO$_3$ secretion requires serosal HCO$_3$, oxidative metabolism (15, 51), and Cl$^-$ in the serosal solution (51). The requirement for mucosal Cl$^-$ is debated (compare 15 and 51). Na$^+$-free serosal solution causes a small ($\leq$ 25%) reduction in HCO$_3$ transport with Cl$^-$-containing solution on the mucosal side and nearly complete inhibition with Cl$^-$-free solution on the mucosal side. Addition of 0.6-mM DIDS to the mucosal solution had no effect, but there was a 50% reduction of HCO$_3$ secretion when 0.6-mM DIDS was added to the serosal solution. Addition of acetazolamide had no effect (51). The relationships among these observations on various effects in intact tissue and apparent Na$^+$-H$^+$ exchange (38) and HCO$_3$ (18) conductance observed in isolated SEC remain to be determined.

Impermeability/Permeability of Membranes to H$^+$ and Its Relation to Ulcers

One of the most interesting questions about the stomach is how it is able to withstand enormous transmembrane pH gradients. One possibility is that the HCO$_3$ secreted by SEC is trapped in the rich mucus gel, thereby providing an unstirred layer of HCO$_3$-rich fluid to neutralize the luminal H$^+$ (1, 20). Indeed, a stable pH gradient across the mucus layer that adheres to the surface cells of rabbit gastric mucosa has been measured using antimony pH electrodes. The pH on the luminal side of the mucus is 2.31 and moves to 7.26 at the apical membrane of the SEC. The pH gradient within the mucus was reduced, but not abolished, by 10-mM potassium cyanide, which suggests that active processes are involved in this apparent pH gradient (56).

We would like to add a note of caution regarding the idea that HCO$_3$ entrapped in the mucus protects the SEC. First, measurements of pH gradients in mucus are technically difficult. Second, the rates of HCO$_3$ secretion are very low. Third, the blocking effects of low luminal pH on Na$^+$ transport are nearly identical for fundic SEC (32), which are covered with mucus, and for isolated frog skin cells (34), which do not secrete base and which are not covered to any great extent with mucus. It appears that reducing the pH of the bulk luminal solution has the same effect on pH at the epithelial cell surface in both frog skin and rabbit gastric mucosa, i.e. the mucus/HCO$_3$ gel does not significantly buffer the luminal surface of gastric mucosa.

A recent study on primary monolayer cultures of canine chief cells (which secrete no mucus) showed that the apical membranes of these cells were able to withstand a luminal pH of 3 for up to 4 hr, even when transepithelial ion transport was inhibited by adding ouabain to the serosal solution (49). These data are consistent with recent measurements of pH_i in *Necturus* antrum: When serosal pH_i of antral epithelium was 7.5, pH_i ($=7.3$) was unaffected by changes of luminal pH between 2 and 7.5 (M. Townsley & T. E. Machen, unpublished data). It appears that the apical membranes of both CC and SEC are, under normal conditions, virtually impermeable to H^+. In contrast to the apparent impermeability of the *apical* membranes of gastric cells to H^+, the *serosal* membranes are very permeable to H^+. For example, when pH of the serosal Ringer's solution of either rabbit gastric glands (50) or *Necturus* antrum is reduced below 7, pH_i is also reduced as a linear function of pH_o (M. Townsley & T. E. Machen, unpublished results). The large H^+ permeability of the serosal membranes of gastric cells is probably provided by the anion and cation exchangers located there. Interestingly, when rabbit gastric glands are incubated in K-gluconate Ringer's (which eliminates the substrates for both Na^+-H^+ and Cl^--HCO_3 exchange), pH_i ($= 7.3$) is independent of pH_o between pH_o values of 6.5 and 8.5 (50).

These data lead to the following hypothesis for the role of H^+ in the formation of ulcers: Under normal conditions the lumen-facing membranes of all cells of the stomach are effectively impermeable to H^+. Although the luminal membranes of the different cells have specialized permeation pathways for K^+, Cl^-, Na^+, and possibly HCO_3, H^+ is excluded. Any small amount of H^+ that leaks into the cells is transported into the blood by the pH_i regulatory mechanisms located at the serosal membranes. The HCO_3 and mucus gel are not important factors in maintenance of the H^+ impermeability of the luminal membrane of SEC. H^+ gains access to the cytoplasm across the *luminal* membranes only if an artificial H^+ permeability is induced (by mechanical damage, oxidation products, alcohol, bile salts, or weak acids, for example). Once H^+ gets into the cells or gains access to the *serosal* membrane (e.g. via broken tight junctions), damage will spread quickly to adjacent cells because the H^+ permeability (via Na^+-H^+ and Cl^--HCO_3 exchange) of the serosal membranes is very high. Once the permeability barrier has been broken, other factors also become important in the ultimate generation of an ulcer. These include the rate at which leaked H^+ can be eliminated via the blood and the rate at which damaged areas are covered by migration of adjacent cells ("restitution," see 8). It will be interesting to determine how the pH_i regulatory mechanisms (or their failure) may be involved in the etiology of gastric ulcers.

SUMMARY

The following picture emerges from the relatively small literature concerned with pH_i regulation in the stomach. *Oxyntic cells* have a H,K-ATPase at the luminal membrane and both Na$^+$-H$^+$ and Cl$^-$-HCO$_3$ exchangers at the serosal membrane. The intrinsic buffer capacity is 40–50 mM/pH. In the resting state, when the H,K-ATPase is inactive, pH$_i$ is 7.1. The Na$^+$-H$^+$ exchanger prevents acidic shifts of pH$_i$, and the Cl$^-$-HCO$_3$ exchanger prevents alkaline shifts. The combined operation of the two appears to contribute directly to the net Cl$^-$ secretion (and short-circuit current) generated by resting OC. In the stimulated state, H$^+$ secretion into the gland lumen via the H,K-ATPase increases, and Cl$^-$ movement across the serosal membrane via exchange for HCO$_3$ doubles or triples; however, pH$_i$ remains roughly constant (ΔpH$_i$ $\leq$ 0.1 units). The large increase in Cl$^-$ and HCO$_3$ movement across the serosal membrane requires one (or all) of the following events: The anion exchanger changes its characteristics (K_m or V_{max}); [Cl$^-$]$_i$ decreases; or other membrane mechanisms must be activated. *Chief cells* also have a pH$_i$ of 7.1 and a B_i of 40–50 mM/pH. They exhibit Na$^+$-dependent and Cl$^-$-dependent changes of pH$_i$ that are consistent with the presence of both Na$^+$-H$^+$ and Cl$^-$-HCO$_3$ exchangers. The Na$^+$-dependent changes of pH$_i$ are larger and the Cl$^-$-dependent changes are smaller in CC than in OC. *Surface cells* exhibit changes of AO fluorescence that indicate that there is a Na$^+$-H$^+$ exchanger and a HCO$_3$ conductance. The H$^+$ permeability of the luminal membranes of *all* cells is very low, while that of the serosal membrane (via the cation and anion exchangers) is high.

ACKNOWLEDGMENTS

We would like to thank: Jeffrey Demarest, Wendy McLennan, Eric Manning, Paul Negulescu, and Michael Starlinger for their contributions during the various stages of our work on pH$_i$ regulation and ion transport in the gastric mucosa; Roger Y. Tsien for his continuing and invaluable contributions to much of the work reviewed here. Work from this laboratory is supported by NIH grants AM17328 and AM19520.

Literature Cited

1. Allen, A., Garner, A. 1980. Mucous and bicarbonate secretion in the stomach and their possible role in mucosal protection. *Gut.* 21:249–62
2. Aronson, P. S., Nee, J., Suhm, M. A. 1982. Modifier role of internal H$^+$ in activating the Na$^+$-H$^+$ exchanger in renal microvillus membrane vesicles. *Nature* 299:161–163
3. Aronson, P. S., Suhm, M. A., Nee, J. 1983. Interaction of external H$^+$ with Na$^+$-H$^+$ exchanger in renal microvillus membrane vesicles. *J. Biol. Chem.* 258:6767–71
4. Benos, D. J. 1982. Amiloride: A molecular probe of sodium transport in tissues and cells. *Am. J. Physiol.* 242:C131–45
5. Berglindh, T. 1977. Absolute dependence on chloride for acid secretion in isolated gastric glands. *Gastroenterology* 73:874–80
6. Boron, W. F., Boulpaep, E. L. 1983. Intracellular pH regulation in the renal proximal tubule of the salamander. Basolateral HCO$_3$ transport. *J. Gen. Physiol.* 81:53–94
7. Boron, W. F., Russell, J. M. 1983. Stoichiometry and ion dependencies of the intracellular pH regulating mech-

anism in squid giant axons. *J. Gen. Physiol.* 81:373–99

8. Critchlow, J., Magee, D., Ito, S., Takeuchi, K., Silen, W. 1985. Requirements for restitution of the surface epithelium of the frog stomach after mucosal injury. *Gastroenterology* 88:237–49

9. Croft, D. N., Ingelfinger, F. J. 1969. Isolated gastric parietal cells: Oxygen consumption, electrolyte content and intracellular pH. *Clin. Sci.* 37:491–501

10. Cuppoletti, J., Sachs, G. 1984. Regulation of gastric acid secretion via modulation of a chloride conductance. *J. Biol. Chem.* 259:14952–59

11. Curci, S., Schettino, T. 1984. Effect of external Na^+ on intracellular chloride activity in the surface cells of frog gastric mucosa. *Pflügers Arch.* 401:152–59

12. Davies, R. E. 1951. The mechanism of hydrochloric acid production by the stomach. *Biol. Rev.* 26:87–120

13. Demarest, J. R., Scheffey, C., Machen, T. E. 1986. Identification of separate cells for Cl^- and Na^+ transport in gastric mucosa. *Biophys. J.* 49:398a

14. Ekblad, E. B. M. 1980. Increase of intracellular pH in secreting frog gastric mucosa. *Biochem. Biophys. Acta* 632: 375–85

15. Flemstrom, G. 1977. Active alkalinization by amphibian gastric fundic mucosa in vitro. *Am. J. Physiol.* 233:E1–E2

16. Flemstrom, G., Garner, A. 1982. Gastroduodenal HCO_3 transport: Characteristics and proposed role in acidity regulation and mucosal protection. *Am. J. Physiol.* 242:G183–93

17. Forte, J. G., Machen, T. E. 1975. Transport and electrical phenomena in resting and secreting piglet gastric mucosa. *J. Physiol.* 244:33–51.

18. Furukawa, T., Olender, E., Fromm, D., Kolis, M. 1985. Effects of cyclic adenosine monophosphate and prostaglandins on Na^+- and HCO_3-induced dissipation of a proton gradient in isolated gastric mucosal cells of rabbits. *Gastroenterology* 89:500–6

19. Grinstein, S., Cohen, S., Rothstein, A. 1984. Cytoplasmic pH regulation in thymic lymphocytes by an amiloride-sensitive Na^+/H^+ antiport. *J. Gen. Physiol.* 83:341–69

20. Heatly, N. G. 1959. Mucosubstance as a barrier to diffusion. *Gastroenterology* 37:313–17

21. Hersey, S. J. 1971. The energetic coupling of acid secretion in gastric mucosa. *Philos. Trans. R. Soc. London, Ser. B.* 262:261–77

22. Hersey, S. J. 1979. Intracellular pH measurements in gastric mucosa. *Am. J. Physiol.* 237:E82–E89

23. Hersey, S. J., High, W. L. 1971. On the mechanism of acid secretory inhibition by acetazolamide. *Biochim. Biophys. Acta* 233:604–9

24. Kafoglis, K., Hersey, S. J., White, J. F. 1984. Microelectrode measurements of K^+ and pH in rabbit gastric glands: Effect of histamine. *Am. J. Physiol.* 246:G433–44

25. Koefoed-Johnsen, V., Ussing, H. H. 1958. The nature of the frog skin potential. *Acta Physiol. Scand.* 42:298–308

26. Lee, H. C., Breitbart, H., Berman, M., Forte, J. G. 1979. Potassium-stimulated ATPase activity and H^+ transport in gastric microsomal vesicles. *Biochim. Biophys. Acta* 553:103–31

27. Lee, H. C., Quintanilha, A. T., Forte, J. G. 1976. Energized gastric microsomal vesicles. An index using metachromatic dyes. *Biochem. Biophys. Res. Commun.* 72:1179–86

28. Lepke, S., Fasold, H., Pring, M., Passow, H. 1976. A study of the relationship between the inhibition of anion exchange and binding to the red cell membrane of 4,4'-diisothiocyanostilbene-2,2'-disulfonic acid (DIDS) and its dihydroderivative (H_2DIDS). *J. Membr. Biol.* 29:147–77

29. Machen, T. E., Forte, J. G. 1984. Anion secretion by gastric mucosa. In *Chloride Transport Coupling in Biological Membranes and Epithelia,* ed. G. A. Gerencser, pp. 415–46. Amsterdam: Elsevier

30. Machen, T. E., McLennan, W. L. 1980. Na^+-dependent H^+ and Cl^- transport by in vitro frog gastric mucosa. *Am. J. Physiol.* 238:G403–13

31. Machen, T. E., Rutten, M. J., Ekblad, E. B. M. 1982. Histamine, cyclic AMP and activation of piglet gastric mucosa. *Am. J. Physiol.* 242:G79–G84

32. Machen, T. E., Silen, W., Forte, J. G. 1978. Na^+ transport by mammalian stomach. *Am. J. Physiol.* 234:E228–35

33. Machen, T. E., Zeuthen, T. 1982. Cl^- transport by gastric mucosa: Cellular Cl^- activity and membrane permeability. *Philos. Trans. R. Soc. London Ser. B* 299:559–73

34. Mandel, L. J. 1978. Effects of pH, Ca, ADH, and theophylline on kinetics of Na entry in frog skin. *Am. J. Physiol.* 235:C35–C48

35. Manning, E. C., Machen, T. E. 1982. Effects of bicarbonate and pH on chloride transport by gastric mucosa. *Am. J. Physiol.* 243:G60–G68

36. Michelangeli, F. 1978. Acid secretion

and intracellular pH in isolated oxyntic cells. *J. Membr. Biol.* 38:31–50

37. Muallem, S., Burnham, C., Blissard, D., Berglindh, T., Sachs, G. 1985. Electrolyte transport across the basolateral membrane of the parietal cells. *J. Biol. Chem.* 260:6641–53

38. Olender, E. J., Fromm, D., Furukawa, T., Kolis, M. 1984. H$^+$ disposal by rabbit gastric mucosal surface cells. *Gastroenterology* 86:698–705

39. Paradiso, A. M., Negulescu, P. A., Machen, T. E. 1986. Na$^+$-H$^+$ and Cl$^-$-OH$^-$ (HCO$_3$) exchange in gastric glands. *Am. J. Physiol.* 250:G524–34

40. Paradiso, A. M., Tsien, R. Y., Machen, T. E. 1984. Na$^+$-H$^+$ exchange in gastric glands as measured with a cytoplasmic-trapped, fluorescent pH indicator. *Proc. Natl. Acad. Sci. USA* 81:7436–40

41. Paradiso, A. M., Tsien, R. Y., Machen, T. E. 1986. Measurements of intracellular pH (pH$_i$) in parietal and chief cells of rabbit gastric glands using dual wavelength microspectrofluorimetry and digital image processing. *Biophys. J.* 49:155a

42. Paradiso, A. M., Tsien, R. Y., Machen, T. E. 1986. Regulation of intracellular pH (pH$_i$) in parietal cells and chief cells of rabbit gastric glands. Submitted for publication

43. Rehm, W. S., Sanders, S. S. 1975. Implications of the neutral carrier Cl$^-$/HCO$_3$ exchange mechanism in gastric mucosa. *Ann. NY Acad. Sci.* 264:442–35

44. Reuss, L., Petersen, K.-U. 1985. Cyclic AMP inhibits Na$^+$/H$^+$ exchange at the apical membrane of *Necturus* gallbladder epithelium. *J. Gen. Physiol.* 85:409–30

45. Rink, T. J., Tsien, R. Y., Pozzan, T. 1982. Cytoplasmic pH and free Mg^{2+} in lymphocytes. *J. Cell Biol.* 95:189–96

46. Roos, A., Boron, W. F. 1981. Intracellular pH. *Physiol. Rev.* 61:296–434

47. Rose, I. A. 1968. The state of magnesium in cells as estimated from the adenylate kinase equilibrium. *Proc. Natl. Acad. Sci. USA* 61:1079–86

48. Sachs, G., Chang, H., Rabon, E., Schackmann, R., Lewin, M., Saccomani, G. 1976. A nonelectrogenic H$^+$ pump in plasma membranes of hog stomach. *J. Biol. Chem.* 251:7690–98

49. Sanders, M. J., Ayalon, A., Roll, M., Soll, A. H. 1985. The apical surface of canine chief cell monolayers resists H$^+$ back-diffusion. *Nature* 313:52–54

50. Starlinger, M., Paradiso, A., Machen, T. E. 1986. Intracellular pH regulation in isolated gastric glands. *Am. Gastroenterol. Assoc. Meet. Abstr.*

51. Takeuchi, K., Merhav, A. M., Silen, W. 1982. Mechanism of luminal alkalinization by bullfrog fundic mocosa. *Am. J. Physiol.* 243:G377–88

52. Thomas, R. C. 1977. The role of bicarbonate, chloride and sodium ions in the regulation of intracellular pH in snail neurons. *J. Physiol.* 273:317–38

53. Thomas, J. A., Kolbeck, P. C., Langworthy, T. A. 1982. Spectrophotometric determination of cytoplasmic and mitochondrial pH transitions using trapped pH indicators. In *Intracellular pH: Its Measurement Regulation and Utilization in Cellular Functions*, pp. 105–23. New York: Liss

54. Tsien, R. Y., Rink, T. J., Poenie, M. 1985. Measurements of cytosolic free Ca^{2+} in individual small cells using fluorescence microscopy with dual excitation wavelengths. *Cell Calcium* 6:145–57

55. Waddell, J. C., Butler, T. C. 1959. Calculation of intracellular pH from the distribution of 5,5-dimethyl-2,4-oxazolidinedione (DMO). Application to skeletal muscle of dog. *J. Clin. Invest.* 38:720–29

56. Williams, S. E., Turnberg, L. A. 1981. Demonstration of pH gradient across mucus adherent to rabbit gastric mucosa: Evidence for a "mucus-bicarbonate" barrier. *Gut* 22:94–96

57. Wolosin, J. M., Forte, J. G. 1984. Stimulation of oxyntic cell triggers K$^+$ and Cl$^-$ conductances in aptical H$^+$-K$^+$-ATPase membrane. *Am. J. Physiol.* 246:C537–45

Ann. Rev. Physiol. 1987. 49:35–49

ROLE OF H$^+$ AND HCO$_3^-$ IN SALT TRANSPORT IN GALLBLADDER EPITHELIUM

Luis Reuss and James S. Stoddard

Department of Cell Biology and Physiology, Washington University School of Medicine, 660 South Euclid Avenue, St. Louis, Missouri 63110

INTRODUCTION

The gallbladder epithelium has been used extensively for more than 20 years as a model system for investigations of the mechanisms of isosmotic salt and water transport. In particular, the transporting gallbladder of *Necturus maculosus* has been employed successfully in intracellular microelectrode and quantitative microscopic studies. The main advantages of this preparation are its simple structure (a monolayered epithelium of only one cell type that can be mounted as a flat sheet) and the large size of the cells. Experimental studies in *Necturus* gallbladder have permitted the formulation of well-founded working hypotheses to explain the mechanisms of salt and water transport. The main purpose of this review is to summarize recent experimental results in support of the notion that apical membrane NaCl entry occurs via a double ion exchange mechanism, namely the operation of independent Na$^+$-H$^+$ and Cl$^-$-HCO$_3^-$ exchangers. Since alternative entry mechanisms have been proposed, we present and illustrate criteria to distinguish between double exchange and other NaCl entry models. In addition, we briefly discuss the effects of cyclic AMP (cAMP) on these transport mechanisms and thus on the regulation of salt transport.

BASIC TRANSPORT FUNCTIONS OF GALLBLADDER EPITHELIUM

The epithelium of the gallbladder absorbs salt and water in isosmotic proportions (7, 8, 9, 34, 50) and hence causes an increase in the luminal

35

0066-4278/87/0315-0035$02.00

concentration of the impermeant components of bile. In all species, NaCl is absorbed under physiologic conditions. In some species, $NaHCO_3$ is absorbed as well. The presence of Na^+ in the lumen is necessary for fluid absorption, whereas the requirement for Cl^- is not absolute (see 10 and 38 for review).

The rate of fluid absorption in *Necturus* gallbladder ranges from ~5 to ~20 μl cm^{-2} h^{-1} (6, 38, 39) and is greater in mammals (for reviews see 10 and 38). Incubation in bathing media containing HCO_3^- and CO_2 stimulates fluid absorption in both mammalian (8, 24) and amphibian gallbladders (39). This effect is partly attributable to the fact that $NaHCO_3$ is absorbed, but in addition, NaCl transport is stimulated.

The epithelium of the gallbladder can perform active transport of both Na^+ and Cl^- (see 10, 18, 38, for reviews). Transepithelial ion transport involves salt entry at the apical membrane and exit across the basolateral membrane. The transported ions pass through a transport pool that includes the entire cytosolic compartment, as evidenced by the rapid changes in cytosolic ionic activities observed during perturbations of ion transport induced by changes in extracellular ion concentrations (see below).

Water absorption is coupled to salt transport and in all likelihood occurs by an osmotic mechanism. In general, it is believed that salt transport causes small osmotic gradients across both cell membranes, making the cell interior hyperosmotic to the mucosal solution and hyposmotic to the fluid in the lateral intercellular spaces. The resulting elevation of the hydrostatic pressure in the lateral spaces causes the solution to flow towards their open ends, i.e. to the subepithelial space (5, 11).

Paracellular salt transport may play an important role in overall transepithelial transport under in vivo conditions. However, under in vitro conditions significant paracellular net fluxes are unlikely because the electrochemical driving forces are insignificant. The spontaneous voltage generated across transporting gallbladders bathed symmetrically with identical solutions is generally less than $\pm$ 2 mV (10, 38, 39). The small magnitude of this voltage is attributable in part to the high conductance of the paracellular pathway relative to that of the cellular pathway (19). In addition, recent data indicate that most cell membrane pathways responsible for transepithelial salt transport are electroneutral, i.e. do not cause net transfer of charge.

Figure 1 summarizes measurements of intracellular ionic activities in *Necturus* gallbladder epithelium under control in vitro conditions. These data, together with the extracellular activities and the cell membrane voltages, indicate that the steady-state electrochemical gradients favor entry of Na^+ and exit of K^+ and Cl^- across both cell membranes. Since NaCl is transported from the mucosal to the serosal fluid, there are net influxes of Na^+ and Cl^- at the apical membrane and net effluxes of both ions at the basolateral membrane. Comparison of the directions of these fluxes with those of the thermodynamic driving forces shown in Figure 1 indicates that apical membrane Cl$^-$ influx and basolateral membrane Na$^+$ efflux must be active processes, whereas Na$^+$ entry at the apical membrane and Cl$^-$ exit at the basolateral membrane could be electrodiffusive. However, in *Necturus*, as well as in other species, both cell membranes are primarily K$^+$ conductive, whereas the apical membrane P$_{Na}$ and the basolateral membrane P$_{Cl}$ are both very small (16, 21, 26, 37, 41, 47). Electrodiffusion can account for only small fractions of the steady-state rates of Na$^+$ entry and Cl$^-$ efflux, which indicates that other transport mechanisms must exist for these ions.

Entry of NaCl across the apical membrane is thought to occur via electroneutral transport mechanisms. At the basolateral membrane, Na$^+$ is extruded from the cell by the Na$^+$ pump, which also transports K$^+$ inwards, and Cl$^-$ is extruded by cotransport with K$^+$. The Na$^+$ pump appears to be the only primary active transporter. All other transporters operate in an *overall* downhill fashion. The magnitude and direction of the thermodynamic forces that drive electrodiffusive and carrier-mediated transport across the cell membranes ultimately depend on the work of the Na$^+$ pump.

MECHANISMS OF Na$^+$ AND Cl$^-$ TRANSPORT AT THE APICAL MEMBRANE

Investigators agree that apical entry of Na$^+$ and Cl$^-$ occurs by electroneutral, carrier-mediated transport mechanisms. In the recent literature pertaining to the gallbladders of several species, the following mechanisms have been proposed: (*a*) NaCl cotransport (2, 15, 17, 29, 44); (*b*) NaKCl$_2$ cotransport (6); (*c*) double exchange (Na$^+$-H$^+$, Cl$^-$-HCO$_3^-$) (1, 23, 36, 39, 40, 48, 49); and (*d*) combinations of the preceding mechanisms (4, 6). We discuss these possibilities below, emphasizing results obtained in *Necturus* gallbladder. Although there is still controversy as to the precise mechanism of NaCl entry in this tissue under control conditions, a strong case can be made for the double-exchange model. In addition, experimental evidence has been presented that indicates that apical membrane Na$^+$-H$^+$ and Cl$^-$-HCO$_3^-$ exchangers play a role in cell volume regulation after osmotic shrinkage (44).

Apical Membrane NaCl Cotransport

The first arguments in favor of apical membrane NaCl cotransport were based on measurements of transepithelial Na$^+$ and Cl$^-$ fluxes and unidirectional fluxes from the apical solution into rabbit gallbladder epithelium (2, 17). Both groups of investigators found that the absorptive flux of either ion depended on the presence of the counter-ion, results consistent with the possibility of NaCl cotransport. Using intracellular ion-sensitive microelectrodes, it was

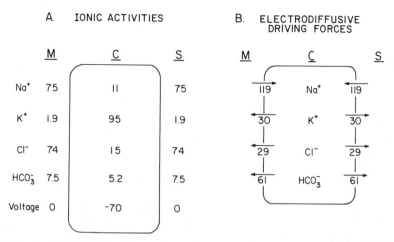

Figure 1 (A) Membrane voltages, extracellular and intracellular ionic activities in *Necturus* gallbladder under control conditions (1% CO_2, 99% air). (B) Net driving forces for electrodiffusive ion movements across the cell membranes, expressed as $\Delta\bar{\mu}_i/F$, in millivolts. Note that the passive driving forces favor outward transport of K^+, Cl^-, and HCO_3^-, and inward transport of Na^+, at both membranes. The activity values shown are those employed in the calculations according to the equations in the text (see also 39 and 40). The values of membrane voltages and intracellular activities shown here are representative, although the means may vary somewhat among laboratories.

also shown, in gallbladders of rabbit and *Necturus,* that luminal Na^+ removal caused a decrease in intracellular Cl^- activity (14, 20, 42).

Although the above results are consistent with the NaCl cotransport hypothesis, alternative explanations are possible: (*a*) Cotransport might involve K^+ as well, as was demonstrated later in other tissues (22, 33), or (*b*) NaCl entry could be via cation (Na^+-H^+) and anion (Cl^--HCO_3^-) exchangers, as first suggested for apical membrane of small intestine (30–32). With regard to these possibilities, it should be noted that steady-state measurements alone cannot distinguish between cotransport and double exchange. In the case of cotransport, the fluxes of Na^+ and Cl^- are obligatorily coupled, both under transient and steady-state conditions. In the case of double exchange, the fluxes are equal at steady state but can be dissociated under non-steady-state conditions.

In the studies described above, tracer fluxes were measured after 20- or 30-min incubations in Na^+-free or Cl^--free medium (2, 17). These intervals are long enough to permit sizable changes in intracellular ionic composition. Therefore, the observed counter-ion dependence of the Na^+ and Cl^- fluxes could have been indirect; for instance, it could have been caused by alterations of the intracellular pH (pH_i).

Further support for the NaCl cotransport hypothesis has been presented by

Spring and his associates (see 44 for review). These authors employed optical techniques to measure the rate of cell swelling upon serosal addition of ouabain. The rationale of these experiments was that ouabain abolishes basolateral salt transport, leaving apical NaCl entry initially unchanged. Thus, these investigators took the initial rate of cell swelling to be a measure of the rate of NaCl entry. Ouabain-induced cell swelling did not require K$^+$ in the apical bathing solution, was inhibited by the diuretic bumetanide ($K_i \approx 10^{-8}$ M), and was insensitive to both amiloride (an inhibitor of Na$^+$-H$^+$ exchange) and the disulfonic stilbene derivative SITS (an inhibitor of Cl$^-$-HCO$_3^-$ exchange) (15, 29, 44). In addition, bumetanide was found to reduce transepithelial fluid transport and to cause decreases in the intracellular activities of Na$^+$ and Cl$^-$ (29). Some of these results have not been confirmed by others. Davis & Finn (6), also using optical techniques, found a rate of ouabain-induced cell swelling of about one third that reported by Ericson & Spring (15). On the basis of their data, Davis & Finn questioned the validity of the assumption that ouabain stops basolateral NaCl exit, while entry remains unchanged. Davis & Finn also claimed that swelling was prevented by removing K$^+$ from the luminal solution, a result they interpreted as an indication of NaKCl$_2$ cotransport (6).

Results from our laboratory are inconsistent with a sizable contribution of either cotransport mechanism to apical NaCl entry. Bumetanide had no effect on fluid absorption or on intracellular activities of Na$^+$ or Cl$^-$ (39, 40, 49, and L. Reuss, unpublished observations). In addition, K$^+$ removal from the luminal solution (with simultaneous addition of Ba^{2+} to reduce K$^+$ leak from the cells) caused no measurable changes in intracellular activities of Na$^+$ or Cl$^-$ (39).

Apical Membrane Na$^+$-H$^+$ Exchange

Early studies on mammalian gallbladders revealed that the luminal fluid acidifies during absorption (3, 25, 45, 46, 51), although the precise mechanism of this acidification was not established. The first demonstration of apical membrane Na$^+$-H$^+$ exchange in gallbladder epithelium was made in *Necturus* (48), by measurements of extra- and intracellular pH and intracellular Na$^+$ activity under a variety of experimental conditions.

The first of these studies involved measurements of acidification of a poorly buffered luminal solution (1-mM HEPES, pre-equilibrated with air). *Necturus* gallbladders were mounted horizontally in a chamber (apical side up), and the luminal fluid volume was kept small and was replaced continuously at the beginning of the experiment. The pH of the solution near the apical surface of the epithelium was measured with a miniature glass or liquid-membrane pH electrode. Upon arrest of superfusion, the mucosal solution acidified. This acidification was observed in the presence of Na$^+$ in the luminal solution and when luminal Na^+ was replaced with Li^+, but not when K^+, Rb^+, Cs^+, or tetramethylammonium (TMA^+) were employed. The presence of amiloride (0.1 to 1 mM) in the apical bathing solution inhibited acidification.

Addition of ouabain to the serosal bathing solution caused a slow, progressive decrease of the rate of luminal acidification. However, when ouabain-treated epithelia were depleted of Na^+ by prolonged exposure to a Na^+-free apical bathing medium, restoration of the inward Na^+ gradient by brief reexposure to Na^+ resulted in recovery of H^+ secretion. The apparent K_m for external Na^+ was about 11 mM, a value close to that found in renal cortical brush border vesicles (27, 28).

These results indicate that secretion of H^+ (or an equivalent flux) is coupled to Na^+ transport at the apical membrane and driven by the inward Na^+ gradient. The transport rate was shown to be independent of the apical membrane voltage. The rates of acidification were not significantly different when the apical membrane was depolarized to -16 mV or hyperpolarized to -93 mV by exposure to either a high-K^+ or a high-TMA^+ mucosal solution, respectively (48). In summary, the ionic requirements, electroneutrality, apparent K_m for external Na^+, and the amiloride sensitivity of the process are all consistent with a Na^+-H^+ exchange mechanism similar to that described in apical membranes of renal proximal tubule (27, 28).

Studies were also conducted to assess the influence of Na^+-H^+ exchange on intracellular pH. If the above conclusions are correct, addition of amiloride to the apical bathing solution should cause a decrease in pH_i, since H^+ extrusion is reduced while metabolic H^+ production continues. Complete removal of Na^+ from the apical bathing solution should also cause a decrease in pH_i, due to reversal of apical membrane Na^+-H^+ exchange. These predictions were confirmed by measuring pH_i with intracellular glass or liquid-membrane microelectrodes (48).

Straightforward predictions can also be made concerning the effects of amiloride and of changing luminal solution pH on the intracellular Na^+ activity (aNa_i^+). Exposure to amiloride should cause a decrease of aNa_i^+, since Na^+ entry is inhibited without an immediate effect on basolateral exit. This was shown to be the case, both in tissues incubated in HEPES (49) and in HCO_3^--CO_2-buffered solutions (39). Amiloride also halved the unidirectional uptake of $^{22}Na^+$ across the apical membrane (49). In 1-mM HEPES solution, reduction of the luminal solution pH from 7.7 to 6.1 caused a reversible fall in aNa_i^+. This effect was abolished by 1-mM amiloride (49). As expected from the effects of amiloride on apical membrane tracer Na^+ uptake and on aNa_i^+, exposure to 1-mM amiloride decreased the rate of fluid absorption by about 50% (39).

In conclusion, these studies demonstrate that amiloride-sensitive Na^+-H^+

exchange is present at the apical membrane of *Necturus* gallbladder, under control conditions, both in HEPES-buffered and in HCO$_3^-$-CO$_2$-buffered solutions. The process is electroneutral, and its rate influences pH$_i$, aNa$_i^+$, and transepithelial salt and water transport. Intracellular acidification upon Na$^+$ removal from the apical bathing medium was also observed by Zeuthen & Machen (56). In addition, these authors confirmed the observation of Na$^+$-dependent apical solution acidification.

Apical Membrane Cl$^-$-HCO$_3^-$ Exchange

Apical membrane Cl$^-$-HCO$_3^-$ exchange has been demonstrated in *Necturus* gallbladder by measurements of extra- and intracellular pH and intracellular Cl$^-$ activity (40). Luminal solution pH was measured with the technique described in the preceding section. Luminal alkalinization was observed when mucosal superfusion was stopped immediately after luminal Na$^+$ removal or addition of 1-mM amiloride. The magnitude of the alkalinization was reduced when the duration of Na$^+$ removal or exposure to amiloride was prolonged. These results can be best explained by apical membrane Cl$^-$-HCO$_3^-$ (or Cl$^-$-OH$^-$) exchange, whereby immediately after inhibition (by amiloride) or reversal (by Na$^+$-free medium) of Na$^+$-H$^+$ exchange, the secretion of base is manifest. The anion exchange rate falls with time after these perturbations because in both cases the increase in intracellular H$^+$ activity will reduce [HCO$_3^-$] (or [OH$^-$]), thus reducing the net driving force for anion exchange. Finally, stopping mucosal superfusion shortly after luminal Cl$^-$ removal resulted in an increased rate and magnitude of mucosal solution acidification compared to control (NaCl Ringer's solution) conditions. This rate fell if the period of Cl$^-$ removal was prolonged, as expected from the reduction of aCl$_i^-$, or if the tissue was exposed to the disulfonic stilbene derivative SITS (0.5 mM), as expected from inhibition of anion exchange.

The effects of changes in luminal solution [Cl$^-$] on pH$_i$ were measured with liquid-membrane intracellular microelectrodes. If Cl$^-$ entry is via exchange with intracellular HCO$_3^-$ or OH$^-$, removing luminal Cl$^-$ should reverse the direction of the anion fluxes: Cl$^-$ should then leave the cell while HCO$_3^-$ (or OH$^-$) enters, causing intracellular alkalinization. Measurements of pH$_i$ before, during, and after Cl$^-$ removal confirmed this prediction (40). In addition, SITS (0.5 mM) reduced the steady-state change in pH$_i$ caused by removal of luminal Cl$^-$. Interestingly, the rise in pH$_i$ upon Cl$^-$ removal was larger in tissues incubated in 10-mM HCO$_3^-$/1% CO$_2$ than in 1-mM HEPES. Inasmuch as the total intracellular buffering power should be greater in the former condition, these results suggest that the base efflux was greater in HCO$_3^-$ medium and therefore that the anion exchanged for Cl$^-$ is HCO$_3^-$ and not OH$^-$ (40). Zeuthen & Machen (56) also found that removal of apical solution Cl$^-$ caused rapid intracellular alkalinization.

Changes in luminal solution [HCO_3^-] should also have predictable effects on aCl_i^-. Reduction of extracellular [HCO_3^-] from 10 to 1 mM at constant P_{CO_2} caused a reversible increase of aCl_i^-. In five experiments, aCl_i^- rose from 21.3 ± 1.5 to 25.6 ± 1.2 mM after 3 min in the low-HCO_3^- medium ($p <$ 0.005; L. Reuss and J. L. Costantin, unpublished observations). In addition, SITS reduced the initial rate of fall of aCl_i^- upon removal of Cl^- from the mucosal solution (40); SITS also inhibited fluid absorption by about 60% (39).

These results demonstrate that there exists a Cl^--HCO_3^- exchanger at the apical membrane of *Necturus* gallbladder epithelium. This exchanger appears to be active under control in vitro conditions, is sensitive to SITS, and can operate in either direction, according to the net chemical driving force.

Rates of Apical Membrane Ion Exchange

Although the results described above suggest that the rates of Na^+ entry via cation exchange and of Cl^- entry via anion exchange are sizable, they do not demonstrate that these are the dominant or sole mechanisms of NaCl entry across the apical membrane. To quantify such rates, the following principle was employed: At the steady state preceding an external change in solution composition, the intracellular ionic contents are invariant with time. Thus, if the chemical gradients on either exchanger are instantaneously altered such that the net driving force becomes zero, and if basolateral ion transport remains initially unchanged, then the initial rate of fall of the intracellular content of the ion of interest is an estimate of the preceding steady-state rate of entry. For the case of Na^+ entry via Na^+-H^+ exchange, the Na^+ net flux will be zero at an extracellular Na^+ activity satisfying the condition

$$aNa_o^+ \cdot aH_i^+ = aNa_i^+ \cdot aH_o^+ \qquad \qquad 1.$$

where extracellular and intracellular chemical activities are indicated by the subscripts o and i, respectively.

Since aNa_i^+ and the two pH values at steady state had been measured, the value of aNa_o^+ at which net exchange would stop could be easily calculated. This value corresponded to an extracellular [Na^+] of 10 mM. When this maneuver was performed by partial replacement of mucosal solution Na^+ with TMA^+, aNa_i^+ fell at an average initial rate of 3.7 mM/min. If we assume no initial change in cell volume and a cell height of 35 μm, the calculated fall in intracellular Na^+ content was equivalent to 75% of the value predicted from the average rate of transepithelial Na^+ transport (39). This is a minimum estimate, since cell shrinkage and reduced basolateral Na^+ exit both tend to decrease the rate of fall of aNa_i^+. To test that the net flux via the exchanger is indeed zero in this experiment, the initial rate of fall of aNa_i^+ was also measured upon reduction of mucosal [Na$^+$] to 10 mM and simultaneous addition of 1-mM amiloride. Amiloride had no effect on the initial rate of fall of aNa$_i^+$ (39).

The rate of Cl$^-$ entry via the anion exchanger was estimated using the same principle. The extracellular [Cl$^-$] that should cause cessation of net Cl$^-$ entry via this pathway is given by

$$a\text{Cl}_o^- \cdot a\text{HCO}_3^-{}_i = a\text{Cl}_i^- \cdot a\text{HCO}_3^-{}_o \qquad \qquad 2.$$

where the intracellular bicarbonate activity is calculated assuming equal intra- and extracellular P$_{CO_2}$ values and identical activity coefficients in the intra- and extracellular compartments. From Equation 2 it was calculated that a reduction in extracellular [Cl$^-$] to 29 mM should immediately stop anion exchange. When this condition was met, aCl$_i^-$ fell at an initial average rate of 5.9 mM/min, which fully accounts for the average rate of net transepithelial Cl$^-$ transport determined from transepithelial fluid transport measurements (39). To test that net Cl$^-$ flux via anion exchange indeed ceases in this experiment, measurements of aCl$_i^-$ were made upon reducing external [Cl$^-$] and simultaneously adding SITS. SITS had no effect on the rate of fall of aCl$_i^-$, which indicates that net anion exchange was effectively stopped by the reduction of external Cl$^-$ (39).

Measurements of acid and base secretion into the apical solution and kinetic analysis of ^{36}Cl$^-$ entry under a variety of experimental conditions support the existence of both Na$^+$-H$^+$ and Cl$^-$-HCO$_3^-$ exchange at the apical membrane of rabbit (4) and guinea pig gallbladders (36, 53). However, the rates of ion transport by these exchangers have not been established.

Independence of Na$^+$ and Cl$^-$ Entry

The thermodynamic predictions of NaCl cotransport and double exchange under steady-state conditions are identical (1, 6); therefore, it is impossible to distinguish between these two modes of electroneutral NaCl entry from steady-state measurements of cell volume, ion fluxes, transepithelial fluid transport, or intracellular ion activities. This is evident from the following equations (6):

for cotransport:

$$U_{net} = RT \ln [a\text{Na}_o^+ \cdot a\text{Cl}_o^-/a\text{Na}_i^+ \cdot a\text{Cl}_i^-] \qquad \qquad 3.$$

and for double exchange:

$$U_{net} = RT \ln [a\text{Na}_o^+ \cdot a\text{H}_i^+ \cdot a\text{Cl}_o^- \cdot a\text{HCO}_{3i}^-/a\text{Na}_i^+$$
$$\cdot a\text{H}_o^+ \cdot a\text{Cl}_i^- \cdot a\text{HCO}_3^-{}_o], \qquad \qquad 4.$$

where U_{net} denotes net chemical potential difference.

If the P_{CO_2} and the pK' are the same on both sides of the membrane, Equation 4 reduces to Equation 3. In other words, the steady-state result of any change in extracellular Na^+ or Cl^- concentrations is the same for each of the two transport models. However, these models behave differently during transient alterations in transport, because in the case of cotransport the Na^+ and Cl^- fluxes are *obligatorily coupled,* whereas in the case of double exchange the *coupling is indirect,* and the Na^+ and Cl^- fluxes can be dissociated.

If the NaCl cotransport model is correct, the following predictions can be made: (*a*) If either Na^+ or Cl^- is removed from the mucosal bathing solution the intracellular activities of both ions should *initially* fall at equal rates, given that efflux across the basolateral membrane continues at the preceding steady-state rate and apical net transport of both Na^+ and Cl^- is reversed. The numerator in Equation 3 falls to zero and the coupling between the fluxes of Na^+ and Cl^- is obligatory. (*b*) The value of aNa_o^+ at which NaCl entry will stop can be calculated from Equation 3 to be about 3 mM. A similar calculation indicates that NaCl entry will cease when aCl_o^- is reduced to essentially the same value. (*c*) Changes in aNa_o^+ or aCl_o^- should have no direct effects on intracellular pH.

In contrast, if the double-exchange model is correct, and if the exchangers are independent, the net driving forces are given by

$$U_{net} = RT \ln [aNa_o^+ \cdot aH_i^+ / aNa_i^+ \cdot aH_o^+] \qquad 5.$$

and

$$U_{net} = RT \ln [aCl_o^- \cdot aHCO_{3i}^- / aCl_i^- \cdot aHCO_{3\ o}^-]. \qquad 6.$$

The predictions for transient behavior of this system are different from those for cotransport: (*a*) Na^+ removal from the external solution will cause a decrease in aNa_i^+ at a rate faster than the decrease of aCl_i^-, because the driving force for Na^+-H^+ exchange will be instantaneously reversed, whereas that for Cl^--HCO_3^- exchange will initially be unchanged. Eventually, aCl_i^- falls as intracellular acidification leads to a decrease in $aHCO_{3\ i}^-$. Similarly, Cl^- removal will cause a much faster initial fall in aCl_i^- than in aNa_i^+. (*b*) The value of aNa_o^+ at which net Na^+ entry will cease is dependent on pH_i and pH_o but is independent of the Cl^- activities. This value can be calculated from Equation 5 to be about 7.5 mM (equivalent to a concentration of 10 mM). The value of aCl_o^- necessary to reduce Cl^- entry to zero, calculated from Equation 6, is about 22 mM, equivalent to a concentration of 29 mM. (*c*) Changes in aNa$_o^+$ or aCl$_o^-$ should cause immediate changes in intracellular pH.

When these studies were done the results were those expected for the double-exchange, not the cotransport, hypothesis. (*a*) When Na$^+$ was removed from the mucosal solution, aNa$_i^+$ fell at an initial rate 4.3 times greater than the rate of fall of aCl$_i^-$ (6.5 versus 1.5 mM/min). When Cl$^-$ was removed, aCl$_i^-$ fell 7.5 times faster than aNa$_i^+$ (12.0 versus 1.6 mM/min) (39). Similar results were obtained by Baerentsen et al (1). (*b*) Net entry of either Na$^+$ or Cl$^-$ did stop upon reduction of the respective external concentration to the value predicted by the double-exchange model, as demonstrated by the lack of effect of amiloride or SITS on the initial rates of fall of activity of Na$^+$ or Cl$^-$, respectively (39). (*c*) Removal of Na$^+$ from the mucosal compartment caused rapid cellular acidification; removal of Cl$^-$ caused intracellular alkalinization. It is worth mentioning that Ericson & Spring (15) found cessation of ouabain-induced cell swelling when they reduced mucosal [Na$^+$] to 10 mM, a concentration at which the driving force for NaCl cotransport should still favor entry.

The possibility still exists that removal of either Na$^+$ or Cl$^-$ from the luminal solution could cause rapid activation of the countertransport pathways, which would be either inoperative or operating at a reduced rate in the control condition (6). This possibility is difficult to reconcile with the magnitude of the effect of 1-mM amiloride on aNa$_i^+$. Under control conditions, 1-mM amiloride causes a decrease in aNa$_i^+$ at an initial rate of 2.4 mM/min, which accounts for about 50% of the rate of transepithelial Na$^+$ transport, whereas there is no measurable change in aCl$_i^-$ (39). This concentration of amiloride also causes rapid intracellular acidification (48). Taken together, these results demonstrate that the transport pathway inhibited by amiloride is Na$^+$-H$^+$ exchange and not NaCl cotransport and that this pathway is functioning at a high rate under control conditions and accounts for most, if not all, of apical membrane Na$^+$ entry.

Cremaschi and his coworkers suggested the possibility of coexistence of cotransport and countertransport systems at the apical membrane of rabbit gallbladder (4). A similar suggestion has been made for *Necturus* gallbladder by Davis & Finn (6). In our opinion, the major arguments for NaCl or NaKCl$_2$ cotransport in *Necturus* gallbladder are based on results obtained with bumetanide. We have no explanation for the different effects of this diuretic on fluid absorption and intracellular ionic activities reported by different groups of investigators (6, 29, 39). Regardless of this controversy, the hypothesis of cotransport cannot be proven on this pharmacological basis alone, because bumetanide has been shown to inhibit not only cotransport but also anion exchange (52).

ROLE OF CYCLIC AMP IN APICAL MEMBRANE ION TRANSPORT

In recent years significant progress has been made in our understanding of the mechanisms of inhibition of fluid transport in gallbladder by elevation of intracellular cAMP levels (see 54 for review). Since agents such as prostaglandins, secretin, and vasoactive intestinal peptide (VIP) elevate intracellular cAMP, cAMP may play a central role in fluid transport regulation in this epithelium, as it does in many other systems.

Cyclic AMP inhibits fluid absorption and in some cases causes net secretion (53). The inhibition of absorption observed in rabbit gallbladder was attributed to inhibition of coupled NaCl influx at the apical membrane, as studied with transepithelial unidirectional fluxes and determinations of Na^+ and Cl^- influx across the apical membrane (17). This conclusion was consistent with early results in *Necturus* gallbladder, in which cAMP was claimed to cause reductions of both aNa_i^+ and aCl_i^-, with no measurable membrane voltage changes (12). These results were questioned on the basis of later studies in the same preparation that demonstrated that cAMP causes apical membrane depolarization together with a large increase in apical membrane conductance (13). Both the depolarization and the increase in conductance were shown to be caused by a large increase in apical membrane electrodiffusive Cl^- permeability (35). This increase in apical membrane Cl^- conductance results in recycling of Cl^- that enters by Cl^--HCO_3^- exchange. Because of the cAMP-induced apical membrane P_{Cl}, aCl_i^-, falls to electrochemical equilibrium levels, and basolateral membrane Cl^- extrusion is reduced.

In addition, cAMP inhibits apical membrane Na^+-H^+ exchange, as shown by reductions of aNa_i^+ and pH_i, inhibition of luminal solution acidification, reduction of the rates of change of aNa_i^+ upon changes in external $[Na^+]$, and inhibition of the Na^+-dependent pH_i recovery from an intracellular acid load (43). This inhibition of Na^+-H^+ exchange accounts for the fall in apical Na^+ entry, which combined with the reduced net Cl^- influx explains the inhibition of NaCl and fluid absorption.

In guinea pig gallbladder, PGE_1, which elevates intracellular cAMP levels, induces fluid secretion and a net HCO_3^- flux from serosa to mucosa (24). This could be caused by stimulation of Cl^--HCO_3^- exchange at the apical membrane, an effect expected as a result of the fall in aCl_i^-. In contrast, in *Necturus* gallbladder, cAMP appears to inhibit Cl^--HCO_3^- exchange, as shown by a decrease in the luminal alkalinization elicited by brief exposure to amiloride (35) or by mucosal Na^+ removal (L. Reuss, J. L. Costantin, J. Bazile, unpublished observations).

It has also been proposed that cAMP induces an increase in electrodiffusive HCO_3^- permeability at the apical membrane in *Necturus* gallbladder (55).

This conclusion was based on the different effects of the phosphodiesterase inhibitor IBMX on the cell membrane voltage in HCO$_3^-$-free medium and in 25-mM HCO$_3^-$. A transient hyperpolarization was observed in the latter condition only. However, this interpretation would require a very large apical membrane HCO$_3^-$ equilibrium potential, which would be incompatible with the intracellular HCO$_3^-$ concentrations estimated from pH$_i$ measurements (43). The same group of investigators found evidence consistent with an IBMX-induced reduction in basolateral P$_K$, which could account in part for the cell membrane depolarization elicited by elevations of intracellular cAMP levels.

CONCLUSIONS

The results summarized in this review provide strong evidence that double ion exchange is the major mechanism of apical membrane NaCl entry in *Necturus* gallbladder epithelium. Coupling of the inward fluxes of Na$^+$ and Cl$^-$ across the apical membrane is indirect and modulated by intracellular pH. A complete picture of acid and base transport across the basolateral membrane is not yet available, but clearly the transporters present at the apical membrane can export a sizable fraction of the intracellular acid load. The apical membrane ion transport mechanisms proposed for this model system have also been found in apical membranes of other epithelia, such as small intestine and renal proximal tubule. The possibility of apical salt entry via double ion exchange should be carefully considered in preparations in which the evidence for cotransport consists only of steady-state measurements of ion transport.

ACKNOWLEDGMENTS

We thank C. U. Cotton, D. C. Howe, and Y. Segal for useful comments on the manuscript; J. L. Costantin and J. E. Bazile for technical assistance; and C. A. Krah and J. E. Jones for secretarial help. This work was supported in part by NIH Grant AM19580 (LR) and a National Kidney Foundation Fellowship to JSS.

Literature Cited

1. Baerentsen, H., Giraldez, F., Zeuthen, T. 1983. Influx mechanisms for Na$^+$ and Cl$^-$ across the brush border membrane of leaky epithelia: A model and microelectrode study. *J. Membr. Biol.* 75:205–18
2. Cremaschi, D., Hénin, S. 1975. Na$^+$ and Cl$^-$ transepithelial routes in rabbit gallbladder. Tracer analysis of the transports. *Pflügers Arch.* 361:33–41
3. Cremaschi, D., Hénin, S., Meyer, G. 1979. Stimulation by HCO$_3^-$ of Na$^+$ transport in rabbit gallbladder. *J. Membr. Biol.* 47:145–70

4. Cremaschi, D., Meyer, G., Bermano, S., Marcati, M. 1983. Different sodium chloride cotransport systems in the apical membrane of rabbit gallbladder epithelial cells. *J. Membr. Biol.* 73:227–35
5. Curran, P. F., MacIntosh, J. R. 1962. A model system for biological water transport. *Nature* 193:347–48
6. Davis, C. W., Finn, A. L. 1985. Effects of mucosal sodium removal on cell volume in *Necturus* gallbladder epithelium. *Am. J. Physiol.* 249:C304–12
7. Diamond, J. M. 1962. The reabsorptive

function of the gall-bladder. *J. Physiol.* 161:442–73

8. Diamond, J. M. 1964. Transport of salt and water in rabbit and guinea pig gallbladder. *J. Gen. Physiol.* 48:1–14

9. Diamond, J. M. 1964. The mechanism of isotonic water transport. *J. Gen. Physiol.* 48:15–42

10. Diamond, J. M. 1968. Transport mechanisms in the gallbladder. In *Handbook of Physiology: Section 6, Alimentary Canal, Bile, Digestion, Ruminal Physiology,* ed. W. Heidel, C. F. Code, V:2451–82. Washington: Am. Physiol. Soc.

11. Diamond, J. M., Bossert, W. H. 1967. Standing-gradient osmotic flow. A mechanism for coupling of water and solute transport in epithelia. *J. Gen. Physiol.* 50:2061–83

12. Diez de los Ríos, A., DeRose, N. E., Armstrong, W. McD. 1981. Cyclic AMP and intracellular ionic activities in *Necturus* gallbladder. *J. Membr. Biol.* 63:25–30

13. Duffey, M. E., Hainau, B., Ho, S., Bentzel, C. J. 1981. Regulation of epithelial tight junction permeability by cyclic AMP. *Nature* 294:451–53

14. Duffey, M. E., Turnheim, K., Frizzell, R. A., Schultz, S. G. 1978. Intracellular chloride activities in rabbit gallbladder: Direct evidence for the role of the sodium-gradient in energizing "uphill" chloride transport. *J. Membr. Biol.* 42:229–45

15. Ericson, A.-C., Spring, K. R. 1982. Coupled NaCl entry into *Necturus* gallbladder epithelial cells. *Am. J. Physiol.* 243:C140–45

16. Fisher, R. S. 1984. Chloride movement across basolateral membrane of *Necturus* gallbladder epithelium. *Am. J. Physiol.* 247:495–500

17. Frizzell, R. A., Dugas, M. C., Schultz, S. G. 1975. Sodium chloride transport by rabbit gallbladder. Direct evidence for a coupled NaCl influx process. *J. Gen. Physiol.* 65:830–34

18. Frizzell, R. A., Heintze, K. 1980. Transport functions of the gallbladder. In *International Review of Physiology; Liver and Biliary Tract Physiology I,* ed. N. B. Javitt, pp. 221–47. Baltimore: Univ. Park Press.

19. Frömter, E. 1972. The route of passive ion movement through the epithelium of *Necturus* gallbladder. *J. Membr. Biol.* 8:259–301.

20. Giraldez, F. 1984. Active sodium transport and fluid secretion in the gallbladder epithelium of *Necturus. J. Physiol.* 348:431–55

21. Graf, J., Giebisch, G. 1979. Intracellular sodium activity and sodium transport in *Necturus* gallbladder epithelium. *J. Membr. Biol.* 47:327–55

22. Greger, R. 1981. Chloride reabsorption in the rabbit cortical thick ascending limb of the loop of Henle. A sodium dependent process. *Pflügers Arch. Eur. J. Physiol.* 390:38–43

23. Heintze, K., Petersen, K.-U. 1980. Na/H and Cl/HCO₃ exchange as a mechanism for HCO₃-stimulated NaCl absorption by gallbladder. In *Hydrogen Ion Transport in Epithelia,* ed. I. Schulz, G. Sachs, J. G. Forte, K. J. Ullrich, pp. 345–54. Amsterdam: Elsevier/North-Holland Biomed.

24. Heintze, K., Petersen, K.-U., Olles, P., Saverymuttu, S. H., Wood, J. R. 1979. Effects of bicarbonate on fluid and electrolyte transport by the guinea pig gallbladder: A bicarbonate-chloride exchange. *J. Membr. Biol.* 45:43–59

25. Heintze, K., Petersen, K.-U., Wood, J. R. 1981. Effects of bicarbonate on fluid and electrolyte transport by guinea pig and rabbit gallbladder: Stimulation of absorption. *J. Membr. Biol.* 62:175–81

26. Hénin, S., Cremaschi, D. 1975. Transcellular ion route in rabbit gallbladder. Electrical properties of the epithelial cells. *Pflügers Arch. Eur. J. Physiol.* 355:125–39

27. Ives, H. E., Yee, V. J., Warnock, D. G. 1983. Mixed type inhibition of the renal Na⁺/H⁺ antiporter by Li⁺ and amiloride. *J. Biol. Chem.* 258:9710–16.

28. Kinsella, J. L., Aronson, P. S. 1980. Properties of the Na⁺-H⁺ exchanger in renal microvillus membrane vesicles. *Am. J. Physiol.* 238:F451–69.

29. Larson, M., Spring, K. R. 1983. Bumetanide inhibition of NaCl transport by *Necturus* gallbladder. *J. Membr. Biol.* 74:123–29

30. Liedtke, C. M., Hopfer, U. 1977. Anion transport in brush border membrane isolated from rat small intestine. *Biochem. Biophys. Res. Commun.* 76:579–85

31. Liedtke, C. M., Hopfer, U. 1982. Mechanism of Cl⁻ translocation across small intestinal brush-border membrane. I. Absence of Na⁺-Cl⁻ cotransport. *Am. J. Physiol.* 242:G263–71

32. Liedtke, C. M., Hopfer, U. 1982. Mechanism of Cl⁻ translocation across small intestinal brush-border membrane. II. Demonstration of Cl⁻-OH⁻ exchange and Cl⁻ conductance. *Am. J. Physiol.* 242:G272–80

33. Musch, M. W., Orellana, S. A., Kimberg, L. S., Field, M., Halm, D. R., et al. 1982. Na⁺-K⁺-Cl⁻ co-transport in

the intestine of a marine teleost. *Nature* 300:351–53

34. Onstad, G. R., Schoenfield, L. J., Higgins, J. A. 1967. Fluid transfer in the everted human gallbladder. *J. Clin. Invest.* 46:606–14

35. Petersen, K.-U., Reuss, L. 1983. Cyclic AMP-induced chloride permeability in the apical membrane of *Necturus* gallbladder epithelium. *J. Gen. Physiol.* 81:705–29

36. Petersen, K.-U., Wehner, F., Winterhager, J. M. 1985. Na/H exchange at the apical membrane of guinea-pig gallbladder epithelium: Properties and inhibition by cyclic AMP. *Pflügers Arch. Eur. J. Physiol.* 405:S115–20.

37. Reuss, L. 1979. Electrical properties of the cellular transepithelial pathway in *Necturus* gallbladder. III. Ionic permeability of the basolateral cell membrane. *J. Membr. Biol.* 47:239–59

38. Reuss, L. 1979. Transport in gallbladder. In *Membrane Transport in Biology, Vol. IVB. Transport Organs,* ed. G. Giebisch, D. C. Tosteson, H. H. Ussing, pp. 853–98. Berlin: Springer-Verlag

39. Reuss, L. 1984. Independence of apical membrane Na$^+$ and Cl$^-$ entry in *Necturus* gallbladder epithelium. *J. Gen. Physiol.* 84:423–45

40. Reuss, L., Costantin, J. L. 1984. Cl$^-$/ HCO$_3^-$ exchange at the apical membrane of *Necturus* gallbladder. *J. Gen. Physiol.* 83:801–18

41. Reuss, L., Finn, A. L. 1975. Electrical properties of the cellular transepithelial pathway in *Necturus* gallbladder. II. Ionic permeability of the apical cell membrane. *J. Membr. Biol.* 25:141–61.

42. Reuss, L., Grady, T. P. 1979. Effects of external sodium and cell membrane potential on intracellular chloride activity in gallbladder epithelium. *J. Membr. Biol.* 51:15–31

43. Reuss, L., Petersen, K.-U. 1985. Cyclic AMP inhibits Na$^+$/H$^+$ exchange at the apical membrane of *Necturus* gallbladder epithelium. *J. Gen. Physiol.* 85:409–29

44. Spring, K. R., Ericson, A.-C. 1982. Epithelial cell volume modulation and regulation. *J. Membr. Biol.* 69:167–76

45. Sullivan, B., Berndt, W. O. 1973. Transport by isolated rabbit gallbladders in phosphate-buffered solutions. *Am. J. Physiol.* 225:838–44.

46. Sullivan, B., Berndt, W. O. 1973. Transport by isolated rabbit gallbladders in bicarbonate-buffered solutions. *Am. J. Physiol.* 225:845–48

47. Van Os, C. H., Slegers, J. F. G. 1975. The electrical potential profile of gallbladder epithelium. *J. Membr. Biol.* 24:341–63

48. Weinman, S. A., Reuss, L. 1982. Na$^+$-H$^+$ exchange at the apical membrane of *Necturus* gallbladder. Extracellular and intracellular pH studies. *J. Gen. Physiol.* 80:299–321.

49. Weinman, S. A., Reuss, L. 1984. Na$^+$-H$^+$ exchange and Na$^+$ entry across the apical membrane of *Necturus* gallbladder. *J. Gen. Physiol.* 83:57–74.

50. Whitlock, R. T., Wheeler, H. O. 1964. Coupled transport of solute and water across rabbit gallbladder epithelium. *J. Clin. Invest.* 43:2249–65.

51. Whitlock, R. T., Wheeler, H. O. 1969. Hydrogen ion transport by isolated rabbit gallbladder. *Am. J. Physiol.* 217:310–16

52. Wieth, J. O., Brahm, J. 1985. Cellular anion transport. In *The Kidney: Physiology and Pathophysiology,* ed. D. W. Seldin, G. Giebisch, 1:49–89. New York: Raven

53. Winterhager, J. M., Stewart, C. P., Heintze, K., Petersen, K.-U. 1986. Electroneutral secretion of bicarbonate by guinea pig gallbladder epithelium. *Am. J. Physiol.* 250:C617–28

54. Wood, J. R., Svanvik, J. 1983. Gallbladder water and electrolyte transport and its regulation. *Gut* 24:579–93

55. Zeldin, D. C., Corcía, A., Armstrong, W. McD. 1985. Cyclic AMP-induced changes in membrane conductance of *Necturus* gallbladder epithelial cells. *J. Membr. Biol.* 84:193–206.

56. Zeuthen, T., Machen, T. 1984. HCO$_3^-$/ CO$_2$ stimulates Na$^+$/H$^+$ and Cl$^-$/HCO$_3^-$ exchange in Necturus gallbladder. In *Hydrogen Ion Transport in Epithelia,* ed. J. G. Forte, D. G. Warnock, F. C. Rector, Jr., pp. 97–108. New York: Wiley

Ann. Rev. Physiol. 1987. 49:51–67

PROTON AND BICARBONATE TRANSPORT MECHANISMS IN THE INTESTINE

Ulrich Hopfer and Carole M. Liedtke

Departments of Physiology and Biophysics, Pediatrics, and Developmental Genetics and Anatomy, Case Western Reserve University, Cleveland, Ohio 44106

INTRODUCTION

The intestinal mucosa regulates the pH of chyme by secretion and absorption of protons and/or bicarbonate. These transport processes have not only local importance, but also serve in the acid-base homeostasis of the body. For example, acid balance studies in man and experimental animals have shown that the gastrointestinal tract responds to acute oral acid loads by reducing the quantity of base secreted in the stools (9, 76, 77); similarly, an oral alkali load appears to increase the secreted base (9, 68, 76, 77). Furthermore, the observation that chloridorrhea, an inherited disease, is associated with metabolic alkalosis, convincingly demonstrates the importance of the intestinal electrolyte transport for overall acid-base balance. Congenital chloridorrhea apparently is a defect of Cl^--HCO_3^- exchange in the intestine (4, 113).

From a physiological point of view, H^+ transport in one direction is equivalent to HCO_3^- transport in the other. The physiological equivalence of the two processes is the result of several factors, such as relatively high CO_2 and HCO_3^- concentrations; a high permeability of biological membranes to CO_2, which allows rapid equilibration of CO_2 between different compartments; and the presence of carbonic anhydrase, which accelerates the conversion of CO_2 to HCO_3^- and vice versa. Carbonic anhydrase is found throughout the intestine in soluble and membrane-bound forms. Particularly high concentrations are present in the colon (11, 81). Therefore, for most physiological conditions, the P_{CO_2} values in adjacent compartments are sim-

51

0066-4278/87/0315-0051$02.00

ilar, and proton, CO_2, and HCO_3^- concentrations are in equilibrium with each other and cannot be varied independently.

TRANSPORT AT THE TISSUE LEVEL

General Considerations

In general, two different sources for acidification of the luminal compartment have to be considered: (a) organic acids generated by the small intestinal epithelium through metabolism and released into the lumen; (b) transepithelial transport of H^+ into, or HCO_3^- out of, the lumen, which means blood is the ultimate source of protons (or sink for HCO_3^-). The converse applies to alkalinization. Metabolic CO_2 only makes contributions to the acidification or alkalinization if the resulting HCO_3^- and H^+ are transported out of the epithelium into opposite extracellular compartments, i.e. one solute enters the lumen and the other the interstitium (blood). This vectorial transport of H^+ and HCO_3^- appears as transepithelial proton flow (or bicarbonate flow in the opposite direction) because of the high membrane permeability for CO_2.

Elucidation and characterization of different bicarbonate and proton transport mechanisms are important from biochemical and pharmacological points of view (32). Table 1 lists mechanisms shown to operate in a number of different epithelia but not necessarily in the intestine. This review is concerned with the evidence available for the different membrane transport mechanisms in the intestine, both at the tissue and isolated plasma membrane level (for previous reviews that touch on this subject see References 21, 85, 86, 94). Intestinal electrolyte transport has traditionally been viewed as consisting of only a few, fairly well-defined mechanisms that are similar for all vertebrates, including fish (35, 88, 98, 99). For Na^+ absorption, three different kinds of mechanisms have been distinguished: (a) nutrient-coupled Na^+ transport; (b) amiloride-sensitive, electrogenic (uncoupled) Na^+ absorption; and (c) electroneutral, coupled Na-Cl absorption. Extensive data about electrolyte fluxes and electrophysiology in intact fish intestine and in isolated membrane vesicles from mammalian intestine have, however, substantially changed the views about the so-called coupled, electroneutral Na-Cl absorption. Data from the mammalian intestine are not consistent with molecularly coupled cotransport of Na^+ and Cl^- but instead suggest parallel Na^+-H^+ and Cl^--HCO_3^- exchanges across the brush border membrane (Figure 1A). Fish intestine appears to possess cotransport of Na^+, K^+, and Cl^- with a stoichiometry of $1:1:2$, rather than just cotransport of Na^+ and Cl^- (47). The cellular mechanism for NaCl absorption in fish intestine resembles the one present in the ascending loop of Henle of the mammalian kidney rather than that in the mammalian intestine (41) (Figure 1B). One of the proposed mechanisms of electrolyte transport has remained unaltered, namely the basolateral location of the Na,K-ATPase and its central role in "energizing" electrolyte transport, both secretion and absorption.

Functional Differences Along the Intestinal Tract

OVERVIEW   Regional differences in acidification or alkalinization of the luminal compartment have been recognized for a long time. In many species, alkalinization of chyme occurs in the duodenum and ileum, and acidification takes place in the jejunum. One interesting question is whether a single set of transporters is present throughout the intestine and can produce regional differences, or whether region-specific membrane and cellular mechanisms exist.

DUODENUM   Flemström & Garner (29–31) have shown for many species that the duodenal mucosa possesses a considerable capacity for bicarbonate secretion, independent of the presence of submucosal glands. So far, investigations at the tissue level suggest that two different transport mechanisms exist. Part of the bicarbonate secretion is electrically silent, is dependent on luminal Cl$^-$, and could result from Cl$^-$-HCO$_3^-$ exchange. Another part is associated with an electrical current, which is equivalent to anions moving from blood to the lumen. This portion of the bicarbonate secretion is inhibited

Table 1 Mechanisms of bicarbonate absorption (proton secretion) and bicarbonate secretion (proton absorption)

Mechanism	Cellular site	Organ	References
Bicarbonate absorption			
Na$^+$-H$^+$ exchange	luminal membrane	intestine	87, 70
H$^+$-ATPase	luminal membrane	renal medulla	101
		turtle bladder	65, 39, 40
H,K-ATPase	luminal membrane	stomach,	94
		jejunum of *Amphiuma*	120
		colon	104
Na$^+$-(HCO$_3^-$)^n			
cotransport	basolateral membrane	proximal tubule	127
Cl$^-$-HCO$_3^-$ exchange	basolateral plasma membrane	small intestine	123
Bicarbonate secretion			
Na$^+$-H$^+$ exchange	basolateral membrane	cortical collecting tubule	14
		intestine	3
H$^+$-ATPase	basolateral membrane	turtle bladder	107, 108
Cl$^-$-HCO$_3^-$ exchange	luminal plasma membrane	small intestine	73, 79, 80
HCO$_3^-$ conductance	luminal plasma membrane	duodenum	30, 103
H$^+$ conductance	basolateral plasma membrane	small intestine	3

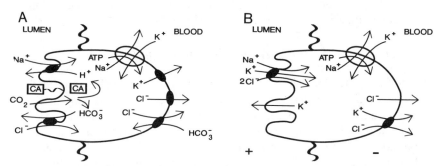

Figure 1 (A) Model for NaCl absorption in mammalian small intestine. Cl⁻ transport pathways in the basolateral plasma membrane and the location of carbonic anhydrase (CA) are speculative. (B) Model for NaCl absorption in fish intestine (47).

by serosal ouabain and is stimulated by prostaglandins. The electrogenic HCO_3^- secretion could result from cytosolic accumulation of HCO_3^- as a consequence of Na^+-H^+ exchange and active Na^+ removal from the cell at the basolateral pole in conjunction with HCO_3^- exit across the brush border membrane via a conductance pathway. A similar mechanism may be responsible for HCO_3^- secretion in *Amphiuma* small intestine (103, 121, 122).

JEJUNUM   The apparent absorption of HCO_3^- by the jejunum is an active, metabolically driven process (7, 57, 63, 90, 90a, 113, 123). The mechanisms in mammalian and amphibian jejunum may be different. Podestra & Mettrick (90a) concluded on the basis of the Na^+ dependence of bicarbonate absorption and the changes in luminal P_{CO_2} under nonequilibrium conditions that the rat jejunum primarily secretes H^+ and that apparent HCO_3^- absorption can be explained on the basis of proton secretion and formation of CO_2 from HCO_3^- within the intestinal lumen. The Na^+ dependence of proton secretion suggests the existence of Na^+-H^+ exchange across the brush border membrane. This conclusion has been criticized by Feldman et al (25), who assert that tissue sources of CO_2 from metabolism and absorbed HCO_3^- have not been considered. They suggest the existence of a mechanism that catalyzes absorption of HCO_3^- directly across the jejunal epithelial cell layer. This idea is based mainly on the insensitivity of HCO_3^- absorption to blood P_{CO_2} and to pH gradients across the epithelium. In *Amphiuma* jejunum, the apparent absorption of bicarbonate seems to result also from H^+ secretion, but it appears to be a primary active process, which may be carried out by a K,H-ATPase in the luminal membrane. The involvement of a K,H-ATPase is suggested by inhibition of H^+ secretion by omeprazole, an inhibitor of gastric K,H-ATPase (120), and by the dependence of HCO_3^- absorption on luminal $[K^+]$ (62, 119).

ILEUM   Rabbit ileum has served as a prototype of small intestine in many in vitro investigations of electrolyte transport. In many species, including the rabbit, the ileum has a considerable capacity for alkalinization (apparent bicarbonate secretion) of chyme (20, 91, 92). An interrelationship between bicarbonate secretion and NaCl absorption is indicated by the mutual effects of the presence of one of the ions on transport of the others and by the types and potencies of agents that inhibit NaCl absorption. HCO$_3^-$ secretion is dependent on the presence of luminal Cl$^-$, and the presence of HCO$_3^-$ increases NaCl absorption (91). These observations taken together suggest the existence of Na$^+$-H$^+$ and Cl$^-$-HCO$_3^-$ exchange mechanisms in the brush border membrane. Studies using inhibitors also support these proposed mechanisms. For example, Nellans et al (89) demonstrated that acetazolamide, a carbonic anhydrase inhibitor, decreases NaCl absorption in rabbit ileum. Furthermore, Humphreys (58) and Liedtke & Hopfer (80) showed for intact rat ileum that NaCl transport and bicarbonate secretion are sensitive to inhibitors of Cl$^-$-HCO$_3^-$ exchange in erythrocytes, such as furosemide and stilbene disulfonates, albeit only at relatively high concentrations.

COLON   Electrolyte transport in the colon has been of considerable interest during the last decade. The proximal and distal regions are quite different with respect to handling of electrolytes under baseline conditions and in response to hormones that affect salt absorption or secretion (18, 102, 106). In land vertebrates that need to conserve Na$^+$ or water, such as herbivores (rabbit) or desert mammals (gerbils), active Na$^+$ absorption in the distal colon occurs predominantly via amiloride-sensitive Na$^+$ conductances in the luminal plasma membrane (99). In contrast, in the proximal colon and in Na$^+$-replete omnivores, such as the laboratory rat, NaCl absorption is predominantly electroneutral and appears to be accomplished by similar mechanisms as in the small intestine (6, 33, 126).

The colon normally secretes bicarbonate into the lumen (112). The secretion is electroneutral, depends on the presence of Cl$^-$ in the lumen, and is inhibited by anion transport inhibitors, such as SITS[1], DIDS, and furosemide (36, 49, 105). It is also inhibited by carbonic anhydrase inhibitors, such as acetazolamide (49). Therefore, it has been assumed that the luminal plasma membrane contains Cl$^-$-HCO$_3^-$ exchangers (99). The intracellular HCO$_3^-$ concentrations are sufficient to "energize" Cl$^-$ absorption via an exchange (22). The observation that genetic chloridorrhea affects not only the ileum but also the colon (64) is consistent with this proposal.

[1]Abbreviations: CA = carbonic anhydrase; DIDS = 4,4'-diisothiocyanostilbene-2,2'-disulfonate; SITS = 4-acetamido-4'-isothiocyanostilbene-2,2'-disulfonate.

Influence of Acid-Base Status On Intestinal Electrolyte Transport

Charney and his colleagues have systematically investigated the effects of arterial and luminal pH and HCO_3^- concentration on small intestinal and colonic electrolyte transport in vivo in both rat and rabbit (15, 16, 26, 27, 74, 117). Changes in the blood parameters were achieved by metabolic or respiratory alkalosis and acidosis. Blood pH and bicarbonate influenced HCO_3^- and Na^+ transport in the ileum of rat and rabbit and in the colon of rat but not in the jejunum of either species or the descending colon of rabbit. In the sensitive regions, net Na^+ absorption decreased with an increase in blood pH and vice versa, while HCO_3^- secretion correlated with plasma HCO_3^-, independently of blood pH and P_{CO_2}. Net Cl^- absorption correlated with blood P_{CO_2} (17). These results suggest that blood pH affects a NaCl absorptive process, possibly by Na^+-H^+ exchange and Cl^--HCO_3^- exchange, and that the plasma HCO_3^- affects an exchange process involving Cl^- absorption and HCO_3^- secretion. The unresponsiveness of rabbit colon to changes in blood pH and HCO_3^- can be explained on the basis of Na^+ absorption via a conductive pathway and lack of Na^+-H^+ exchange (100).

Cellular Sites of Electrolyte and Fluid Transport

Besides regional heterogeneity in transport functions, the intestine displays heterogeneity along the crypt-villus axis. There is considerable reason to believe that salt and fluid secretion are functions of crypt epithelium and that the villus epithelium carries out absorption (28). The best data are available for rabbit colon; they show that crypts are the site of salt and fluid secretion in response to secretagogues (56, 118). Studies with the human colonic cell line T84 suggest that differentiated cells with microvilli and occluding junctions are capable of secretion (19, 82, 83). The existence of different cells along the crypt-villus axis could explain the findings of two different mechanisms of HCO_3^- secretion in the duodenum: electrogenic HCO_3^- secretion and electroneutral Cl^--HCO_3^- exchange (29).

TRANSPORT AT THE ISOLATED MEMBRANE LEVEL

General Considerations

The availability of isolated, highly purified intestinal brush border (51, 54, 67, 96) and basolateral plasma membranes (95) has provided new experimental systems to test membrane mechanisms. In contrast to intact tissue studies, the vesicle system is suited for ion flux measurements under non-steady-state conditions after acute changes of driving forces. This experimental set-up is preferable for probing the nature of transport mechanisms. In addition, a wide range of variables, such as pH, temperature, or ionic compositions of the intravesicular and the extravesicular medium, are experimentally accessible in the isolated vesicle system. However, the physiological significance of findings in isolated membranes can come into question because either lipids (50), membrane proteins, or associated cytoskeletal components may be altered during membrane isolation, or cytosolic components important for normal transport may be missing. To distinguish between specific transport and nonspecific "leakiness", the usual criteria for mediated processes can be employed; these include saturation, co- or countertransport, and inhibition by known transport inhibitors. Ion fluxes have been measured in vesicles either directly with radiolabeled isotopes or indirectly with pH- or potential-sensitive indicator dyes. In addition, light scattering has been used to follow volume changes and thus, indirectly, electrolyte transport (115, 116).

Ion Transport In the Brush Border Membrane

Na^+/H^+ EXCHANGE Evidence for the existence of a transporter mediating Na^+-H^+ exchange comes from rat and rabbit small intestinal brush border membrane vesicles. Essentially three types of experimental results support Na^+-H^+ exchange (13, 23, 43, 70, 87): (*a*) pH gradients stimulate Na^+ transport and support Na^+ movements against a Na^+ concentration gradient. The stimulation persists even in the absence of a diffusion potential. (*b*) Na^+ fluxes down Na^+ gradients stimulate H^+ fluxes in the opposite direction, against H^+ concentration gradients. (*c*) pH-gradient-stimulated Na^+ fluxes are inhibited by concentrations of amiloride and harmaline that typically inhibit Na^+-H^+ exchange. Finally, (*d*) pH-gradient-stimulated cation transport exhibits saturation kinetics and cation specificity similar to those obtained for other Na^+-H^+ exchangers.

Although the existence of intestinal Na^+-H^+ exchange seems well established, relatively little is known about the transporter and its properties (see Reference 2 for reports on other tissues). One of the experimental difficulties in attempting to characterize the transporter is the presence of Na^+ conductance in isolated membrane vesicles (13, 43). The Na^+ conductance was shown to be the dominant pathway for Na^+ movement in the absence of substrates for cotransporters in rabbit jejunal vesicles (43). Since electrophysiological measurements do not show a large Na^+ conductance in intact small intestine, its presence in the membrane probably represents an artifact introduced during isolation. The magnitude of the Na^+ conductance seems to be dependent on intravesicular Ca^{2+} (114).

The properties of jejunal and ileal Na^+-H^+ exchangers appear to be similar, to the extent they have been measured. In addition, Na^+-H^+ exchange behaves similarly in rabbit and rat brush border membrane vesicles. The stoichiometry of Na^+-H^+ exchange is assumed to be 1 : 1 since the initial rates of proton-driven Na^+ fluxes are not influenced by electrical potentials (13, 43, 70, 87) or the presence of anions (13). The exchanger also accepts Li^+ and NH_4^+ as substrates. The pH-gradient-driven Na^+ transport is saturable with reported K_t values between 5 and 16 mM (13, 23, 43, 70) and can be inhibited by amiloride ($I_{50} = .2$ mM at 1 mM Na^+) or harmaline (70). The Na^+-H^+ exchange activity of the isolated membranes explains the apparent Na^+ dependency of bicarbonate absorption in the jejunum (13, 43) and, in conjunction with Cl^--HCO_3^- exchange, the apparently coupled NaCl absorption in the ileum (70, 79, 80). Binder & Murer (6) recently identified a K^+-H^+ exchange, analogous to Na^+-H^+ exchange but distinct from it, in rat ileal brush border membranes.

Cl^-/HCO_3^- (OH^-) EXCHANGE   Evidence for the existence of Cl^--OH^- exchange is similar to that for Na^+-H^+ exchange. Data are available from rat and rabbit: (a) H^+ flux down a pH gradient across the brush border membrane induces Cl^- flux in the same direction, which can be uphill (23, 73, 80). The H^+-driven Cl^- flux is seen in the absence of a diffusion potential, which suggests molecular coupling in the form of either Cl^--H^+ cotransport or Cl^--OH^- exchange. (b) The presence of Cl^- accelerates the dissipation of pH gradients (13, 78). And (c) H^+-driven Cl^- transport is inhibitable by several anion transport inhibitors, such as the stilbene disulfonates (DIDS and SITS), furosemide, and carbonyl cyanide phenylhydrazones (73, 78, 80).

Characterization of the Cl^--OH^- exchanger in rat intestinal and rabbit ileal brush border membranes indicates that HCO_3^- is an effective substrate for the exchanger, more so than OH^- under physiological conditions of 5% CO_2 and 50-mM HCO_3^- (73; U. Hopfer & R. Pienkowski, unpublished observations). This observation suggests that the transporter functions in the intact cell mainly as a Cl^--HCO_3^- exchanger, which would explain the large stimulatory effect of HCO_3^- on intestinal NaCl absorption. Other anions transported by this exchanger are: Br^-, I^-, NO_3^-, and SCN^-.

On the basis of competition and sensitivity to inhibitors, Dobbins and his colleagues (71–73, 97) have provided evidence in rabbit ileal brush border membranes for the existence of at least two different anion exchangers in addition to the Cl^--OH^- transporter. These catalyze SO_4^{2-}-OH^- and oxalate^{2-}-Cl^- exchange. DIDS inhibits these two exchange processes at much lower concentrations than are required to inhibit the Cl^--OH^- exchanger (I_{50} for SO_4^{2-}-OH^- = 9 μM; for Cl^--OH^- = 0.3 mM). Interestingly, HCO_3^- is not a substrate for the SO_4^{2-}-OH^- exchanger.

Cl^- also moves across the isolated brush border membrane in response to diffusion potentials (80). The Cl^- conductance is not inhibitable by stilbene disulfonates and accounts for about one third of Cl^- movement under isotope exchange conditions in rat intestinal brush border membranes.

ABSENCE OF COUPLED NaCl TRANSPORT   The demonstrations of pathways for Na$^+$-H$^+$ and Cl$^-$-HCO$_3^-$ exchange do not exclude the simultaneous presence of coupled NaCl transport. Indeed, one group observed in rabbit ileal vesicles that a small portion of NaCl uptake was apparently coupled and could be inhibited by relatively high concentrations of furosemide (0.2 mM) and intravesicular Ca^{2+} (23, 24). However, the mechanism of coupling between Na$^+$ and Cl$^-$ transport across the vesicle membrane by either cotransport or double exchange was not established. Several arguments suggest that the observations of coupled furosemide-sensitive NaCl uptake occur by double exchange. Apparent coupling of Na$^+$ and Cl$^-$ transport in vesicles was observed at low intravesicular buffer capacity, but not with high pH buffers, which suggests indirect coupling via intravesicular pH changes (73). The pattern of anion inhibition of Cl$^-$-HCO$_3^-$ exchange in vesicles is similar to that found by Frizzell et al (38) for Na$^+$-coupled Cl$^-$ influx across the brush border of intact rabbit ileum. In addition, the K_t for the putative Cl$^-$-coupled Na$^+$ uptake was 4.5 mM, a value similar to that of 5–16 mM reported for Na$^+$-H$^+$ exchange.

Hopfer & Liedtke (53, 79) used kinetic criteria to investigate the question of cotransport. A common feature of models of cotransport is that the transport rates for either substrate are increased by low concentrations of the cosubstrate (53). This prediction can be tested particularly well in vesicles under conditions of isotope exchange at equilibrium, an experimental situation that facilitates interpretation of (unidirectional) solute fluxes in terms of transporter properties because of the absence of net fluxes. Experiments with Na$^+$-glucose (52), Na$_2^+$-lactate (84), and Na-K-Cl$_2$ cotransport (48) have demonstrated the high sensitivity of the method. Interestingly, the approach failed to reveal any cotransport or molecular coupling of Na$^+$ and Cl$^-$ flows in rat and rabbit intestinal brush border membrane vesicles: The exchange rates for Na$^+$ were independent of the concentrations of Cl$^-$, when sulfate served as the replacement. Likewise, Cl$^-$ exchange rates were independent of the Na$^+$ concentrations, when K$^+$ was used to replace Na$^+$ in the incubation media (34, 79). These experiments were sensitive enough that activation by the cosubstrate should have been evident if NaCl cotransport were a major transport pathway across the membrane. These results argue strongly for the absence of a NaCl cotransport mechanism, at least in the isolated intestinal brush border membrane.

ROLE OF CARBONIC ANHYDRASE IN ION TRANSPORT   The role of carbonic anhydrase in intestinal acidification has largely been defined by studies of the effect of carbonic anhydrase inhibitors, such as acetazolamide (69, 90, 113). Speculations that acetazolamide inhibits coupled NaCl flux across the brush border membrane (89) could not be confirmed in isolated brush border membranes (73). The findings of inhibition of HCO_3^- transport in the intact epithelium by acetazolamide or similar compounds are therefore best explained by an intermediate step involving carbonic anhydrase. As judged from the effects of carbonic anhydrase inhibitors, the enzyme is essential for sustaining physiological rates of HCO_3^- transport but is not needed for transport of HCO_3^- derived solely from metabolism (37).

Enzyme activity has been detected by histochemical and biochemical techniques in the epithelium throughout the intestine (10–12, 81). However, the activity in the small intestine is considerably lower than in the colon, and is located predominantly in non-brush border cells, as judged from histochemistry. Most of the residual activity in chief (brush border) cells is found at the basolateral pole (81). Thus, the levels of activity detected by histochemistry do not correlate with NaCl absorption. Maybe an association of one of the isoenzymes with the membrane, as observed by Knickelbein et al (73), is physiologically important for obtaining high rates of bicarbonate fluxes. In the kidney, a membrane-bound form of carbonic anhydrase has been identified in addition to the soluble isoenzymes. It is thought to be functionally located on the luminal surface and to play a role in HCO_3^- absorption (125). A similar mechanism could operate in the small intestine (Figure 1).

DOUBLE EXCHANGE IN INTACT SMALL INTESTINE? The major arguments for initially proposing a coupled NaCl entry mechanism in mammalian small intestine were based on transport data obtained in intact epithelial preparations. They were summarized by Schultz (99) as follows: (a) Replacement of Cl^- in the mucosal solution by relatively impermeant anions inhibits Na^+ absorption, and replacement of Na^+ by an impermeant cation decreases Cl^- absorption to the same degree. (b) Manipulations that increase intracellular cAMP inhibit Na^+ and Cl^- absorption to the same degree. (c) Acetazolamide inhibits Na^+ and Cl^- absorption equally well. And (d) the changes in NaCl absorption are not associated with electrical currents.

None of the intact tissue observations, however, provide a compelling reason to invoke molecular coupling of NaCl movements across the brush border membrane. The studies were carried out under steady-state conditions (with a typical preincubation time of 20 min), which allow the cytosolic pH to change dependent on the particular electrolyte flux conditions. The steady-state condition implies a balanced flux of acid (proton donors) and base (proton acceptors) into or out of the cell, regardless of the molecular mechanism of transport. Additionally, most cells, including epithelial cells, maintain a constant intracellular pH, usually by modulating specific electrolyte transport pathways in their plasma membrane (8, 42). In terms of NaCl absorption, a decrease in the flux of one of the ions would therefore result in a decrease of both, even in the absence of molecular coupling. Actually, a number of observations in intact tissue support the double exchanger mechanism: (a) Acetazolamide (a carbonic anhydrase blocker) inhibits NaCl absorption, which suggests that bicarbonate is involved. (b) Short-chain fatty acids in the colon can support high rates of Na^+ absorption, which suggests that Na^+-H^+ exchange occurs in conjunction with diffusion of the protonated form of the fatty acid. (c) The congenital disease of chloridorrhea appears to be a defect of Cl^--HCO_3^- exchange.

PRIMARY ACTIVE PROTON TRANSPORT The existence of primary active transport for protons in the luminal plasma membrane of the intestine has been suggested but not unequivocally demonstrated. Two types of H^+-secreting ATPase appear to exist in the plasma membrane of vertebrate cells. They differ in a number of respects, most notably in the existence of a phosphorylated intermediate (vanadate-sensitive enzymes) or their sensitivity to mitochondrial ATPase inhibitors (vanadate-insensitive enzymes) (93). Anion-stimulated ATPase activity has been measured in the intestinal brush border membrane by several investigators (59, 61, 110, 111), but it has been difficult to distinguish from alkaline phosphatase, which is abundant in small intestinal membranes and also hydrolyzes ATP. The arguments that connect the anion-stimulated ATPase activity to transport are based on (a) a correlation between stimulation of ATPase activity by certain anions and fluid and Na^+ absorption (60), (b) a gradient of ATPase activity along the intestine with the highest activity in the duodenum (109), and (c) regulation of such activity by the same steroids that modulate renal ion transport (110). These findings, however, are not convincing because anion stimulation of ATPase activity correlates with stimulation of alkaline phosphatase activity by the same solute (61), and the duodenum secretes bicarbonate (29) rather than protons, as predicted for H^+-ATPases located in the luminal plasma membrane and as found in the renal or turtle bladder luminal membranes (40, 65).

A K^+-stimulated, ouabain-insensitive ATPase has been relatively well characterized in brush border membranes from the descending colon (44, 45). The enzyme is vanadate sensitive and could function in a manner similar to that of the gastric K,H-ATPase (94, 104). ATP-dependent H^+ transport with properties that would be expected if this enzyme were involved in H^+ transport has recently been demonstrated in membrane vesicles isolated from descending colon epithelial cells (66).

Ion Transport In the Basolateral Plasma Membrane

Information about H^+ and HCO_3^- transport at the basolateral plasma membrane is even scarcer than for that at the brush border membrane. Intact tissue studies with amphiuma small intestine suggest that bicarbonate transport across the basolateral membrane depends on serosal Cl^- and is inhibited by stilbene disulfonates (124). These observations suggest Cl^--HCO_3^- exchange. Although application of stilbene disulfonates to the serosal medium also inhibits Cl^- transport in the intact mammalian intestine (75, 105), it is not clear whether Cl^--HCO_3^- exchange exists in the basolateral plasma membrane. Rat and rabbit basolateral plasma membranes contain stilbene disulfonate-sensitive SO_4^{2-}-Cl^- exchange (75) that, however, does not accept HCO_3^- (46).

The Cl^--HCO_3^- exchanger in the basolateral plasma membrane could play a role in Cl^--secretion by mediating concentrative Cl^- uptake from the blood into the cell. Such uptake would ultimately be driven by Na^+-H^+ exchange and Na^+ removal from the cell by the Na,K-ATPase. This model has recently received some support by the demonstration of Na^+-H^+ exchange in rabbit small intestinal basolateral plasma membranes (3).

CONCLUSIONS

For the mammalian small intestine, there is strong evidence that the so-called electroneutral, coupled NaCl transport is actually the result of two exchange mechanisms, Na^+-H^+ and Cl^--HCO_3^- (or Cl^--OH^-), in the luminal (brush border) plasma membrane. Coupling in the intact cell could come about in a number of ways. For example, steady-state changes of the cellular pH would differentially change the driving forces for the two exchange processes and hence the ratio of their rates. Additionally, increases in cellular $[H^+]$ could directly activate Na^+-H^+ exchange by an internal modifier site (1), independent from its effects on the driving force. Alternatively, the levels of the two exchange activities in the membrane could be differentially regulated to maintain a constant cellular pH. Regional differences in the ratios of the activities of the two types of exchangers could explain proton secretion in the jejunum, in which the rate of Na^+-H^+ exchange exceeds that of Cl^--HCO_3^-, and bicarbonate secretion in the ileum, in which the rate of Cl^--HCO_3^- exchange exceeds that of Na^+-H^+ exchange. The last decade has seen a considerable increase in the description of transport at the isolated membrane level. Further progress in understanding intestinal electrolyte transport will require information at the molecular level, including the biochemical identities of the transporters and their kinetics, regulation, and density within the membrane.

ACKNOWLEDGMENTS

We acknowledge support from the Cystic Fibrosis Foundation and NIH (AM-27651) for CML and from NIH (AM-35818 and AM-25170) for UH.

Literature Cited

1. Aronson, P. S. 1982. Pathways for solute transport coupled to H$^+$, OH$^-$ or HCO$_3^-$ gradients in renal microvillus membrane vesicles. In *Membranes and Transport*, Vol. 2, pp. 225–30. ed. A. N. Martonosi. New York: Plenum
2. Aronson, P. S. 1985. Kinetic properties of the plasma membrane Na$^+$-H$^+$ exchanger. *Ann. Rev. Physiol.* 47:545–60
3. Barros, F., Dominguez, P., Velasco, G., Lazo, P. S. 1986. Na$^+$/H$^+$ exchange is present in basolateral membranes from rabbit small intestine. *Biochem. Biophys. Res. Commun.* 134:827–34
4. Bieberdorf, F. A., Gordon, P., Fordtran, J. S. 1972. Pathogenesis of congenital alkalosis with diarrhea. Implications for the physiology of normal ileal electrolyte absorption and secretion. *J. Clin. Invest.* 51:1958–68
5. Binder, H. J., Murer, H. 1986. K-H exchange: A new intestinal apical membrane transport process. *Gastroenterology* 90:1346
6. Binder, H. J., Rawlins, C. L. 1973. Electrolyte transport across isolated large intestinal mucosa. *Am. J. Physiol.* 225:1232–39
7. Blair, J. A., Lucas, M. L., Matty, A. J. 1975. Acidification in the rat proximal jejunum. *J. Physiol.* 245:333–50
8. Boron, W. F. 1986. Intracellular pH regulation in epithelial cells. *Ann. Rev. Physiol.* 48:377–88
9. Camien, M. N., Gonick, H. C. 1967. Relationship of renal "net acid" excretion to titratable ash-acidity (ash-TA) in diet and feces. *Proc. Soc. Exp. Biol. Med.* 126:45–51
10. Carter, M. J., Parsons, D. S. 1968. Carbonic anhydrase activity of mucosa of small intestine and colon. *Nature* 219:176–77
11. Carter, M. J., Parsons, D. S. 1971. The isoenzymes of carbonic anhydrase: Tissue, subcellular distribution and functional significance with particular reference to the intestinal tract. *J. Physiol.* 215:71–94
12. Carter, M. J., Parsons, D. S. 1972. The isoenzymes of carbonic anhydrase: Kinetic properties with particular reference to the functions of the intestinal tract. *J. Physiol.* 220:465–78
13. Cassano, G., Stieger, B., Murer, H. 1984. Na/H- and Cl/OH-exchange in rat jejunal and rat proximal tubular brush border membrane vesicles. Studies with

acridine orange. *Pflügers Arch.* 400:309–17
14. Chaillet, J. R., Lopes, H. G., Boron, W. F. 1985. Basolateral Na-H exchange in the rabbit cortical collecting tubule. *J. Gen. Physiol.* 86:795–812
15. Charney, A. N., Arnold, M., Johnstone, N. 1983. Acute respiratory alkalosis and acidosis and rabbit intestinal ion transport in vivo. *Am. J. Physiol.* 244:G145–50
16. Charney, A. N., Feldman, G. M. 1984. Systemic acid-base disorders and intestinal electrolyte transport. In *Mechanisms of Intestinal Electrolyte Transport and Regulation by Calcium*, ed. M. Donowitz, G. W. G. Sharp, pp. 101–17. New York: Liss
17. Charney, A. N., Haskell, L. P. 1984. Relative effects of systemic pH and HCO$_3$ concentration on ileal ion transport. *Am. J. Physiol.* 246:G159–65
18. Clauss, W., Horch, I., Hornicke, H. 1985. Electrolyte transport across rabbit late proximal colon in vitro. *Comp. Biochem. Physiol.* 82A:71–75
19. Dharmasathaphorn, K., Pandol, S. J. 1986. Mechanism of chloride secretion induced by carbachol in a colonic epithelial cell line. *J. Clin. Invest.* 77:348–54
20. Dietz, J., Field, M. 1973. Ion transport in rabbit ileal mucosa. IV. Bicarbonate secretion. *Am. J. Physiol.* 225:858–61
21. Donowitz, M., Welsh, M. J. 1986. Ca^{2+} and cyclic AMP in regulation of intestinal Na, K, and Cl transport. *Ann. Rev. Physiol.* 48:135–50
22. Duffey, M. E. 1984. Intracellular pH and bicarbonate activities in rabbit colon. *Am. J. Physiol.* 246:C558–61
23. Fan, C.-C., Faust, R. G., Powell, D. W. 1983. Coupled sodium-chloride transport by rabbit ileal brush-border membrane vesicles. *Am. J. Physiol.* 244:G375–85
24. Fan, C.-C., Powell, D. W. 1983. Calcium/calmodulin inhibition of coupled NaCl transport in membrane vesicles from rabbit ileal brush border. *Proc. Natl. Acad. Sci. USA* 80:5248–52
25. Feldman, G. M., Arnold, M. A., Charney, A. N. 1984. On the mechanism of luminal CO$_2$ generation during jejunal bicarbonate absorption. *Am. J. Physiol.* 246:G687–94
26. Feldman, G. M., Charney, A. N. 1980. Effect of acute metabolic alkalosis and acidosis on intestinal electrolyte trans-

port in vivo. *Am. J. Physiol.* 239:G427–36

27. Feldman, G. M., Charney, A. N. 1982. Effect of acute respiratory alkalosis and acidosis on intestinal ion transport in vivo. *Am. J. Physiol.* 242:G486–92

28. Field, M. 1981. Secretion of electrolytes and water by mammalian small intestine. In *Physiology of the Gastrointestinal Tract*, ed. L. R. Johnson, pp. 963–82. New York: Raven

29. Flemström, G., Garner, A. 1982a. Gastroduodenal HCO_3^- transport: Characteristics and proposed role in acidity regulation and mucosal protection. *Am. J. Physiol.* 242:G183–93

30. Flemström, G., Garner, A. 1984. Some characteristics of duodenal mucosa. *Ciba Found. Symp.* 109:94–108

31. Flemström, G., Garner, A., Nylander, O., Hurst, B. C., Heylings, J. R. 1982b. Surface epithelial HCO_3 transport by mammalian duodenum in vivo. *Am. J. Physiol.* 243:G348–58

32. Fondacara, J. D. 1986. Intestinal ion transport and diarrheal disease. *Am. J. Physiol.* 250:G1–G8

33. Foster, E. S., Budinger, M. E., Hayslett, J. R., Binder, H. J. 1984. Na/H exchange: Predominant Na absorptive process in rat proximal colon. *Gastroenterology* 86:1080

34. Frankel, M. H., Hopfer, U. 1980. Independence of sodium transport from chloride in rabbit ileum brush border membranes. *Gastroenterology* 78:116

35. Frizzell, R. A., Field, M., Schultz, S. G. 1979. Sodium-coupled chloride transport by epithelial tissues. *Am. J. Physiol.* 236:F1–F8

36. Frizzell, R. A., Kochs, M. J., Schultz, S. G. 1976. Ion transport by rabbit colon. I. Active and passive components. *J. Membr. Biol.* 27:297–316

37. Frizzell, R. A., Markscheid-Kaspi, L., Schultz, S. G. 1974. Oxidative metabolism of rabbit ileal mucosa. *Am. J. Physiol.* 226:1142–48

38. Frizzell, R. A., Nellans, H. N., Rose, R. C., Markscheid-Kaspi, L., Schultz, S. G. 1973. Intracellular Cl^- concentration and influxes across the brush border of rabbit ileum. *Am. J. Physiol.* 224:328–37

39. Gluck, S., Al-Awqati, Q. 1984. An electrogenic proton-translocating adenosine triphosphatase from bovine kidney medulla. *J. Clin. Invest.* 73:1704–10

40. Gluck, S., Cannon, C., Al-Awqati, Q. 1982. Exocytosis regulates urinary acidification in turtle bladder by rapid insertion H^+ pumps into the luminal membrane. *Proc. Natl. Acad. Sci. USA* 79:4327–31

41. Greger, R. 1985. Ion transport mechanisms in thick ascending limb of Henle's loop of mammalian nephron. *Physiol. Rev.* 65:760–97

42. Grinstein, S., Rothstein, A. 1986. Mechanisms of regulation of the Na^+/H^+ exchanger. *J. Membr. Biol.* 90:1–12

43. Gunther, R. D., Wright, E. M. 1983. Na^+, Li^+, and Cl^- transport by brush border membranes from rabbit jejunum. *J. Membr. Biol.* 74:85–94

44. Gustin, M. C., Goodman, D. B. P. 1981. Isolation of brush border membrane from the rabbit descending colon epithelium. Partial characterization of a unique K-activated ATPase. *J. Biol. Chem.* 256:10651–56

45. Gustin, M. C., Goodman, D. B. P. 1982. Characterization of the phosphorylated intermediate of the K^+-ouabain-insensitive ATPase of the rabbit colon brush border membrane. *J. Biol. Chem.* 257:9629–33

46. Hagenbuch, B., Stange, G., Murer, H. 1985. Transport of sulphate in rat jejunal and rat proximal tubular basolateral membrane vesicles. *Pflügers Arch.* 405:202–8

47. Halm, D. R., Krasny, E. J., Frizzell, R. A. 1985. Electrophysiology of flounder intestinal mucosa. II. Relation of the electrical potential profile to coupled NaCl absorption. *J. Gen. Physiol.* 85:865–84

48. Hannafin, J., Kinne-Saffran, E., Friedman, D., Kinne, R. 1983. Presence of a sodium-potassium-chloride cotransport system in the rectal gland of squalms acanthias. *J. Membr. Biol.* 75:73–83

49. Hatch, M., Freel, R. W., Goldner, A. M., Earnest, D. L. 1984. Oxalate and chloride absorption by the rabbit colon: Sensitivity to metabolic and anion transport inhibitors. *Gut* 25:232–37

50. Hauser, H., Howell, K., Dawson, R. M. L., Boyer, D. E. 1980. Rabbit small intestinal brush border membrane preparation and lipid composition. *Biochim. Biophys. Acta* 602:567–77

51. Hopfer, U., Crowe, T. D., Tandler, B. 1983. Purification of brush-border membrane by thiocyanate treatment. *Anal. Biochem.* 131:447–52

52. Hopfer, U., Groseclose, R. 1980. The mechanism of Na-dependent D-glucose transport. *J. Biol. Chem.* 255:4453–62

53. Hopfer, U., Liedtke, C. M. 1981. Kinetic changes of cotransport mechanisms under isotope exchange conditions. *Membr. Biochem.* 4:11–29

54. Hopfer, U., Nelson, K., Perrotto, J., Isselbacher, K. J. 1973. Glucose transport in isolated brush border membrane from rat small intestine. *J. Biol. Chem.* 248:25–32
55. Deleted in proof
56. Horvath, P. J., Ferriola, P. C., Weiser, M. M., Duffey, M. E. 1986. Localization of chloride secretion in rabbit colon: Inhibition by anthracene-9-carboxylic acid. *Am. J. Physiol.* 250:G185–90
57. Hubel, K. A. 1976. Intestinal ion transport: Effect of norepenephrine, pilocarpine and atropine. *Am. J. Physiol.* 231:252–57
58. Humphreys, M. H. 1976. Inhibition of NaCl absorption from perfused rat ileum by furosemide. *Am. J. Physiol.* 230:1517–23
59. Humphreys, M. H., Chou, L. Y. N. 1979. Anion-stimulated ATPase activity by brush border from rat small intestine. *Am. J. Physiol.* 236:E70-E76
60. Humphreys, M. H., Chou, L. Y. N. 1983. Anion effects on fluid absorption from rat jejunum perfused in vivo. *Am. J. Physiol.* 244:G33–G39
61. Humphreys, M. H., Kaysen, G. A., Chou, L. Y. N., Watson, J. B. 1980. Anion-stimulated phosphohydrolase activity of intestinal alkaline phosphatase. *Am. J. Physiol.* 238:G3–G9
62. Imon, M. A., White, J. F. 1984. Association between HCO$_3^-$ absorption and K$^+$ uptake by *Amphiuma* jejunum: Relations among HCO$_3^-$ absorption, luminal K$^+$, and intracellular K$^+$ activity. *Am. J. Physiol.* 246:G732–44
63. Jackson, M. J., Morgan, B. N. 1975. Relation of weak electrolyte transport and acid-base metabolism in rat small intestine in vitro. *Am. J. Physiol.* 228:482–87
64. Kalser, M. H. 1985. Water and mineral transport. In *Gastroenterology*, ed. J. E. Berk. Philadelphia: Saunders 1538 pp. 4th ed.
65. Kaunitz, J. D., Gunther, R. D., Sachs, G. 1985. Characterization of an electrogenic ATP and chloride-dependent proton translocating pump from rat renal medulla. *J. Biol. Chem.* 260:11567–73
66. Kaunitz, J. G., Sachs, G. 1986. Isolation and characterization of potassium-dependent proton pump from rabbit colon. *Fed. Proc.* 45:1489
67. Kessler, M., Acuto, O., Storelli, C., Murer, H., Mueller, M., Semenza, G. 1978. A modification procedure for the rapid preparation of efficiently transporting vesicles from small intestinal brush

border membranes. Their use in investigating some properties of D-glucose and choline transport systems. *Biochim. Biophys. Acta* 506:136–54
68. Kildeberg, P., Engel, K., Winters, R. W. 1969. Balance of net acid in growing infants. *Acta Paediatr. Scand.* 58:321–29
69. Kinney, V. R., Code, C. F. 1964. Canine ileal chloride absorption: Effect of carbonic anhydrase inhibitor on transport. *Am. J. Physiol.* 207:998–1004
70. Knickelbein, R., Aronson, P. S., Atherton, W., Dobbins, J. W. 1983. Sodium and chloride transport across rabbit ileal brush border. I. Evidence for Na-H exchange. *Am. J. Physiol.* 245:G504–10
71. Knickelbein, R., Aronson, P. S., Dobbins, J. W. 1985a. Substrate and inhibitor specificity of anion exchangers on the brush border membrane of rabbit ileum. *J. Membr. Biol.* 88:199–204
72. Knickelbein, R. G., Aronson, P. S., Dobbins, J. W. 1986. Oxalate transport by anion exchange across rabbit ileal brush border. *J. Clin. Invest.* 77:170–75
73. Knickelbein, R., Aronson, P. S., Schron, C. M., Seifter J., Dobbins, J. W. 1985b. Sodium and chloride transport in rabbit ileal brush border. II. Evidence for Cl-HCO$_3$ exchange and mechanism of coupling. *Am. J. Physiol.* 249:G236–45
74. Kurtin, P., Charney, A. N. 1984. Effect of arterial carbon dioxide tension on amiloride-sensitive sodium absorption in the colon. *Am. J. Physiol.* 247:G537–41
75. Langridge-Smith, Y. E., Field, M. 1981. Sulfate transport in rabbit ileum: Characterization of the serosol anion exchange process. *J. Membr. Biol.* 63:207–14
76. Lemann, J. Jr., Lennon, E. J. 1972. Role of diet, gastrointestinal tract and bone in acid-base homeostasis. *Kidney Int.* 1:275–79
77. Lennon, E. J., Lemann, J. Jr., Litzow, J. R. 1966. The effects of diet and stool composition on the net external acid balance of normal subjects. *J. Clin. Invest.* 45:1601–7
78. Liedtke, C. M., Hopfer, U. 1977. Anion transport in brush border membranes isolated from rat small intestine. *Biochem. Biophys. Res. Commun.* 76:579–85
79. Liedtke, C. M., Hopfer, U. 1982. Mechanism of Cl$^-$ translocation across small intestinal brush-border membrane. I. Absence of Na$^+$-Cl$^-$ cotransport. *Am. J. Physiol.* 242:G263–71
80. Liedtke, C. M., Hopfer, U. 1982.

Mechanism of Cl⁻ translocation across small intestinal brush-border membrane. II. Demonstration of Cl^--OH^- exchange and Cl^- conductance. *Am. J. Physiol.* 242:G272–80

81. Lönnerholm, G. 1983. Carbonic anhydrase in the monkey stomach and intestine. *Acta Physiol. Scand.* 117:273–79

82. Madara, J. L., Dharmasathaphorn, K. 1985. Occluding junction structure-function relationships in a cultured epithelial monolayer. *J. Cell Biol.* 101:2124–33

83. Mandel, K. G., Dharmasathaphorn, K., McRoberts, J. A. 1986. Characterization of a cyclic AMP-activated transport pathway in the apical membrane of a human colonic epithelial cell line. *J. Biol. Chem.* 261:704–12

84. Mengual, R., Leblanc, G., Sudaka, P. 1983. The mechanism of Na^+-L-lactate cotransport by brush border membrane vesicles from horse kidney. *J. Biol. Chem.* 258:15071–78

85. Murer, H., Ahearn, G., Biber, J., Cassano, G., Gmaj, P., Stieger, B. 1983. Co- and counter-transport mechanisms in brush border membranes and basallateral membranes of intestine and kidney. *J. Exp. Biol.* 106:163–80

86. Murer, H., Burckhardt, G. 1983. Membrane transport of anions across epithelia of mammalian small intestine and kidney proximal tubule. *Rev. Physiol. Biochem. Pharmacol.* 96:1–51

87. Murer, H., Hopfer, U., Kinne, R. 1976. Sodium/proton antiport in brush-border-membrane vesicles isolated from rat small intestine and kidney. *Biochem. J.* 154:597–604

88. Nellans, H. N., Frizzell, R. A., Schultz, S. G. 1974. Brush border processes and transepithelial Na and Cl transport by rabbit ileum. *Am. J. Physiol.* 226:1131–41

89. Nellans, H. N., Frizzell, R. A., Schultz, S. G. 1975. Effect of acetazolamide on the Na and Cl transport by isolated rabbit ileum. *Am. J. Physiol.* 228:1808–14

90. Parsons, D. S. 1956. The absorption of bicarbonate-saline solutions by the small intestine and colon of the white rat. *Q. J. Exp. Physiol. Cogn. Med. Sci.* 41:410–20

90a. Podestra, R. B., Mettrick, D. F. 1977. HCO_3 transport in rat jejunum: Relationship to NaCl and H_2O transport in vivo. *Am. J. Physiol.* 232:E62–68

91. Podestra, R. B., Mettrick, D. F. 1977. HCO_3^- and H^+ secretion in rat ileum in vivo. *Am. J. Physiol.* 232:E574–79

92. Powell, D. W., Binder, H. J., Curran, P. F. 1972. Electrolyte secretion by the guinea pig ileum in vitro. *Am. J. Physiol.* 223:531–37

93. Rudnick, G. 1986. ATP-driven H^+ pumping into intracellular organelles. *Ann. Rev. Physiol.* 48:403–13

94. Sachs, G., Faller, L. D., Rabon, E. 1982. Proton-hydroxyl transport in gastric and intestinal epithelia. *J. Membr. Biol.* 64:123–35

95. Scalera, V., Storelli, C., Storelli-Joss, C., Haase, W., Murer, H. 1980. A simple and fast method for the isolation of basolateral plasma membranes from rat small-intestinal epithelial cells. *Biochem. J.* 186:177–81

96. Schmitz, J., Preiser, H., Maestracci, D., Ghosh, B. K., Cerda, J. J., Crane, R. K. 1973. Purification of the human intestinal brush border membrane. *Biochim. Biophys. Acta* 323:98–112

97. Schron, C. M., Knickelbein, R. G., Aronson, P. S., Della Puca, J., Dobbins, J. W. 1985. pH gradient-stimulated sulfate transport by rabbit ileal brush-border membrane vesicles: Evidence for SO_4-OH exchange. *Am. J. Physiol.* 249:G607–13

98. Schultz, S. G. 1980. Cellular models of sodium and chloride absorption by mammalian small and large intestine. In *Secretory Diarrhea,* ed. M. Field, J. S. Fordtran, S. G. Schultz, pp. 1–9. Bethesda, MD: Am. Physiol. Soc.

99. Schultz, S. G. 1981. Salt and water absorption by mammalian small intestine. In *Physiology of the Gastrointestinal Tract,* ed. L. R. Johnson, pp. 983–90. New York: Raven

100. Schultz, S. G. 1981. Ion transport by mammalian large intestine. In *Physiology of the Gastrointestinal Tract,* ed. R. Johnson, pp. 991–1002. New York: Raven

101. Schwartz, G. J., Al-Awqati, Q. 1986. Regulation of transepithelial H^+ transport by exocytosis and endocytosis. *Ann. Rev. Physiol.* 48:153–61

102. Sellin, J., DeSoignie, R. 1984. Rabbit proximal colon: A distinct transport epithelium. *Am. J. Physiol.* 246:G603–10

103. Simpson, J. N. L., Merhav, A., Silen, W. 1981. Alkaline secretion by amphibian duodenum. III. Effect of DBcAMP, theophylline, and prostaglandins. *Am. J. Physiol.* 241:G528–36

104. Smith, P. L., McCabe, R. D. 1984. Mechanism and regulation of transcellular potassium transport by the colon. *Am. J. Physiol.* 247:G445–56

105. Smith, P. L., Sullivan, S. K., McCabe, R. D. 1986. Concentration-dependent effects of disulfonic stilbenes on colonic chloride transport. *Am. J. Physiol.* 250: G44–G49

106. Snipes, R. L., Clauss, W., Weber, A., Hornicke, H. 1982. Structural and functional differences in various divisions of rabbit colon. *Cell. Tiss. Res.* 225:331–46

107. Stetson, D. L., Beauwens, R., Palmisano, J., Mitchell, P. P., Steinmetz, P. R. 1985. A double-membrane model for urinary bicarbonate secretion. *Am. J. Physiol.* 249:F546–52

108. Stetson, D. L., Steinmetz, P. R. 1985. α and β types of carbonic anhydrase–rich cells in turtle bladder. *Am. J. Physiol.* 249:F553–65

109. Suzuki, S. 1981. Properties and distribution of Mg^{2+}-HCO$_3$-ATPase in brush border membranes isolated from rat small intestine. *Comp. Biochem. Physiol.* 70B:703–12

110. Suzuki, S., Ozaki, N., Yoshida, J., Takamura, S., Takeuchi, Y., Kudo, S. 1983. Brush border Mg^{2+}-HCO$_3$-ATPase, supernatant carbonic anhydrase and other enzyme activities isolated from rat intestinal mucosa: Effect of adrenalectomy and aldosterone administration. *J. Steroid Biochem.* 19:1419–33

111. Suzuki, S., Takamura, S., Yoshida, J., Ozaki, N. 1985. Effect of aldosterone antagonists on aldosterone-induced activation of Mg^{2+}-HCO$_3^-$-ATPase and carbonic anhydrase in rat intestinal mucosa. *J. Steroid Biochem.* 23:57–66

112. Turnberg, L. A. 1971. Abnormalities in intestinal electrolyte transport in congenital chloridorrhea. *Gut* 12:544–50

113. Turnberg, L. A., Bieberdorf, F. A., Morawski, S. G., Fordtran, J. S. 1970. Interrelationships of chloride, bicarbonate, sodium, and hydrogen transport in the human jejunum. *J. Clin. Invest.* 49:557–67

114. Vaandrager, A. B., Ploemacher, M. C., de Jonge, H. R. 1986. Modulation of salt permeabilities of intestinal brush-border membrane vesicles by micromolar levels of internal calcium. *Biochim. Biophys. Acta* 856:325–36

115. Van Heeswijk, M. P. E., van Os, C. H. 1985. Water and salt permeabilities of brush border membrane vesicles from rat small intestine and kidney cortex. In *Ion Gradient-Coupled Transport*, ed. F. Alvarado, C. H. van Os, pp. 329–32. Amsterdam: Elsevier

116. Verkman, A. S., Dix, J. A., Seifter, J. L. 1985. Water and urea transport in renal microvillus membrane vesicles. *Am. J. Physiol.* 248:F650–55

117. Wagner, J. D., Kurtin, P., Charney, A. N. 1985. Effect of systemic acid-base disorders on colonic intracellular pH and ion transport. *Am. J. Physiol.* 249:G39–G47

118. Welsh, M. J., Smith, P. L., Fromm, M., Frizzell, R. A. 1982. Crypts are the site of intestinal fluid and electrolyte secretion. *Science* 218:1219–21

119. White, J. F. 1982. Intestinal electrogenic HCO$_3^-$ absorption localized to villus epithelium. *Biochim. Biophys. Acta* 687:343–45

120. White, J. F. 1985. Omeprazole inhibits H$^+$ secretion by *Amphiuma* jejunum. *Am. J. Physiol.* 248:G256–59

121. White, J. F., Burnup, K., Ellingsen, D. 1986. Effect of sugars and amino acids on amphibian intestinal Cl$^-$ transport and intracellular Na$^+$, K$^+$, and Cl$^-$ activity. *Am. J. Physiol.* 250:G109–17

122. White, J. F., Ellingsen, D., Burnup, K. 1984. Electrogenic Cl$^-$ absorption by *Amphiuma* small intestine: Dependence on serosal Na$^+$ from tracer and Cl$^-$ microelectrode studies. *J. Membr. Biol.* 78:223–33

123. White, J. F., Imon, M. A. 1981. Bicarbonate absorption by in vitro amphibian small intestine. *Am. J. Physiol.* 241:G389–96

124. White, J. F., Imon, M. A. 1983. A role for basolateral anion exchange in active jejunal absorption of HCO$_3^-$. *Am. J. Physiol.* 244:G397–G405

125. Wistrand, P. J. 1984. Properties of membrane-bound carbonic anhydrase. *Ann. NY Acad. Sci.* 429:195–206

126. Will, P. C., Lebowitz, J. L., Hopfer, U. 1980. Induction of amiloride-sensitive sodium transport in the rat colon by mineralocorticoids. *Am. J. Physiol.* 238:F261–68

127. Yoshitomi, K., Burckhardt, B. C., Fromter, E. 1985. Rheogenic sodium-bicarbonate cotransport in the peritubular cell membrane of rat renal proximal tubule. *Pflügers Arch.* 405:360–66

Ann. Rev. Physiol. 1987. 49:69–85

PROTON TRANSPORT BY HEPATOCYTE ORGANELLES AND ISOLATED MEMBRANE VESICLES

Bruce F. Scharschmidt and Rebecca W. Van Dyke

Liver Center and Department of Medicine, 1120 HSW, University of California, San Francisco, California 94143

INTRODUCTION

Mechanisms of proton (H^+) transport in hepatocytes are of particular interest because (*a*) liver cells are active in endocytosis and secretion (both of which may involve acidification of organelles), and (*b*) hepatocytes secrete bile, probably in part via active H^+-HCO_3^- transport. The purpose of this review is to concisely summarize current information regarding the mechanisms of proton transport by hepatocyte organelles and plasma membranes and the roles that these H^+ transport mechanisms may play in hepatocellular function.

PRIMARY PROTON TRANSPORT

Overview

Although it has been known for several decades that rat liver lysosomes have an acidic interior (12), the mechanisms responsible remained uncertain until recently, when several workers independently reported unequivocal evidence for active, ATP-dependent lysosomal acidification (H^+-ATPase or H^+ pump) (55, 67). Subsequent studies have indicated that a variety of nonlysosomal organelles in hepatocytes and other cells are also actively acidified by an apparently similar mechanism.

A detailed treatment of the experimental techniques used to study proton transport is beyond the scope of this review; however, some appreciation of

69

the advantages and limitations of various approaches is helpful. In sealed vesicles, an electrogenic H^+-pumping ATPase (or H^+-ATPase) may exhibit the following characteristics under appropriate conditions: (*a*) ATPase activity that is stimulated by ionophores or other substances that diminish rate-limiting electrochemical gradients, (*b*) generation of a pH gradient, (*c*) generation of an electrical gradient. Each of these aspects of "pump" function has been used to characterize the H^+-ATPase(s) under discussion, and their respective advantages and/or limitations are considered briefly in turn.

Organelle-associated ATPase activity, in general, has correlated inconsistently with direct measures of pump function (e.g. acidification, electrical potential generation), probably due to multiple factors, including the presence of a variety of ATPases in some vesicles, possible variability in coupling between ATP hydrolysis and H^+ transport, and lack of a specific H^+-ATPase inhibitor. Thus, while stimulation of ATPase activity by ionophores is of considerable interest when present, its absence is difficult to interpret.

A variety of approaches are available for measurement of pH or electrical gradients in vesicles (Table 1). Certain fluorescent dyes can be used to indicate that a vesicle interior is relatively acidic (e.g. weak bases such as acridine orange) or positively charged (e.g. anions such as Oxonol V) and are useful for studying relative rates of H^+ transport by isolated organelles in suspension. The use of radiolabeled markers of pH (e.g. methylamine) or electrical potential (e.g. SCN^-) gradients permits better quantitation of gradients, but these markers have poor time resolution and are therefore of little utility in measuring rates of H^+ transport. Finally, the emission spectrum of fluorescein-labeled ligands or fluid phase markers can be used to measure the internal pH of endocytic organelles in intact cells or after isolation.

Most studies have characterized organelle H^+ transport by measurement of a pH gradient. Less information is available regarding the development of an electrical potential gradient, and the two manifestations of electrogenic H^+ transport have often not been studied in parallel. This approach may lead to problems in interpretation. For example, Cl^- has repeatedly been shown (see below and Table 1) to accelerate the development of a pH gradient and yet inhibit the development of an electrical gradient. Measurement of the electrical gradient alone might lead to the (incorrect) interpretation that Cl^- inhibits the H^+ pump, while the opposite interpretation might be made based on measurement of the pH gradient alone. This situation is conceptually analogous to measuring the work generated by a mechanical hoist capable of performing 10^3 g·cm of work with *either* a ruler or a scale, when in fact the work involved in lifting 1 kg 1 cm is equivalent to that involved in lifting 1 g a total of 10 m.

Finally, as of this writing, no H^+-ATPase associated with a nonmitochondrial hepatocyte organelle has been isolated, nor has such an H^+-ATPase been studied under conditions in which both sides of the membrane are directly accessible; e.g. by incorporation into a planar membrane, as has been done for bacterial H^+-ATPases (39).[1] Thus, comparison of the H^+-ATPase(s) in various organelles has rested on a comparative study of properties such as apparent sensitivity to inhibitors and dependence upon ions.

Proton Transport by Isolated Organelles

A variety of hepatocyte organelles, including clathrin-coated vesicles, endosomes, multivesicular bodies, lysosomes, Golgi, and endoplasmic reticulum, have been reported to be actively acidified via an electrogenic H^+-ATPase. One of the most striking features of these studies to date has been the apparent similarity of H^+ transport among these organelles in hepatocytes and other animal cells (17, 46a, 75, 77–79). While this similarity may reflect the presence of the same, or closely related, H^+-ATPase(s) in these various locations, this conclusion at present must remain tentative as most organelle preparations are contaminated to varying degrees with other cellular constituents. Thus, determination of the distribution of H^+-ATPase(s) among organelles will likely await the use of immunoelectron-microscopic techniques.

The principal characteristics of H^+ transport by isolated hepatocellular organelles are summarized below and outlined in more detail in Table 1.

EFFECTS OF INHIBITORS   Common characteristics of hepatocellular H^+-ATPases include complete inhibition by micromolar concentrations of N-ethylamaleimide (a sulfhydryl reagent) and dicyclohexylcarbodiimide (a nearly universal H^+-ATPase inhibitor), insensitivity to ouabain and vanadate, and relative resistance to oligomycin.

SUBSTRATE UTILIZATION   Hepatocyte organelles, in general, exhibit a rather specific requirement for ATP (Table 1). Lysosomes are exceptional in this regard; however, this may reflect the ability of lysosomes to interconvert high-energy substrates (e.g. GTP $\rightarrow$ ATP) rather than being a unique feature of the lysosomal H^+-ATPase, per se.

CATION DEPENDENCE   In general, H^+ transport by hepatocyte organelles has no specific cation requirement. Stimulation of acidification in the presence of K^+ and valinomycin presumably reflects the ability of K^+ to move counter to H^+ as a charge-compensating cation (23, 75, 77, 78). Its lack of a requirement for K^+ and its insensitivity to vanadate (above) distinguish this H^+-ATPase(s) from the H,K-ATPase of parietal cells (18), and its lack of a

---

[1]Solubilization and reconstitution into proteoliposomes has been successfully achieved for rat liver lysosomal H^+-ATPase (49) and the H^+-ATPase of bovine-brain coated vesicles (84).

Table 1 Characteristics of ATP-dependent H^+ transport by hepatocyte organelles

Characteristics	Coated vesicles	Endosomes	Multivesicular bodies	Lysosomes	Golgi	Endoplasmic reticulum	Mitochondria
Intact cells							
Data available	no	yes	no	yes	no	no	—
Method(s)	—	fluorescein-labeled ligands	—	fluorescein-labeled dextran	—	—	—
Isolated Organelles							
Data available	yes	yes	yes	yes	yes	yes	Submitochondrial particles
Method(s)	acridine orange	9-aminoacridine, fluorescein-labeled ligands	acridine orange, Oxonol V	^{14}C-methylamine, acridine orange, fluorescein-labeled dextran, carbocyanine dyes, Oxonol V	neutral red, acridine orange, carbocyanine dyes, ^{14}C-methylamine	acridine orange	acridine orange
Electrogenic	yes[a]	not established	yes	yes[b]	yes	yes[a]	—
Substrates utilized	ATP>>GTP = UTP	ATP	ATP>>GTP = UTP	ATP = GTP = ITP>>UTP = CTP	ATP (not GTP)	ATP (not GTT, ITP)	—

73

Substrate inhibition (IC_{50})							
Ouabain	no[c]	—	no	no	no	no	no
Vanadate	no[c]	—	no	no	no	no	no
Oligomycin	yes[d] (10^{-4}–10^{-5} M)	—	no	no	no	no	yes (~10^{-7} M)
N-ethylmaleimide	yes (≤ 10^{-4} M)	—	yes (~ 5×10^{-6} M)	yes (< 10^{-4} M)	yes (10^{-5}–10^{-6} M)	yes (< 5×10^{-5} M)	no
DCCD	yes (< 10^{-5} M)	—	yes (5×10^{-5} M)	yes (~ 10^{-5} M)	yes (< 10^{-4} M)	yes (< 10^{-4} M)	yes (< 10^{-6} M)
Ionic dependence							
Cations	no dependence	—	no dependence	no dependence	—	—	—
Anions	acidification: Cl^- = Br^- > NO_3^- > SO_4^{-2} > HPO_4^{-2}, gluconate	—	acidification: Cl^- >> Br^- > NO_3^- = SO_4^{-2} = gluconate	acidification: Cl^- = Br^- > HPO_4^{-2} > SO_4^{-2}	Cl^- >> gluconate	—	—
pH_i[e]	—[f]	5.5	—	≥ 4.5	6	—	—
Ionophore-stimulated ATPase activity	yes[g]	yes	yes	yes	—	—	—
References	17, 78, 79, 85	21, 64	75, 76	29, 48, 55-57, 67, 68	8, 23, 88	60	77

[a]Based upon enhanced acidification in the presence of K⁺ and valinomycin.
[b]Controversial point, table represents view of authors based on most recent data.
[c]"No" designates no inhibition at concentrations of ouabain (≈10^{-3} M) or vanadate (≈10^{-4} M) that completely inhibit Na,K-ATPase and parietal cell H,K-ATPase, respectively.
[d]Not all investigators have observed inhibition by oligomycin; those listed are the lowest concentrations at which inhibition is reported.
[e]Lowest value recorded at an extravesicular pH of 7.0.
[f]pH ≈ 5–6 in coated vesicles from bovine brain (17, 84, 85).
[g]Reported for coated vesicles from bovine brain only.

requirement for Na^+ and its ouabain insensitivity distinguish it from H^+ transport via Na^+-H^+ exchange coupled to Na,K-ATPase (5).

ANION DEPENDENCE   A reciprocal relationship between H^+-ATPase-generated electrical and chemical gradients has been perhaps most clearly demonstrated in studies of anion dependence, in which the presence of Cl^- was found to stimulate acidification and diminish the electrical gradient (e.g. 75, 76). In addition, uptake of tracer amounts of $^{36}Cl^-$ by multivesicular bodies is stimulated by ATP, is enhanced when total extravesicular Cl^- concentration is reduced, and is further stimulated by monensin, an electroneutral cation-proton-exchanging ionophore (76). These findings suggest that Cl^- enters organelles and thus offsets the electrical potential difference generated by the H^+-ATPase and facilitates the development of a pH gradient. These findings do not, however, exclude the possibility that Cl^- may also directly stimulate H^+-ATPase activity. Indeed, studies of the renal endosome H^+-ATPase under apparent voltage-clamped conditions suggest this possibility (34).

The apparent permeability to anions of clathrin-coated vesicles and multivesicular bodies, as evidenced by the ability of these anions to facilitate transiently the development of a pH gradient and to inhibit or reverse an electrical gradient, seems to be $Cl^- > Br^- > NO_3^- > SO_4^{2-} = PO_4^{3-} =$ gluconate (74a; R. W. Van Dyke, unpublished observations). However, the effects of anion substitution are more complex than simple replacement of a permeant by an impermeant species. Apart from the direct stimulatory effect of anions such as Cl^- on pump function (above), certain anions directly inhibit ATP-dependent proton transport. This has been most clearly demonstrated in multivesicular bodies for NO_3^-, and SO_4^{2-} and PO_4^{2-} may have minor inhibitory effects (74a). This observation is of interest in light of a similar inhibition by NO_3^- and stimulation by Cl^- of the proton pump of plant cell vacuoles (tonoplasts) (74). The physiological significance of this potential regulatory mechanism in animals, as in plants, remains uncertain.

ORGANELLE-ASSOCIATED ATPASE ACTIVITY   ATPase activity is associated with each of the isolated hepatocellular organelles demonstrated to transport H^+ ions. It is very likely that vesicle-associated ATPase(s) include the H^+-ATPase(s). Indeed, with isolated organelles, several characteristics of ATPase activity are similar to those of H^+ transport including (a) dependence on divalent cations, e.g. Mg^{2+} (48); and (b) sensitivity to inhibitors, e.g. N-ethylmaleimide and DCCD (48, 75, 76, 77). However, organelle-associated ATPase activity and H^+ transport do not consistently vary in parallel. For example, inhibitors such as SITS or DIDS have apparently disparate effects in some preparations (inhibition of H^+ transport but not

ATPase activity; 48); ATPase activity is incompletely inhibited by N-ethylmaleimide and DCCD, which abolish H^+ transport (48, 75–77); and certain agents show different inhibition curves in the two systems (e.g. IC_{50} for N-ethylmaleimide in multivesicular bodies is 5×10^{-6} M for H^+ transport and 10^{-3} M for ATPase activity) (75).

H^+-ATPase in Intact Cells

ORGANELLES   Relatively little is known regarding the distribution of H^+-ATPases in intact cells. Studies in cultured fibroblasts involving localization by immunoelectron microscopy of a weak base have demonstrated that acidic organelles are diffusely distributed throughout the cytoplasm and include lysosomes, probable endosomes, multivesicular bodies, cisternae and vesicles associated with the trans Golgi complex, and some (but not all) coated vesicles (2, 3). Although the same technique has not been applied to hepatocytes, an antibody raised against rat liver lysosomal membranes, which cross-reacts with parietal cell H,K-ATPase and may therefore recognize a component of the lysosomal H^+-ATPase, has been shown to bind to coated vesicles, putative endosomes, certain elements of the Golgi complex, and pericanalicular dense bodies, as well as lysosomes (61). Fluorescence-microscopic studies of living hepatocytes in primary culture, in which acidic compartments were identified by acridine orange, have similarly demonstrated the presence of numerous acidic compartments (reversibly alkalinized by chloroquine or protonophores) throughout the cytoplasm. Only a minority of these are accounted for by acid phosphatase–positive lysosomes (42). Collectively, these studies confirm that a variety of intracellular compartments are acidified, presumably via an H^+-ATPase, and there is a general congruence between the compartments identified in intact cells and those identified in isolated organelles.

PLASMA MEMBRANE   The presence of an H^+-ATPase in hepatocyte plasma membranes is of particular interest because H^+-ATPase may play a role in regulation of pH_i and bile formation (see below), and it is anticipated based on the presence of the H^+-ATPase in endocytic organelles, such as coated vesicles and endosomes, which are presumably derived from the plasma membrane. At present, however, evidence supporting the presence of a plasma membrane–associated H^+-ATPase is, at best, indirect. Certain characteristics of plasma membrane–associated ATPase activity (DCCD and N-ethylmaleimide sensitivity, resistance to oligomycin) are similar to those of organelle-associated H^+ transport (54), and antibodies that may be directed against the lysosomal H^+-ATPase bind to the plasma membrane (61). Preliminary evidence for amiloride-insensitive H^+ extrusion from isolated hepatocytes has also been reported (4). At present, however, ATP-dependent acidification in plasma membranes that is clearly separable from Na^+-H^+ exchange (see below) has not been demonstrated in plasma membranes isolated from normal rat liver (5, 68; R. W. Van Dyke, unpublished observations).

Possible Roles in Hepatocellular Function

Our current understanding of the functional importance of H^+-ATPase(s) in hepatocytes, as well as in other cells, is incomplete. Indeed, current concepts are based largely on the effects of amines or ionophores, which alkalinize intracellular vesicles but also have other effects. Probable functions of hepatocellular H^+-ATPase(s) as of this writing are briefly summarized below.

RECEPTOR-MEDIATED ENDOCYTOSIS   A variety of ligands, including asialoglycoproteins, lipoproteins, and diferric transferrin, are taken up into hepatocytes via receptor-mediated endocytosis. Many of the organelles now recognized to be actively acidified are on the endocytic pathway (Table 1), including clathrin-coated vesicles, CURL (compartment for uncoupling of receptor and ligand) (22), multivesicular bodies (75), endosomes (a general term that refers to all vesicular structures involved in receptor-mediated uptake and processing "proximal" to lysosomes), and lysosomes. Vesicle acidification appears to alter receptor-ligand interactions. For example, binding of asialoglycoprotein to its receptor and binding of iron to transferrin is diminished at an acidic pH. Thus, acidification of endocytic organelles promotes uncoupling of these ligands from their receptors, facilitating transport of ligands to lysosomes and the return of receptors (as well as apotransferrin) to the cell surface for reutilization (28, 35, 36, 81, 82). Indeed, acidosomotropic amines such as chloroquine, when present in concentrations sufficient to alkalinize acidic vesicles, have been shown to alter receptor recycling. For example, asialoglycoprotein receptors become trapped inside the hepatocyte, and consequently the cell surface receptor population is depleted (69). Amines also inhibit the degradation of ligands (31, 69), perhaps via pH-mediated inhibition of lysosomal enzymes, as well as impaired delivery to lysosomes. Interestingly, amines seem to have little effect on the uptake, recycling, and transport to bile or sequestration compartments of fluid phase markers such as dextran or inulin (41, 65). This could reflect either a lack of importance of acidification on the handling of such markers or the involvement of a heterogeneous population of vesicles in their uptake, only some of which are acidic.

EXOCYTOSIS   Endo- and exocytosis are complementary cellular processes, and a number of observations suggest that vesicle acidification plays an important role in exocytosis, just as it does in endocytosis: (*a*) Studies of isolated hepatic Golgi indicate that this organelle is actively acidified (23), and immunocytochemical studies in cultured fibroblasts demonstrate that the trans Golgi is acidified (3). (*b*) The ionophore monensin inhibits the transport of Semliki Forest virus membrane proteins, transferrin, and albumin at the level of the medial Golgi cisternae (1, 25, 73) and inhibits the glycosylation of these and other proteins, which is believed to occur in the trans Golgi (1, 73). These findings suggest a pH-sensitive step at the level of the medial and/or trans Golgi. (*c*) A variety of endocrine and exocrine secretory granules have been shown to be actively acidified by a mechanism that is apparently similar to that operating in endocytic vesicles. These include neurosecretory granules from the neurohypophysis (10, 63), serotonin-containing platelet granules (33), insulin secretory granules (32), adrenal chromaffin granules (11), and zymogen granules from pancreatic acinar cells (53). (*d*) Moreover, chloroquine has been shown in certain systems to divert newly synthesized proteins from the regulated secretory pathway involving secretory granules into the constitutive or unregulated secretory pathway (46a). Collectively, these observations provide strong evidence for the involvement of an H^+-ATPase(s) in secretion as well as endocytosis, although its precise role(s) remains largely undefined.

CANALICULAR BILE FORMATION   Hepatic formation of bile is an energy-requiring process that has traditionally been divided into formation of ductular bile (by bile ductular cells) and canalicular bile (by hepatocytes). Canalicular bile formation is operationally divided into bile acid–dependent bile flow (BADBF), which is ascribed to biliary secretion of osmotically active bile salts, and bile acid–independent bile flow (BAIBF), which has been ascribed to active secretion of inorganic electrolytes (66). This division, however, may be too simplistic; indeed, several lines of evidence suggest that BADBF may also involve stimulation by bile acids of the secretion of inorganic electrolytes, in particular HCO_3^- (66).

Active HCO_3^- transport by epithelia is generally attributed to the active transport of H^+ ions. For example, in liver, H^+-ATPase pump units localized to the basolateral (sinusoidal) plasma membrane would be expected to extrude protons, raise pH_i and intracellular bicarbonate activity, and, in conjunction with canalicular Cl^--HCO_3^- exchange (46), produce canalicular HCO_3^- secretion and bile formation (Figure 1). There has been little formal investigation of the role of H^+-ATPase in BADBF, a process for which intact Na^+-H^+ exchange does appear important (see section on Na^+-H^+ exchange, below). Indirect evidence supporting a role for ATP-dependent H^+ transport in BAIBF includes: (*a*) BAIBF is reduced in perfused rat liver by removal of perfusate HCO_3^- but not other ions, which suggests a role for active HCO_3^-

Space of Disse'

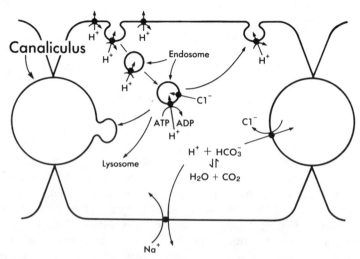

Figure 1   Proposed mechanisms of proton transport by hepatocyte organelles and plasma membrane.

secretion (27, 80). (*b*) BAIBF is minimally reduced by elimination of Na^+ or exposure to amiloride or amiloride analogues, which implies that BAIBF (in contrast to BADBF; see below) does not require intact Na^+-H^+ exchange (41, 80). (*c*) Preliminary results suggest that about 50% of proton extrusion by isolated hepatocytes occurs via an amiloride-insensitive mechanism (4); however, unambiguous evidence for the presence of this pump in the basolateral membrane is lacking (see above).

REGULATION OF pH_i Intracellular pH (pH_i) of hepatocytes, measured by a variety of methods, is more alkaline (6.88–7.27) than would be predicted based on passive distribution of protons (4, 13, 14, 59, 83). The presence of H^+-ATPase pump units on the hepatocyte plasma membrane would imply a role in regulation of pH_i. Indeed, it is tempting to speculate that the "same" H^+-ATPase responsible for acidification of endocytic vesicles also plays a role in canalicular bile formation and maintenance of pH_i, and that pH_i and bile formation are regulated in part via changes in the rate of ATP-dependent H^+ extrusion due to insertion of H^+-ATPase pump units into, or their removal from, the plasma membrane via a vesicular mechanism (Figure 1). This system would be consistent with the mechanisms proposed for regulation of H^+ extrusion by turtle bladder and distal nephron (24, 70, 72) and represents an interesting avenue of investigation.

Na^+-H^+ EXCHANGE

Identification and Characterization of Na^+-H^+ Exchange

Rat hepatocytes exhibit (a) a decrease in pH_i after addition of ouabain or removal of sodium (4), (b) amiloride-sensitive recovery from an acid (NH_4Cl) load (30), and (c) sodium-dependent H^+ efflux (4). These observations suggest the presence of a Na^+-H^+ exchanger similar to that in other cell types (6, 7, 40). Studies using purified basolateral (sinusoidal) hepatocyte membrane vesicles have provided more direct evidence for Na^+-H^+ exchange. Two groups (19, 52) have demonstrated electroneutral, H^+-gradient-stimulated $^{22}Na^+$ uptake and Na^+-gradient-stimulated vesicle acidification in basolateral membrane vesicles, which is consistent with Na^+-H^+ exchange (6, 7, 40). A third group used ^{14}C-methylamine to identify ATP-, Na^+-, and K^+-dependent, amiloride-sensitive acidification of inside-out basolateral membrane vesicles (5), thus demonstrating the presence of Na,K-ATPase and Na^+-H^+ exchange in the same vesicle population.

Further characterization of hepatocyte Na^+-H^+ exchange has revealed many similarities to renal Na^+-H^+ exchange (6, 7, 40). Hepatic Na^+-H^+ exchange is asymmetrically localized to the basolateral plasma membrane; studies of two different purified canalicular membrane preparations failed to show Na^+-H^+ exchange (5, 52). Hepatocyte Na^+-H^+ exchange also is electroneutral, amiloride-sensitive ($IC_{50} \approx 600$ μM), and inhibited by 1-mM harmaline but not by 1-mM bumetanide, furosemide, SITS, DIDS, or acetazolamide (52). Li^+ and NH_4^+, but not K^+, partially substitute for Na^+ (52). Hepatocyte Na^+-H^+ exchange exhibits a high affinity for Na^+ [$K_m \approx 5.4$ mM (52)]. Estimates for V_{max} of 14 nmol Na^+ min^{-1} mg $protein^{-1}$ (52) are, however, about tenfold less than the estimated V_{max} (119 nmol min^{-1} mg $protein^{-1}$) in renal membrane vesicles (7). This difference may reflect differences in the antiporter density and proton transport capacity of the two tissues.

Function of Hepatocyte Na^+-H^+ Exchange

REGULATION OF pH_i The studies cited above suggest that hepatocyte pH_i is regulated in part by Na^+-H^+ exchange (4, 59). However, other potential mechanisms for pH_i regulation, including a plasma membrane proton pump (see discussion above) similar to that in renal epithelia (6, 87) and Cl^--HCO_3^- exchange, may occur also in liver, and the relative contributions of these various proton transport mechanisms to hepatocyte pH_i regulation remain unclear.

CANALICULAR BILE FORMATION   A role for Na^+-H^+ exchange has been proposed for both BAIBF and BADBF (15, 43, 52, 66). For example, BAIBF might be due to basolateral Na^+-H^+ exchange (driven by a basolateral Na,K-ATPase) working in concert with canalicular Cl^--HCO_3^- exchange, canalicular Cl^- conductance, and paracellular Na^+ movement to effect net biliary secretion of HCO_3^- and Na^+ (52) (Figure 1). This hypothesis, however, is inconsistent with the lack of effect of Na^+ substitution, amiloride, or amiloride analogues on BAIBF (43, 62, 80). There is more evidence to support a role for Na^+-H^+ in BADBF. The bile acid ursodeoxycholic acid (UDCA) produces a bicarbonate-rich (39–49 mM) choleresis (15, 43, 62) that is supported by permeable buffers other than HCO_3^- (20) and inhibited by treatments (amiloride, amiloride analogues, or substitution of Li^+ for Na^+) that inhibit Na^+-H^+ exchange but have little effect on UDCA secretion (43, 80). UDCA (200 μM) also stimulates Na^+-H^+ exchange in rat liver basolateral plasma membrane vesicles (50). In addition, amiloride also decreases taurocholate-stimulated bile flow (43). Collectively, these findings suggest that UDCA- and perhaps taurocholate-stimulated bile flow may be attributable in part to stimulation of basolateral Na^+-H^+ exchange.

HEPATIC REGENERATION   Mitogenesis induced by growth factors such as epidermal growth factor (EGF) and platelet-derived growth factor (PDGF) is associated with cytoplasmic alkalinization (26, 47, 58), which is attributed to enhanced Na^+-H^+ exchange (26, 58) that is stimulated via diacylglycerol and protein kinase C (26). Liver has a remarkable capacity to regenerate, and a similar role for Na^+-H^+ exchange in hepatic regeneration has been proposed (37, 38, 44). This suggestion is based on the observations that (a) proliferation of cultured rat hepatocytes, induced by insulin, glucagon, and EGF, is blocked by amiloride, ouabain, and sodium ionophores (37); (b) stimulated hepatocytes exhibit increased amiloride-sensitive sodium uptake (37, 38); (c) amiloride and ouabain impair regeneration of rat liver after 70% hepatectomy (44); and (d) after partial hepatectomy, Na^+-H^+ exchange in basolateral liver plasma membrane vesicles is increased (51). A causal relationship between cytoplasmic alkalinization and cell proliferation, however, remains controversial, as proliferation can be dissociated from alkalinization (9, 47), and amiloride at the concentrations used to block Na^+-H^+ exchange inhibits protein synthesis in both fibroblasts and hepatocytes (9, 45).

Cl^--HCO_3^- EXCHANGE

Cl^--HCO_3^- exchange, originally described in erythrocytes, occurs in many cell types. Studies using purified rat liver plasma membrane vesicles (46) demonstrate pH-gradient- (pH_i > pH_o) and HCO_3^--gradient-stimulated ^{36}Cl uptake into canalicular membrane vesicles, which is consistent with the presence of Cl^--HCO_3^- exchange. HCO_3^--stimulated Cl^- uptake is (a) inhibited by DIDS, (b) electroneutral, (c) saturable with respect to Cl^-, and (d) partially inhibited by bumetanide, furosemide, probenecid, and SITS. These properties are similar to those of Cl^--HCO_3^- exchange in other tissues (71). Hepatic Cl^--HCO_3^- exchange is also "cis-inhibited" by both Cl^- and NO_3^-, but not by other anions, which suggests that the exchanger utilizes only a limited range of substrates (46). In contrast, basolateral membrane vesicles exhibit neither HCO_3^- nor Na^+-stimulated Cl^- transport (46). These findings confirm other observations that hepatocyte Cl^- transport is passive and not coupled to sodium (16, 66).

Although these studies establish the existence of Cl^--HCO_3^- exchange in liver cells, the physiological role(s) of this transporter remains unclear. Cl^--HCO_3^- exchange may participate in pH_i regulation of cells exposed to bicarbonate and may facilitate bicarbonate secretion and bile formation by mediating canalicular efflux of cytoplasmic bicarbonate produced by basolateral Na^+-H^+ exchange or an H^+-ATPase.

OTHER MECHANISMS OF H^+ TRANSPORT

Certain poorly conjugated bile acids such as UDCA and the 23-carbon bile acid analogue nor-ursodeoxycholate acid (nor-UDCA) produce an increase in bile flow that is greater in amount ($\geq 2x$) and richer in bicarbonate (15, 43, 86) than that of physiologic bile acids. These bile acids are secreted partly in unconjugated form, have a relatively high pK_a (~5), and readily cross membranes by nonionic diffusion. These observations have led Yoon and colleagues (86) to postulate an alternative mechanism for HCO_3^- secretion that involves the following sequence of events: (a) protonation of these bile acid anions in the bile ductules, (b) reabsorption of the protonated species across the bile ductule cell, (c) recycling of bile acid back to the hepatocyte via the periductular plexus connecting the bile ducts to the hepatic sinusoid, (d) ionization and reuptake as the anion by hepatocytes and resecretion into bile. This sequence would effect net biliary bicarbonate secretion (86). Similar recycling may also occur across the basolateral membrane of the hepatocyte. Although the driving forces for such a mechanism remain poorly defined, this hypothesis is indirectly supported by the consistent relationship observed under a variety of experimental conditions between the hypercholeresis produced by these bile acids and their appearance in bile in unconjugated form (86).

SUMMARY

It is apparent that proton transport plays an important role in many essential hepatocyte functions. Important unanswered issues include (a) the location of the H^+-ATPase and its role in hepatic functions, (b) the regulators of Na^+-H^+ exchange, (c) the exact role of Na^+-H^+ exchange in bile formation and in hepatic regeneration, and (d) the role of bile acids such as UDCA and nor-UDCA in mediating transepithelial proton transport.

Literature Cited

1. Alonso-Caplin, F. V., Compans, R. W. 1983. Modulation of glycosylation and transport of viral membrane glycoproteins by a sodium ionophore. *J. Cell Biol.* 97:659–68
2. Anderson, R. G. W., Falck, J. R., Goldstein, J. L., Brown, M. S. 1984. Visualization of acidic organelles in intact cells by electron microscopy. *Proc. Natl. Acad. Sci. USA* 81:4838–42
3. Anderson, R. G. W., Pathak, R. K. 1985. Vesicles and cisternae in the trans Golgi apparatus of human fibroblasts are acidic compartments. *Cell* 40:635–43
4. Anwer, M. S. 1985. Direct determination of the role of sodium in H^+-efflux from isolated rat hepatocytes. *Hepatology* 5:1008 (Abstr.)
5. Arias, I. M., Forgac, M. 1984. The sinusoidal domain of the plasma membrane of rat hepatocytes contains an amiloride-sensitive Na^+/H^+ antiport. *J. Biol. Chem.* 259:5406–8
6. Aronson, P. S. 1983. Mechanisms of active H^+ secretion in the proximal tubule. *Am. J. Physiol.* 245:F647–59
7. Aronson, P. S. 1985. Kinetic properties of the plasma membrane Na^+/H^+ exchanger. *Ann. Rev. Physiol.* 47:545–60
8. Barr, R., Sofranski, K., Sun, I. L., Crane, F. L., Morré, D. J. 1984. An electrogenic proton pump associated with the Golgi apparatus of mouse liver driven by NADH and ATP. *J. Biol. Chem.* 259:14064–67
9. Besterman, J. M., Tyrey, S. J., Cragoe, E. J. Jr., Cuatrecasas, P. 1984. Inhibition of epidermal growth factor-induced mitogenesis by amiloride and an analog: Evidence against a requirement for Na^+/H^+ exchange. *Proc. Natl. Acad. Sci. USA* 81:6762–66
10. Breslow, E. 1979. Chemistry and biology of the neurophysis. *Ann. Rev. Biochem.* 48:251–74
11. Cidon, S., Ben-David, H., Nelson, N. 1983. ATP-dependent proton fluxes across membranes of secretory organelles. *J. Biol. Chem.* 258:11684–88
12. Coffey, J. W., de Duve, C. 1968. Digestive activity of lysosomes: II. The digestion of proteins by extracts of rat liver lysosomes. *J. Biol. Chem.* 243:3255–63
13. Cohen, R. D., Henderson, R. M., Iles, R. A., Smith, J. A. 1982. Metabolic inter-relationships of intracellular pH measured by double-barrelled microelectrodes in perfused rat liver. *J. Physiol.* 330:69–80
14. Cohen, S. M., Ogawa, S., Rottenberg, H., Glynn, P., Yamane, T., et al. 1978. ^{31}P nuclear magnetic resonance studies of isolated rat liver cells. *Nature* 273: 554–56
15. Dumont, M., Erlinger, S., Uchman, S. 1980. Hypercholeresis induced by ursodeoxycholic acid and 7-ketolithocholic acid in the rat: Possible role of bicarbonate transport. *Gastroenterology* 79:82–89
16. Fitz, J. G., Scharschmidt, B. F. 1986. Intracellular chloride activity in intact rat liver. *Am. J. Physiol.* In press
17. Forgac, M., Cantley, L., Wiedenmann, B., Altstiel, L., Branton, D. 1983. Clathrin coated vesicles contain an ATP-dependent proton pump. *Proc. Natl. Acad. Sci. USA* 80:1300–3
18. Forte, J. G., Lee, H. C. 1977. Gastric ATPases: A review of their possible role in HCl secretion. *Gastroenterology* 73:921–26
19. Fuchs, R., Graf, J., Peterlik, M., Thalhammer, T. 1984. Sodium-proton antiport in sinusoidal liver cell membrane. *Hepatology* 4:761 (Abstr.)
20. Garcia-Marin, J. J., Corbic, M., Dumont, M., de Couet, G., Erlinger, S. 1985. Role of H^+ transport in ursodeoxycholate-induced biliary HCO_3^- secretion in the rat. *Am. J. Physiol.* 249: G335–41
21. Geisow, M. J., Evans, W. H. 1984. pH in the endosome: Measurements during pinocytosis and receptor-mediated endocytosis. *Exp. Cell Res.* 150:36–46
22. Geuze, H. J., Slot, J. W., Strous, G. J. A. M., Peppard, J., von Figura, K., et al. 1984. Intracellular receptor sorting during endocytosis: Comparative immunoelectron microscopy of multiple receptors in rat liver. *Cell* 37:195–204
23. Glickman, J., Croen, K., Kelly, S., Al-

Awqati, Q. 1983. Golgi membranes contain an electrogenic H^+ pump in parallel to a chloride conductance. *J. Cell Biol.* 97:1303–8

24. Gluck, S., Cannon, C., Al-Awqati, Q. 1982. Exocytosis regulates urinary acidification in turtle bladder by rapid insertion of H^+ pumps into the luminal membrane. *Proc. Natl. Acad. Sci. USA* 79:4327–31

25. Griffiths, G., Quinn, P., Warren, G. 1983. Direction of the Golgi complex. I. Monensin inhibits the transport of viral membrane proteins from medial to trans Golgi cisternae in baby hamster cells infected with the Semliki Forest virus. *J. Cell Biol.* 96:835–50

26. Grinstein, S., Cohen, S., Goetz, J. D., Rothstein, A., Gelfand, E. W. 1985. Characterization of the activation of Na^+/H^+ exchange in lymphocytes by phorbol esters: Change in cytoplasmic pH dependence of the antiport. *Proc. Natl. Acad. Sci. USA* 82:1429–33

27. Hardison, W. G. M., Wood, C. A. 1978. Importance of bicarbonate in bile salt independent fraction of bile flow. *Am. J. Physiol.* 235:E158–64

28. Harford, J., Bridges, K., Ashwell, G., Klausner, R. D. 1983. Intracellular dissociation of receptor-bound asialoglycoproteins in cultured hepatocytes. A pH-mediated nonlysosomal event. *J. Biol. Chem.* 258:3191–97

29. Harikumar, P., Reeves, J. P. 1983. The lysosomal pump is electrogenic. *J. Biol. Chem.* 258:10403–10

30. Henderson, R. M., Graf, J., Boyer, J. L. 1985. The effect of amiloride upon recovery from an intracellular acid load in isolated rat hepatocyte couplets in the absence of external bicarbonate. *Hepatology* 5:1016 (Abstr.)

31. Hornick, C. A., Jones, A. L., Renaud, G., Hradek, G., Havel, R. J. 1983. Effect of chloroquine on low-density lipoprotein catabolic pathways in rat hepatocytes. *Am. J. Physiol.* 246:G187–94

32. Hutton, J. C. 1982. The internal pH and membrane potential of the insulin-secretory granule. *Biochem. J.* 204:171–78

33. Johnson, R. G., Scarpa, A., Salganicoff, L. 1978. The internal pH of isolated serotonin containing granules of pig platelets. *J. Biol. Chem.* 253:7061–68

34. Kaunitz, J. O., Gunther, R. D., Sachs, G. 1985. Characterization of an electrogenic ATP and chloride-dependent proton translocating pump from the rat renal medulla. *J. Biol. Chem.* 260:11567–73

35. Klausner, R. D., Ashwell, G., von Renswoude, J., Harford, J. B., Bridges, K. R. 1983. Binding of apotransferrin to K562 cells: Explanation of the transferrin cycle. *Proc. Natl. Acad. Sci. USA* 80:2263–66

36. Klausner, R. D., Renswoude, J. V., Ashwell, G., Kempf, C., Schechter, A. N., et al. 1983. Receptor-mediated endocytosis of transferrin in K562 cells. *J. Biol. Chem.* 258:4715–24

37. Koch, K. S., Leffert, H. L. 1979. Increased sodium ion influx is necessary to initiate rat hepatocyte proliferation. *Cell* 18:153–63

38. Koch, K. S., Leffert, H. L. 1980. Growth control of differentiated adult rat hepatocytes in primary culture. *Ann. NY Acad. Sci.* 349:111–27

39. Korenbrot, J. I., Hwang, S.-B. 1980. Proton transport by bacteriorhodopsin in plasma membranes assembled from air-water interface films. *J. Gen. Physiol.* 76:649–82

40. Krulwich, T. A. 1983. Na^+/H^+ antiporters. *Biochim. Biophys. Acta* 726:245–64

41. Lake, J. R., George, P., Licko, V., Scharschmidt, B. 1985. Vesicular transport of fluid phase markers (FPM) and ligands by liver: Effects of colchicine and chloroquine. *Clin. Res.* 33:322A (Abstr.)

42. Lake, J. R., Van Dyke, R. W., Scharschmidt, B. F. 1984. Characterization of acidic compartments within living cultured hepatocytes. *Hepatology* 4:1070 (Abstr.)

43. Lake, J. R., Van Dyke, R. W., Scharschmidt, B. F. 1985. Effects of Na^+ replacement and amiloride on ursodeoxycholic acid–stimulated choleresis and biliary bicarbonate secretion. *Am J. Physiol.* In press

44. Leffert, H. L., Koch, K. S. 1980. Ionic events at the membrane initiate rat liver regeneration. *Ann. NY Acad. Sci.* 339:201–15

45. Leffert, H. L., Koch, K. S., Fehlmann, M., Weiser, W., Lad, P. J., et al. 1982. Amiloride blocks cell-free protein synthesis at levels attained inside cultured rat hepatocytes. *Biochem. Biophys. Res. Commun.* 108:738–45

46. Meier, P. J., Knickelbein, R., Moseley, R. H., Dobbins, J. W., Boyer, J. L. 1985. Evidence for carrier-mediated chloride/bicarbonate exchange in canalicular rat liver plasma membrane vesicles. *J. Clin. Invest.* 75:1256–63

46a. Mellman, I., Fuchs, R., Helenius, A. 1986. Acidification of the endocytic and exocytic pathways. *Ann. Rev. Biochem.* 55:663–700

47. Mills, G. B., Cragoe, E. J. Jr., Gelfand, E. W., Grinstein, S. 1985. Interleukin 2 induces a rapid increase in intracellular pH through activation of a Na^+/H^+ antiport. *J. Biol. Chem.* 260:12500–7

48. Moriyama, Y., Takano, T., Okhuma, S. 1984. Proton translocating ATPase in lysosomal membrane ghosts. Evidence that alkaline Mg^{2+}-ATPase acts as a proton pump. *J. Biochem.* 95:995–1007

49. Moriyama, Y., Takano, T., Okhuma, S. 1984. Solubilization and reconstitution of a lysosomal H^+-pump. *J. Biochem.* 96:927–30

50. Moseley, R. H., Ballatori, N., Smith, D., Boyer, J. L. 1985. Ursodeoxycholate stimulates Na^+-H^+ exchange in rat liver basolateral plasma membrane vesicles. *Hepatology* 5:1017 (Abstr.)

51. Moseley, R. H., Barrett, C., Boyer, J. L. 1986. Na^+/H^+ exchange activity is enhanced in liver plasma membrane (LPM) vesicles derived from partially hepatectomized rats. *Gastroenterology* 90:1749 (Abstr.)

52. Moseley, R. H., Meier, P. J., Aronson, P. S., Boyer, J. L. 1986. Na-H exchange in rat liver basolateral but not canalicular plasma membrane vesicles. *Am. J. Physiol.* 250:G35–G43

53. Niederau, C., Van Dyke, R. W., Scharschmidt, B. F., Grendell, J. H. 1985. Rat pancreatic zymogen granules: An acidified compartment. *Gastroenterology* In press

54. Oertle, M., Van Dyke, R. W., Scharschmidt, B. F. 1984. Characterization of the ouabain-insensitive ATPase of rat liver plasma membranes. *Arch. Int. Physiol. Biochem.* 92:107–18

55. Ohkuma, S., Moriyama, Y., Takano, T. 1982. Identification and characterization of a proton pump on lysosomes by fluorescein isothiocyanate-dextran fluorescence. *Proc. Natl. Acad. Sci. USA* 79:2758–62

56. Ohkuma, S., Moriyama, Y., Takano, T. 1983. Electrogenic nature of lysosomal proton pump as revealed with a cyanine dye. *J. Biochem.* 94:1935–43

57. Ohkuma, S., Poole, B. 1978. Fluorescence probe measurement of the intralysosomal pH in living cells and the perturbation of pH by various agents. *Proc. Natl. Acad. Sci. USA* 75:3327–31

58. Paris, S., Pouyssegur, J. 1984. Growth factors activate the Na^+/H^+ antiporter in quiescent fibroblasts by increasing its affinity for intracellular H^+. *J. Biol. Chem.* 259:10989–94

59. Pollack, A. S. 1984. Intracellular pH of hepatocytes in primary monolayer culture. *Am. J. Physiol.* 246:F738–44

60. Rees-Jones, R., Al-Awqati, Q. 1984. Proton-translocating adenosine-triphosphatase in rough and smooth microsomes from rat liver. *Biochemistry* 23:2236–40

61. Reggio, H., Bainton, D., Harms, E., Coudrier, E., Loward, D. 1984. Antibodies against lysosomal membranes reveal a 100,000-mol-wt protein that cross-reacts with purified H^+,K^+-ATPase from gastric mucosa. *J. Cell Biol.* 99:1511–26

62. Renner, E., Lake, J. R., Cragoe, E., Van Dyke, R. W., Scharschmidt, B. F. 1985. Ursodeoxycholic acid (UDCA) chloresis: Relationship to biliary HCO_3^- secretion and further evidence of a role for Na^+/H^+ exchange. *Hepatology* 5:1011

63. Russell, J. T. 1984. ΔpH, H^+ diffusion potentials and Mg^{2+} ATPase in neurosecretory vesicles isolated from bovine neurohypophyses. *J. Biol. Chem.* 259:9496–9507

64. Saermark, T., Flint, N., Evans, W. H. 1985. Hepatic endosome fractions contain an ATP-driven proton pump. *Biochem. J.* 225:51–58

65. Scharschmidt, B. F., Lake, J. R., Licko, V., Van Dyke, R. W. 1985. Fluid phase endocytosis by cultured rat hepatocytes and perfused rat liver. *Proc. Natl. Acad. Sci. USA* In press

66. Scharschmidt, B. F., Van Dyke, R. W. 1983. Mechanisms of hepatic electrolyte transport. *Gastroenterology* 85:1199–1214

67. Schneider, D. L. 1983. ATP-dependent acidification of membrane vesicles isolated from purified rat liver lysosomes. *J. Biol. Chem.* 258:1833–38

68. Schneider, D. L., Manara, F. S. 1985. Alcohol ingestion alters the proton pump activity of rat liver: Decreased activity in lysosomes parallels the presence of activity in plasma membranes. *Res. Commun. Substance Abuse* 6:117–26

69. Schwartz, A. L., Bolognesi, A., Fridovich, S. E. 1984. Recycling of the asialoglycoprotein receptor and the effect of lysosomotropic amines in hepatoma cells. *J. Cell Biol.* 98:732–38

70. Schwartz, G. J., Al-Awqati, Q. 1985. Carbon dioxide causes exocytosis of vesicles containing H^+ pumps in isolated perfused proximal and collecting tubules. *J. Clin. Invest.* 75:1638–44

71. Seifter, J. L., Aronson, P. S. 1984. Cl⁻ transport via anion exchange in *Necturus* renal microvillus membranes. *Am. J. Physiol.* 247:F888–95

72. Stanton, B. A. 1984. Regulation of ion transport in epithelia: Role of membrane recruitment from cytoplasmic vesicles. *Lab. Invest.* 51:255–57

73. Strous, G. J. A. M., Willemsen, R., van Kerkhof, P., Slot, J. W., Geuze, H. J., et al. 1983. Vesicular stomatitis versus glycoprotein, albumin, and transferrin are transported to the cell surface via the same Golgi vesicles. *J. Cell Biol.* 97: 1815–22

74. Sze, H. 1985. H⁺-translocating ATPases: Advances using membrane vesicles. *Ann. Rev. Plant Physiol.* 36: 175–208

74a. Van Dyke, R. W. 1986. Anion inhibition of the proton pump in rat liver multivesicular bodies. *J. Biol. Chem.* In press

75. Van Dyke, R. W., Hornick, C. A., Belcher, J., Scharschmidt, B. F., Havel, R. J. 1985. Identification and characterization of ATP-dependent proton transport by rat liver multivesicular bodies. *J. Biol. Chem.* 26:11021–26

76. Van Dyke, R. W., Matsumoto-Pon, J. K. 1985. Proton transport in rat liver multivesicular bodies (MVB): Effects of anions. *Hepatology* 5:977 (Abstr.)

77. Van Dyke, R. W., Scharschmidt, B. F., Steer, C. J. 1985. ATP-dependent proton transport by isolated brain clathrin-coated vesicles: Role of clathrin and other determinants of acidification. *Biochim. Biophys. Acta* 812:423–36

78. Van Dyke, R. W., Steer, C. J., Scharschmidt, B. F. 1984. Clathrin-coated vesicles from rat liver; enzymatic profile and characterization of ATP-dependent proton transport. *Proc. Natl. Acad. Sci. USA* 81:3108–12

79. Van Dyke, R. W., Steer, C. J., Scharschmidt, B. F. 1984. Characterization of ATP-dependent proton transport in rat liver chathrin-coated vesicles. In *Hydrogen Ion Transport in Epithelia*, ed. J. G. Forte, D. Warnock, R. C. Rector, Jr.,

pp. 231–38. New York: Wiley

80. Van Dyke, R. W., Stephens, J. E., Scharschmidt, B. F. 1982. Effects of ion substitution on bile acid-dependent and -independent bile formation by rat liver. *J. Clin. Invest.* 70:505–17

81. Van Renswoude, J., Bridges, K. R., Harford, J. B., Klausner, R. D. 1982. Receptor-mediated endocytosis of transferrin and the uptake of Fe in K562 cells: Identification of a nonlysosomal acidic compartment. *Proc. Natl. Acad. Sci. USA* 79:6186–90

82. Weigel, P. H., Oka, J. A. 1983. The large intracellular pool of asialoglycoprotein receptor functions during the endocytosis of asialoglycoproteins by rat hepatocytes. *J. Biol. Chem.* 258:5095–5102

83. Williams, J. A., Withrow, C. D., Woodbury, D. M. 1971. Effects of ouabain and diphenylhydantoin on transmembrane potentials, intracellular electrolytes, and cell pH of rat muscle and liver *in vivo*. *J. Physiol.* 212:101–15

84. Xie, X.-S., Stone, D. K. 1986. Isolation and reconstitution of the clathrin-coated vesicle proton translocating complex. *J. Biol. Chem.* 261:2492–95

85. Xie, X.-S., Stone, D. K., Racker, E. 1983. Determinants of clathrin-coated vesicle acidification. *J. Biol. Chem.* 258:14834–38

86. Yoon, Y. B., Hagey, L. R., Hofmann, A. F., Gurantz, D., Michelotti, E. L., et al. 1986. Effect of side chain shortening on the physiological properties of bile acids: Hepatic transport and effect on biliary secretion of 23-nor-ursodeoxycholate in rodents. *Gastroenterology* 90:837–52

87. Zeidel, M. L., Silva, P., Seifter, J. L. 1986. Intracellular pH regulation and proton transport by rabbit renal medullary collecting duct cells. *J. Clin. Invest.* 77:113–20

88. Zhang, P., Schneider, D. L. 1983. The bioenergetics of Golgi apparatus function: Evidence for an ATP-dependent proton pump. *Biochim. Biophys. Res. Commun.* 114:620–25

Ann. Rev. Physiol. 1987. 49:87–103

ROLE OF PROTON AND BICARBONATE TRANSPORT IN PANCREATIC CELL FUNCTION

Gemma A. J. Kuijpers and Jan Joep H. H. M. De Pont

Department of Biochemistry, University of Nijmegen, 6500 HB Nijmegen, The Netherlands

INTRODUCTION

One of the main functions of the exocrine pancreas is the release into the duodenum of digestive enzymes dissolved in an alkaline, HCO_3^--rich fluid. The HCO_3^- in the pancreatic fluid neutralizes the gastric acid content, which is important in preventing acid damage to the duodenal epithelium.

Two main aspects of the role of HCO_3^- and H^+ transport in the pancreas have been studied. First, the role of HCO_3^- in the secretion of fluid by the pancreatic ducts has been extensively studied. Many of these studies were carried out at the organ level, some of these were at the level of the isolated main duct. Only a few studies were performed on ductular cells because of their inaccessibility and the problems encountered in isolating ducts or ductular cells due to the small volume fraction of these cells in the pancreas (less than 4%). Second, a limited number of studies have been dedicated to the role of HCO_3^- transport in the Ca^{2+}-dependent secretion of enzymes and fluid by the acinar cells. In this chapter we focus on the mechanism of H^+-HCO_3^- transport and its relation to the transport of other ions by the ductular cells, and we briefly summarize the literature on the role of H^+ and HCO_3^- transport in the acinar cells.

MORPHOLOGY OF THE PANCREAS

The exocrine pancreas consists of a system of anastomozing tubules or ducts (5). The ductal tree is terminated by groups of acinar cells, forming the acini,

87

0066-4278/87/0315-0087$02.00

and by irregularly shaped ductular cells or "centroacinar" cells wedged between the acinar cells. Intercalated ducts arise from the acini and subsequently fuse into intralobular and interlobular ducts and finally into the main duct. The cells of the ductal tree are structurally similar to the centroacinar cells, but as one moves down the duct system the cell shape changes from an irregular, elongated form to a cubic and finally columnar form. Ductular cells are small and have relatively few mitochondria, a poorly developed endoplasmic reticulum, a small Golgi complex, and moderate numbers of secretory granules and lysosomes. The cells are attached to each other by junctional complexes (for review see Reference 12). Acinar cells are clearly distinguished from ductular cells. The cells contain numerous secretory granules, an elaborate network of rough endoplasmic reticulum, and a Golgi complex close to the nucleus. Junctional complexes with "tight" junctions are present at the apical pole of acinar cells. The epithelial configuration of the pancreas creates three barriers to the movement of solutes and ions in the organ: the basolateral and apical cell membranes and the intercellular junctions.

METHODS OF STUDYING PANCREATIC FLUID AND ELECTROLYTE SECRETION

Studies on pancreatic fluid secretion have been conducted in vivo on conscious and anaesthetized animals, including dog, rat, and pig (47, 50, 65), and in vitro on isolated pancreas preparations, e.g. the secretin-stimulated perfused cat pancreas (13), the superfused isolated rabbit pancreas (53), and the perfused pig (33) and rat pancreas (35). Most studies using these preparations employ analysis of the final secretion or micropuncture and analysis of the ductal fluid at several points in the duct system. Some micropuncture studies have also provided electrophysiological data on the duct cell epithelium (28, 61, 68, 72).

The advantage of the use of intact organ preparations is obviously the integrity of the epithelial tissue structure. However, its limitations are the poor access to the site of secretion and the lack of data on intracellular ion concentrations, membrane potentials, etc. Purification of ductalar tissue and isolation of ductular cells has been carried out using microdissection and enzymatic tissue dissociation (3, 26, 57). A helpful procedure in these studies is to first cause acinar cell atrophy by the administration of a special diet to rats (23). This procedure also provides a method of studying the intact duct system in vivo without interference from acini. Recently, short-term culture of functionally intact duct fragments separated from collagenase digests of adult rat pancreas has been established and appears to be a suitable system to study both fluid transport and electrophysiology of the duct cell epithelium (2).

PHYSIOLOGY AND CONTROL OF SECRETION

The secretory processes in the exocrine pancreas are regulated by hormones and neurotransmitters. Enzyme secretion originating from the acinar cells is stimulated by acetylcholine and CCK in all species. In some species bombesin, substance P, secretin, and VIP also stimulate this process (73). Fluid secretion is stimulated by secretin and VIP in all species (14, 44, 53, 65) and by acetylcholine and CCK in some species, including rat and mouse (48, 58, 65, 70). Both types of fluid secretion are isotonic with blood or perfusion medium and contain plasma-like Na$^+$ and K$^+$ concentrations. The fluid secretion stimulated by secretin and VIP is HCO$_3^-$-rich and Cl$^-$-poor and is assumed to originate from the ductular cells, although an acinar component may exist. The acetylcholine- and CCK-stimulated scretion is HCO$_3^-$-poor and Cl$^-$-rich and probably originates from the acinar cells. In rabbit and rat a relatively large basal secretion exists, which at least in the rabbit is dependent on HCO$_3^-$ and probably originates in the ductular regions of the gland (35, 61).

In recent reviews on pancreatic electrolyte secretion, Case & Argent (12) and Schulz (58) extensively summarized the evidence that the ductular cells are responsible for the secretin-stimulated HCO$_3^-$ secretion. In support of this argument are the presence of high-affinity secretin receptors on ductular cells (45), the secretin-activated adenylate cyclase (55) and the second-messenger nature of cAMP in duct cells (3, 24, 37), the stimulatory effect of dbcAMP and cholera toxin on HCO$_3^-$ and fluid secretion (36, 66), the secretin sensitivity of a pancreas in which the acinar cells have been destroyed (23), and the enrichment of transport-related enzymes such as Na, K-ATPase and carbonic anhydrase in the ductular part of the pancreas (9, 26, 41, 42).

From the analysis of the ductal and final secretion, the following picture of fluid secretion emerges: In the pancreas of the cat, there is almost no basal secretion, and secretin elicits a HCO$_3^-$-rich (142 mM) fluid secretion from the intralobular and especially from the interlobular ducts, which is subject to transepithelial HCO$_3^-$-Cl$^-$ exchange in the extralobular and main ducts (14). The exchange is manifest especially at low flow rates and is at least partly responsible for the relatively low HCO$_3^-$ concentration of the final secretion at low degrees of stimulation by secretin (16). In the rabbit, a continuous secretion with a HCO$_3^-$ concentration of ~90 mM and a Cl$^-$ concentration of ~70 mM is manufactured in the acinar regions of the gland and is probably produced by centroacinar or duct cells at the top of the duct system (44, 61). Secretin stimulates the secretion of a HCO$_3^-$-rich fluid, especially in the interlobular ducts (61, 68). Modification of the basal and secretin-stimulated secretion by HCO$_3^-$-Cl$^-$ exchange apparently occurs in the small interlobular ducts and in the main duct; however, its overall importance appears to be questionable (11, 61). In the rat, the basal acinar fluid secretion has a Cl$^-$

concentration of $\sim$115 mM and a HCO_3^- concentration of 30 mM. Upon stimulation with secretin, a fluid secretion with a relatively high HCO_3^- concentration is produced in the duct system, resulting in a HCO_3^- concentration with a maximum of $\sim$70 mM in the final secretion (44, 65). In this species, CCK causes the acinar cells to vigorously secrete a fluid with a plasma-like Cl^- concentration ($\sim$120 mM) and a low HCO_3^- concentration ($\sim$30 mM) (48, 65). Thus the common phenomenon in all species is that secretin elicits a HCO_3^--rich secretion in the duct system.

CELLULAR MECHANISMS OF DUCTULAR HCO_3^- AND H^+ TRANSPORT

Ductular fluid secretion is strongly dependent on exogenous HCO_3^-, and only a small percentage of the secreted HCO_3^- is derived from metabolically produced CO_2 ($\sim$6%) (18, 56). Since the HCO_3^- concentration in the secreted fluid (30–150 mM) is much higher than in the blood or bathing medium (20–25 mM) and the transepithelial electrical potential is lumen negative, it is generally assumed that there is at least one primary or secondary active HCO_3^- transport step involved in the secretion process. The transport mechanisms for HCO_3^- and the other major ions, namely Cl^-, Na^+, and K^+, are obviously interrelated. In this section we discuss these mechanisms, their relationships, and the derived cellular models for ductular electrolyte secretion.

Ion Requirements of HCO_3^- and Fluid Secretion

SODIUM   Under physiological conditions, the Na^+ and K^+ concentrations in the pancreatic fluid are equal to, or slightly higher than, those in the blood or the perfusing or bathing medium (6, 17, 53). The concentrations are not significantly affected by changes in the medium HCO_3^- or Cl^- concentration. Sodium, however, has an important role in the fluid secretion process. Reduction of the Na^+ concentration in the medium by replacement of NaCl by KCl, LiCl, choline chloride, or sucrose decreases both the fluid secretion rate and the Na^+ concentration of the secreted fluid (6, 13, 17, 54, 69). The degree of effectiveness of the Na^+-replacing substance in sustaining fluid secretion appears to be related to its concentration in the secreted fluid. Replacement of Na^+ by Li^+ or K^+ inhibits secretion rate in a linear fashion, up to 90% at full replacement, and like Na^+ both cations appear in the secreted fluid in concentrations equal to those in the medium (17, 38, 54). Replacement by choline inhibits fluid secretion rate more strongly than substitution with Li^+ or K^+, and the concentration of choline in the secreted fluid is lower than in the medium. Sucrose inhibits secretion to an even larger extent and appears in the lowest concentration in the secreted fluid (6, 13, 38, 69). Concurrently, a large Na^+ concentration gradient is set up between the medium and the secreted fluid. The concentration ratio may reach a factor of three (perfusate 55 mM, secreted fluid 165 mM). Under these conditions, a concentration gradient for K^+ also builds up, with a concentration ratio about equal to that for Na^+ (6, 17).

The equal concentrations in the secreted fluid and the medium of both Na^+ and K^+ under normal conditions, together with the secretory concentration pattern of Na^+, K^+, and the Na^+-replacing substances, have led to the suggestion that the secretion of Na^+ (or a replacing cation) and K^+ is passive and proceeds through a paracellular pathway. The overall rate of paracellular secretion would depend on the permeability coefficients of the available cations and molecules and would determine the degree of inhibition upon replacement (6). This hypothesis is confirmed by the finding of Kuijpers (38) that the fluid secretion rate may be stimulated upon increasing the paracellular pancreatic permeability by CCK after replacement of Na^+ by choline.

However, if Na^+ secretion is passive, the concentration difference mentioned above should be paralleled by a lumen-negative electrical potential of up to 28 mV. Although a negative potential could be established by electrogenic HCO_3^- transport, such a high transepithelial potential has not been found: Measured potential values vary from -5 to -9 mV (61, 68, 72). However, these values were recorded in the main duct and along the duct system and may quantitatively differ from the values at the site of maximal fluid secretion. It also needs to be emphasized that if Na^+ is replaced by an equally permeable cation such as K^+ or Li^+, fluid secretion is still inhibited. The inhibition is accompanied by a decrease in the HCO_3^- concentration and an increase in the Cl^- concentration in the secreted fluid, as found upon replacement of HCO_3^- in the medium (39). It thus seems likely that, although the secretion of Na^+ itself is passive, Na^+ is directly involved in the active HCO_3^- (or H^+) and fluid transport mechanism. In conclusion, the inhibition of fluid secretion by Na^+ replacement appears to depend on the effectiveness of the replacing cation or molecule to substitute for Na^+ in the Na^+-dependent HCO_3^- secretion mechanism and its ability to be transported paracellularly.

POTASSIUM   Potassium is also required for maximal fluid secretion. Omission of K^+ from the perfusate or bathing medium reduces secretion up to 65%, but Rb^+ can substitute for K^+ (17). The inhibition is probably due to the dependence of fluid secretion on the activity of the Na,K-ATPase, which is dependent on the extracellular K^+ concentration (62). The role of the Na,K-ATPase in the fluid secretion process was first discovered in a study on the effect of ouabain on pancreatic fluid secretion: Fluid secretion can be fully inhibited by ouabain, and the activity of the Na,K-ATPase parallels the fluid secretion rate (52). This is in agreement with the results from the Na^+-replacement studies discussed above and suggests an important role for the cellular Na^+ gradient in maintaining fluid secretion (6, 17, 69). Upon replacement of Na^+ by less permeable ions or molecules the K^+ concentration in the secreted fluid is increased in parallel with the increased Na^+ gradient. This may indicate that there is indeed a negative transepithelial potential build up under these conditions.

BICARBONATE   Bicarbonate is essential in the spontaneous or secretin-sensitive secretion by the ductular part of the pancreas. In the cat and rabbit pancreas, an increase in the medium HCO_3^- concentration results in an increased flow rate and an increase in the HCO_3^- concentration and a decrease in the Cl^- concentration of the secreted fluid (18, 39, 54, 56). As part of a buffer system, HCO_3^- can be transported via the movement of any of the buffer components (HCO_3^-, H^+ (OH^-), or CO_2). Experiments have been carried out to identify the primary transported species by altering the concentration of the buffer components in blood or perfusate (18, 32, 51, 68, 69). However, according to the Henderson-Hasselbalch equation, varying one component of the HCO_3^- buffer system (pH, $[CO_2]$, or $[HCO_3^-]$) will always cause one other component to vary simultaneously, which complicates the correct analysis of the results considerably.

Nevertheless, it has been concluded that both medium pH and HCO_3^- concentration determine the rate of HCO_3^- and fluid secretion (18, 32, 56, 69). This would mean that either H^+ or HCO_3^- is the primary transported ion species. HCO_3^- secretion would then be based on the primary, active transport of HCO_3^- from the interstitium to the lumen (or cell) or on the transport of H^+ derived from the dissociation of H_2CO_3 from the lumen (or cell) to the medium, which would result in the transport of HCO_3^- in the reverse direction.

The requirement for HCO_3^- in the medium is not absolute. Various other organic acids, such as formic, acetic, or butyric acid (or the organic acid anions), or sulfonamides can replace HCO_3^- in maintaining fluid secretion (15, 39, 56, 59, 69). Acetate is most effective in replacing HCO_3^- and sustains the fluid secretion rate in the cat and rabbit pancreas at ~60% of the control rate. The order of effectiveness of the other buffers in the cat pancreas is: acetate > propionate > butyrate > formate > sulfamerazine > glyco-diazine. For all buffers except sulfamerazine both anion concentration and pH determine the rate of buffer secretion. In the case of sulfamerazine, only the concentration of the undissociated acid determines the rate of secretion.

Since the structures of the buffer anions listed above are all quite different, it seems likely that H^+ transport is the underlying primary transport step in buffer and fluid secretion. The undissociated acid would permeate from medium to cell (or lumen), where it would dissociate into an anion and a proton, and the proton would be transported back into the medium. The differences in effectiveness of the substituted buffers would be the result of differences in the lipid solubility of the undissociated acid species. In the case of sulfamerazine, the passive acid transport step appears to be the only rate-limiting step, which may be due to a low lipid solubility of this substance and thus an inherently low replacing effectiveness.

However, the order of effectiveness in sustaining fluid secretion of short-chain fatty acids (acetate > propionate > butyrate > formate) (15) apparently is not simply related to the lipid solubility, i.e. the chain length, of the carboxylic acids. In addition, the secretion of these buffers and of glyco-diazine depends on the concentration of their anionic form. Therefore, it appears that anion transport, which probably takes place in the basolateral membrane, is an important determining factor in buffer and fluid secretion. The proton transport mechanism would then be located in the luminal membrane.

CHLORIDE   The Cl$^-$ concentration in the pancreatic juice is inversely related to the HCO$_3^-$ concentration and the secretion rate. At low secretory rates it may reach a concentration of 120 mM, at high rates it falls down to 30 mM, and it is always lower than the medium concentration (58). In the cat pancreas, in which the secretory Cl$^-$ concentration normally is about 30 mM, replacement of Cl$^-$ by various inorganic ions inhibits the rate of fluid secretion up to 70% and leads to an increase of the secretory HCO$_3^-$ concentration (15, 39). The degree of inhibition of fluid secretion rate and the accompanying increase of the secretory HCO$_3^-$ concentration is a measure of the degree of effectiveness of an anion in replacing Cl$^-$ (Cl$^-$ = Br$^-$ > NO$_3^-$ > I$^-$ > SO$_4^{2-}$ > CH$_3$SO$_4^-$ > isethionate) (15). This anion sequence probably reflects the ability of these anions to cross the epithelium, i.e. to substitute in the cellular or paracellular Cl$^-$ transport steps. However, full replacement of Cl$^-$ by isethionate causes a 70% inhibition of fluid secretion, while the secretory HCO$_3^-$ concentration only increases from 121 to 151 mM. This indicates that the removal of Cl$^-$ may inhibit HCO$_3^-$ output, which suggests that Cl$^-$ or another permeable anion is needed for optimal HCO$_3^-$ secretion (15). Although it is less prominent, the stimulation of HCO$_3^-$ secretion by Cl$^-$ is also found in the isolated rabbit pancreas. In this preparation, the removal of Cl$^-$, which is normally present in the secreted fluid in a concentration of ~70 mM, inhibits fluid secretion by about 60% and HCO$_3^-$ secretion by about 20% at full replacement by isethionate or phosphate (39, 54).

The low negative transepithelial potential and the concentration gradient for Cl$^-$ between medium and secreted fluid suggests that Cl$^-$ or a replacing anion is passively transported and that the inhibition of HCO$_3^-$ secretion by Cl$^-$ omission is indirect. The latter might be due to an increase of the electrochemical potential gradient against which HCO$_3^-$ is transported from cell to lumen as a result of the increase of the secretory HCO$_3^-$ concentration. Alternatively, Cl$^-$ removal might lead to inhibition of a coupled or cotransport of Cl$^-$ and HCO$_3^-$ (or H$^+$) in the basolateral membrane from interstitium to cell (30, 43).

In some experiments, however, the Cl^- concentration in the secreted fluid exceeded the bathing medium concentration at very low medium concentrations (e.g. 6 mM in medium, 15 mM in secreted fluid) (39, 54). If one assumes a low negative or zero transepithelial potential, this indicates active Cl^- transport.

Involvement of Ion Pumps and Carriers

Various transport inhibitors have been applied in attempts to identify the ion transport carriers involved in HCO_3^- and fluid secretion. The role of the Na,K-ATPase and active Na^+ transport has been firmly established in a number of studies using ouabain and Na^+ replacement (17, 40, 52, 69). However, primary active Na^+ secretion from cell to lumen via the Na,K-ATPase is unlikely, due to the basolateral location of the transport ATPase (9). Hence, it has been suggested by several authors that the role of the Na,K-ATPase is the maintainance of a Na^+ gradient across the basolateral cell membrane. This would energize a Na^+ co- or countertransport, e.g. Na^+-H^+ exchange, that could bring about transcellular HCO_3^- transport. This is in agreement with the results from the Na^+ and HCO_3^- replacement studies, which lead to the conclusion that a Na^+-dependent H^+ or HCO_3^- transport is the most likely mechanism underlying secretion.

Acetazolamide, an inhibitor of the carbonic anhydrase, has been shown to inhibit secretin-stimulated secretion in the cat pancreas by 60–70% (18) and unstimulated secretion in the rabbit pancreas by 20–40% (40, 69). The inhibition is found only in HCO_3^-/CO_2-buffered media and suggests an important role for the enzyme carbonic anhydrase. An inhibitory effect in a study with sulfamerazine-buffered medium has been ascribed to endogenous CO_2 production (61). The enzyme has been demonstrated histochemically in pancreatic ducts, and its activity is enriched in ductal tissue (41, 42).

Although Na^+-H^+ exchange has frequently been suggested to underlie secretion, amiloride, which is an inhibitor of Na^+-H^+ exchange in a variety of cells and tissues (4), appears to have no effect on fluid secretion in the isolated rabbit pancreas, not even at concentrations as high as 10^{-3} M with 10-mM Na^+ in the medium (40). In the cat pancreas, 23–54% inhibition is found with 2–4 mM amiloride. However, at this concentration amiloride completely inhibits the Na,K-ATPase (74).

The diuretics furosemide, bumetanide, and piretanide have been shown to inhibit pancreatic fluid secretion (40, 63). In a number of epithelia, these diuretics inhibit Cl^- transport via Na^+-Cl^- or Na^+-K^+-Cl^- cotransport (22, 25, 29), but at high concentrations anion-exchange is also inhibited, at least by furosemide (8, 46). In the pancreas, high concentrations of furosemide, piretanide, and bumetanide (10^{-3}–5.10^{-3} M) are required for 50% inhibition of fluid secretion. This concentration dependence points to an effect of these drugs on anion exchange rather than on Na^+-Cl^- cotransport (71). The involvement of anion exchange is also supported by the finding that SITS, a disulfonic stilbene derivative, inhibits pancreatic fluid secretion (40, 63). The inhibition is obtained in the same concentration range as for inhibition of anion exchange, e.g. in red blood cells (10). However, SITS, bumetanide, and furosemide have also been shown to inhibit carbonic anhydrase (21) and Na,K-ATPase activity (19).

Thus the dubious specificity of the inhibitors used in these studies prevents any definite conclusions regarding the role of specific ion transporters in HCO$_3^-$ and fluid secretion. Nevertheless, the lack of inhibition by amiloride necessitates a thorough investigation of the role of mechanisms other than Na$^+$-H$^+$ exchange in ductular fluid secretion.

Electrophysiology of Ductular Secretion

Although electrophysiological data from individual duct cells are scarce, some measurements of ductal electrical parameters have been performed. In the rabbit, the transductal electrical potential was found to be -5 mV and -9.1 mV in intralobular ducts and -2.4 and -7.4 mV in interlobular ducts (61, 68). The low transductal potential differences recorded are in agreement with the "leakiness" of the pancreatic epithelium for cations.

Ion permeability studies indicate that the main duct possesses highly hydrated ion-permeable channels, probably located in the tight junctions, with weak positive charges on the surrounding membrane-bound sites (28, 72). There is no appreciable selectivity between the cations Li$^+$, Na$^+$, K$^+$, Rb$^+$, and Cs$^+$, while there is a definite selectivity sequence for the anions: I$^-$ > Br$^-$ > Cl$^-$ > HCO$_3^-$ > F$^-$. Secretin does not cause a change in the relative ion permeabilities, but in the absence of ion concentration gradients it depolarizes the electrical potential across the main duct from $+2$ to -5 mV (72). This negative potential must be due to some active ion transport, e.g. HCO$_3^-$ secretion or H$^+$ absorption.

The intracellular electrical potential has been estimated in a micropuncture study of rabbit duct cells in situ (61) and in a study employing random impalement of mouse pancreatic cells (27). The values found were -50 mV and -23 mV respectively, while secretin hyperpolarized the latter cells from -23 to -41 mV. In isolated duct cells, an electrical potential of -80 mV was calculated from the distribution ratio of the lipid-permeable cation tetraphenylphosphonium (TPP) (60). In this case, however, secretin depolarized the cell membrane potential by 10 mV.

To determine the location of the HCO$_3^-$ transport steps, the transcellular electrochemical potential differences, i.e. the intracellular pH and ion concentrations, need to be determined. If we assume basolateral and apical cell membrane potentials of -50 and -45 mV and interstitial and luminal HCO$_3^-$ concentrations of 25 and 100 mM, simple calculation shows that the active transport step for HCO$_3^-$ is located in the basolateral membrane if the intracellular pH (pH_i) is higher than 7.23 ($[HCO_3^-]_i > 17$ mM) and in the apical membrane if the pH_i is lower than 6.54 ($[HCO_3^-]_i < 3.4$ mM), with intermediate pH values indicating active transport steps in both membranes.

Measurement of duct cell pH has been performed using the nicotine bitartrate distribution method. In this way, a cell pH of 6.9 was determined (60). In pieces of pancreatic tissue, Swanson & Solomon (68) estimated the cell pH to be 7.25 using the distribution of the weak acid 5,5'-dimethyl-2,4-oxazolidinedione (DMO). They assumed that this pH reflects the intracellular pH of the secretory duct cells. The former pH_i value of 6.9 was taken to indicate that the active transport step for HCO_3^- or H^+ is at the luminal cell side, whereas the latter value of 7.25 would suggest an active step in the basolateral membrane.

Models for Ductular Electrolyte and Fluid Secretion

Swanson & Solomon (67, 68) have postulated a basolaterally located Na^+-H^+ exchange mechanism, which drives the transport of H^+ out of the cell (Figure 1A). These authors also suggested that there is an ATPase-driven Na^+-H^+ exchange transport in the luminal membrane. The model with the basolateral Na^+-H^+ exchange is attractive and has been adapted and modified by several other authors (6, 58). In its simplest form (Figure 1B), the Na^+-H^+ exchange, energized by the Na,K-ATPase-generated Na^+ gradient, would drive the accumulation of weak acid and thus of weak acid anion in the cell. A passive anion exit step in the apical membrane would maintain anion secretion. Cations, like Na^+, would be transported paracellularly (6).

If we assume only a Na^+-gradient-driven H^+ (or HCO_3^-) transport in the basolateral membrane and passive CO_2 and H^+ (or HCO_3^-) conductances in the basolateral and apical membranes, we can predict the thermodynamically feasible pH profile across the pancreatic epithelium. An electroneutral Na^+-H^+ exchanger could generate a maximal electrochemical potential gradient for H^+ (HCO_3^-) across the basolateral membrane of $\sim$60 mV above equilibrium, assuming an intracellular Na^+-concentration of 15 mM. This is equivalent to 1.0 pH unit and could account for an intracellular pH value of 7.5, instead of 6.5, which would be the value found upon passive distribution of H^+ with a membrane potential of -50 mV. A HCO_3^- (or H^+) conductance in the apical cell membrane would allow the exit of accumulated HCO_3^- from the cell to the lumen. At this cell side, an additional pH (HCO_3^-) gradient of -45 mV or 0.8 pH units, which is equivalent to the electrical membrane potential only, could be set up. Taken together, a net transepithelial pH gradient of 0.9 pH units, i.e. a luminal pH of 8.3 or HCO_3^- concentration of more than 150 mM, could theoretically be established in this model.

The lack of an effect of the specific Na^+-H^+ exchange inhibitor amiloride has led Kuijpers et al (40) to postulate a Na^+-HCO_3^--Cl^- (H^+) exchange mechanism instead of a Na^+-H^+ carrier in the basolateral membrane (Figure

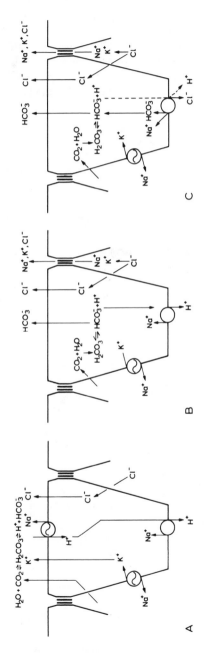

Figure 1 Models for pancreatic electrolyte secretion in ductular cells (slightly modified from the original versions): (A) model proposed by Swanson and Solomon (67), (B) model proposed by Bonting et al (6), (C) model proposed by Kuijpers et al (40).

1C). The advantage of this model is that it not only explains the lack of an effect of amiloride but also gives an explanation for the inhibitory effects of SITS and furosemide via the Na^+-HCO_3^--Cl^- carrier (7). A Cl^--independent Na^+-HCO_3^- cotransport mechanism could also account for the effects of these inhibitors (1, 34). A disadvantage of the latter model is, however, that it does not provide a specific role for the carbonic anhydrase system.

In all of the above models the mode of action of secretin, which is mediated through cyclic AMP, needs to be established. In the models shown in Figure 1B and 1C, secretin might stimulate HCO_3^- and fluid secretion and induce a cell membrane depolarization and a more negative transepithelial potential via an increase of the apical HCO_3^- conductance or via stimulation of the basolateral Na^+-dependent HCO_3^- accumulation and subsequent increase of the intracellular HCO_3^- concentration. However, the latter would result in a secretin-induced increase in pH_i, which has not been found thus far in ductular cells (60). In the more complex Swanson & Solomon model (Figure 1A) secretin might increase the permeability of the plasma membrane to Na^+, and the consequent increase in intracellular Na^+ might stimulate the luminal Na^+-H^+ transporter. The increase of the Na^+-permeability or the stimulation of an electrogenic Na^+-H^+ carrier would cause a depolarization, which might lead to K^+ efflux from the cell (14). In each model, hyperpolarization in response to secretin (27) might be explained by an increase of the K^+ permeability, which would lead to increased Na^+ influx and/or Na^+-H^+ exchange.

In conclusion, the exact location and nature of the active and passive transport mechanisms remain to be established. As long as there are no clear-cut data available from transport studies on isolated duct cells, the models will be helpful but speculative.

CELLULAR MECHANISMS OF ACINAR HCO_3^- AND H^+ TRANSPORT

Acinar Fluid Secretion

In contrast to the ductular fluid secretion, the acinar fluid secretion has a high concentration of Cl^- ($\sim$120 mM) and a low concentration of HCO_3^-, regardless of secretory rate (65). The secretion is dependent on Na^+ and Cl^-, inhibited by ouabain (48), and dependent on extracellular Ca^{2+} (35, 70). The extracellular HCO_3^- concentration appears to be only of minor importance (35, 48). The Ca^{2+} dependence of the fluid secretion is in agreement with the fact that the mode of action of the stimulatory agents is via an effect on the cellular Ca^{2+} metabolism.

Recently studies in isolated acinar cells have been performed to identify the ion transport mechanisms involved in the fluid secretion by these cells. Dufresne et al (20) showed the existence of an amiloride-sensitive Na^+-H^+

antiport that could be stimulated by caerulein in guinea pig pancreatic cells. Hellmessen et al (31) used the fluorescent pH probe 6-carboxyfluorescein-diacetate to identify a Na^+-H^+ exchange mechanism in acinar cells of the rat pancreas. This exchange is inhibited by amiloride and probably regulated by the intracellular pH. Neither secretin nor dbcAMP had any effect on the exchange. More recently, Seow et al (64) carried out an ion replacement and transport inhibition study on caerulein-stimulated fluid secretion by the rat pancreas and showed that furosemide-, SITS-, and amiloride-sensitive carriers, as well as carbonic anhydrase, are involved in the Cl^--rich fluid secretion. Extracellular HCO_3^- may stimulate the secretory process, but it is not a prerequisite. They concluded that acinar cells possess both Na^+-H^+ and Cl^--HCO_3^- exchangers that bring about a net accumulation of Na^+ and Cl^- in the acinar cell with consequent Cl^- and fluid secretion. The role of HCO_3^- in the secretion is not completely elucidated, but it appears that endogenous, metabolically derived CO_2 is sufficient to maintain the secretion under normal, physiological conditions.

Acinar Enzyme Secretion

Enzyme secretion by the acinar cells is stimulated by acetylcholine, CCK, bombesin, and related peptides via a Ca^{2+}-dependent mechanism. In addition, secretin and VIP increase enzyme secretion in acinar cells of some species via a cAMP-dependent process.

The enzyme secretion elicited by the Ca^{2+} agonists is not dependent on the presence of extracellular CO_2/HCO_3^-, nor is it accompanied by a change of the intracellular pH in the acinar cells (49). However, decreasing the extracellular pH from 7.4 to 6.8 decreased the intracellular pH from 6.9 to 6.4 and inhibited the basal and the secretagogue-stimulated amylase release by 30–50%. The change of extracellular pH did not affect basal or stimulated ^{45}Ca efflux. Thus, the pH effect on enzyme secretion is in a more distant step in the Ca^{2+}-mediated exocytosis process.

Secretin-stimulated and basal enzyme secretion are, however, fully dependent on extracellular CO_2/HCO_3^- (48). Although the role of CO_2/HCO_3^- or intracellular pH in the secretion process is not easily understood, the recent results of Hellmessen et al (31) and Seow et al (64) may indicate that the intracellular pH of acinar cells is regulated by a HCO_3^--dependent double ion exchange mechanism (Na^+-H^+ and Cl^--HCO_3^- exchange), which might play a role in the secretin-activated cAMP-mediated enzyme secretion.

CONCLUSION

Transport of H^+/HCO_3^- is important in exocrine pancreatic secretion. Active HCO_3^- transport has a primary role in the secretin-stimulated fluid secretion by the ductular cells. The transepithelial transport of HCO_3^- in the luminal direction, or the reverse transport of H^+, appears to be coupled to Na^+

transport and energized by the Na^+ gradient. The cations Na^+ and K^+ and the anion Cl^- are required for optimal fluid secretion. The transport of H^+/HCO_3^- also plays a role in the Ca^{2+}-mediated fluid and enzyme secretion by the acinar cells, possibly via regulation of intracellular pH. Many questions remain to be answered. Further research on ductular and acinar cell and vesicle preparations will be necessary to obtain information on specific ion pumps and channels in basolateral and apical cell membranes, their mutual interaction, and their hormone and second messenger dependence; on intracellular pH regulation; paracellular permeability characteristics; and H_2O transport.

ACKNOWLEDGMENTS

The authors would like to thank Drs. I. Schulz and B. Argent for their useful comments on the manuscript. Several colleagues are acknowledged for providing us with papers in press. We thank Astrid van Alst for her help in the preparation of the manuscript.

Literature Cited

1. Alpern, R. J. 1985. Mechanism of basolateral membrane $H^+/OH^-/HCO_3^-$ transport in the rat proximal convoluted tubule. *J. Gen. Physiol.* 86:613–36
2. Arkle, S., Argent, B. E. 1985. Morphological and biochemical studies on rat pancreatic ducts maintained in tissue culture. *Gut* 26:A1132
3. Arkle, S., Lee, C. M., Cullen, M. J., Argent, B. E. 1986. Isolation of ducts from the pancreas of copper-deficient rats. *Q. J. Exp. Physiol.* 71:249–65
4. Benos, D. J. 1982. Amiloride: A molecular probe of sodium transport in tissues and cells. *Am. J. Physiol.* 242:C131–45
5. Bockman, D. E. 1980. Architecture of normal pancreas as revealed by retrograde injection. *Cell Tissue Res.* 205:445–51
6. Bonting, S. L., De Pont, J. J. H. H. M., Jansen, J. W. C. M. 1980. The role of sodium ions in pancreatic fluid secretion in the rabbit. *J. Physiol.* 309:533–46
7. Boron, W. F., Boulpaep, E. L. 1983. Intracellular pH regulation in the renal proximal tubule of the salamander. Basolateral HCO_3^- transport. *J. Gen. Physiol.* 81:53–94
8. Brazy, P., Gunn, R. B. 1976. Furosemide inhibition of chloride transport in human red blood cells. *J. Gen. Physiol.* 68:538–99
9. Bundgaard, M., Moller, M., Hedemark Poulsen, J. 1981. Localization of sodium pump sites in cat pancreas. *J. Physiol.* 313:405–14

10. Cabantchik, Z. I., Knauf, P. A., Rothstein, A. 1978. The anion transport system of the red blood cell. The role of membrane protein evaluated by the use of probes. *Biochim. Biophys. Acta* 515:239–302
11. Caflisch, C. R., Solomon, S., Galey, W. R. 1980. In situ micropuncture study of pancreatic duct pH. *Am. J. Physiol.* 238:G263–68
12. Case, R. M., Argent, B. E. 1986. Bicarbonate secretion by pancreatic duct cells: Mechanisms and control. In *The Exocrine Pancreas: Basic and Clinical Aspects*, ed. F. P. Brooks, E. P. Di Magno, J. D. Gardner, V. L. W. Go, E. Lebenthal, L. A. Scheele. New York: Raven. 840 pp.
13. Case, R. M., Harper, A. A., Scratcherd, T. 1968. Water and electrolyte secretion by the perfused pancreas of the cat. *J. Physiol.* 196:133–49
14. Case, R. M., Harper, A. A., Scratcherd, T. 1969. The secretion of electrolytes and enzymes by the pancreas of the anaesthetized cat. *J. Physiol.* 201:335–48
15. Case, R. M., Hotz, J., Hutson, D., Scratcherd, T., Wynne, R. D. A. 1979. Electrolyte secretion by the isolated cat pancreas during replacement of extracellular bicarbonate by organic anions and chloride by inorganic anions. *J. Physiol.* 286:563–76
16. Case, R. M., Scratcherd, T. 1970. On the permeability of the pancreatic duct membrane. *Biochim. Biophys. Acta* 219:493–95

17. Case, R. M., Scratcherd, T. 1974. The secretion of alkali metal ions by the perfused cat pancreas as influenced by the composition and osmolality of the external environment and by inhibitors of metabolism and Na$^+$,K$^+$-ATPase activity. *J. Physiol.* 242:415–28

18. Case, R. M., Scratcherd, T., Wynne, R. D. A. 1970. The origin and secretion of pancreatic juice bicarbonate. *J. Physiol.* 210:1–15

19. Dubinsky, W. P., O'Neil, R. G. 1984. Furosemide, bumetanide and SITS inhibition of carbonic anhydrase. *Kidney Int.* 25:299 (Abstr.)

20. Dufresne, M., Bastie, M.-J., Vaysse, N., Creach, Y., Hollande, E., Ribet, A. 1985. The amiloride sensitive Na$^+$/H$^+$ antiport in guinea pig pancreatic acini. *FEBS Lett.* 187:126–30

21. Ehrenspeck, G., Brodsky, W. A. 1975. Effects of 4-acetamide-4'-isothio-cyano-2-2'-disulphonic stilbene on ion transport in turtle bladder. *Biochim. Biophys. Acta* 419:555–58

22. Frizzell, R., Field, M., Schultz, S. 1979. Sodium-coupled chloride transport by epithelial tissues. *Am. J. Physiol.* 236:F1–F8

23. Fölsch, U. R., Creutzfeldt, W. 1977. Pancreatic duct cells in rats: Secretory studies in response to secretin, CCK and gastrin in vivo. *Gastroenterology* 73:1052–59

24. Fölsch, U. R., Fischer, H., Soling, H.-D., Creutzfeldt, W. 1980. Effects of gastrointestinal hormones and carbamylcholine on cAMP accumulation in isolated pancreatic duct fragments from the rat. *Digestion* 20:277–92

25. Geck, P., Pietzryk, C., Burckhardt, B.-C., Pfeiffer, B., Heinz, E. 1980. Electrically silent cotransport of Na$^+$,K$^+$ and Cl$^-$ in Ehrlich cells. *Biochim. Biophys. Acta* 600:432–47

26. Githens, S., Holmquist, D. R. G., Whelan, J. F., Ruby, J. R. 1980. Characterization of ducts isolated from the pancreas of the rat. *J. Cell Biol.* 85:122–35

27. Greenwell, J. R. 1975. The effects of cholecystokinin-pancreozymin, acetylcholine and secretin on the membrane potentials of mouse pancreatic cells in vitro. *Pflüg. Arch.* 353:159–70

28. Greenwell, J. R. 1977. The selective permeability of the pancreatic duct of the cat to monovalent ions. *Pflüg. Arch.* 367:265–70

29. Greger, R., Schlatter, E. 1983. Properties of the basolateral membrane of cortical thick ascending limb of Henle's loop of the rabbit. A model for secondary active chloride transport. *Pflüg. Arch.* 396:325–34

30. Guggino, W. B., London, R., Boulpaep, E., Giebisch, G. 1983. Chloride transport across the basolateral cell membrane of the *Necturus* proximal tubule: Dependence on bicarbonate and sodium. *J. Membr. Biol.* 71:227–40

31. Hellmessen, W., Christian, A. L., Fasold, H., Schulz, I. 1985. Coupled Na$^+$-H$^+$ exchange in isolated acinar cells from rat exocrine pancreas. *Am. J. Physiol.* 249:G125–36

32. Jansen, J. W. C. M. 1980. Role of the paracellular pathway in pancreatic fluid secretion. PhD Thesis, University of Nijmegen, The Netherlands

33. Jensen, S. L., Fahrenkrug, J., Holst, J., Kuhl, C., Nielsen, O. V., Schaffalitzky de Mucckadell, O. B. 1978. Secretory effects of secretin on isolated perfused porcine pancreas. *Am. J. Physiol.* 235:E381–86

34. Jentsch, T. J., Keller, S. K., Koch, M., Wiederholt, M. 1984. Evidence for coupled transport of bicarbonate and sodium in cultured bovine corneal endothelial cells. *J. Membr. Biol.* 81:189–204

35. Kanno, T., Yamamoto, M. 1977. Differentiation between the Ca^{2+}-dependent effects of CCK and the HCO$_3^-$-dependent effects of secretin in exocrine secretion of the rat pancreas. *J. Physiol.* 264:787–99

36. Kempen, H. J. M., De Pont, J. J. H. H. M., Bonting, S. L. 1975. Rat pancreas adenylate cyclase. III. Its role in pancreatic secretion assessed by means of cholera toxin. *Biochim. Biophys. Acta* 392:276–87

37. Kempen, H. J. M., De Pont, J. J. H. H. M., Bonting, S. L. 1977. Rat pancreas adenylate cyclase. IV. Effect of hormones and other agents on cyclic AMP level and enzyme release. *Biochim. Biophys. Acta* 496:65–76

38. Kuijpers, G. A. J. 1984. Transport mechanisms of pancreatic fluid and enzyme secretion. PhD Thesis, University of Nijmegen, The Netherlands

39. Kuijpers, G. A. J., Van Nooy, I. G. P., De Pont, J. J. H. H. M., Bonting, S. L. 1984. Anion secretion by the isolated rabbit pancreas. *Biochim. Biophys. Acta* 774:269–77

40. Kuijpers, G. A. J., Van Nooy, I. G. P., De Pont, J. J. H. H. M., Bonting, S. L. 1984. The mechanism of fluid secretion in the rabbit pancreas studied by means of various inhibitors. *Biochim. Biophys. Acta* 778:324–31

41. Kumpulainen, T., Jalovoara, P. 1981. Immunohistochemical localisation of

carbonic anhydrase isoenzymes in the human pancreas. *Gastroenterology* 80: 796–99

42. Lakshmanan, M. C., Kahng, M. W., Jones, R. T. 1979. Enzymic profiles of bovine pancreatic ductal and acinar tissues. *Enzyme* 24:107–12

43. Lowe, A. G., Lambert, A. 1983. Chloride-bicarbonate exchange and related transport processes. *Biochim. Biophys. Acta* 694:353–74

44. Mangos, J. A., McSherry, N. R. 1971. Micropuncture study of secretion of water and electrolytes by the pancreas. *Am. J. Physiol.* 221:496–503

45. Okumura, K., Iwakawa, S., Inui, K.-I., Hori, R. 1983. Specific secretin binding sites in rat pancreas. *Biochem. Pharmacol.* 32:2689–95

46. Palfrey, C. H., Feit, P. W., Greengard, P. 1980. cAMP-stimulated cation cotransport in avian erythrocytes: Inhibition by "loop" diuretics. *Am. J. Physiol.* 238:C139–48

47. Pavlov, I. P. 1902. *The Work of the Digestive Glands.* London: Griffin

48. Petersen, O. H., Ueda, N. 1977. Secretion of fluid and amylase in the perfused rat pancreas. *J. Physiol.* 264:819–35

49. Preissler, M., Williams, J. A. 1981. Pancreatic acinar cell function: Measurement of intracellular ions and pH and their relation to secretion. *J. Physiol.* 321:437–48

50. Raeder, M., Mo, A., Aune, S. 1979. Effects of plasma H^+ ion concentration on pancreatic HCO_3^--secretion. *Acta Physiol. Scand.* 105:420–27

51. Raeder, M., Mo, A., Aune, S., Mathisen, O. 1980. Relationship between plasma pH and pancreatic HCO_3^- secretion at different intravenous secretin infusion rates. *Acta Physiol. Scand.* 109:187–91

52. Ridderstap, A. S., Bonting, S. L. 1969. Na^+-K^+-activated ATPase and exocrine pancreatic secretion in vitro. *Am. J. Physiol.* 217:1721–27

53. Rothman, S. S., Brooks, F. P. 1965. Electrolyte secretion from rabbit pancreas in vitro. *Am. J. Physiol.* 208:1171–76

54. Rothman, S. S., Brooks, F. P. 1965. Pancreatic secretion in vitro in "Cl^--free" "CO_2-free" and low-Na^+ environment. *Am. J. Physiol.* 209:790–96

55. Rutten, W. J., De Pont, J. J. H. H. M., Bonting, S. L. 1972. Adenylate cyclase in the rat pancreas. Properties and stimulation by hormones. *Biochim. Biophys. Acta* 274:201–13

56. Schulz, I. 1971. Influence of bicarbonate-CO_2 and glycodiazine buffer on the secretion of the isolated cat's pancreas. *Pflüg. Arch.* 329:283–306

57. Schulz, I. 1980. Bicarbonate transport in the exocrine pancreas. *Ann. NY Acad. Sci.* 341:191–209

58. Schulz, I. 1986. Electrolyte and fluid secretion in the exocrine pancreas. In *Physiology of the Gastrointestinal Tract*, ed. L. R. Johnson. New York: Raven 2nd. ed.

59. Schulz, I., Strover, F., Ullrich, K. J. 1971. Lipid soluble weak organic acid buffer as "substrate" for pancreatic secretion. *Pflüg. Arch.* 323:121–40

60. Schulz, I., Terreros-Aranguren, D. 1982. Sidedness of transport steps involved in pancreatic HCO_3^- secretion. In *Electrolyte and Water Transport across Gastrointestinal Epithelia*, ed. R. M. Case, A. Garner, L. A. Turnberg, J. A. Young, pp. 143–56. New York: Raven

61. Schulz, I., Yamagata, A., Weske, M. 1969. Micropuncture studies on the pancreas of the rabbit. *Pflüg. Arch.* 308:277–90

62. Schuurmans Stekhoven, F., Bonting, S. L. 1981. Transport adenosine triphosphatases: Properties and functions. *Physiol. Rev.* 61:1–76

63. Scratcherd, T., Hutson, D. 1982. The role of chloride in pancreatic secretion. In *Electrolyte and Water Transport across Gastrointestinal Epithelia*, ed. R. M. Case, A. Garner, L. A. Turnberg, J. A. Young, pp. 61–72. New York: Raven

64. Seow, K. T. F., Lingard, J. M., Young, J. A. 1986. Anionic basis of fluid secretion by rat pancreatic acini in vitro. *Am. J. Physiol.* 250:F140–48

65. Sewell, W. A., Young, J. A. 1975. Secretion of electrolytes by the pancreas of the anaesthetized rat. *J. Physiol.* 252:379–96

66. Smith, P. A., Case, R. M. 1975. Effects of cholera toxin on cyclic adenosine $3',5'$-monophosphate concentration and secretory processes in the exocrine pancreas. *Biochim. Biophys. Acta* 399:277–90

67. Swanson, C. H., Solomon, A. K. 1972. Evidence for Na^+-H^+ exchange in the rabbit pancreas. *Nature New Biol.* 236:183–84

68. Swanson, C. H., Solomon, A. K. 1973. A micropuncture investigation of the whole tissue mechanism of electrolyte secretion by the in vitro rabbit pancreas. *J. Gen. Physiol.* 62:407–29

69. Swanson, C. H., Solomon, A. K. 1975. Micropuncture analysis of the cellular mechanisms of electrolyte secretion by the in vitro rabbit pancreas. *J. Gen. Physiol.* 65:22–45

70. Ueda, N., Petersen, O. H. 1977. The dependence of caerulein-evoked pancreatic fluid secretion on the extracellular calcium concentration. *Pflüg. Arch.* 370:179–83

71. Warnock, D., Greger, R., Dunham, P. B., Benjamin, M. A., Frizzell, R. A., et al. 1984. Ion transport processes in apical membranes of epithelia. *Fed. Proc.* 43:2473–87

72. Way, L. W., Diamond, J. M. 1970. The effect of secretin on electrical potential differences in the pancreatic duct. *Biochim. Biophys. Acta* 203:298–307

73. Williams, J. A. 1984. Regulatory mechanisms in pancreas and salivary gland. *Ann. Rev. Physiol.* 46:361–75

74. Wizemann, V., Schulz, I. 1973. Influence of amphotericin, amiloride, ionophores and 2,4 DNP on the secretion of the isolated cat's pancreas. *Pflüg. Arch.* 339:317–38

COMPARATIVE PHYSIOLOGY

SCALING AND STRUCTURE-FUNCTION RELATIONSHIPS

Introduction, Fred N. White, *Section Editor*

The smallest adult shrew is about one-millionth the size of an elephant. While the metabolism of an elephant far exceeds that of a shrew, the metabolism per unit mass of the shrew greatly "outweighs" that of the elephant. The careful measurements by Benedict (1) resulted in the famous "mouse-to-elephant" curve, from which the logarithms of metabolism against mass were found to result in "a most gratifying straight line relationship." Such a relationship implies that metabolism is proportional to a power of body weight: $M = a \cdot W^b$. Early attempts to establish a rule of metabolic intensity, based on a power of mass, derived from the theory that in animals of differing size the metabolic rate should be proportional to surface area. This "surface law" incorporated the 2/3 power of weight into the allometric equation. Max Kleiber vigorously attacked the surface law as insufficiently defined to serve as a basis of measurement and argued for the 3/4 power as the best-fitting function. His statement of his continuing dissatisfaction with the surface law appears in the 1944 volume of the *Annual Review of Physiology* (3).

Advocates of a power of mass near 3/4 were sufficiently persuasive to cause the 1935 National Research Council conference on energy metabolism to endorse a power of 0.73 as the most suitable unit. In his famous monograph (4), Kleiber clung to 3/4, arguing that it was preferable to 0.73 because it can be calculated by using a slide rule (extract the square root of the square root of the cube of the body weight). He concluded that, for all practical purposes, one may assume that the mean standard metabolic rate of mammals (meaning eutherians) is 70 times the 3/4 power of their body weight (in kg) per day. This generality was widely accepted.

Scaling of morphological and physiological variables has become a cornerstone of comparative physiologists' search for unifying principles among animals of differing mass and body form. A host of variables have been subjected to scaling: lung volume, ventilation, respiratory frequency, lung surface area, metabolic cost of swimming, running, and flying, etc. We may discover that the gas conductance of bird eggs, ranging over three orders of magnitude of mass, can be described by: $G_{gas} = 0.432W^{0.78}$. There is more of interest in our breakfast eggs than in coagulated protein! The reader will find many fascinating allometric relationships in two recent monographs (2, 5).

Two reviews in this series are concerned with the theoretical bases and practical utility of our current methods of scaling. Heusner presents the case that much of our present approach to scaling is insufficiently rigorous in the analysis of data, mathematical relationships, and statistical treatments, which underpin the validity of concepts. The reader will find a reevaluation of a power function of mass resembling that of the surface law, about which Kleiber complained so vigorously. He also examines the theoretical basis of the 3/4 power of mass.

Calder's review supports the position of the National Research Council's resolution of 1935, which favored a mass exponent near 3/4. He argues that any lack of sophisticated statistical refinement in support of the 3/4 power of mass is offset by the utility it provides in revealing consistent patterns of biological significance.

Two companion reviews in this section deal with supply-demand aspects of oxidative metabolism. Weibel poses the question of how structural components of the gas exchanger respond to energy demand. He is especially concerned with the hypothesis of symmorphosis, a concept that postulates that structures supporting a function should be no larger than required by the demand at the limit of performance. The review by Taylor considers this concept at the level of tissues where O_2 is consumed.

These reviews, taken collectively, offer insights into current concerns about the mathematical and theoretical bases and utility of scaling, and the application of morphometry at the two ends of the oxygen cascade—acquisition and consumption.

Literature Cited

1. Benedict, F. G. 1938. *Vital Energetics: A Study in Comparative Basal Metabolism*, Washington, D. C.: Carnegie Inst. Washington Publ. 503
2. Calder, W. A. III. 1984. *Size, Function and Life History*. Cambridge, Mass.: Harvard Univ. Press
3. Kleiber, M. 1944. Energy metabolism. *Ann. Rev. Physiol.* 6:123–43
4. Kleiber, M. 1961. *The Fire of Life*. New York: Wiley
5. Schmidt-Nielsen, K. 1984. *Scaling. Why is Animal Size so Important?* Cambridge, England: Cambridge Univ. Press

Ann. Rev. Physiol. 1987. 49:107–20

SCALING ENERGETICS OF HOMEOTHERMIC VERTEBRATES: AN OPERATIONAL ALLOMETRY

William A. Calder III

Department of Ecology and Evolutionary Biology, University of Arizona, Tucson, Arizona 85721

INTRODUCTION: THE SCALING OF BIOLOGICAL PHENOMENA[1]

Design principles and quantitative functional interactions are often revealed through analysis of animal size diversity. Allometric patterns have guided comprehension of physiological data for half a century (29). It is easier to

[1]The symbols used in this review are as follows:

A = area $\propto l^2$;
a = allometric coefficient (Y intercept of log Y/log X plot);
b = scaling exponent (slope of log Y/log X plot);
h = heat transfer coefficient ("thermal conductance");
l = a linear dimension;
M = mass;
P = metabolic power = energy/time;
P_{sm} = standard metabolic rate;
r = correlation coefficient;
r^2 = variability accounted for;
T = temperature;
T_a = ambient or environmental T;
T_b = body T;
T_{lc} = lower critical T (limit of thermoneutrality);
V = volume $\propto l^3$;
$\dot{V}$ = volume flow rate;
$\dot{V}_{gf}$ = glomerular filtration rate;
ρ = density = M/V;
f = frequency;
$\propto$ = is proportional to.

0066-4278/87/0315-0107$02.00

review allometry (5–9, 15, 17, 19–23, 32, 35–37, 41, 42, 46, 49) than to identify its underlying causes and physical constraints. The frequent use of "reappraisal," "reevaluation," "reexamination," "rethinking," and "revisited" in titles of such reviews suggests that the field is not at the cutting edge on the frontiers of knowledge. However, we must clarify patterns and resolve controversies to facilitate further progress. To stay within space limitations, I generally cite only the above reviews, wherein the original sources are credited.

Scaling Generalities

GEOMETRY   For animals, as for spheres and cubes, volumes and surface areas are power functions of linear dimensions: $V \propto l^3$; $A \propto l^2 \propto V^{2/3}$. With constant density ($\rho = M/V$) A scales as $M^{2/3}$, as confirmed empirically for mammals and birds (52, 58). When physiological variables Y of a subclass of animals are expressed in terms of body mass, exponent b shows size effects, and coefficient a seems to be related to ancestry and habits:

$$Y = a \cdot M^b. \qquad\qquad 1.$$

MECHANICS   Similarly constructed and functioning animals lead similar lives and perform similar actions. Animals are subjects of the laws of mechanics. As with pendulums, the periodicity of a repetitive action depends on physical dimensions such as length. The work of the heart or of locomotion is minimal at the natural frequency for heartbeat, stepping, or wing-beat (5, 6).

BODY SIZE: INDEPENDENT OR DEPENDENT VARIABLE?   On the evolutionary time scale, body size is a dependent variable relative to climate (31), food (12, 13), and interspecific competition (10). On a lifetime scale, body size is an independent variable that dominates support requirements. Organ capacities, flow, and turnover rates scale for adequacy (symmorphosis; 53).

INTERRELATIONS   "Organisms may be pictured as systems of precise multiple interrelations" (1). Algebraic combinations (51, 52) show the quantitative nature of the interrelations.

CORRELATIONS   Causation may be suggested by allometric correlation but not proven thereby. Incorporation of mass in both Y as well as M (e.g. mass-specific metabolism or conductance; 3, 19, 36) results in autocorrelation and meaningless r^2 values. If two variables are scaled similarly to M (i.e. have the same b value), they will scale linearly with each other ($b = 1$) and may show stronger r because $b = 1$ is greater than the original b of, say, 3/4.

METABOLIC ALLOMETRY

Standard ("Basal") Metabolism

In practice, the standard metabolic rate (P_{sm}) is the lowest sustained rate of a postabsorptive, resting animal, euthermic in thermoneutrality during the inactive phase of its daily cycle. P_{sm} provides a reference for comparison of different species; it can be considered a physiological summation of energy expended in basic homeostatic maintenance. One would expect natural selection to have favored minimized energy costs with the lowest mass coefficient, a, possible for all homeotherms. However, passerine birds pay a premium for this "minimum" compared to other birds, while marsupials get a 33% discount (11, 24). Desert mammals and birds have P_{sm} values consistently lower than their nondesert equivalents, probably to avoid greater heat dissipation problems. What is compromised by this lower energy expenditure while "idling"? Whatever the nature of differences in a, $M^{3/4}$ scaling seems to be common. In other words, for all homeothermic vertebrates, a 10^4 increase in body mass requires a 10^3 increase in P_{sm}; but compared at one size, a 100-g euthermic mammal has a greater P_{sm} than a 100-g marsupial, but less than a 100-g passerine bird. Nonpasserine birds are similar to euthermic mammals in P_{sm} for any given body mass. Does $M^{3/4}$ scaling reflect fundamental biological organization? Certainly the scaling of resting support functions shows many parallels, with approximately $M^{1.0}$ volumes, $M^{-1/4}$ frequencies, and $M^{3/4}$ rates (6, 41, 46). Some scaling exponents for birds (respiratory f, heart mass) differ from those found for mammals (4, 15).

The $M^{3/4}$ scaling of thermoneutral P_{sm} may be a composite of scalings for heat transfer coefficients (whole-body thermal conductance, $h \propto M^{1/2}$) and the differential between body and lower critical temperatures scaled as $M^{1/4}$. [However, T_{lc} scaling has been *derived* from metabolic heat production (P_m) and h to bypass the imprecision of individual T_{lc} determinations (6).] For constant T_b:

$$P_m = h(T_b - T_{lc}) \propto M^{1/2} \cdot (M^{1/4}) \propto M^{3/4}. \qquad 2.$$

During cold stress, below the size-dependent thermoneutral zone, metabolic scaling approaches $M^{0.5}$ because less insulated small animals are affected more by a given $T_b - T_a$. Resting metabolic differences between marsupials and eutherians disappear below T_{lc} (11, 24). From the skin outward, h combines thermal conductivity [heat flux/(unit area × °C differential per unit thickness)], body surface area, and insulation thickness. The fur of small mammals is "as thick as these small animals can bear without hindrance to movement of their legs" (27); a geometric ($M^{1/3}$) similarity with body length has been suggested for fur thickness. Conductivity is inversely related to the fur thickness, but the empirical body mass exponents of 1/2, 1/4, and 3/4 in Equation 2 have yet to be derived from physical principles (6).

PHYSIOLOGICAL TIME

As is well known, the smaller the animal, the greater proportion of its body mass consumed per day. One day is, however, a larger fraction of a smaller animal's life, so per diem expressions distort our perceptions. Misconceptions about efficiency persist, as if few are aware of Kleiber's (29) hay conversion (rabbit versus steer) example. Rather than compare daily rates, we can compare the "physiological times" required for equivalent actions, which often scale as $M^{1/4}$ (6, 32). A b of 0.28 to 0.30 for food retention time in the gut has been derived from $M^{1.05}$ scaling of gut contents and $M^{0.75}$ scaling of ingestion rates (12, 13). A lower limit for ruminant size can be hypothesized to occur at the point where retention time falls short of the time needed to digest coarse plant material (13). Small species must feed on food of greater energy content that can be digested quickly. Similarly, transit time in pulmonary capillaries scales as $M^{0.21}$, so small mammals need steeper oxygen tension gradients (30). Half-lives after administration of antibiotics scale with a mean $M^{0.25}$ (b ranges from 0.12 to 0.44 across five species) (38).

THE UTILITY OF INTERSPECIFIC ALLOMETRY

Interspecific allometry has contributed fundamentally to the analysis of mammalian respiratory capacity and energetics in locomotion, as documented elsewhere in this series (53–55, 59). In extending the study of energetics from captive animals to wild animals in nature, allometry finds productive use (25a, 40). Quantitative details of the structure and respiratory dynamics of birds' eggs and incubation were incomprehensible before the allometric studies of Rahn and coworkers (43, 44). Interspecific allometry has been useful for interclass comparative physiology. Cardiovascular function of marsupials (11a) and birds (16) and avian respiration (4, 34) are amenable to quantitative comparison with better-known eutherians (see the nephron example detailed below).

Nephron Function, Metabolism, and Environment

A consistent scaling pattern ($M^{0.75}$ to $M^{0.81}$) is found for not only mammalian metabolism but also for its support functions such as cardiac output, renal plasma flow (about 1/5 of cardiac output), glomerular filtration rate (V_{gf}), and urine production (9, 15, 60). The effects of phylogenetically and environmen-

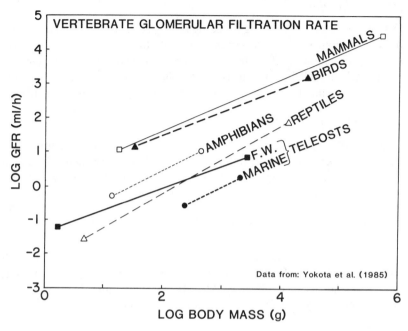

Figure 1. Interspecific scaling for glomerular filtration rates shows, in general, a functional parallel with the metabolic rates that it helps to support. $M^{3/4}$ scaling is included within the 95% confidence limits for the slopes of all regressions except for those of the reptiles. Vertical positions of the lines have been explained (data from Reference 60) in terms of metabolic intensity or osmotic situations (see text).

tally adaptive patterns on these values are confounded by size differences if the values are compared species by species; but basic adaptive principles are apparent in $\dot{V}_{gf}$ allometric equations (60; see Figure 1). Mammalian $\dot{V}_{gf}$ scales in clear parallel with P_{sm} ($M^{0.77}$; $r = 0.976$; reduced major axis (RMA) $b= 0.78$). Furthermore, $M^{0.75}$ scaling is included within the 95% confidence intervals (ci) for $\dot{V}_{gf}$ of birds, amphibians, and teleosts. The smallest r value was 0.803 for the amphibians (note small size range in Figure 1). The slopes for freshwater (0.65) and marine teleosts (0.89) were not statistically distinct (probably because of small sample sizes and the small size range for marine teleosts). The high-metabolism endotherms have the highest $\dot{V}_{gf}$. The ranking of the ectotherms reflects the environmental and/or integumentary status of each category. Freshwater fish and even more permeable amphibians require higher $\dot{V}_{gf}$ than xeric reptiles or marine fish to counteract high osmotic water uptake. Single nephron $\dot{V}_{gf}$ ($5.12\,M^{0.21}$), derived by dividing $\dot{V}_{gf}$ allometry by the allometry of nephron number, reasonably approximated a direct regression ($4.21\,M^{0.28}$) of average data for nine species (Table IV in Reference 60).

Pharmacokinetics

Determination of proper dosages in drug testing depends on an understanding of scaling from smaller experimental animals to humans (2, 29). Human serum concentrations of ceftizoxime were predicted fairly accurately by allometric extrapolations for distribution volumes, clearance rates, and time constants of animals ranging in mass from that of mice to dogs (39).

Muscle-Shortening Rates

Mass-specific metabolic scaling is $M^{-1/4}$ (converted after regression). Small mammals expend proportionally more energy for muscular contractions than do larger animals. Energy expenditure for force-generation is inversely related to size and may be set by rates of shortening:

$$\text{shortening velocity/muscle length } (s^{-1}) \propto M^{-0.23}. \qquad 3.$$

This relationship was derived from correlation of extensor muscle length changes [$\propto M^{0.26}$ (calculated from arc-segments of rotation by femur condyles at mammals' knee joints, $\propto M^{0.38}$)], extension times [$\propto M^{0.14}$ (from stride frequency)], and femur lengths ($\propto M^{0.35}$) (33).

QUESTIONS OF PROPER USE

As useful as allometry may be, we lack general consensus on principles of its application. Reexaminations of allometric procedures have provided valuable insight (as well as controversy) into statistics, the adequacy of data, proper taxonomic levels, and the interpretation of the data (18, 20–23, 49).

Kleiber's $M^{3/4}$ scaling for P_{sm}, once widely accepted, is now questioned. His extensive reliance upon data from domesticated species (75% in Reference 29) has been noted (19). Artificial logistical support and selection may be perpetuating lines incapable of survival in nature, and which may be scaled unnaturally. Daytime measurement of metabolic rates may have imposed a size-dependent bias, because the larger species are active in the daytime, while the smaller ones used by Kleiber were nocturnal. When active and resting temporal phases of small mammals were treated separately, P_{sm} scaled as $M^{0.61}$ ($M = 8$–270 g; 28, 42).

The crucial scaling may not be for thermoneutrality or resting metabolic levels, but for the demands of maximum aerobic activity or for the total energy turnover needed for the complex, varied schedule of natural existence. Kleiber's scaling may have no simple explanation. "$M^{3/4}$ scaling" is usually not exactly $M^{0.750}$ scaling, but scaling that does include $M^{0.75}$ within the 95% confidence interval of b. For example, maximum oxygen consumption of wild mammals scaled as $M^{0.79}$ with a 95% confidence interval of 0.754 to 0.833 (54), and daily field metabolism of eutherian mammals in nature determined by doubly labelled water turnover scales as $M^{0.81}$, 95% ci 0.77 to 0.86 (40). Daily field metabolism of birds scales at a level similar to the scaling for surface area [$M^{0.61}$ (57) to $M^{0.64}$ (40)]; but if passerine and nonpasserine birds are separated, the scaling is Kleiberian [$M^{0.75}$ (40)].

PROPER TAXONOMIC LEVEL

Intermediate Taxonomic Distinctions

Size has a major, but not exclusive, influence on scaling of animal function. The influences of habitat, phylogeny, and diet on metabolism cannot be shown without scaling for size. To show the effects of body size, we need a wide body size range. Ideally, size effects should be shown with other factors held constant, including phylogeny (18, 19), diet (37), environment (6, 27), means of locomotion (46), physiological state, and reproductive status (29). The influences of those other factors are seen either by comparing species of the same size, or via separate allometries representing diverse phylogenies, feeding habits, and habitats. Alternatively, we can derive a general relationship and compare departures from general predictions, looking for adaptive or inherited characteristics.

Sizes are not equally represented in all orders. Mouse-sized elephants and elephant-sized elephant-shrews have not evolved! Kleiber (29, p. 207) required a nine-fold size range to distinguish between $M^{0.75}$ and $M^{0.67}$, but small sample size, inconsistant techniques, and/or variations in the conditions of measurement may confound this. Nevertheless, size range is important in allometry, and there must be a trade-off between lumping together animals of different shapes and lifestyles and splitting them into such small groups that the body size range is insufficient to yield meaningful scaling expressions. Between intraspecific and interclass allometry lies a continuum within which subjective judgement may be as important as statistical methods (Table 1). Mass-scaling exponents found for orders, families, or finer categories may differ because of size-range limitations. This can be appreciated if we hypothesize ±20% error in metabolic determinations and assess the effect of such errors on the slope or exponent b (Table 1). Note that log(y values + 20%/y value − 20%) is less than 3% of log(maximum x/minimum x) and therefore affects the slope only slightly, whereas the same proportionate error on the y axis distributed over the small mass range within a species can have a profound effect on the slope, equal to 28–48% of the variability in log x, which limits the precision of b estimation. Publication of *size range* should be mandatory.

Table 1 The relative influences of phylogenetic and size span (X axis) and $\pm 20\%$ variation in Y axis values on regression slopes (body mass exponents).

Taxon	Size range	$\log(Y+20\%/Y-20\%)$	$\log M$ (max/min)	Ratio*
Class Mammalia	2 g to 100 tons	0.176	7.70	0.023
Class Mammalia (terrestrial)	2 g to 30,000 kg	"	7.18	0.025
Class Mammalia (extant, terrestrial)	2 g to 4500 kg	"	6.35	0.028
Order Artiodactyla	2.5–4500 kg	"	3.26	0.055
Order Rodentia	0.006–50 kg	"	3.70	0.048
Family Sciuridae	0.10–2.5 kg	"	2.88	0.061
Family Cervidae	7–825 kg	"	2.07	0.085
Genus *Felis*	1.6–72 kg	"	1.65	0.107
Genus *Odocoileus,Microtus*	22–215 kg; 18–143 g	"	0.90	0.196
Genus *Peromyscus*	15–38 g	"	0.40	0.436
Peromyscus maniculatus	15–35 g	"	0.37	0.477
Mus musculus (lab, domestic)	16–68 g	"	0.63	0.280

$*\dfrac{\log(y + 20\%/y - 20\%)}{\log(M_{max} - M_{min})}$ = effect of hypothetical 20% measurement error on slope

Intraspecific Versus Interspecific Allometry

The descriptive accuracy and physiological meaning of interspecific analysis have been challenged (20–23). Heusner stated (Reference 22, pp. R-840–42) that "the dimensional structure of extensive quantities" (size-dependent variables such as mass and energy metabolism) "determines the mathematical form of their relationship, whereas the intensive properties" (such as density, temperature, and form) "determine the magnitude of the mass coefficient." Differences in intensive properties, as suggested by differences in a, made pooled interspecific regression seem improper. [Iberall argued that the intensive-extensive distinction may be unnecessary (26).]

Heusner's rigorous criteria (20, 21) insured comparability of data within each species and yielded mass exponents from 0.56 (cattle) to 0.91 [*Peromyscus M.* (sic); the only natural species] that were inversely dependent ($p < 0.05$) on mid-range sizes ($r^2 = 0.469$):

$$b = 0.689\, M^{-0.04} \qquad\qquad 4.$$

Dimensional analysis convinced Heusner that the proper b is 2/3. This theoretical b was included empirically in his 95% confidence intervals (as was 3/4 in most cases), so Heusner adjusted the exponents to 0.67 and recalculated the mass coefficients a as the ratio $P/M^{2/3}$. The recalculated a appears strongly size-dependent ($p < 0.001$; $r^2 = 0.902$):

$$a = 3.32 \, M^{0.12}. \tag{5.}$$

The "explanation" of empirical body mass exponents may lie not in a single factor, but in a combination of factors. The interspecific $b = 3/4$ could combine a surface-area term and some other factor. For example, combining a log-transform of Equation 1 with Equation 5 and its adjusted b, then combining log M terms yields:

$$\log P_{sm} = \log 3.32 + 0.12 \log M + 0.67 \log M$$
$$= \log 3.32 + 0.79 \log M, \tag{6.}$$

or

$$P_{sm} = 3.32 \, M^{0.79}. \tag{7.}$$

The Kleiber equation is essentially rederived, but the scaling with a is unexplained. A b of 3/4 could, for example, combine surface and gravitational terms; the latter (derived from maximum tolerances to gravitational force in centrifuged mice, rats, and dogs; 14) scaled with a b of 0.14, which is close to the value (0.12) Heusner found for a.

The size-dependence of a was suggested (Reference 20, p. 10) to be related to the smaller proportions of metabolically active tissues in large animals. Relevant interspecific allometries (6) of the metabolically less active components (fat, bone) of mammal bodies increase with body size: $M_{fat} = 0.075 \, M^{1.19}$; $M_{skeleton} = 0.061 \, M^{1.09}$. However, these proportionate increases in less active tissues should decrease the metabolic mass coefficient, in contrast to Heusner's proposed increase in a with size.

Physical laws are taxonomically blind, so size effects within a species must apply beyond as well. Interspecific and intraspecific analyses each have shortcomings. Interspecific allometries may obscure real differences reflected in the intercept values (a) of finer phylogenetic categories or in biological diversity of Y values within a given body size range. Wider phylogenetic and size ranges include greater variability due to factors other than body size and yield poorer predictions.

Limiting analysis to the intraspecies level may have worse consequences. The precision of scaling exponent determination depends upon using a size range great enough to overwhelm the variability within a size group due to emaciation, obesity, ontogeny, aging, and experimental artifact. There is a great loss of data and phylogenetic and ecological breadth. For example, P_{sm} data are available for 248 eutherian species (19), but intraspecific allometry (20, 56) has been able to use only 9 (4%).

What can intraspecific allometry tell us about interactions between physiological and ecological functions? Need we measure every variable in every species to understand the interrelations? Can we overlook the considerable variability in intraspecific exponents (see 20, 25, 56)? Small size ranges within species obscure overall trends, patterns, and constraints of size. They preclude interclass comparisons and derivation of unmeasured relations.

The Choice of Regression or Correlation Models

We have found many patterns and learned much from the least squares regression, but we need to consider carefully our methods. Rayner (45) distinguishes an unobservable, true, or *functional relation* from the *general structural relation* (GSR). Two of a family of correlation models, derivable from the GSR, are used and debated widely. Least squares regressions (LSR) assume that body mass is an essentially error-free, independent (presumably causal) variable that should be used with caution (10, 45). Reduced major axis (RMA) analysis "assumes that error variance is the same proportion of the total variance on each axis, which may be closer to reality . . ." (10) and is less biased (45).

The choice between regression and structural analysis is not an easy one (47). Consider the following types of scaling:

1. Correlation coefficients (r) are very high. LSR and RMA lines are identical if the correlation is perfect ($r = 1$), but as the correlation weakens, the two differ increasingly. The RMA slope is "the ratio of the standard deviations of points measured on the y axis and on the x axis", s_y/s_x (18), while b_{lsr} is the product r (s_y/s_x) (50). Therefore:

$$b_{RMA} = b_{LSR}/r. \qquad \qquad 8.$$

Note for example, the LSR scaling for V_{gf} above, $M^{0.77}$, with $r = 0.976$ gives RMA scaling of $M^{0.78}$. Thus one can use LSR in calculations and computer software and from it calculate the RMA allometry. The coefficient a is obtainable via simultaneous solution of the LSR and RMA equations for the same M at the mid-point of the range in log M (where $M = $ antilog[(log M_{min} +log M_{max})/2]:

$$a_{LSR} M^b = a_{RMA} M^{b/r} \qquad \qquad 9.$$

2. Y measurements are less exact than X measurements. Physiologically, body size is more likely to dictate metabolic rate or cardiac output than the reverse. The variability and chance of error on the Y axis is probably

greater because of the possibility of instrument and calculation errors, and the variable emotional, hormonal, and digestive states of subjects, their sex, genetic strain, and level of handling shock. In contrast, weighing errors are less problematic; the subject is simply but precisely weighed at the beginning and end of a metabolic run. Thus LSR is more appropriate than RMA (but r is usually very high as well).

3. Y and X are measured similarly, but differ in variability. If Y is the brain M, which is limited by the bony cranium, and X is body M, which ranges from emaciation to obesity levels, a model that distributes the variances proportionately between the two axes would be more appropriate than LSR. However, the choice is academic because correlations have been so high that LSR and RMA mass exponents are nearly the same.

4. Data for Y and X are from different sources. Physiological and ecological data have been published in abundance without listing the body M of the animals. Explorations of allometric patterns have taken their M values for various species from standard descriptive references. Additional error in X is introduced by combining data from animals living under natural, disturbed, or captive conditions, those in different biogeographic clines, with different adaptations, genomes, and seasonal states.

5. It seems only reasonable that scaling constraints extend across the interface between physiology and ecology, since small and large animals must survive and reproduce in specific environments. Discussions of the appropriateness and relative merits of LSR and RMA (10, 18, 45, 47) have not considered the fact that higher correlation coefficients are more likely with data from simpler measurements in controlled laboratory conditions than from technically difficult experiments or uncontrollable field conditions. Two hypothetical variables similarly constrained by size (b = 0.75, with equivalent mass errors), one determined simply (e.g. P_{sm} with r = 0.98) and the other determined by more complex relations (e.g. V_{gf}) or less precisely measureable (e.g. food intake or metabolic rates in nature with r = 0.70), would show $b_{RMA} = 0.77$ and 1.07, respectively. In such a case any hint of quantitative coupling would be obscured. Thus sensitivity to r due to the technology or conditions under which Y was measured could limit the usefulness of RMA scaling exponents, although the independent variable common to both, body mass, is the same and a less likely cause of variation in r. If data include r, s_b, s_a, confidence intervals, and size range, options are preserved for future reexamination.

CONCLUSION

Allometry is only a tool; its usefulness depends on the particular application. What is the goal of an allometric analysis? Strict statistical goals are to summarize the data with minimal residual variation, to account for the variation, or to maximize predictive power. A comparative physiologist might give higher priority to quantifying size effects, to studying scaling as evolutionary or physiological engineering, or to evaluating physiological adaptations indicated by variability after size has been taken into account (48).

Even more useful is the derivation of expressions that can be combined to elucidate functional interactions between organ systems that must respond in concert to the environment (1, 51, 52). In this case, consistency in pattern assumes a significance of its own. Simple tests for statistical significance do not reflect the mutual reinforcement of scaling parallels between rates of metabolism, cardiac output, respiratory minute volume, glomerular filtration, and food intake. While there is more consistent evidence for an approximately $M^{3/4}$ rate and $M^{1/4}$ time system than for a $M^{2/3}$ surface system, $M^{3/4}$ is neither precise nor magical, only approximate and empirical. Statistical mistakes assembled into a house of cards can and should be pulled down, but there could be a trade-off between statistical refinement and the opportunity to see consistent patterns.

ACKNOWLEDGMENTS

I am grateful to Kenneth Nagy for sharing an unpublished manuscript, to George Bakken for reading a draft of this review and offering many helpful suggestions, and to Fred White and Mary Lee MacKichan for editorial improvements.

Literature Cited

1. Adolph, E. F. 1949. Quantitative relations in the physiological constitutions of mammals. *Science* 109:579–85
2. Boxenbaum, H., Ronfeld, R. 1984. Interspecies pharmacokinetic scaling and the Dedrick plot. *Am. J. Physiol.* 245:R768–74
3. Bradley, S. R., Deavers, D. R. 1980. A re-examination of the relationship between thermal conductance and body weight in mammals. *Comp. Biochem. Physiol.* 65A:465–76
4. Bucher, T. 1985. Ventilation and oxygen consumption in *Amazona viridigenalis*: A reappraisal of resting respiratory parameters in birds. *J. Comp. Physiol. B* 155:269–76
5. Calder, W. A. III. 1981. Scaling of physiological processes in homeothermic animals. *Ann. Rev. Physiol.* 43:301–22
6. Calder, W. A. III. 1984. *Size, Function, and Life History.* Cambridge, Mass.: Harvard Univ. Press. 431 pp.

7. Calder, W. A. III. 1985. Size and metabolism in natural systems. *Can. Bull. Fish Aquat. Sci.* 213:65–75
8. Calder, W. A. III. 1985. The comparative biology of longevity and lifetime energetics. *Exp. Geront.* 20:161–170
9. Calder, W. A. III, Braun, E. J. 1983. Scaling osmotic regulation and body size in mammals and birds. *Am. J. Physiol.* 244:R601–6
10. Clutton-Brock, T. H., Harvey, P. H. 1984. Comparative approaches to investigating adaptation. In *Behavioural Ecology: An Evolutionary Approach*, ed. J. R. Krebs, N. B. Davies, Ch. 1, pp. 7–29. Oxford: Blackwell
11. Dawson, T. J., Grant, T. R., Fanning, D. 1979. Standard metabolism of monotremes and the evolution of homeothermy. *Aust. J. Zool.* 27:511–15
11a. Dawson, T. J., Needham, A. D. 1981. Cardiovascular characteristics of two resting marsupials: An insight into the

cardiorespiratory allometry of marsupials. *J. Comp. Physiol.* 145:95–100
12. Demment, M. W. 1983. Feeding ecology and the evolution of body size of baboons. *Afr. J. Ecol.* 21:219–33
13. Demment, M. W., Van Soest, P. J. 1985. A nutritional explanation for body-size patterns of ruminant and nonruminant herbivores. *Am. Nat.* 125:641–72
14. Economos, A. C. 1979. Gravity, metabolic rate, and body size of mammals. *Physiologist* 22:s71–s72
15. Edwards, N. A. 1975. Scaling of renal functions in mammals. *Comp. Biochem. Physiol.* 52A:63–66
16. Grubb, B. R. 1983. Allometric relations of cardiovascular function in birds. *Am. J. Physiol.* 245:H567–72
17. Harvey, P. H. 1982. On rethinking allometry. *J. Theor. Biol.* 95:37–41
18. Harvey, P. H., Mace, G. M. 1982. Comparisons between taxa and adaptive trends: Problems of methodology. In *Current Problems in Sociobiology*, ed. King's College Sociobiology Group, pp. 343–61. Cambridge: Cambridge Univ. Press
19. Hayssen, V., Lacy, R. C. 1985. Basal metabolic rates in mammals: Taxonomic differences in the allometry of BMR and body mass. *Comp. Biochem. Physiol.* 81A:741–54
20. Heusner, A. A. 1982. Energy metabolism and body size. I. Is the 0.75 mass exponent of Kleiber's equation a statistical artifact? *Resp. Physiol.* 48:1–12
21. Heusner, A. A. 1982. Energy metabolism and body size. II. Dimensional analysis and energetic non-similarity. *Resp. Physiol.* 48:13–25
22. Heusner, A. A. 1984. Biological similitude: Statistical and functional relationships in comparative physiology. *Am. J. Physiol.* 246:R839–45
23. Heusner, A. A. 1985. Body size and energy metabolism. *Ann. Rev. Nutr.* 5:267–93
24. Hinds, D. S., MacMillen, R. E. 1984. Energy scaling in marsupials and eutherians. *Science* 225:335–37
25. Hudson, R. J., Christopherson, R. J. 1985. Maintenance metabolism. In *Bioenergetics of Wild Herbivores*, ed. R. J. Hudson, R. G. White, Ch. 6, pp. 121–42. Boca Raton, Fla.: Chemical Rubber Corp.
25a. Hudson, R. J., White, R. G., eds. 1985. *Bioenergetics of Wild Herbivores*. Boca Raton, Fla: Chemical Rubber Corp. 314 pp.
26. Iberall, A. S. 1984. Commentary on the

article of A. A. Heusner. *Am. J. Physiol.* 246:R845–46
27. Irving, L. 1964. Terrestrial animals in cold: Birds and mammals. *Handbook of Physiology: Adaptation to the Environment*, ed. D. B. Dill, pp. 361–77. Washington, D.C.: Am. Physiol. Soc.
28. Kenagy, G. J., Vleck, D. 1982. Daily temporal organization of metabolism in small mammals: Adaptation and diversity. In *Vertebrate Circadian Systems*, ed. J. Aschoff, S. Daan, G. Groos, pp. 322–38. Berlin: Springer-Verlag
29. Kleiber, M. 1961. *The Fire of Life*. New York: Wiley. 454 pp.
30. Lindstedt, S. L. 1984. Pulmonary transit time and diffusing capacity in mammals. *Am. J. Physiol.* 246:R384–88
31. Lindstedt, S. L., Boyce, M. S. 1985. Seasonality, fasting endurance, and body size in mammals. *Am. Nat.* 125:873–78
32. Lindstedt, S. L., Calder, W. A. III 1981. Body-size, physiological time, and longevity of homeothermic animals. *Q. Rev. Biol.* 56:1–16
33. Lindstedt, S. L., Hoppeler, H., Bard, K. M., Thronson, H. A. Jr. 1985. Estimate of muscle-shortening rate during locomotion. *Am. J. Physiol.* 249:R699–R703
34. Maina, J. N., Settle, J. G. 1982. Allometric comparisons of some morphometric parameters of avian and mammalian lungs. *J. Physiol.* 330:28P
35. McMahon, T. A., Bonner, J. T. 1983. *On Size and Life*. New York: Freeman. 255 pp.
36. McNab, B. K. 1983. Energetics, body size, and the limits to endothermy. *J. Zool.* 199:1–29
37. McNab, B. K. 1986. The influence of food habits on the energetics of eutherian mammals. *Ecology Monogr.* 56:1–19
38. Mordenti, J. 1985. Forecasting cephalosporin and monobactam antibiotic half-lives in humans from data collected in laboratory animals. *Antimicrob. Agents Chemother.* 27:887–91
39. Mordenti, J. 1985. Pharmacokinetic scale-up: Accurate prediction of human pharmacokinetic profiles from animal data. *J. Pharm. Sci.* 74:1097–99
40. Nagy, K. A. Field metabolic rate and food requirement scaling in mammals and birds. *Ecol. Monogr.* 57:In press
41. Peters, R. H. 1983. *The Ecological Implications of Body Size*. Cambridge: Cambridge Univ. Press. 329 pp.
42. Prothero, J. 1984. Scaling of standard energy metabolism in mammals: I. Ne-

glect of circadian rhythms. *J. Theor. Biol.* 106:1–8

43. Rahn, H., Paganelli, C. V. 1981. *Gas Exchange in Avian Eggs*, Vol. I. Buffalo: State Univ. New York. 358 pp.

44. Rahn, H., Whittow, G. C., Paganelli, C. V. 1985. *Gas Exchange in Avian Eggs*, Vol. II. Buffalo: State Univ. New York. 491 pp.

45. Rayner, J. M. V. 1985. Linear relations in biomechanics: The statistics of scaling functions. *J. Zool. A* 206:415–39

46. Schmidt-Nielsen, K. *Scaling: Why is Animal Size So Important?* Cambridge: Cambridge Univ. Press. 241 pp.

47. Seim, E., Saether, B.-E. 1983. On rethinking allometry: Which regression model to use? *J. Theor. Biol.* 104:161–68

48. Smith, R. J. 1984. Determination of relative size: The "criterion of subtraction" problem in allometry. *J. Theor. Biol.* 108:131–42

49. Smith, R. J. 1984. Allometric scaling in comparative biology: Problems of concept and method. *Am. J. Physiol.* 246:R152–60

50. Snedecor, G. W., Cochran, W. G. 1967. *Statistical Methods*. Ames: Iowa State Univ. Press. 177 pp.

51. Stahl, W. R. 1962. Similarity and dimensional biology. *Science* 137:205–12

52. Stahl, W. R. 1967. Scaling of respiratory variables in mammals. *J. Appl. Physiol.* 22:453–60

53. Taylor, C. R. 1986. Maximum oxidative potential and energetics. *Ann. Rev. Physiol.* 49:135–46

54. Taylor, C. R., Maloiy, G. M. O., Weibel, E. R., Langman, V. A., Kamau, J. M. Z., et al. 1981. Design of the mammalian respiratory system. III. Scaling maximum aerobic capacity to body mass: Wild and domestic mammals. *Resp. Physiol.* 44:25–37

55. Taylor, C. R., Weibel, E. R. 1981. Design of the mammalian respiratory system. I. Problems and strategy. *Resp. Physiol.* 44:1–10

56. Thonney, M. L., Touchberry, R. W., Goodrich, R. D., Meiske, J. C. 1976. Intraspecies relationship between fasting heat production and body weight: A reevaluation of $W^{0.75}$. *J. Anim. Sci.* 43:692–704

57. Walsberg, G. E. 1983. Avian ecological energetics. In *Avian Biology*, ed. D. S. Farner, J. R. King, Vol. VII, Ch. 3, pp. 161–220. Orlando, Fla.: Academic

58. Walsberg, G. E., King, J. R. 1978. The relationship of the external surface area of birds to skin surface area and body mass. *J. Exp. Biol.* 76:185–89

59. Weibel, E. R. 1986. Scaling of structural and functional variables in the respiratory system. *Ann. Rev. Physiol.* 49:147–59

60. Yokota, S. D., Benyajati, S., Dantzler, W. H. 1985. Comparative aspects of glomerular filtration in vertebrates. *Renal Physiol.* 8:193–221

Ann. Rev. Physiol. 1987. 49:121–33

WHAT DOES THE POWER FUNCTION REVEAL ABOUT STRUCTURE AND FUNCTION IN ANIMALS OF DIFFERENT SIZE?

A. A. Heusner

Department of Physiological Sciences, School of Veterinary Medicine, University of California, Davis, California 95616

INTRODUCTION

Since its introduction by Snell (40), the power function has become a basic mathematical tool for analyzing form, structure, and function in animals of different size. To date about 750 power functions or allometric equations have been reported (7). The power function can be derived from exponential growth curves (19), from dimensional analysis (16), from principles of similitude (10), and from fractal geometry (29, 37, 38).

The general aim of this review is to critically examine the power function within the theoretical framework of dimensional analysis and principles of similitude. The specific aim is to analyze the interpretations proposed for the metabolic power function. A seminal theoretical approach was put forth by Sarrus & Rameaux (33, 35) and has been continued by von Hoesslin (18), Lambert & Teissier (25), Kayser & Heusner (20), and Heusner (13–17). A more empirical approach can be traced back to Rubner (34) through the works of Brody (5), Kleiber (21–23), and McMahon (26, 27). Both approaches are based on concepts of dimensional analysis and similitude; they differ with respect to their aims and conclusions.

In Heusner's homomorphism (13, 16, 17), the concept of similitude is defined in terms of qualitative sameness (i.e. same intensive properties). Criteria for mass-independent qualitative changes are defined that focus on

121

0066-4278/87/0315-0121$02.00

intraspecific and interspecific qualitative differences in animals. Homomorphism does not explain these qualitative differences, but it orients further research toward an experimental identification of their true nature (structural, compositional, or functional).

McMahon's theory of elastic similarity (26, 27) establishes a basic principle of design according to which trees and mammals are built. This theory offers an explanation of Kleiber's 0.75 interspecific mass exponent in mammals.

In this study I demonstrate that the power function provides *necessary* but not *sufficient* criteria for similitude and, in particular, that the statistical equality between experimentally and theoretically derived mass exponents is not sufficient for establishing any type of similitude.

CONCEPTS OF DIMENSIONAL ANALYSIS AND SIMILITUDE

There are basic differences between dimensional analysis and the concepts of similitude, although the disciplines are often confused (43). Dimensional analysis is the study of mathematical relationships between physical variables. It is a mathematical tool that is based on a specific choice of *independent* primary quantities (mass [M], length [L], and time [T]) from which secondary quantities (density $[ML^{-3}]$, power $[ML^2T^{-3}]$, etc) are derived.

In a theory of similitude, relationships between the magnitudes (or values) of primary and/or secondary quantities are postulated. A similitude transformation is formally defined as a multiplication of the magnitude (or value) of a primary or secondary quantity by a positive constant. A property that can be subjected to this operation is by definition an extensive property (44).

THE POWER FUNCTION AND THE CONCEPT OF GEOMETRIC SIMILITUDE

From a simple analysis of geometrical forms we can show that the classical derivation of geometrical similitude is a *necessary* but not a *sufficient* condition for establishing geometrical similitude.

Solids are geometrically similar when they have the *same form*. This condition can be mathematically expressed by the following relation:

$$l_1/l_2 = k, \hspace{4cm} 1.$$

where l_1 and l_2 represent homologous lengths of solid 1 and solid 2 and k is the scaling factor. Equation 1 must hold for all homologous lengths of solids 1 and 2. The constancy of the above ratio is a *sufficient* condition for geometric similitude, and Equation 1 is a defining relation.

From Equation 1 we can derive the following relationships:

$$A_1/A_2 = k^2 \tag{2}$$

$$V_1/V_2 = k^3, \tag{3}$$

where A_2 and A_1 are the surface areas and V_1 and V_2 the volumes of the two solids. Equations 2 and 3 are consequences of Equation 1 and express *necessary* but not *sufficient* conditions for geometric similitude.

Taking into account Equations 1, 2, and 3, we derive Equation 4:

$$A_1/V_1^{0.67} = A_2/V_2^{0.67}, \tag{4}$$

which states that Meeh's constants ($A/V^{0.67}$; 30) for the two solids are equal. The numerical value of this constant depends on the form of the solid (a qualitative property). For platonic solids, Meeh's constant ranges from 5.15 to 7.20 (tetrahedron, 7.20; hexahedron, 6.00; octahedron, 5.72; dodecahedron, 5.31; and icosahedron, 5.15). However, it is not a quantitative measure of form, i.e. these numbers cannot be subjected to arithmetic operations. In particular, we do not know the meaning of their average value since there is no definition of an "average form." Except in the case of spheres, Meeh's constant does not unequivocally define a specific form—it may be the same for different forms. Therefore, contrary to common belief, *Equation 4 is not a sufficient condition for geometric similitude*.

From Equation 4 we can derive the power function between body surface area (A) and body mass (M) in geometrically similar solids assuming constant density:

$$A = cM^{2/3}, \tag{5}$$

where c is Meeh's constant expressed for mass.

A statistical fit of Equation 5 to a set of data is no proof of geometrical similitude, because the 2/3 mass exponent is not a sufficient condition for geometric similitude and Meeh's constant, c, is not form specific. In fact, Equation 5 may express one of three different types of relationships:

1. a *similitude relation* between mass and surface area in solids of the *same* form. In this case c is truly constant within errors of measurements.
2. Equation 5 may express a *bivariate distribution* of surface area and mass in solids of *different* forms randomly distributed over the mass range. Here c is not constant nor is it correlated with body mass. (Note that if c were

correlated with mass the observed mass exponent would be different from 2/3, and Equation 5 would not be applicable.)

3. Finally, Equation 5 may express *a nonsimilitude relationship* in which solids of different forms exist over a large size range. This is shown by Equation 6, which has been derived by simple geometry:

$$b_o = 2/3 + [\log(c_2/c_1)]/[\log(m_2/m_1)], \qquad\qquad 6.$$

where b_o (the mass exponent) is the observed slope on a bilogarithmic plot, m_1 and m_2 are the respective masses of the compared solids, and c_1 and c_2 are their Meeh's constants. If Equation 6 is applied to a 1 g sphere and a 10^6 g cube, the observed exponent would be equal to 0.68, a value that is not statistically different from 2/3 given the errors of measurement. Clearly, however, the sphere and the cube are not of similar form. Thus, a power function over a large range of mass does not necessarily describe a similitude relation.

In summary, Equation 5 can represent a relationship between mass and surface area in solids of different size of the same form, or different forms. If the solids are of the *same* form and density, the relationship between mass and surface area is a relation of similitude. If the forms are *different*, the solids may be randomly distributed over the size range. A mass exponent of 2/3 is not sufficient for establishing geometrical similitude. But a mass exponent different from 2/3 is sufficient for rejecting this hypothesis (assuming constant density). The mass exponent alone can be used to falsify a hypothesis of similitude, but not to prove it. The exclusive focus on the mass exponent in allometry casts serious doubt on the theoretical validity of most interpretations.

INTERPRETATIONS OF SOME BIOLOGICAL POWER FUNCTIONS

Hemmingsen's Relationship Between Body Mass and Body Surface Area in Vertebrates

The foregoing theoretical considerations allow us to give a biologically meaningful interpretation to Hemmingsen's data on body mass and body surface area in vertebrates (11). Hemmingsen concluded that "the body shape of young or adult vertebrate animals is sufficiently constant to ensure an overall variation of the body surface with the 0.67 power of the body weight when animals of different species with widely varying body weights are considered."

Figure 1 *(top)* shows Hemmingsen's data in a bilogarithmic plot. The figure has been redrawn from digitized data. Independent digitizing by four persons

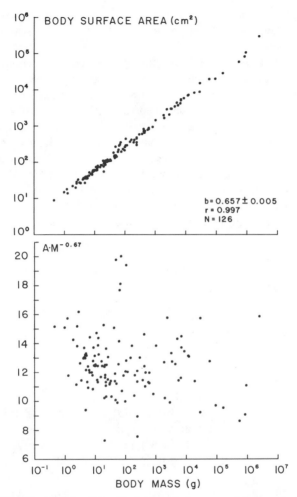

Figure 1   Top: bilogarithmic relationship between body mass and body surface area in vertebrates. The data have been digitized from a graph published by Hemmingsen (11). *Bottom:* bivariate distribution of body mass M and the $AM^{-2/3}$ ratio for the same data.

yielded mass exponents ranging from 0.654 to 0.657, i.e. within the same range as the standard error (SE = 0.005). The distribution of the values of Meeh's constant, which range from 7 to 20, is shown at the bottom of Figure 1. There is no correlation between Meeh's constant and mass: The different forms of vertebrates are randomly distributed over the mass range. Hemmingsen's plot represents a *bivariate distribution* of body mass and body surface area in vertebrates of different form and not a similitude relation. Since the effect of a change in form on surface area is small with respect to that of a large change in mass, the mass exponent will tend toward 2/3 (see Equation 6). Hemmingsen's data do not provide evidence for a geometrically similar design in vertebrates.

This example shows that bilogarithmic plots of power functions mask the variability about the regression line, i.e. the variability of mass-independent or qualitative properties in which even small changes may be biologically very significant. The nature and importance of the residual variance determines whether a power function represents a relation of similitude or a bivariate distribution. If the residual variance is relatively small and represents true random errors of measurement, the power function may reflect a relation of similitude or an allomorphic transformation (16, 17), depending on the value of the mass exponent. However, if the residual variance is due to biological variability in form, structure, or function, then the power function is a bivariate distribution of properties in qualitatively different animals.

McMahon's Relationship Between Height and Diameter of Trees

McMahon's power function describing the relation between the height and diameter of trees does not satisfy the sufficient conditions for elastic similarity. McMahon has claimed that "the proportions of trees, like the proportions of large animals, are determined by the rules of elastic similarity" (27) and that the Brody-Kleiber 0.75 exponent is a consequence of this principle (26).

According to the theory of elastic similarity, the height of trees (h) is proportional to the 2/3 power of diameter (d); i.e. the ratio h^3/d^2 is constant (26). In 528 trees (41, 42, 45; same data as McMahon's except for 48 trees for which the data were not easily available), this ratio varies by a factor of 3880! Regression analysis of height and diameters yields a diameter exponent of 0.596 ± 0.019, significantly different from the theoretical 2/3 value ($t = 3.6$, $p < 0.001$). In trees in which the height is greater than or equal to 10 m, the exponent is even smaller ($b = 0.525 ± 0.026$, $N = 429$). In 41 beech trees (27) $b = 0.569 ± 0.028$ (also different from 2/3; $t = 3.4$, $p < 0.001$). In 55 oak trees, $b = 0.366 ± 0.067$ ($t = 4.48$, $p < 0.001$). In trees of 22 m height, the diameter ranges from 24 to 446 cm. This relative independence of diameter and height, and the fact that the diameter increases to a lesser extent than elastic similarity predicts, suggest that the diameter is relatively oversized in small trees.

In conclusion, there is no sufficient statistical evidence for elastic similarity in trees. McMahon's visually fitted line (27) is not an acceptable proof of the validity of his theory.

THEORETICAL INTERPRETATIONS OF THE 0.75 MASS EXPONENT

Theory of Elastic Similarity

McMahon's theory of elastic similarity is based on concepts of statics dealing with the deformation of elongated cylinders under their own weight (26, 27). Cylinders are elastically similar when the relative sag is constant; i.e. their sag is geometrically similar. This condition is realized in cylinders in which the h^3/d^2 ratio is constant. The form of elastically similar cylinders therefore changes systematically with their size.

McMahon assumed that the form of animals can be conceptually decomposed into elementary cylinders, each of which follows his similarity rule. The connection between form and basal metabolism of an animal is then established via muscular physiology and maximum metabolism. McMahon's theory is based on structural and morphological considerations—it suggests that structure and form determine function.

Are mammals elastically similar? If so, the mass exponent for the relation between body mass (M) and body-head length (L) should be 0.25 (8, 26). Economos' (8) data from 240 mammalian species show that this exponent is 0.314, which is different from 0.25. (Digitized data yield a mass exponent b = 0.325 ± 0.003 that is significantly different from 0.25; t = 25.0, N = 240). The $L \cdot M^{-0.25}$ ratio, which should be constant if mammals are elastically similar, varies by a factor of about four.

Hemmingsen's (11) relationship between body mass and body surface area has a mass exponent of b = 0.657 ± 0.005, which is significantly different from b = 0.625 (t = 6.4, N = 126, p < 0.001), the predicted mass exponent for elastically similar bodies (26). Thus, contrary to McMahon's claim (26, 27), these data do not provide evidence for elastic similitude in mammals.

A simple computation shows that mammals of extreme size differences are not elastically similar. Indeed, a 6.25 × 10⁶ g elephant that is elastically similar to a 24 g mouse with a body-head length of 80 mm (tail not included) would have a body-head length of 1.8 m. The actual body-head length of a 6.25 × 10⁶ g elephant is 6.75 m (46). The real elephant is almost four times longer than predicted and apparently does not sag under its own weight. The size limit set by the constraints of elastic similarity does not appear to be very critical.

In summary, data on body form demonstrate that mammals are not elastically similar (1, 8, 11).

McMahon's theory raises the question of what constitutes a biologically satisfactory explanation in physiology. Even if an elastically similar design could be established in mammals, this would not explain the interspecific metabolic power function, since there is no experimentally established direct link with basal metabolism. A simple mechanical principle of design may be a limiting factor for maximum size or function, but it does not follow that this principle necessarily *determines* function below that limit. For example, the assumption that alveolar surface area sets a limit to maximum oxygen consumption does not mean that alveolar surface area *determines* submaximal oxygen consumption. There is no logical connection between basal metabolism and a design based on elastic similarity. An elastic design, even with all the additional ad hoc assumptions (constant velocity of shortening in muscles, constant force of contraction per cross-sectional area, constant ratio between maximum and basal metabolism), does not explain the decline in tissue metabolism with body size (24, 39).

Calder's Dimensional Derivation of the 0.75 Mass Exponent

Calder (7) has derived the 0.75 mass exponent from the theory of elastic similarity using the following equation:

$$y = m^{0.25(4\alpha + \beta + \gamma)}, \qquad\qquad 7.$$

where y is "anything physically measurable in biology"; "α = the exponent of the mass ratios m_1/m_2 of two different species; β = the exponent of the length ratio l_1/l_2; γ = the ratio of the times they require to perform the same function, such as one heartbeat cycle or one pace t_1/t_2. . . ." Calder has shown that when y is energy metabolism, it is proportional to the 3/4 power of body mass, since $\alpha = 1$, $\beta = 2$, and $\gamma = -3$.

Calder assumed constant density in animals in the derivation of Equation 7. However, if y = density ($\alpha = 1$, $\beta = -3$) Equation 7 shows that y is proportional to the 1/4 power of body mass. This is inconsistent with Calder's initial assumption of constant density. Equation 7 also shows that a 500 kg cow whose basal metabolism varies with the 0.75 power of body mass would have a density of 12.56, assuming a 20 g mouse has a density of 1.

The inconsistency of Calder's equation results from conceptual errors in its derivation (see Reference 7, pp. 83–85). Calder confused a dimensional equation with a geometrical relation and a specific geometric length (height) with the primary quantity of length.

In summary, to date there is no biologically satisfactory theoretical explanation of the 0.75 power of mass.

HOMOMORPHISM AND THE METABOLIC POWER FUNCTION

Principles determining form, structure, and function of living beings must be compatible with physical laws, but this does not imply that they can be derived from or reduced to such laws. Physical laws describe the behavior of qualitatively well-defined conceptual models. They describe actual phenomena only to the extent that there is a relation of similitude between them and the model.

A general principle governing structure and function in mammals can only be found if similitude between mammals can be unambiguously established. If mammals are qualitatively different, then it would be difficult to discover a general law. So the question arises whether the interspecific metabolic power function is a relation of similitude, and if so, is there a general conceptual model to explain it?

Nature of the Interspecific Metabolic Power Function

What facts can give us some insight into the nature of this relationship? Dimensional analysis within the framework of Lambert & Teissier's theory of biological similitude (25) shows that: (*a*) if the mass exponent *b* is equal to 2/3, then the mass coefficient *a* is a mass-independent expression of metabolism (MIM = mass-independent metabolism; 17); and (*b*) if *b* is different from 2/3, then *a* (MIM) is correlated with, but not determined by, mass. The correlation of *a* with mass may be mathematically expressed by a continuous or a discontinuous function.

Figure 2 shows the relationship between the a_2/a_1 ratio and the mass exponent (b_e) that we expect to observe in animals of different *a* and size.

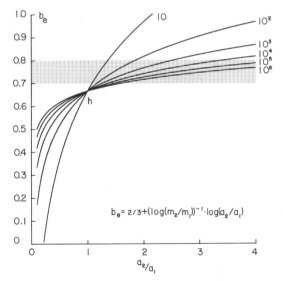

Figure 2 Relationship between the mass coefficient ratio (a_2/a_1) and the expected mass exponent (b_e) for mass ratios from 10 to 10^6.

Each curve corresponds to a given mass ratio (from 10 to 10^6). All the curves converge at point h at which $a_1/a_2 = 1$ and $b_e = 2/3$. This particular point is unique to homomorphic animals, i.e. animals whose metabolic differences are solely due to differences in mass. This ideal case can be approximated in mature animals belonging to the same species in which energy exchange with the environment is minimal (12, 16, 17).

As both a_2/a_1 and m_2/m_1 increase, the curves flatten and tend to be confined within a range of b_e extending from 0.7 to 0.8, a range that contains many of the observed values of the metabolic interspecific mass exponent.

The results of covariance analysis of 273 individual metabolic data points in seven mammalian species from mice to cattle demonstrate that the interspecific metabolic power function is not a relation of similitude (12; see also 9). The interspecific mass exponent is 0.776 ± 0.004, which is different from 2/3. The mass coefficient is not the same in various species. The intraspecific mass exponents range from 0.48 to 0.91, the mean value being 0.67 ± 0.03. These results demonstrate that the mass coefficient is not constant.

Figure 3 shows the distributions of MIM in 163 mammalian (2) and 190 avian species (6) within the same mass range (mass < 100 kg). The MIM ranges from 2.5 to approximately 16 ml O_2 hr$^{-1}M^{-0.67}$ in both groups. However, the average MIMs are significantly different (for mammals, $MIM_M = 5.76 \pm 0.24$; for birds, $MIM_B = 6.91 \pm 0.16$; $t = 6.57$, $p < 0.001$). The larger MIM in birds reflects their higher body temperature.

Figure 3 also shows that MIM is not specific to any particular structure or function: It may be the same in birds and rodents. The power function reveals

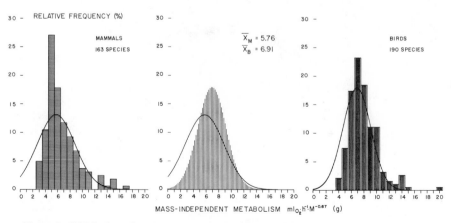

Figure 3 Distribution of mass-independent metabolism (MIM) in mammals *(left)* and birds *(right)*. The center figure shows the superposed adjusted normal distributions to illustrate the considerable overlap.

changes in form, structure, function, and composition with respect to an initial state but does not tell us anything about the initial state itself (17).

A recent statistical analysis of the interspecific metabolic function by Bartels (3, 4, see also 32) reveals that the interspecific mass exponent b varies with the mass range: from shrew to elephant (2.4 to 3.8 $\times$ 10^6 g) $b = 0.66$; from 2.4 to 100 g, $b = 0.23$; from 2.4 to 260 g, $b = 0.42$; from 260 to 3.8 $\times$ 10^6 g, $b = 0.76$. According to Schmidt-Nielsen (36), Bartels' results "raise problems that are difficult to resolve at the present time." The difficulties of interpretation arise because Bartels' results are inconsistent with a relation of similitude between body mass and basal metabolism, but they *are* consistent with a bivariate distribution of body mass and basal metabolism in qualitatively different mammals. Bartels' data lend strong support to the idea that we are dealing with a bivariate distribution in which the mass exponent reflects the sampling of the chosen mammalian species, rather than a general design common to the chosen species. Bartels' results and Heusner's covariance (12) show that since there is no definite value for either the intraspecific or the interspecific mass exponents, the distinction between intraspecific and phylogenic mass exponent proposed by Wieser (47) does not give any new insight into the nature of the power function. The most important finding is that the interspecific metabolic power function is discontinuous, i.e. there is no first derivative (slope) of its bilogarithmic expression. Hence, this function cannot be used for extrapolation (31). Neither can it be used for standardizing basal metabolism with respect to body mass.

In summary, the Brody-Kleiber power function is an empirical statistical relationship, and given this status one cannot ask whether it is right or wrong but only whether it is expedient and useful (28). This power function represents a bivariate distribution of body mass and basal metabolism in qualitatively different animals, and therefore, any attempt to explain the Brody-Kleiber exponent by a general physical principle is most likely to fail.

CONCLUDING REMARKS

The power function reveals *qualitative changes* in form, structure, composition, and function associated with changes in size. However, the logarithmic form of this function that is commonly used in allometry tends to obscure rather than reveal these biologically important changes. The result is a distorted view of biological reality. The power function may describe relations of similitude, allomorphic transformations, or bivariate distributions. Unless the true nature of this function is clearly established in each case, it cannot serve as a valid basis for biologically meaningful and theoretically sound interpretations.

ACKNOWLEDGMENTS

I gratefully acknowledge the suggestions, criticisms, and editorial advice I have received from Drs. M. L. Tracy, B. Horwitz, and B. Moore.

Literature Cited

1. Alexander, R. McN. 1985. Body support, scaling and allometry. In *Functional Vertebrate Morphology*, ed. M. Hildebrand, D. M. Bramble, K. F. Liem, D. B. Wake, pp. 26–37. Cambridge, Mass./London: Belknap Press of Harvard Univ. Press. 430 pp.
2. Altman, P. L., Dittmer, D. 1971. Oxygen consumption: Part I, Mammals. In *Respiration and Circulation, Biological Handbook*, pp. 460–67. Bethesda, Maryland: Fed. Am. Soc. Exp. Biol. 930 pp.
3. Bartels, H. 1980. Aspekte des Gastransports bei Säugetieren mit hoher Stoffwechselrate. *Verh. Dtsch. Zool. Ges.* 1980:188–201
4. Bartels, H. 1982. Metabolic rate of mammals equals the 0.75 power of their body weight. *Exp. Biol. Med.* 7:1–11
5. Brody, S. 1945. *Bioenergetics and Growth.* New York: Reinhold. 1023 pp.
6. Bucher, T. L. 1986. Ratios of hatchling and adult mass-independent metabolism, a physiological index to the altricial-precocial continuum. *Respir. Physiol.* 65:69–83
7. Calder, W. A. III 1984. *Size, Function, and Life History,* pp. 34–83. Cambridge, Mass.: Harvard Univ. Press. 431 pp.
8. Economos, A. C. 1983. Elastic and/or geometric similarity in mammalian design. *J. Theor. Biol.* 103:167–72
9. Feldman, H. A., McMahon, T. A. 1983. The 3/4 mass exponent for energy metabolism is not a statistical artifact. *Respir. Physiol.* 52:149–63
10. Gunther, B. 1975. On theories of biological similarity. In *Fortschritte der Experimentellen und Theoretischen Biophysik,* ed. W. Beier, 19:1–111. Leipzig: Thieme
11. Hemmingsen, A. M. 1960. Energy metabolism as related to body size and respiratory surfaces and its evolution. *Rep. Steno Mem. Hosp. Nord. Insulinlab.* 9:1–110
12. Heusner, A. A. 1982. Energy metabolism and body size. I. Is the 0.75 mass exponent of Kleiber's equation a statistical artifact? *Respir. Physiol.* 48:1–12
13. Heusner, A. A. 1982. Energy metabolism and body size. II. Dimensional analysis and energetic non-similarity. *Respir. Physiol.* 48:13–25
14. Heusner, A. A. 1983. Mathematical expression of the effects of changes in body size on pulmonary function and structure. *Am. Rev. Respir. Dis.* 128:S72–74
15. Heusner, A. A. 1983. Body size, energy metabolism, and the lungs. *J. Appl. Physiol.* 54:867–73
16. Heusner, A. A. 1984. Biological similitude: Statistical and functional relationships in comparative physiology. *Am. J. Physiol.* 15:R839–45
17. Heusner, A. A. 1985. Body size and energy metabolism. *Ann. Rev. Nutr.* 5:267–93
18. von Hoesslin, H. 1888. Ueber die Ursache der scheinbaren Abhängigkeit des Umsatzes von der Grösse der Körperoberfläche. *Du Bois-Reymond Arch. Anat. Physiol.* 323–79
19. Huxley, J. S. 1932. *Problems of Relative Growth.* New York: Dial. 276 pp.
20. Kayser, Ch., Heusner, A. 1964. Etude comparative du métabolisme énergetique dans la série animale. *J. Physiol. Paris* 56:489–524
21. Kleiber, M. 1931–32. Body size and metabolism. *Hilgardia* 6:315–53
22. Kleiber, M. 1947. Body size and metabolic rate. *Physiol. Rev.* 27:511–41
23. Kleiber, M. 1961. *The Fire of Life.* New York: Wiley. 454 pp.
24. Krebs, H. A. 1950. Body size and tissue respiration. *Biochem. Biophys. Acta* 4:249–69
25. Lambert, R., Teissier, G. 1927. Théorie de la similitude biologique. *Ann. Physiol.* 3:212–46
26. McMahon, T. 1973. Size and shape in biology. *Science* 179:1201–4
27. McMahon, T. A., Bonner, J. T. 1983. *On Size and Life.* New York: Sci. Am. Libr. 255 pp.
28. Medawar, P. B. 1950. Transformation of shape. *Proc. R. Soc. London Ser. B.* 137:474–79
29. Mandelbrot, B. B. 1982. *A Fractal*

Geometry of Nature. San Francisco: Freeman. 461 pp.

30. Meeh, K. 1789. Oberflächenmessungen des menschlichen Körpers. *Z. Biol.* 15:425–58

31. Poczopko, P. 1979. Remarks on the metabolic rate in mammals, birds and reptiles of small body size. *Bull. Acad. Pol. Sci. Ser. Sci. Biol.* 27:407–11

32. Prothero, J. 1984. Scaling of standard energy metabolism in mammals: I. Neglect of circadian rhythms. *J. Theor. Biol.* 106:1–8

33. Rameaux, J. F. 1857. Des lois, suivant lesquelles les dimensions du corps, dans certaines classes d'animaux, déterminent la capacité et les mouvements fonctionnels des poumons et du coeur. *Bull. Acad. R. Sci. Lett. Beaux-Arts Belg.* 26ᵉ année, 2ᵉ série, 3:94–104

34. Rubner, M. 1883. Ueber den Einfluss der Körpergrösse auf Stoff- und Kraftwechsel. *Z. Biol.* 19:535–62

35. Sarrus, F., Rameaux, J. F. 1838–39. Rapport sur un mémoire adressé à l'Académie royale de Médecine. Commissaire Robiquet et Thillaye, rapporteurs. *Bull. Acad. R. Med. Paris* 3:1094–1100

36. Schmidt-Nielsen, K. 1984. *Scaling. Why is Animal Size so Important?* Cambridge, England: Cambridge Univ. Press. 241 pp.

37. Sernetz, M., Gelleri, B., Hofman, J. 1985. The organism as bioreactor. Interpretation of the reduction law of metabolism in terms of heterogeneous catalysis and fractal structure. *J. Theor. Biol.* 117:209–30

38. Sernetz, M., Rufeger, H., Kindt, R. 1982. Interpretation of the reduction law of metabolism. *Exp. Biol. Med.* 7:21–29

39. Smith, R. E. 1956. Quantitative relations between liver mitochondria and total body weight in mammals. *Ann. NY Acad. Sci.* 62:403–22

40. Snell, O. 1891. Die Abhängigkeit des Hirngewichts von dem Körpergewicht und den geistigen Fähigkeiten. *Arch. Psychiatr. Nervenkr.* 23:436–46

41. Social Register of Big Trees, 1966. *Am. For.* 72:16–35

42. Social Register of Big Trees, 1971. *Am. For.* 77:25–31

43. Staicu, C. I. 1982. *Restricted and General Dimensional Analysis, Treatment of Experimental Data.* Tunbridge Wells, England: Abacus. 303 pp.

44. Suppes, P. A. 1951. A set of independent axioms for extensive quantities. *Port. Math.* Vol. 10, Fasc. 4, pp. 163–72

45. U.S. Dept. Agric. 1900. *Report on the Big Trees of California.* Washington, D.C.: GPO

46. Walker, E. P. 1975. *Mammals of the World.* Baltimore: Johns Hopkins Univ. Press

47. Wieser, W. 1984. A distinction must be made between the ontogeny and phylogeny of metabolism in order to understand the mass exponent of energy metabolism. *Respir. Physiol.* 55:1–9

Ann. Rev. Physiol. 1987. 49:135–46

STRUCTURAL AND FUNCTIONAL LIMITS TO OXIDATIVE METABOLISM: INSIGHTS FROM SCALING

C. Richard Taylor

Concord Field Station, Museum of Comparative Zoology, Harvard University, Old Causeway Road, Bedford, Massachusetts 01730

INTRODUCTION

A small (30 g) mouse is capable of mass-specific rates of oxygen consumption that are nearly ten times greater than those of a 300-kg steer. This review addresses a simple question: What are the physiological and structural bases for these large differences? I first consider how maximal rates of oxygen consumption scale with body size and then consider the processes in the muscle that consume ATP and set the demand for oxygen. Finally, I consider the role of the mitochondria of muscle, the organelles where the oxygen is consumed and ATP is produced, in setting this upper limit. The review by Ewald Weibel that follows considers the structures involved in moving the oxygen from the environment to the mitochondria. This review and that of Weibel address the general question of whether or not there is a match between structures and their function under rate-limiting conditions of $\dot{V}_{O_{2max}}$. The tenfold differences in maximal rates of oxygen flow per unit mass that occur with body size provide an excellent opportunity to test for this match (24).

AN UPPER LIMIT TO OXYGEN CONSUMPTION, $\dot{V}_{O_{2max}}$

In mammals, the rate of oxygen consumption increases with the intensity of exercise up to a certain point. Increases in intensity beyond this point do not

135

0066-4278/87/0315-0135$02.00

cause higher rates of oxygen consumption; instead, the additional ATP required by the muscles is produced by anaerobic glycolysis and can be quantified by measuring the rate of accumulation of lactate (26). This maximal rate of oxygen consumption has been measured in mammals ranging in body mass from 7 g (pygmy mice) to 250 kg (cattle) (30). It varies in a regular manner with body mass and can be expressed by a simple allometric equation:

$$\dot{V}_{O_{2max}} = 1.92 \, M_b^{0.81}, \qquad\qquad 1.$$

where $\dot{V}_{O_{2max}}$ has the units ml O_2/sec and M_b is in kilograms. The 95% confidence limits of the scaling factor, 0.81, are 0.75 and 0.87. On average, $\dot{V}_{O_{2max}}$ is about ten times the standard resting metabolic rate ($\dot{V}_{O_{2std}}$) calculated by Klieber's equation (20):

$$\dot{V}_{O_{2std}} = 0.188 \, M_b^{0.75}, \qquad\qquad 2.$$

where $\dot{V}_{O_{2std}}$ has the same units as $\dot{V}_{O_{2max}}$.

The average tenfold difference between resting and maximal rates of oxygen consumption encompasses a great deal of variability between animals of the same size. Large differences in $\dot{V}_{O_{2max}}$ occur with adaptational differences in levels of aerobic performance. For example, a 20-kg dog has a $\dot{V}_{O_{2max}}$ that is 2–3 times that of a goat of similar size (30), and we have observed similar 2–3 fold differences between the $\dot{V}_{O_{2max}}$ values for 500-kg horses and cows and 200-g ground squirrels and white rats. Large differences also occur within species as the result of differences in daily exercise regimes and/or genetic makeup. For example, $\dot{V}_{O_{2max}}/M_b$ of adult humans can vary by nearly a factor of two and is dependent on both training and genetic makeup (13, 14). These large differences in maximal rates of oxygen consumption, like the large differences in $\dot{V}_{O_{2max}}/M_b$ that occur with body size, provide powerful tools for examining the physiological mechanisms and structures that determine the upper limit to oxygen consumption and the rate of delivery of oxygen from the air to the mitochondria.

FORCE GENERATION BY MUSCLES SETS THE DEMAND FOR ATP

When animals exercise at high intensities, their muscles use most of the energy being consumed. The rate of breakdown of ATP increases 400–700 fold during a steady isometric tetanus of an isolated muscle (23). Two processes account for most of the ATP breakdown during muscular activity: (a) force generation, which involves the breaking of the cross-bridges between actin and myosin by actomyosin ATPase; and (b) the activation-deactivation process, which involves the pumping of Ca^{2+} into the sarcoplasmic reticulum by the Ca^{2+} transport ATPase system of the sarcoplasmic reticulum. The relative contributions of these two processes have been evaluated by stretching a resting muscle to the point where there is no overlap between actin and myosin filaments, physically preventing the formation of cross-bridges and force development, and thereby preventing ATP breakdown by the actomyosin ATPase system. These types of experiments indicate that about 30% of energy utilized during contraction can be attributed to activation-deactivation and about 70% to force generation (12, 23).

The maximum force or stress exerted by a mammalian muscle is independent of body size (approximately 300–400 kN/m^2 cross section of muscle fiber) because of the basic similarity in the structures of the contractile proteins, actin and myosin. The maximum relative shortening, or strain, is also independent of body size (approximately 0.3). From these constants A. V. Hill (11) pointed out that the maximum work (force times distance) performed in a single contraction is also constant and independent of body size. If the work per contraction is constant, then the work per unit time (power output) is proportional to the speed of shortening. It is the speed of shortening that increases with decreasing body size and accounts for the higher rates of ATP utilization by smaller animals. For example, Lindstedt et al (21) found that the rate of shortening of the knee extensors is much faster in small than in large animals and scales with $M_b^{-0.23}$, which is approximately the same scaling factor as observed for $\dot{V}_{O_{2max}}/M_b$.

Higher speeds of muscular shortening require higher rates of cycling of the cross-bridges. Barany (3) suggested that the actomyosin ATPase activity is directly proportional to the rate of shortening of unloaded muscles and reflects the rate of cross-bridge cycling. Lindstedt et al (21) reviewed data on actomyosin ATPase activity for animals of different sizes and found that, like speed of shortening and $\dot{V}_{O_{2max}}/M_b$, it scales with $M_b^{-0.23}$ to $M_b^{-0.31}$. Thus maximal rates of energy consumption for force generation by the proteins of an animal's muscles appear to be matched to the large differences in maximal rates of energy consumption that occur as a function of animal size.

Many normal activities, like running, involve regular cyclic muscular activities during which muscles stay the same length or are alternatively stretched and then shortened, rather than simply shortened. These muscular activities occur at higher frequencies in smaller animals, and their requirements for energy per unit time are higher. The energetic cost of locomotion along the ground, like $\dot{V}_{O_{2max}}$, increases in a regular manner with decreasing body size and can be described by a simple allometric equation (29):

$$\dot{V}_{O_2}/M_b = 0.533\ M_b^{-0.316} \cdot vg + 0.300 M_b^{-0.303}, \qquad\qquad 3.$$

where $\dot{V}_{O_2}/M_b$ has the units ml O_2/sec·kg, M_b is body mass in kg, and vg is ground speed in m/sec. One finds, however, that the cost per step is a constant at speeds where stresses (force/cross-sectional area) in the muscles and bones of the limbs are the same (28). At the point of transition from a trot to a gallop, muscle and bone stresses in the limbs are independent of body size (4, 5). If one divides the rate of oxygen consumption at this speed by stride frequency, then the cost per step (muscular event) is constant (Table 1). Thus it appears that the higher frequencies of the complex muscular events occurring during locomotion, like faster shortening velocities in simple contractions, in part determine the higher demand for energy in small animals. Both the activation-deactivation costs and the cross-bridge cycling costs should be directly proportional to frequency, thus both should be higher in small animals.

THE CONSUMERS OF OXYGEN, THE MITOCHONDRIA

The mitochondrion is bounded by a continuous outer membrane and contains a second inner membrane that forms multiple infoldings, the cristae. The respiratory chain enzymes involved in phosphorylation of ATP and consumption of O_2 are built into the inner membrane, whereas the Krebs cycle enzymes are all contained in the matrix of the mitochondrion (31).

It is possible to estimate the surface area of the inner mitochondrial membrane (where the oxygen is consumed during oxidative phosphorylation) using stereological techniques and to compare this surface area with biochemical measurements of the oxidative activity of the respiratory chain and the concentrations of the membrane-bound redox complexes. From this type of measurement on liver mitochondria, Schwerzmann et al (25) estimated that 40% of the surface of the inner mitochondrial membrane is made up of the proteins of energy transduction and that the maximal rate of O_2 consumption per area of inner membrane is 0.156 ml O_2/min m^2.

The area of inner mitochondrial membrane per unit volume of mitochondria in skeletal muscle is relatively constant at 20–40 m^2/ml mitochondria (14, 22), and it does not depend on whether the mitochondria is in a muscle that is highly aerobic and continuously active (e.g. the diaphragm) or one that is relatively inactive with a low oxidative potential. Importantly for our considerations, the constant relationship between surface area and volume of mitochondria is independent of body mass. This constant relationship suggests that the maximal rate of oxygen consumption per unit volume of mitochondria should also be constant and is independent of the aerobic capacity of the particular muscle and of body size.

It is possible to estimate a maximal rate of oxygen consumption for each milliliter of mitochondria in skeletal and cardiac muscle by multiplying the

Table 1 The energetic cost of each stride is the same for animals of different size at speeds where muscle stress (force/cross-sectional area) is the same. Cost of locomotion is directly proportional to stride frequency at these speeds. Speed and frequency at the trot-gallop transition are calculated from allometric equations given by Heglund et al (10), and $\dot{V}_{O_2}/M_b$ is calculated from Equation 3 in the text.

Body mass (kg)	Speed at trot-gallop transition (m/sec)	$\dot{V}_{O_2}/M_b$ at trot-gallop transition (ml O_2/sec·kg)	Stride frequency at trot-gallop transition (stride/sec)	Cost/stride at trot-gallop transition (ml O_2/stride·kg)
0.1	0.51	2.38	8.54	0.28
1.0	1.53	1.12	4.48	0.25
100	4.61	0.65	2.35	0.28

maximal rate of oxygen consumption per square meter of inner membrane by the constant ratio of inner membrane to mitochondrial volume (Table 2). This calculation indicates that each milliliter of mitochondria in skeletal muscle is capable of consuming 3–6 ml O_2/min. From these calculations one would anticipate that the higher mass-specific metabolic rates of smaller animals would require higher mitochondrial volumes in their muscles.

Mathieu et al (22) and Else & Hulbert (6) investigated the allometry of mitochondrial volume in mammalian skeletal muscles. Each group found that the total mitochondrial volume of a given skeletal muscle had the same scaling factor as $\dot{V}_{O_{2max}}$. This agrees with the findings of Emmett & Hochachka (7) that the catalytic capacities of several oxidative enzymes scale with the same scaling factor as $\dot{V}_{O_{2max}}$. Thus the demand for oxygen under rate-limiting conditions seems to be directly proportional to the number of respiratory chain units in the mitochondria that are present to consume oxygen and produce ATP. The tenfold higher rates of mass-specific oxygen consumption in the mouse compared to the cow are accompanied by tenfold greater volumes of mitochondria, whereas the rate of oxygen consumption per surface area of inner mitochondrial membrane appears to be constant and independent of the body size and the aerobic capacity of the animal.

More than 80% of the total mitochondrial volume of a mammal is present in its skeletal muscles (14), and under conditions of $\dot{V}_{O_{2max}}$ more than 90% of the cardiac output is directed towards these muscles (8). Therefore, it seems reasonable to conclude that the majority of oxygen is consumed by skeletal muscles at $\dot{V}_{O_{2max}}$. If we divide the $\dot{V}_{O_{2max}}$ of an animal by the total mitochondrial volume of its skeletal muscles, we obtain an estimate of mitochondrial oxygen consumption that can be compared to maximal values calculated for

Table 2 Maximal rate of oxygen consumption for each milliliter of mitochondria in skeletal muscle estimated from maximal rates of oxygen consumption per unit surface area of inner mitochondrial membrane (25) multiplied by the constant ratio of inner mitochondrial membrane per milliliter of mitochondria (mt) (14, 22).

Respiratory chain enzymes as a % of inner membrane surface	40%
Maximal oxygen consumption per unit surface area of inner membrane ($\dot{V}_{O_{2max}}/S_{im}$)	0.156 ml O_2/min·m^2
Surface area of inner membrane per volume of mitochondria [$S_v(im,mt)$]	20–40 m^2/ml
Maximal oxygen consumption per milliliter of mitochondria estimated by multiplying $\dot{V}_{O_{2max}}/S_{im}$ by S_v (im,mt)	3.1–6.2 ml O_2/min·ml mt

isolated mitochondria (Table 2). Assuming that the mean volume density of mitochondria in the two leg muscles, which has been measured in a variety of mammals, reflects the density of the whole body, I have calculated the oxygen consumption of each milliliter of mitochondria for animals ranging from 20 g to 240 kg (Table 3). These calculations show that when animals exercise at $\dot{V}_{O_{2max}}$, each milliliter of mitochondria (mt) in their body consumes about 3.4 ml O_2/min.

It is surprising that this value of 3.4 ml O_2/min·ml mt is within the range of the value of 3–6 ml O_2/min calculated in Table 2 for maximal oxygen consumption by isolated skeletal muscle mitochondria. The calculation of total-body mitochondrial oxygen consumption in Table 3 seems to set a lower boundary for oxygen consumption by active mitochondria under rate-limiting conditions of $\dot{V}_{O_{2max}}$, because it assumes that all of the mitochondria in the animal are consuming oxygen. It seems unlikely that all of the mitochondria of all of the skeletal muscles are active. If only 50% of the mitochondria were active, then $\dot{V}_{O_2}$ per unit volume of the active mitochondria would be doubled. The observation that this lower boundary value is nearly identical to the upper limit calculated for isolated mitochondria suggests that almost all of the animals' mitochondria consume oxygen at these maximal rates when animals exercise at $\dot{V}_{O_{2max}}$.

Recently, total skeletal muscle mitochondria was directly measured using a new whole-body sampling technique (16). These measurements allow us to check the assumption that the volume density of the leg muscles is representative of the density of all skeletal muscles and thus to check the value for total volume of skeletal mitochondria. Values for mitochondrial oxygen consumption calculated from measurements of $\dot{V}_{O_{2max}}$ and mitochondrial volume using this new sampling technique are 4.9 ml O_2/min·ml mt for a 20-g woodmouse (16) and 4.6 ml O_2/min·ml mt in a 500-kg horse (Hoppeler, personal communication). These values are very close to those calculated from the two limb muscles.

These calculations of mitochondrial oxygen consumption suggest that most of the mitochondria of skeletal muscles are operating at close to their maximal rates when animals exercise at $\dot{V}_{O_{2max}}$. However, only 30–40% of the muscle fibers of the major limb muscles appear to be active at $\dot{V}_{O_{2max}}$ (2). How does one reconcile these two observations? Mitochondria are not distributed uniformly within muscle groups, instead, they are concentrated in the 30–40% of the muscle fibers that are active at $\dot{V}_{O_{2max}}$ (1, 17). The remainder of the muscle is available for high peak forces that may be necessary for short bursts of speed, but these activities can be supplied by high-energy phosphates stored as creatine phosphate and/or by anaerobic pathways. The depleted stores could later be slowly replaced by oxidative metabolism, which would involve relatively few mitochondria.

Table 3 Rates of oxygen consumption per unit volume of skeletal muscle mitochondria (mt) at $\dot{V}_{O_{2}max}$ are independent of body size. Rates are calculated by assuming that skeletal muscle accounts for 45% of body mass and that the mitochondrial volume densities of semitendinosus and vastus medialis muscles are representative of skeletal muscles of the whole body.

Species	M_b (kg)	$\dot{V}_{O_{2}max}/M_b$ (ml O_2/sec·kg)	$V_{(mt)}/M_b$ (ml mt/kg)	$\dot{V}_{O_{2}max}/V_{(mt)}$ (ml O_2/sec·ml mt)	(ml/min·ml mt)
[a]European woodmouse (*Apodemus slyvaticus*)	0.020	4.4	53	0.083	4.9
Dwarf mongoose (*Helogale pervula*)	0.58	2.1	34	0.062	3.7
Banded mongoose (*mungos mungo*)	1.14	1.9	27	0.070	4.2
Genet cat (*Genetta tirina*)	1.4	1.8	29	0.062	3.7
Suni (*Nesotragus moschatus*)	3.3	1.6	25	0.064	3.8
Dik-dik (*Madoqua kirkii*)	4.2	0.91	23	0.040	2.4
Grant's gazelle (*Gazella granti*)	10.1	0.89	20	0.045	2.7
African goat (*Capra hircus*)	20.9	0.87	20	0.044	2.6

African sheep (*Ovis aries*)	21.8	0.78	17	0.047	2.8
Dog (*Canis familiaris*)	28.0	2.29	41	0.056	3.4
Goat (*Capea hircus*)	30.0	0.95	19	0.050	3.0
Wildebeest (*Connochaetes taurinus*)	102.0	0.73	13	0.056	3.4
Waterbuck (*Kobus defassa*)	109.8	0.79	15	0.053	3.2
Hereford calf (*Bos taurus*)	141	0.61	12	0.051	3.1
Pony (*Equus caballus*)	171	1.48	20	0.074	4.4
Zebu cattle (*Bos indicus*)	232	0.49	7.9	0.072	3.7
Eland (*Taurotragus oryx*)	240	0.60	12	0.050	3.0

[a]The values for the woodmouse were obtained using an innovative new whole-body sampling procedure (16) and did not require these assumptions. Values for V_{mt} were calculated using measurements of $V_{v(mt,f)}$ and muscle mass reported by Mathieu et al (22) for the African mammals and by Hoppeler et al (18) for the dog, goat, pony, and calf.

There is, however, one muscle that is completely active and for which it is possible to quantify its work rate and estimate its oxygen consumption—the heart. The mitochondrial volume of heart muscle V(mt,h) was recently determined for animals ranging from 2.4 g (shrews) to 920 kg (cattle) (15):

$$V(mt,h) = 185\ M_b^{0.927},\qquad\qquad 4.$$

where V(mt,h) is the total volume of mitochondria in the heart in ml and M_b is body mass in kg. The 95% confidence limits for the scaling factor, 0.927, are from 0.852 to 1.00. A comparison of this allometric relationship for mitochondrial volume of the heart and the allometric relationship for $\dot{V}_{O_{2max}}$ given in Equation 1 shows that the mitochondrial volume of the heart does not change in direct proportion to $\dot{V}_{O_{2max}}$. However, this finding does not necessarily indicate that the $\dot{V}_{O_2}$ of heart mitochondria varies with body size. A more likely explanation is that the work rate and oxygen consumption of the heart scale differently with body size. The work rate of the heart under resting conditions has the same scaling factor as V(mt,h); but allometric data are not available for the work rate of the heart during exercise at $\dot{V}_{O_{2max}}$.

A recent study by Karas et al (19) measured both the work rate of the heart at $\dot{V}_{O_{2max}}$ and the mitochondrial volume in two pairs of species of the same body size (dog versus goat and pony versus calf), where $\dot{V}_{O_{2max}}$ differed by 2–3 fold within each pair. If one uses the reported value of 20% for the efficiency of the heart in converting metabolic energy into mechanical work (using an energy equivalent of 20.1 J/ml O_2) (9, 27), then it is possible to calculate the oxygen consumption of the heart from the work rate. Using these values for oxygen consumption and measurements of mitochondrial volume, one obtains a value of 3.5 ml O_2/min ml mt for all four species during exercise at $\dot{V}_{O_{2max}}$. This is the same rate of mitochondrial oxygen consumption calculated for skeletal muscle mitochondria.

CONCLUSIONS

We began by asking: What are the physiological and structural bases for the tenfold difference in maximal rates of oxidative metabolism in 30-g mice and 300-kg steers? We observed that skeletal muscles consume most of the energy at $\dot{V}_{O_{2max}}$ and use it to generate force. The higher rates of energy consumption by small animals are due to their higher cost for generating force. This cost is directly proportional to the frequency of regular, cyclic events (e.g. stride frequency) and to the maximal shortening velocity of the muscles. It reflects the higher rates of cycling in smaller animals, and the resulting higher ATP consumption by the cross-bridges between actin and myosin that generate the force. The other elements of the musculoskeletal system (e.g. stress and strain) are conservative and independent of animal size. They reflect the invariant dimensions of actin and myosin, the sarcomeres, and the spacing of the cross-bridges. The ATP required for force generation at $V_{O_{2max}}$ is produced by the respiratory chain units located on the inner membrane of the mitochondria. These units are densely packed, occupying 40% of the surface of this membrane. Each milliliter of skeletal muscle mitochondria contains approximately 30 m^2 of inner membrane regardless of body size. The maximal rate of ATP production and oxygen consumption by mitochondria also does not appear to vary with body size: Each milliliter of skeletal muscle mitochondria consumes 3–6 ml O_2/min at $\dot{V}_{O_{2max}}$. It is the total volume of mitochondria in skeletal muscle that changes with body size, and this volume is directly proportional to $\dot{V}_{O_{2max}}$.

We conclude that the machinery that consumes O_2 and produces ATP is matched to the demand for ATP under the rate-limiting condition of $\dot{V}_{O_{2max}}$. The review by Weibel considers whether or not a match also exists in the diffusive steps whereby oxygen is transferred from the blood in the capillaries to the mitochondria and from the air of the lung to the blood in its capillaries.

ACKNOWLEDGMENT

This review was prepared with support from National Science Foundation Grant PCM-83-17800.

Literature Cited

1. Armstrong, R. B., Laughlin, M. H., Schwane, J. A., Taylor, C. R. 1983. Differential inter- and intramuscular responses to exercise: Considerations in use of the biopsy technique. *Int. Ser. Sports Sci. Biochem. Exercise* 13:775–80

2. Armstrong, R. B., Taylor, C. R. 1982. Relationship between muscle force and muscle area showing glycogen loss during locomotion. *J. Exp. Biol.* 97:411–20

3. Barany, M. 1967. ATPase activity of myosin correlated with speed of muscle shortening. *J. Gen. Physiol.* 50:197–218

4. Biewener, A. A. 1983. Allometry of quadrupedal locomotion: Scaling duty factor, bone curvature, and limb orientation to body size in quadrupeds. *J. Exp. Biol.* 105:147–71

5. Biewener, A. A. 1983. Scaling relative mechanical advantage: Implications for muscle function in different sized animals. *Fed. Proc.* 42:469

6. Else, P. L., Hulbert, A. J. 1985. Mammals: An allometric study of metabolism

at tissue and mitochondrial level. *Am. J. Physiol.* 248:R415–21

7. Emmett, B., Hochachka, P. W. 1981. Scaling of oxidative and glycolytic enzymes in mammals. *Respir. Physiol.* 45:261–72

8. Folkow, B., Neil, E. 1971. *Circulation.* London: Oxford Univ. Press. 593 pp.

9. Gibbs, C. J., Chapman, J. B. 1985. Cardiac mechanics and energetics: Chemomechanical transduction in cardiac muscle. *Am. J. Physiol.* 249:H199–H206

10. Heglund, N. C., Taylor, C. R., McMahon, T. A. 1974. Scaling stride frequency and gait to animal size: Mice to horses. *Science* 186:1112–13

11. Hill, A. V. 1950. The dimensions of animals and their muscular dynamics. *Sci. Prog. London* 38:209–30

12. Homsher, E., Mommaerts, W. F. H. M., Ricchiuti, N. V., Wallner, A. 1972. Activation heat, activation metabolism and tension-related heat in frog semiten-

dinosus muscles. *J. Physiol. London* 220:601–25

13. Hoppeler, H., Howald, H., Conley, K., Lindstedt, S. L., Claassen, H., et al. 1985. Endurance training in humans: Aerobic capacity and structure of skeletal muscle. *J. Appl. Physiol.* 59:320–27

14. Hoppeler, H., Lindstedt, S. L. 1985. Malleability of skeletal muscle tissue in overcoming limitations: Structural elements. *J. Exp. Biol.* 115:355–64

15. Hoppeler, H., Lindstedt, S. L., Claassen, H., Taylor, C. R., Mathieu, O., et al. 1984. Scaling mitochondrial volume in heart to body mass. *Respir. Physiol.* 55:131–37

16. Hoppeler, H., Lindstedt, S. L., Uhlmann, E., Niesel, A., Cruz-Orive, L. M., et al. 1984. Oxygen consumption and the composition of skeletal muscle tissue after training in the European woodmouse *(Apodemus sylvaticus). J. Comp. Physiol. B* 155:51–61

17. Hoppeler, H., Mathieu, O., Krauer, R., Claassen, H., Armstrong, R. B., et al. 1981. Design of the mammalian respiratory system. VI. Distribution of mitochondria and capillaries in various muscles. *Respir. Physiol.* 44:87–112

18. Hoppeler, H., Kayar, S., Claassen, H., Uhlmann, E., Karas, R. 1987. Adaptive variation in the mammalian respiratory system in relation to energetic demand: III. Skeletal muscles: Setting the demand. *Respir. Physiol.* In press

19. Karas, R. H., Taylor, C. R., Rösler, K., Hoppeler, H. 1987. Adaptive variation in the respiratory system in relation to energetic demand: IV. Limits to oxygen transport by the circulation. *Respir. Physiol.* In press

20. Kleiber, M. 1961. *The Fire of Life, An Introduction to Animal Energetics.* New York: Wiley. 454 pp.

21. Lindstedt, S. L., Hoppeler, H., Bard, K. M., Thronson, H. A. Jr. 1985. Estimate of muscle-shortening rate during locomotion. *Am. J. Physiol.* 249:R699–R703

22. Mathieu, O., Krauer, R., Hoppeler, H., Gehr, P., Lindstedt, S. L., et al 1981.

23. Rall, J. R. 1985. Energetic aspects of skeletal muscle contraction: Implications of fiber types. *Exercise Sport Sci. Rev.* 13:33–74

24. Schmidt-Nielsen, K. 1984. *Scaling, Why is Animal Size So Important?* Cambridge, England: Cambridge Univ. Press. 241 pp.

25. Schwerzmann, K., Cruz-Orive, L. M., Eggman, R., Sänger, A., Weibel, E. R. 1986. Molecular architecture of the inner membrane of mitochondria from rat liver: A combined biochemical and stereological study. *J. Cell Biol.* 102:97–103

26. Seeherman, H. J., Taylor, C. R., Maloiy, G. M. O., Armstrong, R. B. 1981. Design of the mammalian respiratory system. II. Measuring maximum aerobic capacity. *Respir. Physiol.* 44:11–23

27. Suga, H., Hayashi, T., Shirahata, M. 1981. Ventricular systolic pressure-volume area as a predictor of cardiac oxygen consumption. *Am. J. Physiol.* 240:H39–H44

28. Taylor, C. R. 1985. Force development during sustained locomotion: A determinant of gait, speed and metabolic power. *J. Exp. Biol.* 115:253–62

29. Taylor, C. R., Heglund, N. C., Maloiy, G. M. O. 1982. Energetics and mechanics of terrestrial locomotion. I. Metabolic energy consumption as a function of speed and body size in birds and mammals. *J. Exp. Biol.* 97:1–21

30. Taylor, C. R., Maloiy, G. M. O., Weibel, E. R., Langman, V. A., Kamau, J. M. Z., et al. 1981. Design of the mammalian respiratory system. III. Scaling maximum aerobic capacity to body mass: Wild and domestic mammals. *Respir. Physiol.* 44:25–37

31. Weibel, E. R. 1984. *The Pathway for Oxygen, Structure and Function in the Mammalian Respiratory System.* Cambridge, Mass.: Harvard Univ. Press. 425 pp.

Design of the mammalian respiratory system: VII. Scaling mitochondrial volume in skeletal muscle to body mass. *Resp. Physiol.* 44:113–28

Ann. Rev. Physiol. 1987. 49:147–59

SCALING OF STRUCTURAL AND FUNCTIONAL VARIABLES IN THE RESPIRATORY SYSTEM

Ewald R. Weibel

Department of Anatomy, University of Berne, Berne, Switzerland

Dependencies in the Respiratory System

In his companion review C. R. Taylor (38) concludes that the capacity for oxidative metabolism in the mitochondria sets the limit for energy supply to muscles. Consequently, to supply O_2 to the mitochondria at the rate required by oxidative phosphorylation is a critical process that involves the entire respiratory system, from the lung through the circulation to the muscle microvasculature and finally to the mitochondria (Figure 1). At all levels, this process is determined by both structural and functional features. In a crude way one can say that the conductance terms of the equations given in Figure 1 are affected importantly by structural properties, whereas functional effects predominate in setting the driving forces for O_2 flow. The steady-state rate of O_2 flow through the system is set by the rate at which O_2 is consumed in the mitochondria, which under conditions of maximal exercise is essentially that in mitochondria of the skeletal muscle.

In this review I examine how the different parts of the respiratory system respond to the variations in the rate of energetic demand observed in the animal kingdom. I am particularly concerned with design features of each part because they establish the "stable" framework within which functional variables can operate. Structural features also have an impact on the efficiency with which the system operates. To express this notion in general terms we have proposed the hypothesis of symmorphosis (47), which postulates that the structures supporting a function should be no larger than needed to satisfy the functional demand at the limit of performance. Since symmorphosis should result from "regulation of morphogenesis," this hypothesis depends on the

147

0066-4278/87/0315-0147$02.00

148   WEIBEL

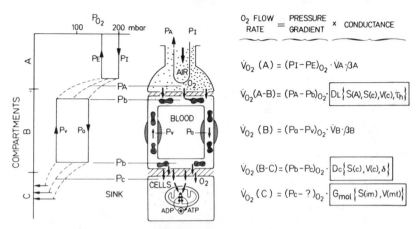

Figure 1 Model of the entire respiratory system. The driving force for O_2 is shown as a P_{O_2} cascade. At steady state the flow rates through all steps must be equal. [From Weibel & Taylor (47).]

adaptability of the structures concerned, at least during the phase of growth. Mitochondria have been shown to increase in amount as energetic needs increase, such as in training for higher levels of endurance work (21). The potential for adaptation is not so clearly established for the lung; in contrast, the elements of the circulatory system appear to respond to higher needs for O_2 delivery (6). We must, however, also consider evolutionary adaptations that are genetically fixed.

Peripheral Gas Exchange: Matching Capillaries with Mitochondria

Krogh introduced the classical notion that the capillary density in muscle determines the conditions for O_2 delivery (27). The radius of what is now called a Krogh cylinder is estimated from the number of capillaries counted on the unit area of muscle cross-section; it estimates the distance O_2 must diffuse from its capillary source. Krogh and his followers used the average $\dot{V}_{O_2}$ in the unit tissue volume to estimate whether capillary supply was adequate for O_2 demand.

Two main refinements of this idea are relevant for our purposes:

1. Capillary density can be expressed as the length of capillaries per unit tissue volume, JV(c), from which one can estimate, among other parameters, the volume of capillary blood per unit tissue volume, VV(c). The length density JV(c) is a function of the number of capillary profiles counted on the unit area of muscle cross-section, NA(c). This function depends on the architecture of the capillary network; specifically, it de-

pends on the degree of anisotropy in the network (31). If one knows the muscle volume, one can then calculate the total capillary length, J(c) (22).

2. Local tissue O_2 consumption can be estimated from the volume density of mitochondria, $VV(mt)$, since at $\dot{V}_{O_{2max}}$, 1 ml of mitochondria consumes an approximately constant amount of O_2, namely about 5 ml O_2/min (21).

These two refinements allow one to determine whether or not the capillary blood supply to the muscle cells is locally and globally matched to the O_2 needs of the mitochondria by estimating the level of proportionality between capillary length or capillary blood volume and mitochondrial volume. Figure 2 shows that capillary length density is directly proportional to mitochondrial volume density for a large spectrum of muscles, from the locomotor muscles of cows, which have only ~1% mitochondria by volume, to the myocardium of the shrew, which has 45% mitochondria by volume (22). When the capillary volume is calculated from these data one finds that 1 ml of capillary blood supplies O_2 to 3 ml of mitochondria. This ratio appears to be a "tissue constant" found in a large variety of muscles in diverse species (46); it is compatible with a mean capillary transit time of ~0.5 sec.

We compared many different muscles of various species ranging from the wood mouse (body mass = 20 g) to the calf and pony (150 kg) and found that

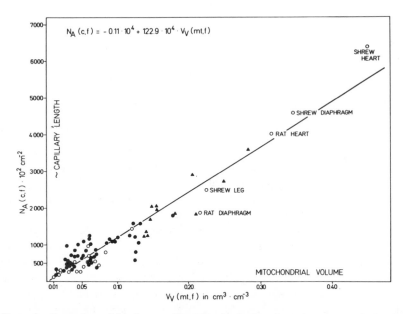

Figure 2   Comparison of data from a wide range of animals and muscle types reveals that the capillary density, expressed as number of capillaries per cm² of muscle cross-section, NA(c,f), increases in proportion to the mitochondrial volume density. [From Hoppeler et al (21).]

total capillary length is linearly proportional to total mitochondrial volume. The tissue constant of this relationship amounted to about 13 km of capillaries per 1 ml of mitochondria, or per 15 ml O_2 consumed per min.

It thus appears that the amount of O_2 supplied by the capillaries closely matches that required by the mitochondria. However, this statement is difficult to interpret as long as several uncertainties remain regarding some of the boundary conditions of gas exchange in tissue. Among the issues that need clarification are: the role of myoglobin in O_2 transport (13, 33); the variability of O_2 diffusion distances due to uneven distribution of mitochondria (26); the effect of capillary transit time and of hemoglobin content of the blood on O_2 transport; and finally some peculiarities of O_2 discharge from the red blood cells on their passage through the capillary (12) need explanation. We must also consider the other functions capillaries serve in addition to supplying O_2, such as substrate delivery, heat absorption, and lactate redistribution (48). In view of this complexity, it is astonishing that such a simple and consistent relationship exists between the structural elements of O_2 supply and O_2 consumption, i.e. between capillaries and mitochondria.

Pulmonary Gas Exchange: Diffusing Capacity and $\dot{V}_{O_{2max}}$

The lung's conductance for O_2 transfer from air to blood, the pulmonary diffusing capacity, DL_{O_2}, is related to morphometric properties of the lung's gas exchanger, e.g. alveolar and capillary surface area, capillary blood volume, and harmonic mean thickness of the tissue and plasma barriers (42, 46).

Several studies comparing animals with differing levels of O_2 consumption report that some of the morphometric determinants, mainly the alveolar surface area, are proportional to O_2 consumption. These studies utilized chronic exercise training in rats forced to swim (17), comparison of Japanese waltzing (14) and artificial waltzing mice (23) with normal mice, and observation of the effects of chronic cold exposure in rats (15). Tenney & Remmers (40) found a linear correlation between alveolar surface and $\dot{V}_{O_2}$ in an allometric study on mammals, but it was later shown that this finding may have been influenced by the inclusion of large marine mammals (16).

Our own first attempts at an allometric study of the mammalian lung revealed that DL_{O_2} scales about linearly with body mass (M_b) rather than with $\dot{V}_{O_2}$ (43, 44), a somewhat unexpected result. All subsequent attempts to bring DL_{O_2} in line with $\dot{V}_{O_2}$ failed. We first thought that the difficulty lay in the values used for $\dot{V}_{O_2}$. We expected DL_{O_2} to be related to the limiting or maximal O_2 consumption, $\dot{V}_{O_{2max}}$, and it appeared possible that $\dot{V}_{O_{2max}}$ might not be proportional to the standard $\dot{V}_{O_2}$ measured in the resting animal (44). A thorough study of this relation (47) did not lend support to this supposition.

$\dot{V}_{O_{2max}}$ was found to be proportional to resting $\dot{V}_{O_2}$ and to scale with $M_b^{0.8}$ (39). Using the same group of animals we found that the densities of mitochondria and capillaries in muscle scaled in proportion to $\dot{V}_{O_{2max}}$ (32), whereas DL_{O_2} did not (16). Figure 3 shows that the alveolar surface area scaled with $M_b^{0.95}$ and that the mean barrier thickness τ increased very slightly with a slope of 0.05. The capillary volume increased linearly with body mass. As a consequence, the DL_{O_2} calculated from these morphometric data also scaled linearly with body mass, in contrast to the slope of 0.81 found for $\dot{V}_{O_{2max}}$ (Figure 4).

We next tested the model for calculating DL_{O_2} from morphometric data. We studied canids of varying size and also estimated DL physiologically using CO as a tracer (49). Figure 5 shows that the morphometric values were larger than the physiologic estimate of DL_{CO} by a factor of about two, but that they were strictly proportional (Figure 5a). However, both estimates of DL increased more steeply with body mass than did $\dot{V}_{O_{2max}}$ (Figure 5b), which confirmed the discordant scaling between DL and $\dot{V}_{O_{2max}}$. The difference in the allometric slopes was similar to that in the total population (Figure 4). This finding indicated that the morphometric estimate of DL_{O_2} did not contain a bias that might explain the discordant scaling with $\dot{V}_{O_2}$. Our findings agreed

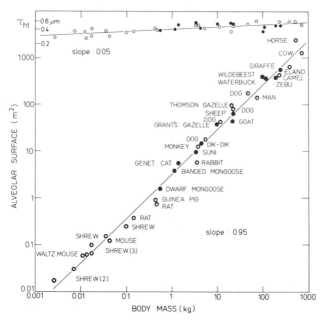

Figure 3 Allometric plot of alveolar surface area and harmonic mean thickness of tissue barrier for 36 mammalian species, ranging in body mass from 2 g (Etruscan shrew) to 700 kg (cow). [From Gehr et al (16).]

with the observation of Stahl (37) and O'Neil & Leith (34) that physiological DL scales about linearly with body mass.

The discordant scaling between DL_{O_2} and $\dot{V}_{O_{2max}}$ is thus established. The implications of this result are substantial. In Figure 6 mouse and cow are compared: Although the body masses of the two species differ by four orders of magnitude (30 g versus 300 kg), both animals have about the same amount of DL_{O_2} available per unit body mass. However, the cow's specific $\dot{V}_{O_{2max}}$ is about ten times smaller than that of the mouse, which means that the unit DL_{O_2} must transfer ten times as much O_2 from air to blood in the mouse as in the cow. This suggests that DL_{O_2} is not matched to resting $\dot{V}_{O_2}$ nor $\dot{V}_{O_{2max}}$. The proportionality between structure and function noted for muscle mitochondria and capillaries is not observed in the pulmonary gas exchanger.

However, such a conclusion, which clearly challenges the hypothesis of symmorphosis, must be carefully examined. It implies, in terms of structure-function correlation, that in the relationship

$$\dot{V}_{O_{2max}} = (P_{A_{O_2}} - \overline{Pc}_{O_2}) \cdot DL_{O_2}$$

the driving force for O_2 diffusion, the partial pressure difference $\Delta P_{O_2} = (P_{A_{O_2}} - \overline{Pc}_{O_2})$, is not a constant but falls as body mass increases (Figure 7). This could be due to either a fall in $P_{A_{O_2}}$ or an increase in $\overline{Pc}_{O_2}$, or both.

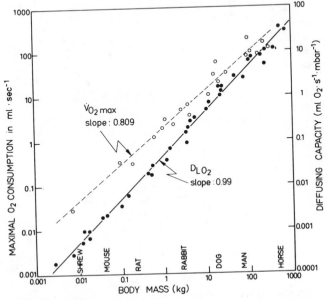

Figure 4 Allometric plot of morphometric pulmonary diffusing capacity for the same species as in Figure 3 (full dots), compared with maximal O_2 consumption for a similar set of species. [From Weibel (46).]

a

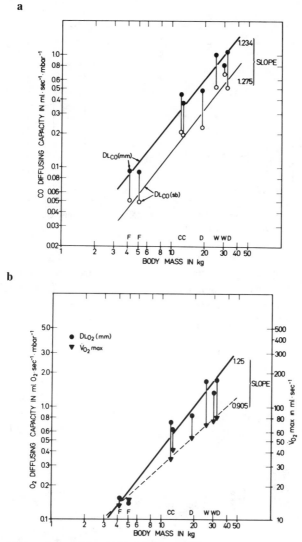

b

Figure 5   (*a*) Comparison of morphometric and physiologic CO diffusing capacity of the lung in four species of canids: foxes (F), coyotes (C), dogs (D), and wolves (W). (*b*) Comparison of morphometric O_2 diffusing capacity with maximal O_2 consumption in the same species. [From Weibel et al (49).]

The possibility that P_{AO_2} may be size dependent has been raised for the case where stratification of P_{O_2} in the air phase of the lung influences P_{AO_2} (35). Thus, the longer path length of acinar airways observed in larger animals of varying size (36, 45) could result in a decline in the average P_{AO_2} with

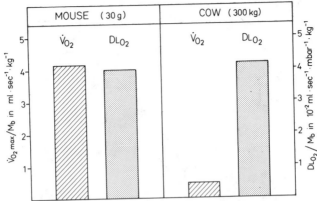

Figure 6   Comparison of oxygen consumption and pulmonary diffusing capacity per unit body mass in mouse and cow. [From Weibel (47).]

increasing body size (46, 48). It remains to be shown how important this effect may be in setting the head pressure for O_2 transfer in the lung.

The mean capillary P_{O_2} could also be size dependent if, for example, there were size-dependent differences in the O_2 binding properties of the blood or capillary transit time increased with body mass (30). Current data do not appear to support these hypotheses. However, the basis for estimating mean capillary P_{O_2} is not very firm; it depends on several assumptions and variables, including DL_{O_2}. The capillary P_{O_2} ranges from mixed venous to end-capillary or arterial P_{O_2}, i.e. between 20 and 100 mm Hg. The pattern of progressive increase from Pv_{O_2} to Pa_{O_2} is calculated by Bohr integration (20). This calculation requires information on the blood flow (transit time), the O_2 binding properties of the blood (hemoglobin content, O_2-hemoglobin equilib-

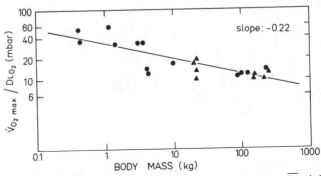

Figure 7   The ratio $\dot{V}_{O_{2max}}/DL_{O_2}$ declines with body mass, indicating that $\overline{Pa_{O_2}-Pc_{O_2}}$ is inversely related to body mass. (See text for further explanation.) [From Weibel et al (48).]

rium curves, O_2 binding rate), and the O_2 transfer conductance of the lung (DM_{O_2} or DL_{O_2}). Variation in any one of these variables greatly affects the estimate of $\overline{P}c_{O_2}$.

Recently we collected the physiological and morphometric data needed to perform Bohr integration for $\dot{V}_{O_{2max}}$ in four species from two size classes and of varying $\dot{V}_{O_{2max}}$: dog, goat, pony, and calf (25). Transit time was found to be about 0.3 sec in all four species. Bohr integration revealed, however, that this transit time was needed for O_2 equilibration of capillary blood with alveolar air in the dog and the pony only; the end-capillary P_{O_2} was reached after 30–50% of the transit time in the goat and the calf. Accordingly, $\overline{P}c_{O_2}$ was considerably higher in the goat and calf than in the two species with high $\dot{V}_{O_{2max}}$. This implies that goat and calf have a DL_{O_2} in excess of that needed to meet the $\dot{V}_{O_{2max}}$ required by their muscles. This conclusion is supported by the recent observation that goats can maintain their $\dot{V}_{O_{2max}}$ under hypoxic conditions (24).

If these new observations are confirmed in other species, then DL_{O_2} is not necessarily a limiting factor for $\dot{V}_{O_2}$ in all cases, i.e. DL_{O_2} is not matched ("adapted") to the body's O_2 needs. The size of the lung would not be determined by the O_2 transfer conditions but perhaps by other constraints, e.g. of a mechanical, design, or simply genetic nature. With respect to genetic control of lung size, the allometric study of the lungs of newborn mammals by Bartlett & Areson (3) is of interest. They found that lung volume was linearly related to body mass in the newborn, as it is in the adult (37, 40, 43). The alveolar surface area, however, was found to increase more steeply than O_2 consumption, with a power of 1.23 of $\dot{V}_{O_2}$. These authors interpreted this finding as indicating that lung size in newborn animals is not matched to $\dot{V}_{O_2}$; this disagrees with the observations of Tenney & Remmers (40) on adults. However, in our view the data indicate that SA is proportional to body mass in the newborn lung, just as in the adult lung (Figure 3), if one excludes marine mammals, in which the gas exchange conditions are significantly different (16). The observation of Bartlett & Areson (3) suggests that "functional lung size" is determined *before* the lung "experiences" the body's O_2 needs, i.e. it is determined genetically, as if in anticipation of O_2 needs. Thus it might be expected that goats would develop a lung large enough to function well in hypoxic conditions, since they were originally mountain animals. We humans may possess a greater capacity for O_2 uptake than modern "civilized" people need because our ancestors were more physically active. In fact, it turns out that top endurance athletes use all their DL_{O_2} at $\dot{V}_{O_{2max}}$, as do dogs.

If DL_{O_2} is set genetically, as we are tempted to conclude from the findings in newborns, then the lung has very little flexibility in adapting to the body's O_2 needs. In contrast, under certain experimental conditions DL_{O_2} adapts to $\dot{V}_{O_2}$ (7, 15, 17, 23, 41) or to environmental P_{O_2} (1, 4, 10). However, neither intermittent exercise nor thyroxine treatment appears to affect lung size, although either condition increases $\dot{V}_{O_2}$ (2, 11). Lechner et al (29) found that in young guinea pigs a combination of hypoxia and cold exposure induced accelerated lung growth: The alveolar surface of the treated animals was larger than that in controls after 2–10 weeks of exposure. However, this difference was abolished when the animals reached the end of their growth period. Thus it remains unclear whether or not the lung can adapt its growth in response to altered functional stresses. This is intriguing because experiments involving partial pneumonectomy unequivocally demonstrated the lung's capacity to regulate and modify its growth rate to fully compensate for lost tissue, even in adult rats (5, 8, 9, 28). Lung size is, therefore, not strictly predetermined genetically. The question clearly is this: If lung size can be regulated during morphogenesis, what characteristics determine the outcome?

Similitude and Symmorphosis

The concepts of similitude and of symmorphosis both seek to extract from nature some of the secret basic rules on how animals are made. We can examine this relationship by comparing animals of various sizes; the use of the allometric power function has been a productive tool in demonstrating consistencies and inconsistencies between related parameters. It is evident that the separation of qualitative (intensive) and quantitative (extensive) factors (18) can sharpen our insight into some of the physical laws underlying the design of organisms of different size.

Our investigations were not designed to distinguish between intensive and extensive factors, however. We are interested in a vital function that is known to have a limit: oxidative energy metabolism. This function depends on a sequence of "auxiliary functions": O_2 uptake in the lung, O_2 transport by the circulation of blood, O_2 delivery to the cells, and oxidative phosphorylation in the mitochondria. We examined how these different levels of the respiratory system (Figure 1) ensure an adequate energy supply, in particular how, and to what extent, the structural design properties may be limiting factors.

The concept of symmorphosis describes an engineering ideal. Intuitively, symmorphosis "makes sense"; it has been implicit in scores of biological studies. However, we must explicitly define the principle of symmorphosis to test it as a scientific theory. We define it as "a state of structural design commensurate to functional needs resulting from regulated morphogenesis." The examination of animals of various sizes has been particularly productive in testing this concept because O_2 needs change dramatically with body size.

This approach has shown that symmorphosis has stood the test at the level of muscle cells and muscle tissue: The densities of mitochondria and capillaries closely match O_2 consumption at the limit. Perhaps the case of mitochondria in muscle cells is comprehensible because (a) oxidative phosphorylation is clearly limited by the turn-over rate of the respiratory chain enzymes and is the exclusive function of mitochondria; (*b*) O_2 consumption occurs only in mitochondria; and because (*c*) the mitochondrial population of muscle cells is quite malleable, thus allowing effective regulation of morphogenesis (21).

Conversely, the lung has a complex structure that is subject to several mechanical stresses that vary with body size and varying boundary conditions, and which may have only limited malleability. The results of our analysis are ambiguous on several points, but it appears that the principle of symmorphosis does not describe the lung, at least not if we take O_2 uptake as the sole functional determinant and exclude the possibility of important effects of boundary conditions.

In any event, the study of the body size–dependent variation of lung morphometry in relation to respiratory function has revealed that at least some characteristics of the mammalian lung (possibly intensive) change with body size. What are they? How are they related to the lung's main respiratory function? Or are they the result of other effects on lung structure and function? For example, the solutions to difficult mechanical problems must certainly be affected by absolute size. If one follows the arguments of Heusner (19), one concludes that the "redundancy" of the lung as gas exchanger increases with body size. Why then should the cow have a lung at least ten times more "redundant" than that of the mouse? The idea that this is simply because of "genetic stubbornness" is hard to believe.

The final question is whether, or to what extent, these findings challenge the concept of symmorphosis. It seems evident that the original form of this concept was too simple. The model must be refined to account for the fact that nature is more complex than our models make us believe.

ACKNOWLEDGMENTS

The continued support of our work by the Swiss National Science Foundation (3.036.84) is gratefully acknowledged.

Literature Cited

1. Bartlett, D. Jr. 1970a. Postnatal growth of the mammalian lung: Influence of low and high oxygen tension. *Respir. Physiol.* 9:58–64

2. Bartlett, D. Jr. 1970b. Postnatal growth of the mammalian lung: Influence of exercise and thyroid activity. *Respir. Physiol.* 9:50–57

3. Bartlett, D. Jr., Areson, J. G. 1977. Quantitative lung morphology in newborn mammals. *Respir. Physiol.* 29: 193–200

4. Bartlett, D. Jr., Remmers, J. E. 1971. Effects of high altitude exposure on the lungs of young rats. *Respir. Physiol.* 13:116–25

5. Berger, L. C., Burri, P. H. 1985. Timing of the quantitative recovery in the regenerating rat lung. *Am. Rev. Respir. Dis.* 132:777–83

6. Blomqvist, C. G., Saltin, B. 1983. Cardiovascular adaptations to physical training. *Ann. Rev. Physiol.* 45:169–89

7. Burri, P. H., Gehr, P., Müller, K., Weibel, E. R. 1976. Adaptation of the growing lung of increased $\dot{V}_{O_2}$. I. IDPN as inducer of hyperactivity. *Respir. Physiol.* 28:129–40

8. Burri, P. H., Pfrunder, H. B., Berger, L. C. 1982. Reactive changes in pulmonary parenchyma after bilobectomy: A scanning electron microscopic investigation. *Exp. Lung Res.* 4:11–28

9. Burri, P. H., Sehovic, S. 1979. The adaptive response of the rat lung after bilobectomy. *Am. Rev. Respir. Dis.* 119:769–77

10. Burri, P. H., Weibel, E. R. 1971. Morphometric estimation of pulmonary diffusion capacity. II. Effect of P_{O_2} on the growing lung. *Respir. Physiol.* 11: 247–64

11. Conley, K. E., Weibel, E. R., Taylor, C. R., Hoppeler, H. 1985. Aerobic capacity estimated by exercise vs. cold-exposure: Endurance training effects in rats. *Respir. Physiol.* 62:273–80

12. Federspiel, W. J., Sarelius, I. H. 1984. An examination of the contribution of red cell spacing to the uniformity of oxygen flux at the capillary wall. *Microvasc. Res.* 27:273–85

13. Gayeski, T. E. J., Honig, C. R. 1978. Myoglobin saturation and calculated p_{O_2} in single cells of resting gracilis muscles. *Adv. Exp. Med. Biol.* 94:77–84

14. Geelhaar, A., Weibel, E. R. 1971. Morphometric estimation of pulmonary diffusion capacity. III. The effect of increased oxygen consumption in Japanese waltzing mice. *Respir. Physiol.* 11:354–66

15. Gehr, P., Hugonnaud, C., Burri, P. H., Bachofen, H., Weibel, E. R. 1978. Adaptation of the growing lung to increased V_{O_2}. III. The effect of exposure to cold environment in rats. *Respir. Physiol.* 32:345–53

16. Gehr, P., Mwangi, D. K., Ammann, A., Maloiy, G. M. O., Taylor, C. R., Weibel, E. R. 1981. Design of mammalian respiratory system. V. Scaling morphometric pulmonary diffusing capacity to body mass: Wild and domestic mammals. *Respir. Physiol.* 44:61–86

17. Gehrig, H. 1951. Ueber tierexperimentelle Einwirkung von körperlicher Ueberanstrengung und sportlichem Training (Schwimmen) auf die Lungenmorphologie. Inauguraldissertation Med. Fak. Univ. Würzburg.

18. Heusner, A. A. 1982. Energy metabolism and body size. II. Dimensional analysis and energetic non-similarity. *Respir. Physiol.* 48:13–25

19. Heusner, A. A. 1983. Body size, energy metabolism and the lung. *J. Appl. Physiol.* 54:867–73

20. Hill, E. P., Power, G. G., Longo, L. D.

1977. Kinetics of O_2 and CO_2 exchange. In *Bioengineering Aspects of the Lung,* ed. J. B. West, pp. 459–514. New York: Dekker. 583 pp.

21. Hoppeler, H., Lindstedt, S. L. 1985. Malleability of skeletal muscle tissue in overcoming limitations: Structural elements. *J. Exp. Biol.* 115:355–64

22. Hoppeler, H., Mathieu, O., Weibel, E. R., Krauer, R., Lindstedt, S. L., Taylor, C. R. 1981. Design of mammalian respiratory system. VIII. Capillaries in skeletal muscles. *Respir. Physiol.* 44:129–50

23. Hugonnaud, C., Gehr, P., Weibel, E. R., Burri, P. G. 1977. Adaptation of the growing lung to increased oxygen consumption. II. Morphometric analysis. *Respir. Physiol.* 29:1–10

24. Jones, J. H., Lindstedt, S. L., Longworth, K. E., Karas, R. H., Taylor, C. R. 1985. Muscle respiration limits aerobic capacity of goats. *Physiologist* 28:342

25. Karas, R. H. 1984. Oxygen delivery during exercise: Limitations to maximal flow. PhD Thesis, Harvard Univ., Cambridge, Mass.

26. Kayar, S. R., Hoppeler, H., Howald, H., Claassen, H., Oberholzer, F. 1986. Acute effects of endurance exercise on mitochondrial distribution and skeletal muscle morphology. *Eur. J. Appl. Physiol.* 54:578–84

27. Krogh, A. 1919. The number and distribution of capillaries in muscles with calculations of the oxygen pressure head necessary for supplying the tissue. *J. Physiol.* 52:409–15

28. Langston, C., Sachdeva, P., Cowan, M. J., Haines, J., Crystal, R. G., Thurlbeck, W. M. 1977. Alveolar multiplication in the contralateral lung after unilateral pneumonectomy in the rabbit. *Am. Rev. Respir. Dis.* 115:7–13

29. Lechner, A. J., Grimes, M. S., Aquin, L., Banchero, N. 1982. Adaptive lung growth during chronic cold plus hypoxia is age-dependent. *J. Exp. Zool.* 219: 285–91

30. Lindstedt, S. L. 1984. Pulmonary transit time and diffusing capacity in mammals. *Am. J. Physiol.* 246:R384–88

31. Mathieu, O., Cruz-Orive, L. M., Hoppeler, H., Weibel, E. R. 1983. Estimating length density and quantifying anisotropy in skeletal muscle capillaries. *J. Microsc.* 131:131–46

32. Mathieu, O., Krauer, R., Hoppeler, H., Gehr, P., Lindstedt, S. L., et al. 1981. Design of the mammalian respiratory system. VII. Scaling mitochondrial

volume in skeletal muscle to body mass. *Respir. Physiol.* 44:113–28

33. Meyer, R. A., Sweeney, H. L., Kushmerick, M. J. 1984. A simple analysis of the "phosphocreatine shuttle". *Am. J. Physiol.* 246:C365–77

34. O'Neil, J. J., Leith, D. E. 1980. Lung diffusing capacity scaled in mammals from 25 g to 500 kg. *Fed. Proc.* 39: 972

35. Piiper, J. 1979. Series ventilation, diffusion in airways, and stratified inhomogeneity. *Fed. Proc.* 38:17–21

36. Rodriguez, M., Bur, S., Favre, A., Weibel, E. R. 1986. The pulmonary acinus: Geometry and morphometry of the peripheral airway system in rat and rabbit. *Am. J. Anat.* In press

37. Stahl, W. R. 1967. Scaling of respiratory variables in mammals. *J. Appl. Physiol.* 22:453–60

38. Taylor, C. R. 1986. Maximum oxidative potential and energetics. *Ann. Rev. Physiol.* 49:00–00

39. Taylor, C. R., Maloiy, G. M. O., Weibel, E. R., Langman, V. A., Kamau, J. M. Z., et al. 1981. Design of the mammalian respiratory system. III. Scaling maximum aerobic capacity to body mass: Wild and domestic mammals. *Respir. Physiol.* 44:25–37

40. Tenney, S. M., Remmers, J. E. 1963. Comparative quantitative morphology of mammalian lungs; diffusing areas. *Nature* 197:54–56

41. Thompson, M. E. 1980. Lung growth in response to altered metabolic demand in hamsters: Influence of thyroid function and cold exposure. *Respir. Physiol.* 40:335–47

42. Weibel, E. R. 1970/71. Morphometric estimation of pulmonary diffusion capacity. I. Model and method. *Respir. Physiol.* 11:54–75

43. Weibel, E. R. 1972. Morphometric estimation of pulmonary diffusion capacity. V. Comparative morphometry of alveolar lungs. *Respir. Physiol.* 14:26–43

44. Weibel, E. R. 1973. Morphological basis of alveolar-capillary gas exchange. *Physiol. Rev.* 53:419–95

45. Weibel, E. R. 1983. Is the lung built reasonably? *Am. Rev. Respir. Dis.* 128:752–60

46. Weibel, E. R. 1984. *The Pathway for Oxygen.* Cambridge, Mass.: Harvard Univ. Press. 425 pp.

47. Weibel, E. R., Taylor, C. R. 1981. Design of the mammalian respiratory system. *Respir. Physiol.* 44:1–164.

48. Weibel, E. R., Taylor, C. R., Gehr, P., Hoppeler, H., Mathieu, O., Maloiy, G. M. O. 1981. Design of the mammalian respiratory system. IX. Functional and structural limits for oxygen flow. *Respir. Physiol.* 44:151–64

49. Weibel, E. R., Taylor, C. R., O'Neil, J. J., Leith, D. E., Gehr, P., et al. 1983. Maximal oxygen consumption and pulmonary diffusing capacity: A direct comparison of physiologic and morphometric measurements in canids. *Respir. Physiol.* 54:173–88

CELL AND MOLECULAR PHYSIOLOGY

PHYSICAL FACTORS IN MEMBRANE FUNCTION

Introduction, Joseph F. Hoffman, *Section Editor*

The focus for this year's Cell and Molecular Physiology section is on physical aspects of membrane function. To this end, the chapters highlight new information on compositional, structural, and material characteristics of membranes that contribute to or underlie certain features of membrane function. It should be apparent that only a few aspects of this burgeoning subject could be reviewed here. It is also worth emphasizing that in concert with the technical advances that allow greater specification of membrane detail at the molecular level, go the integrative aspects of membranes that define the overall properties and functions of cells and organisms. The range and progression of the chapter topics in this section represent an attempt to illustrate this latter point. These themes will undoubtedly be expanded upon in future years.

Readers of previous volumes of the *Annual Review of Physiology* will note that the present section's name has been changed by substituting the word molecular for membrane. There were many reasons for this alteration, but since the primary mission of this section is to survey cellular and subcellular aspects of physiology, it was felt that the new title is more general and better reflects contemporary developments.

Ann. Rev. Physiol. 1987. 49:163–75

LATERAL DIFFUSION OF PROTEINS IN MEMBRANES

Ken Jacobson, Akira Ishihara, and Richard Inman

Laboratories for Cell Biology, Department of Anatomy, and Cancer Research Center, School of Medicine, University of North Carolina at Chapel Hill, Chapel Hill, North Carolina 27514

INTRODUCTION

Numerous measurements of protein lateral diffusion in membranes have been made over the last decade. In most cases, proteins were found to diffuse at considerably lower rates than those seen in artificial membranes. The purpose of this brief review is to examine recent progress, based on biological and biophysical technical developments, in determining the constraints to the "free" lateral diffusion of proteins in animal cell membranes. In most cases, examples are drawn from data on plasma membrane diffusion obtained by techniques using fluorescence recovery after photobleaching (FRAP). However, some of the conclusions from these studies probably apply to the membranes of other organelles as well. The important issue of the relationship of lateral diffusion to biological function is not treated here but has been recently reviewed (5, 24).

CLASSIFICATION OF CONSTRAINTS TO LATERAL DIFFUSION

This review focuses on the ways "free" lateral diffusion is restrained in biomembranes. We define "free" diffusion of proteins as the rate of lateral isotropic diffusion in a fluid lipid bilayer in which the particular protein in question and any other proteins are present in dilute concentrations. We also consider free diffusion to mean that the entire membrane in question can be visited by a particular diffusant via diffusional transport, i.e. there are no

163

0066-4278/87/0315-0163$02.00-000

excluded domains. Lateral diffusion of proteins may be restrained relative to free lateral diffusion in several ways. First, the actual rate of lateral diffusion may be *slower* than free diffusion. This may result from two main causes: (*a*) the concentration of protein may be sufficient to impede diffusion by increasing the overall membrane viscosity and/or by restricting diffusion paths through an excluded volume effect. (*b*) Membrane proteins may interact with structures peripheral to the plasma membrane: the membrane-associated cytoskeleton on the cytoplasmic face of the membrane and the extracellular matrix on the outer surface of the membrane.

Second, lateral protein diffusion may be restricted in the sense that particular proteins may be confined to certain domains of the membrane. Finally, protein lateral diffusion may be constrained such that certain directions for diffusive motions are more probable; that is, lateral diffusion may not be a simple isotropic process.

PROTEIN LATERAL DIFFUSION IS SLOWER IN BIOMEMBRANES THAN IN RECONSTITUTED BILAYERS

General Results

A set of experimental lateral diffusion results for several membrane components in both natural and reconstituted artificial membranes is given in Table 1. Lipid probe diffusion is generally rapid and fluorescence recovery complete in cell membranes, although exceptions exist in more specialized cells, such as eggs (43). The rate of diffusion of glycoproteins (e.g. GP80, band 3) in cell membranes is typically much slower than that observed when the protein is reconstituted into artificial bilayers. In addition, the mobile fraction is often appreciably less than 100%. Such results indicate that some structure(s) peripheral to the bilayer determines the diffusion rates of membrane-spanning glycoproteins. Rhodopsin, which is found in the disc membrane, appears to be an exception: Its rapid diffusion (30) suggests that factors intrinsic to the bilayer (e.g. protein concentration and lipid composition) determine its diffusion rate.

Unlike most membrane-spanning proteins, Thy-1, a glycoprotein antigen, is apparently intercalated into the plasma membrane bilayer by a newly discovered phosphatidylinositol "tail" (23, 39). Since Thy-1 is anchored to the membrane by its glycophospholipid tail, its diffusion is expected to be rapid (42). In fibroblasts it's diffusion is as rapid as that of a fluorescent phospholipid analog (A. Ishihara et al, Reference 15a) and is nearly 40 times faster than that of GP80 (17). Thus, the FRAP result indirectly confirms the novel lipid-linked structure of Thy-1 and indicates that the glycoprotein moiety together with the bound monoclonal antibody tag does not appreciably

Table 1 Lateral diffusion in artificial and cell membranes

Probe	Biological system	Artificial Bilayer membrane		Cell membrane		
		$(D \times 10^{10} \text{ cm}^2/\text{sec})$	mobile fraction (%)	$(D \times 10^{10} \text{ cm}^2/\text{sec})$	mobile fraction (%)	Reference
Dihexadecylindocarbo cyanine (a lipid analog)	Human and murine fi- broblast plasma mem- brane	400	100	100–140	> 90	(16, 17)
Thy-1 antigen	Fibroblasts and lymphoid cells	—	—	20–50	~ 50	(15a, 42)
Rhodopsin	Disc membranes of rod outer segment	200	≳ 95%	40	n.a.	(40, 38 and references therein)
GP80	Murine fibroblast plasma membrane	100–300[a]	~ 100[a]	1.2	70	(17)
Band 3	Erythrocyte	100–200	≳ 95%	0.5	~ 10	(6, 13, 34)

[a]Experiment not actually performed; these values were estimated from other experiments with transmembrane glycoproteins reconstituted into liposomal membranes (40).

hinder the diffusion rate of the mobile fraction of Thy-1 via interaction with the glycocalyx.

Increased Membrane Protein Concentration Decreases Membrane Lateral Diffusion Coefficients

EXPERIMENTAL RESULTS   The effect of protein concentration on the bacteriorhodopsin lateral diffusion coefficient (D) has been explored (28, 40): D was found to decrease with increasing amounts of bacteriorhodopsin reconstituted into dimyristoyl phosphatidylcholine liposomes. This effect has also been shown in the inner membrane of the mitochondrion using freeze fracture relaxation after electrophoresis (37). As the surface density of intramembraneous particles (IMPs) decreased from 6400 to 2400 μm^{-2}, the lateral diffusion coefficient of the IMPs increased from 1.3×10^{-10} to 3.5×10^{-9} cm^2/sec. Recently detailed FRAP studies (B. Chazotte & C. Hackenbrock, unpublished results) were performed with inner mitochondrial membranes diluted by fusion with pure lipid vesicles. Both the lipid and protein (Complex III) diffusion coefficients rose from 4×10^{-9} and 7×10^{-10} cm^2/sec, respectively, in the native inner membrane to about 1.3×10^{-8} cm^2/sec for both lipid and protein when lipid enrichments of 700% were obtained by the fusion process. The latter value presumably approaches the "free" lateral diffusion coefficient.

THEORETICAL TREATMENTS   The reduction in diffusion due to increased protein concentration can be qualitatively predicted by various theoretical treatments, but thorough tests have not been performed. In one view, proteins and lipids percolate through an archipelago of static protein complexes, and reduction in the rate of diffusion is related to a decrease in the fraction of the membrane area that is fluid lipid (33). In the milling crowd model simulations of obstructed diffusion (12), the effective lateral diffusion coefficient is calculated with the assumption that jumps to certain sites are prevented by randomly placed, static obstacles (proteins) of various sizes. While these obstacles have little effect on the short range diffusion (over several lattice sites), the long range diffusion coefficient is diminished as obstacle area increases. These results are consistent with the observation that lipid analogue probes in the membranes of erthrocytes diffuse faster over short distances (several nanometers) than over large distances (~1 micrometer), where diffusion is retarded by numerous membrane proteins (12). For a constant total obstacle area, the diminution is greater for smaller obstacle size. The latter result is not predicted by continuum percolation theories (33). Although these calculations were applied to the movement of lipids, the same considerations are expected to apply to proteins. Monte Carlo simulations of the translational movements of a protein in a two-dimensional protein gas also indicate that protein diffusion will be impeded by steric interactions with other proteins. For proteins of ~45 kd, diffusion is reduced by factors of about 5 and 20 when proteins occupy 55 and 82% of the lattice surface area (29), respectively.

One possible functional role of spatially varying protein concentrations was suggested by the recent calculations of J. Eisinger & B. Halperin (12a). This treatment shows that if the concentration of protein proximate to a trap, e.g. a coated pit, drops enough to increase the lateral diffusion coefficient of a selected receptor by an order of magnitude, the mean capture-time for the receptor can be reduced by a factor of ten. Such a local effect could dramatically accelerate the accumulation of ligand-receptor complexes into coated pits.

Peripheral Structure Restrains the Free Lateral Diffusion of Membrane Proteins

MEMBRANE-ASSOCIATED CYTOSKELETON   Earlier evidence clearly implicated the spectrin-actin-ankryin connection in severely retarding band 3 lateral mobility in the erythrocyte plasma membrane. Certain agents (e.g. polyphosphates) and conditions (e.g. low ionic strength or high temperature) that destabilize the submembraneous spectrin-actin protein matrix of normal erythrocytes also increase the lateral mobility of the band 3 integral membrane proteins, whereas the lateral diffusion rates of membrane lipids are largely unaffected (13). Moreover, band 3 diffusion rates were some 50 times higher in spectrin-deficient spherocytic mouse erythrocytes than in normal mouse red cells (34). In addition, protein diffusion in membrane blebs induced on lymphocytes, fibroblasts, or myoblasts was greatly increased compared with that in unperturbed cell surface membranes (38). Actin-specific fluorescent labels showed that the blebs were largely devoid of membrane-associated microfilaments, which suggests that structures peripheral to the plasma membrane govern the rates of lateral diffusion of surface membrane glycoproteins.

The subjacent spectrin meshwork does not always determine the lateral mobility of membrane proteins, however. For example, when the spectrin network in mouse fibroblasts is seen to be aggregated following microinjection of antispectrin antibodies, there is no change in GP80 lateral diffusion (P. Mangeat et al, unpublished observations).

SEMIQUANTITATIVE MODELS FOR PERIPHERAL CONSTRAINTS   Several semiquantitative models have been invoked to explain how peripheral structure might impede diffusion. These models involve either steric or specific interactions of the portion(s) of the protein protruding from the bilayer with the peripheral structure in question. To explain the slow diffusion of band 3 in the erythrocyte membrane, Koppel et al (21) calculated an effective viscosity of the membrane-associated cytoskeleton of about 450 surface poise. This model assumes that the cytoskeleton sterically traps band 3 into small "corrals" via interactions with the protein's cytoplasmic domain and that the cytoskeleton is labile such that occasional breaks in the matrix allow the slow lateral transport of band 3.

Jacobson et al (17) proposed that the lateral diffusion of some membrane proteins can be described by two populations of diffusing species: one that is rapidly exchanged with a large set of peripheral binding elements via relatively nonspecific mechanisms and another that is slowly exchanged with another set of binding elements. According to the model, the latter gives rise to the immobile fraction and the former is responsible for the observed slow diffusion rates. Jacobson et al envisioned these proteins diffusing through a bilayer set on a square lattice composed of peripheral binding sites. Via rapid diffusion through the bilayer, the protein would visit these sites for "dwell" times that are short (<1 sec) compared to the half-time for fluorescence recovery. Such a process would give rise to the measured low lateral diffusion coefficient for the glycoprotein.

MOLECULAR ORIGIN OF PERIPHERAL RESTRAINTS TO LATERAL DIFFUSION   Site-directed mutagenesis of cloned genes for membrane proteins followed by expression of the altered genes in cultured cells offers a new way to determine which parts of the protein critically affect its rate of lateral diffusion. Initial results using this approach are summarized in Table 2. Deletions in the 31-residue cytoplasmic domain of the H-2 antigen down to as few as 4 residues have little effect on the antigen's lateral diffusion rate in the plasma membrane of murine fibroblasts, although that of the mobile fraction is depressed slightly (11). Recently this finding was confirmed and extended in experiments using mutants of the epidermal growth factor receptor. Livneh and coworkers (22) showed that deletions of the large (542-residue) cytoplasmic domain down to as few as 9 residues did not affect the lateral diffusion of the epidermal growth factor receptor but did reduce its rate of receptor-mediated endocytosis. At this juncture, several possible interpretations of these two experiments exist: (a) The residual amino acids in the cytoplasmic domain are critical for interaction with the membrane-associated cytoskeleton. (b) The membrane protein interacts laterally with an unknown protein in the membrane whose diffusion is slow. (c) The protein is restrained by interactions with the extracellular matrix or with elements within the membrane, so mutations in the cytoplasmic domain do not affect the rate of lateral diffusion.

However, studies with mutant vesicular stomatitus virus (VSV) G glycoproteins expressed in COS-1 cells found that when the normal wild-type G glycoprotein cytoplasmic domain (29 residues) was replaced with a mutant

Table 2   Effect of cytoplasmic domain mutations on the lateral diffusion of membrane proteins

Protein	Cell type	Mutation	Length of cytoplasmic domain	D (cm^2/sec)	Mobile fraction (%)	Reference
H-2	Mouse cells	wild-type	31	1.2×10^{-9}	31	11
		mutant	4	1.5×10^{-9}	~20	
EGF receptor	COS-1	wild-type	542	1.2×10^{-10}	61	22
		mutant	9	1.2×10^{-10}	77	
VSV "G" protein	COS-1	wild-type	29	0.8×10^{-10}	~75	
		mutant[a]	3	2×10^{-10}	~66	Scullion et al, unpublished

[a]wild-type cytoplasmic domain deleted and replaced with 3-residue Ig domain (1ys-val-lys).

cytoplasmic domain consisting of the three-residue (lys-val-lys) cytoplasmic domain from surface immunoglobulin (31), the diffusion coefficient of this mutant glycoprotein increased, while the immobile fraction was decreased slightly relative to the wild-type G glycoprotein (B. F. Scullion et al, unpublished observations). The diffusion coefficient of the mutant "G" is near that of surface immunoglobulin in the lymphocyte plasma membrane (8).

Specific connections of some membrane glycoproteins to the extracellular matrix have recently been discovered. Such connections may be partly responsible for the slow diffusion and the immobile fraction observed for many membrane proteins. For example, GP80 of murine fibroblasts coimmunoprecipitates with a chondroitin sulfate glycosaminoglycan found on the cell surface that is presumably linked to a proteoglycan. This putative proteoglycan codistributes with GP80 in motile cells (P. D'Souza et al, unpublished observations). Heparan surface proteoglycan is associated with aggregated acetylcholine receptors in muscle cells (3). In addition, plasma membrane receptors for laminin (32) and, most recently, fibronectin (1, 15), both prominant extracellular matrix components, were found and characterized. Wier & Edidin (41) report that the mobile fraction of murine histocompatibility antigens was decreased in confluent cells. This decrease was also seen when fresh cells were plated on extracellular matrix derived from confluent cells. However, the specific components responsible for immobilizing the antigen could not be identified.

In summary, important new information about the determinants of lateral diffusion of membrane glycoproteins has accumulated, but general rules have not yet emerged. The diversity of these results suggests that the determinants for each protein may differ and may depend on individual structure-function relationships.

LATERAL CONFINEMENT OF PROTEINS TO DOMAINS

How are certain proteins restricted to discrete regions of the plasma membranes of specialized cells and cells organized into tissue? Here we focus briefly on the confinement of proteins to fairly large regions and ignore local specializations such as coated pits, focal contacts, and gap junctions.

In sperm, for example, a particular glycoprotein antigen (PT-1) is confined to the posterior tail region prior to fertilization (25). A band of IMPs separates the posterior and anterior tail regions, which suggests that a physical barrier confines at least some of the antigens to the posterior tail region. Within the tail domain PT-1 undergoes rapid diffusion with a very high mobile fraction (> 90%) (26).

Sodium channels in the membranes of cultured neurons display differential lateral mobility (as measured by FRAP using fluorescently labelled neurotoxins) depending on which morphological region of these cells is examined (4). Over the cell body, diffusion of the Na^+ channels is rapid ($D \approx 10^{-9}$ cm^2/sec) and recovery is nearly complete. However, over the hillock region the Na^+ channels exhibit reduced mobility ($D \approx 10^{-10}$ cm^2/sec), and 60% are immobilized. The channels are essentially immobile at the presynaptic ending.

In epithelia, many components are localized specifically to either the apical or basolateral domain (see, for example, 2, 35), which gives the cell its required functional polarity. At issue is how this polarity is generated and maintained. After experimental dissociation of the tissue into cells, the apical and basolateral proteins of epithelial cell membranes are observed to intermix. In dissociated intestinal epithelial cells, two apical enzymes, alkaline phosphatase and leucine aminopeptidase, were found to be redistributed in the cell membrane via lateral diffusion, although remnants of tight junctions remained in the isolated cells (44). Conversely, mouse H-2 histocompatibility antigens were confined to the basolateral surface of several epithelial cell types until dissociation of the tight junctions; after dissociation they migrated to the apical surface (27).

Apparently, at least some epithelial cell membrane proteins can diffuse within their respective domains. For example, 50% of the Na,K-ATPase in cultured dog kidney (MDCK) cells exhibited a lateral diffusion coefficient of $\sim 5 \times 10^{-10}$ cm^2/sec when the enzyme was confined to the basolateral surface; the remaining 50% were immobile (18). However, lectins bound to MDCK cell surfaces appeared to be fully immobilized, yet they were somehow transported from the apical to basolateral surface when the cells were fully dissociated (8).

Several schemes for maintaining polarity have been proposed (2). The proposed physical confinement mechanisms include (*a*) the tight junction, which would serve as a physical barrier separating the apical and basolateral domains; and (*b*) cytoskeletal attachments, which would immobilize proteins within certain domains. Cellular metabolism has also been suggested to play a role in maintenance of polarity. Clearly, these mechanisms need not be mutually exclusive, and as yet the evidence is not overwhelming in favor of any one.

The idea that tight junctions act as a physical barrier is attractive in its simplicity and is consistent with the evidence. However, the cell dissociation experiments do not prove this mechanism because such dissociation disrupts other cell-cell junctions and interactions as well (14). The cytoskeletal anchorage model is supported by recent evidence (9) showing the colocalization of a band 3 analog with ankyrin analogs and nonerythrocyte spectrin in the basolateral surface of rat kidney cells. The latter cytoskeletal proteins form a meshwork that nearly completely immobilizes band 3 proteins in the erythrocyte cell membrane (see above). Yet, since apparently some proteins such as the Na,K-ATPase can diffuse within their respective domains, the cytoskeletal anchoring mechanism cannot apply to all membrane proteins. The involvement of cell metabolism in maintaining polarity (10) is plausible but somewhat weakly supported. For example, Ziomek et al (44) discount the importance of tight junctions because remnants of them exist in dissociated cells in which the apical marker spreads over the entire cell. But diffusion paths may exist only where these remnant junctions are broken. If, in fact, metabolic energy is used to maintain polarity, it could be accomplished by endocytosis of membrane proteins that had diffused out of the proper domain followed by directed recycling of the endocytotic vesicles to the original membrane domain. Alternatively, a localized membrane protein distribution might be maintained by continual insertion of protein into the domain to balance that lost by diffusion and subsequent degradation beyond the domain boundary. Almers & Stirling (2) argue that the diffusion coefficients are too rapid and the turnover rates are too slow for this latter scheme to be a viable polarity maintenance mechanism.

IS LATERAL DIFFUSION ISOTROPIC? Spatial Details of the Fluorescence Recovery Process

Lateral mobility may be constrained in that all directions of diffusion are not equally likely. In addition, bulk flows within the membrane may convey components laterally. Imaging methods combined with photobleaching can yield detailed information on such lateral transport processes. In spot photobleaching, fluorescence detection is normally done by a photomultiplier, so that unless the laser beam (20) or stage is scanned, no spatial information on the recovery process can be obtained. In the "video-FRAP" technique, the photomultiplier is replaced by a very sensitive video camera, which is calibrated to operate as a time-resolved (30-ms-resolution) spatial photometer (19). Thus, spatial information on the fluorescence redistribution process is obtained. Recent work using this technique challenges an earlier study by pattern photobleaching that indicated that membrane glycoprotein diffusion may be anisotropic (36). In particular, the earlier work found that diffusion of lectin receptors was effectively channeled and that the fastest diffusion occurred in the direction of stress fibers underlying the plasma membrane. However, the video-FRAP experiments indicated that lipid analog diffusion in model and cellular membranes was isotropic. Lectin (wheat germ agglutinin and concanavalin A) receptor diffusion also appeared isotropic, and there was no evidence that diffusion channels were formed parallel to subjacent stress fibers. Recent advances in the analysis of such data promise to be of great utility: The spatial Fourier transform of the image after photobleaching can be calculated, and each spatial frequency of this transform can be "aged" by multiplying it by a factor that describes the suspected lateral transport process (e.g. isotropic diffusion, anisotropic diffusion, flow). The effect of aging by a known process can then be compared to the redistribution measured after a specific time, by inverting the "aged" transform to give back the simulated image at that time. Such analysis (R. Inman et al, unpublished results) indicates that the lateral diffusion of GP80 in mouse fibroblast plasma membranes is most conservatively interpreted as an isotropic process on the distance scale of these measurements ($\sim$1 μm). This does not mean that anisotropic transport does not exist on smaller or larger distance scales. However, it is entirely plausible that the basic mode of lateral transport in cell membranes is isotropic diffusion and that gross lateral position is determined by the position of "sources" (i.e. sites of membrane insertion) and "sinks or traps" (24) for particular membrane components (e.g. receptor plaques and coated pits).

SUMMARY

Membrane protein lateral diffusion can be constrained in several ways: Diffusion can be slower than that predicted for a simple, fluid lipid bilayer; diffusion can be confined to certain regions within the total membrane; and diffusion may not be equally probable in all directions, i.e. it may be anisotropic. We know that protein diffusion is reduced by increasing concentrations of membrane proteins and by interactions of the diffusant with structure(s) peripheral to the membrane. The molecular nature of such peripheral constraints has been difficult to pinpoint, but attention is now being directed to the extracellular matrix in addition to the membrane-associated cytoskeleton. There are many proteins that are confined to lateral domains in differentiated, isolated cells and in cells organized into tissue. The mechanisms that maintain such inhomogeneous distributions should be elucidated in the next few years. Whether lateral diffusion of membrane proteins over distances of a few micrometers is usually isotropic or anisotropic will be ascertained in the near future using imaging methods combined with photobleaching.

ACKNOWLEDGMENTS

The preparation of this manuscript was supported, in part, by American Cancer Society Grant CD181A. We thank Dr. J. Eisinger for his helpful comments on this work.

Literature Cited

1. Akiyama, S., Yamada, S., Yasmada, K. 1986. Characterization of a 140-kD avian cell surface antigen as a fibronectin-binding molecule. *J. Cell Biol.* 102:442–48
2. Almers, W., Stirling, C. 1984. Distribution of transport proteins over animal cell membranes. *J. Membr. Biol.* 77:169–86
3. Anderson, M. J., Fambrough, D. M. 1983. Aggregates of acetylcholine are associated with plaques of a basal lamina, heparan sulfate proteoglycan on the surface of skeletal muscle fibers. *J. Cell Biol.* 97:1396–1411
4. Angelides, K., Elmer, L., Loftus, D., Elson, E. 1986. Diffusion and regionalization of voltage-dependent sodium channels in neuronal cells. *J. Cell Biol.* In press
5. Axelrod, D. 1983. Lateral motion of membrane proteins and biological function. *J. Membr. Biol.* 75:1–10
6. Chang, C.-H., Takeuchi, H., Ito, T., Machida, K., Ohnishi, S. 1981. Lateral mobility of erythrocyte membrane proteins studied by the fluorescence photobleaching recovery technique. *J. Biochem.* 90:997–1004
7. Dragsten, P., Handler, J., Blumenthal, R. 1982. Fluorescent membrane probes and the mechanism of maintenance of cellular asymmetry in epithelia. *Fed. Proc.* 41:48–53

8. Dragsten, P., Henkart, P., Blumenthal, R., Weinstein, J., Schlessinger, J. 1979. Lateral diffusion of surface immunoglobulin, Thy-1 antigen and a lipid probe in lymphocyte plasma membrane. *Proc. Natl. Acad. Sci. USA* 76:5163–67
9. Drenckhahn, D., Schlüter, K., Allen, D. P., Bennett, V. 1985. Colocalization of band 3 with ankyrin and spectrin at the basal membrane of intercalated cells in the rat kidney. *Science* 230:1287–89
10. Edidin, M. 1984. Tissue architecture and lateral diffusion. Comments. *Mol. Cell. Biophys.* 2:285–93
11. Edidin, M., Zuniga, M. 1984. Lateral diffusion of wild-type and mutant L^d antigens in L-cells. *J. Cell Biol.* 99:2333–35
12. Eisinger, J., Flores, J., Petersen, W. 1986. A milling crowd model for local and long-range obstructed lateral diffusion-mobility of excimeric probes in the membrane of intact erythrocytes. *Biophys. J.* 49:987–1001
12a. Eisinger, J., Halperin, B. 1986. Effect of spatial variation in membrane diffusibility and solubility on the lateral transport of membrane components. *Biophys. J.* 50:513–21
13. Golan, D., Veatch, W. 1980. Lateral mobility of band 3 in the human erythrocyte membrane studied by fluorescence

photobleaching recovery: Evidence for control by cytoskeletal interactions. *Proc. Natl. Acad. Sci. USA* 77:2537–41

14. Gumbiner, B., Louvard, D. 1985. Localized barriers in the plasma membrane: A common way to form domains. *Trends Biochem. Sci.* 10:435–38

15. Horwitz, A., Duggan, R., Greggs, R., Decker, C., Buck, C. 1985. The cell substrate attachment (CSAT) antigen has properties of a receptor for laminin and fibronectin. *J. Cell Biol.* 101:2134–44

15a. Ishihara, A., Hou, Y., Jacobson, K. 1987. The Thy-1 antigen exhibits rapid lateral diffusion in the plasma membrane of rodent lymphoid cells and fibroblasts. *Proc. Natl. Acad. Sci. USA* In press

16. Jacobson, K., Hou, Y., Derzko, Z., Wojcieszyn, J., Organisciak, D. 1981. Lipid lateral diffusion in the surface membrane of cells and in multibilayers formed from plasma membrane lipids. *Biochemistry* 20:5268–75

17. Jacobson, K., O'Dell, D., August, J. 1984. Lateral diffusion of an 80,000-dalton glycoprotein in the plasma membrane of murine fibroblasts: Relationships to cell structure and function. *J. Cell Biol.* 99:1624–33

18. Jesaitis, A., Yguerabide, J. 1986. The lateral mobility of the (Na$^+$, K$^+$)-dependent ATPase in Madin-Darby canine kidney cells. *J. Cell Biol.* 102: 1256–63

19. Kapitza, H., McGregor, G., Jacobson, K. 1985. Direct measurement of lateral transport in membranes by using time-resolved spatial photometry. *Proc. Natl. Acad. Sci. USA.* 82:4122–126

20. Koppel, D. E. 1979. Fluorescence redistribution after photobleaching. A new multipoint analysis of membrane translational dynamics. *Biophys. J.* 28: 281–92

21. Koppel, D. E., Sheetz, M. P., Schindler, M. 1981. Matrix control of protein diffusion in biological membranes. *Proc. Natl. Acad. Sci. USA* 78:3576–80

22. Livneh, E., Benveniste, M., Prywes, R., Felder, S., Kam, Z., Schlessinger, J. 1986. Large deletions in the cytoplasmic kinase domain of the EGF-receptor do not affect its lateral mobility. *J. Cell Biol.* 103:327–31

23. Low, M., Kincade, P. 1985. Phosphatidylinositol is the membrane-anchoring domain of the Thy-1 glycoprotein. *Nature* 318:62–64

24. McCloskey, M., Poo, M. 1984. Protein diffusion in cell membranes: Some biological implications. *Int. Rev. Cytol.* 87:19–81

25. Myles, D., Primakoff, P. 1984. Localized surface antigens of guinea pig sperm migrate to new regions prior to fertilization. *J. Cell Biol.* 99:1634–41

26. Myles, D., Primakoff, P., Koppel, D. 1984. A localized surface protein of guinea pig sperm exhibits free diffusion in its domain. *J. Cell Biol.* 98:1095–9

27. Parr, E. L., Kirby, W. N. 1979. An immunoferritin labeling study of W-2 antigens on dissociated epithelial cells. *J. Histochem. Cytochem.* 27:1327–36

28. Peters, R., Cherry, R. 1982. Lateral and rotational diffusion of bacteriorhodopsin in lipid bilayers: Experimental test of the Saffman-Delbrück equations. *Proc. Natl. Acad. Sci. USA* 19:4317–21

29. Pink, D. 1985. Protein lateral movement in lipid bilayers. Simulation studies of its dependence upon protein concentration. *Biochim. Biophys. Acta* 818:200–4

30. Poo, M.-M., Cone, R. 1974. Lateral diffusion of rhodopsin in the photoreceptor membrane. *Nature* 247:438–41

31. Puddington, L., Machamer, C., Rose, J., 1985. Cytoplasmic domains of cellular and viral integral membrane proteins substitute for the cytoplasmic domain of the vesicular stomatitis virus glycoprotein in transport to the plasma membrane. *J. Cell Biol.* 102:2147–57

32. Rao, N., Barsky, S., Terranova, V., Liotta, L. 1983. Isolation of a tumor cell laminin receptor. *Biochem. Biophys. Res. Commun.* 111:804–8

33. Saxton, M. 1982. Lateral diffusion in an archipelago. Effects of impermeable patches on diffusion in a cell membrane. *Biophys. J.* 39:165–73

34. Sheetz, M., Schindler, M., Koppel, D. 1980. Lateral mobility of integral membrane proteins is increased in spherocytic erythrocytes. *Nature* 285:510–12

35. Simons, K., Fuller, S. 1985. Cell surface polarity in epithelia. *Ann. Rev. Cell Biol.* 1:243–88

36. Smith, B., Clark, W., McConnell, H. 1979. Anisotropic molecular motion on cell surfaces. *Proc. Natl. Acad. Sci. USA* 76:5641–44

37. Sowers, A., Hackenbrock, C. 1985. Variation in protein lateral diffusion coefficients is related to variation in protein concentration found in mitochondrial inner membranes. *Biochem. Biophys. Acta* 821:85–90

38. Tank, D. W., Wu, E.-S., Webb, W. W. 1982. Enhanced molecular diffusibility in muscle membrane blebs: Release of lateral constraints. *J. Cell Biol.* 92:207–12

39. Tse, A., Barclay, A., Watts, A., Wil-

liams, A. 1985. A glycophospholipid tail at the carboxyl terminus of the Thy-1 glycoprotein of neurons and thymocytes. *Science* 230:1003–8

40. Vaz, W., Goodsaid-Zalduondo, F., Jacobson, K. 1984. Lateral diffusion of lipids and proteins in bilayer membranes. *FEBS Lett.* 174:199–207

41. Wier, M., Edidin, M. 1986. Effects of cell density and extracellular matrix on the lateral diffusion of major histocompatibility antigens in cultured fibroblasts. *J. Cell Biol.* 103:215–22

42. Woda, B., Gilman, S. 1983. Lateral mobility and capping of rat lymphocyte membrane proteins. *Cell Biol. Int. Rep.* 7:203–9

43. Wolf, D., Kinsey, W., Lennart, W., Edidin, M. 1981. Changes in the organization of the sea urchin egg plasma membrane upon fertilization: Indications from the lateral diffusion rates of lipid-soluble fluorescent dyes. *Dev. Biol.* 81:133–38

44. Ziomek, C., Schulman, S., Edidin, M. 1980. Redistribution of membrane proteins in isolated mouse intestinal epithelial cells. *J. Cell Biol.* 86:849–57

Ann. Rev. Physiol. 1987. 49:177–92

RED CELL DEFORMABILITY AND ITS RELEVANCE TO BLOOD FLOW

Shu Chien

Division of Circulatory Physiology and Biophysics, Department of Physiology and Cellular Biophysics, Columbia University College of Physicians and Surgeons, New York, New York 10032

INTRODUCTION

The resistance to blood flow is a function of the rheological properties of blood as well as the geometric features of blood vessels. While circulatory investigations generally aim at studying the functions of the heart and blood vessels, there is an increasing realization that blood rheology can also play a significant role in circulatory regulation in health and disease (10, 11). The principal factors determining blood viscosity are hematocrit, plasma viscosity, cell aggregation, and cell deformability (8). This review focuses on the role of the deformability of the red blood cell (RBC) in circulatory regulation under physiological and pathophysiological conditions.[1]

Deformability is a relatively general term that describes the ability of a body (RBCs in this case) to change its shape in response to a deforming force. RBC deformation (or strain) can involve a change in cell curvature, a uniaxial deformation, or area expansion (3, 33). The deforming stress (force per unit area) is usually applied from outside the cell, e.g. by fluid shear stress or local membrane aspiration, but it can also originate from within the cell, e.g. RBC swelling in hypotonic medium or fiber formation in deoxygenated sickle cells. The extent, rate, and mode of deformation depend on the magnitude, rate, and direction of the stress. Therefore, the stress-strain (and stress-strain rate) relationships are complex and cannot be described by a single deformability parameter.

---

[1]This review is based primarily on papers published during the past five years. Because of space limitation, the literature citation is incomplete, and the author apologizes for many omissions. The unpublished studies are supported by NHLBI Grant HL16851.

177

0066-4278/87/0315-0177$02.00

Furthermore, the ability of RBCs to deform involves several factors, including (a) the geometric features of the cell, (b) the rheological properties of the intracellular fluid, and (c) the rheological properties of the cell membrane, as well as the interactions of these components. Various methods of measuring RBC deformability may have differential sensitivities for these parameters and hence may yield different results (9).

DETERMINANTS OF RED CELL DEFORMABILITY

Red Cell Geometry

The normal human RBC at rest has a biconcave discoid shape with a major diameter of ~8 μm and a mean cell volume (CV) of ~90 fl. The mean surface area (SA) of the cell is ~140 μm^2, which is considerably greater than the 97 μm^2 required to enclose a sphere with a volume of 90 fl. This excess surface area is a major factor in allowing the RBC to deform uniaxially at constant SA and CV under a variety of physiological conditions, including its deformation during transit through narrow capillaries and passage through the thin slits of splenic sinusoids. The geometry of RBCs varies with cell age. The dense fraction, which is mainly composed of older cells, has smaller mean values for CV and SA; the light fraction, which consists of primarily young cells, has larger mean values for CV and SA (40). The RBCs of neonates have larger CV and SA than the RBCs of adults (41).

Rheological Properties of Intracellular Fluid

The rheological properties of the intracellular fluid of RBCs are dominated by the concentration and physicochemical properties of the hemoglobin. At the normal mean corpuscular hemoglobin concentration (MCHC) of ~32 g/dl, the intracellular fluid viscosity (η_i) is ~7 millipascal-sec (mPa-s), and it has no elastic behavior. η_i rises with MCHC in a nonlinear fashion: It is nearly quadrupled at an MCHC of 40 g/dl.

Rheological Properties of RBC Membrane

The biochemical anatomy of the RBC membrane, which is reviewed elsewhere in this volume (62), forms the molecular basis of its biophysical properties, which are also treated in this volume (33). The membrane bending stiffness is probably important in small deformations and in resting shape changes (e.g. echinocyte-stomatocyte transformation). The membrane shear elastic modulus plays a major role in uniaxial deformation of RBCs at constant SA. The steady-state shape change of normal RBCs during flow in narrow vessels can be simulated by the finite element method by using the available data on bending stiffness and shear modulus (64). The time constant of the dynamic shape change of RBCs, e.g. during entry into a narrow channel, is a function of the ratio of membrane viscosity to shear modulus. The membrane dilatational modulus and viscoplastic properties are relevant to very strong deformation near membrane breakdown, e.g. in cell swelling and uniaxial stretching beyond the yield point, respectively.

MEASUREMENT OF RED CELL DEFORMABILITY

The deformability characteristics of the RBC are derived from measurements on the stress-strain relationship. The deforming stress can be applied in a variety of ways (9); the most common modes are the shear stress applied in a relatively unrestricted geometry and the aspiration pressure applied via a narrow channel. The resulting RBC deformation is then determined either by direct microscopic measurements or indirect estimations.

Measurement of Red Cell Deformability in Narrow Channels

MICROPIPETTE ASPIRATION   As discussed elsewhere in this volume (33), the micropipette aspiration technique, in which the stress-strain relationship is studied on a small portion of the RBC, can be used to derive a variety of rheological properties of the RBC membrane, including the shear elastic modulus and surface viscosity. In such small deformations involving only a fraction of the excess SA in normal RBCs, cell geometric factors are usually not important. The contribution of η_i to the viscous behavior of the cell is also insignificant unless it is markedly elevated (31, 73).

FILTER ASPIRATION   Polycarbonate sieves with pore diameters less than 1 μm have also been used to determine RBC membrane elastic modulus by pressure aspiration (1). The degree of deformation (tongue length/pore diameter) is determined by scanning electron microscopic examination. Because this is a static measurement, it does not allow measurement of membrane viscosity.

Measurement of Red Cell Deformability in Channels Allowing Whole Cell Passage

MICROPIPETTE ASPIRATION OF WHOLE CELLS   By using micropipettes with diameters $\geq$ 3 μm, the entire RBC can be aspirated. The deformability of the whole cell can be estimated from the pressure required for its total aspiration or the time needed for entry at a given pressure (37).

FILTRATION TESTS   RBC deformability can be studied by determining the pressure-flow relationship of RBC suspensions passed through filters (e.g. polycarbonate sieves) with pore diameters $\geq$ 3 μm under a constant pressure

(29) or a constant flow (57). The resistance (pressure/flow ratio) of the suspension relative to that of the suspending medium provides a measure of cell deformability. The presence of a small fraction of poorly deformable cells, e.g. white blood cells (WBCs), causes a time-dependent increase in filtration resistance and dominates the long term behavior of the filtration resistance. In order to derive an average deformation behavior of the entire cell population, the initial relative resistance obtained at the beginning of the filtration process should be used. The average resistance of a single RBC in a single pore can be calculated from this resistance normalized for cell concentration in the suspension and the cell/pore volume ratio (65).

INTERPRETATION OF WHOLE CELL DEFORMABILITY TESTS   Measurements on whole cell deformability reflect a combination of the various determinants. In general, results on channels close to the limiting size for RBC passage (~ 3 μm) are dominated by the geometric relationship between SA and CV (53). In tests on channels with diameters of ~ 7 μm, such geometric factors are relatively unimportant, and the viscous properties of the cell (η_i and η_m) probably play a dominant role by controlling the rate of entry of the RBC into the channel (53). Filtration tests are usually performed with pore diameter of ~ 5 μm, where both cell geometry and cellular viscosity may play a role.

Measurement of Red Cell Deformability in Shear Flow

DEFORMING SHEAR STRESS   In a fluid shear flow the deforming shear stress acting on the cell is a function of the shear rate ($\dot{\gamma}$) and the external viscosity of the suspending medium (η_o). In a concentrated cell suspension, $\dot{\gamma}$ at the cell surface is not the same as the overall $\dot{\gamma}$ for the suspension because fluid shear is concentrated in the external medium, as there is only a limited participation of the cell interior in the shear flow. Raising η_o has a much stronger effect on RBC deformation than does increasing $\dot{\gamma}$. This is because high η_o can induce RBC membrane rotation, which transmits the shear into the cell interior. The interior then participates in flow and behaves more like a fluid (36). In suspensions with very high cell concentrations, the interaction of cells with each other is analogous to an increase in η_o, which would also facilitate RBC deformation (8). In studies on RBC deformation under shear flow, the deforming force is usually expressed in terms of bulk shear stress ($\dot{\gamma}\eta_o$ or $\dot{\gamma}\eta_s$). The effective deforming shear stress acting on the cell may be quite different depending on the cell concentration and η_o.

Rheoscopy   The deformation of individual RBCs under shear flow can be measured directly under microscopic observation (59). This is usually done in dilute suspensions of RBCs in a medium with very high η_o to enhance cell deformation. An elongation index can be measured as $(L-D)/(L+D)$, where L is the length and D the width of the RBC under deformation. The deformed

RBC can maintain a steady shape during shear flow because of membrane rotation and induction of intracellular fluid flow. The degree of deformation at a given shear stress is probably determined primarily by the η_i and η_m in relation to η_o and to a lesser extent by the cell geometric factors.

Ektacytometry   The deformation of a dilute suspension of RBCs in a high η_o medium can be determined by measuring the laser diffraction pattern during shear. The experimental condition is similar to that described above for rheoscopy, except that measurements are made on a population of cells in ensemble. The recent introduction of the osmotic spectrum technique has greatly increased the utility of this method (16). By continuously varying the osmolality of the high η_o medium, the elongation index can be monitored. From various parts of the elongation-osmolality plots, one can evaluate the roles of cell geometry, η_i, and membrane properties in governing cell deformation behavior in response to changing osmolality.

Viscometry   The viscosity of a suspension of RBCs at a controlled hematocrit (e.g. 45%) in a nonaggregating medium with known η_o provides a measurement of RBC deformability. The viscosity of such suspensions shows shear thinning behavior that reflects the progressive RBC deformation by shear. Under high-shear conditions ($\dot{\gamma} > 200$ sec^{-1} in isotonic buffers), η_i is probably a major determinant of the results. In medium-to-low shears, η_m and cell geometry probably assume greater importance. Rheoscopy and ektacytometry are usually carried out in diluted suspensions at high η_o, viscometry is generally performed in concentrated suspensions at low η_o. As in the other methods a rise in η_o increases the degree of deformation in viscometry, as reflected by the lowering of relative viscosity (η_s/η_o), especially at high $\dot{\gamma}$.

ALTERATIONS IN RED CELL DEFORMABILITY IN EXPERIMENTAL AND PATHOPHYSIOLOGICAL CONDITIONS

Altered RBC deformability can be induced experimentally and is found in hematological and nonhematological disorders. In these cases, there are changes in one or more of the determinants of RBC deformability (geometry, η_i, and membrane properties). Some of the conditions involving altered RBC membrane properties are discussed elsewhere in this volume (33). The present discussion focuses primarily on other determinants.

Experimental Alteration in Red Cell Deformability

VARIATIONS IN OSMOTIC CONCENTRATIONS   An increase in osmolality of the suspending medium leads to both a decrease in CV at constant SA (40), which would facilitate the passage of the RBC through narrow channels, and an increase in MCHC and hence η_i (53), which would reduce the ability of the RBC to deform in shear flow. With high osmolality, there may also be some interaction between hemoglobin and membrane components that renders the membrane less deformable. A decrease in osmolality causes an increase in CV and a decrease in η_i, which have opposite actions on RBC deformability. Therefore, alterations in osmolality can exert different effects on RBC deformability, depending on the method of measurement. In general, excessive changes in osmolality tend to decrease RBC deformability, and the best compromise for RBC deformability is reached in some intermediate osmolality range. For example, in filterability tests using polycarbonate sieves with pore diameters of 2.6, 4.5, and 6.8 μm, the least resistance to filtration is obtained at 200, 280, and 400 mOsm/liter, respectively (53). These results reflect the importance of cell geometric factors in passage through the narrowest channel and the relative predominance of η_i in transit through the larger channels.

In an ektacytometer operated in the osmotic spectrum mode, the osmotic concentration is continuously varied while the cell elongation is determined at a constant high shear stress (16). The elongation versus osmotic concentration curve at low osmotic strengths shows an initial minimum (~140 mOsm for normal RBCs) that reflects the critical hemolytic volume of the cells. The subsequent rise in the curve reflects primarily membrane properties and the geometry of the cell. The peak reached thereafter (at or near physiological osmolality) is a function of the relationship of membrane surface area to cell volume. The final downslope of the curve reflects primarily the influence of MCHC and η_i.

CALCIUM   An increase in intracellular [Ca^{2+}], e.g. by using the ionophore A23187 in the presence of elevated [Ca^{2+}] in the medium, results in a decrease in RBC deformability in the ektacytometer (15, 30) and the rheoscope (61), with the older cells in the population being particularly vulnerable (61). The decrease in cell deformability has been attributed mainly to the increase in η_i due to intracellular dehydration (15, 30). There is also a decrease in the surface area of RBCs when treated with this ionophore at extracellular [Ca^{2+}] higher than 200 μM. Micropipette tests on RBCs exposed to ionophore and Ca^{2+} showed no significant changes in membrane shear modulus (68), but there was a slowing of the recovery time of the deformed segment (23). The latter change was diminished by treatment with an anion channel blocker, DIDS, which blocked Ca^{2+}-induced K^+ and water losses (23). These results indicate that calcium has a complicated effect on RBC deformability by affecting several determinants of deformability. An accumulation of intracellular calcium in RBCs subjected to subhemolytic shear stress in vitro has been found to be associated with a decrease in filterability through 3-μm pores (50).

TEMPERATURE   A decrease in temperature causes a slight increase in the shear modulus of the RBC membrane (32, 77); a reduction of temperature from 37 to 6°C leads to almost 40% increase of shear modulus. Over the same range of temperature change, the membrane surface viscosity increases six-fold (32). The critical force required for the induction of structural failure of the RBC membrane does not vary significantly with temperature (75). However, the plastic viscosity, determined from the rate of membrane tether formation after the critical force has been exceeded, increases sharply with a reduction in temperature. The temperature coefficient for membrane plastic viscosity has been estimated to be 18.6 kcal/mol, which is higher than the corresponding value for membrane surface viscosity (10.0 kcal/mol). This difference is believed to stem from the less extensive molecular rearrangements within the membrane skeletal network below the elastic limit compared with those occurring in plastic flow (75).

Heating to above 45°C causes a decrease in elongation index of RBC ghosts in the ektacytometer (30). Following heat treatment of RBCs at 48°C, micropipette tests have shown increases in membrane shear modulus, membrane viscosity, and the pressure required for cell entry into 3-μm pipettes (49). These changes result from alterations in membrane proteins by the heating procedure.

ALTERATIONS IN MEMBRANE PROTEINS   The influence of membrane skeletal proteins on red cell deformability has recently been reviewed by Mohandas et al (45). Treatment of RBCs with glycophorin A–specific ligands, e.g. the lectin wheat germ agglutinin (7, 26, 67) or a monoclonal antibody IgG to glycophorin A (7), causes a dose-dependent decrease in RBC deformability that can be measured with a micropipette or an ektacytometer. Such changes are not observed with ligands specific for band 3 and blood group A and B antigens, but they are induced by treatment with a monovalent Fab of antiglycophorin IgG (7). In spectrin-deficient and protein-4.1-deficient RBCs and in 2,3-diphosphoglycerate-treated resealed membranes, the rigidification effect of antiglycophorin IgG is markedly reduced. These results have led to the conclusion that a ligand-induced interaction between glycophorin A and membrane skeletal proteins can directly affect membrane deformability (7). Selective removal of ankyrin (band 2.1) from RBC ghosts by controlled trypsin digestion, which results in a horizontal displacement of the membrane skeleton from the lipid bilayer, has been found to prevent the decrease in ghost suspension viscosity and the shape change induced by chlorpromazine or MgATP (34).

Coating of RBC membrane with various components of complement in vitro has shown that C3d, either alone or with other components, causes increases in membrane shear modulus and viscosity, as determined by micropipette aspiration (70). Other components (e.g. C4b, C4d, C5, factor Bb) do not have the same effect. Lipid fluidity of RBC membrane, examined by fluorescence depolarization, increases with fixation of all complement components except C5 (70).

Treatment of RBCs by diamides results in reduced RBC elongation in the rheoscope, while the membrane continues to rotate around the cell interior in a shear field. This finding suggests that diamide causes an increase in membrane shear modulus but has little effect on the cytoplasmic viscosity (28). In support of this, RBC resealed ghosts exhibit a dose-dependent decrease of the elongation index in the ektacytometer following the addition of diamide in the concentration range of 1–10 μM (34). The data on micropipette aspiration also provide evidence that diamide treatment leads to an increase in RBC membrane shear modulus as the reduced glutathione is depleted (35).

ALTERATIONS IN MEMBRANE LIPIDS   Modifications of the cholesterol/phospholipid ratio in the RBC membrane have no effect on membrane viscoelastic properties as tested by micropipette aspiration. However, such procedures alter the fluidity of the membrane lipid molecules as determined by fluorescent depolarization with lipid probes (6). Benzyl alcohol, which causes an increase in the fluidity of membrane lipids, also has no effect on membrane viscoelastic properties as tested by micropipette aspiration (5). Tertiary butyl hydroperoxide, an agent that induces the peroxidation of unsaturated fatty acids in membrane phospholipids, markedly increases membrane rigidity and decreases whole cell deformability (17). Malonyldialdehyde, which is formed during lipid peroxidation and may cause polymerization of membrane proteins such as spectrin, results in a decrease in cellular deformability as tested in the rheoscope (52). These results indicate that the deformability of the RBC membrane is not significantly affected by membrane lipids per se, but is influenced by lipid-protein interactions.

MEMBRANE-HEMOGLOBIN INTERACTIONS   The formation of spectrin-hemoglobin cross-links in RBCs by incubation with H_2O_2 leads to a decrease of RBC deformability as measured in an ektacytometer (69). This effect has been attributed primarily to peroxidation of heme proteins, rather than lipid peroxidation. Oxidation of heme proteins has been shown to result in their cross-linking to membrane skeletal proteins, including those of band 3 (74, 78). Studies on RBCs treated with the oxidant phenylhydrazine have shown that the filterability of such cells through 3-μm pores is not affected until Heinz bodies nearly completely line the inner surface of the membrane (54a).

ECHINOCYTE-STOMATOCYTE   TRANSFORMATION   Filtration   resistance through 3- and 5-μm pores is increased for stomatocytes induced by chlorpromazine and is reduced for echinocytes formed by lysolecithin and sodium salicylate (39, 53). These changes can be explained by the alterations in surface area (a decrease for stomatocytes and an increase for echinocytes) at nearly constant cell volume (54). Measurements of RBC deformability in instruments with dimensions much larger than the RBC, e.g. the rheoscope or a viscometer at constant hematocrit (44, 54), indicate that both echinocytes and stomatocytes are less deformable than the normal discoid RBCs.

ATP AND 2,3-DIPHOSPHOGLYCERATE (DPG)   The depletion of ATP from RBCs incubated in vitro is associated with an echinocytic shape change. Such echinocytes differ from those induced by salicylate in that they show a greater resistance in filtration through 3 and 5 μm pores because of a decrease in excess membrane surface area due to cell swelling (54). ATP-depleted RBCs also show a decreased deformability in the rotational viscometer (44), rheoscope (51), and ektacytometer (4). ATP-depleted RBCs were found to have no significant alterations in their membrane viscoelastic properties in a study using the micropipette aspiration technique (43). In experiments using polycarbonate sieves with 0.6-μm pores to aspirate RBCs, however, an increase in membrane shear modulus was found for RBCs depleted of ATP in the presence of Ca^{2+} (1). In intact RBCs an increase of 2,3-DPG (20 mM) was found to have no significant effects on the membrane shear modulus (measured by micropipette) at physiological ionic strength. There is an increase in the viscosity value, which may be related to an elevation in η_i (76). At a reduced ionic strength of 240 mOsm, an increase of 2,3-DPG causes decreases in the shear modulus and the viscosity of intact RBCs but not in those of membrane ghosts (76).

CELL AGE   Studies on RBC fractions separated by density have shown that there is no significant difference in membrane shear modulus, but that the dense (old) cells have a higher viscosity value as determined by micropipette aspiration (40, 48). The higher viscosity in the older cells is only partially attributable to the higher cellular hemoglobin concentration, and these cells must also have an increased membrane viscosity (40, 48). The velocity at which older RBCs enter a pipette with an inner diameter near 2.5 μm has also been found to be slower than that for the younger RBCs (60). At a given hematocrit, suspensions of older RBCs and ghosts prepared from them have a higher viscosity than their younger counterparts (72). Rheoscopic measurements have shown that ~10% of the older RBCs do not have the capability of undergoing membrane rotation to maintain a steady orientation during shear and that the older RBCs that do maintain a steady orientation elongate less than their younger counterparts (71). The membrane changes in older RBCs have been correlated with various alterations in membrane lipids and proteins, as well as an enhanced interaction between membrane proteins and hemoglobin (69).

RELATION OF RBC DEFORMABILITY TO OTHER HEMORHEOLOGICAL PARAMETERS   The deformability of RBCs affects the energy balance in RBC aggregation (25, 66) as rigid RBCs show a reduced tendency to aggregate (8). RBCs with reduced deformability show a stronger Fåhraeus effect, i.e. they show a greater drop in tube hematocrit as tube diameter is reduced (14). Because of the interactions between RBCs and WBCs, RBC deformability can affect WBC flow behavior at branch points (14, 58).

Alterations in Red Cell Deformability in Disease

HEMATOLOGICAL DISORDERS   In hematological disorders involving RBC abnormalities, especially in RBC shape, there is often an altered RBC deformability. Most of these conditions are discussed elsewhere in this volume (33), and there are several recent reviews (e.g. 12, 45). Thus we briefly discuss studies on single cell deformability in sickle cell anemia (SS disease). The fundamental genetic defect in SS disease lies in the molecular structure of hemoglobin S (HbS), which undergoes gelation and fiber formation when deoxygenated. The resulting increase in η_i and the transformation of the intracellular content into a viscoelastic material are the main cause for the decrease in deformability of sickle cells following deoxygenation (13, 49). Even when oxygenated, however, there is also a decrease in RBC deformability in the high-density subpopulation of sickle cells. In addition to the high MCHC and η_i of these cells, there is evidence that the rheological properties of the membrane are abnormal (27, 47). This finding is probably attributable to interactions between the RBC membrane and HbS following repeated cycles of deoxygenation. The interaction of deoxygenated HbS with the cell membrane skeletal proteins can induce skeletal reorganization and alter the rate of transbilayer movement of lipids (46). Because a reduction in RBC deformability leads to a shift of the optimum hematocrit for oxygen transport to a lower level (56), the anemia in many diseases involving RBC rigidification may serve a compensatory purpose (10).

NONHEMATOLOGICAL DISORDERS   There is evidence that abnormal RBC deformability may also occur in cardiovascular and other disorders that are not primarily hematological in nature. These results are controversial in many cases. This is probably attributable in part to the use of test conditions that do not allow a specific assessment of RBC deformability, e.g. the presence of significant amounts of WBCs in filterability tests, as well as the variability in clinical conditions of the patient. In acute myocardial infarction, RBC filterability through 5-μm sieves is reduced in autologous serum, but not in isotonic buffer or normal serum, which suggests the presence of serum factors that interact with the RBC membrane (21). There is evidence suggesting a reduced RBC deformability in hypertension (19). Measurements of viscosity of RBC suspensions in Ringer's solution indicate a reduced RBC deformability in high-renin, but not low-renin, hypertensive patients (10). The earlier reports on abnormal RBC filterability in peripheral vascular disease were subsequently found to be mainly the result of the presence of contaminating WBCs in the test sample (20). In diabetes mellitus, there is a lack of general agreement on whether RBC deformability is abnormal by filterability and micropipette tests (2). A study on doublet formation of diabetic RBCs suggests that they may have an increased membrane bending stiffness (42).

The abnormal RBC deformability in hematological disorders is usually accompanied by a lowering of the hematocrit and a compensatory vasodilation, which minimize the elevation of flow resistance due to the rheological disturbance and maintain oxygen delivery to tissues (10). As a result, the effect of a reduced RBC deformability on blood flow in vivo is generally less than that predicted from in vitro tests on individual RBCs in a system with fixed geometry.

In cardiovascular disorders characterized by an alteration in blood vessels, any abnormalities in blood rheology are superimposed on the vascular disturbance. Thus, even minor changes in RBC deformability may exert a significant effect on blood flow resistance through the microcirculation and aggravate the flow disturbance (11).

The interrelationship between blood rheology and vascular factors in affecting tissue perfusion is illustrated by the ability of phentolamine (an alpha-adrenergic blocker) to prevent the myocardial necrosis in experimental animals produced by microembolization with 25-μm microspheres (24).

EXPERIMENTAL STUDIES ON EFFECTS OF RBCs WITH REDUCED DEFORMABILITY ON BLOOD FLOW IN VIVO

The blood flow through an organ is given by the pressure-resistance ratio. The resistance is determined not only by the geometric features of the vasculature but also by the flow property of the blood. Since RBC deformability is one of the factors governing rheology, it is expected that alterations in RBC deformability will affect hemodynamic functions in vivo. In contrast to the large number of in vitro measurements on RBC deformability, however, there have been few studies on the effects of alterations in RBC deformability on blood flow in vivo.

Studies on ^{51}Cr-labeled diamide-incubated RBCs in the dog have shown a decrease in cell survival and a preferential sequestration in the spleen (35).

Following intravenous injection of labeled diamide-treated RBCs into rats, these RBCs with an increased shear modulus are found to remain in the circulation during the 4-hr experiment period (22). Exchange of native RBCs (up to 70%) with diamide-treated RBCs leads to only a slight reduction of the RBC velocity in mesentery capillaries at normal arterial pressure. However, it causes a drastic reduction of RBC velocity in hemorrhagic hypotension (arterial pressure = 35 mm Hg), which is not reversed following normalization of arterial pressure (22). The diamide-treated RBCs exhibit a prolongation of transit time through stenosis, which suggests that a reduced dynamic response of these RBCs during transient deformations may limit their ability to negotiate the microcirculation (22).

The effects of exchanging native RBCs with RBCs partially hardened with 0.025% glutaraldehyde, which causes a doubling of the filtration resistance of RBCs through 5-μm pores, have been studied in the rat (63). Using a ^{51}Cr and ^{111}In double labeling technique, the circulating concentration of hardened RBCs was found to decrease by more than 70% (<30% remaining) in 30 min, whereas the native RBCs showed no significant decrease over this period. Tissue counting of radioactivities of the double labels demonstrated that hardened RBCs were preferentially trapped in the spleen, lungs, bones, and liver. Measurements of regional blood flows by the microsphere technique showed flow reductions in these same regions. There was a significant correlation between the degree of flow reduction and that of hardened RBC trapping in various regions (63). The differences in the propensity of different organs and tissues to trap such rigidified cells probably reflect regional variations in microarchitecture of the microcirculation.

The rapid disappearance of RBCs rigidified with glutaraldehyde, which causes cross-linking of membrane proteins as well as hemoglobin, from the circulation contrasts with the insignificant loss of RBCs rigidified with diamide, which primarily affects the membrane. These results suggest that the internal viscosity of the RBC and/or the interaction between hemoglobin and membrane proteins may play a more significant role than membrane changes per se in affecting the passage of RBCs through narrow vessels. The degree of reduction in RBC deformability, however, has not been quantitatively compared in these two cases to rule out the possibility that the discrepancy in results may simply be due to the difference in the severity of RBC rigidification.

Although there is only a limited number of experimental studies on the influence of altered RBC deformability on hemodynamic functions in vivo, there is evidence suggesting that the effect depends on the component of RBC deformability altered, the severity of RBC rigidification, the particular body organ system, the hemodynamic conditions, and the vascular responses. The paucity of in vivo data indicates a need for systematic studies to correlate the in vitro deformability behavior of RBCs with their effects on blood flow in vivo.

CONCLUSION AND FUTURE PERSPECTIVES

During the past few years there have been considerable advances in our understanding of the rheological properties of the RBC. These advances have been made possible by the development of new methods of experimental investigation and theoretical analysis. At the same time, there has also been remarkable progress in research on the molecular structure of the RBC, especially its membrane. There is a need to correlate the biophysical and biochemical properties, so that the molecular basis of RBC deformational characteristics can be established.

The normal RBCs are so highly deformable that the effect of their presence on blood flow appears to be minor in normal conditions. Significant decreases in RBC deformability, however, may compromise blood flow through the microcirculation and curtail nutrient transport. There is a need to establish the relationship between the abnormal RBC deformability (in terms of the nature and degree of the abnormality and the quantity of altered cells) and in vivo flow dynamics and transport function, including the interplay between the blood and the vascular components of resistance and the regional differences in microvascular architecture and reactivity.

RBC deformability is the physical link between the molecular organization of the cell and its influence on circulatory functions. An elucidation of their interrelationships would contribute significantly to the understanding of the role of RBC deformability in circulatory regulation in health and hemodynamic derangements in disease.

Literature Cited

1. Baker, R. F. 1981. Membrane deformability of metabolically depleted human red cells. *Blood Cells* 7:551–58
2. Barnes, A. 1986. See Ref. 12, Ch. 10
3. Brooks, D. E., Evans, E. A. 1986. See Ref. 12, Ch. 3
4. Card, R. T., Mohandas, N., Perkins, H. A., Shohet, S. B. 1982. Deformability of stored red blood cells. Relationship to degree of packing. *Transfusion* 22:96–101
5. Chabanel, A., Abbott, R. E., Chien, S., Schachter, D. 1985. Effects of benzyl alcohol on erythrocyte shape, membrane hemileaflet fluidity and membrane viscoelasticity. *Biochim. Biophys. Acta* 816:142–52
6. Chabanel, A., Flamm, M., Sung, K. L. P., Lee, M. M. L., Schachter, D., Chien, S. 1983. Influence of cholesterol content on red cell membrane viscoelasticity and fluidity. *Biophys. J.* 44:171–76
7. Chasis, J. A., Mohandas, N., Shohet, S. B. 1985. Erythrocyte membrane rigidity induced by glycophorin A-ligand interaction. Evidence for a ligand-induced association between glycophorin A and skeletal proteins. *J. Clin. Invest.* 75:1919–26
8. Chien, S. 1975. Biophysical behavior of red cells in suspensions. In *The Red Blood Cell*, ed. D. M. Surgenor, Vol. 2, pp. 1031–1133. New York: Academic. 2nd. ed.

9. Chien, S. 1977. Principles and techniques for assessing erythrocyte deformability. *Blood Cells* 3:71–99
10. Chien, S. 1981. Hemorheology in disease, pathophysiological significance and therapeutic implications. *Clin. Hemorheol.* 1:319–42
11. Chien, S. 1985. Role of blood cells in microcirculatory regulation. *Microvasc. Res.* 29:129–51
12. Chien, S., Dormandy, J. A., Ernst, E., Matrai, A. 1986. *Clinical Hemorheology: Its Applications in Cardiovascular and Hematological Diseases, Diabetes, Gynecology and Surgery.* The Hague: Nijhoff. In press
13. Chien, S., King, R. G., Kaperonis, A. A., Usami, S. 1982. Viscoelastic properties of sickle cells and hemoglobin. *Blood Cells* 8:53–64
14. Chien, S., Usami, S., Skalak, R. 1984. Blood flow in small tubes. In *Handbook of Physiology, Circulation,* ed. E. M. Renkin, C. Michel, Vol. IV:217–49. Bethesda, MD: Am. Physiol. Soc.
15. Clark, M. R., Mohandas, N., Feo, C., Jacobs, M. S., Shohet, S. B. 1981. Separate mechanisms of deformability loss in ATP-depleted and Ca-loaded erythrocytes. *J. Clin. Invest.* 67:531–39
16. Clark, M. R., Mohandas, N., Shohet, S. B. 1983. Osmotic gradient ektacytometry: Comprehensive characterization of red cell volume and surface maintenance. *Blood* 61:899–910
17. Corry, W. D., Meiselman, H. J., Hochstein, P. 1982. Tertiary-butyl hydroperoxide induced changes in the physicochemical properties of human erythrocytes. *Biochim. Biophys. Acta* 597:224–34
18. Deuticke, B., Haest, C. W. M. 1986. Cell membrane function and membrane lipid patterns. *Ann. Rev. Physiol.* 49: 221–35
19. Dintenfass, L. 1982. *Hyperviscosity in Hypertension.* New York: Pergamon. 250 pp.
20. Dormandy, J. A. 1986. See Ref. 12, Ch. 6
21. Dormandy, J., Boyd, M., Ernst, F. 1981. Red cell filterability and myocardial infarction. *Scand. J. Clin. Med.* 156:195–98 (Suppl.)
22. Driessen, G. K., Fischer, T. M., Haest, C. W., Inhoffen, W., Schmid-Schönbein, H. 1984. Flow behaviour of rigid red blood cells in the microcirculation. *Int. J. Microcirc. Clin. Exp.* 3:197–210
23. Eaton, J. W., Branda, R. F., Hadland, C., Dreher, H. 1980. Anion channel blockade: Effects upon erythrocyte

membrane calcium response. *Am. J. Hematol.* 9:391–99
24. Eng, C., Cho, S., Factor, S. M., Sonnenblick, E. G., Kirk, E. S. 1984. Myocardial micronecrosis produced by microsphere embolization. Role of an alpha adrenergic tonic influence on the coronary microcirculation. *Circ. Res.* 54:74–82
25. Evans, E. A., Buxbaum, K. 1981. Affinity of red blood cell membrane for particle surfaces measured by the extent of particle encapsulation. *Biophys. J.* 34:1–12
26. Evans, E. A., Leung, A. 1984. Adhesivity and rigidity of erythrocyte membrane in relation to wheat germ agglutinin binding. *J. Cell Biol.* 98: 1201–18
27. Evans, E., Mohandas, N., Leung, A. 1984. Static and dynamic rigidities of normal and sickle erythrocytes. Major influence of cell hemoglobin concentration. *J. Clin. Invest.* 73:477–88
28. Fischer, T. M., Haest, C. W. M., Stör, M., Kamp, D., Deuticke, B. 1978. Selective alteration of erythrocyte deformability by SH-reagents. Evidence for an involvement of spectrin in membrane shear elasticity. *Biochim. Biophys. Acta* 510:270–82
29. Hanss, M. 1983. Erythrocyte deformability measurement by the initial flow rate method. *Biorheology* 20:199–211
30. Heath, B. P., Mohandas, N., Wyatt, J. L., Shohet, S. B. 1982. Deformability of isolated red blood cell membranes. *Biochim. Biophys. Acta* 691:211–19
31. Hochmuth, R. M., Berk, D. A., Wiles, H. C. 1983. Viscous flow of cytoplasm and red cell membrane: Membrane recovery and tether contraction. *Ann. NY Acad. Sci.* 416:207–24
32. Hochmuth, R. M., Buxbaum, K. L., Evans, E. A. 1980. Temperature dependence of the viscoelastic recovery of red cell membrane. *Biophys. J.* 29:177–82
33. Hochmuth, R. M., Waugh, R. 1986. Curvature moduli and membrane deformability. *Ann. Rev. Physiol.* 49:209–19
34. Jinbo, Y., Sato, S., Nakao, T., Nakao, M., Tsukita, S., et al. 1984. The role of ankyrin in shape and deformability change of human erythrocyte ghosts. *Biochim. Biophys. Acta* 773:237–45
35. Johnson, G. J., Allen, D. W., Flynn, R. P., Finkel, B., White, J. B. 1980. Decreased survival in vivo of diamide-incubated dog erythrocytes. *J. Clin. Invest.* 66:955–61
36. Keller, W. R., Skalak, R. 1982. Motion

RBC DEFORMABILITY AND FLOW 191

of a tank-treading ellipsoidal particle in
a shear flow. *J. Fluid Mech.* 120:27–
47
37. LaCelle, P. L., Smith, B. D. 1981.
Biochemical factors influencing erythrocyte deformability and capillary entrance
phenomena. *Scand. J. Clin. Lab. Invest.*
156:145–49. (Suppl.)
38. Leblond, P. F. 1986. See Ref. 12, Ch. 8
39. Leblond, P. F., Coulmbe, L. 1979. The
measurement of erythrocyte deformability using micropore membranes. A
sensitive technique with clinical applications. *J. Lab. Clin. Med.* 94:133–43
40. Linderkamp, O., Meiselman, H. J.
1982. Geometric, osmotic, and membrane mechanical properties of density-
separated human red cells. *Blood* 59:
1121–27
41. Linderkamp, O., Wu, P. Y. K., Meiselman, H. J. 1983. Geometry of neonatal
and adult red blood cells. *Pediatr. Res.*
17:250–53
42. McMillan, D. E., Utterback, N. G.,
Mitchell, T. P. 1983. Doublet formation
of diabetic erythrocytes as a model of
impaired membrane viscous deformation. *Microvasc. Res.* 26:205–20
43. Meiselman, H. J. 1981. Morphological
determinants of red cell deformability.
Scand. J. Clin. Lab. Invest. 156:27–34
(Suppl.)
44. Meiselman, H. J., Evans, E. A., Hochmuth, R. M. 1978. Membrane mechanical properties of ATP-depleted human
erythrocytes. *Blood* 52:499–503
45. Mohandas, N., Chasis, J. A., Shohet, S.
B. 1983. The influence of membrane
skeleton on red cell deformability, membrane material properties, and shape.
Sem. Hematol. 20:225–42
46. Mohandas, N., Rossi, M., Bernstein,
S., Ballas, S., Ravindranath, Y., et al.
1985. The structural organization of
skeletal proteins influences lipid
translocation across erythrocyte membrane. *J. Biol. Chem.* 260:14264–68
47. Nash, G. B., Johnson, C. S., Meiselman, H. J. 1986. Influence of oxygen
tension on the viscoelastic behavior of
red blood cells in sickle cell disease.
Blood 67:110–18
48. Nash, G. B., Meiselman, H. J. 1983.
Red cell and ghost viscoelasticity—
effects of hemoglobin concentration
and in vivo ageing. *Biophys. J.* 43:63–
73
49. Nash, G. B., Meiselman, H. J. 1985.
Alteration of red cell membrane
viscoelasticity by heat treatment: Effect
on cell deformability and suspension
viscosity. *Biorheology* 22:73–84
50. O'Rear, E. A., Udden, M., McIntire, L.

V., Lunch, E. C. 1982. *Biochim. Biophys. Acta* 691:274–80
51. Pfafferott, C., Meiselman, H. J. 1981.
Microrheologic behavior of crenated human erythrocytes. *Biblio. Anat.* 20:195–
98
52. Pfafferott, C., Meiselman, H. J., Hochstein, P. 1982. The effect of malonyldialdehyde on erythrocyte deformability.
Blood 59:12–15
53. Reinhart, W. H., Chien, S. 1985. Roles
of cell geometry and cytoplasmic viscosity in red cell passage through narrow
pores. *Am. J. Physiol.* C473–79
54. Reinhart, W. H., Chien, S. 1986. Red
cell rheology in stomatocyte-echino-
cyte transformation: Role of cell geometry and cell shape. *Blood* 67:1110–
18
54a. Reinhart, W. H., Sung, K. L. P.,
Chien, S. 1986. *Blood* In press
55. Reinhart, W. H., Usami, S., Schmalzer,
E. A., Lee, M. M. L., Chien, S. 1984.
Evaluation of red blood cell filterability
test. Influences of pore size, hematocrit
and flow rate. *J. Lab. Clin. Med.*
104:501–56
56. Schmalzer, E. A., Lee, J. O., Brown,
A. K., Usami, S., Chien, S. 1986.
Viscosity of mixtures of sickle and normal red cells at varying hematocrits.
Transfusion In press
57. Schmalzer, E. A., Skalak, R., Usami,
S., Vayo, M., Chien, S. 1982. Influence
of red cell concentration on filtration of
blood cell suspensions. *Biorheology*
20:29–40
58. Schmid-Schönbein, G. W., Usami, S.,
Skalak, R., Chien, S. 1980. The interaction of leukocytes and erythrocytes in
capillary and postcapillary vessels. *Microvasc. Res.* 19:45–70
59. Schmid-Schönbein, H., Gaehtgens, P.,
Fischer, T., Stohr, L. M. 1984. Biology
of red cells: Non-nucleated erythrocytes
as fluid drop-like cell fragments. *Int. J.
Microcirc. Clin. Exp.* 3:161–96
60. Shiga, T., Maeda, N., Suda, T., Kon,
K., Sekiya, M. 1979. The decreased
membrane fluidity of in vivo aged human erythrocytes. *Biochim. Biophys.
Acta* 553:84–95
61. Shiga, T., Sekiya, M., Maeda, N., Kon,
K., Okazaki, M. 1985. Cell age-
dependent changes in deformability and
calcium accumulation of human erythrocytes. *Biochim. Biophys. Acta* 814:289–
99
62. Shohet, S. 1986. Red cell biochemical
anatomy and membrane properties. *Ann.
Rev. Physiol.* 49:237–48
63. Simchon, S., Jan, K. M., Chien, S.
1985. Influence of red cell deformability

on regional blood flow distribution. *Fed. Proc.* 44:1005 (Abstr.)
64. Skalak, R., Chien, S. 1981. Capillary flow: History, experiments and theory. *Biorheology* 18:307–30
65. Skalak, R., Impelluso, T., Schmalzer, E. A., Chien, S. 1982. Theoretical modeling of filtration of blood cell suspensions. *Biorheology* 20:41–56
66. Skalak, R., Zarda, P. R., Jan, K. M., Chien, S. 1981. Mechanics of rouleau formation. *Biophys. J.* 35:771–81
67. Smith, B. D., LaCelle, P., Siefring, G. E., Lowe-Krentz, L., Lorand, L. 1981. Effects of the calcium-mediated enzymatic cross-linking of membrane proteins on cellular deformability. *J. Membr. Biol.* 61:75–80
68. Smith, L., Hochmuth, R. M. 1982. Effect of wheat germ agglutinin on the viscoelastic properties of erythrocyte membrane. *J. Cell Biol.* 94:7–11
69. Snyder, L. M., Fortier, N. L., Trainor, J., Jacobs, J., Leb, L., et al. 1985. Effect of hydrogen peroxide exposure on normal human erythrocyte deformability, morphology, surface characteristics, and spectrin-hemoglobin cross-linking. *J. Clin. Invest.* 76:1971–77
70. Sung, K. L. P., Chabanel, A., Freedman, J., Chien, S. 1985. Effect of complement on the viscoelastic properties of human erythrocyte membrane. *Br. J. Haematol.* 61:455–66
71. Sutera, S. P., Gardner, R. A., Boylan,

C. W., Carroll, G. L., Chang, K. C., et al. 1985. Age-related changes in deformability of human erythrocytes. *Blood* 65:275–82
72. Tillman, W., Levin, C., Pridull, G., Schroter, W. 1980. Rheological properties of young and aged human erythrocytes. *Klin. Wochenschr.* 58:569–74
73. Tözeren, H., Chien, S., Tözeren, A. 1984. Estimation of viscous dissipation inside an erythrocyte during aspirational entry into a micropipette. *Biophys. J.* 45:1179–84
74. Vilsen, B., Nielsen, H. 1984. Reaction of phenylhydrazine with erythrocytes. Cross-linking of spectrin by disulfide exchange with oxidized hemoglobin. *Biochem. Pharmacol.* 33:2739–48
75. Waugh, R. E. 1982. Temperature dependence of the yield shear resultant and the plastic viscosity coefficient of erythrocyte membrane. *Biophys. J.* 39:273–78
76. Waugh, R. E. 1986. Effects of 2,3-diphosphoglycerate on the mechanical properties of erythrocyte membrane. *Blood* In press
77. Waugh, R. E., Evans, E. A. 1979. Thermoelasticity of red blood cell membrane. *Biophys. J.* 26:115–31
78. Waugh, S. M., Low, P. S. 1985. Hemichrome binding to band 3: Nucleation of Heinz bodies on the erythrocyte membrane. *Biochemistry* 24:34–39

Ann. Rev. Physiol. 1987. 49:193–208

INTRACELLULAR LIPID TRANSPORT IN EUKARYOTES

Richard G. Sleight

Department of Biochemistry and Molecular Biology, University of Cincinnati College of Medicine, 231 Bethesda Avenue, Cincinnati, Ohio 45267–0522

INTRODUCTION

The metabolic regulation and biological significance of the large number of lipid species found in all biological membranes are not well understood. It has been estimated that there are greater than 1000 chemically distinct phospholipid species in eukaryotic cells (98), all of which must bestow significant evolutionary advantages to the cells. The majority of lipids are synthesized at the endoplasmic reticulum (ER), and yet most lipid species are found throughout the cell, with organelles having differing lipid compositions and displaying an asymmetric distribution of lipid species across their bilayers. An increased interest in the cell biology of lipids has arisen from the realization that lipid molecules act as modulators of a large number of biological processes (93). The maintenance of the complex intracellular distribution of lipids is most likely regulated by several processes, including specific lipid transport mechanisms. The identification of these transport mechanisms in living cells has proven to be a difficult problem and is the subject of this brief review.

The three general mechanisms believed to be responsible for intracellular lipid transport between membranes are: (*a*) *vesicular transport,* the transport of molecules from one organelle to another by vesicles budding and fusing; (*b*) *monomer transport,* the transport of single lipid molecules between membranes through the cytoplasm (this transport may be either spontaneous or protein assisted); (*c*) *lateral diffusion,* the transport of molecules within the plane of the membrane bilayer between two organelles connected by bridges. Lipid molecules may also undergo transmembrane movement, transferring between leaflets of a membrane's lipid bilayer.

193

0066-4278/87/0315-0193$02.00

INTERMEMBRANE TRANSPORT OF SPECIFIC LIPID CLASSES

Phospholipids

VESICLE TRANSPORT   Transport of phospholipid species between organelles by small vesicles has been observed by a number of different techniques. Microscopic visualization of this process was performed using a fluorescent analog of phosphatidylcholine having N-4-nitrobenzo-2-oxa-1,3-diazole-aminocaproic acid esterified in the sn-2 position (C_6-NBD-PC). C_6-NBD-PC can be stably inserted into the plasma membrane of hamster lung fibroblasts at 2°C (112, 124). When these cells are warmed to 37°C, the majority of the internalized fluorescent lipid is transported to the region of the Golgi apparatus (112). The small vesicles responsible for this intracellular translocation can be observed by incubating the cells at 16°C. At this temperature, delivery to the region of the Golgi apparatus is blocked, and a large number of small, fluorescently labeled vesicles appear randomly distributed throughout the cytoplasm (112). Recent experiments have indicated that internalization of fluorescent phosphatidylcholine from the plasma membrane occurs by vesicular transport in a variety of cultured cells lines; however, the sites of lipid delivery differ in some cell types (115). A fluorescent analog of sphingomyelin has also been observed microscopically to enter cells by a vesicle-mediated process (68).

At the onset of chemotactic migration during the development of *Dictyostelium discoideum*, synthesis of phospholipids increases fourfold, and the newly synthesized lipids are transferred preferentially to the plasma membrane (34). De Silva & Siu have isolated very low density vesicles from these cells, which from pulse chase studies appear to be involved in the delivery of new lipids to the plasma membrane (35). Chlapowski & Band, working with *Acanthamoeba palestinesis*, have also identified intracellular vesicles that appear to be involved in delivering phospholipids to the plasma membrane (23).

The delivery of newly synthesized lipid to the plasma membrane via a vesicle-mediated transport mechanism is typically associated with a lag between the time of lipid synthesis and delivery to the plasma membrane. This lag time required for vesicle movement has been observed by only a few investigators. By pulse labeling *Acanthamoeba castellanii* with [3H]acetate followed by isolation of a plasma membrane fraction, Mills et al observed that delivery of newly synthesized sterols and phospholipids to the plasma membrane occurred after a 30-min lag (81). Simoni and coworkers, using pulse chase labeling of Chinese hamster ovary cells followed by rapid plasma membrane isolation on cationic beads, also reported a substantial lag between the times of synthesis and delivery of cholesterol to the plasma membrane

(60). However, these investigators found no lag in the delivery of newly synthesized phosphatidylcholine to the plasma membranes of these cells (59).

MONOMER TRANSPORT   The spontaneous transfer of phospholipid molecules between membranes through the water phase has been observed in a number of model systems. Estimates of the rates of spontaneous transfer have been determined by measuring shifts in transition temperatures (36, 63, 74), loss of pyrene-labeled lipid excitimer formation (45, 101), resonance energy transfer between suitable lipid analogs (85), and rapid separation of radiolabeled donor and acceptor membrane populations (6, 76). Although the rapid transfer of some species has been reported (30), in general, the spontaneous transfer of most native phospholipid species is extremely slow. For example, the half-time for equilibration of 1-palmitoyl, 2-oleoyl phosphatidylcholine between artificial vesicles is greater than 2 days (76). Although little is known about the rates of spontaneous lysophospholipid transfer, their greater solubility in aqueous media suggests they may transfer rapidly. The functional significance of spontaneous phospholipid monomer transfer in vivo is unknown. Because the rates of spontaneous movement of most phospholipid species are much slower than transfer by alternate mechanisms, it seems unlikely that spontaneous transfer plays a significant role in membrane biogenesis and maintenance. In addition, spontaneous transport would lead to randomization of the lipid components of different membranes rather than support differential lipid compositions between organelles.

In 1968 Wirtz & Zilversmit discovered that phospholipids rapidly exchange between rat liver microsomes and mitochondria in vitro (145). This initial observation led to the discovery of a large class of proteins that facilitate the exchange and/or net transfer of phospholipid molecules between membranes. These proteins have been called phospholipid transfer proteins and phospholipid exchange proteins (PLEPs) interchangeably. From the time of their discovery, it has been postulated that PLEPs function in vivo in the translocation of phospholipids between subcellular membranes (78, 145); however, direct evidence of PLEP-assisted transport in vivo has not yet been produced. Within the large body of circumstantial evidence that suggests the involvement of PLEPs in intracellular phospholipid transport, many inconsistencies exist. Several excellent reviews describing the activities and mechanisms of action of PLEPs are available (44, 57, 58, 125, 143, 150). Evidence that PLEPs are not responsible for the rapid movement of phospholipids in living cells has also been reported (61, 72, 136).

The transport of lipids by vesicular movement has been thought to require a transit time greater than that for lipid translocation by PLEPs. Therefore, much of the evidence suggesting that PLEPs are active in intracellular lipid transport consists of the finding of rapid lipid translocation. For example, when the delivery of newly synthesized phosphatidylethanolamine molecules to the cell surface was measured by trinitrobenzene sulfonic acid labeling, no appreciable lag between synthesis at the ER and appearance at the cell surface was observed (112). In contrast, when the delivery of newly synthesized proteins to the plasma membrane was measured, greater than one hour elapsed between synthesis and initial delivery to the plasma membrane (112). These findings are consistent with a slow, vesicle-mediated delivery of proteins and a rapid monomer transport of lipids to the plasma membrane. Other examples of rapid intracellular phospholipid transport consistent with PLEP-assisted movement include rapid transfer of labeled lipids from microsomes to mitochondria (1, 38, 69, 146) and movement of newly synthesized phosphatidylcholine to the plasma membranes of Chinese hamster ovary (CHO) cells (59). Although often overlooked, these types of data are also consistent with translocation via lateral diffusion and spontaneous monomer transport (described below).

Another source of evidence suggesting the action of PLEPs in vivo is the correlation between PLEP activity and lipid metabolism that has been observed in several systems (20, 37, 39, 95, 96, 144); however, exceptions to this correlation have also been reported (61, 72, 136).

LATERAL DIFFUSION   Phospholipids migrate rapidly in the plane of the bilayer in both biological membranes and in model membranes in the liquid-crystalline state. Diffusion coefficients of approximately 10^{-8} cm^2/sec have been measured in both biological and artificial lipid bilayers (54). By lateral movement, phospholipids could move between organelles via permanent or transient interconnections between organelle membranes; however, this has not been observed experimentally. Current evidence for the existence of membrane bridges between organelles is discussed below in connection with the transport of fatty acids by lateral diffusion.

Cholesterol

VESICLE TRANSPORT   The enzymes involved in hepatic cholesterol biosynthesis are located in the ER (25). Simoni and coworkers have measured the time course of intracellular transport of cholesterol from its site of synthesis to the plasma membrane. This was achieved by pulse labeling Chinese hamster ovary cells followed by rapid plasma membrane isolation (31, 60). Cholesterol transport to the plasma membrane in these cells has a half-time of 10 min and appears to be energy dependent. Although the transport process is blocked below 15°C, cholesterol synthesis continues at this temperature. Lange & Matthies have pulse labeled human fibroblasts with [^{3}H]acetate and measured the movement of newly synthesized cholesterol to the plasma membrane by treating the cells with cholesterol oxidase (64). Transfer of labeled cholesterol followed first order kinetics and had a half-time of 1–2 hr. Newly synthesized cholesterol could not be detected in soluble protein fractions of cell homogenates, but was found in an unidentified low density membranous compartment prior to delivery to the plasma membrane (64). Considerable lag times between synthesis and delivery of cholesterol to the plasma membrane have also been reported in other cell types (65, 81).

MONOMER TRANSPORT   Several studies using liposomes have indicated that cholesterol can move spontaneously between membranes by the transfer of monomers through the aqueous phase (5, 21, 76, 77). The lipid content of the artificial vesicles used as donors or acceptors in these experiments has been demonstrated to influence the rate of intermembrane cholesterol movement (97). It appears that cholesterol preferentially partitions into membranes containing sphingomyelin > phosphatidylcholine > phosphatidylethanolamine (32, 134). However, Wattenberg & Silbert have provided evidence suggesting that the differential partitioning of cholesterol observed in vitro cannot account for the large differences in cholesterol distribution found in vivo (138).

A large number of cytosolic sterol binding factors have been identified in a variety of tissues (24, 41, 46, 82, 86, 121, 128, 129, 130, 131). Many of these factors stimulate the enzymatic conversion of intermediates of cholesterol synthesis. Two of the proteins responsible for this effect have been isolated and given various names, including sterol carrier protein (SCP). In rat liver, sterol carrier proteins having molecular weights of 47,000 (SCP-1) and 13,500 daltons (SCP-2) have been characterized (41, 46, 86, 121). Relatively little is known about SCP-1, which appears to participate in the microsomal conversion of squalene to lanosterol (41, 46, 121). Several functions for SCP-2 have been postulated including (a) participation in the microsomal conversion of lanosterol to cholesterol (86), (b) transport of cholesterol from cytoplasmic lipid droplets to mitochondria (24), (c) translocating cholesterol from the outer to the inner mitochondrial membrane (132), (d) regulating pregnenolone production (130), (e) stimulating hydroxycholesterol production (131), and (f) mediating the exchange of phosphatidylinositol between natural and artificial membranes (131). Currently, there is a controversy as to whether SCP-2 and fatty acid binding protein have the same activity (27, 33, 105). Vahouny and coworkers have recently proposed (131), based on amino acid analysis and properties in model systems, that SCP-2 is identical to the nonspecific phospholipid exchange protein (15) and the nonspecific lipid transfer protein (94) described previously by the laboratories of Zilversmit and Wirtz, respectively. The detailed mode of action of the sterol carrier proteins is unknown, as is the correlation between the observed in vitro activities of the proteins and their actual functions in the cell.

Fatty Acids

MONOMER TRANSPORT   Intracellular transport of some fatty acids and their CoA derivatives may require the participation of one or more low molecular weight cytosolic binding proteins. Although a great deal of information about these fatty acid binding proteins (FABPs) has been obtained, their involvement in fatty acid transport in vivo is still based on circumstantial evidence. These proteins appear to keep large amounts of free fatty acids available for metabolism by preventing their partitioning into the phospholipid bilayer (137). Other suggested functions for FABPs include assisting in the cellular uptake of fatty acids (49, 99, 123) and participating in the esterification (22, 89), oxidation (4, 42), and synthesis (22, 71) of free fatty acids and fatty acylCoAs. Fatty acid binding proteins have been found in a variety of eukaryotic tissues but have not been identified in prokaryotes.

Two of the best characterized FABPs are called hFABP (hepatic form) and gFABP (gut form). hFABP is most likely identical to a FABP called the Z protein (71, 88, 126). hFABP was originally identified in the liver, where it represents 3–5% of the cytosolic protein mass and binds 60% of the long chain fatty acids found in the cytosol (88). While approximately 0.2% of translatable liver mRNA specifies this protein in liver, it is coded for by 3.3% of the translatable intestinal mRNA (48). The primary sequences of the 14,184 dalton rat liver hFABP and the 14,178 dalton human liver hFABP were recently determined (47, 70). Intestinal FABP (gFABP) is a 15,063 dalton protein that represents 1–2% of the cytosolic protein mass and is encoded by 2% of translatable mRNA (48, 87).

LATERAL DIFFUSION   For over a decade, Scow and coworkers have examined the intracellular transport of fatty acids by electron microscopy. They have proposed that in adipose tissue, fatty acids released from chylomicrons by lipoprotein lipase are initially inserted into the plasma membranes of endothelial cells. These fatty acids are then transported laterally in a continuum of cellular membranes to the ER of parenchymal cells, where they can be reesterified to triacylglycerol, which accumulates between leaflets of the ER membrane (14, 107–109). This process is thought to be reversible (10, 109).

For lateral mobility to be an effective means of transport, membrane bridges between organelles must exist. To visualize continuities between extracellular space and intracellular channels, cells have been incubated in the presence of nonpermeable marker substances such as tannic acid or lanthanum, and the intracellular distribution of these substances has been examined. Using tannic acid, membrane continuities between the plasma membrane and ER have been identified in white and brown adipose tissue and in hepatocytes (12). Continuities between the plasma membrane and lipid drop-lets in white adipose tissue have also been reported (11). It should be noted that both these studies were performed on cells that had been pretreated with glutaraldehyde, which may have effected normal membrane structure. Similar continuities were observed in brown adipose tissue using lanthanum as a marker (12). Membrane continuities have also been observed between sarcoplasmic reticulum and the outer mitochondrial membrane in canine heart (17) and mouse diaphragm muscle (139), between the ER and the outer mitochondrial membrane in rat liver (43, 83) and mouse oocytes (104), and between lipid droplets and the outer mitochondrial membrane in rat heart (141).

Scow and coworkers have demonstrated that when glutaraldehyde-fixed adipocytes are incubated at 25°C, lipolysis continues to occur and large amounts of fatty acid accumulate in myelin figures (9, 10). The figures appear only if the tissue is exposed to pH 9.0–9.1 and maintained at or above pH 7.4, otherwise the fatty acids appear in smooth-surface droplets (3). Recent-ly, the presence of fatty acid–containing myelin figures was observed in unfixed adipose tissue after quick-freezing and freeze-fracture electron mi-croscopy (3). It has been proposed that these myelin figures occur when the local concentration of fatty acid on one leaflet of a membrane becomes extremely high (3, 10). Supporting this idea is the finding that droplets of oleic acid suspended in water (pH 6.5) spontaneously form myelin figures when the pH is increased (3). This model of fatty acid transport predicts that normally fatty acids are removed from the interfacial continuum by esterifi-cation or binding to proteins and that when these processes are reduced by metabolic events in vivo or by glutaraldehyde fixation in vitro, fatty acids concentrate at some interfaces and spontaneously form bilayered exten-sions (13).

Although a great deal of experimental evidence obtained over the past decade suggests that fatty acids are transported between organelles by lateral diffusion, several unanswered questions remain. Much of the evidence suggesting organelle continuities comes from studies performed after tissue fixation, and it is possible that this fixation caused the continuities. In addition, investigators examining the internalization of fluid phase markers via endocytosis should have also observed continuities between the ex-tracellular space and cellular organelles, but this has not been the case (40, 122). Since all classes of lipid and some integral membrane proteins undergo lateral diffusion within the plane of the bilayer, a priori one might expect that membrane bridges between organelles would result in a randomization of lipid and protein between all interconnected membranes. Since this is clearly not true, it must be postulated that if lateral movement of fatty acids does occur between organelles, "filters" that selectively permit specific molecules to pass between organelles must exist. Bretscher (18, 19) has suggested that coated pits may act as molecular filters at the plasma membrane.

Glycolipids

Recently, Sonderfeld et al demonstrated that cultured human fibroblasts incubated in the presence of radiolabeled G_{M2} rapidly adsorb the ganglioside to their surfaces. Most of the radiolabeled G_{M2} is then internalized and delivered to lysosomes, where it is degraded; however, some of the radiolabel was found in higher gangliosides such as G_{M1} and G_{D1a} (119). These workers postulated that some radiolabeled glycolipid leaves the lysosomes by "membrane flow" before being fully degraded and that the intermediates of glycolipid catabolism are accepted as substrates by glycosyltransferases (presumably in the Golgi apparatus) responsible for new glycolipid biosynthesis (119). Fluorescently labeled ganglioside analogs have also been inserted into fibroblast membranes and their internalization followed (120). Although the sites of fluorescent ganglioside internalization have not been well characterized, it appears that the labeled gangliosides may be moving to the region of the Golgi apparatus, as was previously observed following the internalization of a fluorescent phosphatidylcholine analog (113). The means of intracellular transport of the radiolabeled and fluorescently labeled glycolipids are unknown, but their general transport properties appear to be consistent with vesicular transport. Although the presence of glycosphingolipids on the cytosolic side of cellular membranes has not been detected, cytosolic glycolipid transfer proteins have been identified (16, 79, 80, 148). In some instances it appears that the protein-mediated transport of glycolipid observed in vitro may reflect a lack of lipid specificity by the transfer protein (16). Abe & Sasaki have reported finding a glycolipid-specific transfer protein in pig brain (2, 147, 148).

Activator proteins that stimulate the hydrolysis of glycosphingolipids in vitro have been isolated from a variety of cell types (66, 67). The importance of these proteins in the in vivo degradation of glycosphingolipids has been substantiated by the finding of sphingolipid storage diseases caused by the deficiency of specific activator proteins (28, 51, 53, 73). Although some of the activator proteins also function as transfer proteins in vitro (67, 73), this function has not been demonstrated in living cells.

Neutral Lipids

Triacylglycerol transfer proteins have been identified in the plasma of several mammalian species (50, 56, 84). These proteins also transfer cholesterol esters in vitro, and their role in vivo remains speculative. Recently Wetterau & Zilversmit identified a triacylglycerol transfer protein in bovine liver (140).

This transfer protein is unique since it is not cytosolic but is associated with microsomes. Like the plasma proteins, the microsomal transfer protein also exchanges cholesterol esters, and its function in living cells is unknown.

TRANSMEMBRANE MOVEMENT

The asymmetric distribution of lipids appears to be a common property of biological membranes (for reviews see References 62, 90, 91, 102). This asymmetry may be associated with differences in lipid "fluidity" or mobility; however, there is considerable disagreement about the exact nature of these differences (26, 52, 100, 106, 111, 127, 142). Membrane lipid asymmetry cannot be completely explained by asymmetric synthesis since the majority of phospholipid synthesis occurs on the cytoplasmic face of the ER (7). A much more plausible mechanism for the creation and maintenance of membrane lipid asymmetry is the differential transbilayer movement of lipid species. Initial studies of transmembrane movement were restricted to erythrocytes, in which it was demonstrated that phosphatidylcholine "flip-flop" occurred with a half-time of 8–15 hr (29, 103, 135). Recently, Devaux and coworkers demonstrated that spin-labeled analogs of phosphatidylserine and phosphatidylethanolamine undergo rapid transmembrane movement in human erythrocytes (110), whereas similar analogs of phosphatidylcholine, phosphatidic acid, and sphingomyelin move very slowly (110, 149). The transmembrane movement of the spin-labeled amino phospholipids can be reversibly inhibited by ATP depletion (110). It has been proposed that membrane lipid asymmetry is maintained by the active inward transport of amino phospholipids and a counterbalancing outward passive diffusion of other lipid species (149). This is supported by the finding that although a fluorescent phosphatidylethanolamine analog undergoes transbilayer movement across the plasma membranes of Chinese hamster fibroblasts, a corresponding phosphatidylcholine analog is not transported by transbilayer movement (92, 113, 114). Circumstantial evidence for the rapid transbilayer movement of radiolabeled native phosphatidylethanolamine at the plasma membrane of these cell has also been presented (112).

Transbilayer movement of phospholipids across the ER has been demonstrated to be a rapid process by a variety of techniques (55, 133, 151). Recently, Bishop & Bell reported on the existence of a protein that mediates the transmembrane movement of sn-1,2-dibutyrolphosphatidylcholine across rat liver microsomal vesicles (8).

Although the transbilayer movement of glycolipids has been thought not to occur, some evidence for this phenomenon has recently been presented. The lipid-linked oligosaccharide, dolichol-PP-GlcNac$_2$Man$_9$Glc$_3$, a central intermediate in asparagine-linked glycoprotein biosynthesis, is synthesized in the ER (116). Recent evidence suggests that the initial production of this molecule occurs on the cytoplasmic face of the ER membrane, after which it is translocated to the luminal surface where its synthesis is completed (117, 118). Snider & Rogers have suggested that because dolichol derivatives do not translocate spontaneously across lipid bilayers (75), a protein-mediated transfer of dolichol-PP-GlcNac$_2$Man$_5$ across the ER membrane is likely (118).

CONCLUSIONS AND PERSPECTIVES

A large body of experimental evidence has emerged over the last few years suggesting that several different mechanisms of intracellular lipid transport are involved in maintaining the complex distribution of lipid species in the membranes of eukaryotes. These mechanisms have been characterized to different extents using in vitro model systems. In the coming years, a major goal of the investigators in this field will be the demonstration of the various transport systems in living cells. The emergence of techniques using spin labeled and fluorescently labeled lipid analogs should greatly aid in vivo studies. Another advance likely to be made in the near future is the identification, isolation, and reconstitution into artificial membranes of proteins that mediate the transbilayer movement of several different lipid classes.

Literature Cited

1. Abdelkader, A. B., Mazliak, P. 1970. Exchange de lipides entre mitochondries, microsomes et surnagent cytoplasmique de cellules de pomme de terre ou de chou-fleur. *Eur. J. Biochem.* 15:250–63
2. Abe, A., Sasaki, T. 1985. Purification and some properties of the glycolipid transfer protein from pig brain. *J. Biol. Chem.* 260:11231–39
3. Amende, L. M., Blanchette-Mackie, E. J., Chernick, S. S., Scow, R. O. 1985. Effect of pH on visualization of fatty acids as myelin figures in mouse adipose tissue by freeze-fracture electron microscopy. *Biochim. Biophys. Acta* 837:94–102
4. Appelkvist, E. L., Dallner, G. 1980. Possible involvement of fatty acid binding protein in peroxisomal beta-oxidation of fatty acids. *Biochim. Biophys. Acta.* 617:156–60
5. Backer, J. M., Dawidowicz, E. A. 1981. Mechanism of cholesterol exchange between phospholipid vesicles. *Biochemistry* 20:3805–10
6. Barenholz, Y., Lichtenberg, D., Thompson, T. E. 1983. Spontaneous transfer of sphingomyelin between phospholipid bilayers. *Biochemistry* 22:5647–51
7. Bell, R. M., Ballas, L. M., Coleman, R. A. 1981. Lipid topogenesis. *J. Lipid Res.* 22:391–403
8. Bishop, W. R., Bell, R. M. 1985. Assembly of the endoplasmic reticulum phospholipid bilayer: The phosphatidylcholine transport. *Cell* 42:51–60
9. Blanchette-Mackie, E. J., Scow, R. O. 1971. Sites of lipoprotein lipase activity in adipose tissue perfused with chylomicrons: Electron microscopic cytochemical study. *J. Cell Biol.* 51:1–25
10. Blanchette-Mackie, E. J., Scow, R. O. 1981. Lipolysis and lamellar structures in white adipose tissue of young rats: Lipid movement in membranes. *J. Ultrastruct. Res.* 77:295–318
11. Blanchette-Mackie, E. J., Scow, R. O. 1981. Membrane continuities in cells and intercellular contacts in white adipose tissue of young rats. *J. Ultrastruct. Res.* 77:277–94
12. Blanchette-Mackie, E. J., Scow, R. O. 1982. Continuity of intracellular channels with extracellular space in adipose tissue and liver: Demonstrated with

tannic acid and lanthanum. *Anat. Rec.* 203:205–19

13. Blanchette-Mackie, E. J., Scow, R. O. 1983. Movement of lipolytic products to mitochondria in brown adipose tissue of young rats: An electron microscope study. *J. Lipid Res.* 24:229–44

14. Blanchette-Mackie, E. J., Scow, R. O. 1985. Lipid filling and lipolysis in adipose tissue and cells. *Int. J. Obesity* 9:7–14 (Suppl. 1)

15. Bloj, B., Hughes, M. E., Wilson, D. B., Zilversmit, D. B. 1978. Isolation and amino acid analysis of a nonspecific phospholipid transfer protein from rat liver. *FEBS Lett.* 96:87–89

16. Bloj, B., Zilversmit, D. B. 1981. Accelerated transfer of neutral glycosphingolipids and ganglioside G_{M1} by a purified lipid transfer protein. *J. Biol. Chem.* 256:5988–91

17. Bowman, R. W. 1967. Mitochondrial connections in canine myocardium. *Tex. Rep. Biol. Med.* 25:517–24

18. Bretscher, M. S. 1976. Directed lipid flow in cell membranes. *Nature* 260:21–23

19. Bretscher, M. S., Thomson, J. N., Pearse, B. M. 1980. Coated pits act as molecular filters. *Proc. Natl. Acad. Sci. USA* 77:4156–59

20. Brophy, P. J., Aitken, P. J. 1979. Phosphatidylinositol transfer activity in rat cerebral hemispheres during development. *J. Neurochem.* 33:355–56

21. Brukdorfer, K. R., Sherry, M. K. 1984. The solubility of cholesterol and its exchange between membranes. *Biochim. Biophys. Acta* 769:187–96

22. Burnett, D. A., Lysenko, N., Manning, J. A., Ockner, R. K. 1979. Utilization of long chain fatty acids by rat liver: Studies of the role of fatty acid binding protein. *Gasteroenterology* 77:241–49

23. Chlapowski, F. J., Band, R. N. 1971. Assembly of lipids into membranes in *Acanthamoeba palestinensis. J. Cell Biol.* 50:634–51

24. Chanderbhan, R., Noland, B. J., Scallen, T. J., Vahouny, G. V. 1982. Sterol carrier protein$_2$: Delivery of cholesterol from adrenal lipid droplets to mitochondria for pregnenolone synthesis. *J. Biol. Chem.* 257:8928–34

25. Chesterson, C. J. 1968. Distribution of cholesterol precursors and other lipids among rat liver intracellular structures. *J. Biol. Chem.* 243:1147–51

26. Cogan, U., Schachter, D. 1981. Asymmetry of lipid domains in human erythrocyte membranes studied with impermeant fluorophores. *Biochemistry* 20:6396–6403

27. Conneely, O. M., Headon, D. R., Olson, C. D., Ungar, F., Dempsey, M. E. 1984. Intramitochondrial movement of adrenal sterol carrier protein with cholesterol in response to corticotropin. *Proc. Natl. Acad. Sci. USA* 81:2970–74

28. Conzelmann, E., Sandhoff, K. 1978. AB variant of infantile G_{M2} gangliosidosis: Deficiency of a factor necessary for stimulation of hexosaminidase A–catalyzed degradation of ganglioside G_{M2} and glycolipid G_{A2}. *Proc. Natl. Acad. Sci. USA* 75:3979–83

29. Crain, R. C., Zilversmit, D. B. 1980. Two nonspecific phospholipid exchange proteins from beef liver. *Biochemistry* 19:1440–47

30. De Cuyper, M., Joniau, M., Dangreau, H. 1980. Spontaneous phospholipid transfer between artificial vesicles followed by free-flow electrophoresis. *Biochem. Biophys. Res. Commun.* 95:1224–30

31. DeGrella, R. F., Simoni, R. D. 1982. Intracellular transport of cholesterol to the plasma membrane. *J. Biol. Chem.* 257:14256–62

32. Demel, R. A., Jansen, J. W. C. M., van Dijek, P. W. M., van Deennen, L. L. M. 1977. The preferential interactions of cholesterol with different classes of phospholipids. *Biochim. Biophys. Acta* 465:1–10

33. Dempsey, M. E., McCoy, K. E., Baker, H. N., Dimitriadou-Vafiadou, A. D., Lorsbach, T., Howard, J. B. 1981. Large scale purification and structural characterization of squalene and sterol protein. *J. Biol. Chem.* 256:1867–73

34. De Silva, N. S., Siu, C.-H. 1980. Preferential incorporation of phospholipids into plasma membranes during cell aggregation of *Dictyostelium discoideum. J. Biol. Chem.* 255:8489–96

35. De Silva, N. S., Siu, C.-H. 1981. Vesicle-mediated transfer of phospholipids to plasma membrane during cell aggregation of *Dictyostelium discoideum. J. Biol. Chem.* 256:5845–50

36. Duckwitz-Peterlein, G., Eilenberger, G., Overath, P. 1977. Phospholipid exchange between bilayer membranes. *Biochim. Biophys. Acta* 469:311–25

37. Dyatlovitskaya, E. V., Timofeeva, N. G., Bergelson, L. D. 1978. A universal lipid exchange protein from rat hepatoma. *Eur. J. Biochem.* 82:463–71

38. Eggens, I., Valtersson, C., Dallner, G., Ernster, L. 1979. Transfer of phospholipids between the endoplasmic reticulum and mitochondria in rat hepatocytes *in vivo. Biochem. Biophys. Res. Commun.* 91:709–14

39. Engle, M. J., van Golde, L. M. G., Wirtz, K. W. A. 1978. Transfer of phospholipids between subcellular fractions of the lung. *FEBS Lett.* 86:277–81
40. Farquhar, M. G. 1983. Multiple pathways of exocytosis, endocytosis, and membrane recycling: Validation of a Golgi route. *Fed. Proc.* 42:2407–13
41. Ferguson, J. B., Bloch, K. 1977. Purification and properties of a soluble protein activator of rat liver squalene epoxidase. *J. Biol. Chem.* 252:5381–85
42. Fournier, N., Geoffroy, M., Deshusses, J. 1978. Purification and characterization of a long chain, fatty-acid-binding protein supplying the mitochondrial beta-oxidative system in the heart. *Biochim. Biophys. Acta* 533:457–64
43. Frink, W. W., Kartenbeck, J. 1971. Outer mitochondrial membrane continuous with endoplasmic reticulum. *Protoplasma* 73:35–41
44. Funkhouser, J. D., Read, R. J. 1985. Phospholipid transfer proteins from lung, properties and possible physiological functions. *Chem. Phys. Lipids* 38:17–27
45. Galla, H. J., Theilen, U., Hartman, W. 1979. Transversal mobility in bilayer membrane vesicles: Use of pyrene lecithin as optical probe. *Chem. Phys. Lipids* 23:239–52
46. Gavey, K. L., Scallen, T. J. 1978. Studies on the conversion of enzymatically generated, microsomal bound squalene to sterol. *J. Biol. Chem.* 253:5476–83
47. Gordon, J. I., Alpers, D. H., Ockner, R. K., Strauss, A. W. 1983. The nucleotide sequence of rat liver fatty acid binding protein mRNA. *J. Biol. Chem.* 258:3356–63
48. Gordon, J. I., Smith, D. P., Alpers, D. H., Strauss, A. W. 1982. Cloning of a complementary deoxyribonucleic acid encoding a portion of rat intestinal preapolipoprotein Alu messenger ribonucleic acid. *Biochemistry* 21:5424–31
49. Goresky, C. A., Daly, D. S., Mishkin, S., Arias, I. M. 1978. Uptake of labeled palmitate by the intact liver: Roll of intracellular binding sites. *Am. J. Physiol.* 234:E542–53
50. Ha, Y. C., Barter, P. J. 1982. Differences in plasma cholesteryl ester transfer activity in sixteen vertebrate species. *Comp. Biochem. Physiol.* 71B:265–69
51. Hechtman, P., Gordon, B. A., Kin, N. M. K. N. Y. 1982. Deficiencys of the hexosaminidase A activator protein in a case of GM₂ gangliosidosis; variant AB. *Pediatr. Res.* 16:217–22
52. Henis, Y. I., Rimon, G., Felder, S. 1982. Lateral mobility of phospholipids in turkey erythrocytes: Implications for adenylate cyclase activation. *J. Biol. Chem.* 257:1407–11
53. Hirabayashi, Y., Li, Y.-T., Li, S.-C. 1983. The protein activator specific for the enzymic hydrolysis of GM₂ ganglioside in normal human brain and brains of three types of GM₂ gangliosidosis. *J. Neurochem.* 40:168–75
54. Houslay, M. D., Stanley, K. K. 1982. Mobility of the lipid and protein components of biological membranes. In *Dynamics of Biological Membranes: Influence on Synthesis, Structure and Function*, Ch. 2, pp. 39–91. New York: Wiley. 330 pp.
55. Hutson, J. L., Higgins, J. A. 1982. Asymmetric synthesis followed by transmembrane movement of phosphatidylethanolamine in rat liver endoplasmic reticulum. *Biochim. Biophys. Acta* 687:247–56
56. Ihm, J., Ellsworth, J. L., Chataing, B., Harmony, J. A. K. 1982. Plasma protein-facilitated coupled exchange of phosphatidylcholine and cholesteryl ester in the absence of cholesterol esterification. *J. Biol. Chem.* 257:4818–27
57. Kader, J. C. 1977. Exchange of phospholipids between membranes. In *Cell Surface Reviews*, ed. G. Poste, G. L. Nicolson, Vol. 3, pp. 127–204. New York: North-Holland
58. Kader, J.-C., Douady, D., Mazliak, P. 1982. Phospholipid transfer proteins. In *Phospholipids*, ed. J. N. Hawthorne, G. B. Ansell, pp. 279–311. New York: Elsevier Biochem.
59. Kaplan, M. R., Simoni, R. D. 1985. Intracellular transport of phosphatidylcholine to the plasma membrane. *J. Cell Biol.* 101:441–45
60. Kaplan, M. R., Simoni, R. D. 1985. Transport of cholesterol from the endoplasmic reticulum to the plasma membrane. *J. Cell Biol.* 101:446–53
61. Kennedy, E. P., Yaffe, M. P. 1983. Intracellular phospholipid movement and the role of phospholipid transfer proteins in animal cells. *Biochemistry* 22:1497–1507
62. Krebs, J. J. R. 1982. The topology of phospholipids in artificial and biological membranes. *J. Bioenerg. Biomembr.* 14:141–57
63. Kremer, J. M. H., Kops-Werkhoven, M. M., Pathmamanoharan, C., Gijzeman, O. L. J., Wiersema, P. H. 1977. Phase diagrams and the kinetics of phospholipid exchange for vesicles of differ-

ent composition and radius. *Biochim. Biophys. Acta* 471:177–88

64. Lange, Y., Matthies, H. J. G. 1984. Transfer of cholesterol from its site of synthesis to the plasma membrane. *J. Biol. Chem.* 259:14624–30

65. Lange, Y., Ramos, B. V. 1983. Analysis of the distribution of cholesterol in the intact cell. *J. Biol. Chem.* 258:15130–34

66. Li, Y.-T., Li, S.-C. 1982. Biosynthesis and catabolism of glycosphingolipids. *Adv. Carbohydr. Chem. Biochem.* 40:235–86

67. Li, Y.-T., Li, S.-C. 1983. Activator proteins for sphingolipid hydrolysis. In *The Enzymes*, ed. P. D. Boyer, Vol. XVI, pp. 427–45. New York: Academic. 783 pp.

68. Lipsky, N. G., Pagano, R. E. 1984. Fluorescent sphingomyelin labels the plasma membrane of cultured fibroblasts. *Ann. NY Acad. Sci.* 435:306–8

69. Lord, J. M. 1976. Phospholipid synthesis and exchange in castor bean endosperm homogenates. *Plant Physiol.* 57:218–23

70. Lowe, J. B., Boguski, M. S., Sweetser, D. A., Elshourbagy, N. A., Taylor, J. M., Gordon, J. I. 1985. Human liver fatty acid binding protein: Isolation of a full length cDNA and comparative sequence analyses of orthologous and paralogous proteins. *J. Biol. Chem.* 260:3413–17

71. Lunzer, M. A., Manning, J. A., Ockner, R. K. 1977. Inhibition of rat liver acetyl coenzyme A carboxylase by long chain acyl coenzyme A and fatty acid. *J. Biol. Chem.* 252:5483–87

72. Lutton, C., Zilversmit, D. B. 1976. Phospholipid exchange proteins in rat intestine. *Lipids* 11:16–20

73. Makita, A., Taniguchi, N. 1985. Glycosphingolipids. In *Glycolipids*, ed. H. Wiegandt, pp. 1–99. New York: Elsevier. 314 pp.

74. Martin, F. J., MacDonald, R. C. 1976. Phospholipid exchange between bilayer membrane vesicles. *Biochemistry* 15:321–27

75. McClosky, M. A., Troy, F. A. 1980. Paramagnetic isoprenoid carrier lipids. 2. Dispersion and dynamics in lipid membranes. *Biochemistry* 19:2061–66

76. McLean, L. R., Phillips, M. C. 1981. Mechanism of cholesterol and phosphatidylcholine exchange or transfer between unilamellar vesicles. *Biochemistry* 20:2893–2900

77. McLean, L. R., Phillips, M. C. 1981. Cholesterol desorption from clusters of phosphatidylcholine and cholesterol in unilamellar vesicle bilayers during lipid transfer or exchange. *Biochemistry* 21:4053–59

78. McMurray, W. C., Dawson, R. M. C. 1969. Phospholipid exchange reactions within liver cell. *Biochem. J.* 112:91–108

79. Metz, R. J., Radin, N. S. 1980. Glucosylceramide uptake protein from spleen cytosol. *J. Biol. Chem.* 255:4463–67

80. Metz, R. J., Radin, N. S. 1982. Purification and properties of a cerebroside transfer protein. *J. Biol. Chem.* 257:12901–7

81. Mills, J. T., Furlong, S. T., Dawidowicz, E. A. 1984. Plasma membrane biogenesis in eukaryotic cells: Translocation of newly synthesized lipid. *Proc. Natl. Acad. Sci. USA.* 81:1385–88

82. Morin, R. J., Brun, M. J., Srikantaiah, M. V. 1982. Effect of age and cholestyramine feeding on rat liver 3-hydroxy-3-methyl glutaryl CoA reductase, sterol carrier protein 1 and sterol carrier protein 2 activities. *Lipids* 17:507–10

83. Morre, D. J., Merritt, W. D., Lembi, C. A. 1971. Connections between mitochondria and endoplasmic reticulum in rat liver and onion stem. *Protoplasm* 73:43–49

84. Morton, R. E., Zilversmit, D. B. 1982. Purification and characterization of lipid transfer protein(s) from human lipoprotein-deficient plasma. *J. Lipid Res.* 23:1058–67

85. Nichols, W. J., Pagano, R. E. 1981. Kinetics of soluble lipid monomer diffusion between vesicles. *Biochemistry* 20:2783–89

86. Noland, B. J., Arebalo, R. E., Hansbury, E., Scallen, T. J. 1980. Purification and properties of sterol carrier protein$_2$. *J. Biol. Chem.* 255:4282–89

87. Ockner, R. K., Manning, J. A. 1974. Fatty acid-binding protein in small intestine; identification, isolation, and evidence for its role in cellular fatty acid transport. *J. Clin. Invest.* 54:326–35

88. Ockner, R. K., Manning, J. A., Kane, J. P. 1982. Fatty acid binding protein: Isolation from rat liver, characterization, and immunochemical quantification. *J. Biol. Chem.* 257:7872–78

89. O'Doherty, P. J. A., Kuksis, A. 1975. Stimulation of triacylglycerol synthesis by Z protein in rat liver and intestinal mucosa. *FEBS Lett.* 60:256–58

90. Op den Kamp, J. A. F. 1979. Lipid asymmetry in membranes. *Ann. Rev. Biochem.* 48:47–71

91. Op den Kamp, J. A. F. 1981. The asymmetric architecture of membranes. In *Membrane Structure,* ed. J. B. Finean, R. H. Michell, pp. 83–126. Amsterdam: Elsevier. 271 pp.

92. Pagano, R. E., Sleight, R. G. 1985. Defining lipid transport pathways in animal cells. *Science* 229:1051–57

93. Pagano, R. E., Sleight, R. G. 1985. Emerging problems in the cell biology of lipids. *Trends Biochem. Sci.* 10:421–25

94. Poorthuis, B. J. H. M., Glatz, J. F. C., Akeroyd, R., Wirtz, K. W. A. 1981. A new high-yield procedure for the purification of the nonspecific phospholipid transfer protein from rat liver. *Biochim. Biophys. Acta* 665:256–61

95. Poorthuis, B. J. H. M., Van der Krift, T. P., Teerlink, T., Akeroyd, R., Hostetler, K. Y., Wirtz, K. W. A. 1980. Phospholipid transfer activities in Morris hepatomas and the specific contribution of the phosphatidylcholine exchange protein. *Biochim. Biophys. Acta* 600: 376–86

96. Post, M., Batenburg, J. J., Schuurmans, E. A. J. M., van Golde, L. M. G. 1980. Phospholipid-transfer activity in type II cells isolated from adult lung. *Biochim. Biophys. Acta* 620:317–21

97. Poznansky, M. J., Czekanski, S. 1982. Cholesterol movement between human skin fibroblasts and phosphatidylcholine vesicles. *Biochim. Biophys. Acta* 685: 182–90

98. Raetz, C. R. H. 1982. Genetic control of phospholipid bilayer assembly. In *Phospholipids,* ed. J. N. Hawthorne, G. B. Ansell, pp. 435–77. New York: Elsevier Biomed.

99. Renaud, G., Foliot, A., Infante, R. 1978. Increased uptake of fatty acids by the isolated rat liver after raising the fatty acid binding protein concentration with clofibrate. *Biochem. Biophys. Res. Commun.* 80:327–34

100. Rimon, G., Hanski, E., Levitzki, A. 1980. Temperature dependence of beta receptor, adenosine receptor, and sodium fluoride stimulated adenylate cyclase from turkey erythrocytes. *Biochemistry* 19:4451–60

101. Roseman, M. A., Thompson, T. E. 1980. Mechanism of the spontaneous transfer of phospholipids between bilayers. *Biochemistry* 19:439–44

102. Rothman, J. E., Lenard, J. 1977. Membrane asymmetry: The nature of membrane asymmetry provides clues to the puzzle of how membranes are assembled. *Science* 195:743–53

103. Rousselet, A., Guthmann, C., Matricon, J., Bienvenue, A., Devaux, P. F. 1976. Study of the transverse diffusion of spin labeled phospholipids in biological membranes. I. Human red blood cells. *Biochim. Biophys. Acta* 426:357–71

104. Ruby, J. R., Dyer, R. F., Skalko, R. G. 1969. Continuities between mitochondria and endoplasmic reticulum in the mammalian ovary. *Z. Zellforsch. Mikrosk. Anat.* 97:30–37

105. Scallen, T. J., Noland, B. J., Gavey, K. L., Bass, N. M., Ockner, R. K., et al. 1985. Sterol carrier protein 2 and fatty acid-binding protein: Separate and distinct physiological functions. *J. Biol. Chem.* 260:4733–39

106. Schachter, D., Cogan, U., Abbott, R. E. 1982. Asymmetry of lipid dynamics in human erythrocyte membranes studied with permeant fluorophores. *Biochemistry* 21:2146–50

107. Scow, R. O., Blanchette-Mackie, E. J., Smith, L. C. 1976. Role of capillary endothelium in the clearance of chylomicrons: A model for lipid transport. *Circ. Res.* 49:149–62

108. Scow, R. O., Blanchette-Mackie, E. J., Smith, L. C. 1980. Transport of lipid across capillary endothelium. *Fed. Proc.* 39:2610–17

109. Scow, R. O., Blanchette-Mackie, E. J., Wetzel, M. G., Reinila, A. 1983. Lipid transport in tissue by lateral movement in cell membrane. In *Adipocyte and Obesity,* ed. A. Angel, C. H. Hollenberg, D. A. K. Roncari, pp. 165–69. New York: Raven

110. Seigneuret, M., Devaux, P. F. 1984. ATP-dependent asymmetric distribution of spin-labeled phospholipids in the erythrocyte membrane: Relation to shape changes. *Proc. Natl. Acad. Sci. USA* 81:3751–55

111. Seigneuret, M., Zachowski, A., Hermann, A., Devaux, P. F. 1984. Asymmetric lipid fluidity in human erythrocyte membrane: New spin-label evidence. *Biochemistry* 23:4271–75

112. Sleight, R. G., Pagano, R. E. 1983. Rapid appearance of newly synthesized phosphatidylethanolamine at the cell surface. *J. Biol. Chem.* 258:9050–58

113. Sleight, R. G., Pagano, R. E. 1984. Transport of a fluorescent phosphatidylcholine analog from the plasma membrane to the Golgi apparatus. *J. Cell Biol.* 99:742–51

114. Sleight, R. G., Pagano, R. E. 1985. Transbilayer movement of a fluorescent phosphatidylethanolamine analogue across the plasma membranes of cultured mammalian cells. *J. Biol. Chem.* 260:1146–54

115. Sleight, R. G., Pagano, R. E. 1986. Intracellular transport of a fluorescent phosphatidylcholine analog in a variety of established cell lines. Submitted for publication

116. Snider, M. D. 1984. Biosynthesis of glycoproteins: Formation of N-linked oligosaccharides. In *Biology of Carbohydrates*, ed. V. Ginsburg, P. W. Robbins, Vol. 2, pp. 163–98. New York: Wiley

117. Snider, M. D., Robbins, P. W. 1982. Transmembrane organization of protein glycosylation. Mature oligosaccharide-lipid is located on the luminal side of microsomes from Chinese hamster ovary cells. *J. Biol. Chem.* 257:6796–6801

118. Snider, M. D., Rogers, O. C. 1984. Transmembrane movement of oligosaccharide-lipids during glycoprotein synthesis. *Cell* 36:753–61

119. Sonderfeld, S., Conzelmann, E., Schwarzmann, G., Burg, J., Hinrichs, U., Sandhoff, K. 1985. Incorporation and metabolism of ganglioside G_{M2} in skin fibroblasts from normal and G_{M2} gangliosidosis subjects. *Eur. J. Biochem.* 149:247–55

120. Spiegel, S., Schlessinger, J., Fishman, P. H. 1984. Incorporation of fluorescent gangliosides into human fibroblasts: Mobility, fate, and interaction with fibronectin. *J. Cell Biol.* 99:699–704

121. Srikantaiah, M. V., Hansbury, E., Loughran, E. D., Scallen, T. J. 1976. Purification and properties of sterol carrier protein. *J. Biol. Chem.* 251:5496–5504

122. Steinman, R. M., Mellman, I. S., Muller, W. A., Cohn, Z. A. 1983. Endocytosis and recycling of plasma membrane. *J. Cell Biol.* 96:1–27

123. Stremmel, W., Strohmeyer, G., Borchard, F., Kochwa, S., Berk, P. D. Isolation and partial characterization of a fatty acid binding protein in rat liver plasma membranes. *Proc. Natl. Acad. Sci. USA* 82:4–8

124. Struck, D. K., Pagano, R. E. 1980. Insertion of fluorescent phospholipids into the plasma membrane of a mammalian cell. *J. Biol. Chem.* 255:5405–10

125. Tai, S.-P., Kaplan, S. 1985. Phospholipid transfer proteins in microorganisms. *Chem. Phys. Lipids* 38:41–50

126. Takahashi, K., Odani, S., Ono, T. 1983. Isolation and characterization of the three fractions (DE-I, DE-II and DE-III) of rat liver Z-protein and the complete primary structure of DE-II. *Eur. J. Biochem.* 136:589–601

127. Tanaka, K.-I., Ohnishi, S.-I. 1976. Heterogeneity in the fluidity of intact erythrocyte membrane and its homogenization upon hemolysis. *Biochim. Biophys. Acta* 426:218–31

128. Tanaka, T., Billheimer, J. T., Strauss, J. F. 1984. Luteinized rat ovaries contain a sterol carrier protein. *Endocrinology* 114:533–40

129. Teerlink, T., Van der Krift, T. P., Van Heusden, G. P., Wirtz, K. W. A. 1984. Determination of nonspecific lipid transfer protein in rat tissue and Morris hepatomas by enzyme immunoassay. *Biochim. Biophys. Acta* 793:251–59

130. Vahouny, G. V., Chanderbhan, R., Noland, B. J., Irwin, D., Dennis, P., et al. 1983. Sterol carrier protein$_2$: Identification of adrenal sterol carrier protein$_2$ and site of action for mitochondrial cholesterol utilization. *J. Biol. Chem.* 258:11731–37

131. Vahouny, G. V., Chanderbhan, R., Noland, B. J., Scallen, T. J. 1985. Cholesterol ester hydrolase and sterol carrier proteins. *Endocr. Res.* 10:473–505

132. Vahouny, G. V., Dennis, P., Chanderbhan, R., Fiskum, G., Noland, B. J., Scallen, T. J. 1984. Sterol carrier protein$_2$ (SCP$_2$)-mediated transfer of cholesterol to mitochondria inner membranes. *Biochem. Biophys. Res. Commun.* 122:509–15

133. Van den Besselaar, A. M. H. P., De-Kruijff, B., Van den Bosch, H., Van Deenen, L. L. M. 1978. Phosphatidylcholine mobility in liver microsomal membranes. *Biochim. Biophys. Acta* 510:242–56

134. van Dijek, P. W. M., De Kruijff, B., van Deennen, L. L. M., De Gier, J., Demel, R. A. 1976. The preference of cholesterol for phosphatidylcholine in mixed phosphatidylcholine-phosphatidylethanolamine bilayers. *Biochim. Biophys. Acta* 455:576–87

135. Van Meer, G., Op den Kamp, J. A. F. 1982. Transbilayer movement of various phosphatidylcholine species in intact human erythrocytes. *J. Cell Biochem.* 19:193–204

136. Voelker, D. R. 1985. Disruption of phosphatidylserine translocation to the mitochondria in baby hamster kidney cells. *J. Biol. Chem.* 260:14671–76

137. Voelker, D. R. 1985. In *Biochemistry of Lipids and Membranes*, ed. D. E. Vance, J. E. Vance, pp. 475–502. Menlo Park, Calif: Benjamin/Cummings

138. Wattenberg, B. W., Silbert, D. F. 1983. Sterol partitioning among intracellular membranes. *J. Biol. Chem.* 258:2284–89

139. Waugh, R. A., Spray, T. L., Sommer,

J. R. 1973. Fenestrations of sarcoplasmic reticulum: Delineation by lanthanum acting as a fortuitous tracer *in situ* negative stain. *J. Cell Biol.* 59:254–60

140. Wetterau, J. R., Zilversmit, D. B. 1984. A triglyceride and cholesteryl ester transfer protein associated with liver microsomes. *J. Biol. Chem.* 259:10863–66

141. Wetzel, M. G., Scow, R. O. 1984. Lipolysis and fatty acid transport in rat heart: Electron microscopic study. *Am. J. Physiol.* 246:C467–85

142. Williamson, P., Bateman, J., Kozarsky, K., Mattocks, K. 1982. Involvement of spectrin in the maintenance of phase-state asymmetry in the erythrocyte membrane. *Cell* 30:725–33

143. Wirtz, K. W. A. 1982. Phospholipid transfer proteins. In *Lipid-Protein Interactions,* ed. P. C. Jost, O. H. Griffith, Vol. 1, pp. 151–231. New York: Wiley. 338 pp.

144. Wirtz, K. W. A., Jolles, J., Westerman, J., Neys, F. 1976. Phospholipid exchange proteins in synaptosomes and myelin fraction from rat brain. *Nature* 260:354–55

145. Wirtz, K. W. A., Zilversmit, D. B. 1968. Exchange of phospholipids between liver mitochondria and microsomes in vitro. *J. Biol. Chem.* 243:3596–3602

146. Wirtz, K. W. A., Zilversmit, D. B. 1969. The use of phenobarbital and carbon tetrachloride to examine liver phospholipid exchange. *Biochim. Biophys. Acta* 187:468–76

147. Yamada, K., Abe, A., Sasaki, T. 1985. Specificity of the glycolipid transfer protein from pig brain. *J. Biol. Chem.* 260:4615–21

148. Yamada, K., Sasaki, T. 1982. A rat brain cytosol protein which accelerates the translocation of galactosylceramide, lactosylceramide and glucosylceramide between membranes. *Biochim. Biophys. Acta* 687:195–203

149. Zachowski, A., Fellman, P., Devaux, P. F. 1985. Absence of transbilayer diffusion of spin-labeled sphingomyelin on human erythrocytes. Comparison with the diffusion of several spin-labeled glycerophospholipids. *Biochim. Biophys. Acta* 815:510–14

150. Zilversmit, D. B., Hughes, M. E. 1976. Phospholipid exchange between membranes. In *Methods in Membrane Biology,* ed. E. D. Korn, Vol. 7, Ch. 4, pp. 211–259. New York: Plenum

151. Zilversmit, D. B., Hughes, M. E. 1977. Extensive exchange of rat liver microsomal phospholipids. *Biochim. Biophys. Acta* 469:99–110

Ann. Rev. Physiol. 1987. 49:209–19

ERYTHROCYTE MEMBRANE ELASTICITY AND VISCOSITY

R. M. Hochmuth

Department of Mechanical Engineering and Materials Science, Duke University, Durham, North Carolina 27706

R. E. Waugh

Department of Radiation Biology and Biophysics, University of Rochester, School of Medicine and Dentistry, Rochester, New York 14642

INTRODUCTION

The classical theory of elasticity (35) treats the material of a deformable body as a three-dimensional continuum in which internal stresses occur as the body is deformed by external forces acting over its surface. Although the internal stresses are caused by the displacement of atoms or molecules from an original state of equilibrium, the molecular character of the material is ignored. This means that every volume element within the material must contain enough molecules to guarantee that the thermal fluctuation of any one molecule does not effect the local state of stress.

Since biomembranes in general and red cell membranes in particular are only a few molecules thick, they can form a continuum only in the plane of the membrane. Thus, the methods of classical, three-dimensional continuum mechanics must be compressed into a two-dimensional world in which "stress resultants" or "tensions" (force per unit width of membrane surface) are defined on the surface of the membrane (8, 25, 48). Measurement of the surface stress resultants and the corresponding surface deformations permits the material properties of the membrane surface to be calculated (15, 16, 20). These surface properties represent a summation, over the thickness of the membrane, of the properties of the lamellar, molecular structures that form the membrane.

209

External forces acting over the surface of an elastic body readily deform and stretch it. When the external forces of deformation are removed, an elastic body recovers its original undeformed shape, i.e. it has "memory." As the membrane deforms, viscous dissipation can occur within the membrane material and in the surrounding fluid. Since the cytoplasm of the normal human red cell is a newtonian hemoglobin solution, the shape of the cell comes from the natural shape of the membrane, and the elastic response of the cell is determined by the elasticity of the membrane. However, the viscous response of the cell can be governed by the viscosities of the cytoplasm, membrane, and external plasma or saline solutions. Surprisingly, dissipation within the membrane usually dominates the process of cell deformation, and thus, dissipation in the cytoplasm and external medium can be neglected (13, 33).

MEMBRANE ELASTICITY

Although cell and membrane deformation can be quite complex in general, for a two-dimensional, incompressible, elastic material like the red cell membrane, any deformation can be expressed in terms of three fundamental, independent deformations (16, 20). The deformations are (a) an elongation or "shear" of the membrane without either increasing the surface area or bending it, (b) a dilation (isotropic expansion) of the membrane surface without either shearing or bending it, and (c) a bending of the membrane without either shearing or expanding it. Each of these fundamental elastic deformations is characterized by an elastic modulus: (a) a shear modulus μ with units of N/m, (b) an area expansion modulus K with units of N/m, and (c) a bending modulus B with units of N m. In general, a larger modulus indicates a greater resistance to that particular form of deformation.

Shear Elasticity

For the constant area extension of a two-dimensional material, the maximum shear resultant, T_s, occurs along a line at 45° to the direction of extension. Shear and extension represent the same phenomenon and are characterized by a single elastic constant—the shear modulus μ. The relation between the shear resultant T_s and the extension ratio λ (extended length/original length) is (9, 15):

$$T_s = (\mu/2)(\lambda^2 - \lambda^{-2}).$$ 1.

When the portion of the membrane at the dimple of a flaccid cell is aspirated into a pipette of radius R_p, the relation between the aspiration pressure P (relative to the pressure outside the cell) and the extension up the pipette L is (5, 57):

$$P \cdot R_p/\mu = (L/R_p) - 1 + \ln(2L/R_p).$$

2.

From Equation 2 it is readily seen that μ is proportional to the slope of the P versus L line. This slope can be measured accurately. The major uncertainty in the determination of a value for μ is the uncertainty in the measurement of a value for the pipette radius R_p. A 20% error in the measurement of R_p (say 0.2 μm out of 1.0 μm) gives about a 40% error in the value for μ. Based upon a single datum point for two different human red cells at room temperature, Evans (9) first obtained a value for μ of 5×10^{-3} mN/m. This value agrees with the value for μ obtained from a study of the shear deformation of point-attached red cells (9, 30, 48). Since the original measurements (9), many investigators have measured values for μ (5, 17, 36, 42, 44, 49, 56, 57). Values range from about 4×10^{-3} mN/m (5, 17) to 10×10^{-3} mN/m (56). The typical value is $\mu = 6$–7×10^{-3} mN/m. Recently, however, Evans et al (19) accurately measured the inner diameter of their pipettes from the insertion depth of a tapered microneedle that had been calibrated with the scanning electron microscope. Their value is $\mu = 9 \pm 1.7 \times 10^{-3}$ mN/m. Because this value is based on an accurate measurement for R_p, it must be given greater weight. Thus, for human red cells at room temperature, $\mu = 6$–9×10^{-3} mN/m. For a given pipette and a given sample of cells from the same donor, the standard deviation in the measurement of μ is about $\pm$ 20%. This is caused either by cell-cell variability or by errors in measurement of the slope of the P versus L line. Experimental data indicate that μ, as defined by Equation 1, is constant, although Fischer et al (24) suggest that the value for μ could decrease by a factor of 2.5 at very small membrane strains. Such small strains cannot be measured with present techniques.

The shear modulus is affected by changes in the membrane environment. Over a temperature range from 5 to 45°C, μ decreases from 8.0×10^{-3} to 5.2 $\times 10^{-3}$ mN/m (57). Thus, the reversible change with temperature in the value for μ is -6×10^{-5} mN/m/°C (57). Cells heated to 47–48°C for 6–7 min and then rapidly cooled to room temperature undergo a permanent, irreversible two- to threefold increase in the value for μ (43, 46).

Metabolic depletion caused by 24-hr incubation of red cells at 37°C causes either no change in the value for μ (39) or a slight (15%) decrease in its value when calcium is present (1). Decreasing pH causes a significant increase in the value for μ, while increasing pH above 7.2 has little effect on its value (6). Elevated concentrations of 2,3-diphosphoglycerate appear to have no effect on the value for μ, except at low ionic strengths, where the value for μ decreases (54).

For normal cells, the value for μ is independent of the cytoplasmic hemoglobin concentration (19, 36, 40, 44). Cells with hemoglobin removed (pink resealed ghosts) have a modulus indistinguishable from that of controls (54). However, the membrane shear elasticity of sickle cells begins to increase when the hemoglobin concentration exceeds about 0.38 kg/liter (19). At 0.45 kg/liter, the value for μ is about two and one-half times that of normal cells (19). According to Nash et al (40), the very dense, irreversibly sickled cell (ISC) has a value for μ that is about twice that of normal cells. Surprisingly, prior to morphological sickling, the shear elasticity of sickle cell membrane does not appear to change, even when the cells are deoxygenated to oxygen concentrations as low as 20 mm Hg (41).

The shear modulus is also affected by chemical alteration of the membrane. Small concentrations of membrane-permeable, bifunctional sulfhydryl reagents (e.g. diamide, tetrathionate) decrease the elongation of human red cells freely suspended in a shear field (23), which probably indicates an increase in the value of μ. Above a certain threshold level (0.1 μg/ml/cell), small concentrations of the lectin wheat germ agglutinin (WGA) cause a stiffening of the membrane (18) because of the binding of WGA to glycophorin (3, 37). At higher concentrations (2 μg/ml/cell), a thirtyfold increase in the value for μ occurs, and individual cells respond in an inelastic, plasticlike manner (18). Cholesterol enrichment and depletion of membrane have no effect on the value for μ (2).

In hereditary spherocytosis, the value for μ is smaller than normal (58). A strong correlation is observed between the surface density of the structural membrane protein spectrin and the value for μ (55). This observation supports the idea that spectrin is primarily responsible for the shear elasticity of the membrane. However, there is little correlation between the value for μ and abnormalities associated either with the membrane protein band 4.1 or with the number of high-affinity ankyrin binding sites (55). The elasticity of red cells from males with Duchenne muscular dystrophy and female carriers is slightly elevated (45).

Area Elasticity

An isotropic dilation of the red cell membrane is produced by aspirating a preswollen cell into a micropipette until the portion of the cell outside the pipette forms a sphere. The isotropic tension T is given by (22, 47):

$$T = P \cdot R_p / [2 \cdot (1 - R_p/R_c)], \qquad\qquad 3.$$

where P is the aspiration pressure, R_p is the pipette radius, and R_c is the cell radius. As the aspiration pressure is increased, the area of the cell expands because of an increase in the isotropic tension in the membrane. The expansion of the surface area is measured accurately by measuring the movement up the pipette of the membrane "tongue" within the pipette (21, 22). Extremely small area dilations can be measured in this way.

Evans et al (22) propose a simple linear relation between the isotropic tension in the membrane and the relative area expansion:

$$T = K \cdot \Delta A / A_o, \qquad \qquad \qquad 4.$$

where ΔA is the increase in surface area, A_o is the original area, and K is the area expansion modulus. The value for K at room temperature is $K = 450$ mN/m (21, 57) with a standard deviation of about $\pm$ 15–20% (57).

The value for K decreases from about 560 mN/m at 5°C to about 320 mN/m at 46°C (57). The change with temperature in the value for K is -6 mN/m/°C (57). Note that both μ and K have roughly the same proportional decrease with temperature (57). The unpublished results of L. Smith & R. M. Hochmuth indicate that the value for K is smaller by approximately a factor of two for cells from individuals with hereditary spherocytosis. Finally, the recent, disconcerting results of Katnik & Waugh (34) indicate that the apparent value for K depends strongly on the strength (voltage) of the applied electrical field across the cell. Voltages of $\pm$ 200 mV produce changes in the value for K of $\pm$ 40%. Also, the measured value for K changes with the presence of Cu^{2+} or Zn^{2+} in solution (34).

Bending Elasticity

Although small, the membrane's resistance to bending stabilizes the biconcave shape of the cell during the early phases of the swelling process (24, 60) and during pipette aspiration (11). For a shear elastic modulus of 6×10^{-3} mN/m, the bending modulus has to be about 10^{-19} N m (10^{-12} ergs) for the cell to swell smoothly (without popping) from a biconcave shape into a sphere (24, 60). This value for the bending modulus implies that bending does not contribute significantly to the pressure required to aspirate the membrane into a pipette (11).

In multilamellar membranes, bending resistance can occur because of the differential expansion and compression of a given monolayer or coupled bilayer or coupled multilayer. For a coupled bilayer, the relation between the bending modulus B, the compressibility of the bilayer K, and the bilayer separation distance h is (16, 20)

$$B = h^2 K / 4. \qquad \qquad \qquad 5.$$

For $h = 2.5$ nm and $K = 100$ mN/m, B equals 1.6×10^{-19} N m.

The bending moment, M, per unit length is given by (10, 26)

$$M = B(C_1 + C_2 - C_o), \qquad \qquad \qquad 6.$$

where C_1 and C_2 are the principal curvatures and C_o is the curvature in the stress-free state. Evans (12) has designed an experiment to measure the value for B in Equation 6. In this experiment, a cell is aspirated into a pipette until the circumferential load on the membrane causes it to buckle. The magnitude of the aspiration pressure at buckling depends directly on the value for B and inversely on the cube of the pipette radius. Analysis and measurements (12, 19) indicate that $B = 1.8 \pm 0.2 \times 10^{-19}$ N m. This value for B agrees with previous estimates (11, 24, 60), including the estimate based on Equation 5.

Based on measurements of the buckling pressure, Nash & Meiselman (43) conclude that heat treatment of red cells causes the value for B to change little, if at all. Also, the value for B does not change with cell hemoglobin concentration for both normal and sickle cells (19), except at an extraordinarily high value for the hemoglobin concentration (0.47 kg/liter). Waugh (55) found a strong correlation between the reduction in spectrin and the fractional reduction in the values for both the bending modulus B and the shear modulus μ. For red cell membranes, this suggests a common molecular basis for the values of μ and B, as well as for the value of K (Equation 5).

MEMBRANE VISCOSITY

The elasticity of the membrane characterizes its resistance to deformation, and the viscosity of the membrane characterizes its resistance to a *rate* of deformation. For all experiments discussed in this section, the rate of deformation is one of shear (extension), and thus a shear viscosity is measured.

Viscoelastic Solid Behavior

When the membrane of a flaccid red cell is elongated by micropipette aspiration or fluid shear deformation and then the force of deformation is suddenly removed, the cell rapidly recovers its undeformed shape. For this recovery process, Evans & Hochmuth (13) calculated that the viscous dissipation in the membrane is about two orders of magnitude greater than that in the internal hemoglobin solution. Thus, the membrane is the dominant source of viscous dissipation during the recovery process.

Evans & Hochmuth (13) accounted for the dissipation in a viscoelastic solid membrane by the addition to Equation 1 of a dissipative term analogous to Newton's law of viscosity:

$$T_s = (\mu/2) \, (\lambda^2 - \lambda^{-2}) + 2\eta \, \partial \ln\lambda/\partial t, \qquad 7.$$

where t is time and η is the coefficient of surface viscosity. A characteristic time constant t_c is obtained in Equation 7 simply by dividing η by μ:

$$t_c = \eta/\mu. \qquad 8.$$

The time required for the membrane of a red cell to recover its stress-free state when the force of deformation is removed is given by the integration of Equation 7 with $T_s = 0$ (13, 33). A best fit of this integrated equation to the experimental data gives a value for t_c (33). Typically, $t_c = 0.1$ s, and thus if $\mu = 10^{-2}$ mN/m, $\eta = \mu t_c = 10^{-3}$ mN s/m.

Rapid deformation of a red cell, produced either by rapid aspiration of the membrane into a pipette (5) or by "tank treading" the membrane in a fluid shear field (51), indicates that "shear thinning" of the membrane may occur at high rates of deformation. Values for t_c and, presumably, η (if μ is a constant) may decrease by as much as a factor of six from their values at a very low rate of deformation (5).

The membrane viscosity η is strongly influenced by the concentration of hemoglobin in the cytoplasm, probably because hemoglobin binds to the membrane (4, 7). Surprisingly, however, the value for the shear elastic modulus μ for normal cells is independent of hemoglobin concentration (19, 36, 40, 44, 54). Thus, η increases in direct proportion with t_c, since μ is a constant. Red cells from the bottom 5% of a centrifuge tube have a value for t_c that is about 50% larger than that of those from the top 5% (36, 44). Similar but less dramatic changes were found by Sutera et al (50). Studies in which cells were precisely separated into density fractions with Stractan solutions reveal a dramatic increase in t_c with an increase in hemoglobin concentration (19). For example, at 0.42 kg/liter (an abnormally large value), the value for t_c is about ten times larger than its value at a normal hemoglobin concentration of 0.32 kg/liter (19). For sickle cells the value for t_c increases with hemoglobin concentration, just as it does for normal cells (19, 40). The viscosity of the dense, irreversibly sickled cell (ISC) is very large because of an increase in both the values of μ and t_c (40). In general, rehydration of dense cells by swelling them in a hypotonic solution causes t_c and η to approach normal values (19, 40).

Temperature also has a strong influence on membrane viscosity. For example, the value for t_c decreases from 0.275 s at 6°C to 0.065 s at 37°C (27). With Equation 8 and the data of Waugh & Evans (57), these values for t_c are converted to values for η. At 6°C, $\eta = 2.1 \times 10^{-3}$ mN s/m, and at 37°C, $\eta = 0.36 \times 10^{-3}$ mN s/m (27).

The lectin wheat germ agglutinin (WGA) binds to glycophorin (3, 37). Small concentrations of WGA can cause a threefold increase in the value for η (49). Elevated levels of 2,3-DPG also affect the value for η. High 2,3-DPG levels at physiological ionic strength cause an increase in η because of an increased cellular hemoglobin concentration (54). At lower ionic strength the value for η decreases with high 2,3-DPG (54). ATP depletion via incubation at 37°C for 24 hr has no effect on the value for η (39). Cholesterol enrichment and depletion of human red cell membrane have no effect on the value for η (2). Ghost cells have a normal value for η (42). Diabetic cells have a normal value for t_c and, presumably, a normal value for the membrane viscosity η (59). Nonmammalian nucleated cells have values for η which are 10 to 30 times those for normal, mammalian cells (56). In general, the value for η is reduced in inherited blood disorders involving reductions in the amount of spectrin, reductions in the number of high-affinity ankyrin binding sites, and abnormalities associated with the band 4.1 membrane proteins (55).

Yield and Continuous Flow

When the stress resultant in the membrane of a red cell exceeds a critical value, the membrane material yields and flows from the cell body into a long, thin, apparently hollow membrane filament called a "tether" (31). Evans & Hochmuth (14) modeled this membrane flow process by assuming that the membrane behaves as a two-dimensional version of a "Bingham plastic":

$$\partial\ln\lambda/\partial t = 0 \text{ for } T_s < T_y$$

$$T_s = T_y + 2\eta_p \cdot \partial\ln\lambda/\partial t \text{ for } T_s > T_y, \hspace{2cm} 9.$$

where T_y is the value for the shear resultant at the yield point where the membrane begins to flow, and η_p is the viscosity for plastic flow. If the tether radius is between 20 and 50 nm, Evans & Hochmuth (14) calculate a value for $T_y = 1.6-4.0 \times 10^{-2}$ mN/m. A more recent measurement and calculation by Waugh gives $T_y = 2 \times 10^{-2}$ mN/m (52). The value for η_p (Equation 9) is inversely proportional to the tether growth rate or tether velocity and directly proportional to the stress resultant in the membrane relative to the yield stress. At room temperature, $\eta_p = 3-10 \times 10^{-3}$ mN s/m (14, 29, 32, 52, 58). These values for η_p are about ten times larger than those for η discussed in the previous section. However, the formation of a tether is a drastic process in which the lipid component of the membrane may separate from the cytoskeleton.

At 12°C, $\eta_p = 29 \times 10^{-3}$ mN s/m, while at 40°C, $\eta_p = 1.3 \times 10^{-3}$ mN s/m (52). The dependence of η_p on temperature gives an apparent activation energy of 18.6 kcal/mol, while the dependence of η on temperature gives only 10.0 kcal/mol (52). Surprisingly, the value for T_y does not change with temperature.

In one case of hereditary spherocytosis, the value for T_y is about one-third that of normal, whereas the value for η_p appears to be normal (58). Abnormalities in the binding of ankyrin to the membrane do not affect the value of T_y (53). Abnormalities associated with the function of band 4.1 cause a reduction in the value for T_y, but the extent of the reduction does not correlate well with the extent of the molecular abnormality (53).

Creep and Force Relaxation

Small forces applied for periods of time greater than a few minutes result in permanent deformation of the membrane (17). This process of creep and force relaxation in red cell membrane has been modeled analytically with an elastic membrane component (Equation 1) in series with a linear (Newtonian) viscous component (20). Markle et al (38) measured the permanent deformation of red cell membrane. The magnitude of the permanent deformation is proportional to the total time period of extension and the level of the applied force. When the results are analyzed according to the analytical model, a value for a "creep viscosity" can be calculated. However, the results are strongly influenced by the concentration of albumin in the suspending fluid. For albumin concentrations of 0.0, 0.01, 0.10, and 1.0 g percent, the creep viscosity is equal to 3.6, 15, 26, and 52 mN s/m, respectively (38). These values for the creep viscosity are approximately four orders of magnitude greater than the values for η and η_p. These extremely large values for the membrane creep viscosity probably represent a slow and permanent molecular reorganization of the structural membrane components (e.g. spectrin).

ACKNOWLEDGMENT

This work was supported by National Institutes of Health grants HL23728, HL31524, and HL18208.

Literature Cited

1. Baker, R. F. 1981. Membrane deformability of metabolically depleted human red cells. *Blood Cells* 7:551–58
2. Chabanel, A., Flamm, M., Sung, K. L. P., Lee, M. M., Schachter, D., Chien, S. 1983. Influence of cholesterol content on red cell membrane viscoelasticity and fluidity. *Biophys. J.* 4:171–76
3. Chasis, J. A., Mohandas, N., Shohet, S. B. 1985. Erythrocyte membrane rigidity induced by glycophorin A-ligand interaction. *J. Clin. Invest.* 75:1919–26
4. Chetrite, G., Cassoly, R. 1985. Affinity of hemoglobin for the cytoplasmic fragment of human erythrocyte membrane band 3. *J. Mol. Biol.* 185:639–44
5. Chien, S., Sung, K. L. P., Skalak, R., Usami, S., Tozeren, A. 1978. Theoretical and experimental studies on viscoelastic properties of erythrocyte membrane. *Biophys. J.* 24:463–87
6. Crandall, E. D., Critz, A. M., Osher, A. S., Keljo, D. J., Forster, R. E. 1978. Influence of pH on elastic deformability of the human erythrocyte membrane. *Am. J. Physiol.* 235:C269–78

7. Eisinger, J., Flores, J., Salhany, J. M. 1982. Association of cytosol hemoglobin with the membrane in intact erythrocytes. *Proc. Natl. Acad. Sci. USA* 79: 408–12
8. Evans, E. A. 1973. A new material concept for the red cell membrane. *Biophys. J.* 13:926–40
9. Evans, E. A. 1973. New membrane concept applied to the analysis of fluid shear- and micropipette-deformed red blood cells. *Biophys. J.* 13:941–54
10. Evans, E. A. 1974. Bending resistance and chemically induced moments in membrane bilayers. *Biophys. J.* 14:923–31
11. Evans, E. A. 1980. Minimum energy analysis of membrane deformation applied to pipette aspiration and surface adhesion of red blood cells. *Biophys. J.* 30:265–84
12. Evans, E. A. 1983. Bending elastic modulus of red blood cell membrane derived from buckling instability in micropipette aspiration tests. *Biophys. J.* 43:27–30

13. Evans, E. A., Hochmuth, R. M. 1976. Membrane viscoelasticity. *Biophys. J.* 16:1–11
14. Evans, E. A., Hochmuth, R. M. 1976. Membrane viscoplastic flow. *Biophys. J.* 16:13–26
15. Evans, E. A., Hochmuth, R. M. 1977. A solid-liquid composite model of the red cell membrane. *J. Membr. Biol.* 30:351–62
16. Evans, E. A., Hochmuth, R. M. 1978. Mechanochemical properties of membranes. *Curr. Top. Membr. Transport* 10:1–64
17. Evans, E. A., La Celle, P. L. 1975. Intrinsic material properties of the erythrocyte membrane indicated by mechanical analysis of deformation. *Blood* 45:29–43
18. Evans, E. A., Leung, A. 1984. Adhesivity and rigidity of erythrocyte membrane in relation to wheat germ agglutinin binding. *J. Cell Biol.* 98:1201–8
19. Evans, E. A., Mohandas, N., Leung, A. 1984. Static and dynamic rigidities of normal and sickle erythrocytes. *J. Clin. Invest.* 73:477–88
20. Evans, E. A., Skalak, R. 1980. *Mechanics and Thermodynamics of Biomembranes.* Boca Raton, Fla.: CRC. 245 pp.
21. Evans, E. A., Waugh, R. 1977. Osmotic correction to elastic area compressibility measurements on red cell membrane. *Biophys. J.* 20:307–13
22. Evans, E. A., Waugh, R., Melnik, L. 1976. Elastic area compressibility modulus of red cell membrane. *Biophys. J.* 16:585–95
23. Fischer, T. M., Haerst, C. W. M., Stohr, M., Kamp, D., Deuticke, B. 1978. Selective alteration of erythrocyte deformability by SH-reagents: Evidence for an involvement of spectrin in membrane shear elasticity. *Biochem. Biophys. Acta.* 510:270–82
24. Fischer, T. M., Haerst, C. W. M., Stohr-Liesen, M., Schmid-Schonbien, H., Skalak, R. 1981. The stress-free shape of the red blood cell membrane. *Biophys. J.* 34:409–22
25. Fung, Y. C. 1966. Theoretical considerations of the elasticity of red cells and small blood vessels. *Fed. Proc.* 24:1761–72
26. Helfrich, W. 1973. Elastic properties of lipid bilayers: Theory and possible experiments. *Z. Naturforsch.* 28C:693–703
27. Hochmuth, R. M., Buxbaum, K. L., Evans, E. A. 1980. Temperature dependence of the viscoelastic recovery of red cell membrane. *Biophys. J.* 29:177–82
28. Deleted in proof
29. Hochmuth, R. M., Evans, E. A., Colvard, D. F. 1976. Viscosity of human red cell membrane in plastic flow. *Microvasc. Res.* 11:155–59
30. Hochmuth, R. M., Mohandas, N. 1972. Uniaxial loading of the red cell membrane. *J. Biomech.* 5:501–9
31. Hochmuth, R. M., Mohandas, N., Blackshear, P. L. Jr. 1973. Measurement of the elastic modulus for red cell membrane using a fluid mechanical technique. *Biophys. J.* 13:747–62
32. Hochmuth, R. M., Wiles, H. C., Evans, E. A., McCown, J. T. 1982. Extensional flow of erythrocyte membrane from cell body to elastic tether: II. Experiment. *Biophys. J.* 39:83–89
33. Hochmuth, R. M., Worthy, P. R., Evans, E. A. 1979. Red cell extensional recovery and the determination of membrane viscosity. *Biophys. J.* 26:101–14
34. Katnik, C., Waugh, R. E. 1986. Reduction of the apparent area compressibility modulus of red blood cell membrane by applied electric fields. *Biophys. J.* 49:147a (Abstr.)
35. Landau, L. D., Lifshitz, E. M. 1970. *Theory of Elasticity,* pp. 4–5. Oxford: Pergamon. 165 pp.
36. Linderkamp, O., Meiselman, H. J. 1982. Geometric, osmotic, and membrane mechanical properties of density-separated human red cells. *Blood* 59:1121–27
37. Lovrien, R. E., Anderson, R. A. 1980. Stoichiometry of wheat germ agglutinin as a morphology controlling agent and as a morphology protective agent for the human erythrocyte. *J. Cell Biol.* 85:534–48
38. Markle, D. R., Evans, E. A., Hochmuth, R. M. 1983. Force relaxation and permanent deformation of erythrocyte membrane. *Biophys. J.* 42:91–98
39. Meiselman, H. J., Evans, E. A., Hochmuth, R. M. 1978. Membrane mechanical properties of ATP-depleted human erythrocytes. *Blood* 52:499–504
40. Nash, G. B., Johnson, C. S., Meiselman, H. J. 1984. Mechanical properties of oxygenated red blood cells in sickle cell (HbSS) disease. *Blood* 63:73–82
41. Nash, G. B., Johnson, C. S., Meiselman, H. J. 1986. Influence of oxygen tension on the viscoelastic behavior of red blood cells in sickle cell disease. *Blood* 67:110–18
42. Nash, G. B., Meiselman, H. G. 1983. Red cell and ghost viscoelasticity. *Biophys. J.* 43:63–73
43. Nash, G. B., Meiselman, H. J. 1985. Alteration of red cell membrane

viscoelasticity by heat treatment: Effect on cell deformability and suspension viscosity. *Biorheology* 22:73–84

44. Nash, G. B., Wyard, S. J. 1981. Erythrocyte membrane elasticity during in vivo aging. *Biochem. Biophys. Acta.* 643:269–75

45. Nash, G. B., Wyard, S. J. 1982. Measurement of erythrocyte membrane elasticity as a diagnostic aid in Duchenne muscular dystrophy. *J. Med. Genet.* 19:262–65

46. Rakow, A. L., Hochmuth, R. M. 1975. Effect of heat treatment on the elasticity of human erythrocyte membrane. *Biophys. J.* 15:1095–1100

47. Rand, R. P. 1964. Mechanical properties of the red cell membrane: II. Viscoelastic breakdown of the membrane. *Biophys. J.* 4:303–16

48. Skalak, R., Tozeren, A., Zarda, R. P., Chien, S. 1973. Strain energy function of red blood cell membranes. *Biophys. J.* 13:245–64

49. Smith, L., Hochmuth, R. M. 1982. Effect of wheat germ agglutinin on the viscoelastic properties of erythrocyte membrane. *J. Cell Biol.* 94:7–11

50. Sutera, S. P., Gardner, R. A., Boylan, C. W., Carroll, G. L., Chang, K. C., et al. 1985. Age-related changes in deformability of human erythrocytes. *Blood* 65:275–82

51. Tran-Son-Tay, R., Sutera, S. P., Rao, P. R. 1984. Determination of red cell membrane viscosity from rheoscopic observations of tank-treading motion. *Biophys. J.* 46:65–72

52. Waugh, R. E. 1982. Temperature dependence of the yield shear resultant and the plastic viscosity coefficient of erythrocyte membrane: Implications about molecular events during membrane failure. *Biophys. J.* 39:273–78

53. Waugh, R. E. 1983. Effects of abnormal cytoskeletal structure on erythrocyte membrane mechanical properties. *Cell Motil.* 3:609–22

54. Waugh, R. E. 1986. Effect of 2,3-diphosphoglycerate on the mechanical properties of erythrocyte membrane. *Blood* 68:231–38

55. Waugh, R. E. 1986. Effects of inherited membrane abnormalities on the viscoelastic properties of erythrocyte membrane. *Biophys. J.* In press

56. Waugh, R. E., Evans, E. A. 1976. Viscoelastic properties of erythrocyte membranes of different vertebrate animals. *Microvasc. Res.* 12:291–304

57. Waugh, R. E., Evans, E. A. 1979. Thermoelasticity of red blood cell membrane. *Biophys. J.* 26:115–32

58. Waugh, R. E., La Celle, P. L. 1980. Abnormalities in the membrane material properties of hereditary spherocytes. *J. Biomech. Engr.* 102:240–46

59. Williamson, J. R., Gardner, R. A., Boylan, C. W., Carroll, G. L., Chang, K., et al. 1985. Morphologic investigation of erythrocyte deformability in diabetes mellitus. *Blood* 65:283–88

60. Zarda, P. R., Chien, S., Skalak, R. 1977. Elastic deformations of red blood cells. *J. Biomech.* 10:211–21

Ann. Rev. Physiol. 1987. 49:221–35

LIPID MODULATION OF TRANSPORT PROTEINS IN VERTEBRATE CELL MEMBRANES

B. Deuticke and C. W. M. Haest

Abteilung Physiologie, Medizinische Fakultät, Rheinisch-Westfälische Technische Hochschule Aachen, D-5100 Aachen, West Germany

INTRODUCTION AND GENERAL ASPECTS

In biological membranes interactions among the two major classes of constituents, lipids and proteins, are of paramount importance. A growing literature and a host of recent reviews (2, 10, 11, 26, 33, 41, 58, 79, 99, 108) are therefore available on this subject. The present overview mainly addresses physiologists and will be restricted to aspects within their domain. We emphasize the influence of the lipid environment on transport proteins in animal cell membranes, as studied under in situ conditions.

Present concepts concerning the mechanistic basis of lipid modulation of transport protein function range between two extremes: modulation by bulk properties, and modulation by specific interactions. Interest in bulk properties has mainly been focused on membrane fluidity (2, 79, 91). Other properties of the bilayer to be considered are surface potential (9, 54, 107), dipole potential (63), and polarity (48). Both bulk properties and specific interactions may affect transport proteins in their native conformation by controlling substrate affinity, and/or modulate the rate of conformation changes that go along with substrate transport. Authors who interpret lipid effects in terms of fluidity often apply to integral membrane proteins the concepts originally developed for the dependence of the molecular dynamics of water-soluble proteins on solvent viscosity (8, 31, 91). The fluidity of an anisotropic bilayer is of course not precisely comparable to the viscosity of isotropic solvents. The rigorous physical description of bilayer fluidity has recently

221

0066-4278/87/0315-0221$02.00

become possible, however (for a survey see 99). The fluidity of biomembranes is particularly diminished by cholesterol (92, 108). The fluidizing effect of fatty acyl double bonds seems to be somewhat less important than previously thought, at least in the range of fatty acid patterns relevant for biological systems (99). A direct relationship between membrane fluidity and the activity of membrane proteins was originally claimed (95, 109). Recent data indicate that fluidity may not have the unique relevance originally presumed. Other, more specific requirements have become evident (27, 41, 58, 94). Even carrier activity in a nonfluid (gel) phase (15) and inhibitory effects of increasing fluidity (25, 31) have been reported. Moreover, bilayer thickness may be of greater relevance for the function of membrane-intercalated proteins than was previously appreciated (14, 15, 29, 44).

The suggestion that a particular lipid bilayer environment is required for the activity of membrane proteins (46, see 10 for a review) has been modified and refined (26, 30, 61). Electron spin resonance (ESR) studies have demonstrated that the motion of lipids is slowed by interaction with the surface of proteins (26, 61). This effect is only seen in lipids in contact with the protein. The average number of lipids interacting with a protein roughly correlates with the perimeter of the bilayer-intercalated portion of the protein and with the number of phospholipids required for its full activity in reconstituted systems (30).

Bilayer-spanning, hydrophobic segments of membrane proteins are likely to contain long stretches of α-helix (28, 82), which may be stabilized by surrounding lipids (31, 82). Due to their hydrophobic side chains the surfaces of these segments are uneven. Lipid species able to adapt to a particular protein surface shape will preferentially interact with that protein. Conversely, the protein will adopt the energetically most favorable conformation to minimize lipid bilayer perturbation.

Protein conformation is probably also stabilized by anionic lipids via electrostatic interactions, presumably with clusters of cationic amino acid residues located at the bilayer–bulk solution interface (103). It is not yet clear whether this type of interaction is the major basis for the frequently observed functional requirement (21, 31, 80) of transport proteins for anionic phospholipids (e.g. phosphatidylserine, cardiolipin).

The general features outlined here were mostly obtained on simple reconstituted systems. Biomembranes are more complex by orders of magnitude (10, 99). This results from the chemical heterogeneity of the lipids (there are several hundred species of phospholipid), their asymmetric transmembrane arrangement (69), and the alleged presence of lipid domains (47). Even the bulk properties of such complex systems may exhibit transverse and lateral inhomogeneity (12, 47, 85).

METHODS TO MODIFY LIPID PATTERNS

A considerable number of techniques for lipid modification in biomembranes are now available (Table 1). In transport studies with membrane-modified cells, the experimenter must check for nonspecific leaks and for loss of cell viability. If such precautions are neglected, erroneous conclusions may result. A further experimental requirement is an appropriate chemical or physical method for verifying the changes induced in lipid patterns.

While in situ methods induce only limited changes in the lipid domain, reconstitution of purified proteins into lipid vesicles allows complete replacement of native phospholipids by a defined set of exogenous lipids. It is now possible to overcome some former shortcomings of this approach. One can avoid or cope with vesicle inhomogeneity, the presence of nonspecific leaks, loss of the native orientation of the protein, and changes in the functional parameters (V_{max}, K_T) found in the native membrane (5, 15, 31, 52, 53, 86). Reconstitution of ion-conducting channels into solvent-free, planar bilayers (see 57 for a review) has also become possible.

LIPID MODULATION OF TRANSPORT PROTEINS

Only a few transport systems have been studied using the plasma membrane modifying techniques listed in Table 1. Presently, reconstitution is expected to provide more easily interpretable data on the molecular aspects of membrane protein function. Modification of the natural "habitat" of membrane proteins, however, is ultimately the more physiological approach. Results of both approaches are discussed below. Since complete coverage of the recent literature is not possible because of space limitations, only reviews are cited in many instances.

Anion Transport Systems

BAND 3 PROTEIN   Lipid modulation of band 3 protein, the Cl-HCO$_3$ exchanger of the erythrocyte membrane (73), has been established in situ and by reconstitution. Cholesterol suppresses band 3 activity in situ at cholesterol/phospholipid ratios greater than 0.3 (36, 37, 42) without changing the high activation energy. At ratios less than 0.3, reconstituted band 3 is insensitive to the sterol (51). The inhibitory effects are compatible with the original concept of fluidity-dependent membrane protein catalysis (95, 109). Indirect (88) and direct (90) evidence, however, also supports a direct cholesterol-band 3 interaction. Conformation changes of band 3 in response to cholesterol have been reported (49, 82, 85).

Table 1 Methods for modification of membrane lipid patterns in intact cells or derived membranes

Subject and strategy	Major objects studied	Technical details and comments	References
Phospholipids			
Enzymatic cleavage (phospholipase A_2, C, D; phosphatidylserine decarboxylase)	Erythrocytes Neurons Subcellular membranes Plasma membrane vesicles	Selective modulation of outer layer in intact cells possible Effects due to cleavage of phospholipids or formation of membrane-bound split products Some split products can be removed by albumin	4, 21, 24, 39, 81, 89, 105
Replacement by exogenous phospholipids with transfer proteins of variable specificity	Erythrocytes Platelets Subcellular membranes	Selective modulation of outer layer in intact cells possible Operative in net or exchange mode	19, 70, 110
Modulation by fusion with lipid vesicles	Blood cells Cultured cells	Fusion must be distinguished from adhesion and endocytosis	72, 87
In situ synthesis from exogenous lysophospholipid and fatty acid	Plasma membrane vesicles (lymphocyte, liver)	Extent of modification limited	13, 76, 100
Catalytic hydrogenation of unsaturated lipids	Chloroplasts	Water-soluble catalysts now available Damage of protein should be checked	40, 79
Replacement of fatty acyl chains by diet	Muscle, liver, brain, blood cells	Effects counteracted or modulated by metabolic "homoviscous" regulation Extensive lipid analyses required	99

Method	System	Comments	References
Replacement by supplements to cell culture media	Cultured cells	Allows modification of acyl chains and head groups Complicated by metabolic counterregulation	96, 99
Replacement by homoviscous adaptation to changes of ambient temperature	Fish Hibernating mammals	Restricted to poikilotherms or cold-adapting animals	34, 79, 164
Study of the same transporter in cells of the same type, but different membrane lipid patterns (a) Comparison of animal species	Erythrocytes	(a) Structural homology and kinetic similarity of equi-functional transporters in the same cell type not yet reliably demonstrated	25
(b) Expression of a transporter gene in cells with different membrane lipid patterns		(b) Not yet tested under this aspect	65
Cholesterol			
Removal or enrichment by acceptors or donors in vitro	Blood cells Cultured cells Brush border vesicles Nerve cells Subcellular membranes	Appropriate donors/acceptors: Phospholipid vesicles ($\pm$ transfer protein) Phospholipid/albumin complexes (1:1) Serum lipoproteins Considerable time requirement	6, 35, 37, 53, 68, 96, 97, 108
Inhibition of biosynthesis	Brain Cultured cell mutants	Complicating changes of phospholipid metabolism?	78, 95

Dietary enrichment or varying supplement to growing cells in culture	Cultured cells	Alteration of phospholipid metabolism, changes of phospholipid patterns?	6, 83, 95, 96
Incorporation of water-soluble cholesterol esters (cholesterol-hemisuccinate)	Erythrocytes Cultured cells	Comparability with effects of cholesterol not rigorously tested	59, 91, 109
Enzymatic oxidation (cholesterol oxidase from various sources)	Erythrocytes Brush border vesicles	Intact cells under physiological conditions not sensitive to cholesterol oxidase. Low ionic strength, insertion of cholesterol or of amphipaths required	56, 101

The phospholipid dependence of band 3 activity is not settled. Cleavage of exofacial lecithin by phospholipase A_2 does not induce changes in band 3 activity (105), but removal of the products of this cleavage produces some inhibition (24). Specifically, removal of the sphingomyelin head group inhibits anion transport (105). Changes of the fatty acyl chain pattern by diet, however, do not affect anion transport (25). These results may point to a modulating influence of the external membrane interface (25), a concept that is also supported by reconstitution studies (50) and a comparison of band 3 mediated transport in various mammalian erythrocytes (25). Anionic head groups at levels greater than 30 mol% suppress band 3 activity, most likely by inducing a repulsive surface charge (50).

MONOCARBOXYLATE TRANSPORTER   In contrast to findings on band 3 activity, an anion transport system in erythrocytes that specifically mediates cotransport of H^+ and small aliphatic monocarboxylates (e.g. lactate) (23) is activated by cholesterol (37). Cleavage of exofacial lecithin by phospholipase A_2 inhibits this system by formation of fatty acids. Extraction of these fatty acids restores normal transport activity (24).

ADP-ATP EXCHANGER   The reconstituted ADP-ATP carrier of the inner mitochondrial membrane also senses its lipid environment. Cholesterol, which is nearly absent from the native mitochondrial membrane (21), increases V_{max} without affecting K_m (53). Moreover, the turnover number of the carrier is markedly enhanced by phosphatidylethanolamine and anionic phospholipids (54, 55). Affinity is diminished by these lipids, presumably due to electrostatic repulsion of the anionic substrate. The binding of substrate to the asymmetric transporter is much more sensitive to the surface charge on the matrix side than on the cytosolic side (54). The binding site facing the cytosol is isolated from the lipid head group region, possibly by protruding ~ 2.5 nm from the lipid bilayer, while the binding site facing the matrix is located in the plane of the head groups.

Cation Transport Systems

The lipid modulation of ATP-consuming active cation transport systems has two aspects: enzyme activity and ion transport capacity. Lipid modulation of the latter is less well studied than that of the former. Conclusions concerning lipid effects on the ion transport properties of pumps should not be based on evidence from studies of their enzyme activity, since uncoupling of these functions may occur (66).

CALCIUM ION PUMPS   In native erythrocytes, cleavage of the outer membrane layer phospholipids by phospholipase A_2 and sphingomyelinase does not affect the Ca^{2+}-transporting ATPase. However, in ghosts phospholipases A_2 and C inhibit the enzyme, probably due to the removal of intact phospholipids from the inner membrane layer (80). The reconstituted enzyme does not require particular phospholipids (80). Negatively charged head groups, however, e.g. of anionic phospholipids or free fatty acids, stimulate enzyme activity (38). These effects are additive to those of calmodulin, which is also supposed to activate the pump by providing negative charges (38). The Ca^+ pump of sarcoplasmic reticulum, which differs in its molecular properties from the plasma membrane pump, is slightly stimulated by phospholipase A_2 treatment of membrane vesicles. Removal of the products from this cleavage inactivates the enzyme (80). Enzyme activity can be restored by a variety of amphipaths (lysophospholipids, fatty acids, nonionic detergents), which indicates that there is no specific lipid requirement (80). Exchange of endogenous for synthetic phospholipids demonstrates that, in addition to the requirement for a fluid environment, optimal activity is provided by phospholipids with acyl chains of 16 to 20 carbon atoms (11, 14, 44, 45). This indicates the importance of an appropriate bilayer thickness. Pump-mediated Ca^{2+} uptake into reconstituted lecithin vesicles demonstrates the same dependence on the length of the fatty acid chain (14). Thirty lipid molecules must be bound to the pump for maximal activity. Those that best support activity (61) are segregated from the bulk lipid. Cholesterol is excluded from the protein surface (11, 61, 93).

Na-K PUMPS   Erythrocyte Na,K-ATPase is characterized by a marked requirement for anionic phospholipids. Enzymatic degradation of phosphatidylserine is accompanied by loss of activity (80). Anionic phospholipids bind preferentially to the delipidated enzyme (30) and are essential for complete reactivation (18, 80).

Reconstitution studies with purified Na,K-ATPases from other sources have not demonstrated a requirement for anionic phospholipids (5). In these studies, however, the negative charge may have been provided by cholate, which was used for reconstitution (80). Modulations of the acyl chain patterns in situ (1, 76) and in plasma membrane preparations (13, 100) do not permit unambiguous conclusions.

Na,K-ATPase, like Ca-ATPase, is markedly dependent on bilayer thickness. Pump-mediated K^+ transport and enzymatic activity are best supported by monoenoic lecithins with 18–20 carbon atoms (45, 60). Additional double bonds suppress transport (60). Increasing the bilayer thickness by adding decane stimulates or inhibits ATPase depending on the original bilayer thickness (45, 60).

Cholesterol depresses Na,K-ATPase activity (5, 78, 108, but see 22). This inhibition of the nonvectorial, enzymatic function of the protein has its vectorial counterpart in an inhibitory effect on the pump flux in human erythrocytes (16, 43).

PASSIVE CATION TRANSPORTERS   The furosemide-sensitive Na^+-K^+-$2Cl^-$ cotransport system (102) is inhibited in erythrocytes by exogenous cholesterol (43, 106); V_{max} and K_m are decreased to the same extent (106). In contrast, the Li-Na countertransport system (102) in the erythrocyte membrane is insensitive to cholesterol (-hemisuccinate) enrichment (59). Passive uptake of Ca^{2+} into native erythrocytes, which is supposed to depend in part on the dihydropyridine-sensitive type of channel, is stimulated by cholesterol (67).

CATION-CONDUCTING CHANNELS   Lipid modulation of ion channels has been studied in several systems. In the squid axon, Na^+ and K^+ channels in situ are insensitive to changes of ± 30–40% of the normal cholesterol level (97). Variations of bilayer thickness produced by inserting hydrocarbons or short chain phospholipids into the axon membrane (29) markedly influence the inactivation of the Na^+ channel. Changes of the electric field strength at constant membrane potential may underlie this phenomenon.

Spontaneous electrical activity of *Aplysia* neurons, unlike that in the squid axon, was reported to be suppressed by cholesterol (98). In these neurons phospholipase A_2 injected intracellularly affects membrane resting potential, resistance, and specific ion fluxes (39). The interpretation of such findings is complicated by the problem of distinguishing induced leaks in the bilayer from modified channels.

This problem is less crucial in acetylcholine-activated cation channels, e.g. the acetylcholine receptor from electric organs (77). In reconstituted systems, agonist-induced gating and ion conductivity are markedly dependent on the presence of cholesterol, which may stabilize the association of the protein subunits of the ion channels (31). Moreover, anionic phospholipids seem to be essential for channel function (31, but see 20).

The conformational changes in the acetylcholine receptor that underlie "desensitization," i.e. the transition from a low to a high agonist-affinity state, also require cholesterol and anionic phospholipids, although to a lesser extent (31). The changes in conformation that correspond to desensitization are also induced by treatment with phospholipase A_2 (4), which completely blocks gating. Liberation of fatty acids is probably responsible for this effect (4).

Reconstitution of a K^+-selective channel from sarcoplasmic reticulum recently provided insight into the influence of lipid surface charge on channel conductance (9). The entrance to this channel may be spatially separated from the lipid surface.

Nonelectrolyte Transport Systems

AMINO ACID TRANSPORTERS   Several amino acid transport systems are subject to lipid modulation. Na^+-independent leucine transport in erythrocytes [by the L system (3)] is inhibited by cholesterol as in band 3 mediated transport (75). A detailed analysis of fluxes (75) suggests that cholesterol's predominant effect is to decrease the reorientation rate of the substrate-loaded form of the carrier but that it also diminishes substrate affinity. Cleavage of lecithin suppresses transport activity (75).

In contrast, the Na^+-dependent γ-aminobutyrate transport system in synaptic plasma membranes is activated reversibly by cholesterol, while choline uptake is not affected (68).

The heterogeneous response of transport systems to the same type of lipid modulation illustrated by these findings (see also 25) is further substantiated by studies of the influence of the fatty acyl pattern on amino acid transport systems in cultured cells (96, 99).

MONOSACCHARIDE TRANSPORTERS   The lipid dependence of monosaccharide transporters is ambiguous. In the native membranes of erythrocytes (37, 62, but see 109) and a sterol-auxotroph mutant of fibroblasts (6, 83), cholesterol stimulates transport (V_{max}) without changing substrate affinity. In contrast, the reconstituted glucose transporter [erythrocytes (17), adipocytes (64)] is inhibited by cholesterol in fluid lipid vesicles in the range of physiological cholesterol levels. Cholesterol stimulates monosaccharide transport only in gel state lipids (17). These different findings in plasma membranes and reconstituted systems underline the inherent risks in comparing data for reconstituted systems and intact biological membranes.

The sensitivity of the transporter to fatty acyl patterns also underlines the heterogeneity of responses of proteins to the lipid environment mentioned before: In adipocytes (74) and fibroblasts (7) the transporter is stimulated by monounsaturated acyl chains (18:1); in erythrocytes it is inhibited (24). These opposite effects of the fatty acyl pattern on glucose transporters from different sources were also observed in reconstituted systems (15, 84). The activity of the reconstituted transporter from erythrocytes exhibits a marked dependence on the acyl chain length (18 C was the optimum) (15), while the transporter in situ is sensitive to phospholipase treatment, as is the monocarboxylate transporter (105).

CONCLUSION

In summary, it has to be admitted that our present understanding of lipid modulation of protein functions in biological membranes is very far from satisfactory. Reconstitution studies will probably help to elucidate basic aspects of this complicated issue. In situ studies combining new probes and modification techniques with a more refined characterization of the nature and state of lipids and of the conformation of membrane proteins will, however, be essential to obtain a clear picture of how membrane proteins operate in their native lipid environment.

Literature Cited

1. Abeywardena, M. Y., McMurchie, E. J., Russel, G. R., Sawyer, W. H., Charnock, J. S. 1984. Response of rat heart membranes and associated ion-transporting ATPases to dietary lipid. *Biochim. Biophys. Acta* 776:48–59
2. Aloia, R. C., Boggs, J. M., eds. 1985. *Membrane Fluidity in Biology, Vol. 4: Cellular Aspects.* Orlando: Academic
3. Al-Saleh, E. A., Wheeler, K. P. 1982. Transport of neutral amino acids by human erythrocytes. *Biochim. Biophys. Acta* 684:157–71
4. Andreasen, T. J., Doerge, D. R., McNamee, M. G. 1979. Effects of phospholipase A_2 on the binding and ion permeability control properties of the acetylcholine receptor. *Arch. Biochem. Biophys.* 194:468–80
5. Anner, B. M. 1985. Interaction of (Na^+ + K^+)-ATPase with artificial membranes. I. Formation and structure of (Na^+ + K^+)-ATPase-liposomes. *Biochim. Biophys. Acta* 822:319–34
6. Baldassare, J. J., Saito, Y., Silbert, D. F. 1979. Effect of sterol depletion on LM cell sterol mutants. *J. Biol. Chem.* 254:1108–13
7. Baldassare, J. J., Silbert, D. F. 1979. Membrane phospholipid metabolism in response to sterol depletion. *J. Biol. Chem.* 254:10078–83
8. Beece, D., Eisenstein, L., Frauenfelder, H., Good, G., Marden, M. C., et al. 1980. Solvent viscosity and protein dynamics. *Biochemistry* 19:5147–57
9. Bell, J. E., Miller, C. 1984. Effects of phospholipid surface charge on ion conduction in the K^+ channel of sarcoplasmic reticulum. *Biophys. J.* 45:279–87
10. Benga, G., Holmes, R. P. 1984. Interactions between components in biological membranes and their implications for membrane function. *Progr. Biophys. Mol. Biol.* 43:195–257
11. Bennett, J. P., McGill, K. A., Warren, G. B. 1980. The role of lipids in the functioning of a membrane protein: The sarcoplasmic reticulum calcium pump.
    Curr. Top. Membr. Transport 14:127–64
12. Blatt, E., Sawyer, W. H. 1985. Depth-dependent fluorescent quenching in micelles and membranes. *Biochim. Biophys. Acta* 822:43–62
13. Breton, M., Wolf, C., Colard, O. 1983. Linoleate incorporation into rat liver membranes phospholipids: Effect on plasma membrane ATPase activity and physical properties. *Biochem. Biophys. Res. Commun.* 28:809–16
14. Caffrey, M., Feigenson, G. W. 1981. Fluorescence quenching in model membranes. 3. Relationship between calcium adenosinetriphosphatase enzyme activity and the affinity of the protein for phosphatidylcholines with different acyl chain characteristics. *Biochemistry* 20:1949–61
15. Carruthers, A., Melchior, D. L. 1984. Human erythrocyte hexose transporter activity is governed by bilayer lipid composition in reconstituted vesicles. *Biochemistry* 23:6901–11
16. Claret, M., Garay, R., Giraud, F. 1978. The effect of membrane cholesterol on the sodium pump in red blood cells. *J. Physiol.* 274:247–63
17. Connolly, T. J., Carruthers, A., Melchior, D. L. 1985. Effects of bilayer cholesterol on human erythrocyte hexose transport protein activity in synthetic lecithin bilayers. *Biochemistry* 24:2865–73
18. Cornelius, F., Skou, J. C. 1984. Reconstitution of (Na^+ + K^+)-ATPase into phospholipid vesicles with full recovery of its specific activity. *Biochim. Biophys. Acta* 772:357–73
19. Crain, R. C. 1982. Nonspecific transfer proteins as probes of membrane structure and function. *Lipids* 17:935–43
20. Criado, M., Eibl, H., Barrantes, F. J. 1984. Functional properties of the acetylcholine receptor incorporated in model lipid membranes. *J. Biol. Chem.* 259:9188–98
21. Daum, G. 1985. Lipids of mitochondria. *Biochim. Biophys. Acta* 822:1–42

22. De Pont, J. J. H. H. M., Peters, W. H. M., Bonting, S. L. 1983. Role of cholesterol and other neutral lipids in Na,K-ATPase. *Curr. Top. Membr. Transport* 19:163–66

23. Deuticke, B. 1982. Monocarboxylate transport in erythrocytes. *J. Membr. Biol.* 70:89–103

24. Deuticke, B., Grunze, M., Forst, B., Luetkemeier, P. 1981. Influence of enzymatic phospholipid cleavage on the permeability of the erythrocyte membrane: III. Discrimination between the causal role of split products and of lecithin removal. *J. Membr. Biol.* 59:45–55

25. Deuticke, B., Grunze, M., Haest, C. W. M. 1980. Influence of membrane lipids on ion and nonelectrolyte transport through the erythrocyte membrane. In *Membrane Transport in Erythrocytes, Alfred Benzon Symp. 14*, ed. U. V. Lassen, J. O. Wieth, pp. 143–60. Copenhagen: Munksgaard

26. Devaux, P. F., Seigneuret, M. 1985. Specificity of lipid-protein interactions as determined by spectroscopic techniques. *Biochim. Biophys. Acta* 822:63–125

27. East, J. M., Jones, O. T., Simmonds, A. C., Lee, A. G. 1984. Membrane fluidity is not an important physiological regulator of the $(Ca^{2+} - Mg^{2+})$-dependent ATPase of sarcoplasmic reticulum. *J. Biol. Chem.* 259:8070–71

28. Eisenberg, D. 1984. Three-dimensional structure of membrane and surface proteins. *Ann. Rev. Biochem.* 53:595–623

29. Elliott, J. R., Haydon, D. A., Hendry, B. M., Needham, D. 1985. Inactivation of the sodium current in squid giant axons by hydrocarbons. *Biophys. J.* 48:617–22

30. Esmann, M., Watts, A., Marsh, D. 1985. Spin-label studies of lipid-protein interactions in (Na^+, K^+)-ATPase membranes from rectal glands of *Squalus acanthias*. *Biochemistry* 24:1386–93

31. Fong, T. M., McNamee, M. G. 1986. Correlation between acetylcholine receptor function and structural properties of membranes. *Biochemistry* 25:830–40

32. Gavish, B., Werber, M. M. 1979. Viscosity-dependent structural fluctuations in enzyme catalysis. *Biochemistry* 18:1269–75

33. Gennis, R. B., Jonas, A. 1977. Protein-lipid interactions. *Ann. Rev. Biophys. Bioeng.* 6:195–238

34. Gilles, R., ed. 1985. Comparative aspects of adaptation to cold (Symp.). In *Circulation, Respiration, and Metabo-lism*, pp. 490–563. Berlin: Springer-Verlag

35. Gottlieb, M. H. 1978. A method for the increased extraction of cholesterol from human red blood cells by modified plasma lipoprotein. *Prep. Biochem.* 8:463–69

36. Gregg, V. A., Reithmeier, R. A. F. 1983. Effect of cholesterol on phosphate uptake by human red blood cells. *FEBS Lett.* 157:159–64

37. Grunze, M., Forst, B., Deuticke, B. 1980. Dual effect of membrane cholesterol on simple and mediated transport processes in human erythrocytes. *Biochim. Biophys. Acta* 600:860–69

38. Hanahan, D. J., Nelson, D. R. 1984. Phospholipids as dynamic participants in biological processes. *J. Lipid Res.* 25:1528–35

39. Hinzen, D. H., Tauc, L. 1977. Membrane properties of *Aplysia* neurons intracellularly injected with phospholipases A and C. *J. Physiol.* 268:21–34

40. Horvath, I., Mansourian, A. R., Vigh, L., Thomas, P. G., Joo, F., Quinn, P. J. 1986. Homogeneous catalytic hydrogenation of the polar lipids of pea chloroplasts in situ and the effects on lipid polymorphism. *Chem. Phys. Lipids* 39:251–64

41. Houslay, M. D., Gordon, L. M. 1983. The activity of adenylate cyclase is regulated by the nature of its lipid environment. *Curr. Top. Membr. Transport* 18:179–231

42. Jackson, P., Morgan, D. B. 1982. The relation between the membrane cholesterol content and anion exchange in the erythrocytes of patients with cholestasis. *Biochim. Biophys. Acta* 693:99–104

43. Jackson, P. A., Morgan, D. B. 1982. The relation between membrane cholesterol and phospholipid and sodium efflux in erythrocytes from healthy subjects and patients with chronic cholestasis. *Clin. Sci.* 62:101–7

44. Johannsson, A., Keightley, C. A., Smith, G. A., Richards, C. D., Hesketh, T. R., Metcalfe, J. C. 1981. The effect of bilayer thickness and *n*-alkanes on the activity of the $(Ca^{2+} + Mg^{2+})$-dependent ATPase of sarcoplasmic reticulum. *J. Biol. Chem.* 256:1643–50

45. Johannsson, A., Smith, G. A., Metcalfe, J. C. 1981. The effect of bilayer thickness on the activity of $(Na^+ + K^+)$-ATPase. *Biochim. Biophys. Acta* 641:416–21

46. Jost, P. C., Griffith, O. H., Capaldi, R. A., Vanderkooi, G. A. 1973. Evidence

for boundary lipid in membranes. *Proc. Natl. Acad. Sci. USA* 70:4756–63

47. Karnovsky, K. J., Kleinfeld, A. M., Hoover, R. L., Klausner, R. D. 1982. The concept of lipid domains in membranes. *J. Cell Biol.* 92:1–6

48. Kimura, Y., Ikegami, A. 1985. Local dielectric properties around polar region of lipid bilayer membranes. *J. Membr. Biol.* 85:225–31

49. Klugerman, A. H., Gaarn, A., Parkes, J. G. 1984. Effect of cholesterol upon the conformation of band 3 and its transmembrane fragment. *Can. J. Biochem. Cell. Biol.* 62:1033–40

50. Köhne, W., Deuticke, B., Haest, C. W. M. 1983. Phospholipid dependence of the anion transport system of the human erythrocyte membrane. *Biochim. Biophys. Acta* 730:139–50

51. Köhne, W., Haest, C. W. M., Deuticke, B. 1981. Mediated transport of anions in band 3/phospholipid vesicles. *Biochim. Biophys. Acta* 664:108–20

52. Koepsell, H. 1986. Methodological aspects in purification and reconstitution of transport proteins from mammalian plasma membranes. *Rev. Physiol. Biochem. Pharmacol.* 104:65–137

53. Krämer, R. 1982. Cholesterol as activator of ADP-ATP exchange in reconstituted liposomes and in mitochondria. *Biochim. Biophys. Acta* 693:296–304

54. Krämer, R. 1983. Interaction of membrane surface charges with the reconstituted ADP/ATP-carrier from mitochondria. *Biochim. Biophys. Acta* 735:145–59

55. Krämer, R., Klingenberg, M. 1980. Enhancement of reconstituted ADP/ATP-exchange activity by phosphatidylethanolamine and by anionic phospholipids. *FEBS Lett.* 119:257–60

56. Lange, Y., Matthies, H., Steck, T. L. 1984. Cholesterol oxidase susceptibility of the red cell membrane. *Biochim. Biophys. Acta* 769:551–62

57. Latorre, R., Alvarez, O., Cecchi, X., Vergara, C. 1985. Properties of reconstituted ion channels. *Ann. Rev. Biophys. Biophys. Chem.* 14:79–111

58. Levitzki, A. 1985. Reconstitution of membrane receptor systems. *Biochim. Biophys. Acta* 822:127–53

59. Levy, R., Hevroni, D., Cabantchik, Z. I., Livne, A. 1986. Li_i-Na_o countertransport and Li leak in erythrocytes are differentially affected by membrane enrichment with cholesteryl hemisuccinate. *Biochim. Biophys. Acta* 854:325–28

60. Marcus, M. M., Apell, H.-J., Roudna, M., Schwendener, R. A., Weder, H.

-G., Läuger, P. 1986. (Na^+ + K^+)-ATPase in artificial lipid vesicles: Influences of lipid structure on pumping rate. *Biochim. Biophys. Acta* 854:270–78

61. Marsh, D. 1985. ESR spin label studies of lipid-protein interactions. In *Progress in Protein-Lipid Interactions*, ed. A. Watts, J.J.H.H.M. De Pont, Vol. 1, pp. 143–72. Amsterdam: Elsevier

62. Masiak, S. J., LeFevre, P. G. 1974. Effects of membrane steroid modification on human erythrocyte glucose transport. *Arch. Biochem. Biophys.* 162:442–47

63. McLaughlin, S. 1977. Electrostatic potentials at membrane-solution interfaces. *Curr. Top. Membr. Transport* 9:71–144

64. Melchior, D. L., Czech, M. P. 1979. Sensitivity of the adipocyte D-glucose transport system to membrane fluidity in reconstituted vesicles. *J. Biol. Chem.* 254:8744–47

65. Morgan, M., Hanke, P., Grygorczik, R., Tintschl, A., Fasold, H., Passow, H. 1985. Mediation of anion transport in oocytes of *Xenopus laevis* by biosynthetically inserted band 3 protein from mouse spleen erythroid cells. *EMBO J.* 4:1927–31

66. Navarro, J., Toivio-Kinnucan, M., Racker, E. 1984. Effect of lipid composition on the calcium/adenosine 5-triphosphate coupling ratio of the Ca^{2+}-ATPase of sarcoplasmic reticulum. *Biochemistry* 23:130–35

67. Neyses, L., Locher, R., Stimpel, M., Streuli, R., Vetter, W. 1985. Stereospecific modulation of the calcium channel in human erythrocytes by cholesterol and its oxidized derivatives. *Biochem. J.* 227:105–12

68. North, P., Fleischer, S. 1983. Alteration of synaptic membrane cholesterol/phospholipid ratio using a lipid transfer protein. *J. Biol. Chem.* 258:1242–53

69. Op den Kamp, J. A. F. 1979. Lipid asymmetry in membranes. *Ann. Rev. Biochem.* 48:47–71

70. Op den Kamp, J. A. F., Roelofsen, B., van Deenen, L. L. M. 1985. Structure and dynamic aspects of phosphatidylcholine in the human erythrocyte membrane. *Trends Biochem. Sci.* 10:320–23

71. Deleted in proof

72. Pagano, R. E. 1978. Interaction of liposomes with mammalian cells. *Ann. Rev. Biophys. Bioeng.* 7:435–68

73. Passow, H. 1986. Molecular aspects of band 3 protein-mediated anion transport across the red blood cell membrane.

Rev. Physiol. Biochem. Pharmacol. 103:61–223

74. Pilch, P. F., Thompson, P. A., Czech, M. P. 1980. Coordinate modulation of D-glucose transport activity and bilayer fluidity in plasma membranes derived from control and insulin-treated adipocytes. Proc. Natl. Acad. Sci. USA 77:915–18

75. Piontek, M. K. 1983. Einfluss von Membranlipiden auf Protein-vermittelte Transportprozesse. Dissertation, RWTH Aachen, Aachen, West Germany. 164 pp.

76. Poon, R., Richards, J. M., Clark, W. R. 1981. The relation between plasma membrane lipid composition and physical-chemical properties and enzymatic activities. II. Effect of phospholipid fatty acid modulation on plasma membrane physical properties and enzymatic activities. Biochim. Biophys. Acta 649:58–66

77. Popot, J.-L., Changeux, J.-P. 1984. Nicotinic receptor of acetylcholine: Structure of an oligomeric integral membrane protein. Physiol. Rev. 64:1162–1223

78. Proverbio, F., Rawlins, F. A. 1978. Increment in sodium and potassium dependent adenosine triphosphatase of brain microsomal fraction from rats treated with the cholesterol biosynthesis inhibitor AY 9944. Mol. Pharmacol. 14:911–19

79. Quinn, P. J. 1981. The fluidity of cell membrane and its regulation. Progr. Biophys. Mol. Biol. 38:1–104

80. Roelofsen, B. 1981. The (non)specificity in the lipid-requirement of calcium- and (sodium plus potassium)-transporting adenosine triphosphatases. Life Sci. 29:2235–47

81. Roelofsen, B., Op den Kamp, J. A. F. 1982. Chemical and enzymatic localization of phospholipids in biological membranes. In Techniques in Lipid and Membrane Biochemistry, B414:1–28. Amsterdam: Elsevier

82. Rooney, M. W., Lange, Y., Kauffman, J. W. 1984. Acyl chain organization and protein secondary structure in cholesterol-modified erythrocyte membranes. J. Biol. Chem. 259:8281–85

83. Saito, Y., Silbert, D. F. 1979. Selective effects of membrane sterol depletion on surface function. Thymidine and 3-O-methyl-D-glucose transport in a sterol auxotroph. J. Biol. Chem. 254:1102–7

84. Sandra, A., Fyler, D. J., Marshall, S. J. 1984. Effects of lipids on the transport activity of the reconstituted glucose transport system from rat adipocyte. Biochim. Biophys. Acta 778:511–15

85. Schachter, D., Abbott, R. E., Cogan, U., Flamm, M. 1983. Lipid fluidity of the individual hemileaflets of human erythrocyte membranes. Ann. NY Acad. Sci. 414:19–28

86. Scheuring, U., Kollewe, K., Haase, W., Schubert, D. 1986. A new method for the reconstitution of the anion transport system of the human erythrocyte membrane. J. Membr. Biol. 90:123–35

87. Schlegel, R. A., Lumley-Sapanski, K., Williamson, P. 1985. Insertion of lipid domains into plasma membranes by fusion with erythrocytes. Biochim. Biophys. Acta 846:234–41

88. Schubert, D., Boss, K. 1982. Band 3 protein-cholesterol interactions in erythrocyte membranes. Possible role in anion transport and dependency on membrane phospholipid. FEBS Lett. 150:4–8

89. Schuurmans Stekhoven, F., Bonting, S. L. 1981. Transport adenosine triphosphatases: Properties and functions. Physiol. Rev. 61:1–61

90. Seigneuret, M., Favre, E., Morrot, G., Devaux, P. F. 1985. Strong interactions between a spin-labeled cholesterol analog and erythrocyte proteins in the human erythrocyte membrane. Biochim. Biophys. Acta 813:174–82

91. Shinitzky, M., Borochov, H., Wilbrandt, W. 1980. Lipid fluidity as a physiological regulator of membrane transport and enzyme activities. In Membrane Transport in Erythrocytes, Alfred Benzon Symp. 14, ed. U. V. Lassen, H. H. Ussing, J. O. Wieth, pp. 91–107. Copenhagen: Munksgaard

92. Shinitzky, M., Inbar, M. 1967. Microviscosity parameters and protein mobility in biological membranes. Biochim. Biophys. Acta 433:133–49

93. Silvius, J. R., McMillen, D. A., Saley, N. D., Jost, P. C., Griffith, O. H. 1984. Competition between cholesterol and phosphatidylcholine for the hydrophobic surface of sarcoplasmic reticulum Ca^{2+}-ATPase. Biochemistry 23:538–47

94. Simmonds, A. C., Rooney, E. K., Lee, A. G. 1984. Interactions of cholesterol hemisuccinate with phospholipids and $(Ca^{2+} - Mg^{2+})$-ATPase. Biochemistry 23:1432–41

95. Sinensky, M., Pinkerton, F., Sutherland, E., Simon, F. R. 1979. Rate limitation of $(Na^+ + K^+)$-stimulated adenosinetriphosphatase by membrane acyl chain ordering. Proc. Natl. Acad. Sci. USA 76:4893–97

96. Spector, A. A., Yorek, M. A. 1985. Membrane lipid composition and cellular function. J. Lipid Res. 26:1015–35

97. Steele, J. A., Poznansky, M. J., Douglas, C. E., Brodwick, M. S. 1981. Lipid vesicle-mediated alterations of membrane cholesterol levels: Effects on Na^+ and K^+ currents in squid axon. *J. Membr. Biol.* 63:191–98

98. Stephens, C. L., Shinitzky, M. 1977. Modulation of electrical activity in *Aplysia* neurons by cholesterol. *Nature* 270:267–68

99. Stubbs, C. D., Smith, A. D. 1984. The modification of mammalian membrane polyunsaturated fatty acid composition in relation to membrane fluidity and function. *Biochim. Biophys. Acta* 779:89–137

100. Szamel, M., Resch, K. 1981. Modulation of enzyme activities in isolated lymphocyte plasma membranes by enzymatic modification of phospholipid fatty acids. *J. Biol. Chem.* 256:11618–23

101. Thurnhofer, H., Gains, N., Mütsch, B., Hauser, H. 1986. Cholesterol oxidase as a structural probe of biological membranes: Its application to brush-border membrane. *Biochim. Biophys. Acta* 856:174–81

102. Tosteson, D. C. 1981. Cation countertransport and cotransport in human red cells. *Fed. Proc.* 40:1429–33

103. Weinstein, S., Blumenthal, R., van Renswoude, J., Kempf, C., Klausner, R. D. 1982. Charge clusters and the orientation of membrane proteins. *J. Membr. Biol.* 66:203–12

104. White, F. N., Somero, G. 1982. Acid-base regulation and phospholipid adaptations to temperature: Time courses and physiological significance of modifying the milieu for protein function. *Physiol. Rev.* 62:40–90

105. Wilbers, K. H., Haest, C. W. M., von Bentheim, M., Deuticke, B. 1979. Influence of enzymatic phospholipid cleavage on the permeability of the erythrocyte membrane. II. Protein-mediated transfer of monosaccharides and anions. *Biochim. Biophys. Acta* 554:400–9

106. Wiley, J. S., Cooper, R. A. 1975. Inhibition of cation cotransport by cholesterol enrichment of human red cell membranes. *Biochim. Biophys. Acta* 413:425–31

107. Wojtczak, L., Nalecz, M. N. 1979. Surface charge of biological membranes as a possible regulator of membrane-bound enzymes. *Eur. J. Biochem.* 94:99–107

108. Yeagle, P. L. 1985. Cholesterol and the cell membrane. *Biochim. Biophys. Acta* 822:267–87

109. Yuli, I., Wilbrandt, W., Shinitzky, M. 1981. Glucose transport through cell membranes of modified lipid fluidity. *Biochemistry* 20:4250–56

110. Zilversmit, D. B. 1984. Lipid transfer proteins. *J. Lipid Res.* 25:1563–69

Ann. Rev. Physiol. 1987. 49:237–48

RED CELL BIOCHEMICAL ANATOMY AND MEMBRANE PROPERTIES

Joel Anne Chasis and Stephen B. Shohet

Departments of Medicine and Laboratory Medicine, and Cancer Research Institute, University of California, San Francisco, San Francisco, California 94143

INTRODUCTION

Our understanding of the biochemical composition and organization of the red cell membrane has increased dramatically over the past two decades. Now that the membrane has been comparatively well characterized, it is possible to study the roles of specific membrane components in regulating the important biological membrane properties of deformability and stability. To fulfill its primary physiological function of oxygen delivery, the erythrocyte must be able to undergo repeated passive deformation. Its normally 8-μm diameter must be altered to allow the cell to traverse capillaries with diameters of 2–3 μm. In addition, the cell must have the capacity to resist fragmentation. These two essential qualities require a membrane that is extremely deformable yet very stable. Membrane stability can be defined as the maximum extent of deformation that a membrane can undergo and still completely recover its original shape. Beyond that degree of deformation, the membrane is unable to recover its predeformed state and it fails. An erythrocyte with normal membrane stability can circulate without fragmenting, while a cell with decreased stability may fragment under normal circulatory stresses. Membrane deformability, on the other hand, determines the extent of membrane deformation that can be induced by a defined level of applied force. A more deformable membrane requires less applied force to enable it to pass through tiny capillaries.

In this review, we focus on the recent developments in our understanding of which membrane components influence membrane deformability and stabil-

237

0066-4278/87/0315-0237$02.00

ity. We describe studies employing both normal membranes that have been biochemically perturbed and pathological membranes with defined biochemical abnormalities. We begin by describing the biochemistry and organization of the membrane components involved in determining deformability and stability.

MEMBRANE STRUCTURE

The erythrocyte membrane is composed of a lipid bilayer that contains several integral proteins and a protein lattice that underlies the bilayer and is associated with it through protein-protein and protein-lipid interactions (3, 4, 9, 25, 38, 63). This protein lattice is often referred to as the membrane skeleton; it consists of spectrin, actin, tropomyosin, and proteins 4.1 and 4.9. The evidence accumulated to date suggests that membrane deformability and stability are predominantly determined by these membrane skeletal proteins.

Spectrin

Spectrin is the most abundant skeletal protein (10^5 tetramers per cell). It is composed of an α (240 kd) and a β (225 kd) polypeptide subunit; these subunits self-associate to form heterodimers ($\alpha\beta$), tetramers ($\alpha\beta)_2$, and higher order oligomers (37, 42, 43). By electron microscopy, the dimer appears to be a rod-shaped molecule of about 194 nm in length (51). Within the dimer the α and β subunits lie parallel to one another with the amino terminal of the α subunit aligned and associated with the carboxy terminal of the β subunit. Higher oligomers are formed by the association of dimers with one another. This association occurs in the dimer region containing the α subunit's amino terminal.

By peptide mapping, the alignment of peptides in both the α and β chains has been elegantly determined (55). The site of spectrin self-association (44) is a domain of 80 kd that begins at the amino terminal of the α subunit. Not only does spectrin self-associate, it also forms noncovalent associations with ankyrin (protein 2.1), actin, and protein 4.1. Ankyrin is bound to a 50-kd polypeptide of the β chain (44) that is ~20 nm from the head of the spectrin molecule (58, 59). Actin, protein 4.1, and spectrin appear to form a complex together (12, 13, 45, 65). Several electron microscopic studies using purified proteins have shown that this association occurs at the end of the heterodimer opposite that involved in spectrin self-association (14, 58, 59). In addition to binding structural proteins, spectrin also binds the polyphosphate 2,3-DPG (possibly at as many as seven sites) (48) and calmodulin. The spectrin-calmodulin association is of low affinity ($K_d \simeq 5$ μM) (54), and it is not known whether this complex plays any physiologic role in the erythrocyte.

Recently, exciting, direct visualizations of the native membrane have been made using negative staining (6, 33a, 50). In these preparations, the lattice of condensed proteins has been expanded using low ionic strength and di-thiothreitol (50) or phosphate buffers at a pH of 5.5 (6). The membrane skeletons thus obtained consist of a network of five to eight spectrin tetramers cross-linked by junctional complexes (6, 33a, 50). The junctional complexes are composed of a 33- to 50-nm (6, 33a, 50) regular rod, which is presumably the actin protofilament. About 78 nm along the spectrin tetramer from the junctional complexes, distinct globules are visible (6). These globules appear in the region of the previously described ankyrin binding site and may represent ankyrin and band 3. Thus, these new electron microscopic findings complement and confirm the earlier experiments performed with isolated, purified spectrin and its associated proteins.

Protein 4.1

Erythrocytes contain 2×10^5 copies of protein 4.1 per cell. With the use of the discontinuous buffer systems and peptide mapping, it has been shown that there are two components of protein 4.1 of very similar molecular weights that contain closely related sequences (4.1a, $M_r = 80,000$, and 4.1b, $M_r = 78,000$) (24). Studies comparing the proportion of 4.1a to 4.1b in mouse cells of varying ages show that young cells have proportionally more 4.1b while older cells have more 4.1a (26). Although the relationship between 4.1a and 4.1b is not yet clear, it appears that posttranslational modification may be responsible for the differences between them.

Ultrastructural studies of purified protein 4.1 show that it is globular in form. When a solution of spectrin and protein 4.1 is examined by rotary shadowing, protein 4.1 is seen to be bound to the tail of the spectrin tetramer (58, 59). Such an association has been confirmed by binding studies done in solution (58, 59). Indeed, protein 4.1 may play a pivotal role in the ternary complex of spectrin, 4.1, and actin, since it interacts directly not only with spectrin but also with F-actin (46). The presence of protein 4.1 greatly strengthens the association of spectrin dimers with F-actin (1×10^{12} M^{-2}), which are only weakly associated in the absence of protein 4.1 (5×10^3 M^{-1}) (45). Further, the interaction of protein 4.1 with spectrin facilitates the interaction of spectrin with actin.

Protein 4.1 may also serve as an important link between the skeletal proteins and the membrane. Studies using protein-4.1-depleted, inside out erythrocyte membranes and purified 4.1 suggest that protein 4.1 binds to glycophorin A (1) and that the extent of this binding is determined by the state of phosphorylation of the membrane phosphoinositides. An association be-tween protein 4.1 and a second transmembrane sialoglycoprotein, glycophor-in C, has also been suggested based on the behavior of glycophorin C and protein 4.1 during Triton extraction of the membrane (40). Whether any of these interactions of protein 4.1 with transmembrane proteins play physiologic roles in vivo has yet to be determined.

Actin and Associated Proteins

The actin monomer has a molecular weight of 43,000 and is present at 5×10^5 copies per cell. There is now ample biochemical and ultrastructural evidence that actin is present in the membrane in the polymerized, filamentous form of F-actin (2, 5, 10, 32, 47). Binding studies, sedimentation analysis, and viscometry suggest that F-actin forms weak associations with spectrin and that this association is enhanced by protein 4.1 (10, 11, 23, 33, 47). Electron microscopic studies using purified proteins show that F-actin binds to the tail region of spectrin (14, 65), the same region that binds protein 4.1. The idea that actin in its polymerized, filamentous form is associated with spectrin has been strengthened by recent ultrastructural studies of native membranes (6, 50). In these studies, the junctional complexes from which the spectrin tetramers radiate were found to be composed of regular rods 33–37 nm in length (6, 50). Importantly, 33 nm is also the length of nonmuscle tropomyosin (15, 39), which is known to be present in the erythrocyte with the stoichiometry of one molecule per seven to eight actin monomers (21). Thus this ultrastructural data additionally suggests that the role of tropomyosin in the erythrocyte may be to stabilize actin filaments and to determine their length (21), a role initially proposed based on experiments performed with purified proteins (20, 62).

Although their presence has not yet been confirmed in the ultrastructural studies of native membranes, it is likely that junctional complexes also contain erythrocyte myosin and band 4.9. Myosin is present in the erythrocyte in an actin/myosin ratio similar to that in other nonmuscle cells and may function in an actomyosin contractile apparatus (22). Erythrocyte band 4.9, which has only recently become the focus of careful study, may serve as an actin-bundling protein (52).

MEMBRANE DEFORMABILITY AND STABILITY

Model of Skeletal Protein Regulation

A model of the skeletal protein regulation of membrane deformability and stability has been proposed by Chasis & Mohandas (7). It incorporates the known structural organization and stoichiometry of the skeletal proteins and is an extension of models discussed by Waugh (60) and Shen et al (49). This model proposes that folded spectrin heterodimers form protein-protein associations at both of their ends: At one end is the region of spectrin-actin-protein 4.1 association, and at the other end is the domain involved in spectrin self-association. During reversible deformation the membrane undergoes a change in shape but maintains a constant surface area. In the nondeformed state the spectrin molecules are folded (Figure 1, *top panel*). Under applied shear stress the membrane's shape changes as the protein network is reorganized and some spectrin molecules become more folded while others become more extended *(middle panel)*. The point of maximal reversible deformation is reached when the extending spectrin molecules have achieved their point of maximum linear extension *(bottom panel)*. At this point, any further applied force would necessitate an increase in the membrane surface area, which would be impossible for the cell to achieve without breaking the junction points in the membrane skeleton. Studies by Evans and colleagues have shown that the normal erythrocyte is capable of linear extensions of up to 230% of its original dimension but that surface area increases of as little as 3–4% can result in cell lysis (18, 19). For reversible deformation at constant surface area to occur, the membrane skeletal proteins must be able to rearrange and the spectrin molecules must be able to fold and unfold. From this model, one would predict that membrane deformability would decrease if the number or quality of the protein-protein associations changed. For example, an increase in the intermolecular or intramolecular associations involving the spectrin molecule would hinder its ability to fold and unfold. Likewise, an increased association of the membrane skeletal proteins with the integral proteins of the bilayer might limit the ability of the membrane skeletal proteins to dissociate and reassociate normally.

When the membrane experiences a shear stress of a magnitude that requires an increase in surface area, the membrane fails. It is proposed that the points of spectrin-spectrin or spectrin-actin-protein 4.1 association are the points of failure during membrane fragmentation. This model predicts that alterations in spectrin self-association or in the spectrin-actin-protein 4.1 complex will reduce membrane stability.

Membrane Protein Associations that Influence Membrane Stability

Studies done on both biochemically perturbed normal membranes and on pathological membranes with defined biochemical abnormalities support the importance of spectrin self-association and of spectrin-actin-protein 4.1 association in membrane stability. In these experiments, stability has been measured using three different techniques: a Triton-shell shaking assay (35), a fragmentation assay using the ektacytometer (7), and a series of micropipette measurements (61).

SPECTRIN SELF-ASSOCIATION   Abnormalities in spectrin self-association and membrane stability have now been described in erythrocytes from a number of individuals with hereditary pyropoikilocytosis (HPP) and hered-

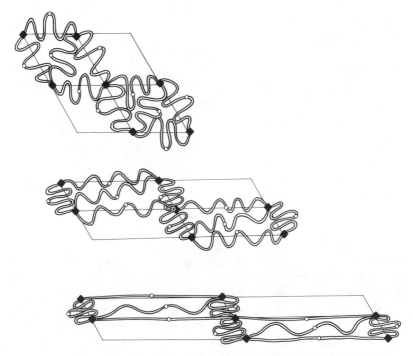

Figure 1 A model of reversible deformation of the erythrocyte membrane. A reversible deformation occurs when the geometric shape changes while the surface area remains constant. The top panel depicts an undeformed membrane. With increased shear stress, the membrane becomes increasingly extended (middle and bottom panels). Further extension of the membrane beyond that shown in the bottom panel would result in an increase in surface area and breaking of junction points. This is the stage at which membrane fragmentation occurs. ■ = protein 4.1, actin, and spectrin association points; ○ = spectrin-spectrin association points; linear coils = spectrin dimers. (Reproduced from the *Journal of Cell Biology,* 1986, 103:343–350 by copyright permission of The Rockefeller University Press.)

itary elliptocytosis (HE). HPP is a hemolytic anemia characterized by microspherocytosis, poikilocytosis, and increased thermal sensitivity of the erythrocytes. When spectrin was extracted at 0°C from the membranes of three individuals from two families with HPP, the percentage of spectrin in the heterodimer state was 15–30% (36). In striking contrast, only a small percentage (5 ± 2%) of the spectrin extracted from normal membranes was in the heterodimer form, and the remainder was predominantly in the tetrameric state (27, 34, 66). Limited tryptic digests prepared from these patients' spectrin showed a decrease in the 80-kd polypeptide of α-spectrin that was proportional to the amount of dimer extracted at 0°C (30). Further, when tryptic peptides were made from dimeric and tetrameric spectrin, the abnormal polypeptide pattern was seen predominantly in the spectrin dimer digest. Since the 80-kd polypeptide contains the domain involved in spectin oligomerization (44), it is not surprising that a defect in this domain would be associated with an inability to form oligomers and would result in an increase in the number of spectrin dimers. When the stability of these HPP membranes was evaluated by the Triton-shell shaking assay, they were found to be less stable than normal membranes (36). Importantly, the degree of instability correlated with both the increase in spectrin dimers and with the decrease in the amount of 80-kd polypeptide. Studies in two other families with HPP (28) also revealed abnormalities in the 80-kd domain of α spectrin and a direct correlation between the amount of the 80-kd polypeptide and the ability of the HPP spectrin to form higher-order oligomers. The stability of these HPP membranes was also measured by ektacytometry. The membranes in which tryptic digests lacked the 80-kd peptide were extremely unstable, while the stability was less impaired in membranes in which this fragment was reduced but present.

Abnormal spectrin heterodimer associations and decreased membrane stability also occur in certain patients with HE, a clinically and biochemically heterogeneous disorder characterized by elliptocytosis and autosomal dominant inheritance. The HE spectrin extracted at 0°C contained an increased level of dimer (15–33%), and the in vitro measurement of membrane stability by Triton-shell shaking assay showed decreased membrane stability (35). Tryptic digests of several of the spectrin samples revealed a decrease in the 80-kd fragment and an increase in a 74-kd fragment (31).

Two families with abnormal spectrin subunits (16, 29) and altered spectrin self-association have been described. One individual had a decreased level of normal β spectrin and an additional 214-kd β chain variant (16). Spectrin tetramer assembly in this subject was abnormal, as evidenced by an excess of spectrin dimer in the spectrin extracted at 4°C and defective self-association of spectrin dimers at 37°C. Since a large proportion of the abnormal chain was found in the dimer form, the defective β chain was probably responsible for the decreased spectrin self-association. Although no in vitro membrane stability assays were done on these cells, membrane fragments were present on the smear of the patient's peripheral blood, which strongly implies in vivo fragmentation due to membrane instability. The second abnormal subunit type is an α chain variant of 4,600 daltons less than the normal α chain (29). The individuals with this abnormality, like those with the β variant, had an increased percentage of dimers, and when membrane stability was assayed using the ektacytometer, it was shown to be decreased. Again, there was a direct correlation between the quantity of the spectrin mutant, the increased percentage of spectrin dimers, and the membrane stability.

These structural and functional studies of pathological erythrocytes support the concept that normal spectrin oligomerization is important for normal membrane stability. Further support for this concept comes from experiments in which normal membranes were treated with N-ethylmaleimide (NEM), a sulfhydryl blocking agent that alters spectrin self-association (53). After incubation in varying concentrations of NEM, there was a dose-dependent decrease in membrane stability as measured by Triton-shell shaking assay (53) and ektacytometry (7).

SPECTRIN-ACTIN-PROTEIN 4.1 ASSOCIATIONS   The idea that spectrin-actin-protein 4.1 associations are also important for normal membrane stability is supported by studies of both pathological membranes and biochemically perturbed normal membranes. An abnormality in this complex of protein associations occurs in several families with protein 4.1 deficiency and in one family with a spectrin variant that does not bind normally to protein 4.1 (40, 41, 57, 64). An Algerian family and an American individual have a total deficiency of protein 4.1 and HE. The Algerian family shows evidence of in vivo fragmentation with fragmented erythrocytes on the peripheral smear (57). When the stability of their red cells was studied in the ektacytometer, the cells were found to be much less stable than normal controls (41). This instability appears to be related to the protein 4.1 deficiency since purified protein 4.1 added to the deficient membranes corrected the instability in a dose-dependent fashion (56). In vitro stability studies were also done on the other, unrelated protein 4.1–deficient individual (61). In this study, the critical force (the force needed to cause yield) was determined by micropipette measurement and found to be decreased. It should be noted that these protein 4.1–deficient membranes may have not only abnormal protein 4.1-actin-spectrin interactions but may also have altered protein 4.1 association with glycophorin C and/or glycophorin A. At this time, it is difficult to sort out the contributions of these possible abnormalities to membrane instability.

Membrane stability was measured with both the ektacytometer and micropipette in a family with a spectrin variant that has abnormal protein 4.1 binding characteristics (7, 61, 64). In these individuals 41% of the spectrin did not bind protein 4.1, although the rest of the spectrin behaved normally. The critical force was determined to be one-half the normal value when evaluated by micropipette measurement (61). The stability of the membranes from three affected individuals was also assayed by ektacytometry and was found to be 45–59% of the normal stability (7).

The data from initially normal membranes treated in vitro with 2,3-DPG complement the data from congenitally abnormal membranes. The polyphosphate 2,3-DPG dissociates spectrin-actin-protein 4.1 complexes, and resealing membranes in the presence of increasing concentrations of 2,3-DPG results in a dose-dependent decrease in membrane stability (7).

Membrane Protein Associations that Influence Membrane Deformability

For reversible deformation at constant surface area to occur, the skeletal proteins need to be able to rearrange, and spectrin molecules need to be able to fold and unfold. Perturbation of the intermolecular or intramolecular spectrin associations would limit the extending capacity of the molecule. In a similar manner, an increase in the associations between skeletal proteins and integral membrane proteins would limit the normal ability of the skeletal proteins to reorganize. Measurement of the deformability of biochemically altered normal membranes suggests that this model (Figure 1) is reasonable.

SPECTRIN ASSOCIATION   Diamide oxidizes sulfhydral groups, thereby cross-linking proteins. Treatment of erythrocytes with this agent creates high molecular weight protein aggregates that consist predominantly of spectrin (25). When membranes were exposed to diamide, there was a dose-dependent decrease in deformability as measured both by ektacytometry (7) and by micropipette (N. Mohandas & E. A. Evans, personal communication). Malonyldialdehyde, an amino group cross-linking reagent, also produced a dose-dependent decrease in membrane deformability when measured in the ektacytometer (7).

INTEGRAL PROTEIN–SKELETAL PROTEIN ASSOCIATION   An increased association between glycophorin A and the skeletal proteins can be induced by glycophorin A–specific ligands. When either wheat germ agglutinin (WGA) or various antibodies with epitopes on the extracellular portion of the sialoglycoprotein were bound to red cells, glycophorin A partitioned with skeletal proteins after Triton extraction (8). This did not occur in nonliganded controls. Interestingly, deformability measurements performed using ektacytometry or a micropipette technique showed that both WGA (8, 17) and antiglycophorin IgG (8) cause membrane rigidity. Since a monovalent Fab fragment of the antiglycophorin was capable of inducing rigidity, this change in membrane deformability may occur because of an increased number of cross-links between the bilayer and the underlying membrane skeleton.

CONCLUSION

In the erythrocyte, increased knowledge of the biochemical structure of the membrane has led to a beginning understanding of the regulation of the mechanical properties of the membrane. The accumulated evidence strongly suggests that spectrin self-association, spectrin-actin-protein 4.1 association, and integral protein–skeletal protein associations play important roles in membrane stability and deformability.

ACKNOWLEDGMENT

Portions of the work performed in the authors' laboratory was supported by the National Institutes of Health AM 16095.

Literature Cited

1. Anderson, R. A., Lovrien, R. E. 1984. Glycophorin is linked by band 4.1 protein to the human erythrocyte membrane skeleton. *Nature* 307:655–58
2. Atkinson, M., Morrow, J., Marchesi, V. 1982. The polymeric state of actin in the human erythrocyte cytoskeleton. *J. Cell. Biochem.* 18:493–505
3. Bennett, V. 1985. The membrane skeleton of human erythrocytes and its implications for more complex cells. *Ann. Rev. Biochem.* 54:273–304
4. Branton, D., Cohen, C. M., Tyler, J. 1981. Interaction of cytoskeleton proteins on the human erythrocyte membrane. *Cell* 254:2533–41
5. Brenner, S. L., Korn, E. D. 1980. Spectrin/actin complex isolated from sheep erythrocytes accelerates actin polymerization by simple nucleation. *J. Biol. Chem.* 255:1670–76
6. Byers, T. J., Branton, D. 1985. Visualization of the protein associations in the erythrocyte membrane skeleton. *Proc. Natl. Acad. Sci. USA* 82:6153–57
7. Chasis, J. A., Mohandas, N. 1986. Erythrocyte membrane deformability and stability: Two distinct membrane properties which are independently regulated by skeletal protein associations. *J. Cell Biol.* 103:343–50
8. Chasis, J. A., Mohandas, N., Shohet, S. B. 1985. Erythrocyte membrane rigidity induced by glycophorin A-ligand interaction: Evidence for a ligand-induced association between glycophorin A and skeletal proteins. *J. Clin. Invest.* 75:1919–26
9. Cohen, C. M. 1983. The molecular organization of the red cell membrane skeleton. *Semin. Hematol.* 20:141–158
10. Cohen, C., Branton, D. 1979. The role of spectrin in erythrocyte membrane-stimulated actin polymerization. *Nature* 279:163–65
11. Cohen, C., Foley, S. 1980. Spectrin-dependent and -independent association of F-actin with the erythrocyte membrane. *J. Cell Biol.* 86:694–98
12. Cohen, C., Foley, S. 1982. The role of

band 4.1 in the association of actin with erythrocyte membranes. *Biochim. Biophys. Acta* 688:691–701
13. Cohen, C. M., Langley, R. C. Jr. 1984. Functional characterization of human erythrocyte spectrin α and β chains: Association with actin and erythrocyte protein 4.1. *Biochemistry* 23:4488–95
14. Cohen, C. M., Tyler, J. M., Branton, D. 1980. Spectrin-actin associations studied by electron microscopy of shadowed preparations. *Cell* 21:875–83
15. Côté, G. P. 1983. Structural and functional properties of the non-muscle tropomyosins. *Mol. Cell. Biochem.* 57:127–46
16. Dhermy, D., LeComte, M. C., Garbarz, M., Bournier, O., Garland, C., et al. 1982. Spectrin β-chain variant associated with hereditary elliptocytes. *J. Clin. Invest.* 70:707–15
17. Evans, E., Leung, A. 1984. Adhesivity and rigidity of erythrocyte membrane in relation to wheat germ agglutinin binding. *J. Cell. Biol.* 98:1201–8
18. Evans, E. A., Waugh, R. E. 1980. Mechanochemical study of red cell membrane structure in situ. In *Erythrocyte Mechanics and Blood Flow*, G. R. Cokelet, H. J. Meiselman, D. E. Brooks, pp. 31–56. New York: Liss.
19. Evans, E. A., Waugh, R., Melnik, L. 1976. Elastic area compressibility modulus of red cell membrane. *Biophys. J.* 16:585–95
20. Fattoum, A., Hartwig, J. H., Stossel, T. P. 1983. Isolation and some structural and functional properties of macrophage tropomyosin. *Biochemistry* 22:1187–93
21. Fowler, V. M., Bennett, V. B. 1984. Erythrocyte membrane tropomyosin. Purification and properties. *J. Biol. Chem.* 259:5978–89
22. Fowler, V. M., Davis, J. Q., Bennett, V. 1985. Human erythrocyte myosin: Identification and purification. *J. Cell Biol.* 100:47–55
23. Fowler, V. M., Taylor, D. L. 1980. Spectrin plus band 4.1 cross-link actin. *J. Cell Biol.* 85:361–76

24. Goodman, S. R., Yu, J., Whitfield, C. F., Culp, E. N., Posnak, E. J. 1982. Erythrocyte membrane skeletal protein bands 4.1a and b are sequence-related phosphoproteins. *J. Biol. Chem.* 257: 4564–69

25. Haest, C. W. M., Plasa, G., Kamp, D., Deuticke, B. 1978. Spectrin as a stabilizer of the phospholipid asymmetry in the human erythrocyte membrane. *Biochim. Biophys. Acta* 509:21–32

26. Jackson, C. W., Mueller, T. J., Dockter, M. E., Morrison, M. 1981. Cytoskeletal alterations during red cell aging. *Blood* 58:29a

27. Ji, T. H., Kiehm, D. J., Middaugh, L. R. 1980. Presence of spectrin tetramers on the erythrocyte membrane. *J. Biol. Chem.* 255:2990–93

28. Knowles, W. J., Morrow, J. S., Speicher, D. W., Zarkowsky, H. S., Mohandas, N., et al. 1983. Molecular and functional changes in spectrin from patients with hereditary pyropoikilocytosis. *J. Clin. Invest.* 71:1867–77

29. Lane, P. A., Shew, R. L., Iarocci, T. A., Mohandas, N., Hays, T., et al. 1985. A unique α-spectrin mutant in a kindred with common hereditary elliptocytosis. *Blood* 66:35a (Suppl 1)

30. Lawler, J., Liu, S. C., Palek, J., Prchal, J. 1982. A molecular defect of spectrin in hereditary pyropoikilocytosis: Alterations in the trypsin-resistant domain involved in spectrin self-association. *J. Clin. Invest.* 70:1019–30

31. Lawler, J., Liu, S. C., Palek, J., Prchal, J. 1984. Molecular defect of spectrin in a subgroup of patients with hereditary elliptocytosis: Alterations in the alpha subunit domain involved in spectrin self-association. *J. Clin. Invest.* 73:1688–95

32. Lin, D. 1981. Spectrin-4.1-actin complex of the human erythrocyte: Molecular basis of its ability to bind cytochalasins with high affinity and to accelerate actin polymerization in vitro. *J. Supramol. Struct.* 15:129–38

33. Lin, D., Lin, S. 1979. Actin polymerization induced by a motility-related high-affinity cytochalasin binding complex from human erythrocyte membrane. *Proc. Natl. Acad. Sci. USA* 76:2345–49

33a. Liu, S. C., Derick, L. H., Palek, J. 1985. High resolution electron microscopic study of normal and abnormal RBC membrane skeletons. *Blood* 66:35a (Suppl 1)

34. Liu, S. C., Palek, J. 1980. Spectrin tetramer-dimer equilibrium and the stability of erythrocyte membrane skeletons. *Nature* 285:586–88

35. Liu, S.-C., Palek, J., Prchal, J. T. 1982. Defective spectrin dimer-dimer association in hereditary elliptocytosis. *Proc. Natl. Acad. Sci. USA* 79:2072–76

36. Liu, S. C., Palek, J., Prchal, J., Castleberry, R. P. 1981. Altered spectrin dimer-dimer association and instability of erythrocyte membrane skeletons in hereditary pyropoikilocytosis. *J. Clin. Invest.* 68:597–605

37. Liu, S. C., Windisch, P., Kim, S., Palek, J. 1984. Oligomeric states of spectrin in normal erythrocyte membranes: Biochemical and electron microscopic studies. *Cell* 37:587–94

38. Marchesi, V. T. 1983. The red cell membrane skeleton: Recent progress. *Blood* 61:1–11

39. Matsumura, F., Yamashiro-Matsumura, S., Jung-Ching Lin, J. 1983. Isolation and characterization of tropomyosin-containing microfilaments from cultured cells. *J. Biol. Chem.* 258:6636–44

40. Mueller, T., Morrison, M. 1981. Glycoconnectin (PAS 2), a membrane attachment site for the human erythrocyte cytoskeleton. In *Erythrocyte Membranes 2: Recent Clinical and Experimental Advances*, ed. W. Kruckeberg, J. Eaton, J. Brewer, pp. 95–112. New York: Liss.

41. Mohandas, N., Clark, M. R., Heath, B. P., Rossi, M., Wolfe, L. C., et al. 1982. A technique to detect reduced mechanical stability of red cell membranes: Relevance to elliptocytic disorders. *Blood* 59:768–74

42. Morrow, J., Haigh, W., Marchesi, V. T. 1981. Spectrin oligomers: A structural feature of the erythrocyte cytoskeleton. *J. Supramol. Struct.* 17:275–87

43. Morrow, J., Marchesi, V. T. 1981. Self-assembly of spectrin oligomers in vitro: A basis for a dynamic cytoskeleton. *J. Cell Biol.* 88:463–68

44. Morrow, J. S., Speicher, D. W., Knowles, W. J., Hsu, C. J., Marchesi, V. T. 1980. Identification of functional domains of human erythrocyte spectrin. *Proc. Natl. Acad. Sci. USA* 77:6592–96

45. Ohanian, V., Wolfe, L., John, K., Pinder, J., Lux, S. E., et al. 1984. Analysis of the tenary interaction of the red cell membrane skeletal proteins: Spectrin, actin, and band 4.1. *Biochemistry* 23: 4416–20

46. Pinder, J., Ohanian, V., Gratzer, W. B. 1984. Spectrin and protein 4.1 as an actin filament capping complex. *FEBS Lett.* 169:161–64

47. Pinder, J., Ungewickell, E., Calvert, R., Morris, E., Gratzer, W. B., et al. 1979. Polymerization of G-actin by spectrin preparations: Identification of

the active constituent. *FEBS Lett.* 104:396–400

48. Shaklai, N., Benitz, L., Ranney, H. M. 1978. Binding of 2,3-diphosphoglycerate by spectrin and its effect on oxygen affinity of hemoglobin. *Am. J. Physiol.* 234:36–40

49. Shen, B. W., Josephs, R., Steck, T. L. 1984. Ultrastructure of unit fragments of the skeleton of the human erythrocyte membrane. *J. Cell Biol.* 99:810–21

50. Shen, B. W., Josephs, R., Steck, T. L. 1986. Ultrastructure of the intact skeleton of the human erythrocyte membrane. *J. Cell Biol.* 102:997–1006

51. Shotton, M. D., Burke, B. E., Branton, D. 1979. The molecular structure of human erythrocyte spectrin. Biophysical and electron microscopic studies. *J. Mol. Biol.* 131:303–29

52. Siegel, D. L., Branton, D. 1985. Partial purification and characterization of an actin-bundling protein, band 4.9, from human erythrocytes. *J. Cell Biol.* 100:775–85

53. Smith, D. K., Palek, J. 1983. Sulfhydral reagents induce altered spectrin self-association, skeletal instability, and increased thermal sensitivity of red cells. *Blood* 62:1190–96

54. Sobue, K., Muramoto, Y., Fujita, M. 1981. Calmodulin-binding protein of erythrocyte cytoskeleton. *Biochem. Biophys. Res. Commun.* 100:1063–70

55. Speicher, D., Morrow, J., Knowles, W. 1982. A structural model of human erythrocyte spectrin: Alignment of chemical and functional domains. *J. Biol. Chem.* 257:9093–9101

56. Takakuwa, Y., Tchernia, G., Rossi, M., Bernabadji, M., Mohandas, N. 1986. Restoration of normal membrane stability to unstable protein 4.1–deficient erythrocyte membranes by incorporation of purified protein 4.1. *J. Clin. Invest.* 78:80–85

57. Tchernia, G., Mohandas, N., Shohet, S. B. 1981. Deficiency of skeletal membrane protein band 4.1 in homozygous

hereditary elliptocytosis. *J. Clin. Invest.* 68:454–60

58. Tyler, J., Hargreaves, W., Branton, D. 1979. Purification of two spectrin-binding proteins. Biochemical and electron microscopic evidence for site-specific reassociation between spectrin and bands 2.1 and 4.1. *Proc. Natl. Acad. Sci. USA* 76:5192–96

59. Tyler, J., Reinhardt, B., Branton, D. 1980. Associations of erythrocyte membrane proteins. Binding of purified bands 2.1 and 4.1 to spectrin. *J. Biol. Chem.* 255:7034–39

60. Waugh, R. E. 1982. Temperature dependence of the yield shear resultant and the plastic viscosity coefficient of erythrocyte membrane. *Biophys. J.* 39:273–78

61. Waugh, R. E. 1983. Effects of abnormal cytoskeletal structure on erythrocyte membrane mechanical properties. *Cell Motil.* 3:609–22

62. Wegner, A. 1982. Kinetic analysis of actin assembly suggests that tropomyosin inhibits spontaneous fragmentation of actin filaments. *J. Mol. Biol.* 161:217–27

63. Williamson, P., Bateman, K. K., Kozarsky, K., Mattocks, K., Hermanowicz, N., et al. 1982. Involvement of spectrin in the maintenance of phase-state asymmetry in the erythrocyte membrane. *Cell* 30:725–33

64. Wolfe, L. C., John, K. M., Falcone, J. C., Byrne, A. M., Lux, S. E. 1982. A genetic defect in the binding of protein 4.1 to spectrin in a kindred with hereditary spherocytosis. *N. Engl. J. Med.* 307:1367–74

65. Ungewickell, E., Bennett, P., Calvert, R. 1979. In vitro formation of a complex between cytoskeletal proteins of the human erythrocyte. *Nature* 280:811–14

66. Ungewickell, E., Gratzer, W. 1978. Self-association of human spectrin. A thermodynamic and kinetic study. *Eur. J. Biochem.* 88:379–85

RENAL AND ELECTROLYTE PHYSIOLOGY

THE JUXTAGLOMERULAR APPARATUS AND TUBULOGLOMERULAR FEEDBACK

Introduction, Carl W. Gottschalk, *Section Editor*

This series of papers discusses the juxtaglomerular apparatus (JGA) and its role in the control of renal hemodynamics and tubular function. As is often the case, these functional studies evolved from earlier morphological studies. In his monumental microdissection study of the nephronic structure of the mammalian kidney, published in 1909, the anatomist and embryologist Karl Peter stressed the finding that the ascending limb of the loop of Henle invariably made contact with the vascular pole of its parent glomerulus. In 1925 the anatomist Ruyter described large granulated "epithelioid" cells in the walls of the afferent arteriole just prior to its entry into the glomerulus, but only in rodents. Several years later similar cells were described in the human kidney by Oberling. In 1932 the Belgian pathologist Norbert Goormaghtigh reinvestigated the juxtaglomerular region in cats and humans and confirmed the presence of large granular cells in the wall of the afferent arteriole and described a second population of small cells, the "lacis" cells, in the angle between the afferent and efferent arterioles. He also remarked on the rich innervation of the structures. A year later Zimmermann described the characteristic form of the tubular cells in that portion of the thick ascending limb of the loop that makes contact with the vascular pole of the glomerulus. He named them the "macula densa" because of their staining characteristics.

In 1937 Goormaghtigh incorporated these three structural elements into his hypothesis of the function of the juxtaglomerular apparatus. "Since the walls of these plaques [macula densa] are in no way related to the capillaries, their function is different from the other elements of the nephron. Taking into account our interpretation of the function of the tissue complex at the vascular pole in the kidney, this structure . . . might communicate the events in the corresponding tubular segment to the intraglomerular circulation. In this context, this group of epithelial cells may be regarded as a sensory plaque, placed downstream from the most important functional segment of the nephron, thus resulting in the possibility of an automatic regulation of the glomerular circulation, controlled either by the 'emptiness or fullness' of the intercalated segment or by the physical chemical composition of the passing urine."[1] In subsequent observations Goormaghtigh explicitly conceived of the granular cells as endocrine cells containing a hypertensive principle, probably renin.

At the Second International Congress of Nephrology in Prague in 1963, Klaus Thurau proposed that the intrarenal mechanism for autoregulation of renal blood flow and glomerular filtation rate (GFR) incorporated a negative feedback loop involving the juxtaglomerular apparatus. A rise in renal perfusion pressure followed by a rise in GFR and tubular flow rate was hypothesized to lead to a change in the physiochemical characteristics of the tubular fluid at the macula densa. This change would be detected by the macula densa cells and transduced in some manner in the JGA, leading to preglomerular vasoconstriction with a decrease in GFR and reestablishment of the filtration rate existing prior to the increase in arterial pressure. Local activation of the renin-angiotensin system was hypothesized to be the vasoactive mechanism. Almost simultaneously Arthur Guyton, on the basis of a computer model, proposed a similar negative feedback hypothesis for the function of the JGA, which differed from Thurau's hypothesis in some details.

The three papers in this section review current knowledge of the juxtaglomerular apparatus and tubuloglomerular feedback control of glomerular and tubular function. Briggs & Schnermann (the latter was one of the original contributors with Thurau to the micropuncture elucidation of tubuloglomerular feedback) review recent work in their laboratory. Bell, Franco, and Navar (who obtained his graduate training with Guyton) discuss calcium as a mediator of tubuloglomerular feedback. Arendshorst reviews the current information, much of which has been provided by him, on altered reactivity of tubuloglomerular feedback.

---

[1]Goormaghtigh, N. 1937. L'appareil neuro-myo-artériel juxtaglomérulaire du rein; les réactions en pathologie et ses rapports avec le tube urinifère. *C. R. Seances Soc. Biol. Paris* 124:293–96. Trans. K. Thurau

Ann. Rev. Physiol. 1987. 49:251–73
Copyright © 1987 by Annual Reviews Inc. All rights reserved

THE TUBULOGLOMERULAR FEEDBACK MECHANISM: Functional and Biochemical Aspects

Josephine P. Briggs and Jurgen Schnermann

Departments of Medicine and Physiology, University of Michigan Medical School, Ann Arbor, Michigan 48109

INTRODUCTION

Changes in NaCl concentration at the macula densa (MD) elicit a response of the smooth muscle cells at the vascular pole of the associated glomerulus. When the NaCl concentration rises, the glomerular plasma flow and glomerular filtration rate (GFR) decrease. The response of the glomerular vascular resistance to changes in the MD NaCl concentration has been termed tubuloglomerular feedback (TGF; 112), in reference to its potential homeostatic effect on distal salt delivery. This mechanism has been investigated extensively by a number of laboratories and has been the subject of several previous reviews (10, 85, 104, 135).

The first section of this review describes the quantitative characteristics of the TGF response and includes attempts to assess the regulatory role of the intact feedback system using control theory. In the second section we summarize new results on the biochemical characteristics of the different cell components of the juxtaglomerular apparatus (JGA) with the expectation that some of this information will eventually lead to an understanding of the cellular mechanisms of JGA function.

PHENOMENOLOGY OF THE TUBULOGLOMERULAR FEEDBACK LOOP

The design of the TGF loop suggests that it serves to maintain distal delivery of NaCl within narrow boundaries and thus regulate the escape of salt into the low-capacity transport system of the distal nephron. When the flow rate in the

251

loop of Henle increases, the filtration rate of the associated glomerulus decreases. The macula densa is not a flow sensor per se, however, but rather reacts to luminal NaCl concentration. The position of the MD is uniquely suited to allow it to sense flow indirectly by sensing NaCl concentration. As a consequence of the transport properties of the thick ascending limb, NaCl concentration is determined almost entirely by tubular flow rate. At low flow rates, the tubular fluid is maximally dilute and Na^+ and Cl^- concentrations are low. When flow increases, these concentrations rise; the physiological range is approximately 25–60 mM. An increase in MD salt delivery, detected as an increase in MD salt concentration, elicits a vasoconstrictor response that reduces GFR and restores distal delivery to near-normal values. This restoration is independent of the cause of increased distal delivery, whether due to an increase in GFR or a decrease in proximal or loop absorption. Maintenance of distal NaCl delivery has primacy over GFR regulation since the effect of TGF regulation on GFR depends upon the nature of the primary perturbation. If the initial disturbance is a change in GFR, the operation of this loop will tend to restore it to, or move it toward, its initial value. However, if the initial change is an alteration in transport, the feedback loop will generate a change in GFR. The efficiency of the system in stabilizing distal salt delivery depends both on the response of glomerular hemodynamics to a change in MD salt concentration (the feedback relationship) and on proximal and loop transport, which determine the relationship between the filtered salt load and the MD signal (the feedforward relationship).

TGF Regulation in Terms of Control Theory

The regulatory efficiency of a control system can be expressed as its open loop gain (OLG), which is an index of how well the system stabilizes its controlled variable in response to an external perturbation (95). OLG is defined as the absolute value of the change in the measured variable with the system inoperative, divided by its change with the system intact, minus one; an OLG of one implies that the deviation from steady state without the feedback loop is twice that found with the feedback loop intact (95). Using conventional microperfusion measurements, Briggs estimated OLG for single-nephron GFR (SNGFR) to be 1, assuming constant fractional absorption along the proximal tubule, and 1.8, when absolute absorption was assumed to be constant (12). Mason & Moore have pointed out that estimates of OLG based on conventional microperfusion experiments may not accurately reflect the regulatory effectiveness of the feedback loop, unless account is also taken of the fact that absorption along the proximal tubule may be altered when the TGF mechanism is activated (72). Changes in absorption may greatly enhance or diminish the regulatory effectiveness and the OLG. In their study Moore & Mason explored the interactions between TGF and the load-dependent adaptive changes in proximal absorption using closed feedback loop analysis (77). They compared the steady-state values of SNGFR and distal flow (a correlate of distal salt delivery) with values measured during perturbation of nephron input produced by adding inulin-free fluid to the flowing early proximal tubule. In hydropenic rats, total system OLG was between 1.5 and 2.1 (72), values similar to those estimated by Briggs. OLG for distal fluid delivery was essentially the same, which suggests that in this experimental condition changes in absorption did not contribute much to error compensation. Consequently, the perturbation in distal delivery was reduced by about 50%, and the regulation was almost entirely a consequence of TGF.

In hemorrhaged rats, OLG for nephron input was lower (1.13) than for distal delivery (2.33). This result indicates that an increase in absorption contributed to compensating for the induced perturbation. Due to this contribution and a more potent TGF response, compensation of the expected deviation from steady state in distal fluid delivery increased to about 70%. Even though the data show only remarkably small changes in absorption, the predictions of the authors' model quantify the extent to which changes in proximal reabsorption that may occur with GFR changes would determine the total effectiveness of the feedback loop. The two phenomena, TGF and the proximal transport adaptation to increased or decreased delivery, are sequential mechanisms that stabilize distal solute delivery: The TGF mechanism is activated only to the extent that more proximal mechanisms have failed to reestablish homeostasis.

The Feedback Relationship

STOP-FLOW PRESSURE   The stop-flow technique is the most convenient method to establish the relationship between loop flow and vascular response. Pressure in a blocked early proximal segment is measured while loop flow rate is varied with a microperfusion pump. Although in one study blocking the nephron was observed to elevate glomerular capillary pressure (P_{GC}) (54), most investigators have found good agreement between P_{GC} estimated as the sum of stop-flow pressure (P_{SF}) and oncotic pressure, and directly measured P_{GC} (1). Changing the loop perfusion rate in small increments revealed a sigmoidal relationship between P_{SF} and flow. In a number of studies no change in P_{SF} was observed when loop flow was increased to about 10–15 nl/min (48, 80, 111). These observations are in good agreement with the failure of Blantz et al to demonstrate a change in glomerular capillary pressure when loop flow was blocked (9). This insensitive region is followed by a sensitive flow band between about 15 and 25 nl/min, and only small responses are seen above 25 nl/min. Since the normal rate of loop flow in rats of the size used in these studies is about 15 nl/min, these results suggest that the TGF mechanism was only activated by supranormal flow rates. However, in some laboratories clear changes in P_{SF} were noted in the flow range between 0 and 15 nl/min (7, 27, 91). Accordingly, values for $V_{1/2}$, the flow rate associated with the half maximum response of P_{SF}, vary substantially among laboratories. A plausible explanation for this variation is not at hand.

FILTRATION RATE   A sigmoidal relationship has also been established between the flow rate in the loop of Henle and SNGFR. In this case the majority of data suggest that the operating point, the steady-state SNGFR at steady-state flow rate, is located somewhere in the steep portion of the curve (7, 12, 17, 91). This position of the operating point is maintained as tubular flow changes as a function of growth (17). In growing rats of different sizes the growth-related increases in filtration rate were accompanied by adaptive changes in the feedback curve, so at each filtration rate the sensitive flow range corresponded approximately to the normal flow range. In 100-g rats with a SNGFR of 15 nl/min and late proximal flow rate of 9 nl/min, the flow rate of maximum sensitivity, $V_{1/2}$, was 10.3 nl/min. In 350-g rats, SNGFR had risen to 49 nl/min and late proximal flow to 26 nl/min, and $V_{1/2}$ had increased correspondingly to 22.3 nl/min. Mueller-Suur et al also documented the necessity of considering body weight when comparing values for $V_{1/2}$ (82). Thus, it appears that TGF exerts a tonic suppressive effect on SNGFR.

The presence of this effect can also be tested by comparing proximal and distal measurements of SNGFR, a method that does not require microperfusion. The standard micropuncture method for measurement of SNGFR is to inject a column of oil into the tubular lumen and collect all fluid arriving at the pipet. In contrast to measurement at a distal tubular site, application of this technique in proximal tubules interrupts flow into the loop of Henle. If TGF tonically suppresses SNGFR, distal values should be systematically lower than proximal values; this supposition was first demonstrated by Schnermann and coworkers (108). Several subsequent studies did not confirm a systematic difference between proximally and distally measured values for SNGFR (3, 71, 80). These investigations included work from researchers who had confirmed the effect of elevated loop flow on filtration (80) and appeared to support the hypothesis that the TGF mechanism was only sensitive to supranormal flows. For unknown reasons, a significant proximal-distal difference appears to have become substantially more common in recent studies (4, 27, 34, 45, 52, 106, 114, 116).

The existence of a TGF mechanism has also been demonstrated for juxtamedullary nephrons of both hamsters and young rats (74, 81, 82). Both the pressure and flow in a descending limb of Henle's loop with a downstream blockade decreased during perfusion of an ascending limb at rates higher than 10 nl/min (81, 82). Furthermore, Ulfendahl et al reported that the flow rate in the loop of Henle, measured from dye bolus velocity and diameter, increased when ascending limb flow was interrupted (129). The demonstrated relationships between flow and SNGFR or virtual P_{SF} suggest a sigmoidal function. The absolute magnitudes of the feedback-induced changes are greater than those in superficial nephrons. This finding is expected because the zero-flow SNGFR is much higher in deep than in surface nephrons. However, percent changes of SNGFR were between 39 and 47% (81, 82) in rats and 54% in hamsters (74). These values are not different from those found in superficial nephrons of both adult and young rats. If flow stimulation was maximal, these results suggest that TGF of deep nephrons is not intrinsically more powerful than that of superficial nephrons.

The position of the operating point between the two nephron populations may be different. Ericson et al (29) assessed the suppressing effect of TGF on SNGFR by comparing measurements obtained using a modified Hanssen technique (MD flow intact) with those obtained by proximal or loop micropuncture (MD flow interrupted). In deep nephrons, micropuncture values exceeded Hanssen values by 54.6 nl/min g^{-1}, while in superficial nephrons the difference was only 3.8 nl/min. At normal flow rates the TGF response appears to be practically maximal in deep nephrons, which would position the operating point at the lower end of the sigmoidal relationship. However, these data suggest that flow can suppress SNGFR of deep nephrons by about 70%, which is quantitatively not in agreement with the microperfusion data cited above (81, 82).

Effects of Changes in the Feedforward Function on the TGF Response

AUTOREGULATION   Changes in transport proximal to the MD may be important for operation of the TGF mechanism in the case of the autoregulatory response of vascular resistance to changes in arterial pressure (AP). There is good experimental support for participation of the TGF mechanism in the resistance changes caused by changes in arterial pressure (104). However, the extent of the TGF contribution is still somewhat unclear. Recent studies by Moore confirmed the earlier conclusion that TGF accounts for no more than half of the total resistance change of superficial nephrons (75). The fact that the fractional change in stop-flow pressure was clearly smaller than the fractional change in arterial pressure was taken as direct evidence for the existence of a TGF-independent mechanism. The results of Schnermann et al (107) suggested that the importance of TGF mediation is pressure dependent, with its contribution diminishing in the subnormal pressure range. However, a recent analysis of the frequency response of renal blood flow by Sakai et al (99) indicates the presence of only one regulator with a frequency characteristics that are compatible with the TGF mechanism. These authors suggest that their earlier finding of a high-frequency regulator may have been an artifact caused by the distance between the sites of flow and pressure measurements (136). Navar also favors the view that TGF can fully account for autoregulation of AP on the basis of his studies in dogs (84).

The nature of the steady-state signal for continued TGF activation once the regulatory response has restored filtration rate to its initial value is unclear. In fact, it is not uncommon to observe a slight rise in SNGFR in response to modest decreases in arterial pressure. Moore recently analyzed the possible contribution of changes in transport to the TGF autoregulatory mechanism (75). He found that when arterial pressure was changed by 30 mm Hg (from 138 to 108 mm Hg), SNGFR fell 0.8 ± 0.8 nl/min with the TGF mechanism intact and fell 6.7 ± 1.4 nl/min with the mechanism interrupted. From model analysis of the TGF loop he demonstrated that small changes in transport could provide the signal for maintained TGF vasodilation (75). The experimental observations could be explained by an increase in single nephron fluid transport of only about 2 nl/min in response to a fall in AP of 30 mm Hg; a slightly greater augmentation of transport would have produced a rise in SNGFR. Such modest pressure-dependent alterations in proximal transport have in fact been observed in a number of studies (22, 75, 78). The phenomenon of pressure natriuresis is based on an inhibitory effect of arterial pressure on tubular absorption. These results and the marked effect of proximal transport changes on the OLG seem to invalidate the conclusion of Jensen & Steven that a contribution of TGF to autoregulation was unlikely because of its insufficient regulatory power (58).

Autoregulation of deep nephron SNGFR was studied by Sjoequist et al (118). During pressure reductions from normal to about 80 mm Hg, SNGFR of both superficial and juxtamedullary nephrons remained constant when the Hanssen technique was used to measure SNGFR but was pressure dependent when assessed by proximal micropuncture. The lower break point of autoregulation appeared to be identical in both nephron populations. In an in vitro preparation that permits study of deep nephron function with maintained tubule-vessel relationships, Casellas et al observed autoregulation of P_{GC} in a small number of nephrons (20). Cohen et al noted a constant vasa recta flow velocity and loop diameter in both hydropenic and volume-expanded rats (24) at pressures between about 75 and 125 mm Hg. At higher pressures vasa recta flow appeared to increase. This result is in agreement with the suggestion of Moore that the position of the operating point of deep nephron TGF at the lower end of the sigmoidal curve should result in relatively poor regulation in response to pressure increases (76).

EFFECTS OF DIETARY PROTEIN CONTENT   A diet high in protein results in an increase in glomerular filtration rate, which appears to be partially accounted for by a loss in the GFR-restraining effect exerted by the TGF mechanism. In rats fed a high-protein diet, interruption of the loop of Henle does not elevate filtration rate as much as it does in control animals (102, 109, 116). The feedback function is shifted to the right: Higher rates of loop flow are required to reduce GFR, but the maximum reduction of GFR produced by TGF is unaltered (102, 116). Recent evidence from Seney and coworkers suggests that these effects may be due to alterations in transport (115). They observed a 30% reduction in Na^+ and Cl^- concentrations in distal fluid during loop perfusion in rats fed a high-protein diet compared with those fed a low-protein diet. More importantly, the TGF response to retrograde perfusion of the loop of Henle was not influenced by the protein content of the diet, which suggests that alterations in the loop rather than in the juxtaglomerular apparatus were responsible for the protein-induced alterations in the feedback function. Bouby et al observed that high-protein fed rats have a widened inner stripe of the outer medulla (11), which might be the anatomical expression of an increased transport activity along thick ascending limbs.

EFFECTS OF ANTIDIURETIC HORMONE ON GFR OF DEEP NEPHRONS
Antidiuretic hormone (ADH) may influence the GFR of deep nephrons via the MD, as a consequence of changes in thick ascending limb (TAL) transport. An effect of ADH on TAL transport was suggested by the marked stimulation of adenyl cyclase activity in medullary TAL segments from mice and rats (55, 79), and this was subsequently confirmed by micropuncture (26) and by in situ and in vitro perfusion studies (40, 43, 100, 134). Hebert et al demonstrated that ADH-stimulated NaCl transport in the isolated, perfused medullary TAL is inhibited by elevated bath tonicity (44). This finding suggests that a functionally important stimulation of transport is most likely to be demonstrable during the transition from water diuresis to antidiuresis. ADH has been shown to increase juxtamedullary nephron filtration rate when measurements are made with the Hanssen technique, which does not interrupt flow through the loop of Henle (25, 127, 128); with conventional micropuncture, which blocks the loop of Henle, no effect on GFR was detected (57, 88).

Juxtamedullary glomeruli in normal rats are substantially larger than superficial glomeruli and have a higher SNGFR. Heterogeneity of both size and function is absent in rats with hereditary DI and is restored by treating the rats with ADH (127, 128). A nonpressor analog of vasopressin, dDAVP, also restored both morphological and functional heterogeneity, which suggests that the increase in deep nephron GFR is not a consequence of direct vascular effects of the hormone (127, 128). Based on these findings, Trinh-Trang-Tan and coworkers proposed that ADH may decrease NaCl concentration at the macula densa of deep nephrons and thereby produce an increase in GFR (128). The vascular effector step for juxtamedullary TGF responses is not known, but the efferent arteriole of juxtamedullary nephrons is thicker walled and better developed than that of superficial nephrons. An efferent mechanism is an attractive possibility, since an increase in GFR and solute delivery without a proportional increase in blood flow would be more effective in reestablishing the medullary solute gradient during the transition from water diuresis to antidiuresis. Evidence from superficial nephrons, discussed below, supports the notion that the TGF response to a decrease in NaCl concentration may involve the efferent arteriole.

Feedback-Loop-Induced Oscillations

It is not uncommon for the operation of a feedback loop to result in periodic fluctuations of the regulated variable. Oscillations can arise for a number of reasons, but feedback loops with a slow response time are particularly vulnerable to oscillatory behavior. As indicated by the time lag between a change in distal flow and a change in P_{SF}, the signal transmission time of the TGF loop is about 5–15 sec. A feedforward or signal propagation time of 3–4 sec was estimated by Young & Marsh from the increase in distal pressure following an abrupt change in arterial pressure (136). Measurements of Leyssac and associates suggest a somewhat more rapid propagation of the signal; they measured a lag of 0.7 sec between proximal and distal tubular pressure changes (69).

Leyssac and coworkers described oscillations in both proximal intratubular pressure and stellate vessel pressure with a periodicity of 2–3 cycles/min and an amplitude of up to 7 or 8 mm Hg that appeared to arise from the operation of the TGF mechanism (67, 68). In their view, the detection of these oscillations is facilitated by using halothane–nitrous oxide anesthetized rats, which have been shown to have a less compliant tubular system (69). The pressure fluctuations observed by Leyssac et al were sometimes observed spontaneously but seemed to be more common or to increase in amplitude when late proximal flow was elevated by a few nanoliters per minute. In spontaneously hypertensive rats, these oscillations were of a highly irregular nature (49). In support of the conclusion that these slow oscillations are TGF-dependent, Leyssac noted that they are abolished by luminal application of furosemide (67), an agent that is also a potent inhibitor of the feedback response to loop microperfusion (104). Furthermore, oscillations measured in two adjacent tubules were out of phase, which is evidence that the periodic phenomenon operates at the single-nephron level; oscillations in one nephron could be abolished by addition of furosemide to the loop perfusate without changing the oscillations in the neighboring tubule (67). The fact that the steady-state pressure during furosemide application was elevated indicates a suppressant effect of normal loop flow on GFR. Since the pressure oscillations were studied with the feedback loop intact, they may simply reflect the time delay between the signal change and the SNGFR response and that between the SNGFR change and the signal response. The cycle length may be a function of the total response time, and the amplitude may reflect the slope of the feedback function. Slow oscillations of approximately the observed frequency are expected in a system with a total delay time of about 20–30 sec/cycle.

Pressure oscillations with other frequencies have also been observed in the renal circulation. We observed very slow cyclic variations (about 1 cycle/min) in stop-flow pressure in animals infused with angiotensin II (103, unpublished observations). These oscillations were most frequently seen when loop flow rate was in the range of maximum TGF sensitivity. They cannot be explained by operation of the TGF loop, since proximal flow is interrupted when stop-flow pressure is measured. These fluctuations would appear to represent the interaction between a TGF-induced change in vasomotor tone and an opposing intrinsic vascular reaction, the nature of which is unclear. Leyssac and coworkers reported rapid oscillations with a frequency of 12–13 cycles/min that were apparent at a high rate of tubular flow (40 nl/min). Although in these studies the feedback loop was not interrupted, the feedback sequence described above seems less likely to explain these observations. At supramaximal rates of tubular flow, decreases in flow have relatively little effect on glomerular function due to the sigmoidal shape of the feedback curve. Oscillations in stop-flow pressure with a similar frequency (14–16 cycles/min) were also observed by Gutsche and coworkers in adrenalectomized rats with or without dexamethasone treatment (39). Oscillations with this frequency do not appear to be generated by the TGF system as they were observed in blocked nephrons microperfused at constant high flow rates.

The Hemodynamic Mechanism

Increasing MD NaCl concentration results in a fall in filtration rate. Measurements of P_{GC} are required to determine the site of the vascular reaction responsible for this decrease in GFR. Studies using P_{SF} as an index of P_{GC} have unequivocally shown that the fall in GFR is accompanied by a fall in this index of glomerular pressure (104). Furthermore, three reports have demonstrated that directly measured P_{GC} also falls with loop perfusion (8, 13, 89) and that the changes in P_{GC} derived from the direct and indirect measurements are essentially identical (89). Ichikawa detected no changes in glomerular pressure with loop perfusion (53). However, it was subsequently demonstrated that the nephrons of the rat substrain utilized in his studies also had very reduced or absent stop-flow pressure responses (F. S. Wright & A. E. G. Persson, personal communication). His data therefore do not appear to invalidate the conclusion that stop-flow pressure and GCP change in parallel.

As has been summarized elsewhere (104), there is reasonably good evidence from several different approaches that the predominant reaction to an increase in loop flow is constriction of the afferent arteriole. Briggs & Wright examined the effect of increasing loop flow from normal (16 nl/min) to high values (40 nl/min) and found that constriction of the afferent arteriole alone could account for the changes in filtration rate (18). Morphological studies have been performed to evaluate the effect of loop perfusion on vascular diameter (104). These studies examined the effect of increasing flow from normal rates to 40 nl/min. Dramatic vasoconstriction of the preglomerular vasculature was demonstrated, and no effect was apparent along the efferent arteriole. Ichikawa examined the effect of increasing flow from 0 to 40 nl/min: His measurements also showed preglomerular vasoconstriction, but in addition they suggested an increase in postglomerular resistance and a decrease in the ultrafiltration coefficient (53). These studies of the effector mechanism all utilized large increments in tubular flow rate. Measurements of segmental resistances in response to small increments in flow are needed to evaluate the exact profile of resistance changes.

When both glomerular filtration rate and stop-flow pressure were measured in the same nephron, a dissociation between the two responses could be demonstrated (15). The flow rate that produced half maximal responses, $V_{1/2}$, was 13.0 nl/min for the filtration rate and 16.7 for the stop-flow pressure. In the flow range between 0 and 10 nl/min, 25% of the total change of filtration rate was observed, while only about 6% of the total response of P_{SF} occurred in this range of flow. A fall in GFR without a change in P_{GC} could be explained by a decrease in the filtration coefficient or an increase in efferent resistance. Inhibition of both angiotensin II formation and prostaglandin synthesis is also associated with a dissociation of the feedback responses of SNGFR and P_{SF} (89). Inhibition of the P_{SF} response despite maintained SNGFR response also suggests parallel changes in afferent and efferent resistances.

Effects of MD-Mediated Renin Release on the TGF Mechanism

Circumstantial evidence suggests that the two events known to be initiated by the MD cells, TGF and renin secretion, may be mechanistically coupled. We recently reviewed the evidence that changes in MD salt concentration are not only followed by the TGF response, but are also followed by a change in renin secretion in the direction opposite that of the change in MD concentration (16, 105). Single-nephron manipulations that change only NaCl concentration at a single macula densa may not adequately mimic the effect of simultaneous activation or deactivation of the two systems in all nephrons. The concentrations of the angiotensins in the tissue may change much more when all nephrons are involved.

Since angiotensin is an agent with both vascular and epithelial effects, a change in its tissue concentration may alter both limbs of the feedback loop. The evidence that angiotensin affects proximal transport was recently reviewed (41). In the critical concentration range, between about 10^{-11} and 10^{-9} M, transport is stimulated, so a rise in angiotensin II concentration with a decrease in the feedback signal would increase proximal transport and thereby increase the OLG. It is conceivable that MD-mediated renin release and angiotensin production are responsible for the increased regulatory efficiency observed during reductions in arterial pressure (75). If TGF vasoconstriction is accompanied by a fall in tissue angiotensin levels, the vasoconstrictor response may be attenuated. One might expect the greatest modulation at the level of the efferent arteriole and the glomerular tuft in view of their greater receptor density.

BIOCHEMICAL CHARACTERISTICS OF THE JG CELLS

Macula Densa

It is likely that the macula densa (MD) plays a key role in mediating the effects of compositional changes in tubular fluid on glomerular vascular tone and renin release. Thus, the elucidation of its biochemical and humoral potential is necessary to eventually understand the mechanism of information transfer. Unfortunately, the size and plaquelike nature of the MD limits the application of the most powerful tool for biochemical studies on the nephron level, that of enzyme analyses in microdissected, defined nephron segments. Nevertheless, sufficient information has been gathered about the biochemical equipment of the MD to establish this small cell group as a distinct nephron segment. We review this evidence with the expectation that it represents a piece of the puzzle that will eventually give a picture of signal generation and transfer by the "sensor plaque" (36).

RNA SYNTHESIS   Vandewalle et al (130, 131) studied the nuclear and cytosolic labelling of microdissected tubular segments after both in vitro and in vivo administration of [^{3}H]uridine. Labelling was virtually absent in the presence of actinomycin D, an inhibitor of transcription of template DNA (131). This observation suggests that uridine labelling reflects incorporation of the pyrimidine precursor into RNA. Substantial differences in the intensity of nuclear labelling were noted among different nephron segments. The most striking finding was that labelling after both in vivo and in vitro exposure to uridine was higher in the MD by a factor of two to three than in any other segment of the nephron. Intense nuclear labelling was also observed in the cortical thick ascending limbs on either side of the MD and in the intercalated cells of the cortical collecting tubules. Vandewalle et al suggest that the intensity of labelling correlates with the mitochondrial density and thus with the metabolic activity of the tubular cells. While this correlation may hold for other segments, it does not appear to explain the dense labelling of MD cells: In the MD, mitochondria are smaller and sparser than in the distal convoluted tubule cells, for example (59, 90). A better morphological correlate may be the volume of cell nuclei. Although morphometric data are not available, the remarkable size of the MD nuclei is evident and accounts for its "dense" appearance. Nuclear volume is also rather high in distal tubule cells, while the lower nuclear volume-to-cytosol relationship of proximal and collecting tubule cells correlates with a lower uridine labelling (90).

The degree of uridine labelling increased significantly in most segments after chronic administration of desoxycorticosterone acetate (DOCA) (130). The highest relative increase was found in cortical and medullary collecting tubules, known target sites for mineralocorticoid action. In macula densa and thick ascending limb, uridine incorporation also tended to rise after treatment with DOCA, but the changes were small compared to the high baseline levels and were not statistically significant. An increase in uridine incorporation after DOCA administration can be taken as a measure of mineralocorticoid-stimulated RNA synthesis; increased RNA synthesis is one step in the events mediating aldosterone action (31). The collecting duct is also the segment in which mineralocorticoids produce the strongest stimulation of Na, K-ATPase and the greatest enlargement of basolateral membrane area (66). The absence of significant changes in uridine labelling by DOCA in thick ascending limb and MD cells suggests that RNA synthesis in these cells is likely to serve a different function. However, Farman & Bonvalet demonstrated that both thick ascending limb cells and MD cells in spontaneously hypertensive rats bind tritiated aldosterone (30). If this binding reflects association with mineralocorticoid binding sites, it is feasible that even in these cells some fraction of RNA synthesis may be related to mineralocorticoid action.

PENTOSE PHOSPHATE SHUNT   Another striking difference in cell biochemistry between MD and surrounding tubular cells is the high activity of glucose-6-phosphate dehydrogenase, G6PD (46). In a recent microenzymatic study Norgaard found G6PD activity in MD to be about two times higher than in proximal tubule cells and about three times higher than in distal tubules (86). The high activity of the pentose phosphate pathway may be related to the high rate of RNA synthesis thought to exist in MD cells (130, 131). Since the pentose pathway generates ribose-5-phosphate, the pentose component of RNA, the increased activity of G6PD may simply reflect a greater need to generate pentose for RNA synthesis.

However, other roles of this high pentose shunt activity are not excluded. Histochemical measurements suggest that the activity of G6PD may vary in parallel to changes in renal renin activity. Quantitative microenzymatic determinations revealed a reduced G6PD activity following NaCl loading, but no increase by salt depletion (87). Thus, the pentose shunt may be coupled to renin synthesis in some unknown way. Recent studies by Rostand & Work support this notion (98). These authors studied the effect of 6-aminonicotinamide, a blocker of the pentose pathway, on renin release from isolated kidneys. They found that 6-aminonicotinamide reduced the renin content of nonfiltering kidneys and virtually abolished its release. This treatment also inhibited furosemide-stimulated renin release in filtering kidneys but did not change renin release stimulated by isoproterenol. Although these are intriguing data, the link between a change in pentose shunt activity in the MD cells and a change in renin synthesis and release from granular cells remains obscure. It has been suggested that the glyceraldehyde-3-phosphate generated in the transketolase reaction of the hexose monophosphate shunt may be transferred to the granular cells, where it might be utilized to drive a glycerol phosphate shuttle providing energy for renin synthesis (47, 98). A high activity of glycerophosphate dehydrogenase has been reported to exist in granular cells, but its cytosolic or mitochondrial localization is not known (47).

NA,K-ATPASE AND TRANSPORT   Several lines of evidence suggest that NaCl transport by MD cells participates in the generation of a signal that leads to a change in glomerular vascular tone. Since luminal concentrations are far below isotonicity, transport of NaCl almost certainly proceeds against an electrochemical gradient and would therefore require energetic support by the sodium pump. The MD cells are stuffed with small mitochondria, especially in their basal cell half, but they are not closely associated with cell membranes (59). Histochemical localization of Na,K-ATPase from the reaction product of p-nitrophenyl phosphate with K-dependent phosphatase detected little or no enzyme in MD cells of rats, rabbits, and dogs (6). Recent studies using a microenzymatic cycling reaction for the detection of ATPase activities in dissected MD segments of rabbits confirmed the finding that Na,K-ATPase activity in this segment is substantially lower than in thick ascending limbs (110). However, MD cells did liberate P_i from ATP at a rate of ~15 pmol/hr, and this rate was reduced by half by treatment with ouabain. Thus MD cells have a Na,K-ATPase activity of about 0.5 fmol/hr per unit tubular cell volume (μm^3), which is similar in order of magnitude to that of thin ascending limbs and cortical and outer medullary collecting tubules but is about 50 times lower than that in thick ascending limbs, distal convoluted tubules, or connecting tubules (35). Low levels of Na,K-ATPase in the basal membranes of MD cells have also been demonstrated using monoclonal antibodies to localize the enzyme (61). The low Na,K-ATPase activity correlates well with the low level of Krebs cycle enzymes found in MD cells (63). Thus, any NaCl transport system in the MD is probably of low capacity. This seems appropriate for a tubular segment without attached blood capillaries for convective solute removal.

Direct evidence for solute and water movement across macula densa segments may come from studies utilizing isolated perfused thick ascending limb segments that include the MD. Two recent reports demonstrate that this approach is technically feasible and that the MD cells are clearly visible (14, 62). The only result possibly related to solute movement is the preliminary demonstration of higher positive potential differences (PDs) at the MD cells compared with cells on either side, when such segments are perfused with symmetrical solutions (14). If the positive PD across thick ascending limb epithelium under these circumstances mainly reflects recycling of potassium absorbed by a NaCl-KCl cotransporter (37), the higher PD is consistent with the presence of this transport system in MD cells. Electron micrographs show that the intercellular spaces of MD cells are wide (60). Narrowing of these spaces has been observed in mannitol and furosemide diuresis and when hypertonic saline was given to animals made hypovolemic by prior administration of furosemide (60). Thus, intercellular space width seems to correlate with the presence of osmotic gradients and may thus indicate osmotic water flow. Kirk and coworkers succeeded in directly observing intercellular space widening in response to the imposition of an osmotic gradient in the perfused MD preparation (62). Even though these results unquestionably establish the MD as a water permeable segment, the magnitude of the actual water flow remains unclear. In the absence of water removal by blood capillaries, intercellular space width may be determined to a greater extent by flow resistance than by flow rate.

GLYCOPROTEINS   The lectin binding specificity of MD cells further supports the idea that they comprise a distinct nephron segment. Although in the rabbit lectin binding does not differ between the thick ascending limb and MD segments (65), MD cells of the rat kidney display a lectin binding pattern quite distinct from that of thick ascending limbs (64). Both soybean and wheat germ lectins bind to the MD but not to the thick ascending limb, while the opposite is true of winged pea lectin (64). Thus, MD cells appear to possess N-acetyl-glucosamine and N-acetyl-galactosamine terminals in their glycoprotein coat, in contrast to the thick ascending limbs, which have 1-fucose binding sites. It is not known whether application of these lectins is associated with differentiated functional responses.

Differences between cells of the MD and of the thick ascending limbs also exist with respect to Tamm-Horsfall (TH) glycoprotein. This constituent of urinary casts is essentially not found in association with MD cells but is located in thick ascending limb cells, where it is also synthesized. Its subcellular localization along basal, basolateral, and luminal cell membranes (51, 117) suggests that coating with a TH-protein-containing gel may render thick ascending limbs water impermeable (51, 117). Thus the absence of this glycoprotein from MD cells may be responsible for the water permeability of this cell group.

Another function suggested for TH protein is related to ion transport (38, 94). Hartmann et al reported binding of mercury chloride and ethacrynic acid to a TH protein subunit and suggested that TH glycoprotein may mediate the effect of diuretics that inhibit chloride transport (42). Greven noted that *Ulex europaeus* agglutinin (UEA), a lectin with affinity for 1-fucose, inhibited NaCl absorption along microperfused loops of Henle (38). Whether UEA binds to ascending limbs is unclear (50), but the binding of winged pea lectin, which is also specific for 1-fucose, makes this a likely possibility (64). Since TH protein contains 1-fucose, albeit in small amounts (132), Greven hypothesized that inhibition of transport might be caused by displacement of NaCl from TH binding sites by the lectin (38). His preliminary observation that purified TH protein in vitro is capable of binding furosemide seems to support this notion (38). This binding required low concentrations of Na^+ and could be augmented by both Cl^- and K^+, which suggests that TH protein has binding sites for Na^+, K^+, and Cl^- that are shared by furosemide. Competitive displacement of Cl^- by furosemide may explain the inhibitory effect of the diuretic. If the presence of TH protein is in fact a prerequisite for NaCl-KCl cotransport and for the transport-inhibiting effect of loop diuretics, the concept of feedback mediation by active MD NaCl transport may require modification. However, an effect of furosemide has also been demonstrated in microperfused distal tubules and collecting ducts, where TH protein is absent (119, 133).

The characterization of TH protein as a surface glycoprotein has recently been questioned by Bachmann et al (2). Using protein A–gold immunocytochemistry these authors conclude that TH protein is located in the entire epithelium, with a particularly high concentration in apical vesicles. In their view the presence of TH protein reflects intracellular storage rather than membrane association. They suggest that the appearance of TH protein along membranes in the earlier studies may at least in part be due to inadequate tissue preservation.

BENZODIAZEPINE RECEPTORS   The existence of a high density of benzodiazepine receptors of the peripheral type in the kidney seems well established (93, 113). Recent autoradiographic studies by Beaumont et al using tritiated flunitrazepam as the radioligand show that these receptors are exclusively located in thick ascending limbs and distal convoluted tubules (5). Some of the material presented in these studies strongly suggests that a high level of benzodiazepine binding activity is associated with some tubular elements at the vascular pole, probably the MD cells (5).

CARBONIC ANHYDRASE   MD cells in rabbit kidneys display cytoplasmic staining when histochemically analyzed for the presence of carbonic anhydrase (28). Even though the reaction is faint, it is distinguishable from the complete absence of such a reaction in thick ascending limbs. In the mouse kidney, in contrast, carbonic anhydrase is present along thick ascending limbs. In this species MD segments were not examined. MD cells of human kidneys showed intense selective staining along both luminal and basolateral membranes, while no cytoplasmic staining was found (70). In adjacent thick ascending limb cells, reaction product was present only along basolateral membranes (70). This result suggests that, at least in some species, MD cells may possess an acidifying transport system such as the Na-H antiporter. Furthermore, the transport systems of MD and thick ascending limb cells may differ.

Goormaghtigh Cells

There is still relatively little known about this peculiar cushion of cells, which fill the wedge-shaped space between the macula densa and the glomerular vascular pole. The anatomic arrangements, particularly the regularity of overlap between the Goormaghtigh cell field and the macula densa (23) and the extensive cell-to-cell coupling (92, 125), suggest a transmitter function. Three-dimensional reconstructions demonstrating an impressive surface enlargement by cytoplasmic extensions seem to support this concept (120). The Goormaghtigh cells are also called extraglomerular mesangial cells, in reference to the similarities of their fine structure with that of the cells of the intraglomerular mesangium. It remains unknown to what extent results accumulating from the study of cultured mesangial cells and glomerular receptors also apply to this cell group. For example, the mesangial cells appear to be the target cells for the rather intense glomerular binding of a number of ligands, including angiotensin II, atrial natriuretic peptide, and vasopressin (97). Studies evaluating the relative binding of intra- and extraglomerular mesangial cells will be of interest.

Schnabel & Kriz studied changes in the interstitial volume of the Goormaghtigh cell field following expansion or depletion of extracellular volume (101). The interstitial volume density of the extraglomerular mesangial cell field increased from 16.9% during volume depletion to 29.0% during volume expansion; no changes were noted in the peritubular interstitium. The demonstration of a fenestrated endothelium in the afferent arteriole and podocyte foot processes facing the Goormaghtigh cell field suggests that the extraglomerular mesangial interstitium could conceivably receive fluid from both the blood and the urinary spaces (96). However, the steep osmotic gradient across the MD cells probably provides a quantitatively more important driving force.

Granular Cells

The presence of angiotensin II in renal tissue was demonstrated by Mendelsohn in 1979 (73). Several groups of investigators have used immunocytochemical methods to show that angiotensin II is not only present in the same cells that contain renin, but that it appears to coexist with renin in the same secretory granules (19, 21, 123). An increase in granular renin following adrenalectomy was accompanied by a parallel increase in granular angiotensin levels (124). Some uncertainty surrounds the question of the origin of the intragranular angiotensin II. Taugner et al have been unable to demonstrate the presence of angiotensin I, renin substrate, or renin converting enzyme within juxtaglomerular granules (124). These authors, as well as Cantin et al (19), suggest that angiotensin II may be taken up by the granular cells either through unspecific pinocytosis or through receptor binding and internalization. However, Naruse et al demonstrated intragranular angiotensin I after the administration of converting enzyme inhibitors, which suggests that angiotensin I levels may normally be too low to detect (83). Angiotensin I, as well as converting enzyme, was also found in juxtaglomerular cells in culture (56). These data suggest that angiotensin II is enzymatically generated within the granules. The results of both groups imply that angiotensin II is secreted together with renin. An action of angiotensin in the immediate vicinity of the site of secretion is therefore likely. This action could be related to the inhibitory effect of angiotensin II on granule release or to its vascular effects.

In addition to renin, juxtaglomerular cell granules appear to contain acid phosphatase (32, 126) and cathepsin B (122). Acid phosphatase and possibly other hydrolytic enzymes may participate in controlling the amount of secretory material awaiting release (126). Cathepsin B has been shown to activate renin in vitro, with a pH optimum of 4–5 (121). If such an acidic pH exists in renin granules, cathepsin B may be importantly involved in intracellular renin activation (122). Taugner et al emphasize that the presence of lysosomal enzymes in renin granules is not typical of most secretory granules and that this finding supports earlier suggestions of the identity of renin granules with lysosomes (32, 126). This concept is further strengthened by the observation that exogenous tracers are taken up by renin granules without apparent interaction with the Golgi complex (126).

To generate angiotensins the JG cells may not exclusively depend upon extraction of liver-produced substrate from the blood. Fried & Simpson have shown that mRNA coding for renin substrate can be demonstrated in the kidney (33). Interestingly, angiotensinogen mRNA was localized primarily, if not exclusively, in the renal medulla.

SUMMARY

Tubuloglomerular feedback is an intrarenal control mechanism designed to regulate the amount of salt entering the distal nephron. Its regulatory efficiency depends upon the magnitude of the vascular response to changes in the luminal signal (the feedback relationship) and on the adjustments in proximal absorption, which determine the macula densa signal (the feedforward relationship). Studies of the feedback relationship have established that the vascular response is related to macula densa solute concentration in a sigmoidal fashion, with the normal operating point located somewhere in the steep portion of the curve. Thus, tubuloglomerular feedback tonically suppresses glomerular filtration rate, an effect that may be even more pronounced in juxtamedullary nephrons. An alteration in the feedforward function and thus in the macula densa signal is likely to participate in the vascular resistance changes initiated by changes in arterial pressure, elevated protein intake, or ADH administration.

Our understanding of the intra- and intercellular mechanisms underlying information transfer across the JGA is currently incomplete, but there is some information about the biochemical characteristics of the cellular components. The enzymatic and surface properties establish the distinct nature of the macula densa cells and indicate a distinct function.

Literature Cited

1. Arendshorst, W. J., Gottschalk, C. W. 1985. Glomerular ultrafiltration dynamics: Historical perspective. *Am. J. Physiol.* 248:F163–74

2. Bachmann, S., Koeppen-Hagemann, I., Kriz, W. 1985. Ultrastructural localization of Tamm-Horsfall glycoprotein (THP) in rat kidney as revealed by protein A–gold immunocytochemistry. *Histochemistry* 83:531–38

3. Bartoli, E., Earley, L. 1973. Measurement of nephron filtration rate in the rat with and without occlusion of the proximal tubule. *Kidney Int.* 3:372–80

4. Baylis, C., Blantz, R. 1985. Tubuloglomerular feedback activity in virgin and 12-day pregnant rats. *Am. J. Physiol.* 249:F169–73

5. Beaumont, K., Healy, D. P., Fanestil, D. D. 1984. Autoradiographic localization of benzodiazepine receptors in the rat kidney. *Am. J. Physiol.* 247:F718–24

6. Beeuwkes, R. III, Rosen, S. 1980. Renal Na-K-ATPase: Localization and quantitation by means of its K-dependent phosphatase activity. *Curr. Top. Membr. Transp.* 13:343–54

7. Bell, P. D., Navar, L. G., Ploth, D. W., McLean, C. B. 1980. Tubuloglomerular feedback responses during perfusion with non-electrolyte solutions in the rat. *Kidney Int.* 18:460–71

8. Bell, P. D., Reddington, M., Ploth, D., Navar, L. G. 1984. Tubuloglomerular feedback-mediated decreases in glomerular pressure in Munich-Wistar rats. 16:F877–80

9. Blantz, R. C., Israelit, A. H., Rector, F. C., Seldin, D. W. 1972. Relation of distal tubular NaCl delivery and glomerular hydrostatic pressure. *Kidney Int.* 2:22–32

10. Blantz, R. C., Pelayo, J. C. 1984. Functional role for the tubuloglomerular feedback mechanism. *Kidney Int.* 25:739–46

11. Bouby, N., Laouari, D., Trinh, M. M., Kleinknecht, C., Kriz, W., Bankir, L. 1984. Protein-induced kidney hypertrophy: Selective increase of the inner stripe of the outer medulla and possible involvement of ADH and/or urine concentrating mechanism (UCM). *Proc. IXth Int. Congr. Nephrol.* Abstr. 405A

12. Briggs, J. 1982. A simple steady-state

model for feedback control of glomerular filtration rate. *Kidney Int.* 22:S12, 143–50

13. Briggs, J. 1984. Effect of loop of Henle flow rate on glomerular capillary pressure. *Renal Physiol.* 7:311–20

14. Briggs, J. P., Kokko, J. P., Jacobson, H. R. 1984. Dissection and in vitro microperfusion of the juxtaglomerular apparatus. *Proc. IXth Int. Congr. Nephrol.* Abstr. 406A

15. Briggs, J. P., Schnermann, J. 1985. Dissociation between stop flow pressure and filtration rate response to changing loop of Henle flow rate. *Kidney Int.* 27:293

16. Briggs, J. P., Schnermann, J. 1986. Macula densa control of renin secretion and glomerular vascular tone: Evidence for common cellular mechanisms. *Renal Physiol.* 9:193–203

17. Briggs, J. P., Schubert, G., Schnermann, J. 1984. Quantitative characterization of the tubuloglomerular feedback response: Effect of growth. *Am. J. Physiol.* 247:F808–17

18. Briggs, J. P., Wright, F. S. 1979. Feedback control of glomerular filtration rate: Site of the effector mechanism. *Am. J. Physiol.* 236:F40–F47

19. Cantin, M., Gutkowska, J., Lacasse, J., Ballak, M., Ledoux, S., et al. 1984. Ultrastructural immunocytochemical localization of renin and angiotensin II in the juxtaglomerular cells of the ischemic kidney in experimental renal hypertension. *Am. J. Pathol.* 115:212–24

20. Casellas, D., Carmines, P., Navar, L. 1985. Microvascular reactivity of in vitro blood perfused juxtamedullary nephrons from rats. *Kidney Int.* 28:752–59

21. Celio, M. R., Inagami, T. 1981. Angiotensin II immunoreactivity coexists with renin in the juxtaglomerular granular cells of the kidney. *Proc. Natl. Acad. Sci. USA* 78:3897–3900

22. Chou, C.-L., Marsh, D. J. 1986. Role of proximal convoluted tubule in pressure diuresis in the rat. *Am. J. Physiol.* 251:F283–89

23. Christensen, J. A., Bjoerke, H. A., Meyer, D., Bohle, A. 1979. The normal juxtaglomerular apparatus in the human kidney. *Acta Anat.* 103:374–83

24. Cohen, H., Marsh, D., Kayser, B. 1983. Autoregulation in vasa recta of the rat kidney. *Am. J. Physiol.* 245:F32–40

25. Davis, J. M., Schnermann, J. 1971. The effect of antidiuretic hormone on the distribution of nephron filtration rates in rats with hereditary diabetes insipidus. *Pflüg. Arch.* 330:323–34

26. De Rouffignac, C., Corman, B., Roinel, N. 1983. Stimulation by antidiuretic hormone of electrolyte tubular reabsorption in rat kidney. *Am. J. Physiol.* 244:F156–64

27. Dilley, J. R., Arendshorst, W. J. 1984. Enhanced tubuloglomerular feedback activity in rats developing spontaneous hypertension. *Am. J. Physiol.* 247:F672–79

28. Dobyan, D., Magill, L., Friedman, P., Hebert, S., Bulger, R. 1982. Carbonic anhydrase histochemistry in rabbit and mouse kidneys. *Anat. Rec.* 204:185–97

29. Ericson, A.-C., Sjoequist, M., Ulfendahl, H. R. 1982. Heterogeneity in regulation of glomerular function. *Acta Physiol. Scand.* 114:203–9

30. Farman, N., Bonvalet, J. P. 1985. Aldosterone binding in isolated tubules. IV. Autoradiography along the nephron of the spontaneously hypertensive rat. *Am. J. Physiol.* 249:F99–F106

31. Feldman, D., Funder, J. W., Edelman, I. S. 1972. Subcellular mechanisms in the action of adrenal steroids. *Am. J. Med.* 53:545–60

32. Fisher, E. R. 1966. Lysosomal nature of juxtaglomerular granules. *Science* 152:1752–53

33. Fried, T. A., Simpson, E. A. 1986. Intrarenal localization of angiotensinogen mRNA by RNA-DNA dot-blot hybridization. *Am. J. Physiol.* 250:F374–77

34. Galla, J. H., Bonduris, D. N., Sanders, P. W., Luke, R. G. 1984. Volume-independent reductions in glomerular filtration rate in acute chloride-depletion alkalosis in the rat. Evidence for mediation by tubuloglomerular feedback. *J. Clin. Invest.* 74:2002–8

35. Garg, L., Knepper, M., Burg, M. 1981. Mineralocorticoid effects on Na-K-ATPase in individual nephron segments. *Am. J. Physiol.* 240:F536–44

36. Goormaghtigh, N. 1937. L'appareil neuro-myoarteriel juxtaglomerulaire du rein: Ses reactions en pathologie et ses rapports avec le tube urinifere. *C. R. Soc. Biol.* 124:293–296

37. Greger, R. 1985. Ion transport mechanisms in thick ascending limb of Henle's loop of mammalian nephron. *Physiol. Rev.* 65:760–60

38. Greven, J. 1983. Studies on the renal receptors of loop diuretics. *Clin. Exp. Hypertension* 5:193–208

39. Gutsche, H.-U., Mueller-Suur, R., Samwer, K. F., Beer, G., Hierholzer, K. 1980. Tubuloglomerular feedback

control in kidneys of adrenalectomized rats. *Pflüg. Arch.* 386:11–19

40. Hall, D. A., Varney, D. M. 1980. Effect of vasopressin on electrical potential difference and chloride transport in mouse medullary thick ascending limb of Henle's loop. *J. Clin. Invest.* 66:792–802

41. Harris, P. J., Navar, L. G. 1985. Tubular transport responses to angiotensin. *Am. J. Physiol.* 248:F621–30

42. Hartmann, L., Delaunay, J., Ollier-Hartmann, M. P., Bringuier, A., Richet, G. 1981. Tamm-Horsfall protein and erythrocyte ghosts immunologically crossreact. *Biomedicine* 35:1–3

43. Hebert, S. C., Culpepper, R. M., Andreoli, T. E. 1981. NaCl transport in mouse medullary thick ascending limbs. II. ADH enhancement of transcellular NaCl cotransport; origin of transepithelial voltage. *Am. J. Physiol.* 241:F432–42

44. Hebert, S. C., Culpepper, R. M., Andreoli, T. E. 1981. NaCl transport in mouse medullary thick ascending limbs. III. Modulation of the ADH effect by peritubular osmolality. *Am. J. Physiol.* 241:F443–51

45. Hermansson, K., Kaellskog, K., Wolgast, M. 1984. Effect of renal nerve stimulation on the activity of the tubuloglomerular feedback mechanism. *Acta Physiol. Scand.* 120:381–86

46. Hess, R., Gross, F. 1959. Glucose-6-phosphate dehydrogenase and renin in kidneys of hypertensive or adrenalectomized rats. *Am. J. Physiol.* 197:869–72

47. Hess, R., Pearse, G. E. 1961. Mitochondrial alpha-glycerophosphate dehydrogenase activity of juxtaglomerular cells in experimental hypertension and adrenal insufficiency. *Proc. Soc. Exp. Biol. Med.* 106:895–98

48. Hierholzer, K., Mueller-Suur, R., Gutsche, H.-U., Butz, M., Lichtenstein, I. 1974. Filtration of stainable glomeruli as regulated by flow through the loop of Henle. *Pflüg. Arch.* 352:315–37

49. Holstein-Rathlou, N.-H., Leyssac, P. P. 1986. TGF-mediated oscillations in the proximal intratubular pressure: Differences between spontaneously hypertensive rats and Wistar-Kyoto rats. *Acta Physiol. Scand.* 126:341–49

50. Holthoefer, H. 1983. Lectin binding sites in kidney. A comparative study of 14 animal species. *J. Histochem. Cytochem.* 31:531–37

51. Hoyer, J. R., Sisson, S. P., Vernier, R. L. 1979. Tamm-Horsfall glycoprotein. Ultrastructural immunoperoxidase localization in rat kidney. *Lab. Invest.* 41:168

52. Huang, C. L., Lewicki, J., Johnson, L. K., Cogan, M. G. 1985. Renal mechanism of action of rat atrial natriuretic factor. *J. Clin. Invest.* 75:769–73

53. Ichikawa, I. 1982. Direct analysis of the effector mechanism of the tubuloglomerular feedback system. *Am. J. Physiol.* 243:F447–55

54. Ichikawa, I. 1982. Evidence for altered glomerular hemodynamics during acute nephron obstruction. *Am. J. Physiol.* 242:F580–85

55. Imbert-Teboul, M., Chabardes, D., Montegut, M., Clique, A., Morel, F. 1978. Vasopressin-dependent adenylate cyclase activities in the rat kidney medulla: Evidence for two separate sites of action. *Endocrinology* 102:1254–61

56. Inagami, T., Okamura, D., Clemens, D., Celio, M. R., Naruse, K., Naruse, M. 1983. Local generation of angiotensin in the kidney and in tissue culture. *Clin. Exp. Hypertens. Ser. A. Theor.* 5:1137–49

57. Jamison, R. L., Buerkert, J., Lacy, F. B. 1973. A micropuncture study of Henle's thin loop in Brattleboro rats. *Am. J. Physiol.* 224:180–85

58. Jensen, P. K., Steven, K. 1982. A model study of the tubuloglomerular feedback mechanism: Effector site and influence on renal autoregulation. *Acta Physiol. Scand.* 115:295–300

59. Kaissling, B., Kriz, W. 1979. *Structural Analysis of the Rabbit Kidney.* Berlin: Springer-Verlag. 121 pp.

60. Kaissling, B., Kriz, W. 1982. Variability of intercellular spaces between macula densa cells: A transmission electron microscopic study in rabbits and rats. *Kidney Int.* 22, Suppl. 12:S9–S17

61. Kashgarian, M., Biemesderfer, D., Caplan, M., Forbush, B. 1985. Monoclonal antibodies to Na,-K-ATPase: Immunocytochemical localization along nephron segments. *Kidney Int.* 28:899–913

62. Kirk, K. L., Bell, P. D., Barfuss, D. W., Ribadeneira, M. 1985. Direct visualization of the isolated and perfused macula densa. *Am. J. Physiol.* 248:F890–94

63. Krompecher-Kiss, E., Bucher, O. 1977. Comparison of the activities of some dehydrogenases in the juxtaglomerular complex of kidneys of Wistar rats and desert rats *(Meriones culati).* *Histochemistry* 53:265–69

64. Le Hir, M., Dubach, U. C. 1982. The cellular specificity of lectin binding in

the kidney. I. A light microscopical study in the rat. *Histochemistry* 74:521–30

65. Le Hir, M., Dubach, U. C. 1982. The cellular specificity of lectin binding in the kidney. II. A light microscopical study in the rabbit. *Histochemistry* 74:531–40

66. Le Hir, M. Kaissling, B., Dubach, U. C. 1982. Distal tubular segments of the rabbit kidney after adaption to altered Na- and K-intake. *Cell Tissue Res.* 224:493–504

67. Leyssac, P. P. 1986. Further studies on oscillating tubulo-glomerular feedback responses in the rat kidney. *Acta Physiol. Scand.* 126:271–78

68. Leyssac, P. P., Baumbach, L. 1983. An oscillating intratubular pressure response to alterations in Henle loop flow in the rat kidney. *Acta Physiol. Scand.* 117: 415–19

69. Leyssac, P. P., Jensen, P. K., Holstein-Rathlou, N. H. 1986. A study of proximal tubular compliances in normotensive and spontaneously hypertensive rats, and the effect of anesthesia on the compliance. *Acta Physiol. Scand.* 126: 341–48

70. Loennerholm, G., Wistrand, P. J. 1984. Carbonic anhydrase in the human kidney: A histochemical and immunocytochemical study. *Kidney Int.* 25:886–98

71. Maddox, D. A., Troy, J. L., Brenner, B. M. 1974. Autoregulation of filtration rate in the absence of macula densa-glomerulus feedback. *Am. J. Physiol.* 227:123–31

72. Mason, J., Moore, L. C. 1982. A new way of investigating tubuloglomerular feedback: The closed-loop mode. *Kidney Int.* 22, Suppl. 12:S151–56

73. Mendelsohn, F. A. O. 1979. Evidence for the local occurrence of angiotensin II in rat kidney and its modulation by dietary sodium intake and converting enzyme blockade. *Clin. Sci. Mol. Med.* 57:173–79

74. Moore, L. C. 1982. Tubuloglomerular feedback in hamster superficial and juxtamedullary nephrons. *Fed. Proc.* 41:A5763

75. Moore, L. C. 1984. Tubuloglomerular feedback and SNGFR autoregulation in the rat. *Am. J. Physiol.* 247:F267–76

76. Moore, L. C. 1984. Intrarenal control of medullary blood flow and the urinary concentrating mechanism. *Proc. IXth. Int. Congr. Nephrol.* pp. 120–29

77. Moore, L. C., Mason, J. 1983. Perturbation analysis of tubuloglomerular feedback in hydropenic and hemorrhaged rats. *Am. J. Physiol.* 245:F554–63

78. Moore, L. C., Schnermann, J., Yarimizu, S. 1979. Feedback mediation of SNGFR autoregulation in hydropenic and DOCA- and salt-loaded rats. *Am. J. Physiol.* 236:F63–F74

79. Morel, F. 1981. Sites of hormone action in the mammalian nephron. *Am. J. Physiol.* 240:F159–64

80. Mueller-Suur, R., Norlen, B. J., Persson, A. E. G. 1980. Resetting of tubuloglomerular feedback in rat kidneys after unilateral nephrectomy. *Kidney Int.* 18:48–57

81. Mueller-Suur, R., Persson, A. E. G. 1986. Influence of water-diuresis or saline volume expansion on deep nephron tubulo-glomerular feedback. *Acta Physiol. Scand.* 126:139–46

82. Mueller-Suur, R., Ulfendahl, H. R., Persson, A. E. G. 1983. Evidence for tubuloglomerular feedback in juxtamedullary nephrons of young rats. *Am. J. Physiol.* 244:F425–31

83. Naruse, K., Inagami, T., Celio, M. R., Workman, R. J., Takii, Y. 1982. Immunohistochemical evidence that angiotensin I and II are formed by intracellular mechanisms in juxtaglomerular cells. *Hypertension* 4, Suppl. II:70–74

84. Navar, L. G., Bell, P. D., Burke, T. J. 1982. Role of a macula densa feedback mechanism as a mediator of renal autoregulation. *Kidney Int.* 22, Suppl. 12: S157–64

85. Navar, L. G., Ploth, D. W., Bell, P. D. 1980. Distal tubular feedback control of renal hemodynamics and autoregulation. *Ann. Rev. Physiol.* 42:557–72

86. Norgaard, T. 1979. Quantitative measurement of G6PDH in cortical fractions of the rabbit nephron. *Histochemistry* 63:103–13

87. Norgaard, T. 1980. Quantitation of glucose-6-phosphate dehydrogenase activity in cortical fractions of the nephron in sodium-depleted and sodium-loaded rabbits. *Histochemistry* 69:49–59

88. Pennell, J. P., Lacy, F. B., Jamison, R. L. 1974. An in vivo study of the concentrating process in the descending limb of Henle's loop. *Kidney Int.* 5:337–47

89. Persson, A. E. G., Gushwa, L. C., Blantz, R. C. 1984. Feedback pressure-flow responses in normal and angiotensin-prostaglandin-blocked rats. *Am. J. Physiol.* 247:F925–32

90. Pfaller, W. 1982. Structure-function

correlation in rat kidney. *Adv. Anat. Embryol. Cell Biol.* 70:1–106

91. Ploth, D. W., Rudulph, J., Lagrange, R., Navar, L. G. 1979. Tubuloglomerular feedback and single nephron function after converting enzyme inhibition in the rat. *J. Clin. Invest.* 64:1325–35

92. Pricam, C., Humbert, F., Perrelet, A., Orci, L. 1974. Gap junctions in mesangial and lacis cells. *J. Cell Biol.* 63:349–54

93. Regan, J. W., Yamamura, H. I., Yamada, S., Roeske, W. R. 1981. High affinity renal [3]flunitrazepam binding: Characterization, localization, and alteration in hypertension. *Life Sci.* 28:991–98

94. Richet, G., 1983. The mechanism of action of some loop-acting diuretics. Role of a binding to Tamm-Horsfall protein. *Clin. Nephrol.* 19:S42–S44

95. Riggs, D. S. 1970. *Control Theory and Physiological Feedback Mechanisms.* Baltimore: Williams and Wilkins.

96. Rosivall, L., Taugner, R. 1986. The morphological basis of fluid balance in the interstitium of the juxtaglomerular apparatus. *Cell Tiss. Res.* 243:525–33

97. Rossier, B. C., Geering, K., Atkinson, J., Roch-Ramel, F. 1985. Renal Receptors. In *The Kidney: Physiology and Pathophysiology,* ed. D. W. Seldin, G. Giebisch, 1:775–806. New York: Raven

98. Rostand, S., Work, J. 1985. Effect of 6-aminonicotinamide on renin release in isolated rat kidney: Possible role for the pentose pathway. *Am. J. Physiol.* 249:F213–19

99. Sakai, T., Hallman, E., Marsh, D. J. 1986. Frequency domain analysis of renal autoregulation in the rat. *Am. J. Physiol.* 250:F364–73

100. Sasaki, S., Imai, M. 1980. Effects of vasopressin on water and NaCl transport across the in-vitro perfused medullary thick ascending limb of Henle's loop of mouse, rat and rabbit kidneys. *Pflüg. Arch.* 383:215–21

101. Schnabel, E., Kriz, W. 1984. Morphometric studies of the extraglomerular mesangial cell field in volume expanded and volume depleted rats. *Anat. Embryol.* 170:217–22

102. Schnermann, J., Briggs, J. P. 1984. The effect of variations in protein intake on tubuloglomerular feedback and single nephron filtration rate in rats with normal and elevated blood pressures. *Renal Physiol.* 7:258–59

103. Schnermann, J., Briggs, J. P. 1986. Effect of angiotensin II infusion on tubuloglomerular feedback responses. *Renal Physiol.* 9:59

104. Schnermann, J., Briggs, J. 1985. Function of the juxtaglomerular apparatus: Local control of glomerular hemodynamics. In *The Kidney: Physiology and Pathology,* ed. D. W. Seldin, G. Giebisch, 1:669–97. New York: Raven

105. Schnermann, J., Briggs, J. P. 1986. The role of the renin angiotensin system in tubuloglomerular feedback. *Fed. Proc.* 45:1426–30

106. Schnermann, J., Briggs, J. P., Schubert, G., Marin-Grez, M. 1984. Opposing effects of captopril and aprotinin on tubuloglomerular feedback responses. *Am. J. Physiol.* 247:F912–18

107. Schnermann, J., Briggs, J. P., Weber, P. C. 1984. Tubuloglomerular feedback, prostaglandins and angiotensin in the autoregulation of glomerular filtration rate. *Kidney Int.* 25:53–64

108. Schnermann, J., Davis, J. M., Wunderlich, P., Levine, D. Z., Horster, M. 1971. Technical problems in the micropuncture determination of nephron filtration rate and their functional implications. *Pflüg. Arch.* 3299:307–20

109. Schnermann, J., Gokel, M., Weber, P. C., Schubert, G., Briggs, J. P. 1986. Tubuloglomerular feedback and glomerular morphology in Goldblatt hypertensive rats on varying protein diets. *Kidney Int.* 29:520–29

110. Schnermann, J., Marver, D. 1986. ATPase activity in macula densa cells of the rabbit kidney. *Pflüg. Arch.* In press

111. Schnermann, J., Persson, A. E. G., Agerup, B. 1973. Tubuloglomerular feedback. Nonlinear relationship between glomerular hydrostatic pressure and loop of Henle perfusion rate. *Clin. Invest.* 52:862–69

112. Schnermann, J., Wright, F. S., Davis, J. M., von Stackelberg, W., Grill, G. 1970. Regulation of superficial nephron filtration rate by tubuloglomerular feedback. *Pflüg. Arch.* 318:147–75

113. Schoemaker, H., Boles, R. G., Horst, W. D., Yamamura, H. I. 1983. Specific high-affinity binding sites for [3]RO 5-4864 in rat brain and kidney. *J. Pharmacol. Exp. Ther.* 225:61–69

114. Selen, G., Persson, A. E. G. 1983. Effects of reduced arterial pressure on feedback control of glomerular filtrate. *Am. J. Physiol.* 244:F342–48

115. Seney, F. D., Persson, A. E. G., Desir, G. V., Wright, F. S. 1985. Dietary protein: Effect on tubuloglomerular signal and sensing mechanism. *Kidney Int.* 27:299

116. Seney, F. D., Wright, F. S. 1985. Dietary protein suppresses feedback control

of glomerular filtration in rats. *J. Clin. Invest.* 75:558–68

117. Sikri, K. L., Foster, C. L., MacHugh, N., Marshall, R. D. 1980. Localization of Tamm-Horsfall glycoprotein in the human kidney using immuno-fluorescence and immuno-electron microscopical techniques. *J. Anat.* 132:597–605

118. Sjoequist, M., Goeransson, A., Kaellskog, O. W., Ulfendahl, H. R. 1984. The influence of tubulo-glomerular feedback on the autoregulation of filtration rate in superficial and deep nephrons. *Acta Physiol. Scand.* 122:235–42

119. Sonnenberg, H. 1978. Effects of furosemide, acetazolamide, and manitol on medullary collecting duct function in the rat kidney. *Pflüg. Arch.* 373:113–23

120. Spanidis, A., Wunsch, H., Kaissling, B., Kriz, W. 1982. Three dimensional shape of Goormaghtigh cell and its contact with a granular cell in the rabbit kidney. *Anat. Embryol.* 165:239–52

121. Takahashi, S., Murakami, K., Miyake, Y. 1982. Activation of kidney prorenin by kidney cathepsin B isozymes. *J. Biochem.* 91:419–22

122. Taugner, R., Buehrle, C. P., Nobiling, R., Kirschke, M. 1985. Coexistence of renin and cathepsin B in epithelioid cell secretory granules. *Histochemistry* 83:103–8

123. Taugner, R., Hackenthal, E. 1981. Angiotensin II in epithelioid (renin containing) cells of rat kidney. *Histochemistry* 72:499–509

124. Taugner, R., Mannek, E., Nobiling, R., Buehrle, C. P., Hackenthal, E., et al. 1984. Coexistence of renin and angiotensin II in epithelioid cell secretory granules of rat kidney. *Histochemistry* 81:39–45

125. Taugner, R., Schiller, A., Kaissling, B., Kriz, W. 1978. Gap junctional coupling between the JGA and the glomerular tuft. *Cell Tiss. Res.* 186:279–85

126. Taugner, R., Whalley, A., Angermueller, S., Buehrle, C. P., Hackenthal, E. 1985. Are renin-containing granules in juxtaglomerular epithelioid cells modified lysosomes? *Cell Tiss. Res.* 239:575–87

127. Trinh-Trang-Tan, M. M., Bouby, N., Doute, M., Bankir, L. 1984. Effect of long- and short-term antidiuretic hormone availability on internephron heterogeneity in the adult rat. *Am. J. Physiol.* 246:F879–88

128. Trinh-Trang-Tan, M. M., Diaz, M., Gruenfeld, J. P., Bankir, L. 1981. ADH-dependent nephron heterogeneity in rats with hereditary hypothalamic diabetes insipidus. *Am. J. Physiol.* 240:F372–80

129. Ulfendahl, H. R., Ericson, A.-C., Goeransson, A., Kaellskog, O., Sjoequist, M. 1982. The tubulo-glomerular feedback mechanism—a determinant for the autoregulation of the glomerular filtration rate in superficial and juxtamedullary nephrons. *Klin. Wochenschr.* 60:1071–76

130. Vandewalle, A., Cluzeaud, F., Chavance, M., Bonvalet, J.-P. 1985. Cellular heterogeneity of uridine incorporation in collecting tubules: Effect of DOCA. *Am. J. Physiol.* 248:F552–64

131. Vandewalle, A., Farman, N., Cluzeaud, F., Bonvalet, J.-P. 1984. Heterogeneity of uridine incorporation along the rabbit nephron. I. Autoradiographic study. *Am. J. Physiol.* 246:F417–26

132. Van Dijk, W., Lasthuis, A.-M., Ferwerda, W. 1979. Preparation and chemical characterization of calf Tamm-Horsfall glycoprotein. *Biochem. Biophys. Acta* 584:121–28

133. Velazquez, H., Good, D. W., Wright, F. S. 1984. Mutual dependence of sodium and chloride absorption by renal distal tubule. *Am. J. Physiol.* 2:F904–11

134. Work, J., Galla, J. H., Booker, B. B., Schafer, J. A., Luke, R. G. 1985. Effect of ADH on chloride reabsorption in the loop of Henle of the Brattleboro rat. *Am. J. Physiol.* 249:F698–F703

135. Wright, F. S., Briggs, J. P. 1979. Feedback control of glomerular blood flow pressure, and filtration rate. *Physiol. Rev.* 59:958–1006

136. Young, D. K., Marsh, D. J. 1981. Pulse wave propagation in rat renal tubules: Implications for GFR autoregulation. *Am. J. Physiol.* 240:F446–58

Ann. Rev. Physiol. 1987. 49:275–93

CALCIUM AS A MEDIATOR OF TUBULOGLOMERULAR FEEDBACK

P. Darwin Bell, Martha Franco, and L. G. Navar

Nephrology Research and Training Center, Departments of Physiology and Biophysics and Medicine, University of Alabama, Birmingham, Alabama 35294

INTRODUCTION

Since the last update on the tubuloglomerular feedback (TGF) mechanism for a previous volume in this series (44) substantial advances have been achieved in our understanding of this intrarenal control system responsible for communication between tubular and vascular components of the kidney. Notably, efforts have been made to elucidate the sequence of events responsible for the transmission of feedback signals from the macula densa cells of the distal tubule to the glomerular contractile cells. These aspects of the TGF mechanism are particularly exciting because they relate to the general issues regarding communication between dissimilar cells (41, 54).

In this article, we first provide a general overview of our current understanding of the intrarenal tubuloglomerular feedback mechanism and then detail recent advances specifically related to the signal transmission process. Additional information on other areas is provided in the other chapters in this section by Briggs & Schnermann (21) and by Arendshorst (2) and in previous reviews (5, 10, 12, 56, 72).

GENERAL CHARACTERISTICS OF THE TUBULOGLOMERULAR FEEDBACK MECHANISM

The morphological basis for the tubuloglomerular feedback (TGF) mechanism resides in the structural contact between the macula densa cells of the distal tubule and glomerulus of each nephron (4, 9). At the point of contact, the macula densa cells occupy the side of the tubule that adjoins the glomerular tuft (37). It is presumed that these cells respond to changes in the composition of the tubular fluid. The macula densa cells rest on an irregular, attenuated basement membrane; below these cells is an array of irregularly shaped intertwining extraglomerular mesangial cells. The extraglomerular mesangial cells form extensive contacts with the other parts of the juxtaglomerular apparatus, including intraglomerular mesangial cells, granular cells, and the smooth muscle cells of the arterioles (55, 67). There is extensive gap junction coupling among all of the cells of this system except between macula densa cells and extraglomerular mesangial cells (29, 68).

In vivo micropuncture and microperfusion techniques have been used to study many aspects of the tubuloglomerular feedback mechanism (5, 11, 13, 19, 50, 59, 63). Measurements of stop flow pressure (SFP), glomerular capillary pressure, and single-nephron glomerular filtration rate (SNGFR) have been utilized to assess feedback responses to changes in macula densa flow rate or composition elicited by perfusion from either a late proximal tubule site or retrograde perfusion from an early distal tubule site. In the rat, perfusion with isotonic solutions decreases stop flow pressure by 8–12 mm Hg (13, 59), and SNGFR by 10–15 nl/min (13, 63).

In a recent study in Munich-Wistar rats (34), nephrons with superficial glomeruli were blocked at a mid proximal site, and direct glomerular pressure was measured during perfusion from a late proximal tubule site. A hole was made in the proximal tubule to allow filtrate to escape onto the kidney surface. Under these conditions there were no significant changes in glomerular capillary pressure when late proximal perfusion rate was increased to 40 nl/min. However, if the proximal tubule was not vented, glomerular capillary pressure was higher (presumably due to blockade of the tubule), and there were significant decreases of about 8 mm Hg in glomerular capillary pressure during orthograde microperfusion. These data suggested that glomerular capillary pressure of unblocked nephrons was not altered during changes in late proximal perfusion rate. In contrast, other investigators have reported decreases in glomerular capillary pressure in both blocked and unblocked tubules during changes in distal perfusion rate. Using young Munich-Wistar rats, Briggs (20) found that glomerular capillary pressure in tubules with proximal tubule wax blockade decreased by 7 mm Hg in response to perfusion rates of 40 nl/min. This decrease in glomerular capillary pressure was not different from the SFP responses obtained in other tubules.

In other studies, Persson et al (48) and Bell et al (76) infused isotonic solutions at 24–25 nl/min into unblocked late proximal tubules. Under these conditions, in which filtration is not interrupted, directly measured glomerular capillary pressure decreased by either 8 (48) or 12 mm Hg (16). Thus the current consensus is that there are feedback-mediated reductions in glomerular capillary pressure that are similar in magnitude to the stop flow pressure feedback responses. The data indicate that, under normal conditions, the feedback-mediated reductions in SNGFR are mediated primarily by reductions in glomerular pressure. However, more subtle mechanisms involving combined constriction of the glomerular arterioles may also contribute to the SNGFR feedback responses at the lower rates of distal volume delivery (56).

During orthograde perfusion experiments with isotonic solutions, the magnitude of the feedback responses are directly related to perfusion rate over the range of 5 to 30 nl/min (10, 72). With the retrograde perfusion technique, the magnitude of the feedback response is independent of perfusion rate. Rather, during retrograde microperfusion the feedback responses are dependent upon the solute concentration of the solution. Maximal feedback responses are obtained at a perfusate concentration of about 120 mOsm/kg and decrease in a linear fashion as perfusate osmolality is reduced below this value (11).

Under normal conditions, the feedback-mediated reduction in glomerular capillary pressure is sufficient to account for the decrease in SNGFR. This suggests that the afferent arteriole serves as the major effector component of the feedback mechanism (23). However, the extraglomerular and glomerular mesangial cells are connected to the arterioles by gap junctions, and thus feedback signals may reach the entire functional syncytium capable of influencing the filtration process. The localization of the major response to the afferent arteriole may simply reflect the predominance of this contractile element. Indeed, recent experiments suggest that certain perturbations can uncouple SNGFR and glomerular capillary pressure feedback responses. Persson et al (48) treated rats for 3–5 days with a combination of converting enzyme inhibitor (MK421) and a cyclooxygenase inhibitor (meclofenamate). Single-nephron GFR feedback responses averaged 9 nl/min in control rats and 8 nl/min in the hormonally blocked rats. In spite of the similar feedback-mediated reductions in SNGFR, there were no changes in glomerular capillary pressure in response to perfusion at 40 nl/min in the rats given MK421 and meclofenamate. Thus, blockade of prostaglandins and the renin-angiotensin system appeared to uncouple glomerular capillary pressure and SNGFR feedback responses. Further studies are needed to determine the mechanism of feedback-mediated reductions in SNGFR when glomerular capillary pressure responses are not evident.

The initial step in the feedback pathway involves a change in the degree of luminal hypotonicity at the level of the macula densa cells (10, 72). The fluid at the terminal part of the ascending loop of Henle is hypotonic due to the powerful transport capability of this relatively water-impermeable segment. The actual concentration is flow dependent such that increases in flow into the thick ascending limb of the loop of Henle result in increases in sodium chloride concentration and osmolality at the macula densa. In this manner, changes in flow rate are transduced into changes in luminal fluid solute concentration, which serves as the activating stimulus to the macula densa cells. In recent years the issue of the specific constituent in the luminal fluid that is detected by the macula densa cells has remained controversial. All workers agree that there is a direct relationship between the luminal concentration and the degree of vasoconstriction. However, some investigators have argued that the feedback signal is activated specifically by chloride (or sodium chloride) transport (22, 60), while others have indicated that changes in total fluid osmolality appear to be detected by the macula densa cells (11). The reader is referred to reviews by Bell & Navar (10) and Wright & Briggs (72) for additional information on the specificity of the luminal signal.

The interpretation that the macula densa cells may be capable of sensing transmembrane osmotic gradients has been supported by other findings indicating (36, 38) that they may be water permeable. Using modified in vitro renal tubule perfusion techniques, the thick ascending limb of the loop of Henle with the attached glomerulus was perfused, and the macula densa cells were observed with differential-interference contrast (DIC) microscopy (38). The macula densa cells were much taller than the surrounding thick ascending limb cells. In response to a decrease in luminal osmolality from isotonic to 70 mOsm/kg, thick ascending limb transepithelial potential difference measured at the perfusion pipette increased from $+4$ to $+11$ mV. Using DIC optics at a magnification of 1250, an increase in the width of the lateral intercellular spaces between macula densa cells was observed upon replacement of the isotonic luminal perfusate with the hypotonic solution. The increase in lateral intercellular space width occurred very rapidly and was reversible. Morphometric analysis of photomicrographs also revealed a small (10%) increase in macula densa cell height. These changes were specifically related to the decreases in osmolality: Similar reductions in luminal sodium chloride concentration did not influence the width of the lateral intercellular spaces when total osmolality was maintained with mannitol. These results are qualitatively similar to those obtained in other systems such as the collecting duct (32, 39) during antidiuretic hormone–induced water flow in response to an osmotic gradients. Thus the macula densa may be a water-permeable plaque of cells located near the end of the water-impermeant thick ascending limb of the loop of Henle.

Similar conclusions were reached by Kaissling & Kriz (36) from their examination of electron micrographs of macula densa cells perfusion-fixed under different experimental conditions. The spaces between the macula densa cells were dilated under control conditions when distal tubular fluid osmolality may be expected to be hypotonic and were closed following experimental manipulations expected to increase luminal osmolality toward isotonic values. Specifically, lateral intercellular spaces were closed during mannitol or furosemide diuresis, conditions under which luminal osmolality at the macula densa should be near isotonic values. These studies also suggest that the macula densa is permeable to water and that there may be movement of water across the macula densa cells in response to an osmotic gradient. It remains unclear whether or not this characteristic of the macula densa cells plays a direct role in the transmission of feedback signals. Nevertheless, these recent studies are in accord with the possibility that changes in the osmotic gradient across the macula densa cells may serve to activate intracellular events.

ROLE OF CYTOSOLIC CALCIUM IN THE TRANSMISSION OF TUBULOGLOMERULAR FEEDBACK SIGNALS

The transient and steady-state characteristics of tubuloglomerular feedback responses indicate that this mechanism must have a fast response time and a high degree of sensitivity (10). Such a mechanism may require the presence of an intracellular messenger system capable of responding to the initial sensing event and activating the transmission of signals from the basolateral side of the cells to the effector components. Recent articles (17, 27) on intracellular messenger systems emphasize the nearly ubiquitous role of intracellular cytosolic calcium as a regulator of various cellular mechanisms. These findings in other systems prompted a consideration of the possible role of macula densa cytosolic calcium as an intracellular transmitter of feedback signals. (Figure 1 is a composite of data from our recent studies on the role of calcium and other intracellular messengers in the transmission of feedback signals. These data are discussed in appropriate sections throughout the remainder of the text.) A schematic of our view of the transmission of feedback signals is shown in Figure 2.

To determine the effects of increases in cytosolic calcium concentration on tubuloglomerular feedback responses, a calcium ionophore (A23187) was added to the luminal perfusion solution to increase membrane permeability to calcium (9). This ionophore was added to a hypotonic solution (70 mOsm/kg). The hypotonic solution alone produced only small feedback responses of ~5 mm Hg. Retrograde microperfusion with the hypotonic solution containing A23187 in concentrations of 5–500 μM produced marked increases in the magnitude of feedback responses to 13–15 mm Hg. This response appeared to be calcium specific, since removal of calcium from the ionophore-containing solution resulted in SFP feedback responses of only 4.8 $\pm$ 1.3 mm Hg (5). Thus, increases in the cytosolic calcium concentration, which presumably occurred in the cells of the macula densa, resulted in the transmission of vasoconstrictive signals.

The pattern of the stop flow pressure feedback responses obtained with A23187 was similar to that found with an isotonic Ringer's solution (9, 14).

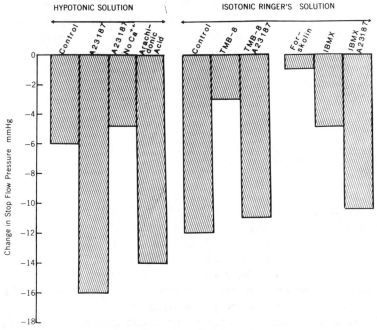

Figure 1 Summary of experimental studies evaluating the tubuloglomerular feedback signal transmission process. All studies utilized in vivo retrograde microperfusion in rats. Studies on the left utilized either a 70 or 38 mOsm per kg hypotonic solution. The control levels are those obtained with the 70 mOsm/kg solution. With the 38 mOsm/kg solution, SFP feedback responses generally averaged between 1 and 2 mm Hg. Studies shown on the right utilized an isotonic Ringer's solution. Data are taken from References 6, 7, 9, 11, 14, and 15.

Stop flow pressure began to decrease within 2–5 sec after the initiation of perfusion and returned to preinfusion values within seconds after termination of perfusion. The return of SFP to control levels was associated with collapse of the distal tubule, which resulted from continued tubular reabsorption after termination of perfusion. Collapse of the distal tubule presumably prevented further entry of calcium into the macula densa cells through these luminal membrane ionophore channels. Once the tubule had been treated with the ionophore, reperfusion of the distal tubule with a hypotonic solution resulted in SFP feedback responses that were the same as those obtained during perfusion with the solution containing A23187. These results suggest that calcium channels were still present in the luminal membrane and were able to allow rapid influx of calcium into the cells during perfusion with a calcium-containing solution. In addition there was no indication that A23187 reached the smooth muscle cells and elicited contraction directly. Such diffusion of the ionophore to the contractile cells should have produced a sustained vasoconstrictive response without recovery of SFP to preinfusion values. These data are consistent with the concept that increases in macula densa

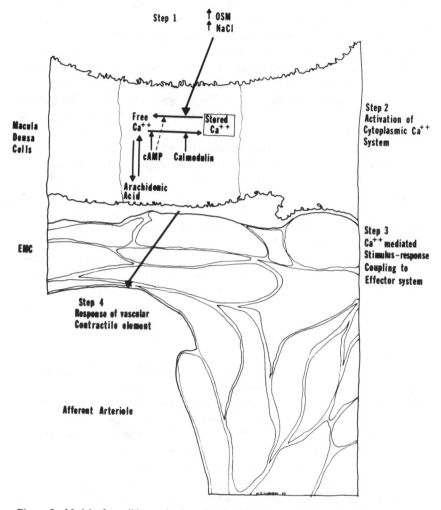

Figure 2 Model of possible mechanisms involved in the transmission of tubuloglomerular feedback signals. The macula densa cells and underlying extraglomerular mesangial cells and smooth muscle cells are represented schematically. Postulated steps in the transmission of feedback signals are shown.

cytosolic calcium can elicit the transmission of constrictor feedback signals to the effector components of the system.

In the experiments using a calcium ionophore, the presumed increases in cytosolic calcium concentration were a consequence of an enhanced calcium influx through the ionophore channels. In the normal setting, however, increases in cytosolic calcium concentration can be due not only to enhanced calcium entry but also to calcium mobilization from intracellular storage sites (17, 52). In this regard, previous studies indicate that calcium influx across the luminal membrane is apparently not essential for the manifestation of normal feedback responses (14, 57). Normal sustained (up to 5-min) feedback responses have been obtained during retrograde perfusion of solutions devoid of calcium, solutions containing a calcium channel blocker (verapamil), or containing calcium chelators (EGTA). These data indicate that in the normal mediation of feedback responses calcium influx into the macula densa cells is not a requisite step.

To determine the effects of intracellular calcium mobilization on the feedback mechanism, the effects of 8-(N,N-diethylamino)-octyl-3,4,5-trimethoxybenzoate (TMB-8) on SFP feedback responses were assessed (14). TMB-8 has been used in a number of studies to prevent or inhibit stimulus-induced release of intracellular sequestered calcium (25, 43, 65). Apparently, TMB-8 binds to bound intracellular calcium to form a stable complex and thereby prevents calcium release. To evaluate the effects of blocking intracellular mobilization on the tubuloglomerular feedback mechanism, retrograde microperfusion studies were conducted using solutions in which TMB-8 was added to isotonic Ringer's solution at concentrations of 100–500 μM. The feedback responses obtained with TMB-8 containing solutions were found to be inhibited by 57% (100-μM), 80% (300-μM), and 76% (500-μM) TMB-8. The inhibitory effects were not observed immediately but required several minutes to develop.

In further studies, it was found that the effects of TMB-8 could be nullified by addition of calcium ionophore (A23187) to the perfusion solution (14). TMB-8 does not inhibit ionophore-induced calcium entry, and therefore cytosolic calcium concentration increases. Addition of 5-μM A23187 to the isotonic Ringer's solution containing 500-μM TMB-8 resulted in augmented SFP feedback responses that were not different from those obtained with an isotonic Ringer's solution alone. Therefore, increased calcium availability was able to overcome the inhibition of feedback responses caused by TMB-8. These experiments demonstrate that the prevention of intracellular calcium mobilization can interfere with the mediation of feedback signals and raise the possibility that this mechanism normally operates by altering cytosolic calcium levels.

The mechanism linking changes in luminal fluid composition to changes in macula densa cytosolic calcium concentration has not been established. In other systems, the increased cytosolic calcium concentration that results from calcium mobilization has been attributed to inositol trisphosphate (IP$_3$)-induced release of calcium from endoplasmic reticulum (18, 26, 33, 69, 71). Generation of IP$_3$ occurs through activation of phospholipase C, which is usually stimulated by occupation of a hormone receptor. In addition, breakdown of phosphatidylinositol-4,5-bisphosphate (PIP$_2$) to form IP$_3$ also results in the generation of 1,2-diacylglycerol, which increases the affinity of protein kinase C for calcium (45). Rasmussen and coworkers (53) found that sustained adrenal aldosterone production requires activation of both the cytosolic calcium system as well as protein kinase C activation. When an increase in cytosolic calcium concentration was induced by a calcium ionophore, which does not activate protein kinase C, aldosterone production was 75–80% of the maximum response and was transient: It returned to the baseline level within several minutes. In contrast, activation of both cytosolic calcium and protein kinase C resulted in a maximal response that was sustained over time.

There are no data that suggest that a "classical" receptor mechanism operates at the luminal membrane of macula densa cells to initiate the transmission of tubuloglomerular feedback signals. Thus, if IP$_3$ is responsible for the mobilization of calcium in the macula densa cells, then IP$_3$ must be generated through a different mechanism. At present there is little information regarding generation of IP$_3$ through non-receptor-mediated mechanisms. It is conceivable, however, that phosphatidylinositol-4,5-bisphosphate breakdown could be sensitive to changes in the transmembrane osmotic gradient, transport of solutes or water into the macula densa cells, or alterations in membrane electrical potentials.

There is also no information regarding the effects of protein kinase C activation per se on feedback responses. However, feedback responses obtained with A23187 are the same as, or somewhat greater than, the maximal responses obtained with an isotonic solution. These responses are sustained for at least 5–10 min, and there is no evidence of waning of the response. It therefore appears that activation of protein kinase C is not essential and that increased cytosolic calcium concentration alone is sufficient for the full activation of maximal, sustained responses.

ROLE OF CALMODULIN IN TUBULOGLOMERULAR FEEDBACK SIGNALS

Calmodulin has been shown to influence a variety of cellular functions (24, 42, 51) upon activation by increased cytosolic calcium concentration. In addition, calmodulin serves to regulate cytosolic calcium concentration through activation of calcium transport mechanisms. The contribution of this nearly universal intracellular protein molecule to the cellular responses to increased cytosolic calcium has generally been assessed using calmodulin antagonists. Agents or substances that interact with calmodulin are characterized by a large hydrophobic region that usually has a positively charged amino group closely associated with it. Because of the diverse effects of calmodulin inhibitors, it has been proposed that these agents are relatively nonselective and influence a variety of cellular functions not dependent on calmodulin. Alternatively, it has been suggested that the wide range of biological actions elicited by these agents simply reflects the many roles that calmodulin plays in the regulation of cellular functions (51).

The contribution of calmodulin to the transmission of tubuloglomerular feedback signals has been examined using trifluoperazine (TFP), a phenothiazine antipsychotic agent, and calmidazolium (R24571), a newly developed calmodulin inhibitor. Calmidazolium is currently one of the most potent and specific calmodulin inhibitors available (30). To test for a role of calmodulin in the tubuloglomerular feedback mechanism, retrograde microperfusion studies were performed using an isotonic Ringer's solution containing TFP or calmidazolium (7). After perfusion for 5 min, these agents, even at very high concentrations, did not influence the magnitude of SFP feedback responses compared to those obtained with isotonic Ringer's solution. Similarly, calmidazolium did not inhibit SNGFR feedback responses.

However, after termination of perfusion, the return of SFP to control preinfusion values took longer in tubules that had been perfused with the calmodulin antagonists. In tubules perfused with the control Ringer's solution, recovery of SFP after termination of perfusion required 65 sec. In tubules perfused with TFP, the recovery time was markedly prolonged to over 100 sec. Specifically, with 50–75 μM TFP, recovery time was 104 sec; with 500 μM TFP, it was 154 seconds; and with 20 μM R24571, recovery time was prolonged to 116 sec. After the tubule was exposed to the calmodulin antagonist, the effect persisted. Prolonged SFP recovery times were still observed upon reperfusion with the control isotonic Ringer's solution alone. This result is consistent with the nearly irreversible interaction of these agents with calmodulin (42). Furthermore, these results suggest that the calmodulin inhibitors reached intracellular sites and that the effects of these agents were not due to their direct action on some property of the luminal membrane. From these results, it seems unlikely that these highly lipophilic agents diffused through the tubule to reach contractile cells. Contraction of smooth muscle is a calmodulin-dependent process, and calmodulin antagonists inhibit smooth muscle contraction (3, 40). The fact that TFP or calmidazolium did not irreversibly inhibit SFP or SNGFR feedback responses suggests that these agents did not reach the contractile machinery responsible for the reduction in stop flow pressure and SNGFR.

The delay in the recovery of SFP to control levels could have been due to inhibition of a calcium-mediated calmodulin-dependent system located at the macula densa. One interpretation of this delayed recovery time is that the ability of the macula densa cells to rapidly restore cytosolic calcium levels is impaired. Since calmodulin enhances calcium extrusion across the plasma membrane (24, 31, 42, 52) and increases calcium uptake into intracellular calcium sequestering sites, cytosolic calcium levels may remain elevated in the presence of the antagonists. Thus, calmodulin may serve an important role in controlling the rapidity with which cytosolic calcium levels are restored to normal after stimulation of the feedback mechanism. The dynamic nature of the tubuloglomerular feedback signal process may be the result of an interplay between two different mechanisms. Activation may result from rapid mobilization of intracellular calcium leading to increases in cytosolic calcium concentration. Second, the calcium-dependent activation of calmodulin may increase the uptake or extrusion of calcium and rapidly lower cytosolic calcium concentration following cessation of the stimulus.

cAMP AND CALCIUM INTERACTIONS WITH THE TRANSMISSION OF FEEDBACK SIGNALS

There is considerable evidence in support of important interactions between the cytosolic calcium system and the cyclic nucleotides; cAMP has been studied most extensively (17, 52, 53). As discussed by Berridge (17), activation of cellular processes occurs principally through calcium and cAMP often serves to modify calcium-mediated events. The nature of the modification by cAMP of calcium-mediated events is cell specific. Rasmussen & Barrett (52) proposed five general categories of interactions between cAMP and calcium. In some cells, cAMP potentiates the actions of increased cytosolic calcium concentration. In other systems, cAMP attenuates or inhibits calcium-mediated responses. For example, Feinstein et al (27) evaluated the effects of cAMP on thrombin-induced increases in the cytoplasmic calcium concentration of platelets. When activators of cAMP were added during stimulation, there were decreases in cytosolic calcium concentration as measured by Quin 2 fluorescence. Thus, depending upon the cells, cAMP can potentiate or inhibit the cytosolic calcium system.

To obtain an idea of the nature of Ca^{2+}-cAMP interactions related to the tubuloglomerular feedback mechanism, phosphodiesterase inhibitors, such as 3-isobutyl-1-methylxanthine (IBMX) or theophylline were perfused retrograde into the distal nephron segment. These agents have been shown to cause concentration-dependent decreases in the magnitude of feedback-mediated decreases in SFP (6) or early proximal flow rate (an index of SNGFR) (58). In one study (6), SFP feedback responses were inhibited by 40% by 50-μM IBM, 60% by 250-μM IBMX, and 89% by 500-μM IBMX. Since there is some uncertainty regarding the specificity of these agents, several additional approaches have been used to increase intracellular cAMP levels. To increase cAMP directly, dibutyryl-cAMP (D-cAMP) plus a low concentration of IBMX (50 μM) was added to an isotonic Ringer's solution (6). IBMX was added to the solution to retard the degradation of cAMP and thereby facilitate the intracellular accumulation of cAMP from D-cAMP. Retrograde perfusion with 50-μM IBMX decreased SFP responses from 12 to 8 mm Hg, and addition of D-cAMP further decreased the magnitude of the SFP feedback response to 3 mm Hg. In other retrograde perfusion studies, we utilized forskolin, an activator of the catalytic subunit of adenylate cyclase, which rapidly and reversibly increases intracellular cAMP concentration (64). Addition of 100-μM forskolin to the isotonic solution resulted in the nearly complete abolition of tubuloglomerular feedback responses. These results indicate that enhanced intracellular cAMP levels can inhibit tubuloglomerular feedback responses and thus reduce the overall sensitivity of the feedback mechanism.

We investigated whether the inhibition of feedback responses during elevations in intracellular cAMP occurs through negative modulation of the intracellular calcium messenger system by assessing the effects of increasing cytosolic calcium concentration, with a calcium ionophore, while simultaneously administering either IBMX or forskolin. A23187 was found to reverse the inhibitory effects of either IBMX or forskolin. In tubules treated with forskolin alone, SFP decreased from only 37 to 35 mm Hg during retrograde microperfusion. With the addition of 5-μM A23187 to the forskolin-containing solution, SFP decreased from 39 to 30 mm Hg during perfusion. These studies support the idea that cAMP may inhibit feedback responses by reducing cytosolic calcium levels, through enhanced calcium uptake into calcium sequestering sites, and/or augmented calcium extrusion across the plasma membrane. Such effects could be a major means for altering sensitivity of the TGF mechanism.

A number of conditions and agents have been reported to affect feedback sensitivity (72). Many of these maneuvers leave the luminal signal unaltered and instead alter feedback responsiveness. Such alterations in feedback sensitivity may occur at several points in the feedback transmission pathway. Persson and colleagues (47) proposed that interstitial pressure or volume in the area of the juxtaglomerular apparatus is an important determinant of the level of feedback sensitivity. However, an adenylate cyclase–cAMP system may also contribute to the observed alterations in feedback sensitivity. The existence of an extensive extracellular network in the mesangial and extraglomerular mesangial region and the finding that the width of these extracellular spaces can vary (55) suggest a dynamic interaction between this interstitial compartment and surrounding tubular and vascular components. Some hormones and other substances in extracellular fluid may reach the basolateral membranes of the macula densa cells and activate adenylate cyclase. Activation of adenylate cyclase would increase cAMP and thereby decrease feedback sensitivity.

Osswald and colleagues (46) suggested that adenosine production is important in feedback signal transduction. The adenosine theory for the transmission of feedback signals has been supported by two experimental findings: First, feedback responses are partially inhibited during administration of a low concentration of theophylline (58). It has been reported that the primary effect of theophylline at low concentrations is as an antagonist of adenosine receptors (66). Second, systemic administration of dipyridamole, an agent that prevents the cellular uptake of adenosine and presumably increases the availability of adenosine to the adenosine receptors, has been shown to enhance feedback responses (1, 46). During orthograde perfusion with a control solution, SFP decreased from around 35 to 25 mm Hg. After administration of dipyridamole at 0.5 mg per 100 g body weight (BW), the SFP feedback response were larger with SFP decreasing from 35 to 19 mm Hg (46). These results suggest that adenosine may be important in the transmission of feedback responses; however, the exact nature of the interactions remains to be determined.

Osswald and coworkers (46) proposed that energy-requiring sodium chloride cotransport by the cells of the thick ascending limb, and perhaps of the macula densa, produces adenosine as a byproduct and that the higher the rate of sodium chloride cotransport, the greater the amount of adenosine generated. The increased amounts of adenosine would thus serve in the signal transmission process as a vasoconstrictor. However, it is also possible that the production of adenosine is not directly dependent upon energy production per se and that, like other messenger systems, it is produced as a result of cellular activation. In addition, it has also been proposed that the macula densa cells produce adenosine, which then serves as a local transmitter that inhibits the release of renin from granular cells (35, 66). Further studies are needed to fully characterize the response of the contractile elements to endogenous adenosine production and to determine whether or not adenosine serves directly in the transmission of feedback signals.

IS A BYPRODUCT OF ARACHIDONIC ACID METABOLISM INVOLVED IN THE TRANSMISSION OF FEEDBACK SIGNALS?

The nature of the communication process between the macula densa cells and the smooth muscle cells remains unknown. The lack of gap junctions between the macula densa cells and the extraglomerular mesangial cells suggests that communication between these components involves the formation by the macula densa cells of a vasoactive substance that diffuses across the extraglomerular mesangial cells to reach the contractile elements. One candidate for this substance is adenosine, as mentioned above. It has also been suggested that a prostanoid may participate in transmission of feedback signals

(70). Studies evaluating the role of prostaglandins in the transmission of feedback signals have produced intriguing results. Initially, Schnermann et al (61) reported that systemic administration of four different cyclooxygenase inhibitors attenuated the tubuloglomerular feedback mechanism as assessed by early proximal flow rate feedback responses to increases in orthograde perfusion rate. In addition, intraluminal infusion of cyclooxygenase inhibitors also decreased feedback responses. In retrograde microperfusion experiments, indomethacin infused at a concentration of 1–5 mM prevented feedback-mediated decreases in early proximal flow rate (61) or SFP (15).

Because of these intriguing findings, we performed additional experiments (15) in an effort to examine the possible role of phospholipids in the transmission of feedback signals. In retrograde microperfusion experiments, arachidonic acid (160 μM) was added to a hypotonic (38 mOsm/kg H_2O) perfusion solution. Perfusion with the hypotonic solution alone resulted in decreases in SFP of 1.4 mm Hg. Addition of arachidonic acid to this solution resulted in an increased magnitude of SFP feedback responses to 14 mm Hg. These results are very similar to those obtained with A23187 and support the idea that an arachidonic acid metabolite participates in some manner in the signalling pathway between the macula densa cells and the smooth muscle cells. The most obvious possibility suggested by the data is that an enhanced cytosolic calcium concentration activates phospholipase A_2 and increases intracellular release of arachidonic acid. In view of the indomethacin data, it seems possible that a cyclooxygenase-derived vasoconstrictor is formed and released.

However, additional findings have raised uncertainty about this conclusion. In the study by Schnermann et al (61) the intravenous administration of 5 mg/kg BW of indomethacin inhibited feedback-mediated reductions in early proximal flow from 39% during the control period to 5%. The inhibition of the feedback responses lasted about 80 min. Thereafter, early proximal flow rate feedback responses returned to control values even though urinary PGE_2 excretion rates, which had decreased markedly (267 to 75 pg/ml) following administration of the cyclooxygenase inhibitor, remained depressed. Thus, feedback responses were restored at a time when prostaglandin excretion rates were very low (45 pg/ml). Further studies (61) demonstrated that the decreases in feedback responses induced with indomethacin were dependent upon dietary salt intake. In rats on a low-salt diet, systemic administration of 5 mg/kg BW of indomethacin failed to affect the magnitude of the feedback response. However, the low-salt diet did not alter urinary PGE_2 or $PGF_{2\alpha}$ concentrations, nor did it prevent the decrease in urinary prostaglandins during indomethacin treatment. These results suggest that the effects of cyclooxygenase inhibitors on feedback responsiveness and renal prostaglandin production are independent.

In preliminary studies, we evaluated the duration of inhibition of SFP feedback responses following perfusion of the nephron with solutions containing indomethacin. SFP decreased by 25% during retrograde microperfusion with a control isotonic Ringer's solution. Subsequent retrograde perfusion for at least 5 min with 5-mM indomethacin resulted in a reduction of feedback responses to only 2%. Upon immediate (15–90 sec) reperfusion of the tubule with an indomethacin-free isotonic Ringer's solution, normal retrograde feedback responsiveness was observed (25%). Since indomethacin is thought to inactivate cyclooxygenase for prolonged periods (28), the restoration of feedback sensitivity within such a short period is puzzling. Another concern is that the intraluminal concentration of indomethacin required for either 50% or 100% inhibition (1–5 mM) of feedback responses is far greater than that required to inhibit prostaglandin synthesis in virtually every other system (1–20 μM) (28). These considerations indicate that the inhibition of feedback responses by indomethacin is probably not directly related to cyclooxygenase inhibition. The inhibition could be due to other effects thought to be exerted by high concentrations of these agents, such as inhibition of other enzyme systems (28). For example, high concentrations of indomethacin have been shown to inhibit phosphodiesterase activity. If this occurs in the macula densa, then inhibition of feedback responses during administration of indomethacin could be due to cAMP accumulation.

In other studies, Schnermann et al (62) infused PGE_2 or $PGF_{2\alpha}$ systemically after inhibition of endogenous prostaglandin formation with intravenous administration of indomethacin. They found that feedback responses were significantly enhanced by the presence of PGE_2 or $PGF_{2\alpha}$, a puzzling observation in view of the vasodilator actions of these agents. They concluded that the presence of certain prostaglandins may be necessary for the normal operation of the feedback mechanism. In other studies, Persson et al (49) infused PGE_2, PGI_2, and $PGF_{2\alpha}$ from a late proximal tubule site and measured SFP feedback responses. They found that the maximum stop flow pressure feedback responses obtained during perfusion at 50 nl/min with an isotonic Ringer's solution was unchanged in the presence of PGE_2 or $PGF_{2\alpha}$. The perfusion rate at which 50% of the maximal feedback response was obtained, however, was slightly lower in tubules perfused with the PGE_2 or $PGF_{2\alpha}$. In addition, 10 min of perfusion with PGI_2 resulted in decreases in SFP feedback responses from 8.4 mm Hg (control) to 0.9 mm Hg. These results are not in agreement with those showing that systemic PGE_2 or $PGF_{2\alpha}$ in the presence of indomethacin restored feedback responses (62). Thus there is presently uncertainty regarding the involvement of prostaglandins in the transmission of feedback signals.

What is the role of phospholipids in the transmission of feedback signals? There are several possibilities. First, increases in macula densa cytosolic calcium levels may activate phospholipase A_2, thereby liberating arachidonic acid. Metabolism of arachidonic acid could then lead to a non-cyclooxygenase-dependent metabolite that would participate in the transmission of vasoconstrictor signals. Second, the actions of arachidonic acid may result from synthesis of some metabolite that participates in the regulation of cytosolic calcium levels. In that case increases in feedback responses during archidonic acid administration would be due to secondary increases in the cytosolic calcium concentration. Third, the actions of arachidonic acid may be indirect and may result from alterations in cellular function unrelated to phospholipid metabolism. Clearly, much more work on the role of phospholipid metabolism remains to be done before a definitive answer emerges.

FUTURE DIRECTIONS

At present, the study of the mechanisms responsible for the transmission of feedback signals is in an exciting period of transition. The isolated perfused tubule preparation has made possible a number of approaches to in vitro study of the intracellular mechanisms involved in signal detection and processing of feedback signals at the macula densa cells (38).

One approach combines fluorescent microscopy with the isolated perfused tubule technique. The recent development of calcium-sensitive fluorescent probes, such as Quin 2 and Fura 2, has provided a means of assessing changes in cytosolic calcium concentration in living cells. Currently, studies are underway to determine changes in macula densa cytosolic calcium concentration in response to changes in the degree of luminal hypotonicity. These agents are also being used to establish an in vitro index of tubuloglomerular feedback responses. Changes in the Quin 2 fluorescence of the entire glomerulus in response to alterations in luminal fluid osmolality have been examined. Preliminary results indicate that when luminal osmolality is increased from 70 to 290 mOsm/kg H_2O, the fluorescence within the glomerulus also increases (8). Thus it may be possible to use changes in total glomerular fluorescence as an in vitro index of tubuloglomerular feedback responses. These approaches should help resolve some of the basic controversies presently existing and extend our understanding of the specific intra- and intercellular steps of the feedback pathway.

ACKNOWLEDGMENTS

We thank our colleagues who participated in previous studies. Our experimental work was supported by NIH grants AM32032 and HL18426 and by a grant from the American Heart Association (831122). We thank Mrs. Joyce Kanute and Ms. Vanessa Hill for secretarial support and Mrs. Ellen

Berstein for the illustrations. P. D. Bell is an Established Investigator of the American Heart Association. M. Franco is a visiting scientist from the Instituto Nacional de Cardiologia, Mexico City.

Literature Cited

1. Arend, L. J., Thompson, C. I., Spielman, W. S. 1985. Dipyridamole decreases glomerular filtration in the sodium-depleted dog. Evidence for mediation by intrarenal adenosine. *Circ. Res.* 56:242–51
2. Arendshorst, W. J. 1987. Altered reactivity of tubuloglomerular feedback. *Ann. Rev. Physiol.* 49:295–317
3. Asano, M., Suzuki, Y., Hidaka, H. 1982. Effects of various calmodulin antagonists on contraction of rabbit aortic strips. *J. Pharmacol. Exp. Ther.* 220: 191–96
4. Barajas, L. 1981. The juxtaglomerular apparatus: Anatomical considerations in the feedback control of glomerular filtration rate. *Fed. Proc.* 40:78–86
5. Bell, P. D. 1982. Luminal and cellular mechanisms for mediation of tubuloglomerular feedback responses. *Kidney Int.* 22:S97–S103 Suppl. 12
6. Bell, P. D. 1985. Cyclic AMP-calcium interaction in the transmission of tubuloglomerular feedback signals. *Kidney Int.* 28:728–32
7. Bell, P. D. 1986. Tubuloglomerular feedback responses in the rat during calmodulin inhibition. *Am. J. Physiol.* 250:F715–19
8. Bell, P. D. 1986. Assessment of tubuloglomerular feedback signal transmission in vitro using glomerular Quin-2 fluorescence. *Proc. 30th Int. Congr. Physiol.* 26:114
9. Bell, P. D., Navar, L. G. 1982. Cytoplasmic calcium in the mediation of macula densa tubulo-glomerular feedback responses. *Science* 215:670–73
10. Bell, P. D., Navar, L. G. 1982. Macula densa feedback control of glomerular filtration: Role of cytosolic calcium. *Miner. Electrolyte Metab.* 8:61–77
11. Bell, P. D., Navar, L. G. 1982. Relationship between tubuloglomerular feedback responses and perfusate hypotonicity. *Kidney Int.* 22:234–39
12. Bell, P. D., Navar, L. G. 1984. Intrarenal control of glomerular filtration: Cellular mechanisms of tubuloglomerular feedback. In *Nephrology, Proc. IXth Int. Congr. Nephrol.*, ed. R. R. Robinson, pp. 130–42. Berlin: Springer-Verlag
13. Bell, P. D., Navar, L. G., Ploth, D. W., McLean, C. B. 1980. Tubuloglomerular feedback responses during perfusion with nonelectrolyte solutions in the rat. *Kidney Int.* 18:460–71
14. Bell, P. D., Reddington, M. 1983. Intracellular calcium in the transmission of tubuloglomerular feedback signals. *Am. J. Physiol.* 245:F295–F302
15. Bell, P. D., Reddington, M., Navar, L. G. 1984. Tubuloglomerular feedback (TGF) responses during delivery of arachidonic acid to macula densa. See Ref. 12
16. Bell, P. D., Reddington, M., Ploth, D., Navar, L. G. 1984. Tubuloglomerular feedback-mediated decreases in glomerular pressure in Munich-Wistar rats. *Am. J. Physiol.* 247:F877–80
17. Berridge, M. J. Cellular control through interactions between cyclic nucleotides and calcium. 1984. *Adv. Cyclic Nucleotide Protein Phosphor. Res.* 17:329–35
18. Berridge, M. J., Irvine, R. F. 1984. Inositol trisphosphate, a novel second messenger in cellular signal transduction. *Nature* 312:315–21
19. Blantz, R. C., Konnen, K. S. 1977. Relation of distal tubular delivery and reabsorptive rate to nephron filtration. *Am. J. Physiol.* 233:F315–24
20. Briggs, J. P. 1984. Effect of loop of Henle flow rate on glomerular capillary pressure. *Renal Physiol.* 7:311–20
21. Briggs, J. P., Schnermann, J. 1987. The tubuloglomerular feedback mechanism: Functional and biochemical aspects. *Ann. Rev. Physiol.* 49:00–00
22. Briggs, J. P., Schubert, G., Schnermann, J. 1982. Further evidence for an inverse relationship between macula densa NaCl concentration and filtration rate. *Pflüger's Arch.* 392:372–78
23. Briggs, J. P., Wright, F. S. 1979. Feedback control of glomerular filtration rate: Site of the effector mechanism. *Am. J. Physiol.* 236:F40–F47
24. Cheung, W. J. 1980. Calmodulin plays a pivotal role in cellular regulation. *Science* 207:19–27
25. Chiou, C. Y., Malagodi, M. H. 1975. Studies on the mechanism of action of

a new Ca^{2+} antagonist, 8-(N,N-diethyl-amino)octyl 3,4,5-trimethoxybenzoate hydrochloride in smooth and skeletal muscles. *Br. J. Pharmacol.* 53:279–85

26. Exton, J. H. 1985. Role of calcium and phosphoinositides in the actions of certain hormones and neurotransmitters. *J. Clin. Invest.* 75:1753–57

27. Feinstein, M. B., Egan, J. J., Sha'afi, R. I., White, J. 1985. The cytoplasmic concentration of free calcium in platelets is controlled by stimulators of cyclic AMP production (PGD_2, PGE_1, forskolin). *Biochem. Biophys. Res. Commun.* 113:598–604

28. Flower, R. J. 1974. Drugs which inhibit prostaglandin biosynthesis. *Pharmacol. Rev.* 26:33–67

29. Forssmann, W. G., Taugner, R. 1977. Studies on the juxtaglomerular apparatus. V. The juxtaglomerular apparatus in typania with special reference to intercellular contacts. *Cell Tissue Res.* 177:291–305

30. Gietzen, K., Wuthrich, A., Bader, H. 1981. R24571: A new powerful inhibitor of red blood cell Ca^{++}-transport ATPase and of calmodulin-regulated function. *Biochem. Biophys. Res. Commun.* 101: 418–25

31. Gmaj, P., Zurini, M., Murer, H., Carafoli, E. 1985. A high affinity calmodulin-dependent Ca^{++} pump in the basal-lateral plasma membranes of kidney cortex. *Eur. J. Biochem.* 136:71–76

32. Grantham, J. J., Ganote, C. E., Burg, M. B., Orloff, J. 1969. Paths of transtubular flow in isolated renal collecting tubules. *J. Cell Biol.* 41:562–76

33. Hokin, L. E. 1985. Receptors and phosphoinositide-generated second messengers. *Ann. Rev. Biochem.* 54:205–35

34. Ichikawa, I. 1982. Direct analysis of the effector mechanism of the tubuloglomerular feedback system. *Am. J. Physiol.* 243:F447–45

35. Itoh, S., Carretero, O. A., Murray, R. D. 1985. Possible role of adenosine in the macula densa mechanism of renin release in rabbits. *J. Clin. Invest.* 76: 1412–17

36. Kaissling, B., Kriz, W. 1982. Variability of intercellular spaces between macula densa cells: A transmission electron microscopic study in rabbits and rats. *Kidney Int.* 22:S9–S17(Suppl. 12)

37. Kaissling, B., Peter, S., Kriz, W. 1977. The transition of the thick ascending limb of Henle's loop into the distal convoluted tubule in the nephron of the rat kidney. *Cell Tissue Res.* 182:111–18

38. Kirk, K. L., Bell, P. D., Barfuss, D. W., Ribadenerira, M. 1985. Direct visualization of the isolated and perfused macula densa. *Am. J. Physiol.* 248: F890–94

39. Kirk, K. L., Schafer, J. A., DiBona, D. R. 1984. Quantitative analysis of the structural events associated with antidiuretic hormone-induced volume reabsorption in the rabbit cortical collecting tubule. *J. Membr. Biol.* 79:65–74

40. Kreye, V. A., Ruegg, J. C., Hofmann, F. 1983. Effect of calcium-antagonist and calmodulin-antagonist drugs on calmodulin-dependent contractions of chemically skinned vascular smooth muscle from rabbit renal arteries. *Naunyn-Schmiedebergs Arch. Pharmakol.* 323:85–89

41. Loewenstein, W. R. 1981. Junctional intercellular communication: The cell-to-cell membrane channel. *Physiol. Rev.* 61:829–913

42. Means, A. R., Tash, J. S., Chafowleas, J. G. 1982. Physiological implications of the presence, distribution, and regulation of calmodulin in eukaryotic cells. *Physiol. Rev.* 62:1–37

43. Misbahuddin, M., Isosaki, M., Houchi, J., Oka, M. 1985. Muscarinic receptor-mediated increase in cytoplasmic free Ca^{2+} in isolated bovine adrenal medullary cells. Effects of TMB-8 and phorbol ester TPA. *FEBS Lett.* 190:25–28

44. Navar, L. G., Ploth, D. W., Bell, P. D. 1980. Distal tubular feedback control of renal hemodynamics and autoregulation. *Ann. Rev. Physiol.* 42:557–71

45. Nishizuka, Y. 1984. The role of protein kinase C in cell surface signal transduction and tumor promotion. *Nature* 308: 693–98

46. Osswald, H., Nabakowski, G., Hermes, H. 1980. Adenosine as a possible mediator of metabolic control of glomerular filtration rate. *Int. J. Biochem.* 12:263–67

47. Persson, A. E. G., Boberg, U., Hahne, B., Muller-Suur, R., Norlen, B.-J., Selen, G. 1982. Interstitial pressure as a modulator of tubuloglomerular feedback control. *Kidney Int.* 22:S122–29

48. Persson, A. E. G., Gushiwa, L. C., Blantz, R. C. 1984. Feedback pressure-flow responses in normal and angiotensin-prostaglandin-blocked rats. *Am. J. Physiol.* 247:F925–31

49. Persson, A. E. G., Hahne, B., Selen, G. 1983. The effect of tubular perfusion with PGE_2, PGF_2, and PGI_2 on the tubuloglomerular feedback control in the rat. *Can. J. Physiol. Pharmacol.* 61:1317–25

50. Persson, B. E., Persson, A. E. G. 1981. The existence of a tubuloglomerular feedback mechanism in the amphiuma nephron. *Pflügers Arch.* 391:129–34

51. Prozialeck, W. C., Weiss, B. 1985. Mechanisms of pharmacologically altering calmodulin activity. In *Calcium in Biological Systems*, ed. R. P. Rubin, C. B. Weiss, J. W. Putney, pp. 255–64. New York: Plenum

52. Rasmussen, H., Barrett, P. Q. 1984. Calcium messenger system: An integrated view. *Physiol. Rev.* 64:938–87

53. Rasmussen, H., Kojima, I., Apfelforf, W., Barrett, P. 1986. Cellular mechanism of hormone action in the kidney: Messenger function of calcium and cyclic AMP. *Kidney Int.* 29:90–97

54. Scheridan, J. D., Atkinson, M. M. 1985. Physiological roles of permeable junctions: Some possibilities. *Ann. Rev. Physiol.* 47:337–53

55. Schnabel, E., Kriz, W. 1984. Morphometric studies of the extraglomerular mesangial cell field in volume expanded and volume depleted rats. *Anat. Histol. Embryol.* 170:217–22

56. Schnermann, J., Briggs, J. P. 1986. Role of the renin-angiotensin system in tubuloglomerular feedback. *Fed. Proc.* 45:1426–30

57. Schnermann, J., Hermle, M. 1975. Maintenance of feedback regulation of filtration dynamics in the absence of divalent cations in the lumen of the distal tubule. *Pflügers Arch.* 358:311–23

58. Schnermann, J., Osswald, H., Hermle, M. 1977. Inhibitory effect of methylxanthines on feedback control of glomerular filtration rate in the rat kidney. *Pflügers Arch.* 369:39–48

59. Schnermann, J., Persson, A. E. G., Agerup, B. 1973. Tubuloglomerular feedback: Nonlinear relation between glomerular hydrostatic pressure and loop of Henle perfusion. *J. Clin. Invest.* 52:862–69

60. Schnermann, J., Ploth, D. W., Hermle, M. 1976. Activation of tubuloglomerular feedback by chloride transport. *Pflügers Arch.* 362:229–40

61. Schnermann, J., Schubert, G., Hermle, M., Herbst, R., Stowe, N. T., et al. 1979. The effect of inhibition of prostaglandin synthesis on tubuloglomerular feedback in the rat kidney. *Pflügers Arch.* 379:269–79

62. Schnermann, J., Weber, P. C. 1982. Reversal of indomethacin induced inhibition of tubuloglomerular feedback by prostaglandin infusion. *Prostaglandins* 24:351–61

63. Schnermann, J., Wright, F. S., Davis, J. M., Stackelberg, W. V., Grill, G. 1970. Regulation of superficial nephron filtration rate by tubulo-glomerular feedback. *Pflügers Arch.* 318:147–75

64. Seamon, K. B., Daley, J. W. 1981. Forskolin: A unique diterpene activator of cyclic AMP-generating systems. *J. Cyclic Nucleotide Res.* 224:201–24

65. Shaw, J. O. 1981. Effects of extracellular Ca^{2+} and the intracellular Ca^{2+} antagonist 8-(N,N-diethylaino)-octyl-3,4,5-trimethoxybenzoate on rabbit platelet conversion of arachidonic acid to thromboxane. *Prostaglandins* 21:571–79

66. Spielman, W. S., Thompson, C. I. 1982. A proposed role for adenosine in the regulation of renal hemodynamics and renin release. *Am. J. Physiol.* 242:F423–35

67. Taugner, R., Buhrle, C. P., Hackenthal, E., Mannek, E., Nobling, R. 1984. Morphology of the juxtaglomerular apparatus and secretory mechanisms. *Contrib. Nephrol.* 43:76–101

68. Taugner, R., Schiller, A., Kaissling, B., Kriz, W. 1979. Gap junctions coupling between JGA and the glomerular tuft. *Cell Tissue Res.* 186:279–85

69. Troyer, D. A., Schwertz, D. W., Kreisberg, J. I., Venkatachalam, M. A. 1986. Inositol phospholipid metabolism in the kidney. *Ann. Rev. Physiol.* 48:51–71

70. Weber, P. C., Scherer, B., Siess, W., Held, E., Schnermann, J. 1979. Formation and action of prostaglandins in the kidney. *Klin. Wochensch.* 57:1021–29

71. Williamson, J. R., Cooper, R. H., Joseph, S. K., Thomas, A. P. 1985. Inositol trisphosphate and diacylglycerol as intracellular second messengers in liver. *Am. J. Physiol.* 248:C203–16

72. Wright, F. S., Briggs, J. P. 1979. Feedback control of glomerular blood flow, pressure and filtration rate. *Physiol. Rev.* 59:958–1006

Ann. Rev. Physiol. 1987. 49:295–317

ALTERED REACTIVITY OF TUBULOGLOMERULAR FEEDBACK

William J. Arendshorst

Department of Physiology, University of North Carolina at Chapel Hill, School of Medicine, Chapel Hill, North Carolina 27514

INTRODUCTION

It is now clearly established that the tubuloglomerular mechanism is a rapidly acting, negative feedback system. This system plays an important functional role in the control of flow and solute delivery to the distal convoluted tubule and in the determination of the filtration rate in the parent glomerulus in many species, including humans. Blantz & Pelayo (3) and Schnermann & Briggs (41, 42) have recently reviewed the role of the juxtaglomerular apparatus and the tubuloglomerular feedback (TGF) mechanism in controlling glomerular hemodynamics. The recent studies of Müller-Suur et al (25, 26) on the rat and of Moore (21) on the hamster demonstrate that this control mechanism exists in juxtamedullary nephrons as well as in superficial nephrons. For a given hydration state, the TGF system regulates glomerular capillary pressure and glomerular filtration rate (GFR) as a nonlinear inverse function of solute delivery to macula densa cells. As first demonstrated by Schnermann and associates, TGF is a dynamic homeostatic regulatory mechanism that is responsive to acute and chronic changes in extracellular fluid (ECF) volume (cf 41). A general definition of "altered reactivity" or "resetting" of TGF is a change in the efficiency of the coupling of salt delivery to the sensing site at the macula densa and the effector response of the glomerular vasculature. The factor(s) responsible for adaptive adjustments in critical elements of TGF during naturally occurring and experimentally induced resetting has been the subject of intensive investigation.

This review focuses on those studies made using the micropuncture technique and published since 1983 that have demonstrated resetting of TGF activity. I particularly emphasize those microperfusion studies that provide

295

quantitative descriptions of several characteristics of the TGF system. Recent evidence concerning several mechanisms proposed to mediate or modulate functional resetting of TGF is also discussed.

QUANTITATION OF FEEDBACK ACTIVITY AND DEFINITION OF RESETTING

The evidence for resetting of TGF comes from in vivo application of micropuncture methodology, mostly in the rat, using three basic experimental designs. One of these approaches employs free-flow collections of tubular fluid from the distal and proximal convolutions of the same nephron. The level of TGF activity is evaluated by the increase in the proximally measured single-nephron GFR (SNGFR) (or early proximal flow rate, EPFR) following complete blockage of early distal flow by insertion of an oil or wax plug in the proximal tubule, which opens the sensor-effector feedback loop. SNGFR increases as a result of the reduced feedback-mediated preglomerular vasoconstriction caused by the absence of flow through Henle's loop and the lack of an input signal. The difference between proximally and distally measured SNGFRs increases when TGF activity is enhanced and decreases when TGF is inhibited. A better index of TGF reactivity to a reduction in distal delivery to a subnormal level is the distal SNGFR or the difference between proximal and distal SNGFRs factored by the change in flow rate or solute delivery to the early distal tubule. The fact that distally measured SNGFR increases in the presence of unchanged or increased distal delivery of fluid and solute is one line of evidence for inhibition of TGF.

A relatively new method for evaluating changes in the TGF system involves a combination of free-flow collection and microperfusion techniques. The "perturbation analysis" introduced by Moore & Mason assesses the strength of the TGF-mediated responses of the SNGFR to an increased distal fluid load. This method more closely approximates the physiological condition of a closed feedback-loop because it does not involve blockade of flow through Henle's loop (22, 23). Multiple measurements of SNGFR are made at the same early distal site before and during perfusion of an early proximal convolution with harvested tubular fluid. Feedback-mediated changes in SNGFR are evaluated as a function of the measured early distal delivery. This approach also gives information on the interaction between TGF and glomerulotubular balance in stabilizing the delivery of salt and water to the distal tubule, because both the filtered load and tubular reabsorption are determined.

The third experimental design, which is most commonly employed in current studies, utilizes loop of Henle microperfusion to evaluate the effect on glomerular responses of changes in tubular flow rate at super- and subnormal levels. A superficial late proximal convolution is usually perfused in the orthograde direction with artificial tubular fluid, and SNGFR, EPFR, or stop-flow pressure (SFP) is measured in an early proximal convolution upstream from the wax block. Early studies primarily used this open feedback loop method to determine the maximum decrease in SNGFR or SFP produced by a large increase in the perfusion rate in the loop of Henle. A more complete feedback curve has been generated in recent studies from measurements of SNGFR or SFP in the same nephron made as the rate of loop perfusion was increased in small steps from 0 to 40 nl/min. Curve fitting of the data shows a nonlinear inverse relation between SNGFR or SFP and the loop perfusion rate that can be satisfactorily described by an equation for a sigmoidal curve (9, 46, 49). The relation plotted for a control group of nondiuretic rats (Figure 1) shows that the most responsive region of the curve is in the normal flow range (12–22 nl/min) and smaller responses are elicited at lower and higher perfusion rates.

In addition to the maximum change elicited by loop perfusion, a feedback curve of TGF-mediated responses can be characterized by its threshold, point of inflection, and maximum reactivity (9, 11, 46, 49). The threshold is defined as the lowest flow rate that elicits a significant (10%) response. The point of inflection (the turning point) is the late proximal flow rate (microperfusion rate) that produces a half-maximal decrease in SNGFR or SFP. The maximum reactivity (gain or sensitivity) at the inflection point is the steepest slope of the sigmoid curve describing the relation between the

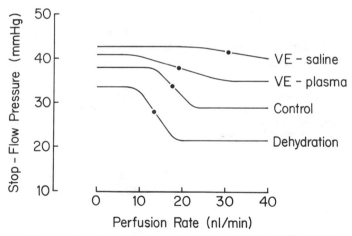

Figure 1   Effect of acute volume expansion and contraction on the feedback curve for stop-flow pressure. VE = volume expansion with isotonic saline or isoncotic plasma. The filled circle on each curve represents the inflection point, i.e. the perfusion rate that elicits a half-maximal decrease in stop-flow pressure. Data were averaged from studies on rats treated with saline expansion (6, 7, 29, 46), plasma expansion (35), or dehydration (46), and hydropenic control rats (6, 7, 9, 11, 16, 26, 29–31, 33–35, 36a, 46, 51).

SNGFR or SFP and the loop of Henle perfusion rate at the rate that elicits a half-maximal response.

Three recent studies indicate that feedback-induced changes in SFP accurately reflect changes in glomerular capillary pressure in nondiuretic Munich-Wistar rats (2, 8, 30). Importantly, feedback curves for both directly measured glomerular capillary pressure and estimated SFP yield identical values for the inflection point and maximum reactivity. In addition, inhibition of feedback-mediated changes in glomerular capillary pressure has an equal effect on SFP (30). The maximum reduction in SNGFR, the inflection point, and the reactivity are the same in normal nondiuretic rats whether the perfusate solution is artificial or native proximal tubular fluid (45).

The results of microperfusion studies, summarized in Table 1, indicate that the shapes of the feedback curves for SNGFR and SFP are virtually identical in terms of the maximum decrease produced by a high rate of loop perfusion, the inflection point, and the maximum reactivity for superficial nephrons in adult nondiuretic rats. The inflection point is in the normal range of late proximal flow measured while TGF is operative; it is approximately 50–60% of the distally measured SNGFR. Although it is less often reported than the inflection point, the threshold response is usually evident at a loop perfusion rate of 10–15 nl/min, which is approximately 5 nl/min less than the inflection point. The findings of Müller-Suur et al (26, 27) and Moore (21) indicate that the TGF mechanism is more active in juxtamedullary than in superficial nephrons during hydropenia. Although the inflection point for the deep nephrons was similar (9–10 nl/min) to that for superficial ones in young rats, the deep nephrons exhibited larger maximum decreases in SFP and SNGFR in response to increased distal delivery (26, 27). Changes in the various measures of TGF activity are associated with different physiological states.

Table 1 Average values for characteristics of feedback curves for superficial nephrons obtained by loop of Henle perfusion with artificial tubular fluid in normal, adult hydropenic or euvolemic[a] rats

	Single nephron glomerular filtration rate (nl/min)		Stop-flow pressure (mm Hg)	
	Mean	Range	Mean	Range
Maximum decrease	14	8–19	9	5–12
Point of inflection	17	15–20	17	9–24
Maximum reactivity (per nl/min)	1.0	0.5–1.7	1.0	0.8–1.6

[a]Control values for SNGFR and SFP averaged 34 nl/min and 38 mm Hg, respectively, in the absence of loop of Henle perfusion. SNGFR values were calculated using data from References 1, 9, and 45. SFP values were calculated using data from References 6, 7, 9, 11, 16, 26, 29–31, 33–35, 36a, 46, 51.

Resetting of TGF activity can be defined as a change in one or more of the characteristics of the feedback response curve constructed using data obtained with different rates of loop perfusion.

CONDITIONS ASSOCIATED WITH RESETTING OF FEEDBACK ACTIVITY

Many recent micropuncture studies provide evidence of TGF resetting during growth, pregnancy, and under a variety of experimental conditions. The general tendency for changes in the free-flow collection and microperfusion indices of TGF activity are summarized qualitatively in Table 2. Microperfusion studies reveal a general tendency for attenuation of TGF activity to be expressed as a reduction in the maximum decrease in SFP or SNGFR, a reduction in the maximum reactivity, and a shift in the inflection point to a higher flow rate. Quantitation of changes in these indices of TGF activity may provide insight into functional alterations that occur at one or more elements in the negative feedback system during resetting. To this end, Seney & Wright (49) proposed that (a) a change in the afferent arteriolar effector mechanism can be expressed as a change in the maximum response, (b) a change in the transmission pathway between the sensing step and the effector mechanism is evidenced by a change in the maximum reactivity, and that (c) a change in the threshold and the inflection point reflects a primary change in the macula densa sensing step.

The results of linear regression analysis performed on the feedback data from most of the recent studies of resetting, which was usually induced by acute intervention, are shown in Figure 2. The top panel illustrates a significant inverse relation between experimentally induced changes in the maximum decrease in SFP and the observed changes in the inflection point. The middle panel shows that changes in the operating point have a significant inverse correlation with changes in the maximum reactivity of SFP. Although the number of observations is smaller in the bottom panel of Figure 2, there is also a general tendency for the maximum decrease in SNGFR to decline as the inflection point increases. This analysis of the data reveals that resetting of TGF is often, but not always, manifested in multiple changes in the measured characteristics of the feedback curve. It remains to be determined if one or several regulatory mechanisms are responsible for the apparently interrelated changes in these characteristics of the feedback response that occur during resetting.

Extracellular Fluid Volume

Since the early work of Schnermann and associates in the 1970s, it has been known that TGF can be reset during acute and chronic changes in ECF

Table 2 Various measures of tubuloglomerular feedback activity that indicate resetting under various experimental conditions

Condition	Free-flow collection[a]		Max. responses		Microperfusion[b]		References
	Prox-dist SNGFR	Dist SNGFR ÷ dist delivery	SNGFR	SFP	1/inflection point	Reactivity	
Acute volume expansion							
Saline	→	→	→	→	→	→	6, 7, 24, 29, 45, 46
Plasma	0	→	—	→	0	→	35
Water	—	—	0	0	0	0	26
Hyperglycemia	0	→	→	—	→	→	4, 5
Chronic volume expansion							
High-salt diet	→→	0↓	→↓	—	0↓	→↓	14, 45
DOCA and high-salt diet	→	→	0↓	—	→	0	23, 24
Acute volume contraction							
After furosemide	←←	←↑	←←	—	—	—	24, 50
Hemorrhage	—	0↑	←	—	←	←	23, 24
Chronic volume depletion							
Dehydration (24 hr)	←←	←←	—	←—	←0	←0	46
Low-salt diet	←0	0	0	—	0	0	14, 45
Protein diet							
Low	←0	←←	←←	—	←	←	44, 48
High	0	→→	←→	←0	0	0	44, 48
Growth/maturation							
Normotensive strains							
Sprague-Dawley	—	—	←←	—	→0	←←	9
Okamoto-Aoki	—	—	←	←	0	←	11
Milan	—	—	—	←0	0	—	7, 29

							Reference
Genetic hypertension							
Development phase							
Okamoto-Aoki	0	↑	↑	↑	↑	↑	11, 12
Milan	0	0	—	0	↑	—	7
Maintenance phase							
Okamoto-Aoki	—	—	0	↑	0	0	11
Milan	0	0	—	↑	0	—	29
Pregnancy	0	—	↑	—	↑	↑	1
Atrial natriuretic factor							
Atrial extract	↓	↓	↓	—	—	—	10
ANF	—	—	↓	↓	↓	↓	17, 36a
Kallikrein-Kinin							
Kininase II inhibition	↓0	↓	↓	↓	0	↓	34, 43
Kallikrein inhibition	↑	↑	↓	↑	—	—	43
Renal venous pressure increase							
Hydropenia	0	↑	—	0	0	—	6
Saline loading	—	—	—	↑	↑	—	6
Ureteral occlusion							
Unilateral (2 hr)	—	—	—	↓	↓	↑	33
Unilateral (24 hr)	—	—	—	↓	↑	—	51
Bilateral (24 hr)	—	—	—	↓	0	—	51
Nephrectomy							
Acute	0	↑	—	↓	↓	—	16, 25, 28, 31
Acute + PGE₂	—	—	—	0	0	—	31
Acute + indomethacin	—	—	—	0	0	—	16
Transplantation	↓	—	0	0	0	—	16, 25, 28

[a]Prox = proximal, dist = distal, SNGFR = single-nephron glomerular filtration rate; ↑, 0, and ↓ indicate TGF activity is increased, unchanged, and decreased, respectively.

[b]Microperfusion of artificial tubular fluid through Henle's loop in the orthograde direction.

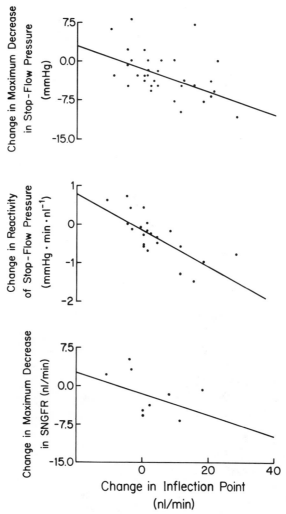

Figure 2 Correlation of changes in different measures of tubuloglomerular feedback activity during resetting associated with the conditions listed in Table 2. Correlation coefficients for the best-fit regression lines are: top panel, $r = -0.52$, $n = 38$, $p < 0.01$; middle panel, $r = -0.74$, $n = 23$, $p < 0.01$; bottom panel, $r = -0.42$, $n = 10$, $p > 0.05$. Data are for normotensive adult rats. (Stop-flow pressure data are from References 6, 7, 29–31, 33–35, 36a, 44, 46, 48, 51. SNGFR data are from References 1, 9, 30, 34, 44, and 49.)

volume (cf 41). Recent studies have extended the inverse relation between ECF volume and TGF activity to include conditions of acute volume contraction produced by hemorrhage (22, 23), furosemide administration (50), and 24 hours of dehydration (46).

The effects of acute changes in ECF volume on SFP feedback curves in adult rats are shown in Figure 1. Very shortly after acute volume expansion (5 ml/100 g body wt) with isotonic saline, SFP responses to loop of Henle perfusion are markedly attenuated (6, 7, 29, 46). Changes in the feedback curve include a smaller maximum decrease in SFP, a shift in the inflection point to a higher flow rate, and a pronounced decrease in maximal reactivity. Qualitatively similar responses have been observed in 4- and 6-week-old rats (7).

Ploth et al (35) obtained somewhat different results during acute expansion (2.5 ml/100 g body wt) with isoncotic plasma. The feedback curve for plasma expansion in Figure 1 shows a smaller maximum decrease in SFP and decreased reactivity as compared with hydropenic control conditions. In contrast to saline loading, plasma expansion produced very little, if any, change in the inflection point from the control curve.

Selén et al (46) demonstrated that the increased TGF activity produced by 24 hours of dehydration is characterized by a lower SFP in the absence of loop perfusion, a larger maximum decrease in SFP, and a lower inflection point; reactivity was only slightly increased. In contrast to the feedback responses to ECF expansion caused by isotonic saline solution or isoncotic plasma, Müller-Suur et al (26) found that acute water loading produced by rapid infusion of 2.5% glucose in water has no demonstrable effect on TGF activity. The maximum reduction in EPFR in superficial nephrons and flow to the descending limb of Henle's loop of juxtamedullary nephrons were unchanged.

It is not known whether the various interventions that affect TGF activity in superficial nephrons cause similar resetting in deeper nephrons. The only evidence available is for young rats with exposed papilla. The results indicate that acute volume expansion (5 ml/100 g body wt) with isotonic saline causes qualitatively similar suppression of TGF activity in the juxtamedullary and superficial nephrons (26).

Moore et al (24) conducted microperfusion studies on rats to compare the time course of TGF resetting following acute and chronic changes in ECF volume. TGF activity did not change detectably until after 4–5 days of sodium retention produced by deoxycorticosterone acetate (DOCA) administration and a high-salt diet. After 14 days of salt loading, feedback-mediated reductions in EPFR were attenuated by more than 90%. Thus, in contrast to the rapid onset of inhibition following acute volume expansion, the inhibition of the TGF response associated with chronic ECF expansion is sluggish, which suggests that this inhibitory mechanism(s) acts slowly.

Other evidence also highlights the involvement of different mechanisms in the resetting of TGF activity during acute and chronic changes in ECF volume. Moore et al (24) showed that the almost complete inhibition of TGF during chronic combined DOCA and high-salt treatment could be reversed within one hour by furosemide-induced volume depletion. Thus the inhibition of TGF produced by chronic treatment with DOCA and a high-salt diet is not caused by DOCA per se. A similar dominant effect of volume depletion was recently observed by Tucker & Blantz (50) during inhibition of TGF activity with furosemide in rats fed a normal diet. Inhibition of salt transport by the loop of Henle and, presumably, macula densa cells produced sustained blunting of feedback responses when ECF volume was maintained by matching the volume of fluid administered with that excreted. However, when volume contraction resulted from excess excretion, the furosemide-induced inhibition of TGF was less pronounced. This reversal suggests that changes in ECF volume affect TGF activity by a potent mechanism that can override drug-induced inhibition of the macula densa transport step.

Recent studies by Schnermann et al (45) and Häberle & Davis (14) have characterized the effect of chronic changes in salt diet on TGF activity in the rat. Although the EPFR of rats consuming a low-salt diet (0.05 mM NaCl/day) was reduced from control values by 20% in the absence of loop perfusion, the maximal response to loop of Henle perfusion at 40 nl/min with artificial perfusate did not differ from that found in control animals. Interestingly, the low-salt diet had no effect on the inflection point or the maximum reactivity. In rats consuming a high-salt diet (26–37 mM NaCl/day), the maximum reactivity of the EPFR was reduced to one-third the normal value. However, the inflection point did not differ appreciably between rats fed high-salt, low-salt, or control diets. Thus, chronic salt loading without DOCA administration has less of an effect (14, 45) than chronic ECF volume expansion with DOCA and high-salt loading, which virtually completely inhibits the SNGFR responses to loop perfusion.

Protein Diet

Two laboratories have characterized the effect of a high- or low-protein diet on TGF responses of the SNGFR and the SFP to orthograde perfusion of Henle's loop. In otherwise normal rats, Seney & Wright (49) found that the threshold and inflection point of the SNGFR and SFP feedback curves were shifted to a higher flow rate in rats fed a high-protein (40%) diet for 10 days as compared to rats fed a low-protein (6%) diet. Neither the maximum decrease in SNGFR and SFP nor the reactivity was affected by the protein diet. It was concluded that the apparent resetting in animals fed a high-protein diet is caused by a change in the sensing step and reflects a reduced input signal or a reduced responsiveness of the macula densa cells. In a subsequent study, Seney et al (48) observed that the selective effect of the high-protein diet on the threshold and inflection point was normalized by perfusing a normal load to the macula densa sensing site via retrograde perfusion from an early distal convolution. The most recent results indicate the sensor and effector mechanisms were able to respond appropriately and were thus unaffected by chronic changes in the amount of dietary protein. Thus the major effect of a high-protein diet in their late proximal orthograde perfusion studies (49) was on reabsorption by the loop of Henle, which was responsible for differences in the load presented to the macula densa and the apparent changes in threshold and inflection point.

Schnermann et al (44) reported somewhat different results on the effect of the amount of dietary protein on TGF for the nonclipped kidney in rats with renovascular hypertension. Rats fed a high-protein (50%) diet exhibited a smaller maximum reduction in EPFR and SFP, an 11 nl/min increase in the inflection point, and a 50% reduction in SFP reactivity relative to rats fed a low-protein (5%) diet. As compared with the normal (10% protein) group, TGF activity was enhanced in rats fed a low-protein diet and was attenuated in rats fed a high-protein diet. In low-protein-fed rats, EPFR was reduced, loop perfusion produced a larger maximum reduction in EPFR, the inflection point was 11 nl/min lower, and EPFR reactivity was twofold that in control rats. In high-protein-fed rats, the inflection point and reactivity were similar to those in the normal-protein group; the maximum decrease in EPFR was 33% less. Arterial pressure was unaffected by the amount of dietary protein (44, 49). A decrease in ECF volume does not appear to explain the relatively greater TGF activity in rats fed a low-protein diet, as Ichikawa et al (18) reported that plasma volume is similar in rats fed 6% and 40% protein diets. Reduced TGF activity can account, at least in part, for the renal vasodilation and elevated GFR and SNGFR observed in animals consuming a high-protein diet.

Growth and Maturation

With body and renal growth and maturation, GFR and SNGFR increase, and the resetting of TGF activity is characterized by a pattern quite different from that observed during changes in ECF volume. Figure 3 shows the change Dilley & Arendshorst (11) observed in the feedback curve for SFP during maturation in normotensive WKY rats. With aging, the inflection point is shifted to a higher flow rate, and there are increases in the maximum decrease in SFP (and SNGFR) and in SFP reactivity. Briggs et al (9) conducted a detailed microperfusion study of SNGFR responses to loop perfusion in 100-, 200-, and 350-g Sprague-Dawley rats and reported similar findings. In Munich-Wistar rats, the growth-related changes in TGF are, in general, similar. An apparent exception is the maximum decrease in SFP and glomerular capillary pressure, which does not appear to increase with age; values of 8–9 mm Hg are reported for both 100 g and 200–300 g Munich-Wistar rats (8, 30). Resetting of TGF may be responsible for the age-related increase in GFR, or this resetting may represent an adaptive change to a primary increase in GFR and renal vasodilation.

Completely different results have been reported by Boberg & Persson for the Milan strain of normotensive rats. They found no evidence of change in

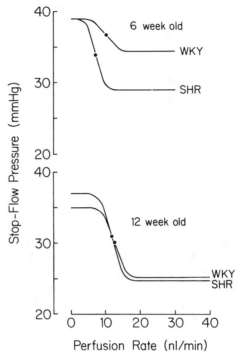

Figure 3   Age- and growth-related changes in tubuloglomerular feedback in 6- and 12-week-old spontaneously hypertensive rats (SHR) and normotensive Wistar-Kyoto rats (WKY) of the Okamoto-Aoki strain. Feedback curves for stop-flow pressure are plotted as a function of late proximal perfusion rate. Filled circle on each curve represents the inflection point. Data are from the study of Dilley & Arendshorst (11).

TGF activity during growth and maturation (7, 29). Their microperfusion studies on young rats at 4 and 6 weeks of age and on adult rats indicate that the SFP feedback curves are essentially the same. Similar values for basal SFP, maximum decrease in SFP, and the inflection point were observed in 75-, 130-, and 240-g rats.

Genetic Hypertension

Recently, the laboratories of Arendshorst and Persson investigated the functional characteristics of TGF in Okamoto-Aoki and Milan strains of genetically hypertensive rats during the developmental and established phases of hypertension (7, 11, 29).

In young Okamoto-Aoki rats, renal blood flow (RBF), GFR, and distally measured SNGFR are lower in spontaneously hypertensive rats (SHR) than in normotensive Wistar-Kyoto control rats (WKY) at 6 weeks of age (12). Resetting of the TGF mechanism during the development of hypertension was suggested by the renal vasoconstriction and reduced SNGFR in the presence of reduced fluid delivery to the distal tubule. The microperfusion studies of Dilley & Arendshorst (11) demonstrated exaggerated feedback responses in moderately hypertensive SHR at 6 weeks of age. Figure 3 shows that loop perfusion at 15–30 nl/min produced 2–3 times larger decreases in SFP in SHR than in WKY rats. Similar strain differences in feedback-induced changes in SNGFR were observed in young SHR and WKY rats. Increased TGF activity was also indicated in young SHR by a lower inflection point and greater maximum reactivity. This abnormality may contribute to the increased renal vascular resistance and reduced RBF, GFR, and sodium excretion previously observed in 6-week-old genetically hypertensive rats (12). The strain differences in TGF-induced changes in SNGFR and SFP were less pronounced in 12-week-old rats, when SHR have established hypertension (11). As Figure 3 shows, a 20–40 nl/min increase in perfusion rate produced a slightly larger maximum decrease in SFP in SHR as the basal value of SFP was higher in these rats. The inflection point and reactivity did not differ significantly between normotensive and hypertensive rats at 12 weeks of age.

Experiments employing aortic constriction to reduce renal perfusion pressure in hypertensive rats to the normotensive level indicated that the enhanced TGF activity in 6- and 12-week-old SHR is independent of an acute change in arterial pressure and renal vascular resistance (11). Both age groups of SHR that underwent aortic constriction demonstrated efficient autoregulation of SFP. Feedback-induced changes in SFP were essentially the same as those in hypertensive SHR not subjected to aortic constriction and were still different from those in WKY rats. More recent studies suggest that neither renal sympathetic nerves, the renin-angiotensin system, nor renal thromboxane is involved in the exaggerated TGF activity that is especially prominent in young SHR. The reduced GFR in 6-week-old SHR is not improved by acute unilateral renal denervation (39), inhibition of the renin-angiotensin system with either captopril or saralasin (38), or inhibition of thromboxane synthesis or thromboxane receptor blockade (13).

Boberg & Persson showed that TGF activity in genetically hypertensive rats of the Milan strain (MHS) differs from that of normotensive controls of the same strain (MNS) as a function of age and arterial pressure (7, 29). At 4 weeks of age, prehypertensive MHS rats displayed blunted feedback responses to loop perfusion. The maximum SFP reduction was 75% less and the inflection point was 23 nl/min higher than in MNS control rats. However, during the developmental phase of hypertension, at 6 weeks of age, MHS rats had a lower SNGFR and a lower inflection point; the maximum reduction in SFP did not differ between strains. Adult MHS rats exhibited a larger maximum SFP reduction than did control rats; the inflection point was normal (20 nl/min) in both MHS and MNS rats. Importantly, the enhanced TGF activity in hypertensive Milan rats is resistant to resetting during acute volume expansion (5 ml/100 g body wt) with isotonic saline. An acute saline load markedly inhibited TGF activity in young and adult normotensive rats but barely affected TGF in the hypertensive rats. There was only a 4 nl/min increase in the inflection point in the MHS rats, versus an 18 nl/min increase in control animals. Persson et al (29) reported that unilateral ureteral occlusion, a maneuver that almost completely abolishes TGF in Sprague-Dawley rats and Milan normotensive rats, does not inhibit the exaggerated TGF activity in adult Milan hypertensive rats.

MECHANISMS INVOLVED IN RESETTING OF THE FEEDBACK SYSTEM

Resetting can result from functional changes in cellular transport, processing, or communication that may involve one or more of the steps in the feedback circuit. Although transport by macula densa cells has not been measured in vivo during the various conditions of resetting, it is generally assumed that transport by the loop of Henle, specifically the thick ascending limb, is a reasonable index of macula densa transport. The rate of flow in the distal tubule and the composition of the fluid delivered to it are not invariant functions of the late proximal perfusion employed in most microperfusion studies of TGF activity. Thus retrograde perfusion from an early distal convolution or the type of perturbation analysis described earlier provides a more precise assessment of TGF characteristics. As mentioned in the section on the effects of dietary protein, Seney and his colleagues (48, 49) found that the effects on the inflection points varied markedly depending on whether the feedback curves were generated with data collected during orthograde perfusion from a proximal site or retrograde perfusion from a distal convolution. This apparent discrepancy could be explained by a change in reabsorption by the loop of Henle that is related to the level of protein in the diet and thus is independent of the sensor or effector mechanisms in the TGF feedback loop, which were functioning normally.

An obvious, albeit elusive, candidate for the factor(s) responsible for TGF resetting is the mechanism mediating transmission of a signal to the glomerular vasculature. Resetting of the TGF system may also involve changes in vascular tone or reactivity in the final effector step that is ultimately responsible for changing GFR. Although a number of intrarenal hormonal mediators have been proposed, the available evidence is inconclusive. An alternative possibility is that the mediator involves signal transduction of an electrical, ionic, or metabolic nature. Vasoactive systems, such as the renin-angiotensin and arachidonic acid–prostanoid systems, may be involved. These two systems were recently reviewed (40–42) and are discussed, along with the role of calcium and other biochemical characteristics of the juxtaglomerular apparatus, in the reviews by Bell et al and Briggs & Schnermann in this volume.

Interstitial Pressure and Volume

In 1979 Persson et al (32) observed that changes in peritubular capillary protein concentration caused parallel changes in SFP responses to loop perfusion. The interpretation of this finding was that capillary colloid osmotic pressure modulates TGF by causing pressure or volume changes in the local interstitial space. It was proposed that a change in interstitial volume influences the concentration or transfer of a mediator substance from the macula densa cells to the glomerular vasculature or that a change in interstitial pressure affects cell volume and transport processes at either the receptor or effector sites. This interesting hypothesis was extended to explain the TGF resetting that occurs during a change in ECF volume and other conditions when TGF activity can be dissociated from the delivery of tubular fluid to the macula densa receptor.

Since 1983 Persson and coworkers have presented a large body of evidence demonstrating an association between changes in interstitial pressures and TGF activity under a variety of experimental conditions. In their studies, net interstitial pressure is calculated as the difference between interstitial hydrostatic pressure (P_i), which is estimated from subcapsular pressure measured with a micropipette, and interstitial colloid osmotic pressure (COP_i), estimated from protein concentration measured in hilar lymph. The results obtained by Persson and associates in Sprague-Dawley and Milan strains of rats during a variety of experimental interventions are graphed in Figure 4. There is an impressive inverse relation between estimated net interstitial pressure and TGF activity, as evaluated based on the inflection point, the maximum decrease in SFP, and the maximum reactivity of SFP determined during loop perfusion. Hydropenic control values for net interstitial pressure averaged -1.6 mm Hg, $P_i = 1.3$ mm Hg, and $COP_i = 2.9$ mm Hg. Control values for the feedback curves during perfusion of the loop of Henle were: inflection point $= 21$ nl/min, maximum SFP decrease $= 8$ mm Hg, and maximum reactivity of SFP $= 1.2$ mm Hg·min·nl^{-1}. These three indices of TGF activity indicate significant, graded inhibition as net interstitial pressure increases, and exaggerated feedback responses when net interstitial pressure decreases.

In the top panel of Figure 4, the inflection point increased above 32 nl/min when net interstitial pressure rose above 0.5 mm Hg during acute isotonic saline loading (6, 7, 29, 46, 47), acute unilateral ureteral occlusion (33), and immediately after contralateral nephrectomy (15, 25, 26). Paradoxically, either intratubular application of PGE_2 or systemic administration of indomethacin eliminated the increase in the inflection point after contralateral nephrectomy (16, 31). During inhibition of prostaglandin synthesis there was an increase of 1.4 mm Hg in the net interstitial pressure (15). The low

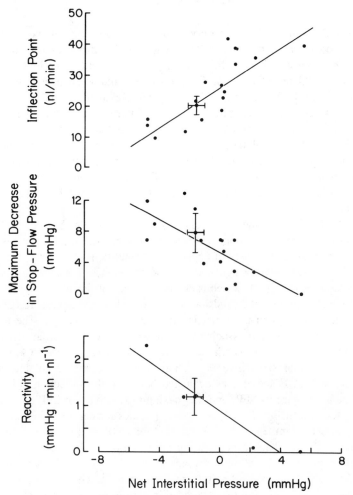

Figure 4 Correlations of different measures of tubuloglomerular feedback activity with net renal interstitial pressure. Correlation coefficients for the best-fit regression lines are: top panel, $r = 0.77$, $n = 17$, $p < 0.01$; middle panel, $r = -0.70$, $n = 17$, $p < 0.01$; bottom panel, $r = -0.95$, $n = 5$, $p < 0.01$. Data are from the studies of Persson and associates (6, 7, 15, 16, 28, 33, 46, 47, 51). Hydropenic control values are indicated with standard error bars.

inflection points of 10–16 nl/min at net interstitial pressures of −4 to −5 mm Hg were observed during 24 hr of dehydration (46, 47) and before and after release of 24-hr unilateral ureteral occlusion (51).

In the middle panel, the maximum SFP decrease was reduced to <4 mm Hg at high net interstitial pressures during acute saline loading (6, 7, 46, 47) and acute unilateral ureteral occlusion (33). The largest maximum SFP decrease (12 mm Hg) was associated with a net interstitial pressure of -4.9 mm Hg after dehydration (46, 47).

As shown in the bottom panel of Figure 4, the reactivity of SFP was decreased by acute saline loading (46, 47) and acute unilateral ureteral occlusion (33); this value was in the normal range after release of acute ureteral occlusion (33); and it increased upon dehydration for 24 hr (45, 46).

It is noteworthy that an acute increase in renal venous pressure (20 mm Hg) in hydropenic rats had no effect on any measure of TGF activity or net interstitial pressure; there were equal increases in P_i and COP_i (6). In contrast, the same increase in renal venous pressure reversed the inhibition of TGF during acute saline loading in conjunction with a decrease in net interstitial pressure due to a large increase in COP_i.

The age-related differences in TGF activity between Milan hypertensive and normotensive rats mentioned earlier tend to correlate with net interstitial pressure during hydropenia. The attenuation of the TGF system in 4-week-old MHS rats was associated with a higher net interstitial pressure (-1.1 versus -2.8 mm Hg). However, the exaggerated feedback response found in 6-week-old MHS rats was present when the interstitial pressure was similar in MHS and MNS rats. In adult rats, net interstitial pressure was more negative in MHS rats (-2.7 versus -1.8 mm Hg) with exaggerated TGF. Acute volume expansion with isotonic saline has a larger inhibitory effect on TGF in normotensive control rats than in Milan hypertensive rats (7, 29). Saline loading produced similar increases in interstitial pressure (2–3 mm Hg) in both strains. Thus factors other than interstitial pressure or volume are probably involved in the inability of volume expansion to suppress TGF in Milan genetically hypertensive rats.

Anatomical evidence provides some support for the hypothesis of Persson. Lateral intercellular spaces between macula densa cells appear to vary in width according to function (19). The spaces are enlarged to widths greater than those of spaces between other cortical nephron segments in normal and saline-loaded animals and are narrow during furosemide or mannitol diuresis. This finding suggests that inhibition of solute transport or a reduced osmotic gradient may reduce fluid movement across macula densa cells. In this regard, Kirk et al (20) observed that a low luminal osmolality expands lateral intercellular spaces and increases the height of the macula densa cells.

Persson cites evidence of albumin appearance in hilar lymph after subcapsular injection to support the view that the subcapsular space has free communication with the deep interstitium. Such an observation, however, does not address the issue of homogeneity of distribution and communication within the region of the juxtaglomerular apparatus. The interstitium at the base of the macula densa cells is a unique region that is devoid of capillaries and lymphatic vessels and that may be isolated from the majority of the cortical interstitium (19). Conversely, this area may slowly equilibrate with other interstitial regions, as suggested by the rather sluggish, time-dependent response to peritubular perfusion with colloid solutions (32). The determination of whether the relation between net interstitial pressure and TGF activity is one of causation or is only a phenomenological association awaits further investigation.

Atrial Natriuretic Factor

A possible mediator of the relation between TGF activity and acute changes in ECF volume is the recently discovered atrial natriuretic peptide or factor (ANF). In 1982 Briggs et al (10) found that systemic infusion of two doses of atrial extract significantly increased distal tubular flow and chloride delivery. Distally measured SNGFR was increased by the high but not the low dose, which suggests that the inhibition of TGF was by a mechanism other than the sensing step in the macula densa. This conclusion is supported by the fact that luminal perfusion of the extract did not affect the SNGFR.

More recent studies have examined the effects of synthetic ANF (28 amino acids) administered systemically. The preliminary results of Pollock & Arendshorst (36a) and Huang et al (17) indicate that ANF is a rapidly acting, potent inhibitor of TGF activity in superficial nephrons of nondiuretic rats. Pollock & Arendshorst observed that infusion of a natriuretic dose (15 μg/kg/hr) of synthetic ANF almost completely blocked glomerular responses to loop feedback activation produced by perfusion at 40 nl/min. The control feedback-mediated decrease in SNGFR of 7 nl/min was reduced to 0 nl/min during ANF administration. With regard to SFP responses to different rates of loop perfusion, ANF reduced the maximum decrease in SFP by 80%, increased the inflection point by 120%, and decreased reactivity by 85%. Interestingly, in the absence of loop perfusion ANF did not affect basal SNGFR, although basal SFP was increased by 30%. An earlier study showed that GFR and RBF were unaffected by the same relatively small amount of ANF (36). Huang et al (17) found that infusion of ANF (5 μg/kg bolus and 30 μg/kg/hr) increased SFP by 25% and SNGFR by 12%. In microperfusion studies, they reported that such doses of ANF reduced by 55% the maximum SFP and SNGFR response to a 50-nl/min increase in loop perfusion. Huang et al (17) proposed that the impaired TGF response during ANF infusion may be mediated by ANF-induced increases in glomerular generation of cGMP. However, Schnermann and associates had shown previously that TGF is unaffected by luminal perfusion with high concentrations of cyclic nucleotides and their more permeant dibutyrl derivatives (cf 41). The effect of ANF on renal interstitial pressures has not been evaluated.

The Kallikrein-Kinin System

Schnermann et al (43) recently investigated the possibility that some of the TGF inhibition produced by angiotensin converting enzyme (kininase II) inhibition is due to reduced degradation of vasodilatory kinins. Enhanced TGF was observed during inhibition of kallikrein activity, and presumably kinin production, by aprotinin, a nonspecific protease inhibitor. Aprotinin administration decreased SNGFR and increased the proximal-distal SNGFR difference without affecting distal fluid delivery. In microperfusion studies, aprotinin treatment increased the maximum decrease in EPFR and reversed the inhibition following captopril administration. The mechanism by which endogenous kinins appear to inhibit TGF is not known. This inhibition may occur through a direct action at the vascular effector site or indirectly via the complex interaction of kinins with the renin-angiotensin and/or arachidonic acid–prostanoid systems. However, Pollock et al (37) recently observed that inhibition of kallikrein activity with aprotinin had no effect on RBF or the GFR in anesthetized or conscious rats studied during various hydration states.

Luminal Factor

The nature of the solution used to perfuse the loop of Henle can influence TGF responses in certain physiological states. Figure 5 presents the results of two studies showing that in rats consuming a very high salt diet (37 mM NaCl/day) for 2–4 weeks, loop perfusion with a Ringer solution produced reductions in the EPFR that were slightly smaller than the normal response of 12 nl/min (14, 45). In contrast, feedback responses were more markedly attenuated during rapid loop perfusion with native fluid harvested from the proximal tubule. Häberle & Davis (14) reported significant inhibition at the intermediate flow rate and 92% inhibition at a rate of 40 nl/min. However, Schnermann et al (44) saw inhibition only at the highest perfusion rate, and the inhibition was only 50%. The native perfusate from the rats fed a very high salt diet was also able to blunt the TGF responses in rats fed a normal or low-salt diet (14). These provocative findings indicate that a constituent of endogenous tubular fluid obtained from salt-loaded rats with a large increase in ECF volume can rapidly inhibit the TGF system. However, Figure 5 also shows that the feedback response to native tubular fluid taken from rats fed a low-salt diet did not differ from the feedback response to Ringer solution in rats fed a low-salt diet. The observations of Schnermann et al (45) are important to the interpretation of the functional importance of the above findings. Schnermann et al found that native tubular fluid from rats consuming a slightly less high salt diet (26 mM NaCl/day) had very little effect on EPFR responses (45). In addition, loop perfusion with artificial and native tubular fluid produced similar feedback responses in rats on a standard diet (3 mM NaCl/day) or on restricted food intake, or in acutely saline-loaded rats.

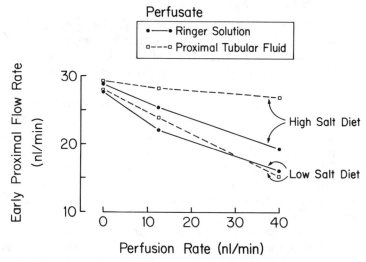

Figure 5 Effect of perfusing loops of Henle with artificial (Ringer solution) or native proximal tubular fluid in rats fed a very high salt diet (37 mM NaCl/day) or low-salt diet (0.05 mM NaCl/day) for 2–4 weeks. (Results are from References 14 and 45.)

The TGF activity, as assessed by the inflection point and reactivity, in response to perfusion with native or artificial perfusate did not differ appreciably in the study of Schnermann et al (45). Based on the findings that chloride reabsorption by the loop of Henle and chloride delivery to the distal tubule were the same whether the perfusate was native or artificial, Schnermann et al (45) concluded that an undefined inhibitory factor in the native proximal tubular fluid from rats in the very high salt group probably interfered with signal transmission or the vascular effector step, rather than with the inhibition of transport by macula densa cells.

Wunderlich et al (52) reported preliminary findings that loop perfusion of rats with urine from a salt-loaded human produced TGF inhibition and that enhanced feedback responses were elicited by perfusion with urine from the same subject during salt restriction. Another recent finding implicating a luminal factor in TGF resetting is that native tubular fluid from rats with acute hyperglycemia has a slightly larger inhibitory effect on TGF than does tubular fluid from normal rats (4).

Thus there is evidence to indicate that an unidentified constituent present in the proximal tubular fluid influences TGF and is in part responsible for its resetting. Although a luminal factor may contribute to TGF resetting during chronic, extreme volume expansion, it is probably not the primary mechanism of resetting during acute or moderate degrees of chronic ECF volume expansion. Clearly, the potential importance of a luminal factor will have to be considered in future quantitative studies of TGF activity.

SUMMARY

The efficiency of coupling between salt delivery to the sensing site in the macula densa and the glomerular vascular effector response is altered by changes in extracellular fluid volume, in the amount of dietary protein, and many other conditions, including growth and maturation, and the development of hypertension in Okamoto-Aoki and Milan strains of genetically hypertensive rats. Examination of feedback-mediated responses by perfusion of Henle's loop reveals a tendency for multiple changes in characteristics of feedback curves for SNGFR and SFP. In general, inhibition of TGF activity is evidenced by a smaller maximum glomerular response, reduced reactivity, and a shift in the inflection point to a higher flow rate. The opposite responses are frequently noted during exaggerated TGF activity. It is not known at present whether one or more mechanisms are involved in mediating or modulating the functional correlates of these characteristics. Insight into these functional correlates may be provided by selective, graded inhibition and stimulation of the sensing and effector elements in the feedback loop. Investigations of potential extrarenal mechanisms of resetting indicate that atrial natriuretic factor and an unidentified factor present in the proximal tubular fluid may play a role under certain circumstances. In addition to the renin-angiotensin and arachidonic acid–prostanoid systems, the kallikrein-kinin system appears to modulate TGF activity. A large body of evidence indicates TGF activity is inversely correlated with renal interstitial pressure. Whether this correlation reflects causality or a phenomenological association awaits further investigation.

ACKNOWLEDGMENT

The work performed in the author's laboratory was supported by NIH grants HL-02334, AM-00808, and AM-07047 and grants from the American Heart Association, North Carolina Affiliate.

Literature Cited

1. Baylis, C., Blantz, R. C. 1985. Tubuloglomerular feedback activity in virgin and 12-day-pregnant rats. *Am. J. Physiol.* 249:F169–73

2. Bell, P. D., Reddington, M., Ploth, D., Navar, L. G. 1984. Tubuloglomerular feedback-mediated decreases in glomerular pressure in Munich-Wistar rats. *Am. J. Physiol.* 247:F877–80

3. Blantz, R. C., Pelayo, J. C. 1984. A functional role for the tubuloglomerular feedback mechanism. *Kidney Int.* 25:739–46

4. Blantz, R. C., Peterson, O. W., Gushwa, L., Tucker, B. J. 1982. Effect of modest hyperglycemia on tubuloglomerular feedback activity. *Kidney Int.* 22:S206–12 (Suppl. 12)

5. Blantz, R. C., Tucker, B. J., Gushwa, L., Peterson, O. W. 1983. Mechanism of diuresis following acute modest hyperglycemia in the rat. *Am. J. Physiol.* 244:F185–94

6. Boberg, U., Persson, A. E. G. 1985. Tubuloglomerular feedback during elevated renal venous pressure. *Am. J. Physiol.* 249:F524–31

7. Boberg, U., Persson, A. E. G. 1986. Increased tubuloglomerular feedback activity in Milan hypertensive rats. *Am. J. Physiol.* 250:F967–74

8. Briggs, J. P. 1984. The effect of loop of

Henle flow on glomerular capillary pressure. *Renal Physiol.* 7:311–20

9. Briggs, J. P., Schubert, G., Schnermann, J. 1984. Quantitative characterization of the tubuloglomerular feedback response: Effect of growth. *Am. J. Physiol.* 247:F808–15

10. Briggs, J. P., Steipe, B., Schubert, G., Schnermann, J. 1982. Micropuncture studies of the renal effects of atrial natriuretic substance. *Pflüg. Arch.* 395:271–76

11. Dilley, J. R., Arendshorst, W. J. 1984. Enhanced tubuloglomerular feedback activity in rats developing spontaneous hypertension. *Am. J. Physiol.* 247:F672–79

12. Dilley, J. R., Stier, C. T. Jr., Arendshorst, W. J. 1984. Abnormalities in glomerular function in rats developing spontaneous hypertension. *Am. J. Physiol.* 246:F12–F20

13. Gröne, H. J., Grippo, R. S., Arendshorst, W. J., Dunn, M. J. 1986. Effect of thromboxane inhibition on renal function in young spontaneously hypertensive rats. *Am. J. Physiol.* 250:F488–96

14. Häberle, D. A., Davis, J. M. 1984. Resetting of tubuloglomerular feedback: Evidence for a humoral factor in tubular fluid. *Am. J. Physiol.* 246:F495–F500

15. Hahne, B., Persson, A. E. G. 1984. Prevention of interstitial pressure change at unilateral nephrectomy by prostaglandin synthesis inhibition. *Kidney Int.* 25:42–46

16. Hahne, B., Selén, G., Persson, A. E. G. 1984. Indomethacin inhibits renal functional adaptation to nephron loss. *Renal Physiol.* 7:13–21

17. Huang, C. L., Ives, H. E., Cogan, M. G. 1985. Atrial natriuretic factor causes glomerular hyperfiltration, blunted tubulo-glomerular feedback, and increased glomerular cGMP generation. *Am. Soc. Nephrol.* 18:235A (Abstr.)

18. Ichikawa, I., Purkerson, M. L., Klahr, S., Troy, J. L., Martinez-Maldonado, M., Brenner, B. M. 1980. Mechanism of reduced glomerular filtration rate in chronic malnutrition. *J. Clin. Invest.* 65:982–88

19. Kaissling, B., Kriz, W. 1982. Variability of intercellular spaces between macula densa cells: A transmission electron microscopic study in rabbits and rats. *Kidney Int.* 22:S9–S17 (Suppl. 12)

20. Kirk, K. L., Bell, P. D., Barfuss, D. W., Ribadeneira, M. 1985. Direct visualization of the isolated and perfused macula densa. *Am. J. Physiol.* 248:F890–94

21. Moore, L. C. 1982. Tubuloglomerular feedback in hamster superficial and juxtamedullary nephrons. *Fed. Proc.* 41:A5763 (Abstr.)

22. Moore, L. C., Mason, J. 1983. Perturbation analysis of tubuloglomerular feedback in hydropenic and hemorrhaged rats. *Am. J. Physiol.* 345:F554–63

23. Moore, L. C., Mason, J. 1986. Tubuloglomerular feedback control of distal fluid delivery: Effect of extracellular volume. *Am. J. Physiol.* 250:F1024–32

24. Moore, L. C., Yarimizu, S., Schubert, G., Weber, P. C., Schnermann, J. 1980. Dynamics of tubuloglomerular feedback adaptation to acute and chronic changes in body fluid volume. *Pflüg. Arch.* 387:39–45

25. Müller-Suur, R., Norlén, B. J., Persson, A. E. G. 1980. Resetting of tubuloglomerular feedback in rat kidneys after unilateral nephrectomy. *Kidney Int.* 18:48–57

26. Müller-Suur, R., Persson, A. E. G. 1986. Influence of water-diuresis or saline volume expansion on deep nephron tubuloglomerular feedback. *Acta Physiol. Scand.* 126:139–46

27. Müller-Suur, R., Ulfendahl, H. R., Persson, A. E. G. 1983. Evidence for tubuloglomerular feedback in juxtamedullary nephrons of young rats. *Am. J. Physiol.* 244:F425–31

28. Norlén, B. J., Müller-Suur, R., Persson, A. E. G. 1978. Tubulo-glomerular feedback response and excretory characteristics of the transplanted rat kidney. *Scand. J. Urol. Nephrol.* 12:27–33

29. Persson, A. E. G., Bianchi, G., Boberg, U. 1985. Tubuloglomerular feedback in hypertensive rats of the Milan strain. *Acta Physiol. Scand.* 123:139–46

30. Persson, A. E. G., Gushwa, L. C., Blantz, R. C. 1984. Feedback pressure-flow responses in normal and angiotensin-prostaglandin blocked rats. *Am. J. Physiol.* 247:F925–31

31. Persson, A. E. G., Hahne, B., Selén, G. 1983. The effect of tubular perfusion with PGE_2 $PGF_{2\alpha}$, and PGI_2 on the tubuloglomerular feedback control in the rat. *Can. J. Physiol. Pharmacol.* 61:1317–23

32. Persson, A. E. G., Müller-Suur, R., Selén, G. 1979. Capillary oncotic pressure as a modifier for tubuloglomerular feedback. *Am. J. Physiol.* 236:F97–F102

33. Persson, A. E. G., Wahlberg, J., Safirstein, R., Wright, F. S. 1984. The effect of two hours of complete uni-

lateral ureteral obstruction on tubuloglomerular feedback control. *Acta Physiol. Scand.* 122:35–43

34. Ploth, D. W., Roy, R. 1982. Renin-angiotensin influences on tubuloglomerular feedback activity in the rat. *Kidney Int.* 22:S114–21 (Suppl. 12)

35. Ploth, D. W., Rudolph, J., Thomas, C., Navar, L. G. 1978. Renal and tubuloglomerular feedback responses to plasma expansion in the rat. *Am. J. Physiol.* 235:F156–62

36. Pollock, D. M., Arendshorst, W. J. 1986. Effect of atrial natriuretic factor on renal hemodynamics in the rat. *Am. J. Physiol.* 251:F795–F801

36a. Pollock, D. M., Arendshorst, W. J. 1986. Atriopeptin resets tubuloglomerular feedback. *Am. Soc. Nephrol.* 19:In press (Abstr.)

37. Pollock, D. M., Butterfield, M. I., Ader, J. L., Arendshorst, W. J. 1986. Dissociation of urinary kallikrein activity and salt and water excretion in the rat. *Am. J. Physiol.* 250:F1082–89

38. Rudd, M. A., Grippo, R. S., Arendshorst, W. J. 1985. Effect of captopril on renal hemodynamics in rats developing spontaneous hypertension. *Kidney Int.* 27:299 (Abstr.)

39. Rudd, M. A., Grippo, R. S., Arendshorst, W. J. 1986. Acute renal denervation produces a diuresis and natriuresis in young SHR but not WKY rats. *Am. J. Physiol.* 251:F655–61

40. Schnermann, J., Briggs, J. P. 1981. Participation of renal cortical prostaglandins in the regulation of glomerular filtrate. *Kidney Int.* 19:802–15

41. Schnermann, J., Briggs, J. 1985. Function of the juxtaglomerular apparatus: Local control of glomerular hemodynamics. In *The Kidney: Physiology and Pathophysiology,* ed. D. W. Seldin, G. Giebisch, pp. 669–97. New York: Raven

42. Schnermann, J., Briggs, J. P. 1986. Role of the renin-angiotensin system in tubuloglomerular feedback. *Fed. Proc.* 45:1426–30

43. Schnermann, J., Briggs, J. P., Schubert, C., Marin-Grez, M. 1984. Opposing effects of captopril and aprotinin on tubuloglomerular feedback responses. *Am. J. Physiol.* 247:F912–18

44. Schnermann, J., Gokel, M., Weber, P. C., Schubert, G., Briggs, J. P. 1986. Tubuloglomerular feedback and glomerular morphology in Goldblatt hypertensive rats on a varying diet. *Kidney Int.* 29:520–29

45. Schnermann, J., Schubert, C., Briggs, J. 1986. Tubuloglomerular feedback responses with native and artifical tubular fluid. *Am. J. Physiol.* 250:F16–F21

46. Selén, G., Müller-Suur, R., Persson, A. E. G. 1983. Activation of tubuloglomerular feedback mechanism in dehydrated rats. *Acta Physiol. Scand.* 117:83–89

47. Selén, G., Persson, A. E. G. 1983. Hydrostatic and oncotic pressures in the interstitium of dehydrated and volume expanded rats. *Acta Physiol. Scand.* 117:75–81

48. Seney, F. D. Jr., Persson, A. E. G., Desir, G. V., Wright, F. S. 1985. Dietary protein: Effect on tubuloglomerular feedback signal and sensing mechanism. *Kidney Int.* 27:299 (Abstr.)

49. Seney, F. D. Jr., Wright, F. S. 1985. Dietary protein suppresses feedback control of glomerular filtration in rats. *J. Clin. Invest.* 75:558–68

50. Tucker, B. J., Blantz, R. C. 1984. Effect of furosemide administration on glomerular and tubular dynamics in the rat. *Kidney Int.* 26:112–21

51. Wahlberg, J., Stenberg, A., Wilson, D. R., Persson, A. E. G. 1984. Tubuloglomerular feedback and interstitial pressure in obstructive nephropathy. *Kidney Int.* 26:294–302

52. Wunderlich, P., Hermle, M., Brunner, F., Thiel, G. 1982. Beeinflussung des Tubulo-glomerulareno-Feedback's mit Urin nach unterschiedlicher Kochsalzbelastung. *Nieren-Hochdruckkr.* 11:183 (Abstr.)

ENDOCRINOLOGY

ACTIONS OF HORMONES IN THE CENTRAL NERVOUS SYSTEM

Introduction, Jack L. Kostyo, *Section Editor*

Much of the past research in the field of neuroendocrinology has focused upon the role of the central nervous system, and particularly the brain, as an endocrine organ that produces a variety of hormones. A number of these substances, the so-called releasing hormones, have been shown to influence the secretory functions of the anterior pituitary gland, whereas others, such as the neurohypophyseal hormones, also have peripheral physiological targets. It has become increasingly clear in recent years, however, that the central nervous system is itself a target for a number of hormones. An abundance of physiological and behavioral data accumulated over many years has strongly suggested that certain hormones, such as the thyroid hormones and sex steroids, have central actions that are essential for the structural maturation of the brain and for the development of sexual cycles and various behaviors. Technical advances during the past two decades have made possible the detection and characterization of receptors for hormones and the detailed structural analysis of the brain. Recent work utilizing this technology has left little doubt that the central nervous system is indeed a target for hormones that alter its structure and function. We now stand at the threshold of a new period during which many of the molecular mechanisms by which hormones influence central nervous system structure and function will be elucidated.

It seemed most appropriate, therefore, to devote the endocrinology section of this volume to recent work and thought on the actions of hormones in the central nervous system. In all, seven chapters cover various aspects of the central actions of thyroid hormones, sex steroids, adrenal cortical steroids, insulin and certain gut peptides, and the renin-angiotensin system.

Ann. Rev. Physiol. 1987. 49:321–34

THYROID HORMONES AND BRAIN DEVELOPMENT

Jean H. Dussault and Jean Ruel

Unité de Recherche en Ontogénèse et Génétique Moléculaire, Le Centre Hospitalier de l'Université Laval, Québec, Canada GIV 4G2

HISTORICAL INTRODUCTION

Although endemic goiter with cretinism was described by Paracelsus (1493–1541) and other physicians living in the Alps and Central Europe, the relation between the disease, cretinism, and the thyroid gland was not recognized at that time (48). The thyroid gland itself was only adequately described for the first time in 1656 by Wharton (91). Even as late as 1850, this relationship was still unrealized, despite Curling's description of two cases of cretinism in children associated with absence of the thyroid gland at autopsy (15). In 1891, Murray reported that the symptoms of hypothyroidism could be relieved by twice weekly injections of an extract of sheep thyroid (53). The discovery of thyroid extract therapy for hypothyroidism is described by Sir William Osler (60): "That we can rescue children otherwise doomed to helpless idiocy is a triumph of experimental medicine. Within six weeks, a poor feeble minded toad like caricature of humanity may be restored to mental and bodily health."

Thus thyroid hormone plays an important role in the central nervous system (CNS). The most striking effects are observed during maturation of the CNS: The absence of thyroid hormones during this period produces multiple morphological and biochemical alterations and in humans leads to irreversible mental retardation. Efforts to understand the mechanism of the hormonal effect have been hampered by the enormous complexity of the developing brain, which is made up of 100 billions of cells and 100 trillions of synapses. Although sparse data exist for humans, it is known that the period between the end of the first trimester of gestation and 6 months after birth is the period of active neurogenesis and the most active phase of the brain growth spurt. The brain is particularly vulnerable to various insults during this period (18–20,

321

51). However, most of our knowledge on the effects of thyroid hormones in the brain comes from experiments on animals, particularly the rat. Figure 1 shows the timing of neurodevelopmental events and of initiation of thyroid function in man, sheep, and rat. It can be seen that, grossly, the newborn rat can be compared to the human fetus during the second trimester of gestation and the 6–10 day-old rat to the newborn infant (14). In this review we summarize what has been learned of the alterations induced by the thyroid hormones on the anatomy, histology, biochemistry, and electrophysiology of the CNS during its maturation and the effects of these changes on neuro-psychological development. Because of space restrictions the reader is re-ferred to other publications for broader reviews on specific aspects of the subject (27, 44, 51).

THYROID HORMONE RECEPTORS

The mechanism of action of thyroid hormone is thought to be initiated by its binding to a specific nuclear receptor (59). The demonstration of local conversion of T_4 to T_3 in the rat brain, with the result that the T_3 receptor is highly saturated under basal conditions, suggests a primary role for the receptor in the maturation of the CNS (38).

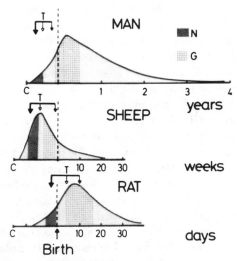

Figure 1 Timing of main neurodevelopmental events and of initiation and activation of thyroid function in man, sheep, and rat. The solid line represents the velocity of the brain growth spurt. The shaded areas N and G indicate the approximate timing of maximal rate of neuroblast and glial cell replication with respect to conception (C) and birth. In the three species, events in the cerebellum are retarded with respect to those shown here. The arrows under T indicate (from left to right) initiation of thyroid function, fetal circulating T_4 levels, and the increase in circulating T_3. (From Reference 51, used with permission.)

In the human fetus, Bernal & Pekonen (8) have been able to demonstrate a high-affinity T_3 binding site with the binding specificity of the nuclear T_3 receptor. The receptor concentration is very low at 10 weeks of gestation but increases tenfold by week 16 (8).

In the rat forebrain, the T_3 receptors are present in comparatively high concentration, with a peak at nine days and a rapid decrease thereafter. The same phenomena can be observed in the cerebellum but with much lower concentrations (Figure 2) (13, 22, 77). In the adult brain (71) we have demonstrated that the distribution of the receptors varies with the region and the cell types studied. The highest concentrations were found in the amygdala, the hippocampus, and the cortex, while the lowest were in the brain stem and the cerebellum; there was a ninefold difference between the lowest and highest capacities observed. No T_3 binding was found in the oligodendrocyte fraction; the neuron-enriched fraction showed an increase in receptor concentration roughly proportional to the level of neuronal purification obtained.

To pursue our investigations of the ontogenesis of the receptor, we have used separate primary cultures of astrocytes and neurons as models. Receptors

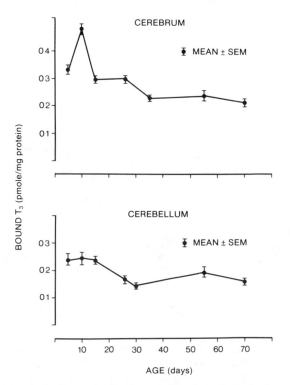

Figure 2   Changes in the T_3 receptor binding capacities during brain development in the rat. (From Ref. 13, used with permission.)

in neuronal cultures show a maximum binding capacity after 12 days of culture, whereas the peak for the astrocytes occurs at 21 days. The receptors of the two cell lines have the same affinity for T_3, but the capacity is threefold higher in the neurons (47).

In summary, specific receptors for triiodothyronine exist both in cerebrum and cerebellum, are present at a higher concentration at early age, and are preferentially found in neuronal cells with regional differences in their distribution.

ANATOMICAL AND HISTOLOGICAL ALTERATIONS

Forebrain

Ruiz-Marcos and coworkers recently studied the effect of hypothyroidism (thyroidectomy) on the number of spines per apical shaft in pyramid cells of the rat visual and auditory cortex (74, 75). Groups of rats thyroidectomized at 10 days of age were treated with thyroxine starting at different times after the operation. Figure 3 shows the results. Pyramidal cells of thyroidectomized rats treated from 12 days of age developed normally. When treatment was delayed until 30 days of age, these cells were severely damaged, as assessed by the distribution of apical shaft spines. More precise studies revealed that when treatment was started at 15 days, the distribution of spines found at 60 days of age was intermediate between the control and the hypothyroid animals; when treatment was begun at 20 days, the damage was irreversible. Thus a critical period appears to occur between day 10, when treatment is

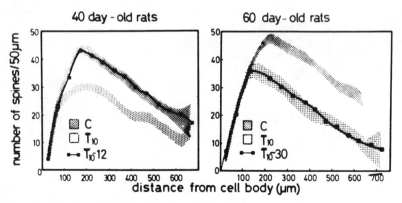

Figure 3   Distribution of spines along the apical shaft of pyramidals from rats thyroidectomized at 10 days of age (T_{10}) and of T_{10} rats treated with 1.5 μg T_4 per 100 g body weight per day since 12 (T_{10-12}) or since 30 (T_{10-30}) days of age. These animals and their age-paired controls (C) were studied at 40 *(left)* and 60 *(right)* days of age. For T_{10} and C rats, 95% confidence intervals are shown by shaded areas. (From Ref. 51, used with permission.)

effective, and day 20, when the sole opportunity for maturation of the cells has been lost (Figure 3).

Cerebellum

Legrand and coworkers (43) have studied in detail the effect of hypothyroid-ism on the development of the rat cerebellum and on the maturation of different "circuits" leading to the establishment of the adult "wiring" pattern in the brain (Figure 4). The only efferent neurons of the cerebellar cortex are the Purkinje cells, which are formed just before birth in the rat. Although the number of Purkinje cells is not decreased by hypothyroidism, their maturation is permanently affected, as reflected by their arborization and number of dendritic spines. After a period of mitotic activity, cells from the external germinal layer migrate toward the internal granular layer, differentiate in the process, and establish contacts with afferent mossy fibers and with Purkinje cells to yield the normal "wiring" pattern. Hypothyroidism delays the dis-appearance of the external germinal layer and decreases the number and density of synaptic contacts with the already defective Purkinje cells, result-ing in a permanent impairment of neuronal connectivity. The critical period appears to occur before day 21 after birth, since treatment given after that date is no longer effective in preventing cellular damage.

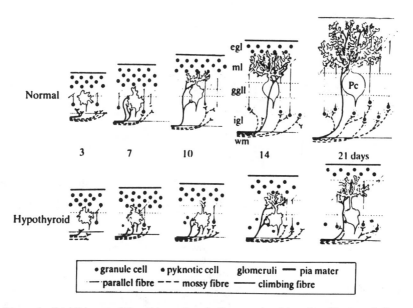

Figure 4 Establishment of the wiring pattern in the normal and hypothyroid rat cerebellum. (From Ref. 43, used with permission.)

BIOCHEMICAL ALTERATIONS

Examples of biochemical effects of thyroid hormones in the developing rat brain are given in Table 1. This list is not exhaustive, but it illustrates well the wide variety of functions sensitive to thyroid hormones. Most of the biochemical effects of hypothyroidism, like the morphological effects, become irreversible if replacement therapy is delayed after the critical period of development, which in rats usually spans the first 10–14 days after birth. Unfortunately, many of these effects can only be detected 2–3 weeks after birth when they can no longer be reversed.

Table 1   Selected examples of effects of thyroid hormones in various biochemical parameters in the developing brain

Parameter	Observations	References
Energy metabolism		
Oxygen consumption	Controversial. Appears to be stimulated by thyroid hormones but only with certain substrates.	65, 78
Glucose and ketone-body metabolism	Hyperthyroidism accelerates developmental changes in glucose transport rate and ketone body metabolizing enzymes. Hypothyroidism delays these changes and prevents the decrease in ketone-body-metabolizing enzymes after weaning.	16, 23, 50, 63
Polyamines		
Content	Transient increases in spermine and spermidine content in hyperthyroid animals.	37
Metabolism	Hyperthyroidism increases ornithine decarboxylase (ODC), S-adenosylmethionine decarboxylase, and methionine adenosyltransferase activities in young animals. Hypothyroidism decreases ODC activity in immature cerebellum.	2, 17, 37, 69
Microtubules		
Tubulin	Content is increased in hyperthyroidism and decreased in hypothyroidism. Rate of synthesis is increased and rate of turnover decreased by thyroid hormones. Decreased tubulin-tyrosine ligase in hypothyroidism.	11, 12, 32, 42, 84
Microtubule-associated protein	Capacity of microtubule to assembly in vitro is delayed in hypothyroid rats due to a defect in microtubule-associated proteins.	25, 28

Table 1 *(continued)*

Parameter	Observations	References
Myelin		
Composition	Hyperthyroidism accelerates and hypothyroidism delays deposition of myelin. Both conditions result in decreased myelin content. Lipid and protein compositions are transiently modified but appear to return to normal at later ages.	3, 7, 24, 29, 61, 86, 89, 90
Metabolism	Hypothyroidism delays the development of a number of myelin-associated enzymes, including fatty acid α-hydroxylase, galactosyltransferase, sialyltransferase, sulfotransferase, myelin basic protein (arginine) methyltransferase, and 2',3'-cyclic nucleotide 3'-phosphohydrolase. Thyroid hormone replacement therapy can restore the activity of these enzymes to normal levels if given early, and hyperthyroidism accelerates their development.	1, 9, 10, 26, 40, 52, 56, 57, 61, 76, 79, 80, 83, 86, 92
Neurotransmitters and neuropeptides		
Content	Changes in the levels of norepinephrine, dopamine, substance P, TRH, and somatostatin have been reported in certain areas of rat brain following manipulation of thyroid status.	21, 39, 45, 58, 66, 67
Metabolism	Thyroid hormones modulate the activity of several synthesizing and degrading neurotransmitter enzymes, such as tyrosine hydroxylase, monoamine oxidase, catachol-O-methyltransferase, choline acetyltransferase, acetylcholinesterase, and glutamic acid decarboxylase, and of the ion fluxes associated with Na,K-ATPase.	4, 5, 6, 33, 36, 46, 66, 67, 87
Receptors	Hyperthyroidism accelerates and hypothyroidism delays the developmental changes in GABAergic, muscarinic, and β-adrenergic receptors.	5, 62, 82

Thyroid hormones affect numerous functions in the brain but do so with a very long lag time in many cases. These observations strongly suggest that many of these late effects are secondary to one or several actions of thyroid hormones at an earlier stage of development. To unravel the mechanism of action of thyroid hormones in the brain, it becomes imperative to determine which are their primary target cells. We have addressed ourselves to this problem by establishing separate cultures of neurons and astrocytes. In this way we have shown that triiodothyronine stimulates glutamine synthetase in astrocytes (70) and modulates protein phosphorylation both in astrocytic and neuronal cultures (72, 73). Thus both neurons and astrocytes appear to be targets for thyroid hormones. These in vitro systems should also allow us to determine whether, for example, all neuronal types are sensitive to thyroid hormones and whether some hormonal actions require interactions between different cell types.

ELECTROPHYSIOLOGICAL ALTERATIONS

The particular susceptibility of the developing peripheral auditory system to thyroid hormone deprivation is well known and can serve as a model for alteration detected by electrical activity. The onset of evoked cochlear electrical activity (which is postnatal in the rat) is delayed by hypothyroidism and is returned to normal by thyroid hormone administration (49, 85). In contrast, relatively few abnormalities are noted in hypothyroid animals when hypothyroidism is induced in adulthood, which again indicates that there is a critical period of peripheral auditory system development that depends on thyroid hormone (34, 68). We determined this period of susceptibility using auditory brain stem response (ABR) technique. Rats were treated with a goitrogen (propylthiouracil or PTU) from 3 days before delivery up to 40 days postnatally, and ABR was assessed at 200 days of age. All groups of rats treated with PTU displayed permanent auditory impairment for each stimulus modality used, as revealed by significantly prolonged wave 1 latencies and elevated thresholds. The severity of these abnormalities was directly related to the duration of PTU treatment. To determine the "critical period," other groups of rats were treated with PTU for 10-day periods beginning at different ages, and peripheral auditory function was evaluated by ABR at 12, 16, 25, and 120 days of age. Figure 5 depicts the results for 120-day-old rats. PTU treatment significantly increased wave 1 latency when administered from 3 days before delivery through 6 days of age but was without permanent effect when administered for 10 days starting 10 days after birth. T_4 administration prevented permanent abnormalities when given during the first 10 days of life. These data suggest that the period of greatest vulnerability to thyroid hormone depletion in the peripheral auditory system extends from at least 3 days before delivery though between 5 and 10 days of age.

In the human, recent data (30) show that treated hypothyroid children have lower scores on hearing speech performance scales as early as 18 months of age, and this may represent the first manifestations of the so-called minimal brain damage syndrome, as recently described (88). In a group of 34 con-

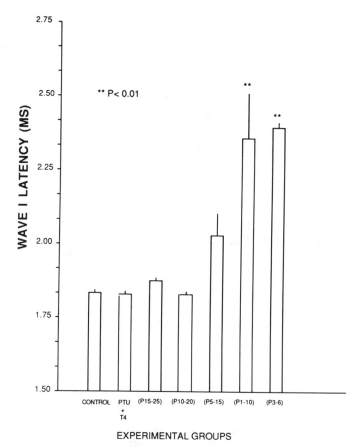

Figure 5 Wave 1 latencies for 4-kHz-evoked responses (80 dB sound pressure level) in the different experimental groups at 120 days of age. PTU + T_4: animals receiving PTU and a replacement dose of T_4 from postnatal day 1 to day 10; Px-y: animals receiving PTU between x and y days of age.

genitally hypothyroid children between ages 5 and 12 under thyroid treatment since the third week of life, significant abnormalities were observed in their auditory brain stem response when compared to a control group (35). Twenty percent showed prolonged wave 1 latencies secondary to a peripheral impairment, and 30% had shortened interpeak latencies.

BEHAVIORAL EFFECTS

As mentioned in the first part of this chapter, the relation between cretinism and the thyroid gland was not established before the nineteenth century. Smith and coworkers (81) were the first to note the importance of initiating treatment within the first few months after birth to maximize the probability that congenitally hypothyroid children can achieve a normal I.Q. They reported improved mental prognosis for children with congenital hypothyroidism when therapy was started before seven months of age. Raiti & Newns (64) and Klein et al (41) found even better results when infants received treatment before three months of age: 85% of those treated achieved an I.Q. greater than 85. With the advent of screening programs that permitted the detection and treatment of hypothyroidism before 1 month of age, these results were corroborated in prospective studies. Of the infants treated, 90% achieved an I.Q. greater than 90 at 3–4 years of age (30, 54). Recent data show that the I.Q.'s of children between 5 and 7 years old are no different than those of a control group (31, 55). However, 10–15% still have an I.Q. below 85. The bone surface area at the age of diagnosis appears to be a good indicator of the severity of the disease during fetal life because almost all the infants with undetectable bone surface have an I.Q. of less than 90 (Table 2). These results are in accordance with those obtained by Vanderschueren et al, who found minimal brain damage in 20% of the children they examined (88). Thus in the human there is a critical period of development during which a minimal amount of thyroid hormones is necessary, and this period appears to extend to fetal life. Depending on the age of onset and/or the severity of the fetal hypothyroidism, some aspects of mental and neurological development may remain impaired even with the early intervention commonly practiced today.

SUMMARY

We have limited ourselves to the deleterious effects of the absence of thyroid hormones on the development of the central nervous system and have not discussed the problems caused by hyperthyroidism. A short "critical period" during which thyroid hormones are essential for normal maturation of the CNS is evident at anatomical, biochemical, and neurophysiological levels. In the last decade we have made progress toward understanding the mechanism of action of thyroid hormones, due in part to numerous studies of the ontogenesis and distribution of the nuclear T_3 receptor. These studies can

Table 2 Developmental quotient in relation to bone surface[a]

Bone surface at diagnosis	Developmental quotient (mean ± S.E.M.)			
	1.5 yr	3 yr	5 yr	7 yr
HC < 0.05 cm²	97 ± 11* (23)	88 ± 15* (18)	93 ± 9* (10)	93 ± 6* (4)
HC ≥ 0.05 cm²	107 ± 8** (46)	106 ± 15** (33)	106 ± 9 (21)	109 ± 12 (7)
Control	110 ± 6 (41)	114 ± 14 (40)	107 ± 9 (45)	

[a]* = $p < 0.001$; ** = $p < 0.05$; HC = hypothyroid children; ( ) = number of individuals studied

indicate where the molecular events that control the growth and maturation of the brain are initiated. However, much further research in this area is needed to comprehend further the relation between thyroid hormones and brain development.

Literature Cited

1. Amur, S. G., Shanker, G., Pieringer, R. A. 1984. Regulation of myelin basic protein (arginine) methyltransferase by thyroid hormone in myelinogenic cultures of cells dissociated from embryonic mouse brain. *J. Neurochem.* 43:494–98

2. Anderson, T. R., Schanberg, S. M. 1975. Effect of thyroxine and cortisol on brain ornithine decarboxylase activity and swimming behavior in developing rat. *Biochem. Pharmacol.* 24:495–501

3. Annunziata, P., Federico, A., D'Amore, I., Corona, R. M., Guazzi, G. C. 1983. Impairment of human brain development: Glycoconjugate and lipid changes in congenital athyroidism. *Early Hum. Dev.* 8:269–78

4. Atterwill, C. K., Atkinson, D. J., Bermudez, I., Balazs, R. 1985. Effect of thyroid hormone and serum on the development of Na$^+$, K$^+$-adenosine triphosphatase and associated ion fluxes in cultures from rat brain. *Neuroscience* 14:361–73

5. Atterwill, C. K., Kingsburg, A., Nicholls, J., Prince, A. 1984. Development of markers for cholinergic neurones in re-aggregate cultures of foetal rats in serum-containing and serum-free media: Effects of triiodothyronine (T$_3$). *Br. J. Pharmacol.* 83:89–102

6. Atterwill, C. K., Reid, J., Athayde, C. M. 1985. Effect of thyroid status on the development of the different molecular forms of Na$^+$, K$^+$-ATPase in rat brain. *Mol. Cell. Endocrinol.* 40:149–58

7. Balazs, R., Brooksbank, B. W. L., Davison, A. N., Eayrs, J. T., Wilson, D. A. 1969. The effect of neonatal thyroidectomy on myelination in the rat brain. *Brain Res.* 15:219–32

8. Bernal, J., Pekonen, F. 1984. Ontogenesis of the nuclear T$_3$ receptor in the human fetal brain. *Endocrinology* 114:677–79

9. Bhat, N. R., Sarlieve, L. L., Subba Rao, G., Pieringer, R. A. 1979. Investigations on myelination in vitro. Regulation by thyroid hormone in cultures of dissociated brain cells from embryonic mice. *J. Biol. Chem.* 254:342–44

10. Bhat, N. R., Shanker, G., Pieringer, R. A. 1981. Investigations on myelination in vitro. Regulation of 2',3'-cyclic nucleotide 3'-phosphohydrolase by thyroid hormone in cultures of dissociated brain cells from embryonic mice. *J. Neurochem.* 37:695–701

11. Chaudhury, S., Chatterjee, D., Sarkar, P. K. 1985. Induction of brain tubulin by triiodothyronine: Dual effect of the hormone on the synthesis and turnover of the protein. *Brain Res.* 339:191–94

12. Chaudhury, S., Sarkar, P. K. 1983. Stimulation of tubulin synthesis by thyroid hormone in the developing rat brain. *Biochim. Biophys. Acta* 763:93–98

13. Coulombe, P., Ruel, R., Dussault, J. H. 1981. Récepteurs nucléaires de la T$_3$ dans le cerveau et le cervelet du rat au cours du développement. *Union Med. Can.* 110:658–61

14. Croskerry, P. G., Smith, G. K., Shepard, B. J., Freeman, K. B. 1973. Perinatal brain DNA in the normal and growth hormone treated rat. *Brain Res.* 52:413–18

15. Curling, T. B. 1850. Two cases of absence of the thyroid body and symetrical swellings of the fat tissues at the side of the neck connected with defective cerebral development. *Med. Chirurg. Trans.* 54:303–6

16. Diez-Guerra, J., Aragon, M. C., Gimenez, C., Valdivieso, F. 1980. Effect of thyroid hormones on the 3-oxoacid CoA-transferase activity in rat brain during development. *Enzyme* 25:106–10

17. DiGiorgio, R. M., Fodale, V., Macaione, S., DeLuca, G. C. 1983. Effects of thyroxine on methionine adenosyltransferase activity in rat cerebral cortex and cerebellum during postnatal development. *J. Neurochem.* 41:607–10

18. Dobbing, J., 1970. Undernutrition and the developing brain. *Am. J. Dis. Child.* 120:411–15

19. Dobbing, J. 1977. The later growth of the brain and its vulnerability. *Pediatrics* 53:2–6

20. Dobbing, J., Smart, J. L. 1974. Vul-

nerability of the developing brain and behaviour. *Br. Med. Bull.* 30:164–68

21. Dupont, A., Dussault, J. H., Rouleau, D., Di Paolo, T., Coulombe, P., et al. 1981. Effect of neonatal thyroid deficiency on the catecholamine, substance P, and thyrotropin-releasing-hormone contents of discrete rat brain nuclei. *Endocrinology* 108:2039–45

22. Eberhardt, N. L., Valcana, T., Timiras, P. S. 1978. Triiodothyronine nuclear receptors: An in vitro comparison of the binding of triiodothyronine to nuclei of adult rat liver, cerebral hemisphere, and anterior pituitary. *Endocrinology* 102: 556–61

23. Escriva, F., Pascual-Leone, A. M., Galan, A., Encinas, J. P. 1983. Circulating glucose, insulin and ketone bodies and enzymes of ketone body utilization in brain mitochondria from suckling rats treated with high L-thyroxine doses. *Rev. Esp. Fisiol.* 39: 363–72

24. Faryna de Raveglia, I., Gomez, C. J., Ghittoni, N. E. 1973. Effects of thyroxine and growth hormone on the lipid composition of the cerebral cortex and the cerebellum of developing rats. *Neurobiology* 3:173–84

25. Fellous, A., Lennon, A. M., Francon, J., Nunez, J. 1979. Thyroid hormones and neurotubule assembly in vitro during brain development. *Eur. J. Biochem.* 101:365–76

26. Flynn, T. J., Deshmukh, D. S., Pieringer, R. A. 1977. Effects of altered thyroid function on galactosyl diacylglycerol metabolism in myelinating rat brain. *J. Biol. Chem.* 252:5864–70

27. Ford, D. H., Cramer, E. B. 1977. Developing nervous system in relation to thyroid hormones. In *Thyroid Hormones and Brain Development,* ed. G. D. Grave, pp. 1–18. New York: Raven

28. Francon, J., Fellous, A., Lennon, A. M., Nunez, J. 1977. Is thyroxine a regulatory signal for neurotubule assembly during brain development? *Nature* 266:188–90

29. Geel, S. E., Gonzales, L. W. 1977. Cerebral cortical ganglioside and glycoprotein metabolism in immature hypothyroidism. *Brain Res.* 128:515–25

30. Glorieux, J., Dussault, J. H., Letarte, J., Guyda, H., Morissette, J. 1983. Preliminary results on the mental development of hypothyroid children detected by the Quebec Screening Program. *J. Pediat.* 102:19–22

31. Glorieux, J., Dussault, J. H., Morissette, J., Desjardins, M., Letarte, J., Guyda, H. 1985. Follow-up at ages 5 and 7 years on mental development in children with hypothyroidism detected by Quebec Screening Program. *J. Pediatr.* 107:913–15

32. Gonzales, L. W., Geel, S. E. 1978. Quantitation and characterization of brain tubulin (colchicine-binding activity) in developing hypothyroid rats. *J. Neurochem.* 30:237–45

33. Gripois, D., Fernandez, C. 1977. Effects of thyroid hormones on the evolution of monoamine oxidase activity in the brain and heart of the developing rat. *Enzyme* 22:378–84

34. Hébert, R., Langlois, J. M., Dussault, J. H. 1985. Permanent defects in rat peripheral auditory function following perinatal hypothyroidism: Determination of a critical period. *Dev. Brain Res.* 23:161–70

35. Hébert, R., Laureau, E., Vanasse, M., Richard, J. E., Glorieux, J., et al. 1986. Auditory brainstem response (ABR) audiometry in congenitally hypothyroid children under early replacement therapy. *Pediatr. Res.* 20:570–73

36. Honegger, P., Lenoir, D. 1980. Triiodothyronine enhancement of neuronal differentiation in aggregating fetal rat brain cells cultured in a chemically defined medium. *Brain Res.* 199:425–34

37. Ientile, R., Macaione, S., Russo, P., Caponetti, A., Ruggeri, P. 1983. Thyroxine effects on polyamine metabolism in rat cerebellum and brain cortex during postnatal development. *Ital. J. Biochem.* 32:9–18

38. Kaplan, M. M., McCann, U. D., Yaskoski, K. A., Larsen, P. R., Leonard, J. L. 1981. Anatomical distribution of phenolic and tyrosyl ring iodothyronine deiodinase in the nervous system of normal and hypothyroid rats. *Endocrinology* 109:397–402

39. Kato, N., Sundmark, V. C., Van Middlesworth, L., Havlicek, V., Friesen, H. G. 1982. Immunoreactive somatostatin and β-endorphin content in the brain of mature rats after neonatal exposure to propylthiouracil. *Endocrinology* 110: 1851–55

40. King, R. A., Smith, R. M., Dreosti, I. E. 1983. Regional effects of hypothyroidism on 5'-nucleotidase and cyclic nucleotide phosphohydrolase activities in developing rat brain. *Dev. Brain Res.* 7:287–94

41. Klein, A. H., Meltzer, S., Kenney, F. N. 1972. Improved prognosis in congenital hypothyroidism treated before age 3 months. *J. Pediatr.* 81:912–15

42. Lakshmanan, J., Mansfield, H., Weich-

sel, M. E., Hoath, S., Scott, S., et al. 1981. Neonatal hypothyroidism—A biochemical disorder of α-tubulin metabolism. *Biochem. Biophys. Res. Commun.* 100:1587–96

43. Legrand, J. 1979. Morphogenetic action of thyroid hormones. *Trends Neurosci.* 2:234–36

44. Legrand, J. 1982–1983. Hormones thyroidiennes et maturation du système nerveux. *J. Physiol. Paris* 78:603–52

45. Lengvari, I., Branch, B. J., Taylor, A. N. 1980. Effects of perinatal thyroxine and/or corticosterone treatment on the ontogenesis of hypothalamic and mesencephalic norepinephrine and dopamine content. *Dev. Neurosci.* 3:59–65

46. Lindholm, D. B. 1984. Thyroxine regulates the activity and the concentration of synaptic plasma membrane Na,K-ATPase in the developing rat brain cortex. *Dev. Brain Res.* 15:83–88

47. Luo, M., Faure, R., Dussault, J. H. 1986. Ontogenesis of nuclear T_3 receptor in primary cultured astrocytes and neurons. *Brain Res.* 381:275–80

48. Major, R. H. 1945. *Classic Descriptions of Disease.* Oxford: Blackwell

49. Meyeroff, W. L. 1979. Hypothyroidism and the ear: Electrophysiological morphological and chemical considerations. *Laryngoscope* 89:1–25

50. Moore, T. J., Lione, A. P., Regen, D. M. 1973. Effect of thyroid hormone on cerebral glucose metabolism in the infant rat. *Am. J. Physiol.* 225:925–29

51. Morreale de Escobar, G., Ruiz-Marcos, A., Escobar del Rey, F. 1983. Thyroid hormone and the developing brain. In *Congenital Hypothyroidism,* ed. J. H. Dussault, P. Walker, pp. 85–126. New York: Dekker

52. Murad, S., Strycharz, G. D., Kishimoto, Y. 1976. α-hydroxylation of lignoceric and nervonic acids in the brain. Effects of altered thyroid function on postnatal development of the hydroxylase activity. *J. Biol. Chem.* 251:5237–41

53. Murray, G. R. 1891. Note on the treatment of myxoedema by hypodermic injections of an extract of the thyroid gland of a sheep. *Br. Med. J.* 2:796–97

54. New England Congenital Hypothyroidism Collaborative. 1984. Characteristics of infantile hypothyroidism discovered on neonatal screening. *J. Pediatr.* 104:539–44

55. New England Congenital Hypothyroidism Collaborative. 1985. Neonatal hypothyroidism screening: Status of patients at 6 years of age. *J. Pediatr.* 107:915–19

56. Noguchi, T., Sugisaki, T. 1984. Hypomyelination in the cerebrum of the congenitally hypothyroid mouse (hyt). *J. Neurochem.* 42:891–93

57. Noguchi, T., Sugisaki, T., Tsukada, Y. 1982. Postnatal action of growth and thyroid hormones on the retarded cerebral myelinogenesis of Snell dwarf mice (dw). *J. Neurochem.* 38:257–63

58. Oliver, C., Giraud, P., Gillioz, P., Conte-Delvolx, B., Usategui, R. 1980. Brain TRH levels during development of the rat, in neonatal hypothyroidism and after caloric deprivation. *Biol. Neonate* 37:1–7

59. Oppenheimer, J. H. 1979. Thyroid hormone action at the cellular level. *Science* 203:971–79

60. Osler, W. 1898. *The Principles and Practice of Medicine,* pp. 840–43. New York: Appleton. 3rd. ed.

61. Pasquini, J. M., Faryna de Raveglia, I. A., Capitman, N., Soto, E. F. 1981. Neonatal hypothyroidism and early undernutrition in the rat: Defective maturation of structural membrane components in the central nervous system. *Neurochem. Res.* 6:979–91

62. Patel, A. J., Smith, R. M., Kingsbury, A. E., Hunt, A., Balazs, R. 1980. Effects of thyroid state on brain development: Muscarinic acetylcholine and GABA receptors. *Brain Res.* 198:389–402

63. Patel, M. S. 1979. Influence of neonatal hypothyroidism on the development of ketone-body metabolizing enzymes in rat brain. *Biochem. J.* 184:169–72

64. Raiti, S., Newns, G. A. 1971. Cretinism: Early diagnosis and its relation to mental prognosis. *Arch. Dis. Child.* 46:692–95

65. Rajan, R. R., Datyare, S. S. 1982. Effect of 3,5,3'-triiodothyronine on cellular growth and oxygen consumption in neonatal rat brain. *Experientia* 38:1110–14

66. Rastogi, R. B., Lapierre, Y. D., Singhal, R. L. 1979. Diazepam modifies L-triiodothyronine-stimulated changes in behaviour and the metabolism of brain norepinephrine, dopamine, and 5-hydroxytryptamine—a possible mechanism of action. *J. Psychiat. Res.* 15:7–20

67. Rastogi, R. B., Singhal, R. L. 1979. Effect of neonatal hypothyroidism and delayed L-triiodothyronine treatment on behavioural activity and norepinephrine and dopamine biosynthetic systems in discrete regions of rat brain. *Psychopharmacol.* 62:287–93

68. Ritter, F. N. 1967. The effects of

hypothyroidism upon the ear, nose and throat. *Laryngoscope* 77:1427–79

69. Ruel, J., Chénard, C., Coulombe, P., Dussault, J. H. 1984. Thyroid hormones modulate ornithine decarboxylase in the immature rat cerebellum. *Can. J. Physiol. Pharmacol.* 62:1279–83

70. Ruel, J., Dussault, J. H. 1985. Triiodothyronine increases glutamine synthetase activity in primary cultures of rat cerebellum. *Dev. Brain Res.* 21:83–88

71. Ruel, J., Faure, R., Dussault, J. H. 1985. Regional distribution of nuclear T_3 receptors in rat brain and evidence for preferential localization in neurons. *J. Endocrinol. Invest.* 8:343–48

72. Ruel, J., Gavaret, J. M., Luo, M., Dussault, J. H. 1986. Regulation of protein phosphorylation by triiodothyronine (T_3) in neural cell cultures: I. Astrocytes. *Mol. Cell. Endocrinol.* 45:223–32

73. Ruel, J., Gavaret, J. M., Luo, M., Dussault, J. H. 1986. Regulation of protein phosphorylation by triiodothyronine (T_3) in neural cell cultures: II. Neurons. *Mol. Cell. Endocrinol.* 45:233–40

74. Ruiz-Marcos, A., Salas, J., Sanchez-Toscano, F., Morreale de Escobar, F., Morreale de Escobar, G. 1983. Effect of neonatal and adult-onset hypothyroidism on pyramidal cells of the rat auditory cortex. *Dev. Brain Res.* 9:205–13

75. Ruiz-Marcos, A., Sanchez-Toscano, F., Escobar del Rey, F., Morreale de Escobar, G. 1979. Severe hypothyroidism and the maturation of the rat cerebral cortex. *Brain Res.* 162:315–29

76. Sarlieve, L. L., Bouchon, R., Koehl, C., Neskovic, N. M. 1983. Cerebroside and sulfatide biosynthesis in the brain of Snell dwarf mouse: Effects of thyroxine and growth hormone in the early postnatal period. *J. Neurochem.* 40:1058–62

77. Schwartz, H. L., Oppenheimer, J. H. 1978. Nuclear triiodothyronine receptor sites in the brain: Probable identity with hepatic receptors and regional distribution. *Endocrinology* 103:267–73

78. Schwartz, H. L., Oppenheimer, J. H. 1978. Ontogenesis of 3,5,3'-triiodothyronine receptors in neonatal rat brain: Dissociation between receptor concentration and stimulation of oxygen consumption by 3,5,3'-triiodothyronine. *Endocrinology* 103:943–48

79. Shanker, G., Amur, S. G., Pieringer, R. A. 1985. Investigations on myelinogenesis in vitro: A study of the critical period at which thyroid hormone exerts its maximum regulatory effect on the developmental expression of two myelin associated markers in cultured brain cells from embryonic mice. *Neurochem. Res.* 10:617–25

80. Shanker, G., Pieringer, R. A. 1983. Effect of thyroid hormone on the synthesis of sialosyl-galactosylceramide (GM_4) in myelinogenic cultures of cells dissociated from embryonic mouse brain. *Dev. Brain Res.* 6:169–74

81. Smith, D. W., Blizzard, R. M., Wilkins, L. 1957. The mental prognosis in hypothyroidism of infancy in childhood. *Pediatrics* 19:1011–22

82. Smith, R. M., Patel, A. J., Kingsbury, A. E., Hunt, A., Balazs, R. 1980. Effects of thyroid state on brain development: β-adrenergic receptors and 5'-nucleotidase activity. *Brain Res.* 198:375–87

83. Sugisaki, T., Noguchi, T., Tsukada, Y. 1985. Cerebral myelinogenesis in the Snell dwarf mouse: Stimulatory effects of GH and T_4 restricted to the first 20 days of postnatal life. *Neurochem. Res.* 10:767–78

84. Takahashi, T., Goto, K., Sudo, S., Suzuki, M. 1981. Effects of L-triiodothyronine on tubulin content in developing male and female rat brain. *Endocrinol. Jpn.* 28:799–808

85. Uziel, A., Rabie, A., Marot, M. 1980. The effect of hypothyroidism on the onset of cochlear potentials in developing rats. *Brain Res.* 182:172–75

86. Valcana, T., Einstein, E. R., Csejtey, J., Dalal, K. B., Timiras, P. S. 1975. Influence of thyroid hormones on myelin proteins in the developing rat brain. *J. Neurol. Sci.* 25:19–27

87. Valcana, T., Timiras, P. S. 1969. Effect of hypothyroidism on ionic metabolism and Na-K activated ATP phosphohydrolase activity in the developing rat brain. *J. Neurochem.* 16:935–43

88. Vanderschueren-Lodeweyckx, M., Debruyne, F., Dooms, L., Eggermont, E., Eekels, R. 1983. Sensorineural hearing loss in sporadic congenital hypothyroidism. *Arch. Dis. Child.* 58:419–22

89. Walravens, P., Chase, H. P. 1969. Influence of thyroid on formation of myelin lipids. *J. Neurochem.* 16:1477–84

90. Walters, S. N., Morell, P. 1981. Effects of altered thyroid states on myelinogenesis. *J. Neurochem.* 36:1792–1801

91. Wharton, T. 1656. Adenographia sive glandularum totius corporis descriptio. London

92. Wysocki, S. J., Segal, W. 1972. Influence of thyroid hormones on enzyme activities of myelinating rat central nervous tissues. *Eur. J. Biochem.* 28:183–89

Ann. Rev. Physiol. 1987. 49:335–47

INSULIN IN THE BRAIN[1]

Denis G. Baskin

Departments of Medicine and Biological Structure, University of Washington, and Veterans Administration Medical Center, Seattle, Washington 98108

Dianne P. Figlewicz and Stephen C. Woods

Departments of Psychology and Medicine, University of Washington, Seattle, Washington 98195

Daniel Porte, Jr.

Department of Medicine, University of Washington, and Veterans Administration Medical Center, Seattle, Washington 98108

Daniel M. Dorsa

Departments of Medicine and Pharmacology, University of Washington, and Geriatric Research, Education and Clinical Center, Veterans Administration Medical Center, Seattle, Washington 98108

INTRODUCTION

The central nervous system (CNS) has traditionally been considered to be independent of the influence of insulin. However, in the last few years new evidence has indicated that insulin and its receptors are present in the CNS, and physiological, behavioral, and developmental influences of central insulin on the CNS have been documented. There is evidence that plasma insulin has relatively rapid access to cerebrospinal fluid (CSF), that CSF insulin concentrations affect feeding behavior and body weight, and that insulin may act as a CNS neuromodulator. The present review focuses on important unanswered questions and problems regarding insulin in the CNS and emphasizes literature published in the last three years. References to earlier papers can be found in these articles, and in general only the most recent work from various laboratories is cited here.

EVIDENCE FOR INSULIN IN THE BRAIN

Radioimmunoassay

Widely divergent values for concentrations of extractable immunoreactive insulin (IRI) in the brain have come from radioimmunoassays from at least eight different laboratories (3, 39, 53, 63). This variability has contributed to the controversy and confusion surrounding the origins of insulin in the CNS, and there is still no general agreement about actual brain IRI levels. Havrankova and coworkers originally reported rat brain IRI concentrations that were 25 times plasma levels, with a range of 3–91 ng/g wet weight, although this group later published values in the 8–9 ng/g range (30a, 39, 46a). In contrast, with a radioimmunoassay detecting 2.8 pg insulin/tube in acid-ethanol extracts of whole rat brain, we found an average IRI concentration of 0.30 ng/g (corrected for recovery), which was 25% of plasma concentrations (3). Other recently published values for rat brain IRI fall in the 0.2–8 ng/g range. IRI in rabbit and dog brain extracts is less than 1 ng/g (63). The variability in rat brain IRI values from different laboratories has been attributed to different methods of extraction and concentration and to different antibodies and insulin standards used in the radioimmunoassays (39, 53, 63).

Biochemistry

IRI in acid-ethanol extracts of rat brain is immunologically similar to pancreatic insulin (3, 6, 63) and elutes with an apparent molecular weight similar to that of pancreatic insulin when subjected to gel filtration (39, 63). It also shows retention times similar to those of authentic pancreatic insulin when analyzed with reverse phase HPLC (10), and its receptor binding and biological activity are like those of native insulin (39). However, an IRI-like peptide that does not coelute with pancreatic insulin and that exhibits more nonpolar properties has been detected in cultures of fetal mouse brain cells (10).

Immunocytochemistry

Immunocytochemical detection of IRI and C-peptide in the cytoplasm of numerous neurons in tissue slices (7, 22, 39) and cultures (44, 59) has been claimed by several laboratories. These reports have been interpreted as evidence for insulinergic neurons in the brain. However, the primary antisera used in these immunocytochemical studies were relatively concentrated, generally 1 : 20–1 : 200. Concentrated antisera may be necessary if the IRI is present in the brain at low concentrations, but there is a high probability of false positive results due to cross-reactivity or nonspecific binding. Recently, LeRoith and coworkers (39) reported that all guinea pig sera produce "staining" of neurons at a dilution of 1 : 50 whether or not the cells contain insulin antibodies. They concluded that the insulinlike immunoreactivity in neurons that was shown in their original paper probably did not represent insulin. This agrees with our immunostaining results, which indicated that immunocyto-chemically detectable insulin is probably not present in neurons of the rat brain (5). The reports of insulinlike immunoreactivity in neurons of in-vertebrates (39) is interesting, although it has yet to be shown that this substance is identical with any vertebrate pancreatic insulin.

LOCALIZATION OF INSULIN IN THE BRAIN

The concentrations of extractable IRI are not uniform throughout various brain regions. However, we found that the absolute values of IRI con-centrations did not differ by more than a factor of two or three among the gross regions sampled (3). The olfactory bulbs and hypothalamus consistently have the highest IRI concentrations (3, 39, 63). The genetically obese Zucker rat is an exception to this rule; we have shown an almost complete absence of IRI in its olfactory bulbs and hypothalamus (4). Since these rats also have fewer insulin receptors in their olfactory bulbs (23), it is tempting to speculate that a major portion of IRI measured in brain extracts represents insulin bound to neural insulin receptors. However, the cellular locations of the IRI that can be extracted from the CNS are not known for sure, and some of it may represent IRI in brain interstitial fluid.

An unanswered question is whether any of the extractable IRI represents insulin synthesized in neurons. If so, regional differences in IRI content could be interpreted as a reflection of differences in the numbers or activity of insulin-secreting neurons. However, the immunocytochemical data showing numerous brain cells that contain IRI (7, 22, 39) seem incompatible with the very low concentrations of IRI present in brain extracts (3, 4, 63). If neurons do in fact secrete insulin, it should not be difficult to demonstrate IRI in a neuron by electron microscopic immunostaining. This has not been reported, even in the case of neurons shown to be filled with insulinlike immunoreactiv-ity by light microscopic immunocytochemistry. Evidence that IRI in brain extracts represents insulin extracted from neuronal cell bodies is still in-conclusive. The data are more compatible with the view that extractable brain IRI is associated with receptors or is carried in extracellular fluid (5, 63).

ORIGIN OF INSULIN IN THE BRAIN

Synthesis by the Brain

Two points of view have emerged regarding the cellular origin of insulin in the brain: (a) It is synthesized by brain cells, or (b) it is taken up from plasma. Several lines of evidence have been interpreted as indicating a neural origin for brain IRI, and this hypothesis was recently reviewed (39, 63). Evidence for both immunoreactive proinsulin in brain extracts and insulin mRNA production in the brain is negative (48a, 63), and electron microscopic immunocytochemical evidence for IRI in secretory granules of neurons has not appeared. However, proinsulinlike immunoreactivity has been detected in cultures of fetal mouse brain cells (11). We cannot exclude the possibility that some neural cells may produce an insulinlike molecule at low concentrations, perhaps by a biosynthetic processing mechanism that does not involve storage in a secretory granule. However, these cells remain to be positively identified.

Uptake from Plasma

Despite the widely held belief that the blood-brain barrier (BBB) is relatively impermeable to the passage of insulin, evidence shows that insulin rapidly enters the CSF of several species (62), including humans (58). Furthermore, parallel changes in CSF and plasma IRI concentrations are well documented (62). We recently found that genetically obese Zucker rats, which have high plasma IRI levels, also have significantly higher CSF IRI levels than do their normoglycemic, lean littermates (50). It has been suggested that insulin may cross the BBB by a receptor-mediated transport system in endothelial cells of brain microvessels (26, 43). Labeled insulin injected into plasma is concentrated on neuron endings in circumventricular organs lacking a BBB, and in some cases it is transported to sites deeper within the brain (55). We have shown that labeled insulin injected into CSF is taken up into hypothalamic tissue surrounding the third ventricle (5). Thus, insulin has access to the brain at circumventricular organs lacking the BBB and is also transported across the BBB into the brain, where it enters neural tissue directly or is taken up into neural tissue from CSF.

INSULIN RECEPTORS IN THE BRAIN

Identification

Investigations of brain insulin receptors are providing insight into the location of insulin action in the brain and the role of insulin in brain function. Evidence that binding sites with the pharmacological characteristics of insulin receptors are present in the brain was reviewed in detail by Havrankova et al (30). A number of papers recently appeared that confirm the conclusion that different regions of the brain have markedly different insulin receptor concentrations (23, 37, 48, 65). Like extractable brain insulin, insulin receptors are concentrated in the olfactory bulb of the rat brain, but relatively high insulin binding is present throughout the limbic system. Insulin receptors are also present in cultures of mixed brain cells and neurons (10, 13, 14, 57), glia (17, 18), retinoblastoma cells (64), and brain endothelial cells (26, 43, 56).

Localization by Quantitative Autoradiography

The cellular location of brain insulin receptors has been probed by autoradiography with radioiodinated insulin. van Houten, Posner, and associates showed the presence of specific uptake sites for plasma insulin in circumventricular organs lacking a BBB (such as the median eminence) and in brain microvessels (55, 56). Their data are consistent with the hypothesis that insulin receptors on neuronal endings in circumventricular organs mediate the action of plasma insulin in the CNS. However, the in vivo method for labeling insulin receptors labels insulin receptors only on the brain side of the BBB.

We have approached the problem of localizing brain insulin receptors with in vitro quantitative autoradiography (QAR). Thawed cryostat sections of rat brain mounted on slides were incubated in labeled insulin under equilibrium binding conditions, which permitted equal access of the label to receptors on both sides of the BBB. The autoradiographic films underwent computer digital image analysis to yield the concentration of bound insulin in small, anatomically defined regions of the brain. With the QAR approach, we found evidence for high- and low-affinity insulin receptors in the external plexiform layer of the olfactory bulb (2), where an earlier report had indicated insulin binding sites are located (39). This localization of insulin receptors suggests that insulin may modulate synaptic activity related to neural processing of olfactory stimuli. Our QAR studies also revealed a high density of insulin receptors in the choroid plexuses of the rat brain (1). More recently, Davidson et al used QAR with competition binding to verify that these insulin binding sites in the choroid plexus are specific for insulin rather than IGF-1 (20). The presence of insulin receptors in the choroid plexus suggests that the transport functions of the choroid plexus, as well as the regulation of CSF composition, may be under the influence of insulin in plasma and CSF, and raises the possibility that the choroid plexus is a site of insulin transport across the BBB.

Recent QAR studies by Corp et al revealed that specific binding sites for insulin are concentrated at many other discrete microanatomical locations throughout the brain (19, 19a). These sites include hypothalamic nuclei which have been implicated in diverse neuroendocrine mechanisms and the neural control of feeding. The physiological significance of insulin binding in these regions is not known, but insulin may have widespread modulatory influences on a variety of neural pathways. In the circumventricular organs, which reportedly have receptors for plasma insulin (55), we find relatively low insulin binding compared with the rest of the brain (19a). In contrast, Bohannon et al found very high concentrations of receptors for IGF-1 in the rat median eminence using QAR (12), and our QAR data suggest that the major neuroanatomical loci of insulin receptors and IGF-1 receptors are distinctly different (12, 19a).

Characteristics

The structural differences reported in the neural insulin receptor indicate it is an insulin receptor subtype. The specificity of this receptor is similar to that of the receptor found in peripheral tissues; however, it may have a higher affinity for insulin analogs that mediate growth activity (28) and a lower affinity for native insulin (7, 57). Unlike the peripheral insulin receptor and that found on brain microvessels, the neural receptor does not show negative cooperativity (28, 57).

Relatively few studies have investigated the regulation of brain insulin receptors. No relationship was found between altered plasma insulin levels and insulin binding to brain membranes of hyperinsulinemic obese mice and of rats made diabetic with streptozotocin. These observations led to the conclusion that brain insulin receptors are not regulated by plasma insulin (30, 30a). In contrast, intracerebroventricular infusions of insulin into the brain of newborn rabbits resulted in a 60% decrease in insulin binding to brain membrane homogenates (21). This result raises the possibility that brain insulin receptors are regulated by CSF insulin. Information about the regulation of the brain insulin receptor is fragmentary, however, and generalizations about the in vivo situation are probably premature.

Evidence from studies on cultured brain cells from neonatal rat indicates that glial cell insulin receptors down-regulate in response to elevated insulin concentrations in vitro, whereas neuronal insulin receptors do not (14, 17). This finding makes it difficult to interpret the in vivo studies in which brain insulin receptor regulation was measured by membrane-binding methods. Membrane homogenates prepared from grossly dissected brain regions contain not only varying proportions of neurons and glia, but also contain functionally different neuronal cells and nuclei, fiber tracts, circumventricular organs, and possibly endothelial cells. The relative contributions of insulin receptors associated with these various structural components of the brain to the binding measured in membrane homogenates are difficult to assess. This problem seriously limits the physiological interpretation of receptor regulation data derived from membrane homogenates from the brain because of that organ's structural complexity. QAR techniques promise to overcome some of these problems. We have shown that binding of insulin and its analogs can be reproducibly measured in very small anatomical locations such as the external plexiform layer of the olfactory bulb (2), the choroid plexus (1, 20), the median eminence (12), and discrete hypothalamic nuclei (19, 19a, 59a). Future studies will undoubtedly use QAR methods to investigate regulation of insulin receptors in specific microanatomical sites within the brain.

The brain insulin receptor is also structurally distinct from insulin receptors in peripheral tissues (28, 31). The alpha subunit of the brain receptor has a lower molecular weight than the alpha subunit of nonneural insulin receptors (28, 31, 32, 39a). This difference is attributed to altered carbohydrate residues, particularly N-linked glycosylation (30b). The beta subunit is also slightly smaller than its nonneural counterpart (45). Like the peripheral insulin receptor, however, the neural insulin receptor has tyrosine kinase activity, and insulin stimulates the autophosphorylation of the receptor's beta subunit (27, 45).

FUNCTIONS OF INSULIN IN THE BRAIN

Insulin has been shown to elicit diverse physiological, developmental, and behavioral responses when introduced into the brain or into culture systems. In this section we summarize some of the recent evidence supporting the conclusion that insulin is an important regulatory peptide in the CNS.

Glucose Utilization

Studies with 2-deoxyglucose uptake support the traditional view that the brain is not responsive to insulin in vivo with respect to whole organ glucose uptake (34), but recent data are challenging this concept. Insulin receptors mediate glucose uptake and stimulate macromolecular synthesis in cultured astrocytes (17, 18), as they do in fat cells. There is also evidence that insulin stimulates glycogen synthesis and glucose metabolism in neurons, and data suggest that it may influence glucose transfer across the BBB in humans (33). Insulin is believed to stimulate the uptake of the glucose analog gold thioglucose by neurons in specific regions of the hypothalamus (see 62). However, other data suggest that insulin has a direct effect on suppressing glucose utilization in the medial basal hypothalamus and elsewhere in the brain (29). Thus, the role of insulin in glucose uptake and metabolism by cells in the CNS is still open to question, and much remains to be learned about this problem.

Neuronal Transmission

Insulin inhibits firing of neurons in the hippocampus (42) and hypothalamus (41, 49). Insulin also alters the response of single units in the olfactory bulb and amygdala to olfactory stimuli (16). Several lines of evidence indicate that insulin may influence synaptic activity. Insulin promotes electrical coupling between sympathetic neurons in culture (38, 60). Insulin modulates

monoamine uptake in cultured neuronal cells (13) and stimulates synaptosomal uptake of neurotransmitter amino acids (46). Insulin increases
catecholamine turnover and release from brain cells (47). High concentrations
of insulin receptors in synaptic layers such as the external plexiform layer of
the olfactory bulb (2) also suggest that insulin may modulate synaptic activity.
Insulin has also been shown to stimulate Na,K-ATPase activity in rat hippocampus (8). Evidence that insulin stimulates membrane ion transport and
hyperpolarization (40) may explain the pronounced inhibitory actions of
insulin on neuronal electrical activity. Therefore, insulin may modulate
neuronal transmission by altering synaptic membrane potentials.

CNS Development

Evidence is increasing that insulin has an important growth-promoting role in
brain development. Insulin stimulates enzyme activity and synthesis of protein, RNA, and DNA in cultured neurons and glial cells (see 18). Insulin also
promotes neuronal regeneration in cell cultures from embryonic mouse brain
(9). Insulin binding in the brain of rats changes during growth and development (36) and is highest in newborn rats (37, 39a). The growth-promoting
effects of insulin in the CNS may be due to interaction with the IGF-1 receptor
(18).

Feeding and Body Weight

Recent evidence indicates that insulin in plasma enters the brain and functions
as a satiety signal to the CNS (62). Insulin infused into CSF inhibits feeding
and results in loss of body weight in baboons (61) and rats (15, 35). We
recently found that CSF insulin levels in obese Zucker rats were disproportionately low as compared with their lean littermates that were made
equally hyperinsulinemic by plasma insulin infusion (51, 52). Extractable IRI
(4) and insulin binding (23) are reduced in the brain of obese Zucker rats,
particularly in the olfactory bulbs and hypothalamus. The Wistar-Kyoto fatty
rat, which has the same allele for obesity, also has reduced brain insulin
binding (24). We recently showed that the obese Zucker rat is insensitive to
the satiety effect of CSF insulin (35). Thus a loss of brain insulin receptors, as
well as defective transport of plasma insulin into CSF, may contribute to the
pathogenesis of obesity in these animals.

In addition to its effects on feeding and body weight, CSF insulin influences other peripheral metabolic events. For example, infusion of insulin
into the CSF stimulates the vagal nerves to the endocrine pancreas and
increases plasma insulin levels (43a, 54a). These results suggest that insulin
in the CSF interacts with central autonomic pathways involved in the regulation of peripheral nutrient homeostasis. The CNS cellular sites of action of
insulin in these processes, as well as the anatomical pathways involved, are

incompletely understood. The hypothalamus, which is well known to be involved in the neural regulation of feeding and body weight, is of special interest because it contains insulin-sensitive neurons (41, 49) and insulin receptors (19a). Several studies show that insulin injections into the hypothalamus cause peripheral hypoglycemia (54, 62). Further, insulin affects turnover of hypothalamic catecholamines (47), which have been shown to influence feeding behavior. However, the presence of a large number of insulin receptors in the olfactory bulb, where insulin alters the electrical response of neurons to odors (16), also suggests that insulin may interact with neural pathways involved in feeding and metabolism at extrahypothalamic locations. For example, injection of insulin directly into the amygdala region produces changes in hepatic acetate metabolism in rabbits (48b). In view of the large numbers of peptides and neurotransmitters shown to affect feeding when administered centrally, it is likely that insulin acts in concert with other neuroactive substances to regulate body weight. Indeed, we have shown that central insulin modulates the ability of cholecystokinin to suppress feeding behavior (25). Future studies hold promise of understanding the precise interrelationship between insulin and the neural basis for feeding, which may lead to new strategies for treatment of human obesity.

CONCLUSIONS

The brain can no longer be considered to be an insulin-insensitive organ. The weight of evidence leaves little room for doubt that the brain contains insulin and insulin receptors and that insulin is taken up relatively quickly into CSF from plasma across the blood-brain barrier. Whether insulin is synthesized by cells in the CNS is still unproven. Therefore, insulin may be unique among the numerous gastroenteropancreatic peptides found in the brain in that it is probably not made in the CNS. A nonneural origin of brain insulin is compatible with its proposed function as a peripheral satiety signal acting within the CNS. The insulin receptors found in the CNS undoubtedly mediate central physiological and behavioral actions of insulin. However, much remains to be learned about the cellular locations of brain insulin receptors, and their mode of regulation is not yet well characterized. Other unsolved problems regarding insulin in the CNS include: (*a*) its role in brain development; (*b*) its influence on the choroid plexus; (*c*) the cellular mechanism of insulin transport across the blood-brain barrier; (*d*) neural pathways involved in the satiety effect of CSF insulin; (*e*) how binding of insulin to CNS receptors is translated into behavioral changes such as reduction in feeding; (*f*) the possible modulation of synaptic transmission by insulin; (*g*) the central pathways involved in the effects of CSF insulin on autonomic activity. These problems offer a fertile field for future investigations on the roles of insulin in brain function.

ACKNOWLEDGMENTS

Our research has been supported by NIH grants AM12829 (DP), AM17844 (SCW), and AM17047 (Diabetes Research Center, University of Washington); by a Career Development Award from the American Diabetes Association (DPF); and by the Veterans Administration (DGB, DMD, DP). We thank Louise Parry for technical assistance in preparation of this manuscript.

Literature Cited

1. Baskin, D. G., Brewitt, B., Corp, E., Davidson, D., Paquette, T., et al. 1986. Quantitative autoradiographic evidence for insulin receptors in the choroid plexus of the rat brain. *Diabetes* 35: 246–49

2. Baskin, D. G., Davidson, D. A., Corp, E. S., Lewellen, T., Graham, M. 1986. An inexpensive microcomputer digital imaging system for densitometry: Quantitative autoradiography of insulin receptors with ^{125}I and LKB Ultrofilm. *J. Neurosci. Meth.* 16:119–29

3. Baskin, D. G., Porte, D. Jr., Guest, K., Dorsa, D. M. 1983. Regional concentrations of insulin in the rat brain. *Endocrinology* 112:898–903

4. Baskin, D. G., Stein, L. J., Ikeda, H., Woods, S. C., Figlewicz, D. P., et al. 1985. Genetically obese Zucker rats have abnormally low brain insulin content. *Life Sci.* 36:627–33

5. Baskin, D. G., Woods, S. C., West, D. B., van Houten, M., Posner, B. I., Dorsa, D. M., Porte, D. Jr. 1983. Immunocytochemical detection of insulin in rat hypothalamus and its possible uptake from cerebrospinal fluid. *Endocrinology* 113:1818–25

6. Benoliel, J. J., Carayon, A., Jean-Joseph, P., Legrand, J. C., Cesselin, F. 1984. Studies on the presence of insulin in rat brain. *Neurochem. Int.* 6:651–57

7. Bernstein, H. G., Dorn, A., Reiser, M., Ziegler, M. 1984. Cerebral insulin-like immunoreactivity in rats and mice. *Acta Histochem.* 74:33–36

8. Bernstein, H. G., Poeggel, G., Dorn, A., Luppa, H., Ziegler, M. 1981. Insulin stimulates sodium-potassium activated ATPase from rat hippocampus. *Experientia* 37:434–35

9. Bhat, N. R. 1983. Insulin dependent neurite outgrowth in cultured embryonic mouse brain cells. *Dev. Brain Res.* 11:315–18

10. Birch, N. P., Christie, D. L., Renwick, A. G. C. 1984. Immunoreactive insulin from mouse brain cells in culture and whole rat brain. *Biochem. J.* 218:19–27

11. Birch, N. P., Christie, D. L., Renwick, A. G. C. 1984. Proinsulin-like material in mouse foetal brain cell cultures. *Fed. Eur. Biochem. Soc.* 168:299–302

12. Bohannon, N. J., Figlewicz, D. P., Corp, E. S., Wilcox, B. J., Porte, D. Jr., Baskin, D. G. 1986. Identification of binding sites for an insulin-like growth factor (IGF-1) in the median eminence of the rat brain by quantitative autoradiography. *Endocrinology* 119: 943–45

13. Boyd, F. T., Clarke, D. W., Muther, T. F., Raizada, M. K. 1985. Insulin receptors and insulin modulation of norepinephrine uptake in neuronal cultures from rat brain. *J. Biol. Chem.* 260: 15880–84

14. Boyd, F. T., Raizada, M. K. 1983. Effects of insulin and tunicamycin on neuronal insulin receptors in culture. *Am. J. Physiol.* 245:C283–87

15. Brief, D. J., Davis, J. D. 1984. Reduction of food intake and body weight by chronic intraventricular insulin infusion. *Brain Res. Bull.* 12:571–75

16. Cain, D. P. 1975. Effects of insulin injection on responses of olfactory bulb and amygdala single units to odors. *Brain Res.* 99:69–83

17. Clarke, D. W., Boyd, F. T., Kappy, M. S., Raizada, M. K. 1985. Insulin binds to specific receptors and stimulates 2-deoxy-D-glucose uptake in cultured glial cells from rat brain. *J. Biol. Chem.* 259:11672–75

18. Clarke, D. W., Boyd, F. T., Kappy, M. S., Raizada, M. K. 1985. Insulin stimulates macromolecular synthesis in cultured glial cells from rat brain. *Am. J. Physiol.* 249:C484–89

19. Corp, E. S., Davidson, D. A., Figlewicz, D. P., Dorsa, D. M., Woods, S. C., Baskin, D. G. 1985. Insulin binding sites are widely distributed in rat brain: In vitro quantitative receptor autoradiography. *Soc. Neurosci. Abstr.* 11: 54

19a. Corp, E. S., Woods, S. C., Porte, D. Jr., Dorsa, D. M., Figlewicz, D. P., Baskin, D. G. 1986. Localization of I-insulin binding sites in the rat hypothalamus by quantitative autoradiography. *Neurosci. Lett.* 70:17–22

20. Davidson, D. A., Corp, E. S., Figlewicz, D. P., Woods, S. C., Porte, D. Jr., et al. 1985. Characterization of insulin receptors in the choroid plexus of the rat brain by quantitative autoradiography and computer densitometry. *Soc. Neurosci. Abstr.* 11:415

21. Devaskar, S. U., Holekamp, N. 1984. Insulin down regulates neonatal brain insulin receptors. *Biochem. Biophys. Res. Commun.* 120:359–67

22. Dorn, A., Rinne, A., Hahn, H. J., Bernstein, H. G., Ziegler, M. 1982. C-peptide immunoreactive neurons in human brain. *Acta Histochem.* 70: 326–30

23. Figlewicz, D. P., Dorsa, D. M., Stein, L. J., Baskin, D. G., Paquette, T., et al. 1985. Brain and liver insulin binding is decreased in Zucker rats carrying the 'fa' gene. *Endocrinology* 117:1537–43

24. Figlewicz, D. P., Ikeda, H., Hunt, T. R., Stein, L. J., Dorsa, D. M., et al. 1986. Brain insulin binding is decreased in Wistar-Kyoto rats carrying the 'fa' gene. *Peptides* 7:61–65

25. Figlewicz, D. P., Stein, L. J., West, D., Porte, D. Jr., Woods, S. C. 1986. Intracisternal insulin alters sensitivity to CCK-induced meal suppression in baboons. *Am. J. Physiol.* 250:R856–60

26. Frank, H. J. L., Pardridge, W. M. 1983. Insulin binding to brain microvessels. *Adv. Metab. Disorders* 10:291–302

27. Gammeltoft, S., Kowalski, A., Fehlmann, M., van Obberghen, E. 1984. Insulin receptors in rat brain: Insulin stimulates phosphorylation of its receptor β-subunit. *Fed. Eur. Biochem. Soc.* 172:87–90

28. Gammeltoft, S., Staun-Olsen, P., Ottesen, B., Fahrenkrug, J. 1984. Insulin receptors in rat brain cortex. Kinetic evidence for a receptor subtype in the central nervous system. *Peptides* 5:937–44

29. Grunstein, H. S., James, D. E., Storlien, L. H., Smythe, G. A., Kraegen, E. W. 1985. Hyperinsulinemia suppresses glucose utilization in specific brain regions: In vivo studies using the euglycemic clamp in the rat. *Endocrinology* 116:604–10

30. Havrankova, J., Roth, J., Brownstein, M. J. 1983. Insulin receptors in brain. See Ref. 26, pp. 259–68

30a. Havrankova, J., Roth, J., Brownstein, M. 1979. Concentrations of insulin and insulin receptors in the brain are independent of peripheral insulin levels. *J. Clin. Invest.* 64:636–42

30b. Heidenreich, K. A., Brandenburg, D. 1986. Oligosaccharide heterogeneity of insulin receptors. Comparison of N-linked glycosylation of insulin receptors in adipocytes and brain. *Endocrinology* 118:1835–42

31. Heidenreich, K. A., Zahniser, N. R., Berhanu, P., Brandenburg, D., Olefsky, J. M. 1983. Structural differences between insulin receptors in the brain and peripheral target tissues. *J. Biol. Chem.* 258:8527–30

32. Hendricks, S. A., Agardh, C. D., Taylor, S. I., Roth, J. 1984. Unique features of the insulin receptor in rat brain. *J. Neurochem.* 42:1302–9

33. Herz, M. M., Paulson, O. B. 1983. Glucose transfer across the blood-brain barrier. See Ref. 26, pp. 177–192

34. Hom, F. G., Goodner, C. J., Berrie, M. A. 1984. A (³H)2-deoxyglucose method for comparing rates of glucose metabolism and insulin responses among rat tissues in vivo. Validation of the model and the absence of an insulin effect on brain. *Diabetes* 33:141–52

35. Ikeda, H., West, D. B., Pustek, J. J., Figlewicz, D. P., Greenwood, M. R. C., et al. 1986. Intraventricular insulin reduces food intake and body weight of lean but not obese Zucker rats. *Appetite* In press

36. Kappy, M. S., Raizada, M. K. 1983. Insulin binding in the brain correlates with brain growth and development in the rat. *Brain Res.* 249:390–95

37. Kappy, M., Sellinger, S., Raizada, M. 1984. Insulin binding in four regions of the developing rat brain. *J. Neurochem.* 42:198–203

38. Kessler, J. A., Spray, D. C., Saez, J. C., Bennett, M. V. L. 1984. Determination of synaptic phenotype: Insulin and cAMP independently initiate development of electrotonic coupling between cultured sympathetic neurons. *Proc. Natl. Acad. Sci. USA* 81:6235–39

39. LeRoith, D., Hendricks, S. A., Lesniak, M. A., Rishi, S., Becker, K. L., et al. 1983. Insulin in brain and other extrapancreatic tissues of vertebrates and non-vertebrates. See Ref. 26, pp. 304–40

39a. Lowe, W. L., Boyd, F. T., Clarke, D. W., Raizada, M. K., Hart, C., LeRoith, D. 1986. Development of brain insulin receptors: Structural and functional studies of insulin receptors from whole brain and primary cell cultures. *Endocrinology* 119:25–35

40. Moore, R. D. 1983. Effects of insulin upon ion transport. *Biochem. Biophys. Acta* 737:1–49

41. Oomura, Y. 1983. Glucose as a regulator of neuronal activity. See Ref. 26, pp. 32–65

42. Palovick, R. A., Phillips, M. I., Kappy, M. S., Raizada, M. K. 1984. Insulin inhibits pyramidal neurons in hippocampal slices. *Brain Res.* 309:187–91

43. Pardridge, W. M., Eisenberg, J., Yang, J. 1985. Human blood-brain barrier insulin receptor. *J. Neurochem.* 44:1771–78

43a. Porte, D. Jr., Woods, S. C. 1981. Regulation of food intake and body weight by insulin. *Diabetologia* 20:274–80

44. Raizada, M. 1983. Localization of insulin-like immunoreactivity in the neurons from primary cultures of rat brain. *Exp. Cell. Res.* 143:351–57

45. Rees-Jones, R. W., Hendricks, S. A., Quarum, M., Roth, J. 1984. The insulin receptor of rat brain is coupled to tyrosine kinase activity. *J. Biol. Chem.* 259:3470–74

46. Rhoads, D. E., Rocco, R. J., Osburn, L. D., Peterson, W. A., Raghupathy, E. 1984. Stimulation of synaptosomal uptake of neurotransmitter amino acids by insulin: Possible role of insulin as a neuromodulator. *Biochem. Biophys. Res. Commun.* 119:1198–1204

46a. Rosenzweig, J., Havrankova, J., Lesniak, M., Brownstein, M., Roth, J. 1980. Insulin is ubiquitous in extrapancreatic tissues of rats and humans. *Proc. Natl. Acad. Sci. USA* 77:572–76

47. Sauter, A., Goldstein, M., Engel, J., Ueta, K. 1983. Effect of insulin on central catecholamines. *Brain Res.* 260:330–33

48. Schlüter, K. J., Andre, J., Enzmann, F., Kerp, L. 1984. Insulin receptor binding in pork brain: Different affinities of porcine and human insulin. In *Lessons from Animal Diabetes*, ed. E. Shafrir, A. E. Renold, pp. 253–56. London: Libbey

48a. Selden, R. F., Skoskiewicz, M. J., Burke Howie, K., Russell, P. S., Goodman, H. M. 1986. Tissue-specific expression of the human insulin gene in transgenic mice. *Endocrine Soc. Abstr., Endocrinology Suppl.* 118:49

48b. Seto, K., Saito, H., Edashige, N., Kawakami, T., Yoshimatsu, K., et al.

1985. Influence of microinjection of insulin into amygdala on acetate metabolism in liver slices of rabbit. *Exp. Clin. Endocrinol.* 86:233–36

49. Shibata, S., Liou, S. Y., Ueki, S., Oomura, Y. 1985. Inhibitory action of insulin on suprachiasmatic nucleus neurons in rat hypothalamic slice preparation. *Physiol. Behav.* 36:79–81

50. Stein, L. J., Dorsa, D. M., Baskin, D. G., Figlewicz, D. P., Ikeda, H., et al. 1983. Immunoreactive insulin levels are elevated in the cerebrospinal fluid of genetically obese Zucker rats. *Endocrinology* 113:2299–2301

51. Stein, L. J., Figlewicz, D. P., Dorsa, D. M., Baskin, D. G., Reed, D., et al. 1985. Effect of insulin infusions on cerebrospinal fluid insulin concentrations in heterozygous lean and obese Zucker rats. *Int. J. Obesity* 9:A31 (Abstr.)

52. Stein, L. J., Hjeresen, D. L., Porte, D. Jr., Woods, S. C., 1982. Genetically obese Zucker rats have inappropriately low immunoreactive insulin levels in cerebrospinal fluid. *Soc. Neurosci. Abstr.* 8:273

53. Stevenson, R. W. 1983. Further evidence for non-pancreatic insulin immunoreactivity in guinea pig brain. *Horm. Metab. Res.* 15:526–29

54. Szabo, A. J., Szabo, O. 1983. Insulin injected into CNS structures or the carotid artery: Effect on carbohydrate homeostasis of the intact animal. See Ref. 26, pp. 385–400

54a. Taborsky, G. J. Jr., Bergman, R. N. 1980. Effect of insulin, glucose, and 2-deoxy-glucose infusion into the third cerebral ventricle of conscious dogs on plasma insulin, glucose, and free fatty acids. *Diabetes* 29:278–83

55. van Houten, M., Nance, D. M., Gauthier, S., Posner, B. I. 1983. Origin of insulin-receptive nerve terminals in rat median eminence. *Endocrinology* 113:1393–99

56. van Houten, M., Posner, B. I. 1983. Circumventricular organs: Receptors and mediators of direct peptide hormone action on brain. See Ref. 26, pp. 269–89

57. van Schravendijk, C. F. H., Hooghe-Peters, E. L., DeMeyts, P., Pipeleers, D. G. 1984. Identification and characterization of insulin receptors on foetal mouse brain-cortical cells. *Biochem. J.* 220:165–72

58. Wallum, B. J., Porte, D. Jr., Figlewicz, D. P., Jacobsen, L., Dorsa, D. 1987. Cerebrospinal fluid insulin levels increase during intravenous insulin infusions in man. *J. Clin. Endocrinol. Metab.* In press.

59. Weyhenmeyer, J. A., Fellows, R. E. 1983. Presence of immunoreactive insulin in neurons cultured from fetal rat brain. *Cell. Mol. Neurobiol.* 3:81–86

59a. Wilcox, B., Corp, E. S., Figlewicz, D. P., Dorsa, D. M., Greenwood, M. R. C., Porte, D. Jr., Baskin, D. G. 1986. Characterization of insulin binding in the hypothalamus of three genotypes of Zucker rat by in vitro quantitative autoradiography. *Soc. Neurosci. Abstr.* 12: In press

60. Wolinsky, E. J., Patterson, P. H., Willard, A. L. 1985. Insulin promotes electrical coupling between cultured sympathetic neurons. *J. Neurosci.* 5:1675–79

61. Woods, S. C., Lotter, E. C., McKay, L. D., Porte, D. Jr. 1979. Chronic intracerebroventricular infusion of insulin reduces food intake and body weight of baboons. *Nature* 282:503–5

62. Woods, S. C., Porte, D. Jr., Bobbioni, E., Ionescu, E., Sauter, J. F., et al. 1985. Insulin: Its relationship to the central nervous system and to the control of food intake and body weight. *Am. J. Clin. Nutr.* 42:1063–71

63. Yalow, R. S., Eng, J. 1983. Insulin in the central nervous system. See Ref. 26, pp. 34–54

64. Yorek, M. A., Spector, A. A., Ginsberg, B. H. 1985. Characterization of an insulin receptor in human Y79 retinablastoma cells. *J. Neurochem.* 45:1590–95

65. Zahniser, N. R., Goens, M. B., Hanaway, P. J., Vinych, J. V. 1984. Characterization and regulation of insulin receptors in rat brain. *J. Neurochem.* 42:1345–62

Ann. Rev. Physiol. 1987. 49:349–64

SEX STEROIDS AND AFFERENT INPUT: Their Roles in Brain Sexual Differentiation

Carlos Beyer

Institute of Animal Behavior, Rutgers, The State University of New Jersey, 101 Warren Street, Newark, New Jersey 07102

Centro de Investigación en Reproducción Animal, CINVESTAV-Universidad Autónoma de Tlaxcala, Tlaxcala, Mexico

Harvey H. Feder

Department of Biological Sciences, Rutgers, The State University of New Jersey, 101 Warren Street, Newark, New Jersey 07102

INTRODUCTION

Sexually dimorphic patterns of sexual behavior and gonadotropin secretion in adult rodents arise as a result of the presence or absence of androgen (or androgen metabolites, primarily estrogen) during the perinatal period (13, 14, 16, 22–24, 44, 51, 70). Central nervous system (CNS) regions underlying control of these reproductive processes show sex differences in various morphological parameters such as size of nuclei in neuronal groups, number of neurons, neuronal volume, extent of dendritic extension and branching, number of dendritic spines, morphology and localization of synapses, and cell nuclear volume and structure (5, 14, 23, 70). Moreover, there are reports of sex differences in the pattern of connectivity between various limbic regions related to reproductive functions (15, 63). The importance of hormones in directing or organizing brain sexual dimorphism has been illustrated convincingly by two types of experiments: (a) Castration of genetic (XY) males during perinatal life demasculinizes and feminizes the neural substrate for sexual behavior and feminizes the brain-pituitary axis destined to mediate adult patterns of gonadotropin secretion, and (b) injection of androgen into

349

genetic (XX) females masculinizes and defeminizes the above-mentioned reproductive processes (16, 22, 24, 44). Studies using brain implants of testosterone (T) in infant rats indicate that sex steroids organize female and male reproductive behavioral capacities by acting primarily at two sites: the mediobasal hypothalamus (MBH) and the medial preoptic area (mPOA) (10, 50).

Several observations indicate that various aspects of sexual dimorphism have different periods during which they are maximally susceptible to the organizing effects of perinatal steroids. For example, in rats, steroids act *prenatally* to virilize neural substrates destined to regulate male sexual behavior, but this is not accompanied by defeminizing effects. In contrast, female sexual behavioral potential and gonadotropin secretion patterns appear to be influenced by the presence or absence of sex steroid during the early *postnatal* period (13, 14, 16, 44).

THESIS

The effects of perinatal steroids on the CNS can be analyzed in terms of the sites and the times of action (7). The primary sites of steroid action include the neurons receiving direct information from steroid molecules. These neurons possess special recognition sites or molecules for decoding such information, i.e. they probably possess classical intracellular steroid receptors. The primary sites of sex steroid action in both male and female animals are some regions in the hypothalamus, mPOA, amygdala, septum, and some scattered cells in the brain stem (56, 66). However, the steroids may affect a considerably larger domain if one considers that steroids also act briefly at recognition sites on the plasma membrane of neurons (42, 71).

The activity and even proper development of a second group of neurons is *indirectly* influenced by steroids through transsynaptic changes or secretory processes of steroid-activated neurons at the primary sites of action. This group of secondary sites of action includes a number of neurons that may be several orders of magnitude greater than the number of neurons responding directly to steroids.

Analysis of the temporal domain of perinatal sex steroids reveals three distinct types of responses:

1. Responses of short latency and duration   Sex steroids (estrogens, androgens, and progestins) can induce with brief latencies (milliseconds) changes in the excitability of neurons (48, 49). The temporal characteristics of these responses rule out the participation of protein synthesis (49). Thus these responses must involve direct actions at the membrane level that alter ionic conductance (49) or modulate the effect of inhibitory neurotransmitters (42).

Although these rapid effects are among the most consistent and clear actions of steroids on brain functioning, they have not been considered by researchers designing models of sex steroid action on brain sexual differentiation.

2. Responses of medium latency and duration   Sex steroids also induce neuronal effects that are apparent within hours and may last for hours or days (16, 44). These effects usually involve the internalization of the sex steroids and their binding to intracellular receptors in the nucleus. Activation of these receptors facilitates interaction of the receptor-hormone complex with the genome (55). Increased transcription of mRNA and protein synthesis results. This type of sex steroid effect, which is typical of some peripheral steroid-sensitive organs, e.g. the uterus, has been the one usually invoked to explain most physiological effects induced by sex steroids in the CNS.

3. Transient responses followed by prolonged alterations in the capacity to respond to steroids   Analysis of the temporal domain of sex steroid actions reveals a response characteristic that may be crucial to understanding the effects of sex steroids on brain organization: An initially transient response is sometimes followed by a prolonged alteration of the target tissue, as revealed by a change in that tissue's capacity to respond to the same or other hormonal stimuli. Such "memory effects" have been described for several estrogen-responsive tissues. These effects consist of a shortening of the latency and an enhancement of the response to a second administration of the hormone. At the cellular level, this change in responsiveness is apparently related to a persistent change in chromatin structure that allows the receptor-hormone complex to interact more efficiently with specific sites on the DNA (8). This type of effect is obviously relevant to sexual differentiation of the brain. Perinatal gonadal steroids produce observable changes in behavior and physiology that are not concurrent with the first administration of hormone but manifest themselves several weeks or months after a second application of the hormonal stimulus. Perinatal steroids probably produce immediate cellular changes that are not manifested until much later, when appropriate hormonal conditions are present (e.g. production of adequate amounts of sex steroids beginning at puberty).

Thus rapid, intermediate, and persistent changes in neuronal function probably result from changes in membrane excitability, protein synthesis, and alterations in chromatin structure, respectively.

Previous writers have emphasized the role of the primary sites of steroid action and those effects of medium latency and duration in discussions of the organization of sexual dimorphism in the brain and in behavior. Clearly, however, sex steroids participate in brain sexual differentiation by influencing various cellular processes at different stages of brain development. For example, T and estradiol appear to stimulate growth of neurites in developing neurons during the fetal period (5, 23, 70). During brain differentiation, sex steroids sensitize the genome of preoptic and hypothalamic neurons to circulating gonadal hormones, probably by altering chromatin structure (8, 44). At a later stage of brain development, most likely during the perinatal period in rodents, sex steroids organize the complex synaptic arrangements of several structures, including the amygdala, the MBH, and the tuberal nuclei. Recent studies performed in several brain regions indicate that detailed synaptic organization results from transsynaptic interactions among neurons. This finding suggests that incoming neuronal activity is of paramount importance for the adequate anatomical and functional development of brain structures (31). Therefore, it is highly likely that sex steroids exert their fine organizational actions during the postnatal period by altering the neuronal firing patterns of some brain regions. The following section reviews the data on the effect of various pharmacological and behavioral manipulations that alter brain neuronal activity and brain sexual dimorphism.

ROLE OF AFFERENT INPUT AND NEURONAL ACTIVITY IN BRAIN SEXUAL DIFFERENTIATION

Sex differences in synaptic pattern have been demonstrated in all brain regions related to the control of reproduction, i.e. the arcuate nucleus (4), the suprachiasmatic nucleus (26), the MBH (43), the mPOA (59), and the medial amygdaloid nucleus (53). Each neuron receives an average of 1000 synaptic contacts from other neurons. Because these contacts are unique and highly specific in their location (on dendritic shafts, spines, soma, or axon), it is unlikely that they result from undirected neurite outgrowth after sex steroid stimulation. Rather, this outgrowth must be tightly controlled both temporally and spatially. Moreover, variations in synaptic organization in sexually dimorphic structures may not all be the result of a direct action of the sex steroids in the developing neurons: For example, the suprachiasmatic nucleus has few or no sex steroid receptors, but it shows sex differences. Therefore, afferent information from steroid-responsive neurons at the primary sites of action may converge on secondary-site neurons to determine the detailed synaptic organization of a nucleus such as the suprachiasmatic nucleus. Indeed, there is solid evidence from studies performed in various brain areas that the establishment of the fine circuitry involved in integrated brain function is mainly controlled by neural activity impinging on developing neurons (6, 12, 25, 32, 60). This afferent input may be generated by the spontaneous activity of neurons projecting to an area or by sensory or internal stimulation of different types, sources, and complexity. Many studies have demonstrated that the afferent supply to a neural region plays a fundamental role in the survival of the young neuron and in its establishment of dendritic arborizations (6, 25, 32, 48, 60). Although an initial stage of neuronal and dendritic development can take place in the absence of afferent input (57, 58), the establishment of synapses (dendritic spines) depends to a large extent on the specific afferent supply to the developing region (32). Deafferentation or reduction in afferent input has been found to have negative and irreversible effects on the development of many brain regions (visual cortex, cerebellum, hippocampus) (6, 25, 32). Interestingly, enrichment of synaptic connections and dendritic arborization has been produced in developing animals by various procedures and conditions (training, electrical stimulation, rearing in complex environments) that have in common the property of increasing the afferent input to the region (25).

Some studies also demonstrate the importance of afferent input to the differentiation of hypothalamic cells. Privat et al (58) found that although immature neurosecretory cells can develop in organotypic cultures of the 40-day-old fetal hypothalamus of the guinea pig (i.e. in the absence of a specific target), these cells appear poorly differentiated with a restricted Golgi zone and no secretory granules. After 10 days in vitro afferent synapses appear, and 5 days later neurosecretory granules are present in the Golgi complex. These results suggest the indispensability of afferent fiber input in the full differentiation of magnocellular hypothalamic cells.

Indeed, the importance of afferent supply for dendritic structure is evident not only in young, developing animals but also in mature animals. Loss or decrease of afferent input has been reported to produce variable degrees of dendritic regression in several brain areas, including the hypothalamus. Histofluorescence studies have shown that the noradrenergic supply of the supraoptic nucleus shifts away from the ventral dendritic zone towards neuronal perikarya before the age of 20 mo. in the F344 rat. This decrease in afferent input is followed by a 35% reduction in dendritic extent per neuron between 20 and 27 mo. (19). Because the supraoptic nucleus is known not to lose neurons with age, the dendritic regression is most likely due to a reduction in afferent input.

From the preceding discussion it seems likely that the development of hypothalamic and preoptic circuitry is influenced by incoming activity from brain areas projecting to this zone. Furthermore, the development of both the ascending and descending pathways through which the sexually dimorphic hypothalamic areas exert their effects almost certainly depends on the activity of these hypothalamic neurons. Despite this very strong likelihood, there are apparently no direct studies of the role of afferent input in the development of fine circuitry in hypothalamic-preoptic structures destined to mediate reproduction. A wealth of indirect data exist, and we have subdivided these data into three sections: (a) electrophysiological studies of the developing hypothalamus, (*b*) studies using pharmacological manipulations that cause generalized or specific functional deafferentations, and (*c*) behavioral studies that imply that altered afferent input to developing hypothalamic structures alters the responsiveness of these structures to steroids.

Electrophysiological Studies

To our knowledge, no information exists on the electrical activity of fetal hypothalamic neurons. Studies made in the spinal cord and brain areas outside the hypothalamus show that fetal neurons are not activated transneuronally until the last days of pregnancy (17). Apparently, development and maturation of synapses, with the consequent capacity for synaptic transmission, are phenomena that occur close to the time of birth in the rat, and in some structures, like the cerebellum, these processes may occur after birth. The lack of development of afferent pathways to the hypothalamus and intrahypothalamic connections may explain why steroid-induced brain sexual differentiation is not complete until the first week of postnatal life, even though several days before birth all the biochemical machinery to produce, process, and respond to the critical sex steroids exists (34, 69, 73), and the hypothalamic nuclei [ventromedial nucleus (VMN), arcuate nucleus, and mPOA] are already morphologically differentiated (2). Another possibility is that these pathways are developed in the prenatal period but are not activated. Activation may be the result of the abrupt changes in endocrine and sensory information that occur at birth and in the first postnatal hours or days.

Some information is available on the activity of the hypothalamic neurons during the postnatal period in rats. Hypothalamic neurons from the VMN and the lateral hypothalamus in one-day-old rats show normal action potentials and usually respond to both external (somatic, gustatory, and olfactory) and internal (saline and glucose solutions) stimulation with increases in their firing rates (1, 18). These results indicate that these afferents to the VMN and lateral hypothalamus are fully functional in the newborn rat (1, 18). The highest proportion of responsive neurons to tactile, gustatory, and olfactory stimuli was found at postnatal day 5. More striking were the data on convergence of the external sensory stimuli. Twenty-five percent of the VMN neurons tested at day 5 of age responded to the three types of input listed above, whereas none showed this degree of convergence at days 1 and 25. When data obtained under conditions of both internal and external stimulation were analyzed, it was clear that during the first 5 days of life there is maximal convergence of sensory influences and that this property sharply diminishes with increasing age. Although rats of both sexes were used, unfortunately no information was provided as to possible differential responsiveness between sexes to sensory or internal stimulation.

The results of this study agree with previous work (68), in which multiunit activity was recorded in the brain stem and forebrain of rats during the first week of life. Although multiunit activity does not provide the fine discrimination that single-unit activity does, it was clear that newborn and 5-day-old rats responded to exteroceptive stimuli with marked increases in neuronal firing in both the mesencephalic reticular formation and in the basal forebrain. Interestingly, this responsiveness decreased during development. The authors concluded that the high level of somatosensory responsiveness was of great importance for the consolidation of the neuronal mechanisms underlying elementary learning and memory processes. Recently, Kimura & Nakamura (37) studied the spontaneous electrical activity and responses to sensory stimulation of locus coeruleus neurons in the neonatal rat of 1–3 days of age. These neurons were not spontaneously active, but both noxious and innocuous stimuli (touch, pinch, etc) induced robust excitatory responses, which sometimes lasted for longer than 1 minute. From these findings in brain stem, the authors concluded that the activity of locus coeruleus neurons in the neonatal rat is predominantly governed by sensory inputs and that if these neurons play an important role in modulating brain development, this influence is intimately related to sensory inputs from the periphery. These results indicate that afferent pathways to the brain stem and forebrain neural structures are actively functioning during the first week of postnatal life in the rat. Moreover, it appears that the responsiveness of hypothalamic neurons to various stimuli, as evidenced by the property of sensory convergence, is greater in neonatal than in adult animals.

There are no data on the direct effect of estradiol (E_2) or T on the excitability of brain neonatal neurons. However, administration of estrogen to infant rats facilitates the appearance of the adult pattern of motor seizures following electric shock. This increased convulsability was interpreted as resulting from an enhanced excitability of some brain areas in response to estrogen (29). Administration of progesterone (P) or some of its metabolites inhibits brain electrical activity and neuronal firing in neonatal rats (21).

Sex steroids may be implicated in the augmented excitability of neural circuits that characterizes the neonatal period in rats. This idea is supported by the well-known stimulatory effect of estrogen in adults of several species on the excitability of various limbic pathways projecting to the hypothalamus. Alternatively or in addition, this increased excitability of perinatal subcortical neurons to peripheral and internal stimulation may be due to their release from the inhibitory action of P. Progesterone is secreted in large amounts during pregnancy by both the mother and the adrenal cortex of the fetus, but these levels fall abruptly in the perinatal period (62). This withdrawal of P may be particularly important because the neonatal brain is exquisitely sensitive to the inhibitory effect of this steroid (30). Dramatic changes in the neuronal activity of the brain would be expected to occur immediately after birth as a result of the combined action of endocrine factors [rises in T and E_2 in males and drop in P in both sexes (62)] and the "catastrophic" alteration in environmental conditions in the passage from fetal to neonatal life. It is obvious that much more information is needed on the pattern of neuronal activity in regions affected by sex steroids during the period of brain sexual differentiation.

Pharmacological Deafferentation of the Hypothalamus-Preoptic Area

An important role for afferent input to the developing hypothalamus in the masculinization and defeminization of the brain is also indirectly supported by several pharmacological observations, in which the effects of neonatal steroid administration have been counteracted by various drugs that affect neuronal activity. Barbiturates and progestins are particularly effective at counteracting the organizing action of androgen. Pentobarbital given to neonatal female rats and mice (52) was found to be the most effective barbiturate in preventing defeminization of gonadotropin release patterns in neonates receiving TP (3, 22, 67). This preventive or protective effect was related to the anesthetic potency of the barbiturate; pentobarbital was much more effective than pheno-barbital (97). Interestingly, the protective effect of barbiturates was counter-acted by the administration of metrazol (22), a drug that increases neuronal excitability and produces seizures when given in large doses. The specific brain site(s) at which barbiturates act to prevent masculinization is not known. Sutherland & Gorski (67) infused pentobarbital directly into the anterior hypothalamus of neonatal rats. This procedure failed to prevent defeminiza-tion of gonadotropin release after neonatal androgen administration. This result suggests that the drug may act diffusely at various neural sites.

Another family of compounds reported to have anti-defeminization effects in neonates is the pregnanes (C21 steroids). Progesterone was the first of these compounds reported to have this action (3, 9, 21, 22, 38). Initially, this effect was considered to be due to the antiandrogenic properties of P (38), but more recent results suggest that P produces this effect by depressing neuronal excitability. Thus, dosages of P effective in preventing defeminization in female neonatal rats also elicited clear depression of EEG and muscular activity in neonatal rats of the same age (21). Other types of studies also show that P is very effective in decreasing brain excitability in the developing brain. Holmes & Weber (30) recently showed that dosages of P even lower than those used to prevent the effects of androgen markedly inhibit kindling produced by repeated low-frequency electrical stimulation of the amygdala in immature rats. Comparable dosages of P were without effect in adult rats. This result is particularly relevant because the amygdala has heavy projections to the hypothalamus.

Progesterone may act by itself or it may be converted to ring A–reduced metabolites, which have a greater depressory action than P on brain electrical activity (21). Arai & Gorski (3) found that pregnanedione (5β-pregnan-3,20-dione) interfered with the defeminizing actions of TP at a lower dosage than did P. More recently, Gonzalez-Mariscal et al (21) studied the anti-defeminization action of various progestins including ring A-reduced P metabolites. They found that protection against TP-induced defeminization was clearly correlated with the capacity of the progestin to depress brain electrical activity in neonatal rats. Thus, $5\beta,3\alpha$-pregnanolone, a potent inhibitor of neuronal activity, was the most effective progestin in blocking neonatal androgen effects. In contrast, chlormadinone acetate, a potent progestational and antiandrogenic pregnane without inhibitory effects on EEG, was ineffective in interfering with neonatal androgen action.

The above-mentioned studies with barbiturates and pregnanes suggest that defeminization and masculinization are achieved through an increase in afferent input or neuronal activity in some of the hypothalamic nuclei related to the control of gonadotropin secretion and perhaps sex behavior. In the absence of this afferent neural bombardment, a feminized and demasculinized anatomical and functional pattern would be expected. This prediction is supported by studies of the development of sexual behavior in hamsters. Clemens et al (11) found that neonatal males treated with 100 μg of pentobarbital on postnatal days 2–4 showed decreased male copulatory behavior as intact adults. This impairment of male sexual behavior was not corrected by TP replacement therapy in adulthood. When tested for estrous behavior, males treated neonatally with 50 μg pentobarbital showed more frequent lordosis as adults. Incidentally, neonatal pentobarbital treatment had no effect in females.

The above-mentioned pharmacological studies were made with dosages of barbiturates and pregnanes that altered neuronal excitability in a generalized manner. Ring A–reduced pregnanes act at the membrane level (21), and barbiturates block postsynaptic activation of excitatory neurotransmitters and enhance the action of inhibitory neurotransmitters (76). Some workers have claimed that protection against defeminization of gonadotropin release can be obtained with drugs that presumably interfere with the afferent input provided by a single neurotransmitter. Kikuyama demonstrated 25 years ago that the administration of the tranquilizing drugs chlorpromazine (36) and reserpine (35) prevented the defeminization of gonadotropin release that normally follows neonatal injection of testosterone or estrogen preparations. Similar results were obtained by other groups and were extended to include demasculinization of sexual behavior (13, 14, 39). These results obtained with tranquilizers were interpreted as being due to specific interference by these drugs with monoamine action at the receptor level (chlorpromazine) or to depletion of noradrenalin (reserpine), but there is an obvious alternative explanation. Namely, in the dose range used to protect neonatal rats from the effects of sex steroids, the tranquilizers exert generalized anesthetic actions. Neonatal rats that received 40 μg of chlorpromazine became unconscious within 15 min and remained so for 3–4 hr (39). Similarly, mice given protective doses of pentobarbital were deeply anesthetized for several hours; those treated with reserpine were sedated and had lowered body temperatures for more than 24 hr (52). Therefore, it appears that tranquilizers, at least at the dosages used in these studies, may exert protective actions against androgen by a generalized, nonspecific mechanism similar to that for barbiturates and pregnanes.

Nevertheless, there are some data to suggest that variations in afferent input limited to a specific neurotransmitter have a facilitative or inhibitory effect on the organizing action of neonatal sex steroids. For example, an important role for serotonin in brain sexual differentiation is supported by the observation that treatment of neonatal female rats with the serotonin precursor 5-hydroxytryptophan inhibits the production of persistent estrus induced by perinatal androgen (64). There is also some indirect evidence that noradrenergic transmission plays a role in the development of sexual dimorphism in behavior. Phenoxybenzamine, an α-adrenergic antagonist, has been found to protect against the defeminizing effect of TP on gonadotropin secretion in both neonatal mice and rats (52, 61). However, in the rat α-methyl-P-tyrosine administration that reduced noradrenergic hypothalamic concentration to one fifth of its normal value failed to prevent the action of testosterone. This finding led Raum & Swerdloff (61) to propose that the effect of α-adrenergic antagonists was exerted by an increase in noradrenergic release and β-receptor stimulation resulting from presynaptic α-receptor blockade. This increase in β-receptor activity was proposed to block androgen aromatization in the hypothalamus, thus preventing defeminization (61). Other studies, however, suggest that an increase in noradrenergic activity may be involved in masculinization. Thus, prenatally stressed males that subsequently develop a stress syndrome (that includes demasculinization and feminization of behavior) show significantly lower levels than control subjects of circulating norepinephrine on the day of birth (14, 72).

Drugs that affect neurotransmission not only may protect neonatal rats from the masculinizing or defeminizing effects of perinatal androgens but themselves may affect these processes. Chlorpromazine injected up to the tenth day after birth into an intact male rat interfered with the organization of a male pattern of gonadotropin control (33). Conversely, p-chlorophenylalanine (a serotonin synthesis inhibitor) administered neonatally increased male sexual behavior in adult male rats in comparison to control noninjected males (14). Dörner and his collaborators (14) tested the effects of neonatal administration of several drugs that affect the concentration or action of some neurotransmitters. In neonatally treated male rats, male sexual behavior was permanently depressed by reserpine (a monoamine depletor) or pargyline (an MAO inhibitor) but permanently increased by pyridostigmine (an acetylcholine inhibitor). Infantile female rats injected with pargyline also showed a decrease in mounting behavior (14). These results suggest that increased catecholaminergic and cholinergic activity stimulate neuronal changes that result in masculinization of behavior, whereas increased serotoninergic activity produces the opposite effect, i.e. demasculinization and feminization. Administration of these drugs resulted in permanent changes in both the concentration of neurotransmitters and in some anatomical features in the amygdala (14, 65).

In summary, the above-mentioned investigations of the pharmacology of brain sexual differentiation support the idea that masculinization and defeminization of hypothalamic and limbic structures result from an altered afferent input to these regions. The relevant information for brain sexual differentiation may be coded for by the number of excitatory impulses impinging on these structures, an idea supported by the results obtained with barbiturates and pregnanes. However, it also appears that the organizing actions of sex steroids may involve various, distinct cellular processes. Each one of these processes may require a type of information more specific than that afforded by quantitative differences in incoming electrical signals. For example, defeminization may be related to an increase in the number of cell deaths in the MBH, and masculinization may involve stimulation of dendritic proliferation as well as reduction in neuronal death in the mPOA.

It is tempting to speculate that each of these cellular processes (e.g. cell death, synaptogenesis, cell survival) is controlled by distinct neurotransmitters, which evoke different types of cellular responses. According to this scheme, sex steroids would act specifically by stimulating or modulating the action of particular neurotransmitters. Some indirect evidence supports this notion. For example, noradrenalin has been proposed to play a role in the organization of some brain areas, probably by stimulating the adenylate cyclase cAMP system, which is known to be involved in growth and differentiation in the central and peripheral nervous system (20). Estrogen administration to infantile rats has been shown to increase cAMP levels through the activation of the noradrenergic system, since noradrenergic blockers interfere with this action (27). Thus estrogen probably exerts some of its growth effects through the modulation of noradrenergic transmission. In addition, neuronal death and loss of synapses can be produced by excitatory neurotransmitters such as glutamate, which is present in the hypothalamus and is under partial estrogen regulation (41). The cell damage that results from glutamate administration is specific to those neurons having glutamate receptors and is due to plasma membrane depolarization and passive chloride influx. Administration of monosodium glutamate to neonatal female rats permanently alters gonadotropin secretion by damaging the arcuate nucleus and other circumventricular structures (54). It has been proposed that a highly effective glutamate uptake system is one of the mechanisms that protects the brain from the potentially toxic effects of glutamate. Any interference with this uptake may lead to neuronal damage by overexposing neurons to glutamate. Interestingly, castration significantly affects the glutamate uptake system of the rat, particularly in the hypothalamus (74). In addition, pentobarbital, which protects neonatal rats from the effects of androgen injections, also specifically antagonizes the effects of glutamate on the postsynaptic membrane (76). The effects of perinatal androgen may be mediated by an increase in the activity of the telencephalohypothalamic pathway, which uses glutamate as a neurotransmitter. Obviously, further pharmacological studies are required to test this idea.

Behavioral Mechanisms that Alter Afferent Input During Perinatal Differentiation

In addition to the electrophysiological and pharmacological studies described above, there is evidence from behavioral work that afferent input to the primary sites of sex steroid action plays a significant role in sexual differentiation of the brain.

Application of stressful stimuli to the pregnant rat at day 16–20 eventually results in demasculinization and feminization of the sexual behavior of the male offspring of stressed mothers (72). The mechanism of this effect is complex. The stress procedure results in a 24-hr advancement of the peak of T that normally occurs during days 18–19 in the fetal rat. This advancement probably leads to a desynchronization in the interaction of the steroid with its competent neural substrate (72, 73). Based on this work, Dörner has proposed that prenatal stress in humans may alter sexual preference in adulthood (13, 14).

Social deprivation during the early postnatal period alters sexual behavioral potential and responsiveness to sex steroids in adulthood in both sexes in a variety of mammalian species (40, 77).

Mother-infant relationships during the first week of postnatal life in rats appear to permanently alter organization of the neural substrates underlying sexual behavior. The key finding is that mothers spend more time with male than with female pups, and they also lick the anogenital region of male pups more frequently than they do that of female pups (45). Administration of androgen or estrogen to female pups resulted in a significant increase in maternal licking rates (46). This finding indicates that sex steroids alter some stimulus characteristics of the pups to which the mothers respond. These interesting behavioral observations suggest that exposure to neonatal sex steroids, besides producing organizational changes in brain tissue, may also alter maternal behavior toward male pups, leading to an increase in the rate of sensory stimulation during the critical postnatal period. Convergence of afferent stimulation presumably triggered by the sex steroid and produced by maternal stimulation may produce optimal masculinization.

A recent study supports this possibility. Male pups that received less maternal anogenital licking than did controls (due to experimental anosmia in the mothers) showed significant alterations in the temporal organization of male copulatory behavior as adults. These males had longer ejaculatory latencies and longer postejaculatory intervals than did normally stimulated males. Moreover, female pups that were licked less frequently than control females performed fewer mounts and intromissions and had longer intromission latencies and intervals (47). These observations demonstrate that maternal care, including licking, contributes to the development of a neural mechanism that underlies the timing of male copulatory rate.

Other types of stimuli active during the postnatal period may also contribute to masculinization of various neuronal functions in animals, including primates. The dramatic disruption in the development of sexual behavior in male monkeys (28) may also be caused by maternal deprivation. These data may also have implications for human behavioral development, because mothers are known to respond differently to infant males and females (75).

All of these behavioral data suggest a dynamic interaction among environmental, behavioral, neurotransmitter, and endocrine factors that influence afferent input to neural substrates destined to underlie reproductive function. These interactions may extend well beyond the immediate postnatal period and continue to shape the circuitry of these substrates.

ACKNOWLEDGMENTS

The authors are grateful to Mrs. Anne Wolff for superb secretarial assistance. This work was supported by Grant NIH HD-04467 to H. H. Feder and a grant from CONACYT, Mexico to C. Beyer. (Publication number 443 of IAB and number 10 of the Department of Biological Sciences.)

Literature Cited

1. Almli, C. R., Fisher, R. S. 1985. Postnatal development of sensory influences on neurons in the ventromedial hypothalamic nucleus of the rat. *Dev. Brain Res.* 18:13–26
2. Altman, J., Bayer, S. A. 1978. Development of the diencephalon of the rat. I. Autoradiographic study of the time of origin and setting patterns of neurons in the hypothalamus. *J. Comp. Neurol.* 182:945–72

3. Arai, Y., Gorski, R. A. 1968. Protection against the neural organizing effect of exogenous androgen in the neonatal female rat. *Endocrinology* 82:1005–9
4. Arai, Y., Matsumoto, A. 1978. Synapse formation of the hypothalamus arcuate nucleus during postnatal development in the female rat and its modification by neonatal estrogen treatment. *Psychoneuroendocrinology* 3:31–45
5. Arnold, A. P. 1985. Gonadal steroid-

induced organization and reorganization of neural circuits involved in bird songs. In *Synaptic Plasticity*, ed. C. W. Cotman, pp. 263–85. New York: Guilford

6. Berry, M., McConnell, P., Sievers, J. 1980. Dendritic growth and the control of neuronal form. *Curr. Top. Dev. Biol.* 15(Pt. 1):67–101

7. Bloom, F. 1979. Chemical integrative processes in the central nervous system. In *Neuroscience: Fourth Intensive Study Program*, ed. F. O. Schmitt, F. G. Worden, pp. 51–58. Cambridge, Mass: MIT Press

8. Burch, J. B. E., Weintraub, H. 1983. Temporal order of chromatin structural changes associated with activation of the major chicken vitellogenin gene. *Cell* 33:65–76

9. Cagnoni, M., Fantini, F., Morace, G., Ghetti, A. 1965. Failure of testosterone propionate to induce the "early androgen" syndrome in rats previously injected with progesterone. *J. Endocrinol.* 35:527–28

10. Christensen, L. W., Gorski, R. A. 1978. Independent masculinization of neuroendocrine systems by intracerebral implants of testosterone or estradiol in the neonatal female rat. *Brain Res.* 146:325–40

11. Clemens, L. G., Popham, T. V., Ruppert, P. M. 1979. Neonatal treatment of hamsters with barbiturate alters adult sexual behavior. *Dev. Psychobiol.* 12: 49–59

12. Coleman, P. O., Buell, S. J. 1985. Regulation of dendritic extent in developing and aging brain. In *Synaptic Plasticity*, ed. C. W. Cotman, pp. 311–33. New York: Guilford

13. Dörner, G. 1976. *Hormones and Brain Differentiation.* Amsterdam: Elsevier/North Holland/Biomed.

14. Dörner, G. 1980. Sexual differentiation of the brain. *Vitam. Horm. NY* 38:325–81

15. Dyer, R. G., MacLeod, N. K., Ellendorf, F. 1976. Electrophysiological evidence for sexual dimorphism and synaptic convergence in the preoptic and anterior hypothalamic areas of the rat. *Proc. R. Soc. London Ser. B* 193:421–40

16. Feder, H. H. 1984. Hormones and sexual behavior. *Ann. Rev. Psychol.* 35:165–200

17. Fishbach, G. D., Nelson, P. 1977. Cell culture in neurobiology. In *Handbook of Physiology. Section 1: The Nervous System*, Vol. 1, Part 2, pp. 719–74. Bethesda, MD: Am. Physiol. Soc.

18. Fisher, R. S., Almli, C. R. 1984. Postnatal development of sensory influences on lateral hypothalamic neurons of the rat. *Dev. Brain Res.* 12:55–75

19. Flood, D. G., Coleman, P. D. 1983. Age-related changes in dendritic extent of neurons in supraoptic nucleus of F344 rats. *Soc. Neurosci. Abstr.* 9:930

20. Friedman, D. L. 1976. Role of cyclic nucleotides in cell growth and differentiation. *Physiol. Rev.* 56:652–708

21. Gonzalez-Mariscal, G., Fernandez-Guasti, A., Beyer, C. 1982. Anesthetic pregnanes counteract androgen-induced defeminization. *Neuroendocrinology* 34:357–62

22. Gorski, R. A. 1971. Gonadal hormones and the perinatal development of neuroendocrine function. In *Frontiers in Neuroendocrinology*, ed. L. Martini, W. F. Ganong, pp. 237–90. New York: Oxford Univ. Press

23. Gorski, R. A. 1985. Gonadal hormones as putative neurotrophic substances. In *Synaptic Plasticity*, ed. C. W. Cotman, pp. 287–310. New York: Guilford

24. Goy, R. W., McEwen, B. S. 1980. *Sexual Differentiation of the Brain.* Cambridge, Mass: MIT Press

25. Greenough, W. T., Cheng, F. F. 1985. Synaptic structural correlates of information storage in mammalian nervous system. In *Synaptic Plasticity*, ed. C. W. Cotman, pp. 335–72. New York: Guilford

26. Güldner, F. H. 1982. Sexual dimorphism of axo-spine synapses and postsynaptic density material in the suprachiasmatic nucleus of the rat. *Neurosci. Lett.* 28:145–50

27. Gunaga, K. P., Kawano, A., Menon, K. M. 1973. *In vivo* effect of estradiol benzoate on the accumulation of adenosine 3'-5' cyclic monophoshate in the rat hypothalamus. *Neuroendocrinology* 16:273–81

28. Harlow, H. F. 1964. Early social deprivation and later behavior in the monkey. In *Unfinished Tasks in the Behavioral Sciences*, ed. A. Abrams, H. H. Garner, J. E. P. Tonnan, pp. 154–73. Baltimore: Williams & Wilkins

29. Heim, L. M., Timiras, P. S. 1963. Gonad-brain relationship; precocious brain maturation after estradiol in rats. *Endocrinology* 72:598–606

30. Holmes, G. L., Weber, D. A. 1984. The effect of progesterone on kindling: A developmental study. *Dev. Brain Res.* 16:45–53

31. Hopkins, W. G., Brown, M. C. 1984. Development of nerve cells and their

connections. Cambridge, England: Cambridge Univ. Press

32. Jones, E. G. 1981. Development of connectivity in the cerebral cortex. In *Studies in Developmental Biology: Essays in Honor of Viktor Hamburger,* ed. W. M. Cowan, pp. 354–94. London: Oxford Univ. Press

33. Kawashima, S. 1964. Inhibitory action of reserpine on the development of male pattern of secretion of gonadotrophins in the rat. *Annot. Zool. Jpn.* 37:79–85

34. Keefer, D., Holderegger, C. 1985. The ontogeny of estrogen receptors: Brain and pituitary. *Dev. Brain Res.* 19:183–94

35. Kikuyama, S. 1961. Inhibitory effect of reserpine on the induction of persistent estrus by sex steroids in the rat. *Annot. Zool. Jpn.* 34:114–16

36. Kikuyama, S. 1962. Inhibition of induction of persistent estrus by chlorpromazine in the rat. *Annot. Zool. Jpn.* 35:6–11

37. Kimura, F., Nakamura, S. 1985. Locus coeruleus neurons in the neonatal rat: Electrical activity and responses to sensory stimulation. *Dev. Brain Res.* 23:301–5

38. Kincl, F. A., Maqueo, M. 1965. Prevention by progesterone of steroid-induced sterility in neonatal male and female rats. *Endocrinology* 77:859–62

39. Ladosky, W., Kesikowski, W. M., Gaziri, I. F. 1970. Effect of a single injection of chlorpromazine into infant male rats on subsequent gonadotrophin secretion. *J. Endocrinol.* 48:151–56

40. Larsson, K. 1978. Experiential factors in the development of sexual behaviour. In *Biological Determinants of Sexual Behaviour,* ed. J. B. Hutchison, pp. 55–86. New York: Wiley

41. Majewska, M. D., Harrison, N. L., Schwartz, R. D., Barker, S. L., Paul, S. M. 1986. Steroid hormone metabolites are barbiturate-like modulators of the GABA receptor. *Science* 232:1004–7

42. Mansky, T., Wuttke, W. 1983. Glutamate in hypothalamic and limbic structures of diestrous, proestrous, ovariectomized and ovariectomized estrogen-treated rats. *Neurosci. Lett.* 38:51–56

43. Matsumoto, A., Arai, Y. 1986. Male-female difference in synaptic organization of the ventromedial hypothalamus in the rat. *Neuroendocrinology* 42:232–36

44. McEwen, B. S., Parsons, B. 1982. Gonadal steroid action on the brain. Neurochemistry and neuropharmaco-

logy. *Ann. Rev. Pharmacol. Toxicol.* 22:565–98

45. Moore, C. L. 1982. Maternal behavior of rats is affected by hormonal condition of pups. *J. Comp. Physiol. Psychol.* 96:123–29

46. Moore, C. L. 1984. Maternal contributions to the development of masculine sexual behavior in laboratory rats. *Dev. Psychobiol.* 17:347–56

47. Moore, C. L., Morelli, G. A. 1979. Mother rats interact differently with male and female offspring. *J. Comp. Physiol. Psychol.* 93:677–84

48. Moss, R. L., Dudley, C. A. 1984. Molecular aspects of the interaction between estrogen and the membrane excitability of hypothalamic nerve cells. *Prog. Brain Res.* 61:3–21

49. Nabekura, J., Oomura, Y., Minami, T., Mizuno, Y., Fukuda, A. 1986. Mechanism of the rapid effect of 17 β estradiol on medial amygdala neurons. *Science* 233:226–28

50. Nadler, R. D. 1971. Sexual differentiation following intrahypothalamic implantation of steroids. Influences of hormones on the nervous system. *Proc. Int. Soc. Psychoneuroendocrinol.* Brooklyn, NY, 1970, pp. 306–21. Basel: Karger

51. Naftolin, F., Ryan, K. J., Davies, I. J., Reddy, V. V., Flores, F., et al. 1975. The formation of estrogens by central neuroendocrine tissues. *Rec. Prog. Horm. Res.* 31:295–319

52. Nishizuka, M. 1976. Neuropharmacological study on the induction of hypothalamic masculinization in female mice. *Neuroendocrinology* 20:152–65

53. Nishizuka, M., Arai, Y. 1981. Organizational action of estrogen on synaptic pattern in the amygdala: Implications for sexual differentiation of the brain. *Brain Res.* 213:422–26

54. Olney, J. W., Schainker, B., Rhee, V. 1976. Chemical lesioning of the hypothalamus as a means of studying neuroendocrine function. In *Hormones, Behavior and Psychopathology,* ed. E. J. Sachar, pp. 153–58. New York: Raven

55. O'Malley, B. W. 1984. Steroid hormone action in eucaryotic cells. *J. Clin. Invest.* 74:307–12

56. Pfaff, D. W., Keiner, H. 1973. Atlas of estradiol concentrating cells in the central nervous system of the female rat. *J. Comp. Neurol.* 151:121–58

57. Privat, A. 1975. Dendritic growth *in vitro. Adv. Neurol.* 12:201–16

58. Privat, A., Marson, A. M., Drian, H. J. 1979. *In vitro* models of neural growth

and differentiation. *Prog. Brain Res.* 51:335–56

59. Raisman, G., Field, P. M. 1973. Sexual dimorphism in the neuropil of the preoptic area of the rat and its dependence on neonatal androgen. *Brain Res.* 54:1–29

60. Rakic, P. 1975. Role of cell interaction in development of dendritic patterns. *Adv. Neurol.* 12:201–16

61. Raum, W., Swerdloff, R. S. 1981. The role of hypothalamic adrenergic receptors in preventing testosterone-induced androgenization in the female rat brain. *Endocrinology* 109:273–78

62. Rhoda, J., Corbier, P., Raffi, J. 1984. Gonadal steroid concentrations in serum and hypothalamus of the rat at birth: Aromatization of testosterone to 17β estradiol. *Endocrinology* 114:1754–60

63. Sakuma, Y., Pfaff, D. W. 1981. Electrophysiological determination of projections from ventromedial hypothalamus to midbrain central gray: Differences between female and male rats. *Brain Res.* 225:184–88

64. Shirama, K., Takeo, Y., Shimizu, K., Maekawa, K. 1975. Inhibitory effect of 5-hydroxytryptophane on the induction of persistent estrus by androgen in the rat. *Endocrinol. Jpn.* 22:575–79

65. Staudt, J., Stuber, P., Dörner, G. 1978. Permanent changes of sexual dimorphism in the rat brain following neonatal treatment with psychotropic drugs. In *Hormones and Brain Development*, ed. G. Dörner, M. Kawakami, pp. 35–41. Amsterdam: Elsevier/North Holland

66. Stumpf, W. E., Sar, M., Reisert, I., Pilgrim, C. 1983. Estrogen receptor sites in the developing central nervous system and their relationship to catecholamine systems. *Monogr. Neural Sci.* 9:205–12

67. Sutherland, S. D., Gorski, R. A. 1972. An evaluation of the inhibition of androgenization of the neonatal female rat brain by barbiturate. *Neuroendocrinology* 10:94–108

68. Tamasy, V., Koranyi, L., Lissak, K. 1975. Multiple units in brain stem and forebrain during the first week of life in the rat. *Exper. Neurol.* 48:29–36

69. Tobet, S. A., Baum, M. J., Tang, H. B., Shim, J. H., Canick, J. A. 1985. Aromatase activity in the perinatal rat forebrain: Effects of age, sex and intrauterine position. *Dev. Brain Res.* 23:171–78

70. Toran-Allerand, C. D. 1984. On the genesis of sexual differentiation of the central nervous system: Morphogenetic consequences of steroidal exposure and possible role of α-fetoprotein. *Prog. Brain Res.* 61:63–97

71. Towle, A. C., Sze, P. Y. 1983. Steroid binding to synaptic plasma membrane: Differential binding of glucocorticoids and gonadal steroids. *J. Steroid Biochem.* 18:135–43

72. Ward, I. I. 1983. Effects of maternal stress on the sexual behavior of male offspring. *Monogr. Neural Sci.* 9:169–75

73. Weisz, J. 1983. Influence of maternal stress on the developmental pattern of the steroidogenic function in Leydig cells and steroid aromatase activity in the brain of rat fetuses. *Monogr. Neural Sci.* 9:184–93

74. Wheeler, D. D., Ondo, J. G. 1982. Effect of castration on the high affinity glutamate transporter in rat hypothalamic and cortical synaptosomes. *Neurochem. Res.* 7:923–42

75. Will, J. A., Self, P. A., Datan, N. 1976. Maternal behavior and perceived sex of infant. *Am. J. Orthopsychiat.* 46:135–40

76. Willow, M., Johnston, G. A. R. 1983. Pharmacology of barbiturates: Electrophysiological and neurochemical studies. *Int. Rev. Neurobiol.* 24:15–49

77. Young, W. C. 1969. Psychobiology of sexual behavior in the guinea pig. *Adv. Study Behav.* 2:1–110

Ann. Rev. Physiol. 1987. 49:365–82

CENTRAL ACTIONS OF OVARIAN STEROIDS IN THE FEEDBACK REGULATION OF PULSATILE SECRETION OF LUTEINIZING HORMONE

Fred J. Karsch

Consortium for Research in Developmental and Reproductive Biology and Department of Physiology, The University of Michigan, Ann Arbor, Michigan 48109

INTRODUCTION

The neural and endocrine actions of gonadal steroids are extensive. These steroids regulate numerous behaviors and influence the secretion of several of the pituitary hormones, including prolactin, follicle-stimulating hormone, and luteinizing hormone (LH). This review focuses on the central actions of ovarian steroids in the feedback regulation of LH secretion. During the past 15 years, there has been a virtual explosion of new information in this area, and it has become increasingly evident that the feedback actions of gonadal steroids are exerted through the systems that govern the *pulsatile* mode of gonadotropin secretion. In reviewing this topic, three areas are emphasized: (*a*) the hypothalamic pulse generator, (*b*) the feedback actions of estradiol, and (*c*) the feedback actions of progesterone.

THE PULSE GENERATOR

The concept of a neural oscillator that governs the secretion of gonadotropin releasing hormone (GnRH) from the hypothalamus, and thus LH from the pituitary, can be traced back to classical observations that the secretion of LH in gonadectomized rhesus monkeys, sheep, rats, and humans is characterized

365

0066-4278/87/0315-0365$02.00

by regular bursts of release, which occur at intervals of 20–60 min (8, 21, 38, 88, 131). Subsequent studies revealed that such episodic secretion may be ubiquitous among mammals and that it also occurs when the gonads are present (17, 42, 79, 81, 82, 84, 103). The existence of these pulses and the finding that comparable ones can be generated experimentally by bolus injections of GnRH when gonadotropin secretion is otherwise blocked (15, 71, 130) prompted the concept that the hypothalamus communicates with the pituitary gonadotroph via quantal, or pulsatile, GnRH signals. As this system was examined in greater detail it became evident that both the frequency and the amplitude of LH pulses change markedly with reproductive state (42, 51, 82, 84, 88, 103, 131), which thus provided early evidence that the pulse-generating system is regulated by gonadal steroid feedback.

Direct evidence for a pulsatile pattern of GnRH release into pituitary stalk portal blood was first obtained in acute studies using anesthetized rhesus monkeys. However, these studies were limited in scope: They did not include simultaneous determinations of GnRH and LH secretion (10). Subsequent refinements in the method for sequential collection of portal blood, and the development of procedures for monitoring GnRH secretion by push-pull perfusion of the median eminence or collection of cerebrospinal fluid from the third ventricle, have enabled simultaneous determination of GnRH and LH secretory profiles in unanesthetized animals (11, 76, 77, 120). It is now established from studies utilizing these approaches that each pulse of LH from the pituitary is coincident with a pulse of GnRH from the hypothalamus. Moreover, there may exist episodes of GnRH secretion that are not accompanied by pulses of LH.

Before turning to the central actions of ovarian steroids in modulating the activity of the pulse generator, we briefly consider the hypothalamic component of this system. What is the GnRH pulse generator? Where is it located? How does it operate? At present, there are no definitive answers to these questions with regard to the GnRH neurosecretory system; however, considerable progress has been made in the study of neurons involved in the secretion of the posterior pituitary hormones. During the process of milk ejection in the lactating rat, electrophysiologically identified oxytocin-secreting cells display a rhythmic pattern of electrical activity (24, 80). These bouts of activity are synchronized among neurons. They correspond directly to, and presumably cause, the pulsatile release of oxytocin in the lactating rat. [A more extensive description of oxytocin-producing neurons is beyond the scope of this article; two excellent reviews recently appeared that describe the posterior pituitary neurosecretory systems and compare them to the GnRH pulse-generating mechanism (26, 79).] Although such electrical recordings have not yet been possible in electrophysiologically identified single GnRH-secreting cells in the hypothalamus, multi-unit recordings in the medial basal hypothalamus of ovariectomized monkeys and sheep have revealed that rhythmic oscillations of activity do exist and that these correlate with the rhythmic pulses of LH secretion (25, 118, 126). Further, the administration of drugs that inhibit the pulsatile pattern of LH secretion in the rhesus monkey produced a corresponding alteration in the pattern of this multi-unit activity (57). By analogy with the posterior pituitary system, therefore, it is reasonable to presume that populations of GnRH-producing neurons are coordinated in such a way that they depolarize rhythmically and in synchrony, thus producing the pulses of GnRH release.

The neurogenic basis for the coupling among GnRH-producing neurons remains speculative. Possibilities include the existence of pacemaker neurons that impinge directly or indirectly upon GnRH neurons (24); alternatively, GnRH cells may be intrinsically oscillatory and coupled electrically. One challenging impediment to the description of the mode of operation of the GnRH pulse-generating system is that, unlike the posterior pituitary neurons, GnRH cells are not clustered into clearly defined hypthalamic loci. Rather, immunocytochemical studies have revealed that perikarya of GnRH neurons are scattered throughout the medial basal hypothalamus and more rostrally and dorsally to the preoptic area, and to extrahypothalamic sites (45, 48, 74, 115, 116, 128). Further, the pattern of distribution varies considerably among species. GnRH neurons in the rat, for example, are distributed rather diffusely in the hypothalamus, the preoptic area, the diagonal band of Brocha, and the medial septal regions (45, 49, 128). They occur in relatively high density in the medial basal hypothalamus of the monkey (115); whereas in sheep, they are relatively concentrated in the medial preoptic area and are sparse (or absent) in the medial basal hypothalamus (74).

Given this widespread distribution of GnRH neurons, it is not known which populations modulate nonendocrine activities such as sexual behavior (61, 91, 100) and which ones subserve the regulation of gonadotropin secretion and hence form a critical component of the pulse generator. Further, with regard to steroid action, the results of studies utilizing a combination of auto-radiographic methods to identify neurons that sequester estradiol, and immunocytochemical methods to localize cells that produce GnRH, suggest that target cells for estradiol in the hypothalamus may be different from GnRH neurons, although the regions of distribution for these neurons overlap (114). The absence of autoradiographically identified binding sites for estradiol in GnRH neurons, however, does not necessarily exclude these cells as targets, as steroid hormones may elicit certain neural effects through pathways other than classical receptor-mediated genomic mechanisms (86).

This brief description of the LH pulse generator, albeit incomplete, sets the stage for describing the specific actions of ovarian steroids in the feedback regulation of pulsatile LH secretion. The following sections focus on the actions of estradiol and progesterone, two ovarian steroids especially important in this system. This review highlights studies in the rhesus monkey and sheep. In these species, the effects of gonadal steroids on pulsatile LH secretion have been particularly well described (31, 42, 51, 63, 64, 79, 82, 84).

FEEDBACK EFFECTS OF ESTRADIOL

Removal of circulating gonadal steroids by ovariectomy or their selective inactivation by immunoneutralization leads to a major increase in both the frequency and the amplitude of LH pulses (42, 83). Physiological replacement with ovarian steroids can reestablish normal values for both aspects of pulsatile LH release (40, 41, 85). Considerable emphasis has been placed on describing the effects of estradiol in this system and on identifying the sites and mechanisms through which the steroid acts. The specific nature of the feedback effects of estradiol on pulsatile LH secretion are complex; they are time and dose dependent, and they can vary markedly with respect to a number of factors, including stage of sexual maturation, state of nutrition and well being, and season. Following the administration of estradiol, a three-stage response in LH secretion is often observed, which consists of an initial suppression (negative feedback); a relatively brief, but explosive, stimulation (positive feedback); and a state of chronic suppression if the estradiol signal is maintained. These respective feedback responses are considered below.

Estradiol Negative Feedback

The earliest description of the effect of a physiological concentration of estradiol on the LH pulse-generating mechanism was made in the ovariectomized rhesus monkey by Knobil and his colleagues. Infusion of a dose of estradiol, which restored the level of circulating steroid found in the early to mid-follicular phase of the menstrual cycle, led to a profound suppression of the hourly discharge of LH pulses, often blocking the next expected secretory episode (129). Subsequent studies showed this inhibition of LH secretion could be maintained for months, provided the estradiol level remained elevated (52, 56). This negative feedback effect of estradiol plays a major role in the regulation of tonic LH secretion during the course of the menstrual cycle of the rhesus monkey (63).

In a series of elegant studies involving hypothalamic lesions to block endogenous GnRH release and hourly infusions of GnRH to restore hypophyseotrophic support, Knobil's group has presented a strong argument that the negative feedback effects of estradiol in the monkey are produced, in large measure, by an action on the pituitary to suppress the response to GnRH (64). Those studies, however, do not discount an additional action of estradiol on the brain to suppress pulsatile GnRH release. A neural site for steroid action was initially suggested by the finding that the inhibitory effect of estradiol on LH pulses in the ovariectomized monkey could be mimicked by the administration of drugs that blocked alpha-adrenergic or dopaminergic neurotransmission (4). These drugs have since been shown to block the rhythmic bursts of hypothalamic multi-unit electrical activity that accompany the rhythmic oscillations of LH, and presumably GnRH release, in the ovariectomized monkey (57). Further support for a neural site of action of estradiol in the monkey is provided by experiments in which pulsatile LH release was blocked by microinjections of the steroid directly into the hypothalamus (29), by observations that estradiol can inhibit pulsatile secretion of GnRH (31), and by autoradiographic localization of neurons that sequester estradiol in the area of GnRH-producing neurons in the medial basal hypothalamus (101, 115). This region is believed to contain the GnRH pulse generator in the rhesus monkey (64). Therefore, the feedback suppression of pulsatile LH secretion by estradiol in the monkey probably involves actions at both pituitary and hypothalamic sites.

Another animal in which the negative feedback effect of estradiol on the LH pulse-generating system has been particularly well studied is the sheep; but in this species the response pattern is considerably more complex than in the monkey. Specifically, over the course of a year there is a very marked seasonal difference in response to the negative feedback effects of estradiol (43, 62, 73, 99, 106, 122). This reflects a photoperiodically mediated change in the activity of the pulse generator and in the ability of estradiol to inhibit pulse frequency (5, 40, 85, 106). During the anestrous season, estradiol is a potent negative feedback agent, and the steroid, in physiological amounts, has a profound ability to inhibit the frequency of LH pulses. This action of estradiol may account for the low pulse frequencies seen during seasonal anestrus (40, 50, 71, 110). During the breeding season, estradiol serves primarily to reduce LH pulse amplitude; physiological levels of estradiol are not able to lower the frequency (41, 85). In fact, under certain conditions, the steroid can actually enhance frequency during the breeding season, and this effect contributes to the five- to ten-fold increase in the pace of LH pulses during the follicular phase of the estrous cycle (2, 13, 53, 60).

Such major variations in the feedback actions of estradiol on pulsatile LH secretion in sheep are not confined to changes with season; comparable variations occur around the time of puberty. Prior to first ovulation, estradiol exerts a profound suppression of LH secretion by inhibiting pulse frequency. Thereafter, the potency of estradiol negative feedback wanes, and the steroid is no longer effective in this regard (32, 34, 35). There is now strong evidence that these changes in the actions of estradiol on the LH pulse-generating system can account for the transition from the immature to the mature reproductive state in lambs, as well as for the transition from anestrus to breeding season in the adult (32, 35, 50, 51).

Most workers agree that changes in the frequency of LH pulses are due to alterations in the oscillatory period of the hypothalamic pulse generator. Changes in amplitude, however, could reflect variations either at the level of the pituitary and its response to GnRH or at the level of the hypothalamus and the amount of GnRH released in each episodic discharge. Based on this logic, the ability of estradiol to reduce LH pulse frequency in sheep during seasonal anestrus, or prior to puberty, would reflect an action on the brain and an alteration in periodicity of the pulse generator. This inhibitory action is then reversed at the transition to the active reproductive state, and estradiol gains the capacity to accelerate the pulse generator, rather than to slow it down. This argument is supported by the demonstration that alpha-adrenergic or dopaminergic blocking drugs can reverse the estradiol inhibition of LH pulse frequency in anestrus but not in the breeding season (87). The latter finding also indicates these neuronal systems participate in the negative feedback action of estradiol in anestrus.

Despite these observations and considerations, studies in which GnRH pulses were monitored directly in serial samples of pituitary stalk portal blood have produced results that are somewhat inconsistent. In one study, pulsatile LH and GnRH secretion was evaluated for several hours before and after injection of estradiol benzoate into one long-term ovariectomized ewe in the anestrous season (13). No reduction in GnRH pulse frequency was observed following the injection of estradiol benzoate. It is noteworthy, however, that LH pulse frequency was also not reduced in this ewe, as would be expected during the anestrous season based on the results of numerous other studies described above (5, 40, 85). In a separate study on a larger number of ewes, insertion of constant-release implants of estradiol at the time of ovariectomy during anestrus was found to block GnRH and LH pulses 8–10 days later when observations were made. A similar blockage, however, was observed when the study was repeated in the breeding season (F. J. Karsch, J. T. Cummins, G. B. Thomas, and I. J. Clarke, unpublished observation).

The sites and modes of action of estradiol in reducing LH pulse amplitude in the breeding season are not easily deduced, but several possibilities exist. First, estradiol could act upon GnRH-secreting neurons to reduce the amount of the neuropeptide discharged in each secretory episode. Such a reduction in the amount of GnRH released could reflect alterations in the pattern of electrical activity of GnRH neurons (27), much as the pattern of electrical activity is critical to the amount of oxytocin released during each secretory episode of that neuropeptide (24, 79). Another way that estradiol could reduce the amount of GnRH discharged in each pulse would be through an inhibition of GnRH synthesis.

Estradiol could also lower LH pulse amplitude in the breeding season of the ewe by acting at the level of the anterior pituitary gland. In this regard, the steroid has been shown to reduce the amount of LH discharged in response to pulse injections or infusions of GnRH (12, 41, 95), much as in the rhesus monkey (92, 102). Although the cellular mechanism for this effect is not known, it is pertinent that prolonged treatment of ewes with physiological doses of estradiol has been found to reduce the amount of messenger RNA for both the alpha and beta subunits of LH in the pituitary, thus suppressing synthesis and lowering pituitary LH content and releasable gonadotropin stores (67, 68, 89, 96).

Yet another mechanism for the amplitude-inhibiting effect of estradiol could be an increase in GnRH pulse frequency. Studies performed to evaluate the importance of variations in the patterning of GnRH signals have shown a clear inverse relationship between GnRH pulse frequency and LH pulse amplitude in the ewe (15, 59). This phenomenon may be explained, in part, by the finding that GnRH can decrease the number of its own receptors in ovine pituitary cells, thereby lowering the amount of LH released during a GnRH challenge (94, 127). Moreover, it has been proposed that high-frequency pulses of GnRH can reduce the releasable store of LH in the pituitary (14). The ability of estradiol to lower LH pulse amplitude in the breeding season, therefore, may be secondary to its ability to increase LH (and presumably GnRH) pulse frequency at that time of the year (13, 53, 60).

Regarding the nature and mechanisms for estradiol negative feedback on the LH pulse-generating system, it is useful to stress that the inhibitory effects of estradiol can be expressed in a number of ways and at several sites within the hypothalamo-hypophyseal axis. Further, the various sites and modes of action of estradiol may well have different time constants, such that the specific negative feedback responses observed shortly after initiation of an estradiol signal may differ greatly from those that prevail during a state of chronic estradiol negative feedback.

Estradiol Positive Feedback

Following the administration of estradiol, the pattern of LH secretion varies with time and depends upon the extent to which circulating estradiol is elevated. If the estradiol level is high enough, e.g. within the upper physiological range, the initial negative feedback response is interrupted by the LH surge, a massive discharge like the one that induces ovulation during the ovarian cycle (43, 50, 63, 111). The latency to onset of this response, referred to as the positive feedback response, depends upon the blood level of estradiol achieved. Within limits, the higher the estradiol level, the shorter the latency to the LH surge (43, 55). The latency is 24–48 hr in the monkey (55) and 12–48 hr in the ewe; however, the latency in the ewe is normally lengthened by the recent exposure to elevated progesterone during the luteal phase of the cycle (43, 54). In the rat, this characteristic is not evident because the onset of the LH surge is confined to a fixed phase of the light-dark cycle (113); latency thus cannot vary outside the limits imposed by the circadian system.

The daily LH surge is another interesting phenomenon related to the participation of circadian rhythms in the LH surge mechanism of the rat. In the ovariectomized rat, injection of estradiol benzoate or treatment with a constant-release Silastic implant of estradiol elicits a daily LH surge that can persist for weeks (9, 70, 72). Under normal circumstances, the daily LH surge is not seen during the estrous cycle because ovulation and corpus luteum formation, both consequences of the LH surge, produce a steroidal milieu (low estradiol, high progesterone) incompatible with a daily LH surge (36, 72). In nonrodent species, estradiol treatment elicits but a single LH surge. In fact, studies in the rhesus monkey suggest that a second surge cannot be induced until a 6–8 day refractory period has elapsed (123).

The characteristics of pulsatile LH release during the surge have been difficult to elucidate because this determination requires extremely frequent blood sampling at a specific point in time, and the exact time of onset of the surge is often difficult to predict. Observations in the rat (37), cow (103), sheep (53), and woman (23) indicate that the LH surge is composed of extremely large pulses of high frequency (up to one pulse per 15–20 min). The positive feedback effect of estradiol, therefore, is likely achieved through the LH pulse-generating mechanism and probably includes modulation of both the frequency and the amplitude of LH pulses.

The mechanisms through which estradiol acts to induce the LH surge have been extensively studied. Like the negative feedback effects of the steroid, the positive feedback response involves multiple sites within the hypothalamo-hypophyseal axis. One major site of action is the anterior pituitary gland, where estradiol enhances the response to GnRH (12, 47, 64, 78, 90, 92, 105). This action of estradiol has been described both in vitro and in vivo in many species, and it may contribute to the increased amplitude of LH pulses during the surge. These pituitary effects of estradiol likely reflect changes in both gonadotropin biosynthesis and the number of GnRH receptors. Just prior to, and during, the LH surge in sheep, for example, there is an increase in pituitary content of messenger RNA coding for gonadotropic hormones; this increase can also be induced by acute exposure to estradiol (65, 66, 68, 69). Further, the number of receptors for GnRH on pituitary cells increases at the time of the LH surge (1, 18, 89, 95, 108, 109).

Another site for the positive feedback action of estradiol is the hypothalamus, where it stimulates GnRH secretion. This too has been demonstrated in vitro and in vivo in many species. For example, an increase in GnRH has been reported in hypophyseal portal blood and in push-pull perfusates from the median eminence during the LH surge in the rat (77, 107), rabbit (119), monkey (75, 93), and sheep (13, 112). In sheep, this change was described as resulting from an increase in the frequency of GnRH pulses (13); in monkeys it was found to be associated with an increase in pulse amplitude (75).

The relative importance of the pituitary and hypothalamus as sites for the positive feedback action of estradiol appears to differ with species. In the rhesus monkey, for example, an action on the pituitary may be especially important (30, 64, 124); although this is a point of considerable controversy. A pituitary site of action is indicated from studies using a number of experimental approaches. Perhaps the most demonstrative of those studies used chronic, hourly pulse infusion of GnRH to restore normal gonadotropin secretion in monkeys whose endogenous GnRH was obliterated by lesions of the arcuate nucleus. In this animal model, injection of estradiol was found to induce an LH surge of normal time course and magnitude, and this response did not require GnRH over and above that provided by the chronic pulsed infusion of the decapeptide (64). In fact, subsequent studies using this model revealed that estradiol could induce the LH surge even when pulsed infusion of GnRH was terminated at the time of the estradiol challenge (124). The premise that endogenous GnRH secretion was abolished in the various animal preparations utilized, however, has recently been challenged by other studies (97). The latter experiments support the view that a further increase in GnRH participates in the generation of the LH surge in the monkey (75, 97).

In the sheep, a pituitary site of action of estradiol cannot completely account for the normal LH surge. Using an experimental model similar to that described above for the monkey (chronic hourly pulse infusion of GnRH into ewes whose own GnRH secretion was presumed to have been abolished), Clarke & Cummins found that injection of estradiol can induce a "surge-like" pattern of LH secretion, but this response was smaller than the normal surge (12). Moreover, we recently observed that an increment of GnRH over and above the chronic pulse infusion is needed to produce an LH surge of normal time course and magnitude in this type of experimental model (A. H. Kaynard & F. J. Karsch, unpublished observation).

In still other species, an acute increase in GnRH secretion seems to be even more critical for the occurrence of the LH surge. In the rat, for example, the surge occurs only within the time constraints imposed by the circadian system, which implies that a neurogenic signal is essential for initiating the preovulatory LH surge (113). This signal presumably triggers the increased secretion of GnRH into the portal circulation on the afternoon of proestrus in the rat (77, 107).

FEEDBACK EFFECTS OF PROGESTERONE

The administration of progesterone can have both inductive and suppressive effects on gonadotropin secretion, and as for estradiol, the nature of these effects is time and dose dependent (104). Although the stimulatory action of acute increases in progesterone may contribute to the generation of the LH surge in a number of species, including the rat, human, and monkey (16, 22, 98, 104), the best documented effects of this steroid on the LH pulse-generating system are its negative feedback actions. It is this aspect of progesterone feedback that is described here.

The earliest indication that progesterone might regulate the LH pulse-generating system was the observation that single injections of this steroid lowered the frequency of LH pulses in ovariectomized rhesus monkeys (129). The physiological significance of that finding, however, was not initially recognized for several reasons: (a) a pharmacological blood level of progesterone was needed to produce the effect; (b) the progesterone treatment did not reduce the mean concentration of LH in serum because decreases in frequency were offset by increases in amplitude; and (c) the concentration of LH in serum obtained during the luteal phase of the menstrual cycle, when progesterone is elevated, was not lower than that obtained during the follicular phase, when progesterone secretion is minimal (63, 129). Subsequent studies, however, indicated that a physiological level of circulating progesterone could lower LH concentrations in the ovariectomized monkey, provided that the treatment was sustained by means of a constant-release implant and that estradiol was also present in low concentrations (56). More recent studies in the monkey, which employed frequent sampling and highly sensitive assays for LH, have revealed that LH pulse frequency does decrease during the luteal phase of the menstrual cycle when progesterone rises (28, 121). Such an inverse relationship between LH pulse frequency and the circulating level of progesterone, and the ability of exogenous progesterone to slow the pace of LH pulses, have also been described for the human (19, 117, 131). Collectively, these observations strongly suggest that progesterone participates in the negative feedback regulation of LH secretion during the menstrual cycle and that it does so by restricting the frequency of the LH pulse-generating system.

Marked changes in the frequency of LH pulses during the course of the cycle have been documented in other species, including the cow (103) and sheep (2, 33, 44, 53). These changes and the negative feedback effects of progesterone on frequency have been particularly well described in sheep. They may be summarized as follows: The frequency of LH pulses in the ewe is high shortly after ovulation when progesterone secretion is low. The frequency decreases during the early to mid-luteal phase as progesterone increases and is minimal at the time of the mid-luteal phase when progesterone secretion is maximal. Finally, the pace of LH pulses increases markedly at the time of luteal regression when progesterone plummets (2, 33, 44, 53). Ovariectomy during the luteal phase causes a prompt increase in LH pulse frequency. Insertion of Silastic implants that maintain a mid-luteal phase level of progesterone can abolish this postcastration increase in LH pulse frequency in the ewe (41). When maintained at a concentration below the luteal phase maximum (for example at an early luteal phase level), progesterone alone is unable to reduce the postcastration increase in LH pulse frequency. This low level of progesterone, however, becomes effective in the presence of a basal concentration of estradiol (39, 85).

The foregoing observations have led to the conclusion that the moment-to-moment changes in LH pulse frequency during the course of the estrous cycle of sheep are governed, in large measure, by cyclic fluctuations in the circulating level of progesterone, which reflects the waxing and waning of the corpus luteum (42, 51). Despite the critical role played by progesterone, it should be stressed that this steroid is not the only ovarian regulator of frequency during the cycle. In this regard, estradiol serves two important functions. First, estradiol acts synergistically with progesterone to allow an otherwise sub-threshold level of progesterone to inhibit frequency in the early luteal phase of the estrous cycle (39, 85). Second, estradiol can actually enhance frequency when unopposed by an elevated level of progesterone, as during the follicular phase of the estrous cycle (13, 53, 60). The marked increase in frequency (five- to tenfold) that occurs during the 2–3 day follicular phase of the estrous cycle of the ewe is thus a consequence of the combined effects of the withdrawal of progesterone inhibition and the presence of estradiol (53).

There is strong evidence that progesterone acts on the brain to reduce LH pulse frequency, thus increasing the interval between episodes of GnRH release. We recently found that maintenance of a luteal phase level of progesterone prevents the increase in GnRH pulse frequency that normally follows ovariectomy of the ewe (F. J. Karsch, J. T. Cummins, G. B. Thomas and I. J. Clarke, unpublished observation). Others have shown that this neural effect of progesterone likely involves the endogenous opioid peptides. In both sheep and monkeys, the suppression of pulse frequency during the luteal phase of the cycle, or during treatment with progesterone, can be interrupted by administration of the opioid antagonist, naloxone (6, 7, 121). Further, the concentration of one of these opioids, beta-endorphin, was found to be greatest in pituitary portal blood of monkeys during the luteal phase of the cycle when progesterone is elevated (31).

Also consistent with a neural site of action for progesterone negative feedback are findings that maintenance of a physiological blood level of progesterone, which by itself can inhibit frequency, has little or no inhibitory effect upon the response of the pituitary to single- or multiple-pulse injections of GnRH (12, 41). Nevertheless, there is some evidence that progesterone can alter LH pulse amplitude and that it may act upon the pituitary to modify its response to GnRH. Depending on the experimental conditions, the effects of progesterone can be stimulatory (12, 41, 129), inhibitory (3, 46), or non-existent (12, 20, 41). Although the specific conditions required for each of these effects of progesterone are not established, the influence of the steroid on pituitary response to pulsatile GnRH secretion may vary with time and appears to depend upon estradiol (12). The physiological relevance of such pituitary effects of progesterone remain to be defined.

One other action of progesterone is its ability to block the preovulatory LH surge. Chronic exposure to a luteal phase level of progesterone prevents an otherwise effective estradiol signal from inducing the LH surge (16, 22, 54, 111). This effect is widespread among spontaneously ovulating mammals, and it can account for the absence of ovulation under conditions of elevated progesterone, for example in the luteal phase of the cycle and during pregnancy. Studies in both the rhesus monkey and the sheep provide strong evidence that this surge-blocking effect of progesterone can be attributed to an action on the brain and a blockade of the pulsatile mode of GnRH release (12, 58, 125). Given that the LH surge is comprised of high-frequency pulses (see section on estradiol positive feedback), the surge-blocking effect of progesterone may well be another manifestation of its ability to lower the frequency of the LH pulse-generating mechanism.

SUMMARY

I have considered the neural organization of the system responsible for pulsatile LH and GnRH secretion and have described the feedback actions of two ovarian steroids, estradiol and progesterone. These steroidal feedbacks are complex: They are time and dose dependent; they include both inductive and inhibitory effects; they reflect actions at multiple sites within the hypothalamo-hypophyseal axis. In this review we emphasized two ovarian steroids especially important to this regulatory system and observations in females of two species that have been particularly well studied in this regard. This emphasis required exclusion of excellent studies in other species, with other steroids, and in the other sex. This focus, however, permitted a more detailed evaluation of current concepts in an area of fundamental importance to the neuroendocrine regulation of reproduction.

Literature Cited

1. Adams, T. E., Norman, R. L., Spies, H. G. 1981. Gonadotropin-releasing hormone receptor binding and pituitary responsiveness in estradiol-primed monkeys. *Science* 213:1388–90
2. Baird, D. T. 1978. Pulsatile secretion of LH and ovarian estradiol during the follicular phase of the sheep estrous cycle. *Biol. Reprod.* 18:359–64
3. Batra, S. K., Miller, W. L. 1985. Progesterone decreases the responsiveness

of ovine pituitary cultures to luteinizing hormone-releasing hormone. *Endocrinology* 117:1436–40
4. Bhattacharya, A. N., Dierschke, D. J., Yamaji, T., Knobil, E. 1972. The pharmacologic blockade of the circhoral mode of LH secretion in the ovariectomized rhesus monkey. *Endocrinology* 90:778–86
5. Bittman, E. L., Kaynard, A. H., Olster, D. H., Robinson, J. E., Yellon, S. M.,

Karsch, F. J. 1985. Pineal melatonin mediates photoperiodic control of pulsatile luteinizing hormone secretion in the ewe. *Neuroendocrinology* 40:409–18

6. Brooks, A. N., Haynes, N. B., Yang, K., Lamming, G. E. 1986. Ovarian steroid involvement in endogenous opioid modulation of LH secretion in seasonally anoestrous mature ewes. *J. Reprod. Fertil.* 76:709–15

7. Brooks, A. N., Lamming, G. E., Lees, P. D., Haynes, N. B. 1986. Opioid modulation of LH secretion in the ewe. *J. Reprod. Fertil.* 76:693–708

8. Butler, W. R., Malvin, P. V., Willett, L. B., Bolt, D. J. 1972. Patterns of pituitary release and cranial output of LH and prolactin in ovariectomized ewes. *Endocrinology* 91:793–801

9. Caligaris, L., Astrada, J. J., Taleisnik, S. 1971. Release of luteinizing hormone induced by estrogen injection into ovariectomized rats. *Endocrinology* 88:810–15

10. Carmel, P. W., Araki, S., Ferin, M. 1976. Pituitary stalk portal blood collection in rhesus monkeys: Evidence for pulsatile release of gonadotropin-releasing hormone (GnRH). *Endocrinology* 99:243–48

11. Clarke, I. J., Cummins, J. T. 1982. The temporal relationship between gonadotropin releasing hormone (GnRH) and luteinizing hormone (LH) secretion in ovariectomized ewes. *Endocrinology* 111:1737–39

12. Clarke, I. J., Cummins, J. T. 1984. Direct pituitary effects of estrogen and progesterone on gonadotropin secretion in the ovariectomized ewe. *Neuroendocrinology* 39:267–74

13. Clarke, I. J., Cummins, J. T. 1985. Increased gonadotropin-releasing hormone pulse frequency associated with estrogen-induced luteinizing hormone surges in ovariectomized ewes. *Endocrinology* 116:2376–83

14. Clarke, I. J., Cummins, J. T. 1985. GnRH pulse frequency determines LH pulse amplitude by altering the amount of releasable LH in the pituitary glands of ewes. *J. Reprod. Fertil.* 73:425–31

15. Clarke, I. J., Cummins, J. T., Findlay, J. K., Burman, K. J., Doughton, B. W. 1984. Effects on plasma luteinizing hormone and follicle-stimulating hormone of varying the frequency and amplitude of gonadotropin-releasing hormone pulses in ovariectomized ewes with hypothalamo-pituitary disconnection. *Neuroendocrinology* 39:214–21

16. Clifton, D. K., Steiner, R. A., Resko, J. A., Spies, H. G. 1975. Estrogen-

induced gonadotropin release in ovariectomized rhesus monkeys and its advancement by progesterone. *Biol. Reprod.* 13:190–94

17. Coquelin, A., Bronson, F. H. 1981. Episodic release of luteinizing hormone in male mice: Antagonism by a neural refractory period. *Endocrinology* 109:1605–10

18. Crowder, M. E., Nett, T. M. 1984. Pituitary content of gonadotropins and receptors for gonadotropin-releasing hormone (GnRH) and hypothalamic content of GnRH during the periovulatory period of the ewe. *Endocrinology* 114:234–39

19. Crowley, W. F. Jr., Filicori, M., Spratt, D., Santoro, N. F. 1985. The physiology of gonadotropin-releasing hormone (GnRH) secretion in men and women. *Rec. Progr. Horm. Res.* 41:473–531

20. Cumming, I. A., Buckmaster, J. M., Cerini, J. C., Cerini, M. E., Chamley, W. A., et al. 1972. Effect of progesterone on release of luteinizing hormone induced by a synthetic gonadotropin-releasing factor in the ewe. *Neuroendocrinology* 10:338–48

21. Dierschke, D. J., Bhattacharya, A. N., Atkinson, L. E., Knobil, E. 1970. Circhoral oscillations of plasma LH levels in the ovariectomized rhesus monkey. *Endocrinology* 87:850–53

22. Dierschke, D. J., Yamaji, T., Karsch, F. J., Weick, R. F., Weiss, G., Knobil, E. 1973. Blockade by progesterone of estrogen-induced LH and FSH release in the rhesus monkey. *Endocrinology* 92:1496–1501

23. Djahanbakhch, O., Warner, P., McNeilly, A. S., Baird, D. T. 1984. Pulsatile release of LH and oestradiol during the periovulatory period in women. *Clin. Endocrinol.* 20:579–89

24. Dreifuss, J. J., Tribollet, E., Muhlethaler, M. 1981. Temporal patterns of neural activity and their relation to the secretion of posterior pituitary hormones. *Biol. Reprod.* 24:51–72

25. Dufy, B., Dufy-Barbe, L., Seal, J., Vincent, J.-D. 1979. An electrophysiological approach to the mechanisms underlying ovulatory processes in the primate. In *Psychoneuroendocrinology in Reproduction*, ed. L. Zichella, P. Pancheri, pp. 167–74. Amsterdam: Elsevier North-Holland

26. Dyer, R. G. 1985. Neural signals for oxytocin and LH release. *Oxford Rev. Reprod. Biol.* 7:223–60

27. Dyer, R. G., Mansfield, S., Yates, J. O. 1980. Discharge of gonadotrophin-releasing hormone from the mediobasal

part of the hypothalamus: Effect of stimulation frequency and gonadal steroids. *Exp. Brain Res.* 39:453–60

28. Ellinwood, W. E., Norman, R. L., Spies, H. G. 1984. Changing frequency of pulsatile luteinizing hormone and progesterone secretion during the luteal phase of the menstrual cycle of rhesus monkeys. *Biol. Reprod.* 31:714–22

29. Ferin, M., Carmel, P. W., Zimmerman, E. A., Warren, M., Perez, R., Vande Wiele, R. L. 1974. Location of intrahypothalamic estrogen-responsive sites influencing LH secretion in the female rhesus monkey. *Endocrinology* 95:1059–68

30. Ferin, M., Rosenblatt, H., Carmel, P. W., Antunes, J. L., Vande Wiele, R. L. 1979. Estrogen-induced gonadotropin surges in female rhesus monkeys after pituitary stalk section. *Endocrinology* 104:50–52

31. Ferin, M., Van Vugt, D., Wardlaw, S. 1984. The hypothalamic control of the menstrual cycle and the role of endogenous opiod peptides. *Rec. Progr. Horm. Res.* 40:441–85

32. Foster, D. L., Karsch, F. J., Olster, D. H., Ryan, K. D., Yellon, S. M. 1986. Determinants of puberty in a seasonal breeder. *Rec. Progr. Horm. Res.* 42: 331–84

33. Foster, D. L., Lemons, J. A., Jaffe, R. B., Niswender, G. D. 1975. Sequential patterns of circulating luteinizing hormone and follicle-stimulating hormone in female sheep from early postnatal life through the first estrous cycles. *Endocrinology* 97:985–94

34. Foster, D. L., Ryan, K. D. 1979. Endocrine mechanisms governing transition into adulthood: A marked decrease in inhibitory feedback action of estradiol on tonic secretion of luteinizing hormone in the lamb during puberty. *Endocrinology* 105:896–904

35. Foster, D. L., Yellon, S. M., Olster, D. H. 1985. Internal and external determinants of the timing of puberty in the female. *J. Reprod. Fertil.* 75:327–44

36. Freeman, M. C., Dupke, K. C., Croteau, C. M. 1976. Extinction of the estrogen-induced daily signal for LH release in the rat: A role for the proestrous surge of progesterone. *Endocrinology* 99:223–29

37. Gallo, R. V. 1981. Pulsatile LH release during the ovulatory LH surge on proestrus in the rat. *Biol. Reprod.* 24:100–4

38. Gay, V. L., Seth, N. A. 1972. Evidence for a periodic release of LH in castrated male and female rats. *Endocrinology* 90:158–62

39. Goodman, R. L., Bittman, E. L., Foster, D. L., Karsch, F. J. 1981. The endocrine basis of the synergistic suppression of luteinizing hormone by estradiol and progesterone. *Endocrinology* 109: 1414–17

40. Goodman, R. L., Bittman, E. L., Foster, D. L., Karsch, F. J. 1982. Alterations in the control of luteinizing hormone pulse frequency underlie the seasonal variation in estradiol negative feedback in the ewe. *Biol. Reprod.* 27:580–89

41. Goodman, R. L., Karsch, F. J. 1980. Pulsatile secretion of luteinizing hormone: Differential suppression by ovarian steroids. *Endocrinology* 107:1286–90

42. Goodman, R. L., Karsch, F. J. 1981. The hypothalamic pulse generator: A key determinant of reproductive cycles in sheep. In *Biological Clocks in Seasonal Reproductive Cycles*, ed. B. K. Follett, D. E. Follett, pp. 223–36. Bristol: Wright

43. Goodman, R. L., Legan, S. J., Ryan, K. D., Foster, D. L., Karsch, F. J. 1981. Importance of variations in behavioural and feedback actions of oestradiol to the control of seasonal breeding in the ewe. *J. Endocrinol.* 89:229–40

44. Hauger, R. L., Karsch, F. J., Foster, D. L. 1977. A new concept for control of the estrous cycle of the ewe based on the temporal relationships between luteinizing hormone, estradiol and progesterone in peripheral serum and evidence that progesterone inhibits tonic LH secretion. *Endocrinology* 101:807–17

45. Hoffman, G. E., Gibbs, F. P. 1982. LHRH pathways in rat brain: 'Deafferentation' spares a sub-chiasmatic LHRH projection to the median eminence. *Neuroscience* 7:1979–93

46. Hooley, R. D., Baxter, R. W., Chamley, W. A., Cumming, I. A., Jonas, H. A., Findlay, J. K. 1974. FSH and LH response to gonadotropin-releasing hormone during the ovine estrous cycle and following progesterone administration. *Endocrinology* 95:937–42

47. Jackson, G. L. 1975. Blockage of estrogen-induced release of luteinizing hormone by reserpine and potentiation of synthetic gonadatropin-releasing hormone-induced release of luteinizing hormone by estrogen in the ovariectomized ewe. *Endocrinology* 97:1300–7

48. Jennes, L., Stumpf, W. E. 1980. LHRH-systems in the brain of the golden hamster. *Cell Tissue Res.* 209:239–56

49. Jennes, L., Stumpf, W. E., Sheedy, M.

E. 1985. Ultrastructural characterization of gonadotropin-releasing hormone (GnRH)-producing neurons. *J. Comp. Neurol.* 232:534–47

50. Karsch, F. J. 1980. Seasonal breeding: A saga of reversible fertility. *Physiologist* 23, No. 6:29–38

51. Karsch, F. J., Bittman, E. L., Foster, D. L., Goodman, R. L., Legan, S. J., Robinson, J. E. 1984. Neuroendocrine basis of seasonal reproduction. *Rec. Progr. Horm. Res.* 40:185–232

52. Karsch, F. J., Dierschke, D. J., Weick, R. F., Yamaji, T., Hotchkiss, J., Knobil, E. 1973. Positive and negative feedback control by estrogen of luteinizing hormone secretion in the rhesus monkey. *Endocrinology* 92:799–804

53. Karsch, F. J., Foster, D. L., Bittman, E. L., Goodman, R. L. 1983. A role for estradiol in enhancing luteinizing hormone pulse frequency during the follicular phase of the estrous cycle of sheep. *Endocrinology* 113:1333–39

54. Karsch, F. J., Legan, S. J., Ryan, K. D., Foster, D. L. 1980. Importance of estradiol and progesterone in regulating LH secretion and estrous behavior during the sheep estrous cycle. *Biol. Reprod.* 23:404–13

55. Karsch, F. J., Weick, R. F., Butler, W. R., Dierschke, D. J., Krey, L. C., et al. 1973. Induced LH surges in the rhesus monkey: Strength-duration characteristics of the estrogen stimulus. *Endocrinology* 92:1740–47

56. Karsch, F. J., Weick, R. F., Hotchkiss, J., Dierschke, D. J., Knobil, E. 1973. An analysis of the negative feedback control of gonadotropin secretion utilizing chronic implantation of ovarian steroids in ovariectomized rhesus monkeys. *Endocrinology* 93:478–86

57. Kaufman, J.-M., Kesner, J. S., Wilson, R. C., Knobil, E. 1985. Electrophysiological manifestation of luteinizing hormone-releasing hormone pulse generator activity in the rhesus monkey: Influence of alpha-adrenergic and dopaminergic blocking agents. *Endocrinology* 116:1327–33

58. Kaynard, A. H. 1984. Evidence to support a neural site of action for progesterone blockade of the LH surge in the ewe. *Biol. Reprod.* Vol. 30, Suppl. 1, Abstr. 7

59. Kaynard, A. H., Karsch, F. J. 1983. The inverse relationship between LH-pulse amplitude and frequency in the ewe may reflect a change in pituitary response to GnRH. *Biol. Reprod.* 28, Suppl. 1, Abstr. 65

60. Kaynard, A. H., Karsch, F. J. 1984.

Estradiol stimulates an increase in LH-pulse frequency in the ewe independent of prior exposure to progesterone. *Abstr. 7th. Int. Congr. Endocrinol. Excerpta Med. Int. Congr.,* Ser. 652, Abstr. 1233

61. Kendrick, K. M., Dixson, A. F. 1985. Luteinizing hormone releasing hormone enhances proceptivity in a primate. *Neuroendocrinology* 41:449–53

62. Kennaway, D. J., Dunstan, E. A., Gilmore, T. A., Seamark, R. F. 1984. Effects of pinealectomy and melatonin on plasma prolactin and LH secretion in ovariectomized sheep. *J. Endocrinol.* 102:199–207

63. Knobil, E. 1974. On the control of gonadotropin secretion in the rhesus monkey. *Rec. Progr. Horm. Res.* 30:1–46

64. Knobil, E. 1981. The neuroendocrine control of the menstrual cycle. *Rec. Progr. Horm. Res.* 36:53–88

65. Landefeld, T., Kaynard, A., Kepa, J. 1985. Pituitary alpha-subunit messenger ribonucleic acid remains elevated during the latter stages of the preovulatory luteinizing hormone surge. *Endocrinology* 117:934–38

66. Landefeld, T. D., Kepa, J. 1984. Pituitary alpha subunit mRNA amounts during the sheep estrous cycle. *J. Biol. Chem.* 259:12817–20

67. Landefeld, T. D., Kepa, J., Karsch, F. J. 1983. Regulation of alpha subunit synthesis by gonadal steroid feedback in the sheep anterior pituitary. *J. Biol. Chem.* 258:2390–93

68. Landefeld, T., Kepa, J., Karsch, F. 1984. Estradiol feedback effects on the alpha-subunit mRNA in the sheep pituitary gland: Correlation with serum and pituitary luteinizing hormone concentrations. *Proc. Natl. Acad. Sci. USA* 81:1322–26

69. Landefeld, T., Maurer, R., Kepa, J. 1985. Luteinizing hormone beta-subunit mRNA amounts increase during the preovulatory surge of luteinizing hormone in the ewe: The highest levels are observed at the completion of the peak. *DNA* 4:249–54

70. Legan, S. J., Coon, G. A., Karsch, F. J. 1975. Role of estrogen as initiator of daily LH surges in the ovariectomized rat. *Endocrinology* 96:50–56

71. Legan, S. J., I'Anson, H., Fitzgerald, B. P., Fitzovich, D. 1985. Does the seasonal increase in estradiol negative feedback prevent luteinizing hormone surges in anestrous ewes by suppressing hypothalamic gonadotropin-releasing hormone pulse frequency? *Biol. Reprod.* 33:117–31

72. Legan, S. J., Karsch, F. J. 1975. A

daily signal for the LH surge in the rat. *Endocrinology* 96:57–62

73. Legan, S. J., Karsch, F. J., Foster, D. L. 1977. The endocrine control of seasonal reproductive function in the ewe: A marked change in response to the negative feedback action of estradiol on luteinizing hormone secretion. *Endocrinology* 101:818–24

74. Lehman, M. N., Robinson, J. E., Karsch, F. J., Silverman, A.-J. 1986. Immunocytochemical localization of luteinizing hormone-releasing hormone (LHRH) pathways in the sheep brain during anestrus and the mid-luteal phase of the estrous cycle. *J. Comp. Neurol.* 244:19–35

75. Levine, J. E., Norman, R. L., Gleissman, P. M., Oyama, T. T., Bangsberg, D. R., Spies, H. G., 1985. In vivo gonadotropin-releasing hormone release and serum luteinizing hormone measurements in ovariectomized, estrogen-treated rhesus macaques. *Endocrinology* 117:711–21

76. Levine, J. E., Pau, K.-Y. F., Ramirez, V. D., Jackson, G. L. 1982. Simultaneous measurement of luteinizing hormone releasing hormone and luteinizing hormone release in unanesthetized, ovariectomized sheep. *Endocrinology* 111:1449–55

77. Levine, J. E., Ramirez, V. D. 1982. Luteinizing hormone-releasing hormone release during the rat estrous cycle and after ovariectomy, as estimated with push-pull cannulae. *Endocrinology* 111:1439–48

78. Libertun, C., Orias, R., McCann, S. M. 1974. Biphasic effect of estrogen on the sensitivity of the pituitary to luteinizing hormone-releasing factor (LRF). *Endocrinology* 94:1094–1100

79. Lincoln, D. W., Fraser, H. M., Lincoln, G. A., Martin, G. B., McNeilly, A. S. 1985. Hypothalamic pulse generators. *Rec. Progr. Horm. Res.* 41:369–419

80. Lincoln, D. W., Wakerley, J. B., 1974. Electrophysiological evidence for the activation of supraoptic neurones during the release of oxytocin. *J. Physiol.* 242:533–54

81. Lincoln, G. A., Kay, R. N. B. 1979. Effects of season on the secretion of LH and testesterone in intact and castrated red deer stags *(Cervus elaphus)*. *J. Reprod. Fertil.* 55:75–80

82. Lincoln, G. A., Short, R. V. 1980. Seasonal breeding: Nature's contraceptive. *Rec. Progr. Horm. Res.* 36:1–52

83. Martenesz, N. D., Baird, D. T., Scaramuzzi, R. J., Van Look, P. F. A. 1976. Androstenedione and the control of luteinizing hormone in the ewe during anoestrus. *J. Endocrinol.* 69:227–37

84. Martin, G. B. 1984. Factors affecting the secretion of luteinizing hormone in the ewe. *Biol. Rev.* 59:1–87

85. Martin, G. B., Scaramuzzi, R. J., Henstridge, J. D. 1983. Effects of oestradiol, progesterone and androstenedione on the pulsatile secretion of luteinizing hormone in ovariectomized ewes during spring and autumn. *J. Endocrinol.* 96:181–93

86. McEwen, B. S., Biegon, A., Davis, P. G., Krey, L. C., Luine, V. N., et al. 1982. Steroid hormones: Humoral signals which alter brain cell properties and functions. *Rec. Progr. Horm. Res.* 38:41–92

87. Meyer, S. L., Goodman, R. L. 1985. Neurotransmitters involved in mediating the steroid-dependent suppression of pulsatile luteinizing hormone secretion in anestrous ewes: Effects of receptor antagonists. *Endocrinology* 116:2054–61

88. Midgley, A. R. Jr., Jaffe, R. B. 1971. Regulation of human gonadotropins: X. Episodic fluctuation of LH during the menstrual cycle. *J. Clin. Endocrinol. Metab.* 33:962–69

89. Moss, G. E., Crowder, M. E., Nett, T. M. 1981. GnRH-receptor interaction. VI. Effect of progesterone and estradiol on hypophyseal receptors for GnRH, and serum and hypophyseal concentrations of gonadotropins in ovariectomized ewes. *Biol. Reprod.* 25:938–44

90. Moss, G. E., Nett, T. M. 1980. GnRH interaction with anterior pituitary. IV. Effect of estradiol-17B on GnRH-mediated release of LH from ovine pituitary cells obtained during the breeding season, anestrous season, and period of transition into or out of the breeding season. *Biol. Reprod.* 23:398–403

91. Moss, R. L., McCann, S. M. 1973. Induction of mating behavior in rats by luteinizing hormone-releasing factor. *Science* 181:177–79

92. Nakai, Y., Plant, T. M., Hess, D. L., Keogh, E. J., Knobil, E. 1978. On the sites of the negative and positive feedback actions of estradiol in the control of gonadotropin secretion in the rhesus monkey. *Endocrinology* 102:1008–14

93. Neill, J. D., Patton, J. M., Dailey, R. A., Tsou, R. C., Tindall, G. T. 1977. Luteinizing hormone releasing hormone (LHRH) in pituitary stalk blood of rhesus monkeys: Relationship to level of LH release. *Endocrinology* 101:430–34

94. Nett, T. M., Crowder, M. E., Moss, G.

E., Duello, T. M. 1981. GnRH-receptor interaction. V. Down-regulation of pituitary receptors for GnRH in ovariectomized ewes by infusion of homologous hormone. *Biol. Reprod.* 24:1145–55

95. Nett, T. M., Crowder, M. E., Wise, M. E. 1984. Role of estradiol in inducing an ovulatory-like surge of luteinizing hormone in sheep. *Biol. Reprod.* 30:1208–15

96. Nilson, J. H., Nejedlik, M. T., Virgin, J. B., Crowder, M. E., Nett, T. M. 1983. Expression of alpha subunit and luteinizing hormone beta genes in the ovine anterior pituitary. *J. Biol. Chem.* 258:12087–90

97. Norman, R. L., Gliessman, P., Lindstrom, S. A., Hill, J., Spies, H. G. 1982. Reinitiation of ovulatory cycles in pituitary stalk-sectioned rhesus monkeys: Evidence for a specific hypothalamic message for the preovulatory release of luteinizing hormone. *Endocrinology* 111:1874–82

98. Odell, W. D., Swerdloff, R. S. 1968. Progestogen-induced luteinizing and follicle-stimulating hormone surge in postmenopausal women: A simulated ovulatory peak. *Proc. Natl. Acad. Sci. USA* 61:529–36

99. Pau, K.-Y. F., Jackson, G. L. 1985. Effect of frontal hypothalamic deafferentation on photoperiod-induced changes in luteinizing hormone secretion in the ewe. *Neuroendocrinology* 41:72–78

100. Pfaff, D. W. 1973. Lutinizing hormone-releasing factor potentiates lordosis behavior in hypophysectomized ovariectomized female rats. *Science* 182:1148–49

101. Pfaff, D. W., Gerlach, J. L., McEwen, B. S., Ferin, M., Carmel P., Zimmerman, E. A. 1976. Autoradiographic localization of hormone-concentrating cells in the brain of the female rhesus monkey. *J. Comp. Neurol.* 170:279–94

102. Plant, T. M., Nakai, Y., Belchetz, P., Keogh, E., Knobil, E. 1978. The sites of action of estradiol and phentolamine in the inhibition of the pulsatile, circhoral discharges of LH in the rhesus monkey (*Macaca mulatta*). *Endocrinology* 102:1015–18

103. Rahe, C. H., Owens, R. E., Fleeger, J. L., Newton, H. J., Harms, P. G. 1980. Pattern of plasma luteinizing hormone in the cyclic cow: Dependence upon the period of the cycle. *Endocrinology* 107:498–503

104. Ramirez, V. D., Kim, K., Dluzen, D. 1985. Progesterone action on the LHRH

and the nigrostriatal dopamine neuronal systems: In vitro and in vivo studies. *Rec. Progr. Horm. Res.* 41:421–72

105. Reeves, J. J., Arimura, A., Schally, A. V. 1971. Changes in pituitary responsiveness to luteinizing hormone-releasing hormone (LH-RH) in anestrous ewes pretreated with estradiol benzoate. *Biol. Reprod.* 4:88–92

106. Robinson, J. E., Radford, H. M., Karsch, F. J. 1985. Seasonal changes in pulsatile luteinizing hormone (LH) secretion in the ewe: Relationship of frequency of LH pulses to day length and response to estradiol negative feedback. *Biol. Reprod.* 33:324–34

107. Sarkar, D. K., Chiappa, S. A., Fink, G. 1976. Gonadotropin-releasing hormone surge in pro-oestrous rats. *Nature* 264:461–63

108. Savoy-Moore, R. T., Schwartz, N. B., Duncan, J. A., Marshall, J. C. 1980. Pituitary gonadotropin-releasing hormone receptors during the rat estrous cycle. *Science* 209:942–44

109. Savoy-Moore, R. T., Schwartz, N. B., Duncan, J. A., Marshall, J. C. 1981. Pituitary gonadotropin-releasing hormone receptors on proestrus: Effect of pentobarbital blockade of ovulation in the rat. *Endocrinology* 109:1360–64

110. Scaramuzzi, R. J., Baird, D. T. 1977. Pulsatile release of luteinizing hormone and the secretion of ovarian steroids in sheep during anestrus. *Endocrinology* 101:1801–6

111. Scaramuzzi, R. J., Tillson, S. A., Thorneycroft, I. H., Caldwell, B. V. 1971. Action of exogenous progesterone and estrogen on behavioral estrus and luteinizing hormone levels in the ovariectomized ewe. *Endocrinology* 88:1184–89

112. Schillo, K. K., Leshin, L. S., Kuehl, D., Jackson, G. L. 1985. Simultaneous measurement of luteinizing hormone-releasing hormone and luteinizing hormone during estradiol-induced luteinizing hormone surges in the ovariectomized ewe. *Biol. Reprod.* 33:644–52

113. Schwartz, N. B. 1969. A model for the regulation of ovulation in the rat. *Rec. Progr. Horm. Res.* 25:1–55

114. Shivers, B. D., Harlan, R. E., Morrell, J. I., Pfaff, D. W. 1983. Absence of oestradiol concentration in cell nuclei of LHRH-immunoreactive neurones. *Nature* 304:345–47

115. Silverman, A. J., Antunes, J. L., Abrams, G. M., Nilaver, G., Thau, R., et al. 1982. The luteinizing hormone-releasing hormone pathways in rhesus (*Macaca mulatta*) and pigtailed (*Macaca*

382   KARSCH

nemestrina) monkeys: New observations on thick, unembedded sections. *J. Comp. Neurol.* 211:309–17

116. Silverman, A. J., Krey, L. C. 1978. The luteinizing hormone-releasing hormone (LH-RH) neuronal networks of the guinea pig brain. I. Intra-and extra-hypothalamic projections. *Brain Res.* 157:233–46

117. Soules, M. R., Steiner, R. A., Clifton, D. K., Cohen, N. L., Aksel, S., Bremner, W. J. 1984. Progesterone modulation of pulsatile luteinizing hormone secretion in normal women. *J. Clin. Endocrinol. Metab.* 58:378–83

118. Thiery, J. C., Pelletier, J. 1981. Multiunit activity in the anterior median eminence and adjacent areas of the hypothalamus of the ewe in relation to LH secretion. *Neuroendocrinology* 32:217–24

119. Tsou, R. C., Dailey, R. A., McLanahan, C. S., Parent, A. D., Tindall, G. T., Neill, J. D. 1977. Luteinizing hormone releasing hormone (LHRH) levels in pituitary stalk plasma during the preovulatory gonadotropin surge of rabbits. *Endocrinology* 101:534–39

120. Van Vugt, D. A., Diefenbach, W. D., Alston, E., Ferin, M. 1985. Gonadotropin-releasing hormone pulses in third ventricular cerebrospinal fluid of ovariectomized rhesus monkeys: Correlation with luteinizing hormone pulses. *Endocrinology* 117:1550–58

121. Van Vugt, D. A., Lam, N. Y., Ferin, M. 1984. Reduced frequency of pulsatile luteinizing hormone secretion in the luteal phase of the rhesus monkey. Involvement of endogenous opiates. *Endocrinology* 115:1095–1101

122. Webster, G. M., Haresign, W. 1983. Seasonal changes in LH and prolactin concentrations in ewes of two breeds. *J. Reprod. Fertil.* 67:465–71

123. Weick, R. F., Dierschke, D. J., Karsch, F. J., Yamaji, T., Knobil, E. 1972. The refractory period following estrogen-induced LH surges in the rhesus monkey. *Endocrinology* 91:1528–30

124. Wildt, L., Hausler, A., Hutchinson, J. S., Marshall, G., Knobil, E. 1981. Estradiol as a gonadotropin releasing hormone in the rhesus monkey. *Endocrinology* 108:2011–13

125. Wildt, L., Hutchinson, J. S., Marshall, G., Pohl, C. R., Knobil, E. 1981. On the site of action of progesterone in the blockade of estradiol-induced gonadotropin discharge in the rhesus monkey. *Endocrinology* 109:1293–94

126. Wilson, R. C., Kesner, J. S., Kaufman, J.-M., Uemura, T., Akema, T., Knobil, E. 1984. Central electrophysiologic correlates of pulsatile luteinizing hormone secretion in the rhesus monkey. *Neuroendocrinology* 39:256–60

127. Wise, M. E., Nieman, D., Stewart, J., Nett, T. M. 1984. Effect of number of receptors for gonadotropin-releasing hormone on the release of luteinizing hormone. *Biol. Reprod.* 31:1007–13

128. Witkin, J. W., Paden, C. M., Silverman, A. J. 1982. The luteinizing hormone-releasing hormone (LHRH) systems in the rat brain. *Neuroendocrinology* 35:429–38

129. Yamaji, T., Dierschke, D. J., Bhattacharya, A. N., Knobil, E. 1972. The negative feedback control by estradiol and progesterone of LH secretion in the ovariectomized rhesus monkey. *Endocrinology* 90:771–77

130. Yen, S. S. C., Lasley, B. L., Wang, C. F., Leblanc, H., Siler, T. M. 1975. The operating characteristics of the hypothalamic-pituitary system during the menstrual cycle and observations of biological actions of somatostatin. *Rec. Progr. Horm. Res.* 31:321–63

131. Yen, S. S. C., Tsai, C. C., Naftolin, F., Vandenberg, G., Ajabor, L. 1972. Pulsatile patterns of gonadotropin release in subjects with and without ovarian function. *J. Clin. Endocrinol. Metab.* 34:671–75

Ann. Rev. Physiol. 1987. 49:383–95

GASTROENTEROPANCREATIC PEPTIDES AND THE CENTRAL NERVOUS SYSTEM[1]

Dianne P. Figlewicz, Francoise Lacour, and Alfred Sipols

Department of Psychology, University of Washington, Seattle, Washington 98195

Daniel Porte, Jr.

Department of Medicine, University of Washington, Seattle, Washington 98195, and Veterans Administration Medical Center, Seattle, Washington 98108

Stephen C. Woods

Departments of Psychology and Medicine, University of Washington, Seattle, Washington 98195

INTRODUCTION

Over the past ten years, it has become widely recognized that "classic" gastrointestinal (GI) hormones are also localized in the central nervous system (CNS), where they may behave as neurotransmitters or neuromodulators, and that peptide transmitters originally found in the CNS are also localized in the GI tract, where they may serve an endocrine or paracrine role in addition to being neurotransmitters.

A major focus of research in many laboratories, including our own, has been the role of GI, or gastroenteropancreatic (GEP), peptides in the regulation of meal size and adiposity. A number of the GEP peptides may interact extensively with the CNS to influence meal size, and this is the focus of the present review. As an extensive literature exists for several of these hormones, only some of the more recent findings are summarized here.

---

[1]The US Government has the right to retain a nonexclusive, royalty-free license in and to any copyright covering this paper.

CHOLECYSTOKININ

Cholecystokinin (CCK) was the first gut peptide reported to reduce meal size (26), and numerous reviews of its action in many species exist. When administered before food is presented, CCK causes a dose-related suppression of meal size. In a free-feeding model, in which rats received CCK before each meal, the rats compensated for the decreased meal size by increasing the number of meals they consumed (87). Thus, it is unlikely that CCK is a regulator of adiposity. As is true of all peptides that reduce meal size, there is controversy as to whether the action of CCK is specific for appetite or whether it is secondary to nonspecific effects, such as illness or depressed activity. Further, CCK is known to act directly on the stomach to decrease gastric emptying. (For discussion of these issues, see Reference 25.)

The presence of CCK in high concentrations in a number of brain areas, its colocalization with dopamine in some central neurons (85), the distinct behavioral effects it is observed to have, and the alterations in certain neurotransmitter systems that are seen following its peripheral or central administration, all implicate CCK as a neuromodulator or neurotransmitter. (For an extensive review of neuronal CCK, see Reference 85.)

There is general agreement that the highest concentrations of CCK in the CNS occur in the cortex (92) and that the predominant form synthesized in vivo is CCK-8 in the pig (28); and that the predominant form extracted in vivo is CCK-8 in man (62), rat, and pig (32, 92), although concomitant biosynthesis of CCK-8 and CCK-4 in rat cerebral cortex has been reported (29). Ontogenetic studies in the rat suggest that CCK content reaches its maximum level in the cortex (36) by 20 days after birth, and that these levels are maintained in adult life.

High concentrations of CCK receptors are found in the caudate nucleus, olfactory bulb, and cortex. This distribution is similar to that of extractable CCK (31). Moderate receptor concentrations were reported in the hippocampus and hypothalamus, and low binding activity levels were found in the hindbrain, midbrain, and thalamus (23). Moran et al identified two types of central CCK receptor, based on differences in their affinity for CCK analogs (55). One receptor subtype in the CNS is essentially protected by the blood-brain barrier, which suggests that some receptors may recognize blood-borne CCK and others may respond to neurally released CCK.

Two major types of central actions of CCK have been reported. CCK decreases exploratory activity in rats when given i.c.v. (9, 35) or i.p. (11), and it can increase hexobarbital-induced sleeping and latency to convulsions in mice when given subcutaneously (94). Centrally administered CCK decreases food intake in chicks (15), sheep (13), dogs (59), golden hamsters (53), and baboons (18). In the latter two species, CCK appears to be more effective i.v.t. than peripherally. Della-Fera et al (14) suggest that the "rostral ventricular compartments" are important in the action of CCK, as they observed no effect of intracisternal CCK but found suppression of food intake when CCK was administered into the lateral ventricle.

The effects of CCK on food intake evidently involve its interaction with major neurotransmitter pathways. McCaleb & Myers (51) reported suppression of norepinephrine-stimulated eating following CCK injection into the paraventricular nucleus (PVN) and medial preoptic hypothalamus. CCK injection into the lateral hypothalamus (LH), but not the olfactory tubercle and nucleus caudate-putamen, decreases food intake (88). Following an intragastric meal, CCK concentrations are increased in perfusate collected from the hypothalamus (66). CCK infused i.c.v. increases dopamine binding in the nucleus accumbens (16).

Peripheral administration of CCK suppresses feeding elicited by central norepinephrine injection (51). We found in baboons (21) and rats (40) that peripheral CCK appears to interact with the central insulin body-weight regulatory system (90). These studies suggest that exogenous CCK may gain access to the CNS. However, $[^{125}I]$-CCK reportedly does not enter the cerebrospinal fluid (CSF) from the blood (60). On the other hand, pretreatment of rats with i.p. CCK prior to sacrifice decreases isoproterenol binding to hypothalamic membranes (37), increases brain dopamine binding (16), and increases dopamine concentrations in the mesencephalon, amygdala, and septum (89). These relatively rapid effects imply a relatively rapid, central access of CCK, perhaps via peripheral nervous receptors for CCK. Smith and his colleagues have demonstrated that peripherally administered CCK interacts with gastric vagal afferents (70) to reduce food intake. Receptors for CCK have been identified in the vagus nerve (65). They are transported in a peripheral direction (93); thus peripheral CCK may have access to them.

The central CCK system has been examined in the obese Zucker rat and ob/ob mouse, but a cohesive picture has not yet developed. There are reports of decreased extractable CCK content (92) and increased brain CCK binding (23, 31) in obese animals as compared to lean controls. In addition, more CCK is released from the hypothalamus of obese animals than from that of lean ones in response to electrical stimulation (54). However, Schneider et al (67) and Hansky & Ho (30) reported no difference in brain CCK content in obese and lean animals. There is also conflicting evidence as to whether obese animal models show normal or decreased sensitivity to the action of exogenous CCK in reducing meal size (77, 52, L. J. Stein & S. C. Woods, unpublished results). Careful regional studies of brain CCK content and receptor number combined with functional studies may clarify a role for CCK, which is altered in obese and hyperphagic animal models.

The ability of exogenous CCK to interact with dopaminergic and catecholaminergic systems in the brain appears well documented at this date. Several basic questions remain to be answered before a specific central role for CCK in the regulation of food intake can be established: How does peripherally released or infused CCK communicate with the CNS? What role does neuronal CCK play in the regulation of meal size? How do CCK's central effects on feeding relate to its ability to decrease arousal?

BOMBESIN AND GASTRIN RELEASING PEPTIDE

The tetradecapeptide bombesin and its 27–amino acid mammalian relative, gastrin-releasing peptide (GRP), have been colocalized in nerve cells throughout the enteric, peripheral, and central nervous systems. Like CCK, these peptides have been shown to reduce meal size in many species, including humans (57), when administered peripherally, and as with CCK, several studies suggest that this action is not due to illness. Bombesin administered i.v.t. also reduces meal size and appears to be more potent than i.v. bombesin in rats and baboons (19, 24). Recent studies from Lacour et al (41) and Ladenheim & Ritter (42) suggest that hindbrain structures accessible to the fourth ventricle may be critical for the effect on food intake of i.v.t. bombesin. This literature was reviewed by Gibbs & Smith (25).

The mechanisms of bombesin-induced satiety may be different for peripheral as compared to central administration. Area postrema lesions eliminate the suppression of food intake by i.v.t., but not i.p., bombesin (39). Following peripheral bombesin administration, a normal behavioral sequence of satiety is observed; specifically, the time spent feeding decreases and the time spent resting increases (24). The dose range over which peripheral bombesin decreases food intake is lower than that which results in decreased water intake. In contrast, central administration of bombesin decreases food and water intake over a similar dose range (24). Additionally, rapid onset of extensive grooming and scratching is reported in rats following i.c.v. bombesin (12, 27). Bilateral injection of bombesin into many CNS sites of rats causes enhanced locomotor activity, licking, and scratching, and diminished sleeping behavior (68). Similar results have been reported in dogs (4).

It has been hypothesized that a primary action of bombesin in the CNS is to cause a generalized arousal. We have observed small increases of plasma norepinephrine levels five minutes after lateral ventricular administration of bombesin in the baboon (20). Brown and his colleagues reported that central administration of bombesin activates the adrenal medulla and results in markedly elevated plasma epinephrine, with secondary increases of plasma glucose and glucagon and a lesser rise in norepinephrine. However, further studies found simultaneous suppression of cold-induced tachycardia and brown fat thermogenesis, which indicates that the central effects of bombesin are complex. In a recent review (5), Brown suggested that central bombesin may play a role in an adaptive response to states that require energy conservation or efficient caloric utilization.

A number of localization studies demonstrate the presence of GRP immunoreactivity in many areas of the CNS; however, there is a dearth of studies examining its potential role there. Like bombesin, GRP induces satiety when given peripherally on either a short- or long-term basis (22, 76). When given intracisternally, it can inhibit gastric acid secretion (78). The ability of centrally administered GRP to influence meal size or chronic feeding behavior has not been tested.

To summarize, centrally administered bombesin can inhibit food intake, but this may not be a specific effect. Rather, it may be a part of a complex behavioral and metabolic repertoire that coincides with generalized arousal and partial activation of the sympathetic nervous system.

PANCREATIC POLYPEPTIDE, NPY, AND PYY

Like cholecystokinin and bombesin, this family of 36–amino acid peptide hormones has been localized throughout the nervous system and GI tract. Recent evidence suggests that all three influence feeding behavior when given centrally, although the results are not totally consistent.

Pancreatic polypeptide (PP) was the first of the three hormones to be isolated. Although original studies localized PP in the pancreas, central and peripheral nervous system, and distal GI tract, it now appears that true PP-secreting cells occur exclusively in islets or cell clusters in the duodenal portion of the pancreas. [This literature was reviewed by Schwartz in 1983 (69).]

Early studies led to the hypothesis that elevated plasma levels of PP might be involved in the mediation of satiety, as PP is released following meal ingestion (69), and its peripheral administration was reported to reduce meal size (49) in obese mice. Thus, PP was hypothesized to be involved in body-weight regulation, although data in obese mice and obese humans are conflicting and, at this point, somewhat inconclusive.

In contrast, i.v.t. administration of PP increases food intake in satiated rats, both by decreasing latency to initiate feeding and by increasing time spent eating (7). This suggests that PP has different actions in the periphery and the brain or perhaps that the reduction of food intake upon peripheral administration of PP may not be a specific action.

Neuropeptide Y (NPY) is found throughout the nervous system, including many areas of the brain, the spinal cord, autonomic ganglia, and enteric nervous system. NPY-containing nerves innervate blood vessels and smooth muscle of the gut, as well as the pancreatic acini. Discussions of the localization and peripheral actions of NPY are found in Polak & Bloom (61) and O'Donohue et al (58).

NPY is colocalized with catecholamines in both the central and the peripheral nervous system (17), and chemical depletion of catecholamines results in depletion of NPY in some, but not all, neurons (47). Colocalization of NPY with central catecholamines implies that NPY plays a role in the regulation of food intake, as central catecholamines are intimately involved in the central regulation of appetitive behaviors (43). NPY is the most potent appetite-stimulating peptide localized in the CNS to date. Both food and water intake are stimulated by NPY injection into the PVN of sated rats (73), and NPY-stimulated eating is not blocked by pretreatment with phentolamine (74), which suggests that catecholamine release does not mediate this effect. NPY injected into the ventromedial hypothalamus (VMH) and LH also stimulates feeding, whereas its injection into the amygdala, periaqueductal gray, or thalamus is without effect (71). A recent report suggests that the chronic administration of NPY into the PVN of rats leads to weight gain (72).

Peptide YY (PYY), a 36–amino acid peptide with an 18–amino acid homology with PP (80) and 25–amino acid homology with NPY (81), has been localized in the mucosa of the intestine, colon, and rectum of a number of mammalian species (48). A few PYY cells have also been reported to coexist with glucagonlike immunoreactivity in some cells of the gut and pancreas (1). PYY has not been observed in the brain, sympathetic ganglia, pituitary, thyroid, or adrenals in the rat or guinea pig (48). Some described actions of PYY include stimulation of vasoconstriction and inhibition of gut motility (58), and inhibition of arginine-stimulated insulin secretion and glucagon secretion (58). Like PP, plasma concentrations of PYY rise in response to a meal (82).

Intraventricular injection of PYY results in dramatic increases in food intake—increases greater than those caused by NPY at every concentration tested in one report (56). In another report, hPYY was found to be about half as effective as pNPY, and as effective as hNPY, in inducing feeding (8). Water intake is also significantly increased by PYY, and this effect does not appear to be secondary to the increased food ingestion. Repeated administration of PYY (every 6 hr for 48 hr) resulted in significantly increased food intake, and rats did not appear to become tolerant to PYY in this regimen (56). As PYY has not been localized centrally and its ability to cross the blood-brain barrier has not been reported, it is difficult to hypothesize at present that PYY has a physiologic role in the central regulation of food intake. The stimulation of food intake by central administration of both PYY and PP is likely due to their interaction with central NPY receptor sites.

SOMATOSTATIN

The peptide somatostatin was originally isolated from a hypothalamic extract (3). It has subsequently been shown to be present in neurons and endocrine cells throughout the brain and GI tract, in either a 14– or 28–amino acid form. For a concise review of its localization, actions, and potential functions see the 1983 review by Reichlin (63, 64).

Somatostatin has been reported to decrease food intake when given peripherally, but not centrally, to rats (45) and baboons (46). This suppression in rats caused by i.p. somatostatin was not associated with the formation of a conditioned taste aversion (45), which suggests that somatostatin may be another peripheral satiety factor.

Numerous central effects of somatostatin have been described, although there appear to be some conflicts in the literature. The consensus appears to be that central somatostatin administration results in a generalized arousal, with concomitant enhancement of grooming and exploratory activities. Metabolically, it has been shown to inhibit the hyperglycemic response to a variety of stressors (6). Further, somatostatin may play a role in the etiology of various brain or neurological diseases, although the literature at present is mainly suggestive.

GLUCAGON

In addition to being found in the pancreas and GI tract, glucagonlike activity has been extracted from brain regions of the dog, rat, pig, and human (83) and demonstrated in situ by immunocytochemistry (10, 44). The highest concentrations appear to be in the hypothalamus with intermediate amounts in the midbrain and low amounts in the cortex.

Glucagon is a putative peripheral satiety factor. However, some controversy surrounds this concept. It has been proposed that glucagon-induced hyperglycemia is the mechanism whereby glucagon can cause satiety and that the hepatic vagus is critically involved in this effect (50). More recent data suggest that the time of day may be critical for testing for glucagon's satiety effects (86), that glucagon's satiating capacity can be separated from the size of releasable glycogen stores (75), and that under certain conditions vagotomized animals show a satiety response to glucagon (2).

Little work has been done to date to establish a possible function of glucagonlike molecules in the CNS. Glucagon and glucagonlike immunoreactivity are released from a synaptosomal preparation of thalamus, hypothalamus, and brain stem in response to K^+ (84). These data support a potential role of glucagon or glucagonlike peptides as neurotransmitters or neuromodulators. Additionally, iontophoretic application of glucagon decreases the activity of glucose-sensitive neurons in the lateral hypothalamus (34). The effect could be mimicked somewhat by intra-arterial injection of glucagon.

The ability of glucagon to influence appetitive behaviors following direct administration in the CNS has not been studied extensively. In a study in which chronic suppression of food intake by i.v.t. insulin infusion was clearly demonstrated, Woods et al observed no effects on food intake or body weight by a chronic infusion of glucagon (90). In contrast, using a much higher i.c.v. dose of glucagon, Inokuchi et al observed suppression of short-term food intake in the rat (33). It is difficult to put together a cohesive picture at present, as different doses of glucagon and measurement intervals were used in central and peripheral studies.

CONCLUSIONS

The general hypothesis under investigation is that food intake stimulates the release of specific GEP hormonal signals (peptides), which interact with the nervous system to regulate the amount and type of food eaten during a meal. Many of these peptides are also localized in the CNS, and their release may be modulated by the onset of a meal.

In most cases, the GEP peptides appear to be feedback suppressors of meal size, but some may stimulate food intake. A summary of the peptides that may modulate food intake is provided in Table 1. These data are derived from

Table 1   Effect of peptide administration on food intake[a]

Peptide	Effect
Insulin (into CNS)	decrease
Cholecystokinin	decrease
Bombesin	decrease
Glucagon	decrease
Somatostatin	decrease
Thyrotropin-releasing hormone	decrease
Pancreatic polypeptide (into CNS)	increase
Caerulein	decrease
Litorin	decrease
Gastrin-releasing peptide	decrease
Enterogastrone	decrease
Calcitonin gene–related peptide (79)	decrease
Galanin (38)	increase
NPY	increase
PYY	increase

[a]See Reference 91 for specific literature citations

studies in which peptides have been exogenously administered. As relatively large peptide doses were used in some of these studies, the reader is cautioned regarding the conclusion that any or all of these peptides play a *physiologic* role in the regulation of meal size. Additionally, it should be noted that insulin is the only GEP peptide to date for which a substantial body of evidence documents a role in the long-term regulation of appetite and body adiposity.

Certain GEP peptides have been shown to interact with peripheral neural receptors, and the possibility of a direct central feedback via the circulation or direct CNS action of the centrally localized GEP peptides is still under active investigation. These effects are separate from the ability of the GEP peptides to regulate gall bladder, stomach, and small and large bowel function. It is, therefore, often difficult to separate direct neural effects from such peripheral actions, which may also affect food-intake behavior. Further study of the peptidergic systems that regulate food intake and body weight should lead to greater insights into the causes and treatment of obesity and anorexia.

ACKNOWLEDGMENTS

The authors' studies described herein were supported by National Institutes of Health Grants AM-17844, AM-14047, AM-12829, and RR-00166 and by the Veterans Administration. Dr. Figlewicz is a recipient of an American Diabetes Association Career Development Award and a Pilot and Feasibility Grant through the University of Washington Clinical Nutrition Research Unit (NIH Grant AM-35816). Dr. Lacour was a Visiting Scholar sponsored by Ministere de l'Industrie et de la Recherche, Paris, France.

Literature Cited

1. Ali-Rachedi, A., Varndell, I. M., Adrian, T. E., Gapp, D. A., Van Noorden, S., et al. 1984. Peptide YY (PYY) immunoreactivity is costored with glucagon-related immunoreactants in endocrine cells of the gut and pancreas. *Histochemistry* 80:487–91
2. Bellinger, L. L., Williams, F. E. 1985. Liver denervation [Hepatic vagal branch (HVB); Artery-portal vein (HAPV); combined (COM)] or sham operation (SCON) on glucagon (GLG) suppression of food intake (FI). *Fed. Proc.* 44:1164 (Abstr.)
3. Brazeau, P., Vale, W., Burgus, R., Ling, N., Butcher, M., et al. 1973. Hypothalamic polypeptide that inhibits the secretion of immunoreactive pituitary growth hormone. *Science* 179:77–79
4. Brown, M. R. 1983. Central nervous system sites of action of bombesin and somatostatin to influence plasma epinephrine levels. *Brain Res.* 276:253–57
5. Brown, M., Fisher, L. 1986. Regulation of the autonomic nervous system by peptides. In *Peptide-Hormones: Effects and Mechanisms of Action*, ed. A. Negro-Vilar, P. M. Conn. Boca Raton, Fla: CRC In press
6. Brown, M., Rivier, J., Vale, W. 1979. Somatostatin: Central nervous system actions on glucoregulation. *Endocrinology* 104:1709–15
7. Clark, J. T., Kalra, P. S., Crowley, W. R., Kalra, S. P. 1984. Neuropeptide Y and human pancreatic polypeptide stimulate feeding behavior in rats. *Endocrinology* 115:427–29
8. Clark, J. T., Kalra, S. P. 1985. Neuropeptide Y (NPY)-induced feeding: Comparison with rat pancreatic polypeptide (rPP), human NPY and peptide

YY (PYY) in male and female rats. *Soc. Neurosci. Abstr.* 11:619

9. Cohen, S. L., Knight, M., Tamminga, C. A., Chase, T. N. 1983. Tolerance to the anti-avoidance properties of cholecystokinin-octapeptide. *Peptides* 4:67–70

10. Conlon, J. M., Samson, W. K., Dobbs, R. E., Orci, L., Unger, R. H. 1979. Glucagon-like polypeptides in canine brain. *Diabetes* 28:700–2

11. Crawley, J. N. 1983. Divergent effects of cholecystokinin, bombesin, and lithium on rat exploratory behaviors. *Peptides* 4:405–10

12. deCaro, G., Massi, M., Micossi, L. G., Perfumi, M. 1984. Drinking and feeding inhibition by ICV pulse injection or infusion of bombesin, ranatensin and litorin to rats. *Peptides* 5:607–13

13. Della-Fera, M. A., Baile, C. A. 1980. CCK-octapeptide injected in CSF decreases meal size and daily food intake in sheep. *Peptides* 1:51–54

14. Della-Fera, M. A., Baile, C. A., Beinfeld, M. C. 1982. Cerebral ventricular transport and uptake: Importance for CCK-mediated satiety. *Peptides* 3:963–68

15. Denbow, D. M., Myers, R. D. 1982. Eating, drinking and temperature responses to intracerebroventricular cholecystokinin in the chick. *Peptides* 3:739–43

16. Dumbrille-Ross, A., Seeman, P. 1984. Dopamine receptor elevation by cholecystokinin. *Peptides* 5:1207–12

17. Everitt, B. J., Hökfelt, T., Terenius, L., Tatemoto, K., Mutt, V., Goldstein, M. 1984. Differential co-existence of neuropeptide Y (NPY)-like immunoreactivity with catecholamines in the central nervous system of the rat. *Neuroscience* 11:443–62

18. Figlewicz, D. P., Sipols, A., Porte, D. Jr., Woods, S. C. 1985. Intraventricular (IVT) cholecystokinin octapeptide (CCK-8) is more effective in suppressing single meal size than intravenous (IV) CCK-8 in baboons. Presented at *Int. Peptide Conf., 5th, Washington, D.C.*

19. Figlewicz, D. P., Sipols, A., Porte, D. Jr., Woods, S. C. 1986. Intraventricular bombesin (IVT BBS) is more effective than intravenous (IV) bombesin in reducing single meal size in the baboon. *Brain Res. Bull.* 17:535–37

20. Figlewicz, D. P., Sipols, A., Porte, D. Jr., Woods, S. C. 1986. Plasma norepinephrine (NE) levels are elevated following intraventricular (IVT) bombesin (BBS) administration in the baboon. *Appetite* In press

21. Figlewicz, D. P., Stein, L. J., Porte, D. Jr., Woods, S. C. 1986. Intracisternal insulin alters sensitivity to CCK-induced meal suppression in baboons. *Am. J. Physiol.* 250:R856–60

22. Figlewicz, D. P., Stein, L. J., Woods, S. C., Porte, D. Jr. 1985. Acute and chronic gastrin-releasing peptide decreases food intake in baboons. *Am. J. Physiol.* 248:R578–83

23. Finkelstein, J. A., Steggles, A. W., Martinez, P. A., Praissman, M. 1984. Cholecystokinin receptor binding levels in the genetically obese rat brain. *Peptides* 5:11–14

24. Gibbs, J., Kulkosky, P. J., Smith, G. P. 1981. Effects of peripheral and central bombesin on feeding behavior of rats. *Peptides* 2:179–83 (Suppl. 2)

25. Gibbs, J., Smith, G. P. 1984. The neuroendocrinology of postprandial satiety. In *Frontiers in Neuroendocrinology*, ed. L. Martini, W. F. Ganong, 8:223–45. New York: Raven

26. Gibbs, J., Young, R. C., Smith, G. P. 1973. Cholecystokinin decreases food intake in rats. *J. Comp. Physiol. Psychol.* 84:488–95

27. Gmerek, D. E., Cowan, A. 1983. Studies on bombesin-induced grooming in rats. *Peptides* 4:907–13

28. Goltermann, N. R. 1982. *In vivo* biosynthesis of cholecystokinin in hog cerebral cortex. *Peptides* 3:101–4

29. Goltermann, N. R. 1982. In vivo synthesis of cholecystokinin in the rat cerebral cortex: Identification of COOH-terminal peptides with labelled amino acids. *Peptides* 3:733–37

30. Hansky, J., Ho, P. 1979. Cholecystokinin-like peptides in brain and intestine of obese-hyperglycaemic mice. *Aust. J. Exp. Biol. Med. Sci.* 57:575–79

31. Hays, S. E., Goodwin, F. K., Paul, S. M. 1981. Cholecystokinin receptors in brain: Effects of obesity, drug treatment, and lesions. *Peptides* 2:21–26 (Suppl. 1)

32. Ichihara, K., Eng, J., Pond, W. G., Yen, J. T., Straus, E., Yalow, R. S. 1984. Ontogeny of immunoreactive CCK and VIP in pig brain and gut. *Peptides* 5:623–26

33. Inokuchi, A., Oomura, Y., Nishimura, H. 1984. Effect of intracerebroventricularly infused glucagon on feeding behavior. *Physiol. Behav.* 33:397–400

34. Inokuchi, A., Oomura, Y., Shimizu, N., Yamamoto, T. 1986. Central action

of glucagon in rat hypothalamus. *Am. J. Physiol.* 250:R120–26

35. Katsuura, G., Hsiao, S., Itoh, S. 1984. Blocking of cholecystokinin octapeptide behavioral effects by proglumide. *Peptides* 5:529–34

36. Kiyama, H., Shiosaka, S., Takami, K., Tateishi, K., Hashimura, K., et al. 1980. CCK pathway from supramamillary region to the nucleus anterior ventralis thalami of the young rats. *Peptides* 5:889–93

37. Kochman, R. L., Grey, T. R., Hirsch, J. D. 1984. Cholecystokinin in vivo reduces binding to rat hypothalamic β-adrenergic sites. *Peptides* 5:499–502

38. Kyrkouli, S. E., Stanley, B. G., Leibowitz, S. F. 1985. Galanin: Stimulation of feeding induced by medial hypothalamic injection of this novel peptide. *Brain Res. Bull.* In press

39. Lacour, F., Kenney, N. J., Kott, J. N., Woods, S. C. 1984. Bombesin suppresses food intake of area-postrema-lesioned rats. *Soc. Neurosci. Abstr.* 10:1014

40. Lacour, F. J., Brief, D., Woods, S. C. 1985. Intracerebroventricular insulin potentiates the satiating effect of CCK-8. *Brain Res. Bull.* In press

41. Lacour, F. J., Kott, J. N., Kenney, N. J., Woods, S. C. 1986. Intraventricular bombesin (BBS) reduces food intake of normal but not area postrema-lesioned rats. *Appetite.* In press

42. Ladenheim, E. E., Ritter, R. C. 1985. Suppression of food intake by low dose infusion of bombesin into the fourth ventricle. *Soc. Neurosci. Abstr.* 11:343

43. Leibowitz, S. F. 1980. Neurochemical systems of the hypothalamus. Control of feeding and drinking behavior and water electrolyte excretion. In *Handbook of the Hypothalamus. Behavioral Studies of the Hypothalamus,* ed. P. J. Morgane, J. Panksepp, 3A:299–437. New York: Dekker

44. Loren, I., Alumets, J., Hakanson, R., Sundler, F., Thorell, J. 1979. Gut-type glucagon immunoreactivity in nerves of the rat brain. *Histochemistry* 61:335–41

45. Lotter, E. C., Krinsky, R., McKay, J. M., Treneer, C. M., Porte, D. Jr., Woods, S. C. 1981. Somatostatin decreases food intake of rats and baboons. *J. Comp. Physiol. Psychol.* 95:278–87

46. Lotter, E. C., Woods, S. C. 1977. Somatostatin decreases food intake of baboons. *Diabetes* 26:358 (Suppl. 1)

47. Lundberg, J. M., Saria, A., Franco-Cereceda, A., Hökfelt, T., Terenius, L., Goldstein, M. 1985. Differential effects of reserpine and 6-hydroxydopamine on neuropeptide Y (NPY) and noradrenaline in peripheral neurons. *Arch. Pharmacol.* 328:331–40

48. Lundberg, J. M., Tatemoto, K., Terenius, L., Hellström, P. M., Mutt, V., et al. 1982. Localization of peptide YY (PYY) in gastrointestinal endocrine cells and effects on intestinal blood flow and motility. *Proc. Natl. Acad. Sci. USA* 79:4471–75

49. Malaisse-Lagae, F., Carpentier, J.-L., Patel, Y. E., Orci, L. 1977. Pancreatic polypeptide: A possible role in the regulation of food intake in the mouse. *Experientia* 33:915–17

50. MacIsaac, L., Geary, N. 1985. Hepatic vagotomy or total liver denervation can block pancreatic glucagon's satiety effect. *Soc. Neurosci. Abstr.* 11:58

51. McCaleb, M. L., Myers, R. D. 1980. Cholecystokinin acts on the hypothalamic "noradrenergic system" involved in feeding. *Peptides* 1:47–49

52. McLaughlin, C. L., Baile, C. A. 1980. Decreased sensitivity of Zucker obese rats to the putative satiety agent cholecystokinin. *Physiol. Behav.* 25:543–48

53. Miceli, M. O., Malsbury, C. W. 1983. Feeding and drinking responses in the golden hamster following treatment with cholecystokinin and angiotensin II. *Peptides* 4:103–6

54. Micevych, P. E., Go, V. L. W., Yaksh, T. L., Finkelstein, J. 1984. In vitro release of cholecystokinin from hypothalamus and frontal cortex of Sprague-Dawley, Zucker lean (Fa/−) and obese (fa/fa) rats. *Peptides* 5:73–80

55. Moran, T. H., Robinson, P. H., Goldrich, M. S., McHugh, P. R. 1986. Two brain cholecystokinin receptors: Implications for behavioral actions. *Brain Res.* 362:175–79

56. Morley, J. E., Levine, A. S., Grace, M., Kneip, J. 1985. Peptide YY (PYY), a potent orexigenic agent. *Brain Res.* 341:200–3

57. Muurahainen, N. E., Kissileff, H. R., Thornton, J., Pi-Sunyer, F. X. 1983. Bombesin: Another peptide that inhibits feeding in man. *Soc. Neurosci. Abstr.* 9:183

58. O'Donohue, T. L., Chronwall, B. M., Pruss, R. M., Mezey, E., Kiss, J. Z., et al. 1985. Neuropeptide Y and Peptide YY neuronal and endocrine systems. *Peptides* 6:755–68

59. Pappas, T. N., Melendez, R. L., Strah, K. M., Debas, H. T. 1985. Cholecystokinin is not a peripheral satiety signal in

the dog. *Am. J. Physiol.* 249:G733–38

60. Passaro, E., Debas, H., Oldendorf, W., Yamada, T. 1982. Rapid appearance of intraventricular administered neuropeptides in the peripheral circulation. *Brain Res.* 241:338–40

61. Polak, J. M., Bloom, S. R. 1984. Regulatory peptides—the distribution of two newly discovered peptides: PHI and NPY. *Peptides* 5:79–89 (Suppl. 1)

62. Reeve, J. R. Jr., Eysselein, V. E., Walsh, J. H., Sankaran, H., Deveney, C. W., et al. 1984. Isolation and characterization of biologically active and inactive cholecystokinin-octapeptides from human brain. *Peptides* 5:959–66

63. Reichlin, S. 1983. Somatostatin. *N. Engl. J. Med.* 309:1495–1501

64. Reichlin, S. 1983. Somatostatin. *N. Engl. J. Med.* 309:1556–62

65. Sankaran, H., Deveney, C. W., Goldfine, I. D., Williams, J. A. 1979. Preparation of biologically active radioiodinated cholecystokinin for radioreceptor assay and radioimmunoassay. *J. Biol. Chem.* 254:9349–51

66. Schick, R. R., Taksh, T. L., Go, V. L. W. 1985. Cholecystokinin octapeptide (CCK-8) is released from the hypothalamus in response to an intragastric meal in anesthetized cats. *Soc. Neurosci. Abstr.* 11:968

67. Schneider, B. S., Monahan, J. W., Hirsch, J. 1979. Brain cholecystokinin and nutritional status in rats and mice. *J. Clin. Invest.* 64:1348–56

68. Schulz, D. W., Kalivas, P. W., Nemeroff, C. B., Prange, A. J. 1984. Bombesin-induced locomotor hyperactivity: Evaluation of the involvement of mesolimbic dopamine system. *Brain Res.* 304:377–82

69. Schwartz, T. W. 1983. Pancreatic polypeptide: A hormone under vagal control. *Gastroenterology* 85:1411–1425

70. Smith, G. P., Jerome, C., Cushin, B. J., Eterno, R., Simansky, K. J. 1981. Abdominal vagotomy blocks the satiety effect of cholecystokinin in the rat. *Science* 213:1036–37

71. Stanley, B. G., Chin, A. S., Leibowitz, S. F. 1985. Feeding and drinking elicited by central injection of neuropeptide Y: Evidence for a hypothalamic site(s) of action. *Brain Res. Bull.* 14:521–24

72. Stanley, B. G., Kyrkouli, S. E., Lampert, S., Leibowitz, S. F. 1985. Hyperphagia and obesity induced by neuro-

peptide Y injected chronically into the paraventricular hypothalamus of the rat. *Soc. Neurosci. Abstr.* 11:36

73. Stanley, B. G., Leibowitz, S. F. 1984. Neuropeptide Y: Stimulation of feeding and drinking by injection into the paraventricular nucleus. *Life Sci.* 35:2635–42

74. Stanley, B. G., Leibowitz, S. F. 1985. Neuropeptide Y injected in the paraventricular hypothalamus: A powerful stimulant of feeding behavior. *Proc. Natl. Acad. Sci. USA* 82:3940–43

75. Stein, L. J., O'Farrell, L., Novin, D. 1985. Circadian variation of hepatic glycogen: Effect of glucagon on food intake and glycogen concentration. *Soc. Neurosci. Abstr.* 11:58

76. Stein, L. J., Woods, S. C. 1982. Gastrin releasing peptide reduces meal size in rats. *Peptides* 3:833–35

77. Strohmayer, A. J., Smith, G. P. 1981. Cholecystokinin inhibits food intake in genetically obese (C57BL/6j-ob) mice. *Peptides* 2:39–43

78. Tache, Y., Marki, W., Rivier, J., Vale, W., Brown, M. 1981. Central nervous system inhibition of gastric secretion in the rat by gastrin-releasing peptide, a mammalian bombesin. *Gastroenterology* 81:298–302

79. Tannenbaum, G. S., Goltzman, D. 1985. Calcitonin gene-related peptide mimics calcitonin actions in brain on growth hormone release and feeding. *Endocrinology* 116:2685–87

80. Tatemoto, K. 1982. Isolation and characterization of peptide YY (PYY), a candidate gut hormone that inhibits pancreatic exocrine secretion. *Proc. Natl. Acad. Sci. USA* 79:2514–18

81. Tatemoto, K. 1982. Neuropeptide Y: Complete amino acid sequence of the brain peptide. *Proc. Natl. Acad. Sci. USA* 79:5485–89

82. Taylor, I. L. 1985. Distribution and release of Peptide YY in dog measured by specific radioimmunoassay. *Gastroenterology* 88:731–37

83. Tominaga, M., Ebitani, I., Marubashi, S., Kamimura, T., Kataguri, T., Sasaki, H. 1981. Species difference of glucagon-like materials in the brain. *Life Sci.* 29:1577–81

84. Tominaga, M., Kaneda, H., Marubashi, S., Kamimura, T., Katagiri, T., Sasaki, H. 1984. Synaptosomal localization and release of glucagon-like materials in the rat brain. *Brain Res. Bull.* 12:373–75

85. Vanderhaegen, J.-J., Crawley, J. N., eds. 1985. Neuronal cholecystokinin. *Ann. NY Acad. Sci.* 448:1–697

86. Weatherford, S. C., Ritter, S. 1985. Glucagon-induced suppression of feeding: neural substrates and circadian variations. *Brain Res. Bull.* In press

87. West, D. B., Fey, D., Woods, S. C. 1984. Cholecystokinin persistently suppresses meal size but not food intake in free-feeding rats. *Am. J. Physiol.* 246:R776–87

88. Willis, G. L., Hansky, J., Smith, G. C. 1984. The role of some central catecholamine systems in cholecystokinin-induced satiety. *Peptides* 5:41–46

89. Wilson, M. C., Denson, D., Bedford, J. A., Hunsinger, R. N. 1983. Pharmacological manipulation of sincalide (CCK-8)-induced suppression of feeding. *Peptides* 4:351–57

90. Woods, S. C., Lotter, E. C., McKay, L. D., Porte, D. Jr. 1979. Chronic intracerebroventricular infusion of insulin reduces food intake and body weight of baboons. *Nature* 282:503–5

91. Woods, S. C., Taborsky, G. J. Jr., Porte, D. Jr. 1986. Central nervous system control of nutrient homeostasis. *Handbook Physiol.* Sect. 1, Vol. IV, pp. 365–411

92. Yalow, R. S., Eng, J., Straus, E. 1983. The role of CCK-like peptides in appetite regulation. *Adv. Metab. Disord.* 10:341–54

93. Zarbin, M. A., Wamsley, J. K., Innis, R. B., Kuhar, M. J. 1981. Cholecystokinin receptors: Presence and axonal flow in the rat vagus nerve. *Life Sci.* 29:697–705

94. Zetler, G. 1982. Ceruletide, ceruletide analogues and cholecystokinin octapeptide (CCK-8): Effects on motor behaviour, hexobarbital-induced sleep and harman-induced convulsions. *Peptides* 3:701–4

Ann. Rev. Physiol. 1987. 49:397–411
Copyright © 1987 by Annual Reviews Inc. All rights reserved

ADRENOCORTICAL STEROIDS AND THE BRAIN

J. W. Funder and K. Sheppard

Medical Research Centre, Prince Henry's Hospital, Melbourne, Victoria
Australia 3004

INTRODUCTION

Adrenal steroids have been reported to have a wide range of actions in the central nervous system—from regulation of cell growth and differentiation, through effects on neuronal and glial metabolism, to changes in appetite, affect, and behavioral patterns. Those who have contributed to our present understanding of the field are drawn from a correspondingly wide range of primary disciplines—developmental neurobiology, cell biology, neurochemistry, neuroendocrinology, and behavioral science. The breadth of the field is similarly reflected in several excellent recent reviews (4, 36, 39, 51), in which the area is considered from a particular vantage point—for example neurochemistry, behavioral studies, or aging. In none of these reviews, however, has the primary focus been on the physiology of the adrenal cortex and the role of its products in the central nervous system.

The review to follow is written with such a primary focus in the hope of providing a complementary vantage point from which to survey a bewildering mass of data. This choice of focus attests to a personal bias of the authors and their feeling that there has to date been insufficient emphasis placed on the adrenal cortex in considering the physiology of corticoids and the central nervous system. This review is an attempt to redress this perceived imbalance. In addition, it seeks to rephrase questions, rather than to provide consensus answers, and is thus to a degree consciously speculative in approach.

CORTICOSTEROID SIGNALS

In mammalian systems there are six commonly recognized classes of steroid hormone: mineralocorticoid, glucocorticoid, estrogen, progestin, androgen, and Ca^{2+}-active, of which the first two are uniquely products of the adrenal cortex. In species from amphibia onwards, in the evolutionary sense, and in some fish, the physiologic mineralocorticoid is aldosterone, which is uniquely a product of the outer zona glomerulosa of the gland. In most mammalian species the physiologic glucocorticoid is cortisol, which is uniquely a product of the zona fasciculata of the adrenal; in rats and mice, however, which are commonly used for in vivo and in vitro studies, the physiologic glucocorticoid is corticosterone.

Definitions and Distinctions

Historically, the distinctions between the six mammalian classes of steroids are based on effector criteria. Whereas the word steroid describes what a certain molecule is, the terms mineralocorticoid or estrogen describe what certain molecules do—regardless of the fact that they may be structurally quite dissimilar (e.g. estradiol 17β, diethylstilbestrol). For some steroids a consensus definition has emerged—for example, that of a mineralocorticoid as a steroid modulating unidirectional transepithelial sodium transport (7). For other steroids—e.g. glucocorticoids—there is no equivalent definition. The word glucocorticoid reflects the effects of such steroids on glucose metabolism, as measured by an early bioassay (mouse liver glycogen deposition). Currently, the most easily recognized description of glucocorticoids is of adrenal steroids that are released in response to stress and that mediate and/or modulate a range of responses to stress. Other well-recognized glucocorticoid effects are on development, on immune suppression, and as anti-inflammatory steroids (4, 17).

In the perhaps inevitable absence of a definition of "glucocorticoid," it is of interest that an additional criterion, over and above those of effects, has become current in describing glucocorticoids—that of release in response to stress. In physiological terms, the adrenal glucocorticoid response is to adrenocorticotropin hormone (ACTH), and stress even very broadly defined is only one of the two physiologic stimuli to ACTH secretion. The other mode of ACTH secretion is circadian: "Baseline" levels of ACTH and glucocorticoids vary markedly in unstressed animals over the course of a day.

Mineralocorticoids

Compared with the description of "glucocorticoid," the definition of mineralocorticoid given above is much more precise—though perhaps this definition is rather too stringent, as will be discussed later. Again in contrast with glucocorticoid secretion, which is dominated by ACTH, the control of mineralocorticoid secretion is physiologically much more complex. The most important factor in this control is the octapeptide angiotensin II. Angiotensin I, a decapeptide, is cleaved from a circulating precursor (angiotensinogen) by the action of renin released from the kidney in response to sodium loss (and other stimuli); its C-terminus is then trimmed by the dipeptidase-converting enzyme to yield angiotensin II. ACTH also modulates aldosterone secretion, producing a circadian variation in the sodium replete, unstressed state; intra-adrenal concentrations of both Na^+ and more particularly K^+ also influence aldosterone secretion rate. Other humoral factors that have been shown to affect aldosterone secretion are pituitary aldosterone-stimulating hormone (ASH) and atrial natriuretic factor (ANF). The precise physiologic circumstances in which these latter two hormones are involved and the extent to which they contribute to the overall control of aldosterone secretion remain to be determined (35).

Circulating Levels of Signal

Just as mineralocorticoids and glucocorticoids have different physiologic actions and have distinct (but overlapping) control systems, their circulating levels differ markedly. Though adrenal androgen precursors are usually the predominant product of the adrenal cortex, glucocorticoids are secreted in relatively high amounts. In contrast, aldosterone secretion and plasma levels are 2–3 orders of magnitude lower, although the ratio depends to some extent on the sodium status of the organism. To a degree this very marked (100–1000 fold) difference in total circulating concentrations is offset by the much higher levels of plasma binding of cortisol and corticosterone than aldosterone, so the difference in free concentrations of steroids able to enter target tissue cells and bind to receptors is correspondingly less. In any consideration of the effects of corticosteroids this difference in level of signal presentation needs to be borne in mind. This is especially true of corticosteroids in the central nervous system, where the definitions and descriptions from classical assay systems (e.g. toad bladder, thymolysis) may or may not apply.

Limits of Signal Specificity

The second caveat of importance in interpreting studies on corticosteroids is that few steroids are absolutely specific in their effects in classical test systems and presumably, by extrapolation, in experimental systems under study in the central nervous system and elsewhere in the body. For example, corticosterone and cortisol have some sodium-retaining activity, though much higher doses are required than for aldosterone, and the maximal response is only a fraction that of aldosterone in mammalian systems (54). In other test systems (e.g. toad bladder), sufficiently high levels of steroids not normally considered mineralocorticoids can produce an essentially maximal Na^+ transport effect. Aldosterone at high levels has been shown to be an excellent glucocorticoid in in vitro test systems (50); whether levels are ever sufficiently high in vivo for such crossover effects remains moot.

The second-generation synthetic glucocorticoids, such as dexamethasone, were developed to obviate the Na^+ retention seen with high doses of cortisone or hydrocortisone given therapeutically. Nonetheless, dexamethasone has not inconsiderable affinity for mineralocorticoid receptors in vitro (33) and, inasmuch as it occupies such receptors after administration in vivo, can be presumed to have effects, presumably largely or completely as an antagonist. Only relatively recently, in fact, have there been developed very specific steroids (glucocorticoid RU26988, RU28362; mineralocorticoid RU28318, RU26752) (56, 57). Though both dexamethasone and the RU-steroids have proven of immense value in delineating mechanisms of steroid action, it must always be remembered that the physiologic steroids do not enjoy similar selectivity. It has been more than five years, for example, since it was noted that corticosterone (and cortisol) have higher affinity for mineralocorticoid receptors than for glucocorticoid receptors (32). Fortunately, there are currently sufficient data to attempt to make physiologic sense of this apparent conundrum, though its resolution is far from complete in all its details.

CORTICOSTEROID RECEPTORS

In any consideration of corticosteroid action, it would in fact appear to make more sense to talk of receptor selectivity rather than steroid selectivity. Whereas there are hundreds of naturally occurring steroid molecules and thousands of synthetic steroids, there appear to be very many fewer receptors, as has been demonstrated by binding studies. With the recent cloning of glucocorticoid (60), estrogen (24, 25), and progesterone receptors (Pierre Chambon; personal communication), and given their shared homology with the *v-erb-A* oncogene product, this may also be able to be shown at the level of the genome.

Two types of receptor have classically been described for corticosteroids (49). This distinction was initially made in rat kidney, in which sites binding aldosterone with high affinity were termed Type I or mineralocorticoid receptors (20). Those that bound aldosterone with lower affinity (Type II sites) were subsequently found to be classical, dexamethasone binding glucocorticoid receptors (21), previously described in a variety of other tissues and cell lines.

Renal Mineralocorticoid (Type I) Receptors

In the initial studies, kidney slices from adrenalectomized rats were incubated with tritiated aldosterone over a range of concentrations, either alone or with competing unlabeled steroids (20). Under such conditions, aldosterone was shown to bind with relatively high affinity to Type I sites ($K_d \approx 1$ nM at 37°C), which is consistent with their representing physiological mineralocorticoid receptors. Corticosterone appeared to bind with much lower (2–5%) affinity to such sites, which was interpreted as evidence for marked aldosterone selectivity of these putative mineralocorticoid receptors. Dexamethasone bound with lower affinity still, which is consistent with its lower salt-retaining activity relative to that of the physiologic glucocorticoids. Following this initial demonstration of renal Type I sites, they were reported in a variety of classical aldosterone target tissues such as salivary gland (19) and gut (45); in classical nontarget tissues for aldosterone, such as heart (18) and liver (15), Type I receptors appeared to be either absent or below detectable limits.

High-Affinity Aldosterone Binding Sites in Tissues Not Classical Mineralocorticoid Targets

In a variety of tissues, however, high-affinity aldosterone binding sites were reported, although such tissues—brain (1, 16, 41), pituitary (14, 29, 33), aortic smooth muscle (40), lung (30), and mammary gland (46)—are not normally considered classical mineralocorticoid targets, at least in terms of the modulation of transepithelial Na^+ transport. In addition, though in many of such tissues specificity studies were incomplete, these high-affinity aldosterone binding sites apparently differed from renal mineralocorticoid receptors in that they appeared to have equivalent, high affinity for aldosterone, corticosterone, and deoxycorticosterone. They did, however, resemble mineralocorticoid receptors in that their affinity for dexamethasone was very much lower than that for aldosterone or corticosterone.

Hippocampal Corticosterone-Preferring Sites

At the same time, work from McEwen's laboratory had clearly distinguished two types of glucocorticoid binding species in the rat hippocampus (12). Whereas there was clear evidence for the existence of classical, dexamethasone-binding glucocorticoid receptors in the hippocampus, there was also overwhelming evidence for a second class of site with a higher affinity for corticosterone than dexamethasone, in clear contrast to classical glucocorticoid receptors. At this time, since there was no evidence that such sites were glucocorticoid receptors, they were conservatively termed "corticosterone-preferring sites". Subsequently, however, there has emerged a body of evidence that such sites are indeed glucocorticoid receptors, although they have a much higher affinity for physiological glucocorticoids than the classical, dexamethasone-preferring species also present in the hippocampus.

The first demonstration of a specific role for such sites came from collaborative studies, between McEwen's laboratory and that of Greengard, on levels of synapsin, an 80-kd phosphoprotein, in the rat hippocampus (43). After adrenalectomy, hippocampal levels of synapsin fall; levels are restored to those found in intact rats by the administration of corticosterone but not by equal doses of dexamethasone. This finding is strong evidence for an action via corticosterone-preferring sites rather than via classical glucocorticoid receptors.

Subsequently, de Kloet and his colleagues published a series of reports on the effects of adrenalectomy and steroid administration on hippocampal levels of serotonin and serotonin receptors (8, 9, 11). The changed levels postadrenalectomy were restored by corticosterone but not by equal doses of dexamethasone, which is also evidence for an action via corticosterone-preferring sites rather than classical glucocorticoid receptors (8). Of particular interest, given the subsequent studies comparing hippocampal corticosterone-preferring sites and renal Type I (mineralocorticoid) receptors, was the demonstration that aldosterone alone did not reverse the effects of adrenalectomy but effectively antagonized the effects of coadministered corticosterone (11).

Taken together, these studies provide powerful evidence supporting the notion that the corticosterone-preferring hippocampal sites represent a class of distinct, physiological, glucocorticoid receptors. This class is distinct in that dexamethasone is ineffective, physiological in that the naturally occuring glucocorticoid reverses the effects of adrenalectomy, and glucocorticoid in that aldosterone is not an agonist but an antagonist.

High-Affinity Aldosterone Binding in the Brain

There have been reports for over a decade that mineralocorticoid receptors may be present in the brain. The first of these (34) used tritiated deoxycorticosterone as a ligand to probe possible differences in mineralocorticoid binding between spontaneously hypertensive and control rats and described high-affinity binding sites for deoxycorticosterone and aldosterone in brain cytosol preparations. Subsequently, the existence of mineralocorticoid receptors in the brain was indirectly inferred from the finding that spirolactone was a more powerful competitor for tritiated aldosterone binding sites than for tritiated dexamethasone binding sites (1).

More recently, there have been two developments that have enabled much more authoritative studies on mineralocorticoid receptors in general and of aldosterone binding sites in the brain in particular—the use of molybdate and the development of highly selective Type II, classical glucocorticoid receptor ligands. The inclusion of molybdate in homogenization media has enabled binding studies to be confidently performed in cytosol preparations, rather than tissue slices (26). Secondly, Roussel-Uclaf has developed a series of steroids (RU26988, RU28362) that have negligible affinity for renal mineralocorticoid receptors but have an affinity similar to that of dexamethasone for classical glucocorticoid receptors (56). Inclusion of excess unlabeled RU26988 or RU28362 with tritiated aldosterone thus excludes tracer from classical glucocorticoid receptors, allowing demonstration of a single population of high-affinity aldosterone binding sites.

In studies using RU26988 to exclude tritiated aldosterone from Type II sites, Moguilewsky & Raynaud (41) reported high-affinity aldosterone binding sites in cytosol preparations from a number of brain areas. On the basis of their high affinity for aldosterone such sites were termed mineralocorticoid receptors by these authors, even though no values for corticosterone were reported in otherwise extensive competition studies.

Renal and Hippocampal Type I Receptors

A series of studies published in 1983 has provided at least a partial resolution of this otherwise confused picture—of a variety of different receptors and thus of potential systematic classes of adrenal steroid action—in the central nervous system. First, Wrange & Yu (62) showed that the renal and hippocampal aldosterone binding sites had identical tryptic fragmentation patterns on isoelectrofocusing, which were clearly distinct from that for classical, dexamethasone binding glucocorticoid receptors. These studies were complemented and extended by those of Krozowski & Funder (31), who showed that the inherent steroid specificity of renal mineralocorticoid receptors was identical to that of hippocampal corticosterone-preferring sites in vitro. In addition, these authors showed that the hippocampal corticosterone-preferring sites had identical affinity for aldosterone, corticosterone, and deoxycorticosterone. Moreover—and importantly, in terms of the prior claims for a hippocampal "mineralocorticoid" receptor—no tritiated aldosterone or tritiated deoxycorticosterone binding sites were corticosterone resistant; whatever tracer was used, corticosterone, aldosterone, and deoxycorticosterone competed equivalently for these high-affinity receptors.

On the basis of these findings, Krozowski & Funder proposed that renal mineralocorticoid receptors and hippocampal corticosterone-preferring glucocorticoid receptors could usefully be characterized as Type I sites, given their identical steroid specificity and tryptic fragmentation patterns in vitro. Inasmuch as renal Type I sites appear to be physiological mineralocorticoid receptors responsive to variations in levels of aldosterone, while hippocampal Type I sites appear to be physiological glucocorticoid receptors, there remains a considerable question. What remains to be resolved are the mechanisms whereby a binding site that appears inherently nonselective in an in vitro cytosol preparation (aldosterone = corticosterone) can distinguish between the two classes of steroid on a tissue-specific basis. Given the much higher free concentrations of corticosterone than aldosterone in the circulation, the problem is primarily one for the kidney rather than the nervous system—that of how aldosterone can occupy inherently nonselective receptors, despite much higher ambient concentrations of corticosterone.

MINERALOCORTICOID SPECIFICITY-CONFERRING MECHANISMS

The problem is not one uniquely for the kidney, however: it is a question that must be asked for any Type I binding site anywhere in the body, including the central nervous system, for which a mineralocorticoid receptor role is postulated or claimed. A physiological mineralocorticoid receptor operationally has to show much higher affinity for aldosterone than for corticosterone (or cortisol, in those species in which it is the physiologic glucocorticoid). This is the case for the kidney and—extrapolating from effector data—the gut, despite equivalent affinity for the two classes of steroid in vitro. Given that there are aldosterone-specific actions within the central nervous system (for example, on blood pressure (23) or salt appetite (37), then mechanisms must exist for enabling such sites to preferentially bind aldosterone rather than corticosterone or cortisol in vivo, i.e. to function as mineralocorticoid receptors, in a slightly expanded sense of the term mineralocorticoid.

Extravascular Transcortin in the Renal Papilla–Inner Medulla

One mechanism for preferential binding of aldosterone proposed (55) for the renal papilla–inner medulla was that of the selective sequestration of corticosterone by the very high extravascular levels of transcortin, which has much higher affinity for the physiologic glucocorticoids than for aldosterone. Such sequestration was proposed to be renewable, i.e. essentially nonsaturable, given the recurrent vasculature in the region, which allows the establishment of a gradient of corticosterone binding by transcortin, thus lowering the level of free corticosterone able to compete with aldosterone for Type I receptor occupancy.

Though such a mechanism may indeed operate, there are at least two serious criticisms of it as a unique mechanism conferring mineralocorticoid specificity on Type I sites. First, though other mineralocorticoid target tissues may have a spectacularly recurrent vasculature (e.g. sweat glands), there is no evidence for a combination of a recurrent vasculature and high concentrations of extravascular transcortin in other well-characterized mineralocorticoid targets—specifically the cortical collecting tubules and connecting segments of the kidney. Secondly, 10-day-old rats, with negligible circulating and renal extravascular levels of transcortin, did not show any diminution of aldosterone-selectivity of their papillary inner medullary Type I receptors in a series of in vivo studies comparing hippocampal and renal binding of tritiated aldosterone and tritiated corticosterone.

Selective Aldosterone Uptake and Retention In Vivo

Almost two decades ago, McEwen and his colleagues in their pioneering studies determined the uptake and retention of tritiated steroids in the brain after their in vivo administration (38). In the intervening period, there have been a number of similar studies, both biochemical (1, 2, 6, 10, 12, 13, 27, 31, 41, 47, 58, 62) and autoradiographic (3, 16, 22, 48, 52, 59), though few have squarely addressed the question of possible mineralocorticoid specificity. In a recent series of studies we have injected tritiated aldosterone or tritiated corticosterone into adrenalectomized rats at various doses, either alone or with unlabeled competitors, and determined binding 10–180 min later, both in the hippocampus and in the renal cortex and papilla–inner medulla (53). In brief, corticosterone is very poorly bound or retained in either renal zone, in either 10-day-old or mature rats, whereas aldosterone is very well bound and retained, as are both aldosterone and corticosterone in the hippocampus.

It would thus appear that there exist tissue-specific mechanisms operating in vivo to confer steroid specificity on what have repeatedly been demonstrated to be nonselective Type I receptors in cytosol preparations. If such mechanisms operate in both zones of the kidney—and as shown in subsequent studies, the colon, parotid gland, and pituitary (53)—they may equivalently operate in the hippocampus and elsewhere in the central nervous system. There is very strong evidence that at least some of the hippocampal Type I sites are physiological glucocorticoid receptors, as reviewed earlier (8, 9, 11, 43). It remains possible, however, that a subpopulation of such sites are aldosterone-selective, physiological mineralocorticoid receptors in vivo, though one must bear in mind that corticosterone competes well for tritiated aldosterone binding sites in both renal and hippocampal cytosol preparations in vitro (2, 31).

If in the kidney, parotid, colon (all of which are classical mineralocorticoid target tissues), and the pituitary (which is not), aldosterone in the presence of excess RU28362 is very much better bound and retained in vivo than corticosterone, then Type I receptors in these sites must have a much higher affinity for aldosterone than for corticosterone. To accomodate this apparent paradox we propose two possible models that might explain how such Type I sites have a much higher affinity for aldosterone in vivo (and, incidentally, in the original kidney slice studies), whereas in cytosol preparations in vitro the Type I receptors have equivalently high affinity for aldosterone and corticosterone. Whether either or both of these models holds true remains to be established by experimental testing, not only for the tissues listed above, but also for discrete areas of the central nervous system, if aldosterone-selective sites can be demonstrated by micropunch and/or autoradiographic techniques.

Mineralocorticoid Receptors: Prebinding Aldosterone Selectivity

Both models entail the predominant binding of the unoccupied Type I receptor to chromatin in the absence of steroid. Such nuclear localization has recently been found, by two different techniques, for estrogen receptors (28, 61). Studies from our laboratory have shown that unoccupied Type I receptors in pituitary GH_3 tumor cells appear to be at least as concentrated in the nuclear fraction as estrogen receptors (44). In the first of the two nonexclusive models, shown as Figure 1, the unoccupied Type I receptor is postulated to exist bound to the chromatin in such a way that it has a markedly higher affinity for aldosterone than for corticosterone. This is represented diagrammatically in Panel *i* of Figure 1. When aldosterone binds to the receptor, a secondary conformational change occurs that increases the affinity of the steroid-receptor complex for chromatin, as represented in Panel *ii*. When, however, a cell is disrupted in the absence of steroid and the Type I receptor is released into the cytosol fraction, the receptor assumes a conformation in which it cannot distinguish between aldosterone and corticosterone, as shown in Panel *iii*. In summary, such a model postulates a chromatin-directed differential in receptor specificity that operates in the absence of steroid and in this sense is "prebinding."

Mineralocorticoid Receptors: Postbinding Aldosterone Selectivity

The alternate—and, it should be emphasized, nonexclusive—model is one of postbinding, chromatin-directed specificity conferral; it is depicted diagramatically in Figure 2.

In such a model the chromatin-bound Type I site is nonselective in the absence of steroid, as shown in Panel *i* of Figure 2, in contrast with the

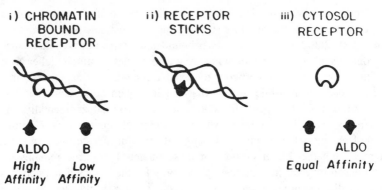

Figure 1   In this model, when the receptor is bound to nuclear chromatin it is postulated to have a high affinity for aldosterone (Aldo) and a low affinity for corticosterone (B); the conformation of the receptor is presumed to be influenced by its association with chromatin (i). When aldosterone binds (ii), there is an increase in the affinity of binding of receptor to chromatin, which does not occur when corticosterone binds. When the unoccupied receptor dissociates from the chromatin, a conformational change occurs so that the receptor can no longer distinguish, in terms of its affinity of binding, between aldosterone and corticosterone; this is shown graphically in (iii).

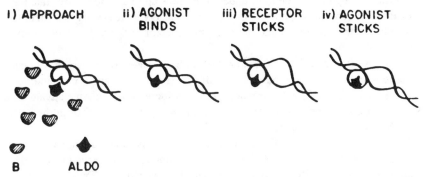

**I) APPROACH   ii) AGONIST   iii) RECEPTOR   iv) AGONIST
                    BINDS   STICKS   STICKS**

B   ALDO

Figure 2 In this model aldosterone (Aldo) and corticosterone (B) are postulated to have equal affinity for the loosely-attached nuclear receptor at the time of initial binding (i). When aldosterone binds (ii), however, a cascade of events takes place. First, the affinity of binding of receptor to chromatin increases (iii); subsequently (and as a consequence of this interaction), there occurs a secondary, chromatin-mediated change in the affinity of the receptor for aldosterone, but not for corticosterone. Under such conditions the dissociation of aldosterone is not favored (iv), giving aldosterone a higher in vivo affinity than corticosterone.

postulated selectivity of the unoccupied chromatin-bound receptor in Figure 1. If the chromatin-bound receptor is nonselective, the chances of an initial encounter with a minor ligand—minor in terms of concentration—are correspondingly low. If a minor ligand—e.g. aldosterone vis-à-vis corticosterone— is to constitute the physiological signal, there needs to be a mechanism of postbinding specificity conferral. Such a mechanism is depicted diagrammatically in Panels *ii–iv*. If the system is one in which aldosterone is to be agonist—for example, in the renal cortex—then the frequency of initial encounters between unoccupied Type I receptors and aldosterone will be relatively low compared with corticosterone. With a frequency dictated by its relative concentration, however, aldosterone will bind to the Type I sites, as shown in Panel *ii*. Consequent upon agonist binding—and common to the two models—there is an increase in affinity of the steroid-receptor complex for the chromatin, as depicted in Panel *iii*.

The postbinding, chromatin-requiring mechanism of specificity conferral postulated by this model is shown in Panel *iv*. We are accustomed to the notion of an increase in the affinity of a steroid-receptor complex for chromatin as a consequence of a primary interaction between agonist and receptor. This time the model proposes a subsequent, additional increase in the affinity of the receptor for the steroid, as a consequence of the agonist-requiring increase in the affinity of the receptor for chromatin. This is depicted graphically as the steroid being "buried" in the receptor in Panel *iv* of Figure 2, as a representation of a decreased dissociation rate of the steroid-receptor complex, i.e. increased affinity, under these circumstances. If this model holds, then even though the frequency of initial encounters between aldosterone and a Type I receptor may be low, under conditions approaching steady state the extent of receptor occupancy will be proportionately increased by the extent to which a chromatin-directed increase in receptor affinity for aldosterone occurs.

Finally, it is possible that features of both models may coexist in a given tissue—that both "prebinding" specificity (Figure 1) and "postbinding" specificity (Figure 2) are combined to further increase the relative advantage of aldosterone over corticosterone, for example, in the kidney, or in the area of the brain subserving salt appetite (37).

There are a number of currently available experimental procedures to examine whether either or both of these models can account for the aldosterone-selectivity of kidney, gut, parotid, and pituitary Type I receptors in vivo, given their equivalent binding of aldosterone and corticosterone in vitro. Ultimate verification (or rejection) of the models will depend upon purification of Type I receptors; demonstration of the identity (or nonidentity) of the steroid-binding and chromatin-binding regions of renal, hippocampal, and other Type I receptors; and comparison of the consensus sequences for Type I receptors in chromatin from various mineralocorticoid and glucocorticoid target tissues, including the brain.

SUMMARY

In summary, a wide variety of effects of adrenal steroids on the brain have been reported and have been recently and exhaustively reviewed. From the viewpoint of endocrine physiology, however, what is often forgotten is the extraordinary difference in signal level between the two unique products of the adrenal cortex, the mineralocorticoid and glucocorticoid hormones. Levels of cortisol or corticosterone are 2–3 orders of magnitude higher than those of aldosterone, a difference that is tempered by perhaps one order of magnitude by the much higher binding of glucocorticoids to plasma protein. The signal-detecting mechanisms for the lower-intensity signal, i.e. the mineralocorticoid receptor, must therefore have powerful specificity-conferring mechanisms to enable it to recognize, bind, and respond to aldosterone. In vitro studies from a number of laboratories have shown that Type I receptors, in both classic mineralocorticoid target tissues (kidney, parotid, gut) and nontarget tissues (pituitary, hippocampus), cannot distinguish between aldosterone and corticosterone. This finding highlights the problem of aldosterone-selectivity in the kidney (Na^+ transport) or the brain (Na^+ appetite). In vivo studies, in contrast, show that corticosterone is very poorly taken up and/or retained in kidney, colon, parotid, and pituitary (but not in hippocampus) in mature and 10-day-old (minimal transcortin) rats, whereas aldosterone is well taken up and/or retained by all tissues, evidence for tissue-specific aldosterone selectivity in vivo. Two nonexclusive (i.e. possibly additive) models for such aldosterone selectivity are proposed, one "prebinding" and the other "postbinding". Both models accomodate the experimental findings of the nonselectivity of cytosol preparations in vitro and the stringent specificity seen in in vivo receptor and effector studies.

In any real sense, the action of adrenal steroids on the brain is still largely an area of unconnected phenomenology, despite the efforts of a number of talented individuals and groups over the past two decades. Without descriptions of phenomena, even of the most basic ablation and replacement type, we have no chance of making physiological statements. It is equally important, in the attempt to make a coherent physiology, to erect a scaffolding of hypothesis that can be tested against the existing experimental findings and that can serve to suggest further studies in a logical sequence. These hypotheses themselves, and the models used to reify them, may be validated, altered, or rejected by the studies over the next few years. They are not the truth; their purpose is to facilitate the search for truth, in terms of the actions of adrenocortical steroids in the brain and other target tissues.

Literature Cited

1. Anderson, N. S. III, Fanestil, D. D. 1976. Corticoid receptors in rat brain: Evidence for an aldosterone receptor. *Endocrinology* 98:676–84
2. Beaumont, K., Fanestil, D. D. 1983. Characterization of rat brain aldosterone receptors reveals high affinity for corticosterone. *Endocrinology* 113:2043–51
3. Birmingham, M. K., Sar, M., Stumpf, W. E. 1984. Localization of aldosterone and corticosterone in the central nervous system, assessed by quantitative autoradiography. *Neurochem. Res.* 9:333–50
4. Bohus, B., de Kloet, E. R., Veldhuis, H. D. 1982. Adrenal steroids and behavioral adaptations: Relationship to brain corticoid receptors. In *Current Topics in Neuroendocrinology*, ed. D. Ganten, D. Pfaff, 1:107–49. Berlin: Springer-Verlag
5. Coirini, H., Magarinos, A. M., De Nicola, A. F., Rainbow, T., McEwen, B. S. 1985. Further studies of brain aldosterone binding sites employing new mineralocorticoid and glucocorticoid receptor markers in vitro. *Brain Res.* 361:212–16
6. Coirini, H., Marusic, E. T., De Nicola, A. F., Rainbow, T. C., McEwen, B. S. 1983. Identification of mineralocorticoid binding sites in rat brain by competition studies and density gradient centrifugation. *Neuroendocrinology* 37:354–60
7. Crabbe, J. 1961. Stimulation of active sodium transport by the isolated toad bladder with aldosterone in vitro. *J. Clin. Invest.* 40:2103–10
8. de Kloet, E. R., Kovacs, G. L., Szabo, G., Telegdy, G., Bohus, B., Versteeg, D. H. G. 1982. Decreased serotonin turnover in the dorsal hippocampus of rat brain shortly after adrenalectomy: Selective normalization after corticosterone substitution. *Brain Res.* 239:659–63
9. de Kloet, E. R., Sybesma, H., Reul, M. H. M. 1986. Selective control by corticosterone of serotonin$_1$ receptor capacity in raphe-hippocampal system. *Neuroendocrinology* 42:513–21
10. de Kloet, E. R., Veldhuis, H. D., Wagenaars, J. L., Bergink, E. W. 1984. Relative binding affinity of steroids for the corticosterone receptor system in rat hippocampus. *J. Steroid Biochem.* 21:173–78
11. de Kloet, E. R., Versteeg, D. H. G., Kovacs, G. L. 1983. Aldosterone blocks the response to corticosterone in the raphe-hippocampal serotonin system. *Brain Res.* 264:323–27
12. de Kloet, E. R., Wallach, G., McEwen, B. S. 1975. Differences in corticosterone and dexamethasone binding to rat brain and pituitary. *Endocrinology* 96:598–609

13. de Kloet, R., McEwen, B. S., Wallach, B. 1976. Interaction in vivo and in vitro of corticoids and progesterone with cell nuclei and soluble macromolecules from rat brain regions and pituitary. *Brain Res.* 105:129–36
14. De Nicola, A. F., Tornello, S., Weisenberg, L., Fridman, O., Birmingham, M. K. 1981. Uptake and binding of [³H]aldosterone by the anterior pituitary and brain regions in adrenalectomized rats. *Horm. Metab. Res.* 13:103–6
15. Duval, D., Funder, J. W. 1974. The binding of tritiated aldosterone in the rat liver cytosol. *Endocrinology* 94:575–79
16. Ermisch, A., Ruhle, H. J. 1978. Autoradiographic demonstration of aldosterone-concentrating neuron populations in rat brain. *Brain Res.* 147:154–58
17. Funder, J. W. 1985. On mineralocorticoid and glucocorticoid receptors. In *BIMR Clinical Endocrinology 4: Adrenal Cortex*, ed. D. C. Anderson, J. Winter, 4:86–95. London: Butterworth
18. Funder, J. W., Duval, D., Meyer, P. 1973. Cardiac glucocorticoid receptors: The binding of tritiated dexamethasone in rat and dog heart. *Endocrinology* 93:1300–8
19. Funder, J. W., Feldman, D., Edelman, I. S. 1972. Specific aldosterone binding in rat kidney and parotid. *J. Steroid Biochem.* 3:209–18
20. Funder, J. W., Feldman, D., Edelman, I. S. 1973. The roles of plasma binding and receptor specificity in the mineralocorticoid action of aldosterone. *Endocrinology* 92:994–1004
21. Funder, J. W., Feldman, D., Edelman, I. S. 1973. Glucocorticoid receptors in rat kidney: The binding of tritiated dexamethasone. *Endocrinology* 92:1005–13
22. Gerlach, J. L., McEwen, B. S. 1972. Rat brain binds adrenal steroid hormone: Radioautography of hippocampus with corticosterone. *Science* 175:1133–36
23. Gomez-Sanchez, E. P. 1986. Intracerebroventricular infusion of aldosterone induces hypertension in rats. *Endocrinology* 118:819–23
24. Green, S., Walter, P., Kumar, V., Krust, A., Bornert, J.-M., et al. 1986. Human oestrogen receptor cDNA: Sequence, expression and homology to v-erb-A. *Nature* 320:134–39
25. Greene, G. L., Gilna, P., Waterfield, M., Baker, A., Hart, Y., Shine, J. 1986. Sequence and expression of human estrogen receptor complementary DNA. *Science* 231:1150–54
26. Grekin, R. J., Sider, R. S. 1980. Aldosterone receptor assay in rat kidney cytosol. *J. Steroid Biochem.* 13:835–37
27. Grosser, B. I., Stevens, W., Reed, D. J. 1973. Properties of corticosterone-binding macromolecules from rat brain cytosol. *Brain Res.* 57:387–95
28. King, W. J., Green, G. L. 1984. Monoclonal antibodies localize oestrogen receptor in the nuclei of target cells. *Nature* 307:745–47
29. Krozowski, Z., Funder, J. W. 1981. Mineralocorticoid receptors in rat anterior pituitary: Toward a redefinition of "mineralocorticoid hormone." *Endocrinology* 109:1221–24
30. Krozowski, Z., Funder, J. W. 1981. Mineralocorticoid receptors in the lung. *Endocrinology* 109:1811–13
31. Krozowski, Z., Funder, J. W. 1983. Renal mineralocorticoid receptors and hippocampal corticosterone-binding species have identical intrinsic steroid specificity. *Proc. Natl. Acad. Sci. USA* 80:6056–60
32. Lan, N. C., Graham, B., Bartter, F. C., Baxter, J. D. 1982. Binding of steroids to mineralocorticoid receptor: Implications for in vivo occupancy by glucocorticoids. *J. Clin. Endocrinol. Metab.* 54:332–42
33. Lan, N. C., Matulich, P. T., Morris, J. A. 1981. Mineralocorticoid receptor-like aldosterone-binding protein in cell culture. *Endocrinology* 109:1963–70
34. Lassman, M. N., Mulrow, P. J. 1974. Deficiency of deoxycorticosterone-binding protein in the hypothalamus of rats resistant to deoxycorticosterone-induced hypertension. *Endocrinology* 94:1541–46
35. MacDougall, J. G., Coghlan, J. P., Scoggins, B. A. 1987. Physiological control of aldosterone secretion. *J. Endocrinol.* In press
36. McEwen, B. S., de Kloet, E. R., Rostene, W. 1986. Adrenal steroid receptors and actions in the nervous system. *Physiol. Rev.* In press
37. McEwen, B. S., Lambdin, L. T., Rainbow, T. C., De Nicola, A. F. 1986. Aldosterone effects on salt appetite in adrenalectomized rats. *Neuroendocrinology* 43:38–43
38. McEwen, B. S., Weiss, J. M., Schwartz, L. S. 1968. Selective retention of corticosterone by limbic structures in rat brain. *Nature* 220:911–12
39. Meyer, J. S. 1985. Biochemical effects of corticosterone on neural tissue. *Physiol. Rev.* 65:946–1020
40. Meyer, W. J., Nichols, N. R. 1981. Mineralocorticoid binding in cultured smooth muscle cells and fibroblasts from

rat aorta. *J. Steroid Biochem.* 14:1157–68

41. Moguilewsky, M., Raynaud, J. P. 1980. Evidence for a specific mineralocorticoid receptor in rat pituitary and brain. *J. Steroid Biochem.* 12:309–14

42. Munck, A., Guyre, P. M., Holbrook, N. J. 1984. Physiological functions of glucocorticoids in stress and their relation to pharmacological actions. *Endocr. Rev.* 5:25–44

43. Nestler, E. J., Rainbow, T. C., McEwen, B. S., Greengard, P. 1981. Corticosterone increases the amount of protein I, neurone specific phosphoprotein, in rat hippocampus. *Science* 212:1162–64

44. Pearce, P. T., McNally, M., Funder, J. W. 1986. Nuclear localization of Type I aldosterone binding sites in steroid-unexposed GH₃ cells. *Clin. Exp. Pharmacol. Physiol.* In press

45. Pressley, L., Funder, J. W. 1975. Glucocorticoid and mineralocorticoid receptors in gut mucosa. *Endocrinology* 97:588–96

46. Quirk, S. J., Gannell, J. E., Funder, J. W. 1983. Aldosterone-binding sites in the pregnant and lactating rat mammary gland. *Endocrinology* 113:812–17

47. Reul, J. M. H. V., De Kloet, E. R. 1985. Two receptor systems for corticosterone in rat brain: Microdistribution and differential occupation. *Endocrinology* 117:2505–11

48. Rhees, R. W., Grosser, B. I., Stevens, W. 1975. Effect of steroid competition and time on the uptake of [³H]corticosterone in the rat brain: An autoradiographic study. *Brain Res.* 83:292–300

49. Rousseau, G., Baxter, J. D., Funder, J. W., Edelman, I. S., Tomkins, G. M. 1972. Glucocorticoid and mineralocorticoid receptors for aldosterone. *J. Steroid Biochem.* 3:219–27

50. Rousseau, G. G., Schmit, J. P. 1977. Structure-activity relationships for glucocorticoids. I. Determination of receptor binding and biological activity. *J. Steroid Biochem.* 8:911–19

51. Sapolsky, R. M., Krey, L. C., McEwen, B. S. 1986. The neuroendocrinology of stress and aging: The glucocorticoid cascade hypothesis. *Endocr. Rev.* In press

52. Sapolsky, R. M., McEwen, B. S., Rainbow, T. C. 1983. Quantitative autoradiography of [³H]corticosterone receptors in rat brain. *Brain Res.* 271:331–34

53. Sheppard, K. E., Funder, J. W. 1986. *In vivo and in vitro studies on mineralocorticoid specificity-conferring mechanisms.* Presented at *68th Ann. Meet. Endocr. Soc., 68th, Anaheim, Calif.*

54. Stephenson, G., Hammet, M., Hadaway, G., Funder, J. W. 1984. Ontogeny of renal mineralocorticoid receptors and urinary electrolyte responses in the rat. *Am. J. Physiol.* 247:F665–71

55. Stephenson, G., Krozowski, Z., Funder, J. W. 1984. Extravascular CBG-like sites in rat kidney and mineralocorticoid receptor specificity. *Am. J. Physiol.* 246:F227–33

56. Teutsch, G., Costerousse, G., Deraedt, R., Benzoni, J., Fortin, M., Philibert, D. 1981. 17α-Alkany-11β,17-dihydroxyandrosterone derivative: A new class of potent glucocorticoids. *Steroids* 38:651–55

57. Torelli, V., Hardy, M., Nedelec, L., Tournemine, C., Deraedt, R., Philibert, D. 1982. 7α-aklyl steroidal spirolactones as potent aldosterone antagonists. Presented at *6th. Int. Congr. Horm. Steroids, Israel. J. Steroid Biochem.* 17:Abstr. 168

58. Veldhuis, H. D., Van Koppen, C., Van Ittersum, M., de Kloet, E. R. 1982. Specificity of the adrenal steroid receptor system in rat hippocampus. *Endocrinology* 110:2044–51

59. Warembourg, M. 1974. Radioautographic study of the rat brain after injection of [1,2-³H]corticosterone. *Brain Res.* 89:61–70

60. Weinberger, C., Hollenberg, S. M., Rosenfeld, M. G., Evans, R. M. 1985. Domain structure of human glucocorticoid receptor and its relationship to the *v-erb-A* oncogene product. *Nature* 318:670–72

61. Welshons, W. V., Lieberman, M. E., Gorski, J. 1984. Nuclear localization of unoccupied oestrogen receptor. *Nature* 307:747–49

62. Wrange, O., Yu, Z.-Y. 1983. Mineralocorticoid receptor in rat kidney and hippocampus: Characterization and quantitation by isoelectric focusing. *Endocrinology* 113:243–50

Ann. Rev. Physiol. 1987. 49:413–35

FUNCTIONS OF ANGIOTENSIN IN THE CENTRAL NERVOUS SYSTEM

M. Ian Phillips

Department of Physiology, Box J-274, College of Medicine, University of Florida, Gainesville, Florida 32610

INTRODUCTION

The existence of the brain-renin angiotensin system has been the subject of several reviews (36, 37, 86, 93). All the components of the renin-angiotensin cascade have been described in the brain, although their exact interaction is not yet defined. Angiotensin (Ang) II in brain has been quantified and characterized by high-pressure liquid chromatography (HPLC) (46, 73, 91, 97). The levels are in the picogram range, but a concentration of 1 picogram of Ang II per gram brain tissue is 1000–3000 times greater than that of 1 picogram per milliliter found in plasma, because brain tissue contains 1–3 μl plasma per gram.

This review attempts to summarize the emerging picture of the physiological functions and significance of brain Ang II. Several diverse effects have been reported for Ang II in the brain. Some of these effects can be achieved with peripherally administered doses, but others occur only with intraventricular (ivt) or direct microinjections into the brain. A brief survey of the effects of central versus peripheral angiotensin indicates that there are substantial differences between these two sources of the hormone (Table 1).

Some of these differences in effect are a matter of degree. For example, the dose required to induce thirst depends on whether Ang II is administered centrally or peripherally, but this may also reflect different mechanisms. It is hard to assess the actual dose equivalency between blood-borne angiotensin and angiotensin injected directly into the brain because the availability of, and the access to, receptors differ. Direct injection into the brain allows angiotensin to reach many receptor sites. Systemic infusion of Ang II, however, can only reach sites in the brain that have no blood-brain barrier (BBB); these

413

0066-4278/87/0315-0413$02.00

Table 1 Effects of angiotensin for different routes of administration

Actions	Route of Ang II administration	
	Central	Peripheral
Drinking	Low dose required	High dose required
Blood pressure increase	Slow rise/long duration	Fast rise/short duration
	Complex mechanisms	Local vasoconstriction
Heart rate	Up or no change	Down
AVP release	Prompt	?
Sympathetic nerve activation	Increases	Local norepinephrin changes
Aldosterone	Decreases	Increases
Na$^+$ appetite	Slow onset/long duration	?
Urinary Na$^+$	Natriuresis	Antinatriuresis
Catecholamines	Levels increase in plasma and brain	Prolongs action in periphery
Adrenocorticotrophic hormone release	Positive	High dose required
Corticotropin releasing factor interaction	Interacts	High dose required
Prolactin release	Inhibits	Stimulates
Luteinizing hormone release	Positive	?
Prostaglandins	?	Increases synthesis

are the circumventricular organs (CVOs). In these organs lies a mechanism for the differences between central and peripheral actions. The CVOs must limit the spread of blood-borne peptides to keep them out of the brain; otherwise, the BBB would be useless. In the CVOs, the plasma peptides have access to only a fraction of the total brain receptors.

There are three areas in which brain Ang II appears to function. The first group of actions suggests that Ang II is a hormone controlling hypovolemia. The central and peripheral actions of Ang II may in some cases be entirely independent but aimed towards the same goal of maintaining body fluid homeostasis. The second effect of Ang II is the cyclic regulation of reproductive hormones by brain and pituitary Ang II. This action may be significant in reproduction and pregnancy. The third function of brain Ang II is as a neurotransmitter that interacts with catecholamines, serotonin, and other peptides.

BRAIN ANGIOTENSIN IN THE REGULATION OF BODY FLUID VOLUME

The peripheral response of Ang II to hypovolemia includes increased blood pressure and aldosterone secretion. In addition, it is claimed that systemic administration of Ang II induces thirst and arginine vasopressin (AVP) release. However, the physiological levels of peripheral Ang II required for these effects are very high, and systemic Ang II may not be involved except under extreme conditions. The brain Ang II appears to be more sensitive for these functions and, therefore, may play an important role in volume homeostasis.

ANGIOTENSIN II AND THIRST

Drinking in response to intraventricular administration of Ang II is one of the most compelling biological effects produced by a peptide. It is unclear how truly physiological the thirst effect of Ang II is, although very low doses injected into the third ventricle induce drinking (64, 84). Hypovolemia produces thirst without osmotic changes. Hypovolemia may affect thirst in two ways. One is via vagal input from volume receptors. Little research has been done on volume receptor input into the brain and its thirst effects. Using inflatable balloons in the atria, Kaufman (52) showed that atrial stretch inhibited drinking in response to Ang II administration. The other way that hypovolemia may affect thirst is by raised plasma Ang II levels acting on CVOs (27).

Circumventricular Organs and Thirst

The subfornical organ (SFO), organum vasculosum laminae terminalis (OVLT), and the area postrema (AP) contain receptors for Ang II. The evidence for angiotensin from the periphery having an action on the brain via the circumventricular organs is voluminous. Lesioning the SFO abolishes drinking in response to intravenous (iv) angiotensin, but injections directly into the brain cause drinking even in the presence of such a lesion (84). One explanation for this might be that the area involved in drinking is not damaged by the SFO lesions. The evidence points to the OVLT and its adjacent median preoptic nucleus (MPO) as the sites of this effect of Ang II. This region has a unique structure. Tanycytes connected by tight junctions (88) on the OVLT surface appear to transport Ang II from the cerebrospinal fluid (CSF) into the OVLT (57) selectively. Gap junctions over the MPO allow free entry of CSF-borne peptides. Therefore the SFO is an important site of action for iv Ang II, the OVLT is an important site for iv or ivt Ang II effects (84), and the MPO is a receptor site for Ang II in CSF. More recent studies on receptor binding using autoradiography have confirmed that in both the SFO and the OVLT/MPO, there are numerous binding sites for Ang II (39, 43, 45, 72).

If systemic Ang II acts on CVOs, is the action physiological? Mann et al (66) infused different amounts of iv Ang II and measured the plasma Ang II levels after infusion. However, their data are incomplete because drinking was not measured. These investigators only compared the infusion rates with those from another study (27). Based on that study (27), we calculate that 500 pg Ang II per ml plasma is the threshold level for induction of drinking by iv Ang II. This is equivalent to water deprivation for over 48 hr, which produces 399 pg Ang II per ml plasma (47). By taking blood at the moment of drinking during iv injection of Ang II, we found an average level of 458 pg/ml (125).

In summary, drinking induced by iv angiotensin, at least in the rat, requires a high plasma level of Ang II. Outside the laboratory this level is probably only reached under dire circumstances such as extreme dehydration or severe hypovolemia. It is more difficult to elicit drinking with peripheral Ang II than with ivt Ang II. The reason for this difference appears to be that the periphery is not a normal site for Ang II induction of thirst but that high doses can overpower the CVO-limited diffusion barrier and reach the MPO.

Angiotensin Antagonists and Acetylcholine in Thirst

Thirst is stimulated by osmotic and hypovolemic stimuli. Efforts to separate the angiotensin component in dehydration by use of the antagonist Sar^1-Ala^8-angiotensin II (saralasin) have had mixed success (62, 85).

Carbachol, a cholinergic agonist, also evokes thirst when injected into rat brains (47). Its effects are strikingly similar to those of angiotensin in dose, time order, and in producing a pressor response (85); however, carbachol does not produce Na^+ appetite. Thus, this cholinergic stimulus may mediate osmotic dehydration, which does not require sodium intake, whereas angiotensin mediates hypovolemic dehydration, which does. However, blockage of dehydration-induced thirst requires both atropine and saralasin (47). Therefore, two different, parallel neural circuits for drinking exist, and when one is inhibited the other takes over (85).

Drinking involves not only motivation but also motor activity and memory. How brain Ang II functions in the latter two processes is not known. For the moment, suffice it to say that there are Ang II receptors in areas associated with motor control (e.g. the inferior olivary nucleus) and with memory (e.g. the hippocampus) (72, 82).

BLOOD PRESSURE AND CENTRAL ANGIOTENSIN II

Blood pressure is increased by ivt Ang II via mechanisms that involve the release of vasopressin and the increase of sympathetic nerve activity (29, 104). Peripheral Ang II may act via vasoconstriction, but evidence now shows a central component is also involved (31). The circumventricular organs and the nucleus tractus solitarius (NTS) are also important (Figure 1).

Microinjections of 0.1 pg Ang II into the SFO were shown to elicit drinking and pressor responses (8, 63, 64). These responses were specifically inhibited by saralasin. Such direct microinjections were used to model the SFO response to blood-borne Ang II. Lesioning of the entire organ significantly

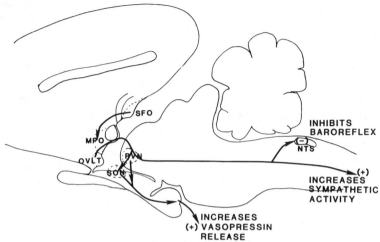

Figure 1   Brain Ang II mechanisms of blood pressure increase.

reduced the pressor response to Ang II but did not alter resting arterial pressure or disturb fluid balance (64). This is in contrast to effects of lesions of the median preoptic nucleus (65) or the entire anteroventral third ventricle (AV3V) area (49). AV3V lesions cause hypernatremia, adipsia, and loss of blood pressure in many models of hypertension.

Other substances also act in the SFO to produce blood pressure effects. When acetylcholine or serotonin was injected into the SFO directly, there was a pressor response (8, 64). Direct electrical stimulation of the SFO produces a short-latency pressor response and resistance changes in various vascular beds (63).

Very low doses of Ang II (50 fmol) applied accurately by microinjections into the OVLT/MPO cause a pressor response (84). When Ang II is injected into the brain ventricles but restricted to the region of the OVLT and MPO by cream plugs in the ventricles, the pressor, drinking, and antidiuretic responses are maintained. The connections of the OVLT and SFO include projections to the supraoptic nucleus (14, 74), and therefore both organs may effect the Ang II pressor response by stimulating AVP release from magnocellular cells. Specific OVLT lesions are very difficult to make without interfering with the adjacent MPO and periventricular tissue. Lesions of these sites result in loss of responsiveness to Ang II administered iv or ivt (4, 49, 65) and to osmotic stimuli (121). These findings suggest that osmoreceptors are located in the OVLT (121). Electrophysiological responses to microiontophoretically applied Ang II showed a line of excited cells that included the OVLT and MPO (56, 87). Stimulation of this area via microelectrodes increases mean blood pressure and alters resistance in the renal and mesenteric vascular beds (64).

Thus, it appears that the OVLT plays an important role in the response to brain Ang II and osmotic stimuli. The profound interconnection between the MPO and OVLT make absolute quantification of their respective roles impossible. Any difference in function most likely lies in their respective locations—the OVLT is able to detect both systemic and brain Ang II. ^{125}I-Ang II given iv is antagonized by ivt saralasin in the OVLT, but there is little inhibition of the label in the SFO or AP (126). This observation confirms the earlier hypothesis that the OVLT "sees" both CSF and blood Ang II but that the SFO and AP detect only blood-borne Ang II (84).

Lesions of the AP in rats (44) but not in dogs (31) do not alter acute responses to ivt or iv Ang II (44). However, the AP is surrounded by a glial border (87), which lesions may disrupt. Also, the lesions impinge on the NTS and could alter the baroreflex so that there is no net change in blood pressure. Thus, the AP may play an important role in the effects of brain Ang II, but a more accurate type of lesion is needed.

Ang II–like material has been reported in the SFO and OVLT (45, 59). The role of this peptide in areas that receive plasma Ang II has not been established, nor has the possibility of uptake of Ang II from plasma into the neurons been investigated. Nevertheless, the cells may be among those connected to the MPO (49). Saralasin inhibits electrical responses in the MPO to SFO stimulation, which indicates that the MPO contains effective Ang II synapses (76).

The OVLT and SFO have many similarities in structure and function and may act in unison to monitor Ang II in plasma. They may also serve as paracrine glands, with Ang II acting as the messenger hormone between cells. Both CVOs impinge on the MPO, but the MPO would not usually detect plasma Ang II because of the CVO-brain barrier. In high-renin hypertension, either Ang II could diffuse from the OVLT to the receptors in the MPO or Ang II–containing cells in the CVOs could synaptically stimulate the receptors. Thus the MPO may be important in relaying the effects of Ang II from brain and/or plasma sources, and therefore it may be critical in the development of hypertension involving Ang II and in Ang II responses to hypovolemia.

Parallel Mechanisms

Because of the parallel organization of AVP release and sympathetic nerve stimulation, if one system is abolished, the other can maintain the blood pressure response. Pretreatment with iv cyclo-dVD AVP, a synthetic AVP analogue, partially reduces the blood pressure response to icv Ang II. Since cyclo-dVD AVP is a specific antagonist for the vasopressor response of AVP, this finding supports the idea that plasma AVP contributes to the central Ang II pressor response (123).

Evidence for an increase in sympathetic nerve activity (SNA) to Ang II is based on pharmacological experiments, recordings of electrical activity in nerves, studies with microspheres, and direct measurement of the levels of norepinephrine in blood (103, 104, 115, 123). The actual vascular beds that respond to Ang II–induced SNA are not well defined. Falcon et al (29) showed that although 6-OH-dopamine (6-OHDA) treatment eliminated sympathetic activation, it did not prevent the rise in blood pressure but only delayed the response. This observation also indicates that there are two systems acting in parallel, and that another system was able to compensate for the lack of sympathetic nerve activity.

The Effects of Angiotensin II in the Nucleus Tractus Solitarius on the Baroreflex

Microinjections of Ang II into the NTS increase blood pressure (16, 17). This response, which has also been found with microinjections of AVP (69), suggests that these peptides control the blood pressure to some extent by dampening the relay synapse of the baroreceptor reflex. In these experiments with Ang II, heart rate did not change. Inhibition of the reflex overcomes the decrease in heart rate (HR) that normally occurs when blood pressure is raised. Without the HR decrease, blood pressure rises even further. The increase in blood pressure was not due to diffusion of Ang II into the AP or blood (16, 17). The response of hypophysectomized rats to Ang II in the NTS did not decline. Hexamethonium-treatment, however, almost completely blocked the effects of Ang II injections (16). The NTS exerts some control over the sympathetic outflow system and can be modified by central Ang II. The source for this central Ang II may be the cells in the PVN containing Ang II. Swanson & Sawchenko (119) have shown that there are extensive projections from the PVN to the brain stem with collateral branches terminating in the NTS. Thus, it seems possible that the brain angiotensin system has its major manufacturing sites in the magnocellular nuclei of the hypothalamus (11, 92) and projects to the NTS, where it releases Ang II. This Ang II alters blood pressure by inhibiting the baroreflex.

A blunting of the baroreflex is found in spontaneously hypertensive rats (SHRs) (16). This finding supports the idea that brain Ang II is a hormone controlling blood pressure in SHRs (86). Central injections of saralasin (90) or infusions of converting enzyme inhibitor (86) reduce blood pressure in SHRs.

The brain Ang II may play a role in hypertension because of its central control of three major mechanisms of blood pressure elevation: vasopressin release, sympathetic activation, and NTS synaptic inhibition of the baroreflex. Each contributing factor is probably independent; such multiple mechanisms normally permit buffering to maintain constant blood pressure under varying conditions. In hypertension, however, brain Ang II may be overactive. In low-renin hypertensive models, such as DOCA-salt, brain Ang II receptors are up-regulated (127). In hypertension characterized by normal renin levels (e.g. SHR), brain Ang II is increased. In high-renin hypertension models, the high circulating Ang II may penetrate by diffusion through the CVO-brain barrier to reach otherwise inaccessible receptors and activate them.

ANGIOTENSIN II AND VASOPRESSIN RELEASE

AVP, also known as antidiuretic hormone (ADH), is one of the three hormones involved in fluid balance; the others are angiotensin and aldosterone. AVP is released when blood volume decreases. Thus it seems logical that peripheral angiotensin should stimulate the release of vasopressin. The evidence that peripheral angiotensin releases vasopressin, however, is controversial. Some investigators have shown increases in ADH when dogs were given iv Ang II (6, 23, 98). Many others, however, have been unable to stimulate vasopressin release in anesthetized and conscious dogs with iv or intracarotid infusions of Ang II (21, 99). The key difference between these studies appears to be in the concentration of Ang II in the plasma. In a study by Reid et al (99), a dose of 20 ng/kg/min increased plasma vasopressin release slightly (1.7 pg/ml), but this effect was only achieved at a very high level of Ang II in the blood (449 pg/ml).

In the rat, iv Ang II does not cause release of ADH (48). In the human, the story is much the same. The Ang II doses given or the levels of Ang II in the plasma must be very high in order to produce quite small vasopressin increases (81, 122). Thus, peripheral Ang II at physiological levels does not release vasopressin. Vasopressin secretion can be induced by high concentrations of Ang II in the plasma or by an interaction between Ang II and plasma osmolality (105). The interaction may be via central Ang II receptors or by the opening of the BBB.

Clearly, central Ang II causes acute or chronic release of AVP (48, 54, 106, 113). In conscious rats, using the bioassay (48) or vasopressin radioimmunoassay (54), researchers found a consistent and prompt release of vasopressin with ivt Ang II (although one cannot state that these were physiological doses).

The site of action of central Ang II for vasopressin secretion is still unknown, but several possibilities exist, including direct or indirect action through osmoreceptors or interneurons. A direct action on the neurons containing AVP would be mediated by localized release of Ang II in the supraoptic nucleus (92). Electrophysiological evidence indicates that Ang II stimulates supraoptic nucleus (SON) cells (78). However, autoradiography does not show such intense binding of Ang II in the SON but does show binding in the PVN (72). Ang II acts directly to release AVP in isolated hypothalamic tissue with the pituitary intact (108). This block of tissue contains the OVLT and the median eminence, as well as the PVN, SON, and neurohypophysis. The hypothalamic block lacks noradrenergic inputs, but interneurons in the block may be the source of stimulation.

Saralasin blocked vasopressin release in response to an osmotic stimulus in the organ-cultured hypothalamo-pituitary explant (108). These data and the demonstration that blood pressure raised by ivt NaCl administration can be blocked by saralasin in vivo (108) point to a role for Ang II in mediating osmotic changes. The actual osmotic receptors are unknown, but they reside within the hypothalamic block used in organ explants.

The circumventricular organs may play a role in vasopressin release. Neural connection to the supraoptic nucleus from the SFO (74) and the OVLT (87) has been demonstrated by horseradish peroxidase (HRP) tracer studies. Lesions of the SFO or the OVLT (or AV3V) inhibit or abolish the vasopressin release in response to ivt Ang II (4, 65). However, in the isolated hypothalamic block taken from AV3V-lesioned rats, in which the OVLT is destroyed and the SFO is absent, Ang II can still cause release of AVP (107). The role of the circumventricular organs in vasopressin release does not necessarily require the presence of blood-borne Ang II. Small spherical cells in the SFO and OVLT that contain Ang II–like immunoreactivity have been reported (59). If these cells are the ones connected to the SON or PVN along the axons demonstrated by HRP and amino acid transport, then central injections of Ang II would mimic the release of endogenous brain Ang II from these cells.

SODIUM APPETITE AND BRAIN ANGIOTENSIN

A low level of salt in the diet leads to hypovolemia, and hypovolemia leads to Na^+ hunger. One of the effects produced by central angiotensin is sodium appetite. Ang II infused at low rates (1 pmol/hr) into the third ventricle causes rats to drink large quantities of 2.7% sodium. This increase in sodium appetite is not secondary to sodium excretion because animals went into positive sodium balance and anuric animals also demonstrated increased sodium appetite in response to centrally injected angiotensin (32). Compared to the water-intake response to ivt infusions of Ang II, the response to sodium is slower. A single hypovolemic stimulus (polyethylene glycol) can induce permanent Na^+ appetite (58). Peripheral infusions of angiotensin do not induce sodium appetite until extremely high doses have been reached, at which point aldosterone levels become elevated. Aldosterone greatly enhances central Ang II induction of Na^+ appetite (32). Aldosterone can cross the blood-brain barrier, and it increases the number of brain Ang II receptors

(127). This may be the mechanism by which a high dose of aldosterone or deoxycorticosterone (DOCA) induces NaCl appetite (32). At the opposite extreme, adrenalectomized rats in the absence of mineralocorticoid hormones also have a profound preference for NaCl over water. It is interesting that ivt administration of Ang II suppresses aldosterone secretion (9, 77). Therefore, the sodium appetite induced by centrally administered Ang II appears to resemble that induced by adrenalectomy. A greater NaCl appetite is produced in rats given ivt Ang II and DOCA than is elicited by either substance alone (33). The increased sodium appetite with Ang II and steroid would be beneficial when there is an extreme lack of sodium in the diet since this would induce more mineralocorticoid release and make sodium ingestion a conscious need.

In sodium-sensitive humans, sodium intake above 20-mmol Na per day is correlated with hypertension. Whether this sodium intake and/or hypertension is related to brain angiotensin is unknown (89).

CENTRAL ANGIOTENSIN II AND KIDNEY FUNCTION

So far, angiotensin in the periphery and in the brain appears to have a single common function, that of conserving volume and maintaining the sodium balance of the extracellular fluid. In the kidney, antinatriuresis (decrease in $U_{Na}V$) is induced by several hormonal agents, including systemic Ang II (80). However, both acute and chronic ivt injections of Ang II produce a natriuresis (increase in $U_{Na}V$) (10). In contrast to the action of peripheral Ang II, ivt Ang II inhibits aldosterone release (9). Aldosterone promotes Na^+ reabsorption in the kidneys, which produces an antinatriuresis. Thus, the systemic Ang II and the brain Ang II have opposite actions on sodium excretion, although ivt Ang II increases sodium appetite, which would seem to counteract the sodium loss. With chronic ivt Ang II, no change in plasma $[Na^+]$ was found (26).

Ang II administered ivt produces natriuresis in dogs that is independent of changes in blood pressure (BP), renal blood flow (RBF), glomerular filtration rate (GFR), and plasma aldosterone (10). Brooks & Malvin used a dose low enough (6 ng/min for 2 hr) to produce natriuresis but no renal hemodynamic changes (10). Converting-enzyme inhibitor (ivt Captopril) caused decreased Na^+ excretion, which indicates that brain Ang II inhibits Na^+ reabsorption in the kidney. It could do this by release of natriuretic hormone (12).

An explanation of the opposite effects of sodium appetite and sodium loss is that brain Ang II may function to regulate brain Na^+. Low Na^+ has been reported to raise the number of Ang II brain receptors (67) and alter drinking in response to Ang II (51). AV3V-lesioned rats lose their responsiveness to central Ang II and enter a state of hypernatremia (5, 49). It may be that brain Ang II increases when brain levels of sodium are raised, so that natriuresis occurs and normal levels of sodium are again achieved. However, in the AV3V lesioned rats without Ang II receptors, this circuit is destroyed, and consequently, persistent hypernatremia develops.

In summary, the two systems, brain and peripheral Ang II, appear to have a reciprocal effect on absolute sodium excretion. Brain Ang II may have a dual role in Na^+ balance: increasing sodium intake in hypovolemia and controlling Na^+ levels in the brain. Modulation of sodium reabsorption when brain angiotensin is stimulated should be studied by afferent neural recording. The exact efferent pathway for the natriuretic response to brain Ang II remains to be investigated. It is possible that central Ang II releases natriuretic hormone (NH), since lesions to the Ang II sites of the AV3V region prevent NH release (12).

Plasma Renin and Brain Angiotensin II

Ang II given intraventricularly inhibits renin secretion and thus decreases plasma renin activity (PRA) with or without parallel variation in plasma angiotensin levels, depending on the species studied and the experimental conditions (28, 60). Malayan et al (61) suggested that the inhibition may be mediated by AVP release.

The infusion of Captopril into the sheep brain elicits an increase in PRA (10). Since Captopril inhibits Ang II, this result implies that endogenous brain angiotensin is involved in decreasing renin. Lowering PRA leads to less reabsorption of Na^+ in the kidney (80).

ATRIAL NATRIURETIC FACTOR AND ANGIOTENSIN

Since DeBold et al (24) first demonstrated profound diuresis and natriuresis in rats following iv infusion of atrial homogenates, there has been great excitement about atrial natriuretic factor (ANF). The active factor is a 28–amino acid peptide that is released when volume expansion causes atrial stretch. Many of its actions appear to be opposite those of iv Ang II (Figure 2). The two hormones may provide off-setting hormonal controls to maintain normal body fluid volume. In vascular strips, ANF inhibits contractions produced by Ang II. ANF inhibits PRA (13, 79), AVP (101), and aldosterone stimulation by Ang II (40). One of the major differences between the two hormones is that ANF is a vasorelaxer and Ang II a vasoconstricter. They have opposite effects on GFR and RBF (3, 7, 79). There is immunocytochemical and receptor binding evidence for ANF in the brain (95), as well as in the periphery. ANF appears to be distributed in the same brain areas as Ang II. In addition, the ANF receptors are localized in the same regions as Ang II receptors, particularly the circumventricular organs. ANF attenuates the drinking induced by ivt Ang II and by dehydration (2). In view of their multiple opposite effects,

ANF and Ang II appear to play a yin-yang role in maintaining volume homeostasis.

ACTH RELEASE, CRF, AND ANGIOTENSIN II INTERACTION

Steroids shift fluid balance, and central Ang II facilitates ACTH release, which in turn increases corticosteroid levels (68, 110). Several possible mechanisms can be considered. Firstly, Ang II may cause the release of corticotrophin releasing factor (CRF); secondly, Ang II may act to potentiate the action of CRF; and thirdly, Ang II causes the release of AVP. AVP itself is able to stimulate ACTH release, either by acting directly at the anterior pituitary or by releasing CRF. There is a partially blunted ACTH response to ivt Ang II administration in the Brattleboro rat, which suggests that the Ang II effect may be mediated partly by AVP and partly by another mechanism (35).

The definitive experiments to distinguish between direct and indirect mechanisms of Ang II–mediated ACTH release in vivo have not yet been reported. When isolated pituitary cells are treated with CRF, ACTH is released, and when Ang II is used in place of CRF, ACTH is released but to a much lower extent (124). CRF and Ang II together have an additive action on ACTH release (124).

The evidence that suggests that Ang II exerts its effects via CRF release comes from Spinedi & Negro-Vilar (110). Rats were pretreated with chlorpromazine–morphine sulphate and Nembutol. When CRF or AVP was infused intravenously, ACTH release occurred; but when Ang II was infused intravenously, ACTH release was blocked. This suggests that Ang II does not act in the pituitary but acts at a higher center, possibly to cause CRF release.

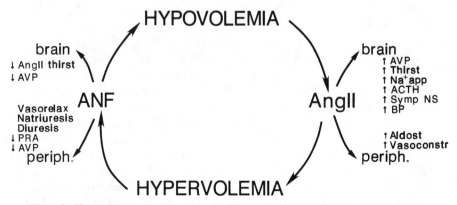

Figure 2 Humoral responses to hypovolemia with Ang II and to hypervolemia with ANF. These effects balance each other to maintain a state of normovolemia.

Recent studies in trained, unstressed dogs infused with Ang II and CRF have shown that systemic Ang II does not cause ACTH release but is permissive to CRF's action on ACTH release (55). A key to obtaining meaningful results in this kind of study is assuring that the animals are initially unstressed, so that baseline ACTH levels are low.

ALDOSTERONE AND ANGIOTENSIN II

Aldosterone is essential for maintaining body fluid volume. Systemic Ang II has a major role in aldosterone release, but central Ang II inhibits this release. In sodium-replete sheep, intraventricular infusion of Ang II results in increased plasma aldosterone levels; however, this response is probably mediated by ACTH, as it can be blocked by dexamethasone.

In anesthetized, sodium-depleted dogs that received ivt infusions of either Captopril or saralasin, both inhibitors of Ang II, plasma aldosterone concentrations rose (9). This finding is significant because peripheral infusions of these inhibitors did not alter aldosterone levels. There may be a negative feedback loop by which adrenal steroids regulate angiotensinogen levels centrally (94) and Ang II receptors (127). However, it is challenging to resolve the ambiguity of Ang II effects on Na^+ conservation. Again, the possibility of a dual role for Ang II, i.e. in hypovolemia and in cerebral Na^+ balance, needs to be studied.

ANGIOTENSIN II AND REPRODUCTIVE HORMONES

Evidence is emerging that central Ang II has a function in regulating the hypothalamo-pituitary sex hormone axis and cyclic reproductive activity. First, during the estrus cycle, spontaneous drinking is reduced, and the number of Ang II receptors in the preoptic area, lateral hypothalamus, septum, olfactory bulbs and pituitary is reduced (18, 19). In contrast, the peripheral effects of estrus are an increase in plasma angiotensinogen and in the number of uterine Ang II receptors (15).

The ability of estrus to alter Ang II binding is probably influenced by estrogen. Several recent studies have shown that estrogen administration decreased Ang II binding centrally and at the same time reduced the amount of water ingested following ivt Ang II (33, 50).

Drinking in response to ivt Ang II was depressed in ovariectomized female rats one day after ivt estradiol benzoate. The interaction of estrogen and central Ang II is specific because drinking in response to carbachol or polyethyleneglycol in the same rats was not altered, and no change in drinking following ivt Ang II occurred in males. The pressor response to ivt Ang II was also reduced by estrogen pretreatment. In a series of clever experiments,

Jonklaas & Buggy (50) altered sexual differentiation in neonatal rats and showed that in adulthood Ang II binding in the OVLT and MPO was reduced by estrogen.

Ang II is present in the median eminence (92), a location that poises it for releasing activity in the anterior pituitary. We have measured brain angiotensin throughout the estrus cycle, and preliminary data indicate an increase in brain Ang II during proestrus. In ovariectomized rats pretreated with estrogen, ivt Ang II increased plasma levels of luteinizing hormone (LH) (111). In ovariectomized rats that did not have estrogen replacement, Ang II lowered the level of LH in blood, the frequency of LH pulse release, and the amplitude of such releases (112). In rats pretreated with both estradiol and progesterone, ivt Ang II increased LH in plasma. Blocking brain Ang II with ivt saralasin or enalapril in the presence of progesterone and estrogen prevented the LH surge during proestrus (112). Oxytocin is also released by Ang II (34). Oxytocin is necessary for parturition and suckling and is involved in impregnation.

These experiments and the report that central Ang II releases prolactin (1) point to a possible role for brain Ang II in the control of reproduction. Ang II is localized in gonadotrophs of the anterior pituitary (25), where it may have paracrine activity. In the OVLT, LH releasing hormone (LHRH) inhibited cells that were excited by Ang II (30). This suggests that Ang II may release LHRH and that a short negative-feedback loop may exist between LHRH and Ang II in OVLT cells.

In summary, there is increasing evidence that central angiotensin has actions related to reproduction in addition to its role in maintaining fluid balance. At times, these two major survival functions are interrelated, e.g. thirst during estrus and water retention during pregnancy, and it may be worth investigating the role of central Ang II in premenstrual water retention and its attendant vascular effects.

BRAIN ANGIOTENSIN II AND NEUROTRANSMITTER FUNCTION

Electrophysiological studies have shown that Ang II has the qualities of a neurotransmitter. It is found in synaptic terminals and excites neurons at very low doses (10^{-12} M) with high specificity (30, 56, 82). It acts on neurons with high affinity and reversible binding (72, 97). Pharmacological experiments indicate numerous interactions between Ang II and other transmitters.

Catecholamines and Angiotensin II

There is an interaction between Ang II and catecholamines (CA) in the brain as well as in the periphery. Central injection of Ang II causes a pressor response that is partly mediated by activation of the sympathetic nervous system (20, 29, 103, 123). In hemorrhage, ivt Ang controls catecholamine release from adrenals, not peripheral Ang II (22). Intraventricular Ang II increases turnover (or utilization) of norepinephrine in specific brain regions associated with blood pressure control without changing the dopamine utilization in these regions (115). These effects are not caused by the blood pressure increases resulting from the central administration of Ang II (115, 116). Central injection of renin increases dopamine (DA) turnover in the external layer of the median eminence and decreases norepinephrine (NE) turnover in the magnocellular paraventricular nucleus and the dorsomedial hypothalamic nucleus (34). Renin also increased epinephrine turnover in a block of brain stem tissue containing the NTS, nucleus commisuralis, and the dorsal motor nucleus of the vagus. These effects are specifically mediated by Ang II (102).

The NTS and locus coeruleus contain a high concentration of both catecholamines (100) and Ang II receptors (71), as do many parts of the hypothalamus, which also contains Ang II (59, 92). Thus, components of the Ang II system and catecholamines are closely related anatomically in areas of the brain associated with the control of blood pressure.

Ang II does not evoke NE release from brain tissue but enhances electrically stimulated NE release (70). Converting-enzyme inhibitors had the same effect on NE release as clonidine, an α_2-adrenoceptor agonist, and could partially inhibit the effects of rauwolscine, an α_2-adrenoceptor antagonist (70). Similarly, Ang II can increase the potassium-evoked release of NE from rabbit hypothalamus in a dose-dependent fashion, an effect blocked by saralasin (38). This stimulation of NE by Ang II can be blunted by placing the animals on a low-sodium diet. The A2 area of the brain contains Ang II receptors and catecholamines and is involved in blood pressure control. Release of NE in response to Ang II in this area is modulated by the sodium status of the animal. Ventriculocisternal infusion of Ang II in rabbits caused an increase in the CSF concentration of NE, which was highly correlated with the increase in blood pressure due to Ang II (20). This result strengthens the evidence for a central Ang II–CA interaction in blood pressure regulation.

Angiotensin II: Catecholamine Negative Feedback

In cell culture, where there is no interference from blood pressure, one can test hypotheses about Ang II–CA mechanisms. In primary rat brain cultures, neurons were shown by fluorescence microscopy to contain NE (117). Ang II in the medium causes significant increases in neuronal and media NE levels (116). In addition, Ang II stimulates NE uptake in rat hypothalamus-brain stem neuronal cocultures (118). Such experiments suggest that (a) Ang II activates catecholamines and (b) there is a negative-feedback loop through which catecholamines inhibit Ang II release and reduce Ang II binding. When catecholamines levels are increased, the number of Ang II receptors decreases and vice versa (96). In SHR brains, there is a defect in the negative-feedback loop, and altered CA levels have no effect on the receptors. The SH rat brains have a lower number of Ang II receptors even when CA levels are high (118). This in turn leads to more CA release. By this mechanism, the increased Ang II release probably contributes to the elevated blood pressure of SHRs. Thus, in the SHR, evidence from in vivo studies and in vitro studies points to an overactive brain angiotensin system.

The effect of Ang II on NE uptake is a little more complex. In neuronal cell culture it has a biphasic effect. At short times after Ang II exposure, NE uptake is enhanced whereas after longer Ang II treatment, NE uptake is inhibited (96).

In summary, the primary cell culture and in vivo studies in the rat indicate a negative feedback of NE on Ang II receptors.

Serotonin and Angiotensin II

Rats treated with parachlorophenylalamine (pCPA), an inhibitor of serotonin (5-HT) synthesis, and then given intraventricular Ang II show a depressor rather than a pressor response (75). Similarly, methylsergide, a 5-HT antagonist, had the same effect. In synaptosomal preparations from hypothalamus and brain stem, Ang II increased 5-HT synthesis. Ang II was shown to affect the rate-limiting enzyme of serotonin synthesis, tryptophan hydroxylase, in a dose-dependent fashion. At low concentrations Ang II decreased the enzyme's activity, and at high concentrations it increased it, as did angiotensin III (42). 5-HT blockers blunt the pressor and drinking responses to Ang II, probably through the inhibition of serotonin binding (75).

5-HT and Ang II appear to interact at the level of the medial forebrain bundle input to the anterior hypothalamic preoptic area. However, this interaction is in turn dependent on an intact brain NE system, as 6-OHDA abolishes it (42).

Peripheral administration of Ang II also leads to increases in the serotonin content of the hypothalamus, brain stem, and pineal gland of dogs (41, 42). A reninlike substance has a diurnal rhythm in the pineal similar to that of norepinephrine and melatonin. When 5-HT synthesis is blocked with pCPA, the reninlike activity in the pineal increases (41). Thus, Ang II may be involved with serotonin in a diurnal rhythm. Preliminary data indicate that brain Ang II has a diurnal rhythm.

Opioid–Angiotensin II Interaction

There is an interrelationship of opioids and Ang II in the brain, but it is poorly understood. At first sight, the interaction seems simple. Enkephalins, β-endorphins, and morphine can inhibit the usual effects of centrally administered Ang II. These effects include dose-dependent increases in plasma vasopressin and oxytocin, drinking behavior, and pressor response (53, 114). Naloxone potentiates the pressor effect of ivt Ang II, and naloxone can disinhibit the opioid inhibition of Ang II–induced effects. It appears that the site of this interaction can be reached from the lateral and third ventricles (114). However, opiates decrease immobility, and naloxone and naltrexone alone also decrease Ang II–induced drinking (93), so the situation is complex. A complete dose-response curve of morphine is biphasic: Low doses potentiate angiotensin-induced effects, while high doses inhibit them. These studies may have missed this effect of dose. Furthermore, naloxone and naltrexone act through inhibition of endogenous opioids, which may have different effects than exogenous opioids. Studies of the effects Ang II and opioid turnover have on each other, along with studies with specific inhibitors of both systems, would help unravel this interaction.

Further evidence that the opioid peptides are involved in Ang II synaptic action is the observation that Ang II induces analgesia (41). Ang II–induced analgesia was measured by the tail-flick method and could be antagonized by naloxone. Angiotensin and the enkephalins are linked by the fact that converting enzyme is also an enkephalinase (120). Captopril, a converting-enzyme inhibitor, prevents the hydrolysis of enkephalins by enkephalinase and also produces analgesia (120).

LOCAL ANGIOTENSIN SYSTEMS

The brain angiotensin is but one of several locally produced angiotensins. Angiotensin and/or its receptors appear in the anterior pituitary (25), kidney (71), uterus (15), bladder (71), adrenals (15), Leydig cells (83), mesenteric arteries, vascular endothelium cells, and microvessels (37, 71, 109). Although Ang II in all these sites may have the same structure, its role will vary. In the brain, there is considerable evidence that Ang II serves as a neurotransmitter as well as a hormone. Local angiotensins may be a mechanism for fine tuning of physiological processes. The distance between the site of Ang II release and the receptor is shorter than that for a circulating hormone, and therefore, the actions of Ang II are more quickly adjustable. However, the levels of peptide in these tissues are relatively small and difficult to measure.

SUMMARY AND CONCLUSIONS

In this review, the emerging functional roles of the brain angiotensin system have been considered. The major effects of Ang II can be classified into three groups, which imply three possible functions:

The first, and largest, group is actions associated with the regulation of body fluid volume in response to hypovolemia. These include thirst, blood pressure increase, vasopressin release, sodium appetite and excretion, and ACTH and aldosterone release. This function alone has important implications for the control of blood pressure and the disease of hypertension.

Another possible function is a role for angiotensin in the activity of gonadotropic hormone releasing hormones and pituitary hormones during the reproductive cycle and pregnancy.

A third group of functions is the synaptic, neurotransmitter interactions of Ang II with catecholamines, serotonin, prostaglandins, and other peptides, not all of which could be reviewed here due to space limitations. This interaction is significant for all functions mentioned and leads to alterations in motivation (thirst, pain), memory (and possibly learning), and motor control. The amount of data available, however, is so limited that to claim angiotensin plays any major role in the latter functions would be premature.

Throughout this review, we compared the central and peripheral effects of Ang II. We suggest that normally, a blood-CVO barrier prevents diffusion of peripheral Ang II to brain receptors inside the BBB. Because of this mechanism, the responses to the two routes of administration are distinctly different. When systemic peptide levels are low, Ang II activates only receptors in the CVOs; however, when these levels are high, the peptide diffuses to receptors that are normally activated only by brain Ang II.

ACKNOWLEDGMENTS

I wish to thank Mrs. C. Gabbard for excellent typing and Elaine Richards Sumners for her input. This work was supported by NIH grant 1-R01-HL27334.

Literature Cited

1. Aguilera, G., Hyde, C. L., Catt, K. J. 1982. Angiotensin II receptors and prolactin release in pituitary lactotrophs. *Endocrinology* 111:1045
2. Antunes-Rodrigues, J., McCann, S. M., Rogers, L. C., Samson, W. K. 1985. Atrial natriuretic factor inhibits dehydration- and angiotensin II–induced water intake in the conscious, unrestrained rat. *Proc. Natl. Acad. Sci. USA* 82:8720–23
3. Atlas, S. A., Kleinert, H. D., Camargo, M. J., Januszewicz, A., Sealy, J. E., et al. 1984. Purification, sequencing and synthesis of natriuretic and vasoactive rat atrial peptide. *Nature* 309:717–19
4. Bealer, S. L., Phillips, M. I., Johnson, A. K., Schmid, P. G. 1979. Effect of anteroventral third ventricle lesions on antidiuretic responses to central angiotensin II. *Am. J. Physiol.* 236:E610
5. Bealer, S. L., Schneider, E. G. 1985. Plasma corticosterone and volume after preoptic recess lesions and volume depletion. *Am. J. Physiol.* 248:R161–65
6. Bonjour, J. P., Malvin, R. L. 1970. Stimulation of ADH release by the renin-angiotensin system. *Am. J. Physiol.* 218:1555
7. Borenstein, H. B., Cupples, W. A., Sonnenberg, H., Veress, A. T. 1983. The effect of a natriuretic atrial extract on renal hemodynamic and urinary excretion in anesthetized cat. *J. Physiol.* 334:133
8. Brody, M. J., Mangiapane, M. L. 1983. *Neuroscience* 9:183 (Abstr.)
9. Brooks, V. L., Malvin, R. L. 1980. Intracerebroventricular infusion of an-

giotensin II inhibits aldosterone secretion. *Am. J. Physiol.* 239:E447

10. Brooks, V. L., Malvin, R. L. 1982. Intracerebroventricular infusion of angiotensin II increases sodium excretion (41385). *Proc. Soc. Exp. Biol. Med.* 169:532

11. Brownfield, M. W., Reid, I. A., Ganten, D., Ganong, W. F. 1982. Differential distribution of immunoreactive angiotensin and angiotensin converting enzyme in rat brain. *Neuroscience* 7: 1759

12. Buckalew, V. M. Jr., Gruber, K. A. 1984. Natriuretic hormone. *Ann. Rev. Physiol.* 46:343–58

13. Burnett, J. C., Granger, J. P., Opgenorth, T. J. 1985. Effects of synthetic atrial natriuretic factor on renal function and renin release. *Am. J. Physiol.* 246:F863

14. Camacho, A., Phillips, M. I. 1981. Horseradish peroxidase study in rat of the neural connections of the organum vasculosum of the lamina terminalis. *Neurosci. Lett.* 25:201

15. Capponi, A. M., Catt, K. J. 1979. Angiotensin II receptors in adrenal cortex and uterus. *J. Biol. Chem.* 254:5120–27

16. Casto, R., Phillips, M. I. 1984. Mechanism of pressor effects by angiotensin in the nucleus tractus solitarius of rats. *Am. J. Physiol.* 247:R575

17. Casto, R., Phillips, M. I. 1985. Neuropeptide action in nucleus tractus solitarius: Angiotensin specificity in hypertensive rats. *Am. J. Physiol.* 249:R341

18. Chen, F. M., Hawkins, R., Printz, M. P. 1982. Evidence for a functional, independent brain angiotensin system: Correlation between regional distribution of brain angiotensin receptors, brain angiotensinogen and drinking during the estrus cycle of rats. *Exp. Brain Res. Suppl.* 4:157

19. Chen, F. M., Printz, M. P. 1983. Chronic estrogen treatment reduces angiotensin II receptors in the anterior pituitary. *Endocrinology* 113:1503

20. Chevillard, C., Duchene, N., Pasquier, R., Alexander, J. M. 1979. Relation of the centrally evoked pressor effect of angiotensin II to central noradrenaline in the rabbit. *Eur. J. Pharmacol.* 58:203

21. Claybaugh, J. R., Share, L., Shimizu, K. 1972. The inability of infusions of angiotensin to elevate the plasma vasopressin concentration in the anesthetized dog. *Endocrinology* 90:1647

22. Corwin, E. J., Seaton, J. F., Hamaji, M., Harrison, T. S. 1985. Central role for angiotensin in control of adrenal

catecholamine secretion. *Am. J. Physiol.* 249:R363–70

23. Cowley, A. W. Jr., Switzer, S. J., Skelton, M. M. 1981. Vasopressin, fluid and electrolyte response to chronic angiotensin II infusion. *Am. J. Physiol.* 240:R130

24. DeBold, A. J., Borenstein, H. B., Veress, A. T., Sonnenberg, H. 1981. A rapid and potent natriuretic response to intravenous injection of atrial myocardial extract in rats. *Life Sci.* 28:89–94

25. Deschepper, C. F., Seidler, C. D., Steele, M. K., Ganong, W. F. 1985. Further studies on the localization of angiotensin-II-like immunoreactivity in the anterior pituitary gland of the male rat, comparing various antisera to pituitary hormones and their specificity. *Neuroendocrinology* 40:471–75

26. DiNicolantonio, R., Mendelsohn, F. A. O., Hutchinson, J. S., Takata, Y., Doyle, A. E. 1982. Dissociation of dipsogenic and pressor responses to chronic central angiotensin II in rats. *Am. J. Physiol.* 242:R498

27. Epstein, A. N. 1976. The physiology of thirst. *Can. J. Physiol. Pharmacol.* 54:639

28. Eriksson, L., Fyhrguist, F. 1976. Plasma renin activity following central infusion of angiotensin II and altered CSF sodium concentration in the conscious goat. *Acta Physiol. Scand.* 98:209

29. Falcon, J. E., Phillips, M. I., Hoffman, W. E., Brody, M. J. 1978. Effects of intraventricular angiotensin II mediated by the sympathetic nervous system. *Am. J. Physiol.* 235:H392

30. Felix, D., Phillips, M. I. 1979. Inhibitory effects of luteinizing hormone releasing hormone (LHRH) on neurons in the organum vasculosum lamina terminalis (OVLT). *Brain Res.* 169:204

31. Ferrario, C. M. 1983. Neurogenic actions of angiotensin II. *Hypertension* 5:V73–79

32. Fluharty, S. J., Epstein, A. N. 1983. Sodium appetite elicited by intracerebroventricular infusion of angiotensin II in the rat: II. Synergistic interaction with systemic mineralocorticoids. *Behav. Neurosci.* 97:746

33. Fregly, M. J. 1980. Effect of chronic treatment with estrogen on the dipsogenic response of rats to angiotensin. *Pharmacol. Biochem. Behav.* 12:131

34. Fuxe, K., Andersson, K., Locatelli, V., Mutt, V., Lundberg, J., et al. 1980. Neuropeptides and central catecholamine systems: Interactions in neuroendocrine and central cardiovascular regulation. In *Neural Peptides and Neuronal*

Communication, ed. E. Costa, M. Trabucchi, P. 37. New York: Raven

35. Gaillard, R. C., Favrod-Coune, C. A., Capponi, A. M., Muller, A. F. 1985. Corticotropin-releasing activity of the renin-angiotensin system peptides in rat and in man. *Neuroendocrinology* 4:511–17

36. Ganten, D., Fuxe, K., Phillips, M. I., Mann, J. F. E., Ganten, H. 1978. The brain isorenin-angiotensin system: Histochemistry, localization and possible role in drinking and blood pressure regulation. In *Frontiers in Neuroendocrinology,* ed. W. F. Ganong, D. Ganten, pp. 61–99. New York: Raven

37. Ganten, D., Printz, M., Phillips, M. I., Scholkens, B. A., eds. 1982. *The Renin Angiotensin System in the Brain.* Heidelberg: Springer-Verlag

38. Garcia-Sevila, J. A., Dubocovich, M. L., Langer, S. Z. 1979. Angiotensin II facilitates the potassium-evoked release of ^{3}H-noradrenaline from the rabbit hypothalamus. *Eur. J. Pharmacol.* 56:173

39. Gehlert, D. R., Speth, R. C., Healy, D. P., Wamsley, J. K. 1984. Autoradiographic localization of angiotensin II receptor in the rat brainstem. *Life Sci.* 34:1565–71

40. Goodfriend, T. L., Elliot, M. E., Atlas, S. A. 1984. Action of synthetic atrial natriuretic factor on bovine adrenal glomerulosa. *Life Sci.* 35:1675–82

41. Haulica, I., Petrescu, G., Stratone, A., Branisteanu, D., Rosca, V., et al. 1982. Possible functions of brain renin. In *The Renin Angiotensin System in the Brain,* ed. D. Ganten, M. Printz, M. I. Phillips, B. A. Scholkens, p. 335. Heidelberg: Springer-Verlag

42. Haulica, I., Petrescu, G., Uluitu, M., Rosca, V., Slatineanu, S. 1980. Influence of angiotensin II on dog pineal serotonin content. *Neurosci. Lett.* 18:329

43. Haywood, J. R., Brennan, T. J., Hinojosa, C. 1985. Neurohumoral mechanisms of sodium-dependent hypertension. *Fed. Proc.* In press

44. Haywood, J. R., Fink, G. D., Buggy, J., Phillips, M. I., Brody, M. J. 1980. The area postrema plays no role in the pressor action of angiotensin in the rat. *Am. J. Physiol.* 239:H108–13

45. Healy, D. P., Printz, M. P. 1984. Distribution of immunoreactive angiotensin II, angiotensin I, angiotensinogen and renin in the CNS of intact and nephrectomized rats. *Hypertension* 6:1–130

46. Hermann, K., Lang, R. E., Unger, T., Bayer, C., Ganten, D. 1984. Combined high-performance liquid chromatography radioimmunoassay for the characterization and quantitative measurement of neuropeptides. *J. Chromatogr.* 312:273

47. Hoffman, W. E., Ganten, U., Phillips, M. I., Schmid, P. G., Schelling, P., Ganten, D. 1978. Inhibition of drinking on water-deprived rats by combined central angiotensin II and cholinergic receptor blockade. *Am. J. Physiol.* 234:F41

48. Hoffman, W. E., Phillips, M. I., Schmid, P. G. 1977. The role of catecholamines in central antidiuretic and pressor mechanisms. *Neuropharmacology* 16:563

49. Johnson, A. K. 1985. The periventricular anteroventral third ventricle (AV3V): Its relationship with the subfornical organ and neural systems involved in maintaining body fluid homeostasis. *Brain Res. Bull.* 15:595

50. Jonklaas, J., Buggy, J. 1984. Angiotensin-estrogen interaction in female brain reduces drinking and pressor responses. *Am. J. Physiol.* 247:R167

51. Kapsha, J. M., Keil, L. C., Klase, P. A., Severs, W. B. 1979. Centrally mediated hydration effects of angiotensin in various states of sodium balance. *Pharmacology* 81:25

52. Kaufmann, S. 1983. Role of right atrial receptors in the control of drinking in the rat. *J. Physiol.* 349:389–96

53. Keil, L. C., Rosella-Dampman, L. M., Emmert, S., Chee, O., Summy-Long, J. Y. 1984. Enkephalin inhibition of angiotensin-stimulated release of oxytocin and vasopressin. *Brain Res.* 297:329

54. Keil, L. C., Summy-Long, J., Severs, W. B. 1975. Release of vasopressin by angiotensin II. *Endocrinology* 96:1063

55. Keller-Wood, M., Stenstrom, B., Shinsako, J., Phillips, M. I. 1986. Interaction between CRF and Ang II in control of ACTH and adrenal steroids. *Am. J. Physiol.* 250:R396–402

56. Knowles, W. D., Phillips, M. I. 1980. Angiotensin II responsive cells in the organum vasculosum lamina terminalis (OVLT) recorded in hypothalamic brain slices. *Brain Res.* 195:256

57. Landas, S., Phillips, M. I., Stamler, J. F., Raizada, M. K. 1980. Visualization of specific angiotensin II binding sites in the brain by fluorescent microscopy. *Science* 210:791–93

58. Leavitt, M. L. 1976. *The Phenomenon of Permanent Na$^+$ Appetite in Rats.* PhD thesis, Univ. Iowa, Iowa City

59. Lind, R. W., Swanson, R. W., Ganten, D. 1985. Organization of angiotensin II immunoreactive cells and fibers in the

rat central nervous system. *Neuroendocrinology* 40:2

60. Lokhandwala, M. F., Buckley, J. P., Jandhyala, B. S. 1978. Reduction of plasma renin activity by centrally-administered angiotensin II in anesthetized cats. *Clin. Exp. Hyperten.* 1:167

61. Malayan, S. A., Keil, L. C., Ramsey, D. J., Reid, I. A. 1979. Mechanism of suppression of plasma renin activity by centrally administered angiotensin II. *Endocrinology* 104:672

62. Malvin, R. L., Mouw, D., Vander, A. J. 1977. Angiotensin: Physiological role in water deprivation-induced thirst of rats. *Science* 197:171

63. Mangiapane, M. L., Brody, M. J. 1983. Electrical stimulation of subfornical organ (SFO) increases arterial pressure and regional vascular resistance. *Fed. Proc.* 42:854

64. Mangiapane, M. L., Thrasher, T. N., Keil, L. C., Simpson, J. B., Ganong, W. F. 1982. Subfornical organ lesions impair the vasopressin (AVP) response to hyperosmolality or angiotensin II (AII). *Fed. Proc.* 41:1105

65. Mangiapane, M. L., Thrasher, T. N., Keil, L. C., Simpson, J. B., Ganong, W. F. 1983. Deficits in drinking and vasopressin secretion after lesions of the nucleus medianus. *Neuroendocrinology* 37:73

66. Mann, J. F. E., Johnson, A. K., Ganten, D. 1980. Plasma angiotensin II: Dipsogenic levels and angiotensin-generating capacity of renin. *Am. J. Physiol.* 238:R372

67. Mann, J. F. E., Schiffrin, E. L., Schiller, P. W. 1980. Central actions and brain receptor binding of angiotensin II: Influence of sodium intake. *Hypertension* 2:437

68. Maran, J. W., Yates, F. E. 1977. Cortisol secretion during intrapituitary infusion of angiotensin II in conscious dogs. *Am. J. Physiol.* 233:E272

69. Matsuguchi, H., Sharabi, F. M., Gordon, F. J., Johnson, A. K., Schmid, P. G. 1982. Blood pressure and heart rate responses to vasopressin microinjection into the nucleus tractus solitarius region of the rat. *Neuropharmacology* 21:687

70. Meldrum, M. J., Xne, C. S., Badino, L., Westfall, T. C. 1984. Angiotensin facilitation of noradrenergic neurotransmission in central tissues of the rat: Effects of sodium restriction. *J. Cardiovas. Pharmacol.* 6:989

71. Mendelsohn, F. A. O. 1985. Editorial review. Localization and properties of

angiotensin receptors. *J. Hyperten.* 3:307–16

72. Mendelsohn, F. A. O., Quirion, R., Saavedra, J. M., Aguilera, G., Catt, K. J. 1984. Autoradiographic localization of angiotensin II receptors in rat brain. *Proc. Natl. Acad. Sci. USA* 81:1575

73. Mikami, H., Suzuki, H., Smeby, R. R., Ferrario, C. M. 1985. Cerebrospinal fluid angiotensin II immunoreactivity is not derived from the plasma. *Hypertension* 7:65–71

74. Miselis, R. R. 1981. The efferent projections of the subfornical organ of the rat: A circumventricular organ within a neural network subserving water balance. *Brain Res.* 230:1

75. Nahmod, V. E., Finkielman, S., Benarroch, E. E., Pirola, C. J. 1978. Angiotensin regulates release and synthesis of serotonin in brain. *Science* 202:1091

76. Nelson, D. O., Johnson, A. K. 1985. Subfornical organ projections to nucleus medianus: Electrophysiological evidence for angiotensin II synapses. *Fed. Proc.* 44:1010

77. Nicholls, M. G., Malvin, R. L., Espiner, E. A., Lun, S., Miles, K. D. 1983. Adrenal hormone responses to cerebroventricular angiotensin II in the sheep (41565). *Proc. Soc. Exp. Biol. Med.* 172:330

78. Nicoll, R. A., Barker, J. L. 1971. Excitation of supraoptic neurosecretory cells by angiotensin II. *Nature New Biol.* 233:172

79. Obana, K., Naruse, M., Naruse, K., Sakurai, H., Demura, H., et al. 1985. Synthetic rat atrial natriuretic factor inhibits *in vitro* and *in vivo* renin secretion in rats. *Endocrinology* 117:1282–84

80. Olsen, M. E., Hall, J. E., Montani, J. P., Guyton, A. C., Langford, H. G., Cornell, J. E. 1985. Mechanisms of angiotensin II natriuresis and antinatriuresis. *Am. J. Physiol.* 249:F299

81. Padfield, P. L., Morton, J. J. 1977. Effects of angiotensin II on arginine-vasopressin in physiological and pathological situations in man. *J. Endocrin.* 74:251

82. Palovcik, R. A., Phillips, M. I. 1984. Saralasin increases activity of hippocampal neurons inhibited by angiotensin II. *Brain Res.* 323:345–48

83. Pandey, K. N., Inagami, T. 1986. Regulation of renin angiotensins by gonadotropic hormones in cultured immune Leydig tumor cells. *J. Biol. Chem.* 261:3934–38

84. Phillips, M. I. 1978. Angiotensin in the brain. *Neuroendocrinology* 25:354–77

85. Phillips, M. I. 1980. Biological effects

of angiotensin in the brain. In *Enzymatic Release of Vasoactive Peptides*, ed. F. Gross, G. Vogel, pp. 337–64. New York: Raven

86. Phillips, M. I. 1984. Brain renin-angiotensin and hypertension. In *Hypertension and the Brain*, ed. G. P. Guthrie, Jr., T. A. Kotchen, pp. 63–81. Mount Kisco, New York: Futura

87. Phillips, M. I., Camacho, A. 1986. The organum vasculosum of the lamina terminalis and median preoptic nucleus: Anatomical connections and physiological functions. In *Circumventricular Organs and Body Fluids*, ed. P. M. Gross. Boca Raton, Fla.: CRC

88. Phillips, M. I., Deshmukh, P., Larsen, W. 1978. Morphological comparisons of the ventricular wall of subfornical organ and organum vasculosum of the lamina terminalis. *Scanning Electron Microsc.* 2:349–56

89. Phillips, M. I., Mann, J. F. E. 1982. Hypertension and sodium intake: Is the brain renin angiotensin system salient? In *Salt and Hypertension. Proceedings of Lewis K. Dahl Symposium*, ed. J. Iwai, pp. 185–202. New York/Tokyo: Igaku-Shoin

90. Phillips, M. I., Mann, J. F. E., Haebara, H., Hoffman, W. E., Dietz, R., et al. 1977. Lowering of hypertension by central saralasin in the absence of plasma renin. *Nature* 270:445–47

91. Phillips, M. I., Stenstrom, B. 1985. Angiotensin II in rat brain comigrates with authentic angiotensin II in HPLC. *Circ. Res.* 56:212–19

92. Phillips, M. I., Weyhenmeyer, J. A., Felix, D., Ganten, D. 1979. Evidence for an endogenous brain renin angiotensin system. *Fed. Proc.* 38:2260–66

93. Printz, M. P., Ganten, D., Unger, T., Phillips, M. I. 1982. Minireview: The brain renin angiotensin system. In *The Brain Renin Angiotensin System*, ed. D. Ganten, M. Printz, M. I. Phillips, B. A. Scholkens, p. 30. Heidelberg: Springer-Verlag

94. Printz, M. P., Hawkins, R. L., Wallis, C. J., Chen, F. M. 1983. Steroid hormones as feedback regulators of brain angiotensinogen and catecholamines. *Chest* 83:308

95. Quirion, R., Dalpe, M., DeLean, A., Gutkowska, J., Cantin, M., Genest, J. 1984. Atrial natriuretic factor (ANF) binding sites in brain and related structures. *Peptides* 5:1167–72

96. Raizada, M. K., Muther, T. F., Sumners, C. 1984. Increased angiotensin II

receptors in neuronal cultures from hypertensive rat brain. *Am. J. Physiol.* 247:C364–72

97. Raizada, M. K., Yang, J. W., Phillips, M. I., Fellows, R. E. 1981. Rat brain cells in primary culture: Characterization of angiotensin II binding sites. *Brain Res.* 207:343–55

98. Ramsay, D. J., Keil, L. C., Sharpe, M. C., Shinsako, J. 1978. Angiotensin II infusion increases vasopressin, ACTH, and 11-hydroxycorticosteroid secretion. *Am. J. Physiol.* 234:R66

99. Reid, I. A., Brooks, V. L., Rudolph, C. D., Keil, L. C. 1982. Analysis of the actions of angiotensin on the central nervous system of conscious dogs. *Am. J. Physiol.* 243:R82

100. Saavedra, J. M., Brownstein, M. J., Kizer, J. S., Palkovits, M. 1986. Biogenic amines and related enzymes in the circumventricular organs of the rat. *Brain Res.* 107:412

101. Saavedra, J. M., Plunkett, L. M. 1985. Autoradiography with computerized microdensitometry: A new tool for the study of receptor and enzyme kinetics in discrete brain areas. Focus on the brain angiotensin system. *IBRO News* 13:1–8

102. Schacht, U. 1984. Effects of angiotensin II and ACE inhibitors on electrically stimulated noradrenaline release from superfused rat brain slices. *Clin. Exp. Hypertension Theory Pract.* A6:1847

103. Scholkens, B. A., Jung, W., Rascher, W., Dietz, R., Ganten, D. 1982. Intracerebroventricular angiotensin II increases arterial blood pressure in rhesus monkeys by stimulation of pituitary hormones and the sympathetic nervous system. *Experentia* 38:469

104. Severs, W. B., Daniels-Severs, A. 1973. Effects of angiotensin on the central nervous system. *Pharmacol. Rev.* 25:415

105. Shimizu, K., Share, L., Claybaugh, J. R. 1973. Potentiation by angiotensin II of the vasopressin response to an increasing plasma osmolality. *Endocrinology* 93:42

106. Simonnet, G., Rodriguez, R., Furnoux, F., Czernichow, P., Vincent, J. 1979. Vasopressin release and drinking induced by intracranial injection of AII in monkey. *Am. J. Physiol.* 237:R20

107. Sladek, C. D., Johnson, A. K. 1983. Effect of anteroventral third ventricle lesions on vasopressin release by organ cultured hypothalamo-neurohypophyseal explants. *Neuroendocrinology* 37:78

108. Sladek, C. D., Joynt, R. J. 1979. An-

giotensin stimulation of vasopressin release from the rat hypothalamo-neurohypophyseal system in organ culture. *Endocrinology* 104:148

109. Speth, R. C., Harik, S. I. 1985. Angiotensin II receptor binding sites in brain microvessels. *Proc. Natl. Acad. Sci. USA* 82:6340–43

110. Spinedi, E., Negro-Vilar, A. 1983. Angiotensin II and ACTH release: Site of action and potency relative to corticotropin-releasing factor and vasopressin. *Neuroendocrinology* 37:446

111. Steele, M. K., Gallo, R. V., Ganong, W. F. 1985. Stimulatory or inhibitory effects of angiotensin II upon LH secretion in ovariectomized rats: A function of gonadal steroids. *Neuroendocrinology* 40:210

112. Steele, M. K., Negro-Vilar, A., McCann, S. M. 1982. Modulation by dopamine and estradiol of the central effects of angiotensin II on anterior pituitary hormone release. *Endocrinology* 111:722

113. Sterling, G. H., Chec, O., Riggs, R. V., Keil, L. C. 1980. Effect of chronic intracerebroventricular angiotensin II infusion on vasopressin release in rats. *Neuroendocrinology* 31:182

114. Summy-Long, J. Y., Keil, L. C., Sells, G., Kirby, A., Chee, O., Severs, W. B. 1983. Cerebroventricular sites for enkephalin inhibition of the central actions of angiotensin. *Am. J. Physiol.* 244: R522

115. Sumners, C., Phillips, M. I. 1983. Central injection of angiotensin II alters catecholamine activity in rat brain. *Am. J. Physiol.* 244:R257

116. Sumners, C., Phillips, M. I., Raizada, M. K. 1983. Angiotensin II stimulates changes in the norepinephrine content of primary cultures of rat brain. *Neurosci. Lett.* 36:305–9

117. Sumners, C., Phillips, M. I., Raizada, M. K. 1983. Rat brain cells in primary culture: Visualization and measurement of catecholamines. *Brain Res.* 264:267–75

118. Sumners, C., Raizada, M. K. 1986. Angiotensin II stimulates norepinephrine uptake in hypothalamus/brainstem neuronal cultures. *Am. J. Physiol.* 250:C236–44

119. Swanson, L. W., Sawchenko, P. E. 1983. Hypothalamic integration: Organization of the paraventricular and supraoptic nuclei. *Ann. Rev. Neurosci.* 6:269

120. Swerts, J. P., Perdrisot, R., Malfroy, B., Schwartz, J. C. 1979. Is "enkephalinase" identical with "angiotensin converting enzyme"? *Eur. J. Pharmacol.* 53:209

121. Thrasher, T. N., Keil, L. C., Ramsay, D. J. 1982. Lesions of the organum vasculosum of the lamina terminalis (OVLT) attenuate osmotically induced drinking and vasopressin secretion in the dog. *Endocrinology* 110:1837

122. Uhlich, E. P., Weber, P., Eigler, J., Groschel-Stewart, U. 1975. Angiotensin stimulated AVP-release in humans. *Klin. Wochenschr.* 53:177

123. Unger, T., Rascher, W., Shuster, C., Pavlovitch, R., Schonig, A., et al. 1981. Central blood pressure. Effects of substance P and angiotensin II: Role of the sympathetic nervous system and vasopressin. *Eur. J. Pharmacol.* 71:33

124. Vale, W., Vaughan, J., Smith, M., Yamamoto, G., Rivier, J., Rivier, C. 1983. Effects of synthetic ovine corticotropin-releasing factor, glucocorticoids, catecholamines, neurohypophyseal peptides, and other substances on cultured corticotropic cells. *Endocrinology* 113:1121

125. van Eekelen, A., Phillips, M. I. 1986. The level of plasma Ang II at the moment of drinking. In press

126. van Houten, M., Mangiapane, M. L., Reid, I. A., Ganong, W. F. 1983. [Sar^1,Ala^8]-angiotensin II in cerebrospinal fluid blocks the binding of blood-borne ^{125}I-angiotensin II to the circumventricular organs. *Neuroscience* 10:1421

127. Wilson, K. M., Sumners, C., Hathaway, S., Fregly, M. J. 1986. Mineralocorticoids modulate central angiotensin II receptors in rats. *Brain Res.* 382:87–96

CARDIOVASCULAR PHYSIOLOGY

CHRONIC ADAPTATION OF THE CARDIOVASCULAR SYSTEM

Introduction, Harvey V. Sparks, Jr., *Section Editor*

The cardiovascular system contributes to homeostasis by means of mechanisms with time constants ranging from seconds to months to years. Although short-term control systems have been emphasized in the past, there have been a number of recent advances in our understanding of long-range adaptations of the heart and blood vessels; some of these are summarized in the following reviews. The underlying theme of most of these papers is the impact of the regulation of protein synthesis and tissue growth on cardiovascular function. This is an area of very fruitful cross-fertilization of modern biology and systems physiology.

Seidel & Schildmeyer review the evidence that increased load on the blood vessel wall stimulates synthesis of connective tissue and contractile proteins and cell growth. The same is true of the heart. This is reviewed at the level of the cardiocyte by Cooper and at a more biochemical level by Morgan and colleagues. Morkin's review stresses exciting work on the molecular basis for the influence of thyroid hormone on contractile protein synthesis. Four other reviews deal with growth of the microvasculature with emphasis on mechanisms of angiogensis (D'Amore & Thompson), blood vessel growth into transplanted muscles (Burton and colleagues), microvascular responses to chronic hypoxia (Banchero), and vascular adaptation to cardiac hypertrophy (Chilian & Marcus). Finally, Lakatta describes biochemical and cellular changes in the heart associated with senescence. These subjects are representative of an exciting area of cardiovascular research that has important implications for understanding disease.

Ann. Rev. Physiol. 1987. 49:439–51

MICROCIRCULATORY ADAPTATION TO SKELETAL MUSCLE TRANSPLANTATION[1]

Harold W. Burton, Bruce M. Carlson, and John A. Faulkner

Departments of Physiology, Anatomy, and Biological Sciences, The University of Michigan Medical School, Ann Arbor, Michigan 48109

INTRODUCTION

Skeletal muscle transplantation involves the removal of a muscle from its normal site and transfer to another region in the body. Various transplantation procedures, with or without neurovascular repair, have been used to correct facial palsy (27, 28), anal (23) and urinary (17) incontinence, and direct trauma to the muscles of the arm (18, 37, 46). Despite the widespread use of muscle transplantation, most of the relevant research has been descriptive, and only a few mechanisms underlying the processes of muscular and vascular degeneration and regeneration are known. Much of this information has been obtained through studies of muscle grafts in small mammals. These studies involved removing muscles and grafting them into the same site (orthotopic grafts) or removing muscles and transplanting them (heterotopic grafts). Comparisons of heterotopic and orthotopic grafts demonstrate no qualitative differences in the processes of degeneration and regeneration of muscles, nerves, or blood vessels nor quantitative differences in structure and function after stabilization of the grafts (14, 58).

In a standard muscle graft the proximal and distal tendons are sutured to the tendon stumps in the host site, but nerves and blood vessels are not repaired. Under these circumstances, skeletal muscle fibers degenerate. If the graft revascularizes and reinnervates spontaneously, the muscle fibers regenerate and the structural and functional characteristics of the muscle eventually

[1]Please send reprint requests to Dr. John A. Faulkner at the above address.

0066-4278/87/0315-0439$02.00

stabilize (5, 24, 26, 55). A muscle graft is considered stable when there is no further increase in maximum force development with time. In grafts of >3 g in mass, spontaneous revascularization is often inadequate to supply blood vessels to fibers in the core of the grafts, and these fibers remain as a necrotic mass infiltrated with connective tissue (8, 38). Consequently, the use of standard muscle grafting is limited to muscle grafts of small masses. When neurovascular anastomoses are made between suitable blood vessels and nerves in the surrounding tissue and the neurovascular pedicle of the graft, original muscle fibers survive (44). Nerve and vascular anastomosis at the time of grafting allows muscles >3 g in mass to be transplanted successfully (16, 21, 27, 28, 37, 44, 46, 52).

The muscle fibers in standard muscle grafts degenerate and then regenerate from a population of myogenic cells, called satellite cells. Satellite cells are located between the sarcolemma and basal lamina of muscle fibers (1, 48). In a whole muscle graft, the process of regeneration proceeds in a centripetal fashion and is linked temporally to the growth of blood vessels into the graft (6, 8, 26). The regeneration of fibers within a muscle graft relies ultimately on the degree to which the graft is revascularized. Although reinnervation of the muscle graft is also an important determinant of the extent to which a graft recovers structure and function (6, 8), it is not discussed in this review. The focus of this review is the process of revascularization of muscles grafted by different procedures and the structure and function of the vascular bed in these muscle grafts.

MODELS OF SKELETAL MUSCLE GRAFTING

The minced muscle model was the earliest procedure for skeletal muscle grafting to receive serious attention (4, 50). In this model, an entire muscle is removed, minced into 1-mm^3 fragments and then replaced into its original bed or into a foreign site. All vascular, tendinous, and neural connections with the host are severed. For function to be restored, the minced muscle must create order out of architectural chaos as the muscle fragments break down, regenerate, and then become reintegrated with the vasculature, nerves, and tendon stumps of the host. Since the vasculature of the muscle is totally disrupted by mincing, formation of the gross vascular pattern within the regenerated muscle cannot be based upon a preexisting vascular network. Standard whole muscle grafts are similar to minces in that all vascular, neural, and tendinous connections are severed at the time of grafting, but with whole muscle grafts the muscle itself is not mechanically disrupted. As a result, the pattern of the original intramuscular vasculature remains, although many cellular changes occur.

Several standard whole muscle models of grafting have been developed whereby an entire muscle is removed from its bed and grafted back into its original bed or into a foreign site. The first model used the technique of predenervation of the muscle a few weeks before transplantation on the premise that predenervation enhanced either the survival of original muscle fibers or regeneration (51, 52, 54, 55). Subsequently, no long-term differences were found between grafts made with or without predenervation (5), and investigators have dispensed with this technique. The second model of standard whole muscle grafting is performed without predenervation. Standard extensor digitorum longus (EDL) muscle grafts, with a mass of 100 mg in rats, and a mass of 3 g in cats, attained a maximum force development of 56 (12) and 31% (14) of control values, respectively. A variant of the standard muscle graft technique is to sever all vascular and tendinous connections to the muscle, but leave the nerve intact (7, 9). Application of the nerve-intact grafting technique resulted in restoration of approximately 90% of the maximum force development of EDL muscles in rats (9) and approximately 65% in EDL muscles in cats (13).

With a neurovascular pedicle of adequate size, muscles of any mass can be transplanted successfully through reestablishment of the blood supply with anastomoses of the blood vessels and facilitation of reinnervation through anastomoses of the nerve (53). If the muscle is ischemic for no longer than 2–3 hr during the grafting procedure, the majority of the muscle fibers in the graft survive, as does the vascular bed (44). The transplantation of large muscles with neurovascular anastomoses results in the restoration of approximately 70% of the maximum force development of the control muscle (21). In reconstructive surgery, grafting with neurovascular anastomoses has been widely adopted for the transplantation of whole skeletal muscles into the face (27, 28) and forearm (37, 46).

The process of revascularization of regenerating muscle fibers has been studied in bundles of fibers grafted onto the hamster cheek pouch (15, 57). Small bundles, containing approximately 20 intact muscle fibers, revascularize spontaneously. Fibers may degenerate spontaneously, or a homogeneous population of degenerating fibers can be obtained by immersing the bundles in bupivacaine. Muscle fiber regeneration, which is completed within 14 days, is more rapid than in 100 mg EDL muscles in rats.

Since the fiber degeneration found in transplanted muscle is induced by muscle ischemia rather than the act of transplantation, ischemic models of muscle regeneration, with (19, 25, 31) and without (31, 36, 49) tenotomy, have been developed. When ischemia is experimentally induced in muscles, the process of muscle degeneration and regeneration closely parallels that described for standard muscle grafts (19, 25, 31). Using different ischemic models, investigators have described the effect of short and prolonged muscle ischemia on capillary structure (36, 49).

REVASCULARIZATION OF MUSCLE GRAFTS

After whole muscle grafting, the graft becomes ischemic, and the endothelium and other elements of the vascular walls degenerate (4, 24, 26). The extent of endothelial cell survival in free muscle grafts has not been determined, but a thin peripheral rim of muscle fibers survives the grafting procedure (5). Vascular elements associated with these fibers are also likely to survive. The degree of spontaneous revascularization of standard grafts depends on the vascularity of the site as well as on the mass of the ischemic graft to be revascularized.

It is not known how functional vascular connections are made between a whole muscle graft and the vessels of the bed in which the graft is placed. The graft may be revascularized by capillary sprouts growing inwards from blood vessels in the host into the graft, outwards from blood vessel fragments in the graft to the blood vessels in the host tissue, or a combination of these processes. Although there are no definitive studies in which inward growth of capillaries into grafts from the host tissue has been observed, this process occurred in pieces of absorbable gelatin sponge (Gelfoam) implanted in place of the plantar flexor muscles of rats (4). Capillary sprouts from blood vessels within the host tissue grew across the surface of the Gelfoam. Conversely, revascularization of small bundles of intact fibers grafted onto the hamster cheek pouch was accomplished by outward growth of blood vessels (15). Fragments of blood vessels longer than 0.5 mm were found inside the graft 12 hours after grafting. Since blood vessels grow at a rate of 0.5 mm/day (11), these fragments appeared to have survived the ischemia of the grafting procedure. The fragments contained endothelial cells that demonstrated mitotic activity. Endothelial cells undergoing mitosis were found most often at the growing tip of the surviving fragments in the grafts. Mitotic activity was rarely observed in blood vessels of the cheek pouch, and the growing tips of the blood vessels from within the graft appeared to play a significant role in establishing contact with the vasculature of the host tissue.

In grafts of whole 100-mg muscles or of minced muscles in rats, India ink injections at the end of the second day show the first traces of injected vessels in scattered patches over the periphery of the grafts (4, 26). Once the vascular bed is established in the periphery of the graft, a regular sequence of cellular associations begins as regenerating blood vessels grow from the periphery toward the center of the graft. It is not evident from these experiments whether endothelial cells that form the first peripheral capillary tubes originate from within the graft or in the surrounding tissue.

The first vessels observed in a whole muscle graft are sinusoidal structures that form a branching network around surviving muscle fibers at the periphery of the graft (26). The inward penetration of vascular sprouts follows closely behind macrophages, which invade the basal laminae of the ischemic muscle fibers and ingest fragments of damaged cytoplasm. Very few mast cells are demonstrable in early muscle grafts (34). As vascular sprouts penetrate into the graft, they use the empty basal laminae of degenerated blood vessels, nerve fibers, or muscle fibers as a substrate (26, 56). In a recent histochemical study of free grafts of rat muscles, the alkaline phosphatase reaction was used to distinguish the arterial segments of capillaries, and the dipeptidyl peptidase IV reaction was used to identify the venous segments (20). These techniques showed that the enzymatic differentiation characteristic of arterial capillary segments appeared before that characteristic of venous segments.

Injection studies of free muscle grafts soon after grafting show a transient period during which connections are made between newly regenerating capillaries and larger vascular remnants located in the center of the muscle graft, which is still ischemic (26). Characteristically, the larger vessels are dilated and are packed with erythrocytes (15, 26, 57). At this stage little evidence of an active circulation is observed. In grafts of entire muscles, congestion of large vessels lasts only a few days before an active circulation is established throughout the muscle.

Shortly after regenerating capillaries first penetrate into an area of ischemic muscle and cytoplasmic removal of the original ischemic muscle fibers is almost complete, mononuclear myoblastic cells appear beneath the persisting basal laminae of the muscle fibers. As muscle fiber regeneration begins, the new blood vessels begin to differentiate. The earliest vessels are simple endothelial tubes and are often surrounded by degenerating cells and debris from the walls of the original vessels (26, 57). The endothelial cells of such vessels show a high degree of mitotic activity. Pericapillary cells are found around endothelial cells in some of the smallest vessels, and presumptive smooth muscle cells form irregular layers around larger diameter vessels. It is unclear whether these cells are derived from surviving elements of original vessels or migrate inward along with the endothelial sprouts.

The blood vessels that first grow into a muscle graft, particularly a minced one, are poorly oriented (4). Within a few days, as the regenerating muscle is subjected to the environment of a functioning extremity, both regenerating muscle fibers and their accompanying capillaries become aligned parallel to the newly developing lines of tension.

The time required for revascularization of all regions of a grafted muscle depends upon both the size of the muscle and the nature of the vascular bed surrounding the graft. Five to seven days are required for blood vessels to reach the most central region of 100- to 150-mg EDL grafts in the rat (8), whereas penetration into the center of a 3-g EDL graft in the cat takes six to eight weeks (43). The effects of differences between species, the mass of the graft, and of the vascularity of the grafting site on the rate of revascularization cannot be distinguished at this time. Although Markley et al (38) did not specifically study the vasculature, they found that in monkeys, long-term standard grafts of 3- to 4-g palmaris longus muscles consisted of a central core of dense connective tissue surrounded by a rim of regenerated muscle fibers. Based on the close association between revascularization and regeneration, the rate of revascularization was interpreted to be a limiting factor in the development of these grafts. The site of the palmaris longus muscle is less well vascularized than the EDL muscle site, but the possibility of a species difference cannot be excluded on the basis of available data.

STRUCTURE OF BLOOD VESSELS IN MATURE GRAFTS

Although many blood vessels in stabilized regenerated muscle appear normal (57), other vessels show distinct abnormalities in the structure of their walls. A characteristic feature of small blood vessels is the presence of multiple layers of basal lamina around the endothelial cells (26, 29, 56). Multiple basal laminae, whether around capillaries, muscle fibers, or nerve fibers, are considered to indicate one or more cycles of degeneration and regeneration of the structure in question (56).

Normal muscle capillaries are lined by a continuous sheet of endothelial cells. In damaged guinea pig cremaster muscle, however, McKinney et al (41) described fenestrations in regenerating capillaries. Ludatscher (35) noted that fenestrae were also frequently encountered in polymyositis and other inflammatory human myopathies in which muscle regeneration occurs.

Larger vessels in mature free muscle grafts showed a broad spectrum of structural abnormalities, primarily in the smooth muscle and the elastic lamina (26). In some cases smooth muscle cells were located on the luminal side of the elastic lamina. In other cases, regenerated smooth muscle cells were scattered on both sides of the original elastic lamina but were far removed from the walls of new vessels that had grown into the remains of the original vessel.

Arterial and venous segments of capillaries can be distinguished by the alkaline-phosphatase/dipeptidyl-peptidase-IV reaction (33). The arterial portion of the capillary bed reacts positively for alkaline phosphatase activity and the venous portion reacts positively for dipeptidyl peptidase IV activity. Capillaries within a longitudinal section of normal skeletal muscle fibers are in parallel with arterial and venous segments aligned, whereas in a cross section, capillaries form a mosaic pattern of patches that stain with characteristics of either arterial or venous segments (42). Such a mosaic arrangement is restored in stabilized regenerated muscle.

Microvascular Damage in Ischemic Muscle

Microvascular changes have been examined in skeletal muscles in which ischemia was induced for varying lengths of time (36, 49). Capillary endothelial cell damage was observed in rat anterior tibialis muscle after 150 min of muscle ischemia (49) and in rat quadriceps muscles after 180 min of ischemia (36). Cell damage became more extensive as the time of ischemia increased. At 360 min cell death was observed in all capillary endothelial cells (36). Endothelial cells in regenerated capillaries of ischemic muscle had a normal ultrastructure by 45 days, but the endothelial fraction of the cross-sectional area for capillaries was increased and the luminal fraction was decreased (36). By 90 days post-ischemia, both the mean endothelial and luminal areas were similar to those of controls. These results have implications for clinical applications of muscle transplantation in which the muscle is ischemic for at least 180 min while a neurovascular anastomosis is performed. Abnormalities in capillary structure resulting from ischemic damage to the endothelial cells could affect blood flow and ultimately muscle performance, at least until the capillary damage is repaired.

Capillary Architecture

Capillarity of regenerated skeletal muscle has been examined in 3–4 g standard (39, 58) and nerve-anastomosed grafts in cats (13, 39) and monkeys (40), in nerve-intact grafts in cats (13), in chronically stimulated standard and nerve-intact grafts in rats (10), in rat hindlimb muscles after temporary ischemia (36), and in mouse hindlimb muscles after injection of crude snake venom (22). White et al (58) reported that the capillary density of standard muscle grafts in cats averaged 75% of control values between 50 and 179 days, but decreased to 45% of control values between 180 and 518 days after grafting. The capillary-to-fiber ratio averaged approximately 50% of the control value between 180 and 518 days. Similarly, in 240-day-old nerve-intact and nerve-anastomosed EDL grafts in cats, Faulkner et al (13) observed that both capillary density and capillary-to-fiber ratio were significantly lower than in control EDL muscles. In this study there was no difference in fiber cross-sectional area between grafted muscles and control muscles. Maxwell (39) found no difference in capillary density between either 100-day-old nerve-intact or standard grafts and control EDL muscles in cats. He attributed this finding to a lower average fiber cross-sectional area in grafted muscles than in control muscles. However, compared to control muscles, a significant reduction was observed in capillary-to-fiber ratios in both nerve-intact and in standard grafts. In both standard and nerve-anastomosed palmaris longus muscle grafts in monkeys, values for capillary density and capillary-to-fiber ratio were lower than in control muscles (40). The decreased capillarity observed in EDL muscle grafts in cats and in palmaris longus muscle grafts in monkeys suggests that there is inadequate recapillarization in grafts of this mass.

Hakelius & Nyström (24) found that capillary density in standard EDL muscle grafts in cats was greater in areas that had been reinnervated than in areas without innervation. Areas with a predominance of oxidative fiber types had a higher capillary density than areas with a predominance of glycolytic fiber types. This capillary distribution was similar to that observed in control EDL muscles.

In 100–150 mg EDL muscle grafts in rats, there is a consensus that grafting has no effect on capillary-to-muscle fiber ratio (10, 20, 26). In nerve-intact grafts, Ciske & Faulkner (10) reported a 38% reduction in mean fiber area and a 43% increase in capillary density compared to control values, but they found no significant difference in capillary-to-fiber ratio. Hansen-Smith et al (26) and Grim et al (20) found low capillary-to-muscle fiber ratios in early regenerating EDL grafts in rats, but these ratios approached normal values by 30 days.

Chronic, low-frequency (10 Hz) stimulation of nerve-intact EDL grafts in rats for 8 hr/day for 26 days resulted in a 30% reduction in fiber area when compared to nonstimulated grafts (10). Capillary density was 46% higher, and capillary-to-fiber ratio was 29% higher in stimulated grafts than in nonstimulated grafts. In addition, both capillary density and capillary-to-fiber ratio in the stimulated grafts were significantly higher than the contralateral nonstimulated control EDL muscles. Thus, chronic stimulation of grafts of 100–150 mg in mass greatly stimulated capillary growth.

In rats, a distributional abnormality of capillaries occurs in regenerated muscle spindles. Normally, vascular elements are not seen within the capsule of the muscle spindle, but both Schmalbrüch (47) and Rogers (45) observed capillaries among intrafusal muscle fibers within the capsules of regenerated spindles. This suggests that during the period of degeneration the continuity of the "blood-spindle" barrier is disrupted, and regenerating vessels are allowed to penetrate the interior of the spindle.

Tenotomy of skeletal muscles with blood vessels and nerves left intact caused fiber atrophy and limited degeneration of both muscle fibers and blood vessels (30). Tenotomy of guinea pig crural muscles resulted in a progressive decrease in capillary density up to six weeks (30). Subsequent tendon suture at either six, three, or two weeks after tenotomy resulted in an increasing capillary density towards control values, when evaluated 12 weeks after tendon suturing.

Muscle regeneration and recapillarization have been studied in models that do not involve the mechanical disruption of the muscle (22, 36). Twenty-eight days after myonecrosis was induced in mouse hindlimb muscles by injection of crude snake venom, muscle regeneration was incomplete and capillary-to-muscle fiber ratio was significantly lower than in control muscles (22). Evidence that the recovery process had stabilized was lacking, so the ultimate status of the capillarity of the muscle bed remains unclear. Ninety days after 6 hr of muscle ischemia, capillary density and capillary-to-fiber ratio in regenerated rat anterior tibial muscles were similar to control values (36).

BLOOD FLOW AND FUNCTION OF ARTERIOLES

To meet the increase in metabolism during contractile activity, skeletal muscles require an increased blood flow. The structure of blood vessels in regenerated skeletal muscle has been described, but few studies have investigated the response of blood flow in grafts to muscle contraction. White et al (58) examined blood flow of standard EDL grafts in cats at rest and during twitch contractions. The resting blood flow in grafted muscle increased from total ischemia at the time of grafting to as much as 400% of control values during muscle regeneration. Resting blood flow decreased by 400 days post-grafting and was not different from control values of 3 ± 0.5 ml $\cdot$ 100 $g^{-1} \cdot min^{-1}$. In response to a stimulation frequency of one Hz, blood flow of 24 ± 1.4 ml $\cdot$ 100 $g^{-1} \cdot min^{-1}$ in grafted muscles was not different from blood flow in control muscles. Blood flow in grafted muscle did not increase as stimulation frequency was increased above one Hz, whereas a maximum blood flow of 85 ± 6.0 ml $\cdot$ 100 $g^{-1} \cdot min^{-1}$ was reached at a frequency of four Hz in control muscles. Since avascular connective tissue in the grafts may have affected blood flow values when expressed per gram of whole muscle, the blood flow was estimated relative to the amount of viable muscle tissue in the grafts. Expressed in this manner, maximum blood flow in grafts was 70% higher than maximum blood flow in control muscles. In rabbits, the mass and specific tension of rectus femoris muscle grafts with nerves and vasculature intact was significantly less than control values, but the blood flow was not different from control values either at rest or during twitch contractions (3). The lack of an effect of the grafting procedure on blood flow in the neurovascular-intact grafts was attributed to the absence of a period of ischemia following grafting and the preservation of the original vascular bed.

In small bundles of intact fibers grafted onto the hamster cheek pouch, blood flow was not observed until 2.5 days after grafting (15). From a slow, oscillating, intermittent flow between 2 and 3 days, blood flow in 30-μm diameter vessels increased fivefold over the next 7 days. When compared to the change in the diameter of control arterioles following topical application of either adenosine or norepinephrine, the change in arteriolar diameter in small bundles of grafted fibers was diminished, even 180 days post-grafting (2). Coupled with the results of White et al (58), these findings suggest that arterioles in grafted muscle have a diminished capacity to regulate blood flow when metabolism is increased. No direct evidence is available, but the abnormalities in blood flow response to twitch contractions (58) and in arteriolar function (2) may be associated with structural abnormalities found in blood vessels in grafted muscle (26) or to the lack of regeneration of either afferent and efferent nerve endings or nerve plexi in the arteriolar walls (32).

SUMMARY

A standard whole muscle graft, in which all neural and vascular connections with the host tissue are severed, reinnervates and revascularizes spontaneously. The extent to which a standard graft regains structure and function depends largely on the degree and timing of revascularization. Whether the endothelial cells that form the first capillary tubes in a whole muscle graft originate inside or outside of the graft is unknown. Blood vessel growth into a graft proceeds in a centripetal fashion and precedes muscle fiber regeneration. Abnormalities have been observed in the structure of capillaries and of the larger vessels in stable muscle grafts. The ability of the vascular bed in large standard grafts to regulate blood flow in response to twitch contractions is impaired, as is the ability of arterioles in small grafts to respond following topical application of norepinephrine and adenosine. The dysfunction of arterioles in standard grafts may be related to structural abnormalities. Blood flow at rest and in response to twitch contractions in stable grafts in which nerves and blood vessels are left intact is not different from control muscles. The following should be investigated to provide further insights into the revascularization process in regenerating skeletal muscle and the structure and function of the microcirculation in stable muscle grafts: the origin of mitotic endothelial and smooth muscle cells; the stimulus for blood vessel growth; the overall architecture and organization of the vascular bed; the presence or absence of adrenergic innervation of blood vessels; and the development of receptors involved in blood flow regulation in muscle grafts.

ACKNOWLEDGMENTS

The authors thank the many investigators who collaborated with them in the studies of microcirculatory adaptation following the transplantation of skeletal muscles. The research investigations and preparation of this review were supported by grants HL-34164 and EY-05813 and Program Project DE-07687 from the National Institutes of Health.

Literature Cited

1. Allbrook, D. 1975. Transplantation and regeneration of striated muscle. *Ann. R. Coll. Surg. Engl.* 56:312–24
2. Burton, H. W., Faulkner, J. A. 1985. Arteriolar response in grafted skeletal muscle to adenosine and norepinephrine. *Fed. Proc.* 44:433
3. Burton, H. W., Stevenson, T. R., Dysko, R. C., Gallagher, K. P., Faulkner, J. A. 1986. Blood flow of grafted skeletal muscles in rabbits. *Fed. Proc.* 45:419
4. Carlson, B. M. 1972. *The Regeneration of Minced Muscles.* Basel: Karger. 128 pp.
5. Carlson, B. M. 1976. A quantitative study of muscle fiber survival and regeneration in normal, predenervated and Marcaine-treated free muscle grafts in the rat. *Exp. Neurol.* 52:421–32
6. Carlson, B. M., Faulkner, J. A. 1983. The regeneration of skeletal muscle fibers following injury: A review. *Med. Sci. Sports Exercise* 15:187–98
7. Carlson, B. M., Foster, A. H., Bader, D. M., Hník, P., Vejsada, R. 1983. Restoration of full mass in nerve-intact muscle grafts after delayed reinnervation. *Experientia* 39:171–72
8. Carlson, B. M., Hansen-Smith, F. M., Magon, D. K. 1979. The life history of a free muscle graft. In *Muscle Regeneration,* ed. A. Mauro, pp. 493–507. New York: Raven
9. Carlson, B. M., Hník, P., Tuček, S., Vejsada, R., Bader, D. M., Faulkner, J. A. 1981. Comparison between grafts with intact nerves and standard free grafts of the rat extensor digitorum longus muscle. *Physiol. Bohemoslov.* 30:505–13
10. Ciske, P. E., Faulkner, J. A. 1985. Chronic electrical stimulation of nongrafted and grafted skeletal muscles in rats. *J. Appl. Physiol.* 59:1434–39
11. Clark, E. R., Clark, E. L. 1939. Microscopic observations on the growth of blood capillaries in the living mammal. *Am. J. Anat.* 79:15–32
12. Faulkner, J. A., Carlson, B. M. 1985. Contractile properties of standard and nerve-intact muscle grafts in the rat. *Muscle & Nerve* 8:413–18
13. Faulkner, J. A., Markley, J. M., McCully, K. K., Watters, C. R., White,

T. P. 1983. Characteristics of cat skeletal muscles grafted with intact nerves or with anastomosed nerves. *Exp. Neurol.* 80:682–96
14. Faulkner, J. A., Niemeyer, J. H., Maxwell, L. C., White, T. P. 1980. Contractile properties of transplanted extensor digitorum longus muscles of cats. *Am. J. Physiol* 238:C120–26
15. Faulkner, J. A., Weiss, S. W., McGeachie, J. K. 1983. Revascularization of skeletal muscle transplanted into the hamster cheek pouch: Intravital and light microscopy. *Microvasc. Res.* 26:49–64
16. Frey, M., Gruber, H., Havel, M., Weiner, E., Freilinger, G. 1983. Experimental free muscle transplantation with microneurovascular anastomoses. *Plast. Reconstr. Surg.* 71:609
17. Gierup, J., Hakelius, L. 1979. Free autogenous muscle transplantation in 5 children with urinary incontinence. *Z. Kinderchir.* 104:1424–28
18. Gilbert, A. 1981. Free muscle transfer. *Int. Surg.* 66:33–35
19. Gordon, L., Buncke, H. J., Townsend, J. J. 1976. Histological changes in skeletal muscle after temporary independent occlusion of arterial and venous supply. *Plast. Reconst. Surg.* 61:576–80
20. Grim, M., Mrázková, O., Carlson, B. M. 1986. Enzymatic differentiation of arterial and venous segments of the capillary bed during the development of free muscle grafts in the rat. *Am. J. Anat.* 177:149–59
21. Guelinckx, P. J., Faulkner, J. A., Essig, D. 1985. Rectus femoris muscles of rabbits autografted with microvascular repair with nerves intact or nerves anastomozed. In *Proc. 2nd Vienna Muscle Symp.,* ed. M. Frey, G. Freilinger, pp 75–83.
22. Gutierrez, J. M., Ownby, C. L., Odell, G. V. 1984. Skeletal muscle regeneration after myonecrosis induced by crude venom and a myotoxin from the snake bothrops asper (fer-de-lance). *Toxicon* 22:717–31
23. Hakelius, L. 1974. Free autogenous muscle transplantation in two cases of total anal incontinence. *Acta Chir. Scand.* 141:69–75

24. Hakelius, L., Nyström, B. 1975. Blood vessels and connective tissue in auto-transplanted free muscle grafts of the cat. *Scand. J. Plast. Reconstr. Surg.* 9:87–91

25. Hall-Craggs, E. C. B. 1978. Ischemic muscle as a model of regeneration. *Exp. Neurol.* 60:393–99

26. Hansen-Smith, F. M., Carlson, B. M., Irwin, K. L. 1980. Revascularization of freely grafted extensor digitorum longus muscle in the rat. *Am. J. Anat.* 158:65–82

27. Harii, K., Ohmori, K., Torii, S. 1976. Free gracilis muscle transplantation, with microneurovascular anastomoses for the treatment of facial paralysis. *Plast. Reconstr. Surg.* 57:133–43

28. Harrison, D. H. 1985. The pectoralis minor vascularized muscle graft for the treatment of unilateral facial palsy. *Plast. Reconstr. Surg.* 75:206–13

29. Jerusalem, F., Rakusa, M., Engel, A. G., MacDonald, R. N. 1974. Morphometric analysis of skeletal muscle capillary ultrastructure in inflammatory myopathies. *J. Neurol. Sci.* 23:391–402

30. Józsa, L., Bálint, B. J., Vándor, E., Riffz, A., Damel, Z. 1985. Recapillarization of tenotomized skeletal muscles after delayed tendon suture. *Res. Exp. Med.* 185:163–68

31. Karpati, G., Carpenter, S., Melmed, C., Eisen, A. 1974. Experimental ischemic myopathy. *J. Neurol. Sci.* 23:129–61

32. Lassman, F. 1982. Afferent innervation of the vascular system: A neglected entity. *Z. Mikrosk-Anat. Forsch.* 96:517–26

33. Lojda, Z. 1979. Studies on dipeptidyl (amino) peptidase IV (glycyl-proline naphthylamidase). II. Blood vessels. *Histochemistry* 59:153–66

34. Lu, D. 1985. Mast cell numbers in freely grafted muscles of rats. *Anat. Rec.* 211:114A

35. Ludatscher, R. M. 1981. Patterns of regeneration in vessels of human diseased muscle and skin: An ultrastructural study. *Virchows Arch. Cell Pathol.* 36:65–75

36. Mäkitie, J. 1977. Microvasculature of rat striated muscle after temporary ischemia. *Acta Neuropathol.* 37:247–53

37. Manktelow, R. T., McKee, N. H. 1978. Free muscle transplantation to provide active finger flexion. *J. Hand Surg.* 3:416–26

38. Markley, J. M., Faulkner, J. A., Carlson, B. M. 1978. Regeneration following transplantation of skeletal muscles in monkeys. *Plast. Reconstr. Surg.* 62:415–22

39. Maxwell, L. C. 1984. Muscle fiber regeneration in nerve-intact and free skeletal muscle autografts in cats. *Am. J. Physiol.* 246:C96–C105

40. Maxwell, L. C., Faulkner, J. A., Markley, J. M., Winborn, D. R. 1979. Neuroanastomosis of orthotopically transplanted palmaris longus muscles. *Muscle Nerve* 2:44–52

41. McKinney, R. V., Singh, B. B., Brewer, P. D. 1977. Fenestrations in regenerating skeletal muscle capillaries. *Am. J. Anat.* 150:213–18

42. Mrázková, O., Grim, M., Carlson, B. M. 1986. Enzymatic heterogeneity of the capillary bed of rat skeletal muscles. *Am. J. Anat.* 177:141–48

43. Mufti, S. A., Carlson, B. M., Maxwell, L. C., Faulkner, J. A. 1977. The free autografting of entire limb muscles in the cat: Morphology. *Anat. Rec.* 188:417–30

44. Prendergast, F. J., McGeachie, J. K., Edis, R. H., Allbrook, D. 1977. Whole-muscle reimplantation with microneurovascular anastomoses. *Ann. R. Coll. Surg. Engl.* 59:393–400

45. Rogers, S. L. 1982. Muscle spindle formation and differentiation in regenerating rat muscle grafts. *Dev. Biol.* 94:265–83

46. Schenck, R. P. 1978. Rectus femoris muscle and composite skin transplantation by microneurovascular anastomoses for avulsion of forearm muscles. A case report. *J. Hand Surg.* 3:60–69

47. Schmalbrüch, H. 1977. Regeneration of soleus muscles of rat autografted in toto as studied by electron microscopy. *Cell Tissue Res.* 177:159–80

48. Snow, M. H. 1977. Myogenic cell formation in regenerating rat skeletal muscle injured by mincing. I. A fine structural study. *Anat. Rec.* 188:181–99

49. Strock, P. E., Majano, G. 1969. Microvascular changes in acutely ischemic rat muscle. *Surg. Gynecol. Obstet.* 129:1213–24

50. Studitsky, A. N. 1958. The experimental surgery of muscle. *Izdatel-stvo Akademii Nauk SSSR.* 338 pp. (In Russian)

51. Studitsky, A. N. 1977. The transplantation of muscles in animals. *Meditsina.* Moscow. 248 pp. (In Russian)

52. Studitsky, A. N., Bosova, N. N. 1960. The development of atrophic muscular tissue when transplanted in place of mechanically damaged muscle. *Arch. Anat.* 39:18–32 (In Russian)

53. Tamai, S., Komatsu, S., Sakamoto, H., Sano, S., Sasauchi, N., et al. 1970. Free

muscle transplants in dogs with micro-surgical neurovascular anastomoses. *Plast. Reconstr. Surg.* 46:219–25

54. Thompson, N. 1971. Autogenous free grafts of skeletal muscle. *Plast. Reconstr. Surg.* 48:11–27

55. Thompson, N. 1974. A review of auto-genous skeletal muscle grafts and their clinical applications. *Clin. Plast. Surg.* 1:349–403

56. Vracko, R., Benditt, E. P. 1972. Basal lamina: The scaffold for orderly cell replacement. *J. Cell Biol.* 55:406–19

57. Weiss, S. W., Faulkner, J. A. 1983. Revascularization of skeletal muscle transplanted into the hamster cheek pouch: Electron microscopy. *Microvasc. Res.* 26:65–73

58. White, T. P., Maxwell, L. C., Sosin, D. M., Faulkner, J. A. 1981. Capillarity and blood flow of transplanted skeletal muscles of cats. *Am. J. Physiol.* 241:H630–36

Ann. Rev. Physiol. 1987. 49:453–64

MECHANISMS OF ANGIOGENESIS

Patricia A. D'Amore and Robert W. Thompson

Laboratory of Surgical Research and Departments of Pathology and Surgery, The Children's Hospital and Harvard Medical School, Boston, Massachusetts 02115

CAPILLARY GROWTH

The growth of endothelial cells (EC) as a part of angiogenesis is now recognized to be an important component of many disease processes. The mechanisms of angiogenesis and EC growth control, particularly with regard to collateral vessel development, are becoming an increasingly important area of cardiovascular physiology.

Turnover of Vascular Endothelium

Vascular endothelial cells (EC) are, under normal conditions, remarkably quiescent cells. The fraction of rat aortic endothelium labeled following injection of [^{3}H]thymidine is at a maximum of 13% at birth and then decreases to 0.1–0.3% by 5 months of age (54). The labeling index (a measure of cell turnover) of capillary EC in the retina and the myocardium of adult rats has been measured to be 0.01% and 0.14%, respectively (16). These rates compare to a labeling index of 14% for duodenal mucosal epithelium.

Despite the normally low level of EC turnover, certain conditions are associated with accelerated EC growth. Corpus luteum formation, wound healing, chronically exercised muscle, psoriasis, diabetic retinopathy, and tumor vascularization are all characterized by new blood vessel growth. The [^{3}H]thymidine labeling index of EC in tumors has been measured at levels as high as 9.0%, an increase of more than 100-fold over that reported for other microvascular beds (14). This suggests that the proliferation of vascular endothelium is closely regulated under normal circumstances, but that it can be dramatically increased by altered conditions.

453

0066-4278/87/0315-0453$02.00

Experimental Models

Several in vivo models have been utilized to study the process of neovascularization. The most widely used among these are the chick chorioallantoic membrane (1), the hamster cheek pouch (66), and the rabbit corneal pocket assays (27). These systems have proven to be invaluable tools for descriptive and morphological studies of angiogenesis, and they have provided a means for the assay of angiogenic activity. However, since these assays are expensive, time consuming, and do not lend themselves to quantification, they do not provide a feasible means for monitoring angiogenic activity throughout extensive purification schemes.

To overcome these difficulties, in vitro systems have been applied to the study of angiogenesis. The establishment of large vessel EC in culture by Jaffe et al in 1974 (35) and of capillary EC by Folkman et al in 1979 (23) allowed further study of the mechanisms underlying new vessel formation. The assays that have been developed to facilitate the purification of angiogenic factors and to study the process of angiogenesis are based on the descriptions of neovascularization given below. EC proliferation, migration, protease release, lumen formation, and basement membrane synthesis have all been examined. Further, the establishment of microvascular pericytes in culture (7, 28) has permitted investigation of the role of this cell in angiogenesis.

Elements of Capillary Formation

There are a number of studies describing the formation of capillaries in vivo (for review see 34, 65). The following description summarizes the current view of the steps involved in new vessel growth, illustrated in Figure 1.

New vessel growth generally proceeds from a preformed vessel, usually a venule (53). This growth involves "activation" of EC, which is characterized by an increase in the number of organelles in the cells and the formation of projections from their surfaces (2, 69). The basement membrane of the parent vessel becomes fragmented at the time the EC are activated. It has been postulated that proteases synthesized and secreted by the EC are active at this stage (50).

Next, the EC migrate from the vessel wall into the interstitial space. In the case of tumor-induced angiogenesis this migration appears to be directed toward a tumor-derived stimulus. To examine the role of migration in the process of angiogenesis, Sholley et al (59) inhibited EC proliferation by irradiation and then induced vascularization in the rabbit ear chamber. New vessel formation was limited, but it was not abolished, which suggests that initial vascular sprouting does not require EC proliferation.

Concomitant with migration, EC proliferation is observed proximal to the migrating tip. Ausprunk & Folkman (2) suggested that the movement of cells

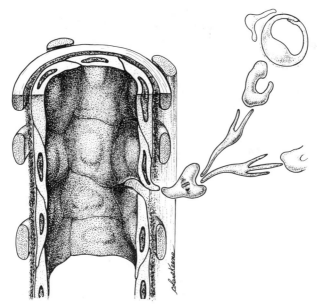

Figure 1 Schematic representation of the formation of a new blood vessel.

from the parent vessel, which causes loosening of the intercellular junctions, may release EC from contact inhibition and allow cell proliferation. These areas of active proliferation are also associated with increased vascular permeability, presumably due to the disrupted cell contacts (2).

Of all the phases of new capillary growth, the least is known about the mechanism of lumen formation. Folkman & Haudenschild (22) observed the formation of capillary-like structures in culture as the development of intracellular vacuoles in contiguous cells, which then connect to form capillary-like tubes. Following lumen formation, pericytes migrate along the capillary sprout and become intimately associated with the abluminal surface of the EC. The final step in capillary formation is the production of basement membrane. Although both the EC (51) and the pericyte (10) are known to synthesize and secrete components of the basement membrane, the relative contribution of these two cell types in vivo is not yet known.

FACTORS INFLUENCING VESSEL GROWTH

There is no doubt that a number of factors contribute to the regulation of new blood vessel growth. The four considered to have the strongest influence are mechanical factors, intercellular interactions, the extracellular matrix, and growth factors.

Mechanical Factors

Folkman & Moscona (24) examined the effect of cell shape on proliferation. They found that DNA synthesis varied with cell shape: the flatter the cells, the higher the rate of DNA synthesis. Rounder cells, such as confluent EC, had a lower rate of DNA synthesis. In vivo changes in EC shape induced by vasodilation, intravascular pressure, or shear stress (due to rapid flow or turbulence) could lead to changes in EC growth rate (33, 68).

Cell-Cell Interactions

Interactions between adjacent EC have been postulated to regulate EC growth. Cell membranes isolated from cultures of confluent EC can inhibit DNA synthesis in actively growing cultures of EC, which suggests a role for membrane interactions in growth control (32).

It has also been postulated that pericytes can suppress the proliferation of EC (12). Neovascularization is often characterized by an absence of pericytes: The proliferative phase of diabetic retinopathy is proceeded by "pericyte dropout;" tumor vasculature is devoid of pericytes; and hemangiomas, vascular malformations characterized by large vascular channels, have few pericytes. Proliferation of capillary EC is inhibited by coculture with microvascular pericytes or smooth muscle cells, but not by coculture with fibroblasts or epithelial cells. EC growth is not inhibited by pericyte-conditioned media, which suggests a cell-mediated effect (A. Orlidge & P. A. D'Amore, manuscript submitted). Another level of control is suggested by the finding that heparin suppresses the proliferation of smooth muscle cells (8) and pericytes (47), and that heparin is synthesized by postconfluent EC in culture (8).

Extracellular Matrix

The extracellular matrix has been shown to modulate the growth and differentiation of a wide variety of cells (for review see 37) including the endothelium. Madri & Williams reported phenotypic modulation of capillary EC by matrix components (43). EC plated onto interstitial collagens proliferated and migrated, but they formed capillary tubes only after a long period in culture. In contrast, cells plated onto basement membrane neither proliferated nor migrated but formed tubelike structures at an early time in culture. Young & Herman (70) evaluated the effect of purified matrix components on the response to injury of EC and correlated the rates of recovery with the staining pattern of the cytoskeleton. The most rapid recovery occurred on substrates of glass, fibronectin, and interstitial collagen and the slowest on gelatin and Type IV collagen. D. Ingber and coworkers (manuscript submitted) demonstrated that the ability of EC to respond to mitogens is determined by the nature of the substrata; Type III collagen provides the most conducive substrate and laminin the least. The mode of action of extracellular matrix modulation of EC phenotype is not known. It may be direct, or it may reflect changes in cell shape mediated by effects on the cytoskeleton. Furthermore, certain matrix components may act to sequester mitogens or present growth factors to the cell.

Growth Factors

A number of tissue and cell extracts have been reported to stimulate neovascularization (for reviews see 19 and 57). Only those that have been purified to homogeneity or are very well characterized are reviewed here. These factors may be arbitrarily divided into two groups: those that bind heparin and those that do not.

NON-HEPARIN BINDING GROWTH FACTORS

Small molecular weight   Small molecular weight factors (less than 1000 daltons) have been isolated from tumors by several groups. Using antisera raised against an angiogenic activity isolated from a Walker 256 rat carcinoma (48), Shahabuddin et al demonstrated a cross-reactive material in tumors, myocardial infarcts, activated macrophages, lymphocytes, retina, wound fluid, and arthritic joints (55). Fenselau et al isolated a factor of 400–800 daltons that was mitogenic for EC and angiogenic in vivo from the same tumor system (20).

Several studies indicate that copper may be involved in angiogenesis. Copper-deficient rabbits were unable to respond to an angiogenic stimulus (71); ceruloplasmin (the serum copper carrier), heparin, and glycyl-L-histidyl-L-lysine were angiogenic in vivo but only when complexed with copper ions (49). In addition, McAuslan and coworkers showed that copper modulates the synthesis of fibronectin by EC and suggested that alterations in this matrix component may be a controlling event in EC migration (31, 44).

Form & Auerbach (25) reported that PGE_2 stimulates new vessel formation in the chick chorioallantoic membrane (CAM) assay, showed that the levels required for angiogenesis are similar to those reported for a variety of tumors and inflammatory exudates, and suggested that PGE_2 may play a role in the initiation of vascularization in a variety of conditions. Castellot and his coworkers demonstrated differentiation-dependent stimulation of neovascularization by conditioned media of 3T3 adipocytes (9). The factor from the differentiated 3T3 cells that stimulates the migration of EC has been identified as a member of the prostanoid family that is distinct from currently known prostaglandins (15).

Large molecular weight   Banda et al (5) isolated an angiogenic factor from wound fluid with a molecular weight between 2,000 and 14,000 that stimulates the migration but not the proliferation of EC. The release of this angiogenic factor from macrophages has been shown to be modulated by oxygen tension: Cells cultured under hypoxic conditions (2% oxygen) secreted this factor, whereas those cultured under normoxic conditions (20% oxygen) did not (38).

A 14,000 dalton peptide, termed angiogenin, has been isolated from a human tumor line and reported to be angiogenic in the CAM assay (21). Sequence analysis of the factor revealed a 35% homology with human pancreatic ribonuclease (60); recent reports indicate that the factor itself exhibits ribonuclease activity (55a). Since ribonuclease is not angiogenic, the significance of this homology is uncertain.

HEPARIN BINDING GROWTH FACTORS (HBGFs)   Following the development of methods for the culture of EC in 1974, a large number of peptides were described that stimulated EC growth. However, because of the small amount of activity in the tissues and the losses suffered in conventional purification schemes, none of these factors were purified to homogeneity. A major breakthrough in the biochemistry of EC mitogens was the discovery by Shing and coworkers (58) that a cationic EC mitogen from rat chondrosarcoma bound heparin with high affinity. Subsequently, anionic EC mitogens that exhibited a strong affinity for heparin were reported (13, 42). Similarly charged peptides that were not EC mitogens did not bind to heparin with equal avidity, which led to the suggestion that heparin binding may be a common property of all peptide EC mitogens.

The HBGFs have now been classified into two groups based on their biochemical characteristics (41). Class 1 HBGFs are anionic peptides with isoelectric points between 5.0 and 6.0, elute from immobilized heparin at approximately 1.0-M NaCl, and have molecular weights in the range of 15,000–17,000. Class 2 HBGFs are cationic proteins with isoelectric points of 8.0–9.8. These factors are eluted from heparin at concentrations of NaCl of 1.5 M or greater and have molecular weights between 17,000 and 20,000. HBGFs have been demonstrated in a wide variety of tissues; interestingly, cationic HBGFs have been isolated from a number of different tissues, but anionic HBGFs have been reported only in neural tissues (Table 1).

The HBGFs have been shown to stimulate the in vitro proliferation of a variety of mesenchymal cells. The mitogenic effect of Class 1 HBGFs on EC is potentiated by the addition of exogenous heparin (47, 62), whereas the activity of Class 2 HBGFs is either unaffected or inhibited by the presence of heparin (P. A. D'Amore et al, manuscript submitted). Both the anionic (64) and the cationic (63) HBGFs have been demonstrated to induce neurite outgrowth in PC12 cells, a model system for sympathetic neurons. Heparin potentiates neurite induction in PC12 cells by anionic HBGF at concentrations similar to those required to potentiate EC proliferation, which suggests a

Table 1   Heparin-binding growth factors

Tissue	Class	Reference
Adrenal gland	2	29
Brain	1, 2	17, 40, 42
Cartilage	2	61
Hypothalamus	1, 2	36
Kidney, spleen, liver, and		
thymus	2	45
Macrophage	2	4
Myocardium	1, 2	*
Pituitary	2	6
Placenta	2	30
Retina	1, 2	3, 11, 13
Tumor	2	58

*Thompson & D'Amore, unpublished data

common mechanism of heparin growth factor action in these two embryologically distinct cell types.

The role of HBGFs in vivo is still unclear. Both anionic (40) and cationic (57) factors have been shown to stimulate the growth of new blood vessels in vivo. This finding, along with the fact that at least one HBGF has been found in every tissue studied to date, suggests that HBGFs may have a role in the maintenance of the normal vasculature, the ability of tissues to respond to injury (as in inflammation or collateralization), and the pathological neovascularization associated with diabetic retinopathy, arthritis, and tumor growth.

COLLATERAL VESSELS

Collateral vessels may be simply defined as routes of blood supply to an organ or tissue that are not functional or present under normal circumstances. The collateralization that develops in response to chronic myocardial ischemia is a good example of "response to injury" at the level of the microvasculature (Figure 2). These alternate routes of blood supply to jeopardized myocardium arise both from preformed collateral channels and from neovascular collateral vessel formation. Although the precise mechanism for the development of these vessels is not known, mechanical as well as biochemical signals have been implicated.

Preformed Collateral Vessels

Anatomical injection studies have shown that normal myocardium contains approximately 5000 capillaries/mm^2 (67). Physiological studies demonstrate

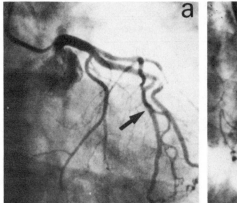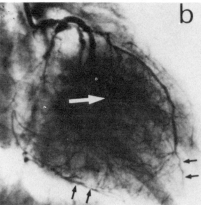

Figure 2   Coronary collateral vessels in ischemic heart disease. Left coronary arteriograms from two patients: (A) normal left anterior descending artery (LAD, *arrow*) with few collaterals; (B) occluded LAD *(white arrow)* with extensive collaterals and retrograde filling of distal LAD and posterior descending artery *(black arrows)*. (Courtesy of Dr. Lawrence M. Boxt, Department of Radiology, Brigham and Women's Hospital, Boston, MA.)

that the beating heart at rest perfuses capillaries at an average density of 900 capillaries/mm^2, that is, only 20% of the available channels are used (46). Thus, preexisting capillary collateral channels serve as an important adjunctive source of blood supply to the myocardium. Mechanical stimuli, such as pressure changes across the capillary bed, and biochemical signals that act as vasodilators have both been implicated in the recruitment of preformed collateral vessels in the exercising normal heart and during the progression of coronary artery disease.

Neovascular Collateral Vessels

In addition to dilation of preexisting capillary channels, chronic exercise and coronary artery disease may lead to the formation of new capillary vessels.

ROLE OF MECHANICAL FACTORS   It has been suggested that the mechanical forces acting on capillary EC provide a stimulus for new vessel formation. The shear stress resulting from a pressure differential between two vascular beds may initiate vessel remodeling (52). However, the shear stress generated is significantly smaller than the forces resulting from intraluminal pressure. In this regard, stretching of the capillary channels by vasodilation and increased blood flow may be a more important factor. The physical separation of EC may release the cells from their stringent contact inhibition, allowing the normally quiescent cells to proliferate.

ROLE OF BIOCHEMICAL FACTORS   Products of myocardial ischemia and anaerobic metabolism, as well as specific angiogenic factors from ischemic tissues, have been implicated in the development of neovascular growth.

Kumar et al identified a small-molecular-weight angiogenic factor in tissue from human myocardial infarcts (39) that stimulated EC proliferation in vitro. The nature of this factor and its cellular source were not reported. Galloway and his coworkers reported the release of an EC mitogen by rabbit hearts extracted under varying conditions of ischemia (26). The level of EC mitogenic activity released from cardiac tissue paralleled the degree of myocardial injury, as measured by creatine phosphokinase (CPK) release.

More recently, we showed that normal myocardium contains heparin-binding EC mitogens (R. W. Thompson & P. A. D'Amore, unpublished data). Atrial myocardium was excised from a series of patients at the time of cannulation for cardiopulmonary bypass, and whole dog hearts were excised

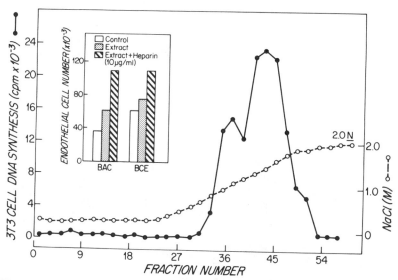

Figure 3   Heparin binding of canine heart growth factor. Normal canine ventricular myocardium was extracted in balanced salt solution for 3 hr at 37°C. Tissue was removed and the extract clarified by centrifugation. Canine heart extract (CHE) was applied to a column of heparin-Sepharose and eluted with a gradient of 0.2–2.0 M NaCl, and 1-ml fractions were collected. Fractions were tested for mitogenic activity (^{3}H-thymidine incorporation) on quiescent BALB/c 3T3 cells. Two peaks of activity were identified that eluted at 1.0- and 1.5-M NaCl, respectively. *(Inset)* Heparin potentiation of CHE mitogenic activity. CHE was assayed for mitogenic activity (72-hr cell proliferation) on bovine aortic endothelial cells (BAC) and bovine capillary endothelial cells (BCE) in vitro. Addition of exogenous heparin (10 μg/ml) potentiated the mitogenic effect of CHE (100 μl/ml) on both cell types (R. W. Thompson & P. A. D'Amore, unpublished data).

shortly after anesthetic overdose. These tissues were extracted for 6 hr in balanced salt solution. The extracts contained EC and 3T3 cell mitogenic activities, which were characterized as both Class 1 and Class 2 HBGFs based on three criteria. First, the mitogen bound to immobilized heparin and was eluted in two peaks at 1.0- and 1.5-M NaCl, concentrations known to elute other HBGFs (Figure 3). Second, the mitogenic activity was potentiated by exogenous heparin (Figure 3, inset). Finally, immunoblot analysis using antibodies raised against various synthetic peptides from Class 1 and 2 HBGFs revealed cross-reactivity with both forms. The amount of capillary EC mitogen released was increased by conditions that produced progressively greater ischemic cell injury, as monitored by CPK release (Figure 4, bar graph) and ultrastructural evidence of irreversible myocardial injury (Figure 4 a and b).

A Model for Collateral Formation

The underlying mechanisms for development of coronary collateral blood vessels are likely to be similar to the mechanisms involved in neovascular growth elsewhere. Tissue ischemia is a common feature of many of the conditions in which neovascular growth is observed. The neovascularization

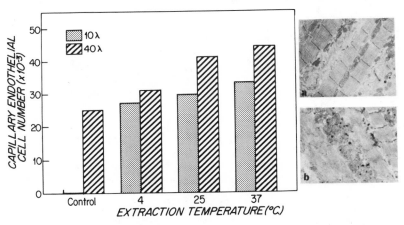

Figure 4   Release of human heart growth factor by ischemic extraction. Human atrial myocardium was extracted in balanced salt solution (100 mg tissue per ml) for 6 hr at various temperatures. The tissue was removed and fixed for electron microscopy. The extract was clarified by centrifugation, and tested for mitogenic activity (72-hr cell proliferation) on bovine capillary endothelial cells in vitro, at doses of 10 and 40 μl per 0.5 ml. There was a progressive increase in activity released with extraction temperature. Ultrastructural analysis revealed progressively greater degrees of irreversible ischemic tissue damage: (*a*) control myocardium (magnified 25,000 times), (*b*) myocardium from 37°C extract, with glycogen depletion, N-band formation, mitochondrial swelling, and multiple amorphous dense bodies (magnified 30,000 times) (R. W. Thompson & P. A. D'Amore, unpublished data).

associated with wound healing, diabetic retinopathy, and tumor vascularization are all preceded by the development of poorly perfused tissue. In addition, it has been shown that all of these tissues under "normal" conditions contain a mitogen(s) that stimulates EC proliferation in vitro, as well as angiogenesis in vivo. Thus, we postulate that the tissue injury/destruction that is associated with ischemia results in the release of mitogens that are sequestered either within the cell or in association with the extracellular matrix. The mechanisms and control of HBGF release are not known for any of the tissues capable of neovascularization. One possibility is that only irreversibly damaged cells release the mitogen; in this case, release of HBGF would not be a "finely regulated" function. Conversely, alterations in the microenvironment associated with ischemia (hypoxia, acidic pH, increase in the concentration of metabolites) may act to modulate the synthesis and release of HBGFs. Regardless of the precise mechanism, it is becoming increasingly clear that HBGFs play an important role in angiogenesis and in the development of neovascular collateral vessels, particularly in tissues at risk of irreversible ischemic injury.

Literature Cited

1. Alfthan, O. S. 1956. *Ann. Med. Exp. Biol. Fenn.* 9:1–78 (Suppl. 34)
2. Ausprunk, D. H., Folkman, J. 1977. *Microvasc. Res.* 14:53–65
3. Baird, A., Esch, F., Gospodarowicz, D., Guillemin, R. 1986. *Biochemistry* 24:7855–60
4. Baird, A., Mormede, P., Böhlen, P. 1985. *Biochem. Biophys. Res. Commun.* 126:358–64
5. Banda, M. J., Knighton, D. R., Hunt, T. K., Werb, Z. 1982. *Proc. Natl. Acad. Sci. USA* 79:7773–77
6. Bohlen, P., Baird, A., Esch, F., Ling, N., Gospodarowicz, D. 1984. *Proc. Natl. Acad. Sci. USA* 81:5364–68
7. Buzney, S. M., Frank, R. N., Robison, W. G. 1975. *Science* 190:985–86
8. Castellot, J. J. Jr., Addonizio, M. L., Rosenberg, R., Karnovsky, M. J. 1981. *J. Cell Biol.* 90:372–79
9. Castellot, J. J. Jr., Karnovsky, M. J., Spiegelman, B. M. 1982. *Proc. Natl. Acad. Sci. USA* 79:5597–5601
10. Cohen, M. P., Frank, R. N., Khalifa, A. A. 1980. *Invest. Ophthalmol.* 19:90–94
11. Courty, J., Loret, C., Moenner, M., Chevallier, B., Lagente, O., et al. 1985. *Biochimie* 67:265–69
12. Crocker, D. J., Murad, T. M., Geer, J. C. 1970. *Exp. Mol. Pathol.* 13:51–65
13. D'Amore, P. A., Klagsbrun, M. 1984. *J. Cell Biol.* 99:1545–49

14. Denekamp, J., Hobson, B. 1982. *Br. J. Cancer* 46:711–20
15. Dobson, D. E., Castellot, J. J. Jr., Spiegelman, B. M. 1985. *J. Cell Biol.* 101:109a
16. Engerman, R. L., Pfaffenbach, D., Davis, M. D. 1967. *Lab. Invest.* 17: 738–43
17. Esch, F., Ueno, N., Baird, A., Hill, F., Denoroy, L., et al. 1985. *Biochem. Biophys. Res. Commun.* 133:554–62
18. Deleted in proof
19. Fenselau, A. 1984. *Growth and Maturation Factors*, ed. G. Guroff, Vol. 2, pp. 87–129. New York: Wiley
20. Fenselau, A., Watt, S., Mello, R. J. 1981. *J. Biol. Chem.* 256:9605–11
21. Fett, J. W., Strydom, D. J., Lobb, R. R., Alderman, E. M., Bethune, J. L., et al. 1985. *Biochemistry* 24:5480–86
22. Folkman, J., Haudenschild, C. 1980. *Nature* 288:551–56
23. Folkman, J., Haudenschild, C. C., Zetter, B. R. 1979. *Proc. Natl. Acad. Sci. USA* 76:5217–21
24. Folkman, J., Moscona, A. 1978. *Nature* 273:345–49
25. Form, D. M., Auerbach, R. 1983. *Proc. Soc. Exp. Biol. Med.* 172:214–18
26. Galloway, A. C., Pelletier, R., D'Amore, P. A. 1984. *Surgery* 96:435–38
27. Gimbrone, M. A. Jr., Cotran, R. S., Leapman, S. B., Folkman, J. 1974. *J. Natl. Cancer Inst.* 52:413–27

28. Gitlin, J. D., D'Amore, P. A. 1983. *Microvasc. Res.* 26:74–80
29. Gospodarowicz, D., Baird, A., Cheng, J., Lui, F., Esch, F., Böhlen, P. 1986. *Endocrinology* 118:82–90
30. Gospodarowicz, D., Cheng, J., Lui, G. M., Fujii, D. K., Baird, A., Böhlen, P. 1985. *Biochem. Biophys. Res. Commun.* 128:554–62
31. Hannan, G. N., McAuslan, B. R. 1982. *J. Cell. Physiol.* 111:207–12
32. Heimark, R. L., Schwartz, S. M. 1985. *J. Cell Biol.* 100:1934–40
33. Herman, I. M., Pollard, T. D., Wong, A. J. 1983. *Ann. NY Acad. Sci.* 401:50–60
34. Hudlicka, O. 1984. *Handbook of Physiology. The Cardiovascular System. Vol. IV. Microcirculation,* Part 1, pp. 165–216, ed. E. M. Renkin, C. C. Michel. Baltimore: Waverly
35. Jaffe, E. A., Nachman, R. L., Becker, C. G., Minick, C. R. 1973. *J. Clin. Invest.* 52:2745–56
36. Klagsbrun, M., Shing, Y. 1985. *Proc. Natl. Acad. Sci. USA* 82:805–9
37. Kleinman, H. K., Klebe, R. J., Martin, G. R. 1981. *J. Cell Biol.* 88:473–85
38. Knighton, D. R., Hunt, T. K., Scheuenstuhl, H., Halliday, B. J., Werb, Z., Banda, M. J. 1983. *Science* 221:1283–85
39. Kumar, S., West, D., Shahabuddin, S., Arnold, F., Haboubi, N., et al. 1983. *Lancet* 2:364–68
40. Lobb, R. R., Alderman, E. M., Fett, J. W. 1985. *Biochemistry* 24:4869–4973
41. Lobb, R., Sasse, Y., Sullivan, R., Shing, Y., D'Amore, P., et al. 1986. *J. Biol. Chem.* 261:1924–28
42. Maciag, T., Mehlman, T., Friesel, R., Schreiber, A. 1984. *Science* 225:932–35
43. Madri, J. A., Williams, S. K. 1983. *J. Cell Biol.* 97:153–65
44. McAuslan, B. R., Reilly, W. G., Hannan, G. N., Gole, G. A. 1983. *Microvasc. Res.* 26:323–38
45. Mormede, P., Baird, A., Pigeon, P. 1985. *Biochem. Biophys. Res. Commun.* 128:1108–13
46. Myers, W. W., Honig, C. R. 1964. *Am. J. Physiol.* 207:653–60
47. Orlidge, A., D'Amore, P. A. 1986. *Microvasc. Res.* 31:41–53
48. Phillips, P., Kumar, S. 1979. *Int. J. Cancer* 23:82–88
49. Raju, K. S., Allesandri, G., Ziche, M., Gullino, P. M. 1982. *J. Natl. Cancer Inst.* 69:1183–88
50. Rifkin, D. B., Gross, J. L., Moscatelli, D., Jaffe, E. 1982. *Pathobiology of the Endothelial Cell,* pp. 191–97. New York: Academic
51. Sage, H., Pritzl, P., Bornstein, P. 1981. *Arteriosclerosis* 1:427–42
52. Scheel, K. W., Fitzgerald, E. M., Martin, R. O., Larsen, R. A. 1979. ed. W. Schaper, pp. 489–518. Amsterdam: Elsevier/North-Holland Biomed.
53. Schoefl, G. I. 1963. *Virchows Arch. Pathol. Anat. Physiol.* 37:97–141
54. Schwartz, S. M., Benditt, E. P. 1977. *Circ. Res.* 41:248–55
55. Shahabuddin, S., Kumar, S., West, D., Arnold, F. 1985. *Int. J. Cancer* 35:87–91
55a. Shapiro, R., Riordan, J. F., Vallee, B. L. 1986. *Biochemistry* 25:3527–32
56. Shepro, D., D'Amore, P. A. 1984. In *Handbook of Physiology. The Cardiovascular System. IV. Microcirculation,* Part 1 pp. 165–216, ed. E. M. Renkin, C. C. Michel. Baltimore: Waverly
57. Shing, Y., Folkman, J., Haudenschild, C., Lund, D., Crum, R., Klagsbrun, M. 1986. *J. Cell Biochem.* 29:275–87
58. Shing, Y., Folkman, J., Sullivan, R., Butterfield, C., Murray, J., Klagsbrun, M. 1984. *Science* 223:1296–99
59. Sholley, M. M., Ferguson, G. P., Seibel, H. R., Montour, J. L., Wilson, J. D. 1984. *Lab. Invest.* 51:624–34
60. Strydom, D. J., Fett, J. W., Lobb, R. R., Alderman, E. M., Bethune, J. L., et al. 1985. *Biochemistry* 24:5486–94
61. Sullivan, R., Klagsbrun, M. 1985. *J. Biol. Chem.* 260:2399–2403
62. Thornton, S. C., Mueller, S. N., Levine, E. M. 1983. *Science* 222:623–25
63. Togari, A., Dickens, G., Kuzuya, H., Guroff, G. 1985. *J. Neuroscience* 5:307–16
64. Wagner, J. A., D'Amore, P. A. 1986. *J. Cell Biol.* 103:1363–67
65. Wagner, R. C. 1975. *Adv. Microcirc.* 9:45–75
66. Warren, B. A., Shubik, P. 1966. *Lab. Invest.* 15:464–78
67. Wearn, J. T. 1928. *J. Exp. Med.* 47:273–92
68. White, G. E., Gimbrone, M. A. Jr., Fujiwara, K. 1983. *J. Cell Biol.* 97:416–24
69. Yamagami, I. 1970. *Jpn. J. Ophthalmol.* 14:41–58
70. Young, W. C., Herman, I. M. 1985. *J. Cell. Sci.* 73:19–32
71. Ziche, M., Jones, J., Gullino, P. 1982. *J. Natl. Cancer Inst.* 69:475–82

Ann. Rev. Physiol. 1987. 49:465–76

CARDIOVASCULAR RESPONSES TO CHRONIC HYPOXIA

Natalio Banchero

Department of Physiology, School of Medicine, University of Colorado Health Sciences Center, Denver, Colorado 80262

INTRODUCTION

Hypoxia exists when O_2 is delivered to the tissues at a partial pressure lower than that for normal individuals of the same species at sea level. Because the partial pressure of O_2 in the air decreases with decreasing barometric pressure, lower partial pressures are found above sea level. However, a certain threshold must be reached before the effects of hypoxia become significant. It has customarily been accepted that the effects of altitude are physiologically important above 3000 m, but some researchers believe that this threshold may be lower, perhaps 2000 m.

For the purposes of this review, "chronic hypoxia" implies that tissue P_{O_2} has been continuously low for more than two weeks. The following discussion excludes experiments concerned with the effects of acute hypoxia on the cardiovascular system. If changes occur through chronic exposure to natural high altitude, the process is called acclimatization; if changes occur through adaptation to simulated high altitude, the process is called acclimation.

A series of articles has provided substantial evidence concerning the effect of cold in combination with hypoxia on the cardiovascular system (5, 8, 12, 17, 35). Cold produces a considerable and sustained increase in the demands of the body for O_2, and ambient hypoxia reduces O_2 availability. Thus, the combination of these two stressors is thought to be very taxing to the individual (35). Most studies conducted at high altitude, however, have ignored the effects of cold.

Cattle and sheep respond with pulmonary arterial hypertension to cold and to hypoxia applied separately (12, 53), and an additive response has been measured (17). Lechner et al (33, 34) exposed guinea pigs separately to cold

465

and to hypoxia, and they assumed that the combination of the two environmental stresses could be deleterious. But in fact, guinea pigs exposed to cold plus hypoxia had a better survival rate than those animals exposed to simple normothermic hypoxia (35). These observations suggest that the addition of cold to hypoxia may, in some species, actually facilitate acclimation to high altitude. Lahiri (31), using theoretical considerations, has suggested that the cold air of high altitudes may be helpful in O_2 transport within the lung.

HOW DOES CHRONIC HYPOXIA OCCUR?

In mammals the most common natural cause of hypoxia is life at high altitude. Animals cannot always protect themselves from low temperatures. Because of their lower ratio of body weight to body surface area, small mammals are more easily affected by environmental temperature than large mammals.

It is difficult to determine precisely the degrees of hypoxia and cold acting on small rodents living at high altitude. The degree of hypoxia appears to be invariant and can be calculated from barometric pressure and the concentration of O_2 in air, but ambient temperatures show considerable diurnal variation and must be measured in the immediate vicinity of the animal. In fact, the animal's living habits may affect both the level of ambient hypoxia and temperature (13). Burrowing mammals, for example, stay warmer inside their burrows, but the air they breathe there has lower O_2 and higher CO_2 concentrations than the outside air (13, 32). In effect, they experience more hypoxia than on the surface, but the warmth enables them to reduce their O_2 consumption. Various physiological adaptations such as a low P_{50}, high O_2 capacity, and high muscle myoglobin have been reported in burrowing rodents (32).

Probably the most common causes of chronic hypoxia in humans are pulmonary and/or cardiac problems that lead to insidious reduction of arterial blood and tissue P_{O_2}, such as chronic obstructive pulmonary disease and cardiac failure. Another cause of chronic hypoxia in humans is residence at high altitude. About 20 million people live at elevations greater than 3000 m. In the Andes, the population is generally less mobile than people in other high altitude areas of the world. Because the weather in the central Andes is relatively warm, with no snow accumulation, Andean natives usually spend their entire lives at high altitude. In contrast, in the Himalayas, where the weather is much colder, the population is more mobile. Because humans can protect themselves from the environment, cold causes fewer physiological adaptations in them than in animals.

Experimentally induced hypoxia can be either hypobaric or dilutional. The degree of hypoxia and its course over time can easily be controlled. In most studies the temperature is kept at about 22°C; thus laboratory conditions are seldom the same as those found at natural high altitude.

IS BODY GROWTH AFFECTED BY HYPOXIA?

Because body weight and fiber cross-sectional area (FCSA) play an important role in skeletal and cardiac capillarity, growth rates deserve attention (2, 5, 21, 24). Some authors have found slower growth rates in rodents in hypoxic or high-altitude conditions than in normoxic animals (40, 52), whereas others have found no difference in growth rates (43). Growth retardation has been reported in human populations native to high altitudes (46, 47). It is difficult to determine whether these differences in growth can be ascribed to hypoxia, and the subject is too complicated for analysis here. However, the reader should keep in mind that the interpretation of results in both humans and animals may depend on the body size.

EFFECTS OF HYPOXIA ON THE CARDIOVASCULAR SYSTEM

Anatomical and biochemical adaptations occur as hypoxia becomes chronic. Exposure to low temperatures (5–10°C) also induces adaptive changes. Some of these changes become measurable only after 2 or 3 weeks, while others occur more rapidly. The following discussion of the effects of chronic hypoxia focuses on five major areas: hematology, oxygen consumption and cardiac output, blood flow distribution, muscle capillarity, and the volume and distribution of mitochondria. These divisions are, as always, highly arbitrary but necessary for clarity.

HEMATOLOGICAL EFFECTS OF CHRONIC HYPOXIA

The higher hemoglobin concentration [Hb] and hematocrit (Hct) found after prolonged exposure to hypoxia are believed to be caused by a sustained increase in erythropoietin (Epo), the glycoprotein hormone that stimulates the formation of red blood cells. The P_{O_2} in the renal tissue appears to regulate red blood cell production through Epo, but other substances, especially E-type prostaglandins, have been implicated (29). The production of Epo is much greater in male than in female rats exposed to the same degree of hypoxia (10). It has not always been possible, however, to consistently measure increased levels of Epo in the blood of chronically hypoxic animals (18). This fact has led some investigators to conclude that the increased erythropoietic activity found in species native to or acclimated to high altitude may not be related to Epo. One should remember that despite improved methodology, inaccuracies and lack of reproducibility continue to exist in the determination of Epo concentrations, especially in animals. The existence of an inhibitor of erythropoiesis that modulates the hematological response to chronic hypoxia has been suggested (42).

Not all mammals respond to chronic hypoxia with large increases in [Hb] and Hct. The Andean Camelids (llamas, alpacas) and the Andean guinea pig, for example, have very modest erythropoietic responses (7, 50). However, exposure of young US guinea pigs to chronic normothermic hypoxia resulted in marked erythropoiesis and large increases in [Hb] and Hct (34). Bartels et al (9) found large differences in the erythropoietic responses of rats and guinea pigs grown in simulated high altitude conditions. Rats showed modest elevations of [Hb] and Hct at 3000 m and no further increases above this altitude, whereas guinea pigs showed significant increases in these parameters above 5000 m. This result may reflect the changing level of Epo in the blood of rats, which diminishes when the polycythemic state is attained (18). However, Snyder et al (47) measured Hct's of 72% in rats exposed to 350 torr for 5 weeks. Strain and sex differences in the hematological adaptation of rats to laboratory hypobaric hypoxia have been well documented (27, 39).

In guinea pigs exposed to 5°C, [Hb] is approximately 10% higher than in controls of similar age and body weight maintained at 22°C (33). Young guinea pigs subjected to cold and hypoxia responded more mildly than those subjected to normothermic hypoxia (35). It appears, therefore, that the hematological response to hypoxia was blunted by concomitant cold stress. Among humans, Sherpas have lower values for [Hb] and Hct than Andean natives (37), but considerable variability has been reported in both populations (56). The Sherpas' lower [Hb] may reflect their lower environmental temperatures.

EFFECTS ON OXYGEN CONSUMPTION AND CARDIAC OUTPUT

Abundant experimental evidence indicates that chronic hypoxia does not affect the standard O_2 consumption of large mammals. To maintain O_2 consumption, their respiratory systems maintain a certain degree of hyperventilation. As altitude increases, the ventilation required to bring into the body the same amount of O_2 per unit of time must increase. However, natives to high altitude ventilate less than do sojourners (30).

At sea level, when O_2 needs increase, much larger volumes of ventilation are necessary. At the same $\dot{V}_{O_2}$ the air volumes are even larger at high altitude. In fact, during exercise at very high elevations, ventilation increases disproportionately to the amount of oxygen consumed; that is, the ratio $\dot{V}_{O_2}/\dot{V}E$ decreases.

Chronic exposure to hypoxia causes a decrease in $\dot{V}_{O_{2max}}$ that is directly proportional to the altitude but varies considerably in magnitude (22, 50). Climbers who had exceptionally high values of $\dot{V}_{O_{2max}}$ at sea level and a good ventilatory response to hypoxia have climbed Mt. Everest without supplemental oxygen (50). The decrease in $\dot{V}_{O_{2max}}$ imposed by altitudes in excess of 6000 m was not enough to prevent the performance necessary to climb to the summit.

Guinea pigs have no ventilatory response to acute hypoxia (10% O_2) (11). In fossorial and semifossorial mammals the ventilatory response to increases in CO_2 and to low O_2 is lower than that of nonfossorial mammals (13). These animals thus avoid excessive respiratory work while still ensuring adequate oxygen delivery to their tissues by other mechanisms (13, 32).

In normoxia, guinea pigs exposed to 5°C experience an $\sim$2.3-fold increase in both $\dot{V}_{O_2}$ (11) and $\dot{Q}$ because of an increase in metabolic rate. At high altitude, the changes in ventilation and cardiac output must reflect adjustments to both cold and hypoxia. At a certain altitude and temperature, these responses may become an impediment to survival. Arieli et al (3) have shown that the increase in $\dot{V}_{O_2}$ induced by low temperatures disappears in severe hypoxia, perhaps as a consequence of lower body temperatures. In fact, some of the small nonfossorial rodents living in the Andes must find shelter at night when the ambient temperature drops (J. Faura, personal communication). The reason for this behavior is that maintaining body temperature requires much more oxygen.

The bulk of the evidence shows that, at rest, $\dot{Q}$ in chronic hypoxia is normal. Systemic oxygen transport, that is, the product of O_2 content times $\dot{Q}$, is maintained within normal levels because an absolute increase in [Hb] sustains an unchanged arterial O_2 content. Experimental results regarding the changes evoked by physical exercise show considerable disparity (20), but most investigators report a decrease in $\dot{Q}_{max}$ that is not as marked as the decrease in $\dot{V}_{O_{2max}}$. Some of the discrepancies in the literature can be explained by detraining in the early part of the exposure to high altitude when the exercise regime could not be followed (20). Stroke volume and heart rate have been found to vary with the type of exercise and body position in subjects with different degrees of acclimation (20). Ou et al (40) found no difference in ventilation and in O_2 transport by blood between two strains of Sprague-Dawley rats with strikingly different susceptibility to hypoxia.

There is considerable controversy about the benefits of increased [Hb] and Hct. For example, some Andean natives show symptoms from excess polycythemia. Lindenfeld et al (36) found that in normoxic dogs with normovolemic polycythemia, systemic O_2 transport to muscle is preserved at rest and during exercise, despite decreased muscle blood flow. Cerretelli (16) suggested that the oxygen uptake of tissues may be impaired in individuals at an altitude of 5400 m during 100% O_2 breathing, possibly due to increased blood viscosity. In contrast with this finding, Buick et al (14) showed that a slight increase in $\dot{V}_{O_{2max}}$ occurred after autologous red cell transfusions in athletes highly trained at sea level. Blood letting has long been claimed to have a beneficial effect for individuals afflicted with chronic mountain sickness, but the data in support of this belief are scarce (38).

The effects of hemodilution on O_2 transport in chronic hypoxia have been examined. Horstman et al (20) removed 450 ml of blood from subjects after 3 weeks at 4300 m, decreasing the mean Hct from 52.7% to 47.7%. During maximal exercise after phlebotomy, the decrease in $\dot{V}_{O_{2max}}$ persisted despite an increase in $\dot{Q}_{max}$, which did not bring systemic O_2 transport to prephlebotomy levels. This experiment also showed that systemic O_2 transport is decreased when O_2 carrying capacity is increased because $\dot{Q}_{max}$ diminishes. Klein studied high-altitude polycythemia in residents of Cerro de Pasco (4390 m) (28). He produced hemodilution with the aid of a cell separator and observed that resting $\dot{Q}$ increased, pulmonary artery pressure declined, and mixed venous O_2 saturation remained unchanged. Winslow (55) measured an increase in arterial P_{O_2} and arterial saturation but found a decrease in arterial O_2 content after hemodilution with a cell separator. However, in two of three subjects an increased ability to perform maximal exercise was measured. Apparently, when the subject is at rest, adaptive mechanisms allow the cardiovascular system to transport a normal amount of O_2 from the lungs to the tissues. During exercise the O_2 transported to the tissues is reduced by an amount equal to the difference in $\dot{Q}$ between the sea-level and the high-altitude conditions (55). In subjects in whom $\dot{Q}$ is not decreased, systemic O_2 transport should be maintained. The question is, then, do all tissues get their adequate share of O_2 and if so, how?

BLOOD FLOW DISTRIBUTION

Blood flow distribution affects O_2 transport but has attracted little attention over the last few years. Data on short-term exposure to hypoxia are available; however, systematic studies with simultaneous determinations in several organs are still lacking. A study conducted in rats subjected to intermittent hypoxia equivalent to that produced by altitudes of up to 7000 m reported elevated $\dot{Q}$ and greater relative blood flows in spleen, intestine, skeletal muscle, and liver (23). The authors recognized, however, that the level of hypoxia induced in this experiment exceeded that caused by permanent residence at high altitude. It is still unclear whether chronic exposure to hypoxia changes the distribution of blood flow in the capillaries or the level of their perfusion.

MUSCLE CAPILLARITY IN CHRONIC HYPOXIA

An effective system of distribution must exist for adequate amounts of O_2 to reach all cells of the body under different metabolic conditions, some of which are as taxing as intense physical activity. Skeletal muscle O_2 consumption may increase 90-fold during exercise. This very high O_2 consumption must be met by increases in blood flow and O_2 extraction, both of which would benefit from a denser network of microvessels. The teleological appeal of such a network explains the belief that simple hypoxia generates increased muscle capillarity.

The most important factor affecting the capillarity of skeletal and cardiac muscles is normal body growth (7). Hence, alterations in body growth rate induced by hypoxia must be considered in the analysis of data on muscle capillarity. The weights of skeletal muscles, as well as of the right and left ventricles and of the whole heart, increase linearly with body weight (24). Skeletal and cardiac muscle growth occurs through fiber hypertrophy; the number of fibers remains practically unchanged. As capillaries can be located only around fibers, fiber growth rearranges the capillary network.

Cardiac muscle has a much denser capillary network and smaller fiber cross-sectional area (FCSA) than skeletal muscle (6). Numerous investigators have established the relationships between FCSA and capillarity in these two muscles (2, 21). Cardiac and skeletal muscle growth is associated with increases in both the ratio of capillary density to fiber density (C/F) and the numbers of capillaries around fibers (CAF). This increase in the absolute number of capillaries, however, is insufficient to maintain a constant capillary density (CD), which decreases hyperbolically as fiber girth increases (1).

Changes in FCSA elicited by other mechanisms, such as starvation or slow growth (A. H. Sillau, personal communication), also result in changes of CD, C/F, and CAF. The changes produced by starvation follow, in reverse direction, those produced by normal growth. Departures from these normal relationships, then, indicate changes in the capillarity of a given muscle. Often, however, investigators fail to report or to measure some of these variables. Such omissions complicate the interpretation of their results. Increases in the number of capillaries are very effective in shortening diffusion distances when the CD is low, but are much less effective when the CD is already high.

The topic of muscle and cardiac capillarity has been comprehensively reviewed by Hudlicka (21). She has shown, as others have done before, that CD is high in muscles with small fiber cross-section and low in muscles with large fiber cross-section, even across species. The regression equation she has calculated, using data reported by numerous investigators, shows a very good correlation ($r = 0.862$) over a wide range of fiber sizes. Hudlicka's equation is valuable for two reasons: It provides a descriptor of muscle growth and changes in capillarity, and it permits comparisons of capillarity in muscles subjected to various environmental or physical conditions. It must be recognized, however, that Hudlicka's graph and equation excluded a series of data points that did not conform with the calculated equation and were probably incorrect due to technical artifact. She also excluded some animal species that seem to depart from this general relationship. Aquin et al (1) investigated the capillarity of dog sternothyroid, gastrocnemius, and flexor digitorum superficialis muscles and found that CD did not change with body growth but that C/F increased with FCSA. Sillau has also reported that the sternothyroid muscle of the dog shows a larger C/F with increasing FCSA (44).

Hudlicka continues to maintain the traditional view that chronic hypoxia is accompanied by increased skeletal muscle capillarity (21). Although her view is based principally on work by Valdivia (51), Cassin et al (15), Banchero (4), and Eby & Banchero (19), none of their data points were used on her graph relating CD and FCSA. It seems important to point out certain aspects of these articles that bear on her view.

The work of Valdivia (51) reporting an increased skeletal muscle capillarity in Andean guinea pigs gives values for CD that exceed values currently accepted as correct. It is almost certain that the histological techniques used by Valdivia produced considerable shrinkage of the tissues, as evidenced by CD's of 1621 and 1542 capillaries/mm^2, FCSA's of about 1400 μm^2, and C/F's of 2.52 and 2.47 in the gastrocnemius of guinea pigs raised at sea level. Valdivia's values for capillarity in Andean guinea pigs were even higher than those for the animals raised at sea level, but his guinea pigs were kept in the open or in unheated quarters at 4,540 m and were thus exposed to cold as well as hypoxia. This combination of stressors results in higher capillarity for the gastrocnemius (8).

Cassin et al (15) compared control, normoxic rats, weighing an average of 287 g with hypoxic rats with an average body weight of 154 g kept at 6150 m for over 30 days. They attributed the smaller rats' higher skeletal muscle CD to opening of previously closed capillaries. Simple calculations using the data collected by Ripoll et al (43) show that the difference was due to the different average body weights of the two groups of rats and not to hypoxia. In fact, the hypoxic rats had fewer capillaries than the normoxic rats.

Banchero's early work showed that the sternothyroid muscle of dogs exposed to hypobaria for three weeks displayed increased CD, no change in C/F, and reduced FCSA (5). But Banchero's dogs were tracheostomized, and the changes in CD could have been related to muscle atrophy caused by denervation or trauma during surgery. As the dogs did not lose weight at simulated altitude, the reduction in FCSA and the concomitant rise in CD could have been confined to this particular muscle. One confusing aspect of this work on dog skeletal muscle is that further studies on Andean dogs not subjected to tracheostomy (19) showed an even larger CD at a smaller FCSA than did the dogs kept under simulated altitude conditions or at sea level. Sillau (44) measured no change in the capillarity of the sternothyroid muscle of dogs native to high altitude.

Sillau & Banchero found no differences in the capillarity of the gastrocnemius and the soleus muscles of guinea pigs purchased from farmers at high altitude and at sea level (46). These Andean guinea pigs were domesticated animals, raised in the single-room houses of the farmers, where the guinea pigs cuddled around the stove and thus experienced ambient temperatures higher than the outside temperature.

The bulk of recent evidence suggests that skeletal muscle capillarity does not respond to simple normothermic hypoxia even when the muscle is active (45). In the diaphragm, a muscle with continuous, low-frequency activity, capillarity remained unchanged after exposure to chronic hypoxia (47). Still, some recent reviews insist that simple hypoxia must lead to increased capillarity, on the basis of teleological reasoning backed by the articles discussed above. These reviews often neglect the severity of the hypoxia at the level of the tissue under consideration, and the presence of spurious technical factors in the studies. Such omissions are due not to carelessness on the part of the writers but to changing patterns of thought about the problem, and they reflect the difficulty of eradicating some erroneous notions in science.

In cardiac muscle, chronic hypoxia has been shown to cause an absolute, transient increase in capillarity independent of fiber hypertrophy. The study of the effects of chronic hypoxia on myocardial capillarity is complicated by the presence of significant right ventricular hypertrophy, which is induced by the greater pressure load on the right ventricle as it works against higher pulmonary vascular resistance caused by elevated Hct and by anatomical and functional alterations in the pulmonary vasculature (24). Right ventricular hypertrophy has been found to reduce CD in adult animals, but it may increase capillarity in young animals. However, a decrease in FCSA due either to smaller body size, fiber elongation (found in some forms of ventricular hypertrophy), or simple hypotrophy would result in a denser capillary network.

EFFECT OF CHRONIC HYPOXIA ON MITOCHONDRIA

Oxygen is useful only as it enters the mitochondria. Hence, considerable attention has focused on the role that the volume and the location of the mitochondria play in O_2 transport, as well as in ATP transfer. It has been shown that the oxidative capacity of a tissue is proportional to the number and volume of mitochondria in its cells. However, it remains to be determined whether the rate-limiting step in aerobic metabolism is related to the capillary-to-mitochondria diffusion distance. Important determinants of O_2 diffusion are the difference in partial pressure of O_2 between capillaries and mitochondria, the distance between these two points, and the rate at which the mitochondria remove O_2. Because mitochondria can operate at very low O_2 pressures, the difference in O_2 pressure from the capillary to the mitochondria may be close to the capillary P_{O_2}.

In situations where the O_2 delivery system is challenged, as in exposure to cold, hypoxia, and exercise, it becomes especially important to consider the geometrical parameters that bear on the delivery of O_2 to the cell. Investigators have mainly directed their attention to exercise and have concentrated less on hypoxia (25). No reports on the effects of cold exposure on these parameters have been made. Nothing is known about the mobilization of skeletal muscle mitochondria in chronic hypoxia, especially during physical activity, when the challenge to the O_2 transport system is maximal. The volume density and the distribution of mitochondria around capillaries have been measured in the myocardium of normoxic and hypoxic guinea pigs (25). The volume density of mitochondria reaches a peak close to the capillary and decreases away from it. No differences in mitochondria distribution were observed in these two groups but because the highest density of mitochondria occurred at about 15% of the maximal diffusion distance, CD values influenced the absolute distance from the capillary, as the intercapillary distance (ICD) can be approximated by $ICD = 0.88 \ (CD^{-1/2})$. No redistribution of mitochondria within the muscle fiber was observed by Kayar et al (26), in well-trained males immediately after endurance exercise at sea level, but the depletion of glycogen and lipids from the muscle produced some fiber shrinkage.

The features of acclimatization and acclimation to chronic hypoxia have long fascinated physiologists. The study of animals well adapted to chronic hypoxia provides a wealth of information that enhances our understanding of the mechanisms that allow them to survive at high altitudes. In addition, these findings improve our ability to unravel pathophysiologic mechanisms in patients with lung and heart disease. Of particular importance are those hematological factors involved in improving O_2 transport to the tissues and O_2 transport from the capillary into the mitochondria. It remains to be determined whether or not an elevated hematocrit and increased blood viscosity affect the transit of red blood cells in the capillaries of chronically hypoxic animals. It is also important to establish what level of tissue hypoxia is necessary for capillary proliferation to occur. Thus, studies on animals in chronic hypoxia must challenge the oxygen delivery system even further by exercise or exposure to cold in order to reproduce conditions encountered in everyday life.

Literature Cited

1. Aquin, L., Banchero, N. 1981. *J. Anat.* 132:341–56
2. Aquin, L., Sillau, A. H., Lechner, A. J., Banchero, N. 1980. *Microvasc. Res.* 20:41–50
3. Arieli, R., Ar, A., Shkolnik, H. 1977. *Physiol. Zool.* 50:61–75
4. Banchero, N. 1975. *Proc. Soc. Exp. Biol. Med.* 148:435–39
5. Banchero, N. 1982. *Physiologist* 25:385–89
6. Banchero, N. 1985. *Proc. Int. Soc. O$_2$ Transport to Tissue*, ed. F. Kreuzer, S. M. Cain, T. K. Goldstick, pp. 355–63. New York: Plenum
7. Banchero, N., Grover, R. F., Will, J. A. 1971. *Resp. Physiol.* 13:102–15
8. Banchero, N., Kayar, S. R., Lechner, A. J. 1985. *Respir. Physiol.* 62:245–55
9. Bartels, H., Bartels, R., Rathschlag-Schaefer, A. M., Robbel, H., Ludders, S. 1979. *Respir. Physiol.* 36:375–89
10. Baumann, R., Bauer, C., Bartels, H. 1971. *Respir. Physiol.* 11:135
11. Blake, C. I., Banchero, N. 1985. *Respir. Physiol.* 61:357–68
12. Bligh, J., Chauca, D. 1983. *Adjustment to High Altitude*. US Dept. Health Human Services, NIH Pub. No. 83-2496, pp. 75–78
13. Boggs, D. N., Kilgore, D. L. Jr., Birchard, G. F. 1984. *Comp. Biochem. Physiol.* 77A:1–7
14. Buick, F. J., Gledhill, N., Froese, A. B., Spriet, L., Meyers, E. C. 1980. *J. Appl. Physiol.* 48:636–42
15. Cassin, S. R., Gilbert, D., Bunnel, C. F., Johnson, E. M. 1971. *Am. J. Physiol.* 220:448–51
16. Cerretelli, P. 1983. *Adjustments to High Altitude*. US Dept. Health Human Services, NIH Pub. No. 83-2496, pp. 61–64
17. Chauca, D., Bligh, J. 1976. *Res. Vet. Sci.* 21:123–24
18. Dunn, C. D. R., Smith, L. N., Leonard, J. I., Andrews, R. J., Lange, R. J. 1980. *Exp. Hematol.* 8:259–79
19. Eby, S. H., Banchero, N. 1976. *Proc. Soc. Exp. Biol. Med.* 151:795–98
20. Horstman, D., Weiskopf, R., Jackson, R. E. 1980. *J. Appl. Physiol.* 49:311–18
21. Hudlicka, O. 1984. *Handbook of Physiology, IV. Microcirculation*, ed. E. M. Renkin, C. C. Michel, pp. 165–216. Bethesda, Maryland: Am. Physiol. Soc.
22. Johnson, E. S., Finch, C. A. 1984. *Am. J. Physiol.* 246:R619–23
23. Kasalicky, J., Ressl, J., Urbanova, D., Widimsky, J., Ostadal, B., et al. 1977. *Pflüg. Arch.* 368:111–15
24. Kayar, S. R., Banchero, N. 1985. *Pflüg. Arch.* 404:319–25
25. Kayar, S. R., Banchero, N. 1986. *Resp. Physiol.* In press
26. Kayar, S. R., Hoppeler, H., Howald, H., Claassen, H., Oberholzer, F. 1986. *Eur. J. Appl. Physiol.* 54:578–84
27. Kentera, D., Susic, D., Zdravkovic, M. 1983. *Respiration* 44:38–43
28. Klein, H. G. 1983. *Adjustments to High Altitude*. US Dept. Health Human Services, NIH Publ. No. 83-2496, pp. 47–51.
29. Kurtz, A., Jelkmann, W., Pfeilschifter, J., Baver, C. 1985. *Am. J. Physiol.* 249:C3–C8.
30. Lahiri, S. 1984. *High Altitude and Man*, ed. J. B. West, S. Lahiri, pp. 147–62. Bethesda, Maryland: Am. Physiol. Soc.
31. Lahiri, S. 1985. *Physiologist* 28:275 (Abstr.)
32. Lechner, A. J. 1976. *J. Appl. Physiol.* 41:168–73
33. Lechner, A. J., Salvato, V. L., Banchero, N. 1980. *Comp. Biochem. Physiol.* 66A:541–44
34. Lechner, A. J., Salvato, V. L., Banchero, N. 1980. *Comp. Biochem. Physiol.* 67A:239–44
35. Lechner, A. J., Salvato, V. L., Banchero, N. 1981. *Comp. Biochem. Physiol.* 70A:321–27
36. Lindenfeld, J., Weil, J. V., Travis, V. L., Horwitz, L. D. 1985. *Circ. Res.* 56:793–800
37. Morpurgo, G., Arese, P., Bosia, A., Pescarmona, G. P., Luzzana, M., et al. 1976. *Proc. Natl. Acad. Sci. USA* 73:747–51
38. Monge, C. C., Lozano, R., Whittembury, J. 1965. *Nature* 207:770
39. Ou, L. C., Cai, Y. N., Tenney, S. M. 1985. *Respir. Physiol.* 62:85–94
40. Ou, L. C., Smith, R. P. 1984. *Proc. Soc. Exp. Biol. Med.* 177:308–11
41. Pietschmann, M., Bartels, H. 1985. *Respir. Physiol.* 59:347–60
42. Reynafarje, C. 1966. *Life at High Altitudes*. Pan American Health Org. Sci. Publ. #140, Washington, D.C.
43. Ripoll, E., Sillau, A. H., Banchero, N. 1979. *Pflüg. Arch.* 380:153–58
44. Sillau, A. H. 1980. *Int. J. Biometeorol.* 24:355–59
45. Sillau, A. H., Aquin, L., Bui, M. V.,

Banchero, N. 1980. *Pflüg. Arch.* 386:39–45

46. Sillau, A. H., Banchero, N. 1979. *Proc. Soc. Exp. Biol. Med.* 160:368–73
47. Snyder, G. K., Wilcox, E. E., Burnham, E. W. 1985. *Respir. Physiol.* 62:135–40
48. Stinson, S. 1980. *Am. J. Phys. Anthropol.* 52:377–85
49. Stinson, S. 1982. *Am. J. Phys. Anthropol.* 59:61–71
50. Turek, Z., Ringnalda, B. E. M., Moran, O., Kreuzer, I. 1980. *Pflüg. Arch.* 394:109–15
51. Valdivia, E. 1958. *Am. J. Physiol.* 194:585–89

52. West, J. B. 1982. *J. Exp. Biol.* 100:147–57
53. Whittembury, J. 1983. *Adjustments to High Altitude.* US Dept. Health Human Services, NIH Publ. No. 83-2496, pp. 79–82
54. Will, D. H., McMurty, I. F., Reeves, J. T., Grover, R. F. 1978. *J. Appl. Physiol.* 45:469–73
55. Winslow, R. M. 1983. *Adjustments to High Altitude.* US Dept. Health Human Services, NIH Publ. No. 83-2496, pp. 43–46
56. Winslow, R. M., 1984. *High Altitude and Man,* ed. J. B. West, S. Lahiri, pp. 59–72. Bethesda, Maryland: Am. Physiol. Soc.

Ann. Rev. Physiol. 1987. 49:477–87

CORONARY VASCULAR ADAPTATIONS TO MYOCARDIAL HYPERTROPHY

William M. Chilian

Department of Medical Physiology, Texas A&M College of Medicine, College Station, Texas 77843, and Department of Internal Medicine, The Cardiovascular Center, University of Iowa, College of Medicine, Iowa City, Iowa 52242

Melvin L. Marcus

Department of Internal Medicine, The Cardiovascular Center, University of Iowa, College of Medicine, Iowa City, Iowa 52242

CHARACTERISTICS OF CARDIAC HYPERTROPHY

Imposition of a pressure or volume overload on the myocardium increases the wall stress of the involved ventricle. Cardiac hypertrophy, which occurs during such a hemodynamic perturbation, is generally viewed as a compensatory process that normalizes wall stress. After complete normalization of wall stress due to increased wall thickness, the hypertrophy stabilizes, and there is no further change in ventricular volume or in total cardiac mass (7, 33). As a consequence of the normalized systolic wall stress, myocardial oxygen consumption per unit mass of hypertrophied left ventricular myocardium is equal to that in controls (30). Also, in the hypertrophied ventricle with normalized wall stress, resting myocardial perfusion per unit mass of myocardium is normal (5, 21, 30, 34, 35).

Although stabilized cardiac hypertrophy is characterized by normal wall stress, oxygen consumption, and perfusion per unit mass, when it is secondary to systemic hypertension, it is associated with many abnormalities. For example, Spann (43) found that cardiac muscle was characterized by impaired

477

0066-4278/87/0315-0477$02.00

contractile responses. Tarazi (46) found that the collagen content of the left ventricular wall was elevated due to diffuse fibrosis. Furthermore, the surface area of the external sarcolemma per myocyte volume, excluding the t-tubular system, was decreased, and mitochondrial density per cell volume was also decreased (36). The hypertrophied myocardium was also characterized by altered electrophysiological properties (3) and impaired diastolic function (14). Thus, although cardiac hypertrophy is generally viewed as a *compensatory* process that normalizes wall stress during chronic hemodynamic perturbation, due to hypertension or aortic insufficiency, for example, there are also several *pathological* consequences associated with this process.

Pathological Manifestations of Cardiac Hypertrophy

Animal studies and human epidemiological studies have found that cardiac hypertrophy secondary to a pressure overload is associated with pathological changes.

In patients, the dominant cause of left ventricular hypertrophy is systemic hypertension. Hypertension is associated with an increased development of atherosclerotic coronary artery disease (25). Also, the incidence of sudden death, myocardial infarction, and cardiovascular morbidity is much higher in patients with left ventricular hypertrophy secondary to systemic hypertension (25). It was reported that patients with such hypertrophy were three times more likely to die suddenly. These epidemiological studies of the pathological manifestations of cardiac hypertrophy secondary to systemic hypertension cannot determine whether the increased adverse effects of coronary occlusion in patients with hypertension are related to their more severe atherosclerosis or to the altered vulnerability of the hypertrophied ventricle to ischemia.

To gain insight into this question, dogs with left ventricular hypertrophy secondary to renal vascular hypertension but without coronary artery disease were examined following circumflex occlusion. Under these experimental conditions, sudden coronary artery occlusion was followed by sudden death three times more frequently than in controls, and a substantial increase in the amount of tissue necrosis per risk area of occluded vessel was observed (27, 28). Thus the factor responsible for the increase in sudden death and tissue necrosis following coronary artery occlusion was hypertension rather than cardiac hypertrophy (24). These investigators reported that an acute reduction in arterial pressure in animals with renal vascular hypertension and hypertrophy prevented increases in the incidence of sudden death and the amount of tissue necrosis. Thus, the increased vulnerability of the hypertrophied ventricle to ischemia and hypertension has a major influence on the deleterious effects of coronary occlusion.

Interaction Between Cardiac Hypertrophy and the Coronary Vasculature

For the last several years, it was thought that the dominant pathological manifestations of cardiac hypertrophy were abnormalities in the coronary vascular system (31). This review presents data that both support and challenge the concept that hypertrophy *always* produces adverse effects on the coronary vasculature. Figure 1 is a schematic diagram of the interaction between left ventricular hypertrophy and the coronary resistance vessels. This diagram provides a framework from which to discuss the effects of hypertrophy on the coronary vascular system. In this figure, the size of each box represents the relative left ventricular mass and the area of each circle within a box represents the cross-sectional area of the coronary resistance vessels. The box in the center represents the normal relationship between the myocardial mass and the cross-sectional area of the resistance vessels. The upper boxes represent an increase of the coronary vasculature to match the increase in myocardial mass *(upper left)* and an expansion of the vasculature cross-sectional area in excess of that of the myocardial mass *(upper right)*. The box at center left represents decreased density of the coronary vasculature during cardiac hypertrophy, i.e. growth of the cardiac mass without expansion of the cross-sectional area of the coronary vasculature. The box at center right shows

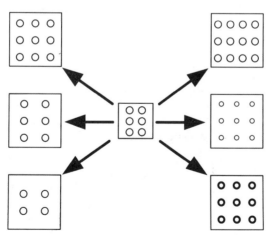

Figure 1   Various possible relationships between the left ventricular mass and the cross-sectional area of the coronary resistance vessels are shown. Left ventricular mass is represented by the size of the box; the cross-sectional area of the vascular bed is represented by the area of the circles within each box. The box in the center represents the normal relationship, and the arrows point to different adaptations of the coronary vasculature to left ventricular hypertrophy. See the text for details. (This figure was adapted from Reference 31 and is published with permission from McGraw-Hill Book Company.)

a functional decrease of the coronary vessel cross-sectional area due either to altered extravascular compressive forces or increased vasomotor tone. The lower boxes represent coronary vascular pathology during cardiac hypertrophy: vascular rarefaction, a decreased number of resistance vessels, *(lower left)* and increased wall-to-lumen ratio of the coronary resistance vessels *(lower right)*. Both of these situations are characterized by increased minimal coronary resistance.

Figure 1 emphasizes the fact that all forms of cardiac hypertrophy do not lead to adverse changes in the coronary vascular system.

Many factors influence the adaptation of the coronary vasculature to cardiac hypertrophy, including (a) the nature of the stimulus that provokes hypertrophy; (b) the age of the animal when the stimulus that causes hypertrophy is imposed; (c) the species (patient studies versus animal studies); (d) the stability of the hypertrophy and the normalization of wall stress; (e) the duration of hypertrophy; and (f) the particular ventricle involved. In the remainder of this review we discuss in detail the coronary resistance vessel adaptations to hypertrophy produced by different initiating stimuli. We intentionally omit most references regarding adaptations of the coronary capillary bed to hypertrophy, since this topic has been reviewed recently (39).

INFLUENCE OF THE STIMULUS THAT INITIATES HYPERTROPHY ON CORONARY VESSEL–CARDIAC MUSCLE INTERACTION

Hypertrophy Secondary To Systemic Hypertension

The effects of cardiac hypertrophy that is secondary to systemic hypertension on the coronary vascular system have been widely investigated (31). There is a plethora of data concerning the pathological manifestations of this type of hypertrophy on coronary anatomy and coronary physiology.

CORONARY ANATOMY: PRESSURE-OVERLOAD HYPERTROPHY   The influence of pressure overload on the epicardial coronary arteries is somewhat controversial. Stack et al (44) found that epicardial coronary arteries did not enlarge during hypertrophy caused by pressure overload. However, other investigators reported that the diameter of epicardial coronary arteries increased in proportion to the extent of similarly induced left ventricular hypertrophy (22). Since epicardial coronary arteries are responsible for only a minor fraction of total coronary resistance (26), there would have to be substantial decrease in their cross-sectional area to have an appreciable influence on coronary reserve. Thus, alterations in the epicardial coronary vascular system are most likely not responsible for pathological manifestations of cardiac hypertrophy that is secondary to systemic hypertension. There is less information concerning the effects of cardiac hypertrophy on the coronary resistance vessels. Tomanek et al (47) found no consistent morphological abnormalities in coronary resistance vessels from dogs subject to six weeks of left ventricular hypertrophy secondary to renal vascular hypertension. These investigators reported that the wall-to-lumen ratios of coronary arteries and arterioles, ranging from epicardial arteries to precapillary arterioles, were not different from the ratios in similarly sized vessels from control animals. Interestingly, larger coronary arteries showed pathological changes. Specifically, there was an increase of the tunica media, and diffuse fibrosis of the coronary arteries was observed. In contrast, in other organ systems an increase in wall-to-lumen ratio is frequently observed during systemic hypertension (13).

Breisch et al (6) recently reported a decrease in the density of arterioles (<100 μm in diameter) during cardiac hypertrophy. This decrease in arteriolar density suggests vascular rarefaction, but it also may represent a reduction in the number of vessels per unit mass of myocardium. It should be emphasized that vascular rarefaction during systemic hypertension has been observed in the skeletal muscle vasculature (38), mesentery (19), and skin (17).

Clearly, additional studies are needed to more fully elucidate coronary vascular adaptations to pressure-overload cardiac hypertrophy. In our opinion such studies should focus on the following: investigation of the effects of long-term hypertrophy on arteriolar wall-to-lumen ratios; more complete documentation of the possibility of rarefaction in the coronary vasculature; and identification of the causal factor for vascular abnormalities, namely hypertension or hypertrophy.

CORONARY PHYSIOLOGY: PRESSURE-OVERLOAD HYPERTROPHY   Although resting myocardial perfusion is normal in the hypertrophied myocardium, other functional parameters of the coronary circulation are impaired compared to those found under normotensive, nonhypertrophied conditions. Such coronary pathophysiology was associated in animals with decreased coronary vasodilator reserve in the left ventricle (4, 32, 37, 40, 49, 52) and increased minimal coronary resistance per unit mass (1, 12, 21, 34, 49, 51).

Impaired vasodilator responses are associated with an increased coronary resistance and decreased vasodilator reserve during left ventricular hypertrophy; this impairment is especially prominent in the subendocardium. Some investigators have reported that left ventricular hypertrophy secondary to pressure overload alters the normal subendocardial-to-subepicardial distribution of perfusion at rest (34, 40). Because of this disturbance, subendocardial vasodilator reserve is compromised during a variety of physiological stresses.

Bache and his colleagues (5) reported that exercise-induced tachycardia markedly attenuates vasodilation in the subendocardium and midmyocardium of dogs with left ventricular hypertrophy. Other investigators also reported that in both dogs (21) and miniswine (50) strenuous exercise is associated with subendocardial underperfusion.

The specific mechanisms of the decrease in coronary reserve during pressure-overload hypertrophy are, as yet, unknown. Tomanek and colleagues (48) recently found that increased minimal resistance in the spontaneously hypertensive rat was related to chronic elevations in arterial pressure rather than left ventricular hypertrophy. Thus, elevations in coronary perfusion pressure may be the cause of coronary vascular abnormalities. Augmented extravascular compressive forces could lead to an increase in minimal coronary resistance and impair vasodilator reserve. Harrison et al (18) reported that the minimal coronary resistance in isolated, unloaded canine hearts was equivalent in normal and hypertrophied ventricles. One implication of this result is that augmented extravascular compressive forces compromised coronary vasodilation. In contrast, Scheel et al (41) reported an increase in minimal coronary resistance in an isolated heart preparation subjected to pressure-overload left ventricular hypertrophy. Although the effects of extravascular compressive forces on minimal coronary resistance remain unsettled, these forces may be involved in coronary vascular abnormalities, especially those observed in the subendocardium, where compressive forces are thought to be greatest.

Some plausible mechanisms for this decrement in coronary flow reserve during pressure-overload hypertrophy are shown in Figure 1. For instance, if the mechanical properties of the ventricle caused inappropriate extravascular compression (either during systole or diastole), the dilator capacity (box at center right) would be impaired. Moreover, it is also possible that coronary resistance vessels in such models of left ventricular hypertrophy are hyperreactive to vasoconstrictor stimuli, which could also impair coronary dilation. There may also be arteriolar rarefaction (box at lower left) and/or increased wall-to-lumen ratios (box at lower right) in the coronary resistance vessels. Decreased vascular density during hypertension (box at center left) would lead to impaired dilator capacity. This decreased density would be especially prominent if the spacing of arterioles was heterogeneous, which could create areas of hypoxia and decreased vasodilator reserve. Thus, pressure-overload hypertrophy is characterized by adverse effects on the coronary vasculature that are most evident in the subendocardium.

Thyroxine-Induced Cardiac Hypertrophy

Cardiac hypertrophy caused by thyrotoxicosis or thyroxine administration is characterized by several biochemical and anatomical parameters that distinguish it from other types of hypertrophy. Goodkind et al (16) found increased myosin adenosine triphosphatase (ATPase) activity. This increased enzyme activity results from a shift of the myosin isozymes to the V_1 (fastest) myosin ATPase (29). In thyroxine-induced hypertrophy, mitochondrial volume and sarcolemma surface area per myocyte (36) increase, and the amount of collagen in the ventricular wall decreases (11), which contrasts with the biochemical characteristics of pressure-overload hypertrophy. Since many of the biochemical and anatomical features of thyroxine-induced hypertrophy are different from left ventricular hypertrophy caused by pressure overload, it is not surprising that the interaction between the myocardial mass and the coronary vasculature is also dissimilar.

Short-term administration of thyroid hormone was reported to reduce the coronary vasodilator reserve (45). Presumably, this decrease was related to the elevated resting blood flow induced by the augmented metabolism resulting from tachycardia or elevated systolic pressure. Left ventricular hypertrophy produced by thyroxine administration over a two-month period was not characterized by a decrease in coronary vasodilator reserve (8). Furthermore, the minimal resistance for the entire left ventricle of thyroxine-treated rats (30–35% hypertrophy) was reduced compared to that of control animals. Importantly, minimal coronary resistance per unit mass was equivalent in the left ventricle of thyroxine-treated and control animals (8). These results can be placed in the scheme in Figure 1. The adaptation of the coronary vasculature to thyroxine-induced hypertrophy is shown by the box on the upper left, in which the cross-sectional area of the coronary vasculature increases to match the increase in the myocardial mass. This is in marked contrast to the interaction between the coronary vasculature and pressure-overload cardiac hypertrophy. These data support the concept that the stimulus that provokes left ventricular hypertrophy strongly influences the adaptation of the coronary vasculature.

Anemia-Induced Left Ventricular Hypertrophy

Cardiac hypertrophy secondary to chronic anemia is related to a volume overload (9). However, in contrast to other types of volume-overload cardiac hypertrophy (e.g. those caused by aortocaval fistula or atrioventricular block), in anemia-induced hypertrophy the oxygen carrying capacity and viscosity of the blood decrease. Since these factors may independently influence tissue oxygenation and vascular shear stresses, we consider anemia-induced left ventricular hypertrophy separately from other models of volume-overload cardiac hypertrophy.

Recently, Scheel & Williams (42) demonstrated that maximal coronary conductance per unit weight of myocardium was increased in dogs with anemia-induced cardiac hypertrophy. They found that chronic anemia (hematocrit of 11%) produced modest cardiac hypertrophy (20%). Maximal coronary conductance was increased by about 25–30% in the left anterior descending and circumflex distributions of the left ventricle. In the septum the maximal coronary conductance was increased to a greater extent (50%) than in the other vascular distributions. These investigators also found increased collateral conductance in the left ventricle.

The relationship between the coronary vasculature and the anemia-induced hypertrophied myocardium may also be analyzed within the framework of Figure 1. In this particular model, the growth of the coronary vasculature actually exceeds that of the myocardium, as represented by the box at upper right. This is markedly different than the situation during pressure-overload cardiac hypertrophy (a decrease in the cross-sectional area of the coronary vasculature in proportion to that of the myocardial mass).

Volume-Overload Cardiac Hypertrophy

In the left ventricular capillary bed, volume-overload hypertrophy produces pathological changes. Volume-overload cardiac hypertrophy in the canine was also found to decrease capillary density (23). Also, myocardial infarction is associated with normal arterial pressure but altered end-diastolic pressure and volume; thus, it may be considered volume-overload hypertrophy. Within this context, it was reported that myocardial infarction produced a substantial (30%) increase in myocyte cross-sectional area (2). These investigators found that capillary density of the left ventricle was reduced by 18% and oxygen diffusion distance was increased by 16% during hypertrophy. Thus, inadequate adaptation of the capillary bed in volume-overload hypertrophy may impair vasodilation and increase the susceptibility of the heart to ischemia.

Cardiac hypertrophy resulting from volume-overload (e.g. due to mitral valvular insufficiency, aortocaval shunt, atrioventricular-block, or myocardial infarction) appears to produce varied physiological responses in the coronary vascular system. In dogs with volume-overload left ventricular hypertrophy, minimal coronary resistance per gram of myocardium was not different from that in control animals (15, 23). It is also worth emphasizing that volume-overload hypertrophy in animals is usually rather modest in magnitude (20–30%) and short in duration; thus, coronary vascular abnormalities may not be apparent. In contrast, volume-overload hypertrophy in humans, secondary to valvular insufficiency, can be substantial (60–100%) and is much longer in duration, which may augment its pathological effects on the coronary circulation. In this regard, Doty and colleagues (10) found that volume-overload-induced hypertrophy in man, secondary to atrial-septal defect, was characterized by a decrease in coronary reserve. Also, Hiratzka et al (20) reported that coronary reserve was depressed in humans with volume-induced hypertrophy caused by mitral or aortic valvular insufficiency. These data suggest that mild hypertrophy resulting from volume overload has few adverse effects on the coronary circulation in dogs, whereas in patients with severe volume-overload hypertrophy there are major decrements in coronary flow reserve.

CONCLUSIONS

The factors that determine the adaptation of the coronary vasculature to cardiac hypertrophy are complex. In our opinion, one very important, *known* factor that influences this relationship is the stimulus that provokes the hypertrophy. This factor can influence the adaptation in a benign or pathological manner. Of course, many other factors also influence coronary adaptation to hypertrophy. *Some* of these include the animal species; the age of the animal; the duration of the hypertrophy; the ventricle involved; the rate of progression of the hemodynamic perturbation, e.g. gradual versus sudden onset; and the extent of hypertrophy.

The mechanism(s) of the varied adaptive coronary responses to hypertrophy is unknown. We can speculate that in thyroxine- and anemia-induced hypertrophy an angiogenesis factor is produced and expressed. In pressure-overload cardiac hypertrophy there must be inadequate production (or suppression) of the angiogenesis factor. We hope that research on such a factor will elucidate the mechanisms that govern the adaptation of the coronary vasculature to cardiac hypertrophy.

ACKNOWLEDGMENTS

The author's original studies summarized in this review were supported by the following grants from the US Public Health Service: Program Project grant HL 14388; National Heart, Lung, and Blood Institute grants HL 20827, HL 06496, HL 01570, HL 29271, HL 18629; and Ischemic SCOR grant HL 32295. We also thank Maureen Kent and Ruth Hurlburt for preparation of this article.

Literature Cited

1. Alyono, D., Anderson, R. W., Parish, D. G., Dri, X., Bache, R. J. 1986. Alterations of myocardial blood flow associated with experimental canine left ventricular hypertrophy secondary to valvular aortic stenosis. *Circ. Res.* 58:47–57
2. Anversa, P., Beghi, C., Kikkawa, Y., Olivetti, G. 1986. Myocardial infarction in rats: Infarct size, myocyte hypertrophy, and capillary growth. *Circ. Res.* 58:26–37
3. Aronson, R. S. 1980. Characteristics of action potentials of hypertrophied myocardium from rats with renal hypertension. *Circ. Res.* 47:433–42
4. Bache, R. J., Vrobel, T. R. 1979. Effects of exercise on blood flow in the hypertrophied heart. *Am. J. Cardiol.* 44:1029–38
5. Bache, R. J., Vrobel, T. R., Ring, W. S., Emergy, R. W., Anderson, R. W. 1981. Regional myocardial blood flow during exercise in dogs with chronic left

ventricular hypertrophy. *Circ. Res.* 48: 78–87

6. Breisch, E. A., White, E. C., Nimmo, L., Bloor, C. M. 1985. The interrelationship of coronary vascular structure and flow during pressure overload hypertrophy. *Circulation* 72:76

7. Burger, S. B., Strauer, B. E. 1981. Left ventricular hypertrophy in chronic pressure load due to spontaneous essential hypertension. I. Left ventricular function, left ventricular geometry, wall stress. In *The Heart In Hypertension*, ed. B. E. Strauer, pp. 13–36. Berlin: Springer Verlag. 464 pp.

8. Chilian, W. M., Wangler, R. D., Peters, K. C., Marcus, M. L., Tomanek, R. J. 1985. Thyroxine-induced left ventricular hypertrophy in the rat. Anatomical and physiological evidence for angiogenesis. *Circ. Res.* 57:591–97

9. Datta, B. N., Silver, M. D. 1975. Cardiomegaly in chronic anemia in rats. *Lab. Invest.* 32:503–14

10. Doty, D. B., Wright, C. B., Hiratzka, L. F., Eastham, C. L., Marcus, M. L. 1984. Coronary reserve in volume-induced right ventricular hypertrophy from atrial septal defect. *Am. J. Cardiol.* 54:1059–65

11. Edgren, J., Vonknorring, J., Lindy, S., Turto, H. 1976. Heart volume and myocardial connective tissue during development and regression of thyroxine-induced cardiac hypertrophy in rats. *Acta Physiol. Scand.* 97:514–18

12. Einzig, S., Leonard, J. J., Trip, M. R., Lucas, R. V., Swayze, C. R., Fox, I. 1981. Changes in regional myocardial blood flow and variable development of hypertrophy after aortic banding in puppies. *Cardiovasc. Res.* 15:711–18

13. Folkow, B., Hallback, M., Lundgren, Y., Sivertsson, R., Weiss, L. 1973. Importance of adaptive changes in vascular design for establishment of primary hypertension, studied in man and in spontaneously hypertensive rats. *Circ. Res.* 32 (Suppl. I):2–10

14. Fouad, F. M., Solominski, J. M., Tarazi, R. C., 1984. Left ventricular diastolic function in hypertension: Relation to left ventricular mass and systolic function. *Am. Coll. Cardiol.* 3:1500–6

15. Gascho, J. A., Mueller, T. M., Eastham, C. L., Marcus, M. L. 1982. Effect of volume overload hypertrophy on the coronary circulation in awake dogs. *Cardiovasc. Res.* 16:288–92

16. Goodkind, M. J., Dambach, G. E., Thyrum, P. T., Luchi, R. J. 1974. Effect of thyroxine on ventricular myocardial contractility and ATPase

activity in guinea pigs. *Am. J. Physiol.* 226:66–71

17. Haack, D. W., Schaffer, J. J., Simpson, J. G. 1980. Comparisons of cutaneous microvessels from spontaneously hypertensive, normotensive Wistar-Kyoto and normal Wistar rats. *Proc. Soc. Biol. Med.* 164:453–58

18. Harrison, D. G., Barnes, D. H., Hiratzka, L. F., Eastham, C. E., Kerber, R. E., Marcus, M. L. 1985. The effect of cardiac hypertrophy on the coronary collateral circulation. *Circulation* 71:1135–42

19. Heinrich, H., Hertel, R., Assmann, R. 1978. Structural difference in the mesentery microcirculation between normotensive and spontaneously hypertensive rats. *Pflüg. Arch.* 375:153–59

20. Hiratzka, L. F., Doty, D. D., Eastham, C. L., Marcus, M. L., White, C. W. 1982. Pressure versus volume has different effects on coronary reserve. *Circulation* 66:II–324 (Abstr.)

21. Holtz, J., Restorff, W. V., Bard, P., Bassenge, E. 1977. Transmural distribution of myocardial blood flow and coronary vascular reserve in canine left ventricular hypertrophy. *Basic Res. Cardiol.* 72:286–92

22. Hort, W. 1981. Microscopic pathology of heart muscle and of coronary arterial hypertension. See Ref. 7, pp. 185–91

23. Hultgren, P. E., Bove, A. A. 1981. Myocardial blood flow and mechanisms in volume overload-induced left ventricular hypertrophy. *Cardiovasc. Res.* 15:522–28

24. Inou, T., Koyanagi, S., Harrison, D. G., Harbuzik, D., Eastham, C. L., Marcus, M. L. 1983a. Relative importance of hypertension versus left ventricular hypertrophy on infarct size and sudden cardiac death. *J. Am. Coll. Cardiol.* 1:660 (Abstr.)

25. Kannel, W. B. 1974. Role of blood pressure in cardiovascular morbidity and mortality. *Prog. Cardiovasc. Dis.* 17:5–17

26. Kelley, K. O., Feigl, E. O. 1978. Segmental alpha-receptor-mediated vasoconstriction in the canine coronary circulation. *Circ. Res.* 43:908–17

27. Koyanagi, S., Eastham, C. L., Harrison, D. G., Marcus, M. L. 1982a. Increased size of myocardial infarction in dogs with chronic hypertension and left ventricular hypertrophy. *Circ. Res.* 50:55–62

28. Koyanagi, S., Eastham, C. L., Marcus, M. L. 1982b. Effects of chronic hypertension and left ventricular hypertrophy on the incidence of sudden

cardiac death after coronary artery occlusion in conscious dogs. *Circulation* 65:1192–97

29. Litten, R. Z. III, Martin, B. J., Low, R. B., Alpert, N. R. 1982. Altered myosin isozyme patterns from pressure-overload and thyrotoxic hypertrophied rabbit hearts. *Circ. Res.* 50:856–64

30. Malik, A. B., Abe, T., O'Kane, H., Geha, A. S. 1973. Cardiac function, coronary flow, and oxygen consumption in stable left ventricular hypertrophy. *Am. J. Physiol.* 225:186–91

31. Marcus, M. L. 1983. *The Coronary Circulation in Health and Disease.* New York: McGraw-Hill. 465 pp.

32. Marcus, M. L., Doty, D. B., Hiratzka, L. F., Wright, C. B., Eastham, C. L. 1982. Decreased coronary reserve. A mechanism for angina pectoris in patients with aortic stenosis and normal coronary arteries. *N. Engl. J. Med.* 307:1362–66

33. Meerson, F. Z. 1969. The myocardium in hyperfunction, hypertrophy and heart failure. *Circ. Res.* 25:1–163

34. Mueller, T. M., Marcus, M. L., Kerber, R. E., Young, J. A., Barnes, R. W., Abboud, F. M. 1978. Effect of renal hypertension and left ventricular hypertrophy on the coronary circulation in dogs. *Circ. Res.* 42:543–49

35. O'Keefe, D. D., Hoffman, J. I. E., Cheitlin, R., O'Neill, M. J., Allard, J. R., Shapkin, E. 1978. Coronary blood flow in experimental canine left ventricular hypertrophy. *Circ. Res.* 43:43–51

36. Page, E., McCallister, I. P., 1973. Quantitative description of heart muscle cells. Application to normal, hypertrophied, and thyroxine-stimulated heart. *Am. J. Cardiol.* 31:172–81

37. Peters, K. G., Wangler, R. D., Tomanek, R. J., Marcus, M. L. 1984. Effects of long-term cardiac hypertrophy on coronary vasodilator reserve in SHR rats. *Am. J. Cardiol.* 54:1342–48

38. Prewitt, R. L., Chen, I. I. H., Dowell, R. 1982. Development of microvascular rarefaction in the spontaneously hypertensive rat. *Am. J. Physiol.* 243:H243–51

39. Rakusan, K. 1987. Microcirculation in the stressed heart. In *The Stressed Heart*, ed. M. Legato. Amsterdam: Martinus Nijhoff. In press

40. Rembert, J. C., Kleinman, L. H., Fedor, J. J., Wechsler, A. S., Greenfield, J. C. Jr. 1978. Myocardial blood flow distribution in concentric left ventricular hypertrophy. *J. Clin. Invest.* 62:379–86

41. Scheel, K. W., Eisenstein, B. L., Ingram, L. A. 1984. Coronary, collateral, and perfusion territory responses to aortic banding. *Am. J. Physiol.* 246:H768–75

42. Scheel, K. S., Williams, S. E. 1985. Hypertrophy and coronary collateral vascularity in dogs with severe chronic anemia. *Am. J. Physiol.* 249:H1032–37

43. Spann, J. F. Jr., 1969. Heart failure and ventricular hypertrophy: Altered cardiac contractility and compensatory mechanisms. *Am. J. Cardiol.* 23:504–9

44. Stack, R. S., Rembert, J. C., Schirmer, B., Greenfield, J. C. Jr. 1983. Relation of left ventricular mass to geometry of the proximal coronary arteries in the dog. *Am. J. Cardiol.* 51:1728–31

45. Talifah, K., Briden, K. L., Weiss, H. R. 1983. Thyroxine-induced hypertrophy of the rabbit heart: Effect of regional oxygen extraction, flow, and oxygen consumption. *Circ. Res.* 52:272–77

46. Tarazi, R. C. 1985. The heart in hypertension. *N. Eng. J. Med.* 312:308–90

47. Tomanek, R. J., Palmer, P. J., Pieffer, G. W., Schreiber, K., Eastham, C. L., Marcus, M. L. 1986. Morphometry of canine coronary arteries, arterioles, and capillaries during hypertension and left ventricular hypertrophy. *Circ. Res.* 58:38–46

48. Tomanek, R. J., Wangler, R. D., Bauer, C. A. 1985. Prevention of coronary vasodilator reserve decrement in spontaneously hypertensive rats. *Hypertension* 7:533–40

49. Wangler, R. D., Peters, K. G., Marcus, M. L., Tomanek, R. J. 1982. Effects of duration and severity of arterial hypertension and cardiac hypertrophy on coronary vasodilator reserve. *Circ. Res.* 51:10–18

50. White, F. C., Sanders, M., Peterson, T., Bloor, C. M. 1979. Ischemic myocardial injury after exercise stress in the pressure-overload heart. *Am. J. Pathol.* 97:473–79

51. Wicker, P., Tarazi, R. C., Kobayashi, K. 1983. Coronary blood flow during the development and regression of left ventricular hypertrophy in renovascular hypertensive rats. *Am. J. Cardiol.* 51:1744–49

52. Wusten, B., Buss, D. D., Heist, H., Schaper, W. 1977. Dilatory capacity of the coronary circulation and its correlation to the arterial vasculature in the canine left ventricle. *Basic Res. Cardiol.* 72:636–50

Ann. Rev. Physiol. 1987. 49:489–99

VASCULAR SMOOTH MUSCLE ADAPTATION TO INCREASED LOAD

C. L. Seidel and L. A. Schildmeyer

Departments of Medicine and Physiology, Baylor College of Medicine, Houston, Texas 77030

INTRODUCTION

This review describes the adaptive response of the vascular wall to a chronic increased load, that is, increased transmural pressure. Because it is not clear whether the changes in the vascular wall in various animal models of systemic or pulmonary arterial hypertension are due solely to an increase in transmural pressure, this review concentrates on experimental models in which increased pressure is the primary stimulus. This restriction means that the great majority of experiments discussed were performed on conduit vessels. Currently, there is insufficient evidence to determine whether changes observed in conduit vessels also occur in microvessels. Vascular heterogeneity is well documented; therefore, it would not be surprising to find that microvessels respond differently than conduit vessels. This review covers the following models of increased load: vessel coarctation, venous-to-arterial autologous grafts, and stretched, in vitro preparations of vessel wall or cultured vascular smooth muscle cells. The known morphological, protein, and functional changes correlated with an increase in load are discussed.

We must begin with a description of morphological, protein, and functional changes in normal vascular smooth muscle because they change over the course of development. Any increase in load is applied to this changing base line; therefore, the characteristics of the vascular response to a given load vary with the age of the animal at the time of onset.

489

0066-4278/87/0315-0489$02.00

NORMAL DEVELOPMENT

Morphological Changes

The great majority of work on the normal developmental changes of the vasculature has been performed on the rat aorta. The early descriptive studies of Cliff (12, 13) indicated that during the first 12 weeks after birth (*a*) wall thickness increases due to an increase in the amount of extracellular protein; (*b*) the smooth muscle cell becomes more obliquely oriented; (*c*) the cells become more widely separated because of the increase in extracellular material; and (*d*) they acquire a more irregular outline with a consequent increase in the surface-to-volume ratio. The number of lamella remain the same, but they become thicker. As the rat ages beyond 12 weeks the amount of connective material continues to increase, and the muscle cells increase in size. The increase in extracellular material is faster than the increase in cell size, so the number of cells per unit area decreases.

Quantitative morphological analysis (34) indicates that the doubling of the wall thickness in rats from 1–11 days of age is due to the combined effect of a 1.8-fold increase in muscle cell volume, a 2.6-fold increase in the number of muscle cells, and an 8- and 10-fold increase in the amount of elastic laminae and collagen, respectively. Because the increase in extracellular material is greater than the increase in the number or size of the muscle cells, the actual volume percent of the wall made up of muscle cells decreases. All subcellular components of the muscle cell increase during this time; the greatest increases are in rough and smooth endoplasmic reticulum (2.3- and 2.7-fold, respectively). The increase in rough endoplasmic reticulum is expected because of the increased production of extracellular proteins.

The aortic DNA content per vessel length has been observed to double between 3 and 7 weeks after birth and then decline (3, 8, 31, 39, 43). It is assumed that increases in DNA reflect increases in cell number. If so, this finding extends the morphological observations and suggests that the increase in media thickness that occurs during the first 7 weeks after birth is due in part to an increase in muscle cell number.

The use of DNA content as an indication of cell number assumes that each cell contains the same amount of DNA during development. Bucher et al (8) found this to be true; however, Owens & Schwartz (37) suggested that the percentage of tetraploid cells increases during the development of rat aorta and reaches a peak of approximately 10% of the cells at 12 weeks of age. Using the total DNA measured in vessels from mature animals would cause one to overestimate the true number of cells by approximately this percentage. However, measurements made on vessels from developing animals where polyploidy is small (10%) and changes in DNA content are large (doubled or tripled) indicate an increase in cell number.

To obtain a more accurate estimate of the changes in smooth muscle cell volume with development, Bucher and coworkers (7, 8) measured the volumes of isolated muscle cells from aorta of rats between 3 and 18 weeks of age. The volume doubled (487 to 1070 μm^3) during this time, with the greatest increase occurring during the first seven weeks. Morphometric analysis of arteries less than 250 μm in outer diameter (OD) indicates that smooth muscle cell size increases during development (33, 48, 49), but the number of smooth muscle cells does not.

In summary, the evidence indicates that the smooth muscle cells of large arteries increase in size and number during the early stages of development and that only cell size increases in small arteries. At later stages of development, the muscle cells of only large arteries increase in size. This developmental heterogeneity is important in studying any model of load-induced changes.

Protein Changes

The findings obtained by direct quantitation of the various protein constituents of the vessel wall during development support the morphological observations. The work of many investigators (2, 22, 31, 50, 51) indicates that the absolute amounts of collagen and elastin per rat aorta continue to increase up to the longest time studied (64 weeks of age): however, the amount of these two proteins relative to the dry weight of the vessel (or its total protein content) does not increase with the same time course. The proportion of elastin increases until approximately 5 weeks after birth (22, 31) and then remains constant for as long as 64 weeks, whereas the proportion of collagen continues to increase even at 64 weeks. These changes in connective tissue protein composition appear to depend upon the location along the length of the aorta (31), the sex of the animal (51), the type of vessel examined (15), and the animal species examined (32). Apparently, the net production of collagen and elastin by the smooth muscle cells in a given vessel is not the same during development, and the relative production of these proteins varies among vessels and species.

Gerrity & Cliff (22) observed that in rat aorta the volume percent of myofilaments increased from 5% at birth to a maximum of 20% at 8 weeks of age. Wolinsky observed that the noncollagenous, alkali-soluble protein fraction, which in part represents the contractile proteins, did not change after 10 weeks of age (50, 51). This finding suggests that the net production of contractile proteins increases during the first 10 weeks after birth and then remains constant. To test this possibility directly, we measured the content of actin and myosin in aorta from rats between 3 days and 43 weeks of age (39, 40, 43). We observed that between 4 and 7 weeks of age the net production of actin and myosin is greater than that of total protein, so the percentage of contractile proteins increases from 5% to over 15% of the total protein. At younger and older ages, the production of contractile proteins again parallels that of total protein. At no time during development is the weight ratio of actin to myosin different. When the amount of actomyosin per cell (estimated from DNA content) is determined, it changes over the same time course as actomyosin per total protein: It increases three times between the third and seventh week after birth. Recently, Kocher et al (27) extended these observations. They demonstrated a shift from the nonmuscle beta-actin form to the muscle alpha-actin form during maturation. In addition, the cellular content of tropomyosin, vimentin, and desmin also increases with maturation.

These studies indicate that in the rat aorta during certain periods of development, cell number, cell size, and cellular contractile and intermediate filament protein content increase. It is not known what stimulates this simultaneous increase in cell size and number.

Functional Changes

The maximum contractile response of vessel preparations changes during development. For more extensive reviews of this area, the reader is referred to the work of Duckles & Banner (19). Many investigators have reported that the maximum contractile response of conduit vessels increases during early postnatal life (14, 16, 40) and then either declines (14) or remains unchanged (20) at later ages. In contrast to large vessels, small arteries do not appear to undergo an increase in force-generating ability with development (48); however, additional studies in younger animals are needed to verify this possibility.

The changes in maximum contractile response with development have not been completely explained but are not due to changes in the active length-tension properties of the muscle (14). The increase in maximum response early in development can be explained in part by the increasing proportion of actomyosin; however, the decline in this response observed in older animals cannot be explained by a loss of contractile material (43). Recent work by Kocher et al (27) indicates that aorta from young rats possess more nonmuscle beta-actin, whereas those from older animals posess more muscle alpha-actin. These actin forms may interact differently with myosin which might result in differences in their force generating ability. Also, the magnitude of the change in the maximum response with development depends on the contractile agent (16). This observation suggests that developmental changes in excitation-contraction coupling also occur.

The reduction in maximum contractile response of vessels seen in older animals could be due to a structural reorganization of muscle cells or of contractile filaments within the muscle cell, a change in the chemomechanical transduction process, or a change in the availability of calcium. None of these possibilities have been adequately tested. Cohen & Berkowitz (14) observed that the contractile effect of serotonin and norepinephrine in the absence of extracellular calcium was reduced in aorta from older rats. Since the mechanism of action of these agents is thought to involve the release of intracellular Ca^{2+}, these observations suggest that either the amount stored or the releasability of this Ca^{2+} is reduced during maturation.

Changes in the ED_{50} value for various contractile agents have been observed during development: Large vessels from young animals show higher sensitivity (21, 40).

STRAIN-INDUCED HYPERTROPHY

Increased load is the primary stimulus acting on the vascular smooth muscle cell in hypertrophy modeled by vessel coarctation, venous-to-arterial autologous grafts, and in vitro preparations of stretched vessel wall or isolated vascular smooth muscle cells.

Coarctation

Over the last decade, the Bevans have extensively studied the morphological and contractile responses of vessels on either side of a coarctation of the abdominal aorta in the rabbit (4–6, 25). Within two weeks, arteries above the coarctation, which are therefore exposed to elevated transmural pressure, exhibit an increase in wall thickness, but only large-diameter vessels exhibit an increase in collagen and elastin content (4, 5). Using [³H]thymidine uptake as a measure of DNA turnover and therefore hyperplasia, the Bevans and their colleagues observed that labelling increased, peaking at 2 weeks (5), and then returned to normal by 8 weeks (6). The extent of labelling varied inversely with the vessel caliber: Small arteries (aural, brachial, gastric) and arterioles were labelled more than large arteries (aorta, carotid). This finding suggests that small vessels undergo more hyperplasia than large vessels. The incorporation of [³H]proline and [³H]lysine into connective and non–connective tissue proteins was also elevated at 2 (25) but not at 8 weeks (6). It was suggested that by 8 weeks the wall had completed its adaptation to the elevated transmural pressure. The contractile ability of vessels above the coarctation was also examined (4), and no change in sensitivity (ED_{50}) or maximum contractile response was observed. It was concluded that the wall hypertrophy due to coarctation was due to both hyperplasia and hypertrophy of the smooth muscle cells; however, neither the sensitivity nor the maximum contractile response of the muscle cells was altered.

Olivetti et al (35) determined the morphological changes occurring above an aortic coarctation in 4-week-old rats. Within 8 days, smooth muscle cell hypertrophy occurred, which included an increased net production of both extracellular connective tissue protein and intracellular contractile protein. The increase in contractile protein content kept pace with the increase in smooth muscle cell volume so there was no change in the cytoplasmic volume percent of myofilaments. A similar study by Owens & Reidy (36), however, suggested that the increase in wall thickness was due to smooth muscle hyperplasia and not hypertrophy. The difference between the conclusions from these two studies may be due to the fact that Owens & Reidy: (a) used older rats (20 weeks old), (b) produced a greater degree of coarctation, and (c) placed the constriction between, rather than above, the renal arteries. Such differences in results emphasize that one must be cautious in generalizing the response of the smooth muscle cell to hypertrophic stimuli.

The portal vein in rats and rabbits has also been used as a coarctation model. Johansson (26) and Uvelius et al (46) examined the morphological and mechanical properties of the portion of the rat portal vein exposed to the high pressure induced by coarctation for up to 15 days. Within a week, there was smooth muscle cell hypertrophy and an increase in the wall cross-sectional area made up of connective tissue, but there was no indication of smooth muscle hyperplasia.

As in arteries subjected to the high pressure of coarctation, in the portal vein no change in sensitivity occurred in response to norepinephrine (26). However, the vein lost its spontaneous contractile activity (44, 46), apparently because of an increase in the resting membrane potential (44).

Unlike arteries subjected to the high pressure of coarctation (4), after 15 days the portal vein exhibited a decrease in maximum active stress (26). After only five days of coarctation, the cell cross-sectional area doubled, but the force per cell area decreased by 40%. This result suggests that the increase in muscle cell area was not accompanied by an equal increase in contractile protein content. This response is different than that observed in arteries of coarctation (4, 35). The increase in pressure is greater in aortic coarctation (26 mm Hg; 4) than it is in portal vein coarctation (7 mm Hg; 26); however, the percent increase in pressure is similar (80 and 100%, respectively). This may suggest that venous and arterial tissue respond differently to an elevation in transmural pressure.

Berner et al (1) produced portal vein hypertrophy in rabbits by coarctation and at two weeks observed an increase in wall thickness and smooth muscle cell cross-sectional area, as had been observed in rat portal veins. However, it was observed that the number of thin and intermediate filaments increased in the hypertrophied cells, but the number of thick filaments did not. This resulted in a significant increase in the thin-to-thick filament ratio, which may contribute to the reduced force-generating ability of the hypertrophied portal vein smooth muscle cell (26). These data also suggest that the net production of actin, intermediate filament protein, and myosin need not change similarly during vascular smooth muscle hypertrophy and that changes in the net production of thin and intermediate filament proteins can occur within two weeks after an increase in pressure.

Venous-to-Arterial Autologous Grafts

We have studied the changes in contractility and protein composition of the intact saphenous vein when it is grafted into the femoral artery (42). Such grafts are subjected to the elevated pressure, shear stress, and P_{O_2} of the arterial circulation, as well as to the physical handling and ischemia associated with the surgical procedure. Because the changes in protein composition that occur in the graft are similar to those that occur in models in which elevated pressure acts directly on smooth muscle cells (see next section), it is likely that elevated strain is responsible for some of the observed changes. Within one week, there is a significant increase in the absolute amount of total protein, which is due to the accumulation of protein other than collagen, actin, or myosin. At one month, the wall thickness and absolute amount of collagen are significantly elevated and continue to increase up to two months after grafting. The content of actin and myosin becomes significantly elevated 8 weeks after grafting. At all times the actin-to-myosin weight ratio is unchanged, contrary to predictions based on morphological studies of hypertrophied rabbit portal veins (1).

The maximum contractile response of grafted saphenous veins is decreased when expressed relative to wall cross-sectional area or myosin content, which suggests that the force-generating ability of myosin may be compromised. This reduction in force-generating ability was observed 1 week after grafting and was maintained throughout the 8 weeks that the grafts were examined. The cause of this decrease is unknown, but it may involve structural reorganization of the contractile system, a change in the force-generating ability of the contractile proteins, or a change in excitation-contraction coupling. As pointed out above, the coarcted portal vein also underwent a decrease in maximum force generation (26), whereas arteries showed no change in this parameter (4).

Stretched In Vitro Preparations

To obtain more direct information about the effect of increased load on smooth muscle cells, in vitro preparations have been used. Hume (24) mounted rabbit ear artery segments on adjustable, spring-loaded frames and incubated these preparations in a sterile culture medium for up to 9 days. An increase in uptake of [^{3}H]thymidine or [^{3}H]proline was first observed 5 days after the application of a step increase in strain, and the magnitude of increase was directly related to the amount of applied strain.

Leung et al (29, 30) performed similar uptake experiments using cultured rabbit aortic smooth muscle cells grown on elastin membranes and subjected to rhythmic strain. The muscle cells were derived from aortic explants and had been passed once before being seeded onto the elastin membrane. The membrane was stretched 10% of its initial length at a rate of 52 times/min. Such conditions mimic the changes in aortic wall dimension produced by the pulse pressure (18). After 8 hr of rhythmic strain, the incorporation of proline into both total protein and collagen increased. Strain did not increase the incorporation of thymidine or the total DNA content, which suggests that hyperplasia did not occur during the period studied (52 hr). In a similar preparation, Sottiurai et al (45) observed that rhythmic stretching increased the number of rough endoplasmic reticulum profiles and retarded the loss of myofilaments that normally occurs in stationary cultures. Recently we performed similar studies using primary cultures of venous smooth muscle cells grown on a polyurethane membrane and subjected to a rhythmic strain comparable to that experienced under arterial conditions (41). These studies indicated that after three days of strain, the total protein content of the cells increased, but the actin and myosin content was unchanged. These data suggest that an elevation of strain first induces an increase in the net production of non–contractile protein and that this increase may occur more rapidly if the strain is rhythmic rather than stepwise (24). If the strain is applied for a sufficient length of time (days), smooth muscle hyperplasia may occur.

Several investigators (9, 10, 17, 41) have observed that when isolated vascular smooth muscle cells are subjected to rhythmic strain, they orient themselves so that their long axis is at a 45–90° angle relative to the direction of the strain. Such an orientation occurs within 24 hr (41) and therefore represents movement of the cell rather than orientation of its progeny. With the short axis of the cell oriented toward the direction of strain, the strain on each cell is minimized. It is not known if such reorientation occurs in vivo in response to an abnormal increase in strain, but Cliff (12) observed that aortic smooth muscle cells become more obliquely arranged during development at a time when arterial pressure increases. If such reorientation occurs during an increase in load, it could contribute to apparent reductions in force development (26, 42, 46), if force is measured circumferentially.

The fact that the pulse pressure induces a circumferential wall strain seems to indicate that a helical rather than a circular orientation of muscle cells would be favored in vivo: However, measurements of cell angle (47) in vivo indicate a circular cell orientation in vessels of widely different diameters. The reason why cells orient differently in vitro and in vivo in response to strain is unknown, but it may involve the dissipation of strain by the connective tissue to which the smooth muscle cells are tethered in vivo and/or the effect of longitudinal strain in vivo.

Mechanism of Load-Induced Adaptations

The mechanism by which an increase in load induces changes in vascular smooth muscle cells has not been studied. An increase in net protein production can be induced by an increase in load on isolated cells that are not undergoing active tension development (29, 30, 41). Thus the contraction of the muscle cell against an increased load is not a necessary stimulus. An obvious stimulus is the direct effect of elevated strain on the permeability properties of the smooth muscle cell membrane. Changes in ion flux, particularly of Na^+, have been shown to stimulate protein production in other cell types (28). Also, since the thin filaments are inserted into the cell membrane of smooth muscle cells, deformation of the membrane could be transmitted to the interior of the cell via these filaments. Finally, the proliferation rate and protein synthetic activity of the smooth muscle cell are influenced by other cells within the vascular wall, especially the endothelial cells (11). In vivo increases in load would also affect the function of non-smooth muscle cells (23, 38), which might influence smooth muscle cells.

CONCLUSIONS

Observations to date indicate that an increase in rhythmically applied load stimulates an increase in net protein production within hours. It is not clear which proteins are involved, but preliminary studies indicate that the net production of connective tissue proteins increases before that of contractile proteins and that the amounts of specific proteins within these general classes can change independently. An increase in protein production is associated with a concomitant increase in the cellular content of the protein synthetic machinery (rough endoplasmic reticulum, golgi, mitochondria) and cellular hypertrophy. Whether longer periods of elevated strain induce cellular hyperplasia is unclear. During the hypertrophic response the maximum contractile ability of the arterial tissue is unaltered; however, in venous tissue the maximum force relative to the cross-sectional area or the myosin content of the cell is reduced. Other intervessel differences exist, which suggests that the vascular response to increased load is heterogeneous. In addition to intervessel heterogeneity, the developmental variability alluded to in the introduction must also be taken into consideration when interpreting and designing studies on the effect of increased load.

Acknowledgments

We would like to express our appreciation to Dr. Julius Allen for his helpful criticisms and Ms. Rainy Lane-Greenleaf for preparation of the manuscript. This work was supported by NIH grants HL 23815 and HL 34280.

Literature Cited

1. Berner, P. F., Somlyo, A. V., Somlyo, A. P. 1981. Hypertrophy-induced increase of intermediate filaments in vascular smooth muscle. *J. Cell Biol.* 88:96–101

2. Berry, C. L., Greenwald, S. E. 1976. Effects of hypertension on the static mechanical properties and chemical composition of the rat aorta. *Cardiovasc. Res.* 10:437–51

3. Berry, C. L., Looker, T., Germain, J. 1972. The growth and development of the rat aorta. *J. Anat.* 113:17–34

4. Bevan, J. A., Bevan, R. D., Chang, P. C., Pegram, B. L., Purdy, R. E., Su, C. 1975. Analysis of changes in reactivity of rabbit arteries and veins two weeks after induction of hypertension by coarctation of the abdominal aorta. *Circ. Res.* 37:183–90

5. Bevan, R. D. 1976. An autoradiographic and pathological study of cellular proliferation in rabbit arteries correlated with an increase in arterial pressure. *Blood Vessels* 13:100–28

6. Bevan, R. D., Eggena, P., Hume, W. R., Van Marthens, E., Bevan, J. A. 1980. Transient and persistent changes in rabbit blood vessels associated with maintained elevation in arterial pressure. *Hypertension* 2:63–72

7. Bucher, B., Travo, P., Laurent, P., Stoclet, J. C. 1982. Vascular smooth muscle cell hypertrophy during maturation in rat thoracic aorta. *Cell. Biol. Int. Rep.* 6:883–92

8. Bucher, B., Travo, P., Stoclet, J. C. 1984. Smooth musle cell hypertrophy and hyperplasia in the thoracic aorta of spontaneously hypertensive rats. *Cell. Biol. Int. Rep.* 8:567–77

9. Buck, R. C. 1983. Reorientation response of cells to repeated stretch and recoil of the substratum. *Exp. Cell. Res.* 127:470–74

10. Buck, R. C. 1983. Behavior of vascular smooth muscle cells during repeated stretching of the substratum in vitro. *Atherosclerosis* 46:217–23

11. Chamley-Campbell, J. H., Campbell, G. R. 1981. What controls smooth muscle phenotype? *Atherosclerosis* 40:347–57

12. Cliff, W. J. 1967. The aortic tunica media in growing rats studied with the electron microscope. *Lab. Invest.* 17:599–615

13. Cliff, W. J. 1970. The aortic tunica media in aging rats. *Exp. Mol. Pathol.* 13:172–89

14. Cohen, M. L., Berkowitz, B. A. 1976. Vascular contraction: Effect of age and extracellular calcium. *Blood Vessels* 13:139–54

15. Cox, R. H. 1977. Effects of age on the mechanical properties of rat carotid artery. *Am. J. Physiol.* 233:H256–63

16. Cox, R. H., Jones, A. W., Swain, M. L. 1976. Mechanics and electrolyte composition of arterial smooth muscle in developing dogs. *Am. J. Physiol.* 231:77–83

17. Dartsch, P. C., Hammerle, H., Betz, E. 1986. Orientation of cultured arterial smooth muscle cells growing on cyclically stretched substrates. *Acta Anat.* 125:108–13

18. Dobrin, P. B. 1978. Mechanical properties of arteries. *Physiol. Rev.* 58:397–460

19. Duckles, S. P., Banner, W. 1984. Changes in vascular smooth muscle reactivity during development. *Ann. Rev. Pharmacol. Toxicol.* 24:65–83

20. Duckles, S. P., Carter, B. J., Williams, C. L. 1985. Vascular adrenergic neuroeffector function does not decline in aged rats. *Circ. Res.* 56:109–16

21. Gray, S. D. 1977. Reactivity of neonatal canine aortic strips. *Biol. Neonate* 31:10–14

22. Gerrity, R. G., Cliff, W. J. 1975. The aortic tunica media of the developing rat. *Lab. Invest.* 32:585–600

23. Grega, G. J., Adamski, S. W., Dobbins, D. E. 1986. Physiological and pharmacological evidence for the regulation of permeability. *Fed. Proc.* 45:96–100

24. Hume, W. R. 1980. Proline and thymidine uptake in rabbit ear artery segments in vitro increased by chronic tangential load. *Hypertension* 2:738–43

25. Hume, W. R., Bevan, J. A. 1978. Amino acid uptake in rabbit blood vessels two weeks after induction of hypertension by coarctation of the abdominal aorta. *Cardiovasc. Res.* 12:106–14

26. Johansson, B. 1976. Structural and functional changes in rat portal veins after experimental portal hypertension. *Acta Physiol. Scand.* 98:381–83

27. Kocher, O., Skalli, O., Cerutti, D., Gabbiani, F., Gabbiani, G. 1985. Cytoskeletal features of rat aortic cells during development. *Circ. Res.* 46:829–38

28. Leffert, H. L., Koch, K. S. 1985. Growth regulation by sodium ion influxes. In *Control of Animal Cell Pro-*

liferation, 1:367–413. New York: Academic

29. Leung, D. Y. M., Glagov, S., Mathews, M. B. 1976. Cyclic stretching stimulates synthesis of matrix components by arterial smooth muscle cells in vitro. *Science* 191:474–77

30. Leung, D. Y. M., Glagov, S., Mathews, M. B. 1977. A new in vitro system for studying cell response to mechanical stimulation. *Exp. Cell Res.* 109:285–98

31. Looker, T., Berry, C. L. 1972. The growth and development of the rat aorta. *J. Anat.* 113:17–34

32. McCloskey, E. I., Cleary, E. G. 1974. Chemical composition of the rabbit aorta during development. *Circ. Res.* 34:828–35

33. Miller, B. G., Overhage, J. M., Bohlen, H. G., Evan, A. P. 1985. Hypertrophy of arteriolar smooth muscle cells in the rat small intestine during maturation. *Microvasc. Res.* 29:56–69

34. Olivetti, G., Anversa, P., Melissari, M., Loud, A. V. 1980. Morphometric study of early postnatal development of the thoracic aorta in the rat. *Circ. Res.* 47:417–24

35. Olivetti, G., Anversa, P., Melissari, M., Loud, A. V. 1980. Morphometery of medial hypertrophy in the rat thoracic aorta. *Lab. Invest.* 42:559–65

36. Owens, G. K., Reidy, M. A. 1985. Hyperplastic growth response of vascular smooth muscle cells following induction of acute hypertension in rats by aortic coarctation. *Circ. Res.* 57:695–705

37. Owens, G. K., Schwartz, S. M. 1983. Vascular smooth muscle cell hypertrophy and hyperploidy in the Goldblatt hypertensive rat. *Circ. Res.* 53:491–501

38. Schwartz, S. 1984. Hypertension as a vascular response to injury. *Hypertension* (Suppl. III) 6:III33–III37

39. Seidel, C. L. 1979. Aortic actomyosin content of maturing normal and spontaneously hypertensive rats. *Am. J. Physiol.* 237:H34–H39

40. Seidel, C. L., Allen, J. C. 1979. Pharmacologic characteristics and acto-

myosin content of aorta from neonatal rats. *Am. J. Physiol.* 237:C81–C86

41. Seidel, C. L., Ives, B. V., Eskin, S. L. 1984. The effect of strain on vascular muscle cells in culture. *Physiologist* 27:236 (Abstr.)

42. Seidel, C. L., Lewis, R. M., Bowers, R., Bukoski, R. D., Kim, H. S., et al. 1984. Adaptation of canine saphenous veins to grafting. *Circ. Res.* 55:102–9

43. Seidel, C. L., Murphy, R. A. 1979. Changes in rat aortic actomyosin content with maturation. *Blood Vessels* 16:98–108

44. Sigurdsson, S. B., Uvelius, B. 1983. Membrane potential in smooth muscle cells from hypertrophic rat portal vein. *Experientia* 39:1288–90

45. Sottiurai, V. S., Kollros, P., Glagov, S., Zarins, C. K., Mathews, M. B. 1983. Morphologic alteration of cultured arterial smooth muscle cells by cyclic stretching. *J. Surg. Res.* 35:490–97

46. Uvelius, B., Arner, A., Johansson, B. 1971. Hypertrophic venous smooth muscle. *Acta Physiol. Scand.* 112:463–71

47. Walmsley, J. G., Owen, M. P., Bevan, J. A. 1983. Medial morphometry and mechanics of sequential rabbit ear arteries and myograph ring segments. *Am. J. Physiol.* 245:H840–48

48. Warshaw, D. M., Mulvany, M. J., Halpern, W. 1979. Mechanical and morphological properties of arterial resistance vessels in young and old spontaneously hypertensive rats. *Circ. Res.* 45:250–59

49. Warshaw, D. M., Root, D. T., Halpern, W. 1980. Effects of antihypertensive drug therapy on the morphology and mechanics of resistance in arteries from spontaneously hypertensive rats. *Blood Vessels* 17:257–70

50. Wolinsky, H. 1970. Response of the rat aortic wall to hypertension. *Circ. Res.* 26:507–22

51. Wolinsky, H. 1971. Effects of hypertension and its reversal on the thoracic aorta of male and female rats. *Circ. Res.* 28:622–37

Ann. Rev. Physiol. 1987. 49:501–18

CARDIOCYTE ADAPTATION TO CHRONICALLY ALTERED LOAD[1]

George Cooper, IV

Cardiology Section of the Department of Medicine and the Department of Physiology, Gazes Cardiac Research Institute, Medical University of South Carolina; Veterans Administration Medical Center, Charleston, South Carolina 29425

INTRODUCTION

The long-standing multidisciplinary interest in myocardial hypertrophy recently has evolved from a description of specific forms of this entity to a more general consideration of the basic mechanisms by which the entire potential spectrum of cardiac loading conditions regulates the biology both of the myocardium and of the constituent striated muscle cell of this tissue, the cardiocyte. This is not to suggest that the understanding of hypertrophied myocardium is now complete. Although there have been significant recent refinements in the pathophysiologically relevant models of cardiac hypertrophy, the most important work in this area, which may lead to a clearer understanding of the bases for the transition from compensated cardiac hypertrophy to decompensated cardiac failure, remains to be done. Nonetheless, other recent work having a broader scope is clarifying the relative importance of loading conditions and other potential regulatory factors to the control of myocardial biology. A natural outgrowth of this investigative interest would be the elucidation of the mechanisms controlling growth and differentiation in both neonatal and adult mammalian myocardium. The expectation that such an approach may allow the basis for cardiocyte adaptation to chronically altered loads to be understood at the molecular level is one of the most exciting prospects in cardiovascular physiology.

501

CARDIAC OVERLOADING

It is now clear that overloaded, hypertrophied myocardium is not inherently abnormal. Rather, the functional consequences of cardiac overloading are the combined result of the type, degree, and duration of overloading, the identity of the affected chamber, and the compensatory mechanisms available to the species.

Pressure Overloading

RIGHT VENTRICLE   For the right ventricle of mammals exposed to an abrupt fixed pressure overload, the preponderance of data (8, 30, 51, 52, 54, 63, 95, 137) indicates that contractile performance per unit mass of hypertrophied myocardium is compromised even before the onset of overt pump failure of the ventricle as a whole (30, 35). When the pressure overload is severe, increased cardiac mass is no longer able to maintain normal ventricular pump function, and contractile performance both of the right ventricle as a whole and of each unit mass of this hypertrophied myocardium is reduced (139). Early studies where this result was not obtained usually involved only modest degrees of hypertrophy (44, 108).

One study (158), although flawed by the use of experimental groups with quite variable degrees of right ventricular hypertrophy and by the use of large superfused papillary muscle preparations in which metabolic support by diffusion was questionable, suggested that the contractile defect might be the result of transient acute injury produced by the abrupt fixed pressure overload and that hypertrophied right ventricular myocardium contracts normally after recovery from this early injury phase. A possible morphological basis for this injury phase was suggested by a study of severely after-loaded right ventricular myocardium (12). Both because any transient injury might contribute to the contractile defects described for the right ventricle hypertrophying in response to an abrupt, fixed pressure overload, and more importantly because this type of after-load increase does not mimic the great majority of clinical pathophysiology, chronic, progressive pressure overload of the cat right ventricle was studied (35). Despite the absence of early injury, a progressive decrement was found in contractile performance per unit mass of isolated cardiac muscle, even while normal ventricular function was maintained. Thus it seems that contractile dysfunction is an intrinsic property of substantial right ventricular pressure-overload hypertrophy.

The question of whether this contractile dysfunction is the result of irreversible changes has been addressed by removing the pressure overload after cardiac hypertrophy has been established. Both for an abrupt, fixed pressure overload and for a chronic, progressive pressure overload of the cat right ventricle, a full return to normal cardiac structure and function follows the restoration of a normal after-load (27, 31). However, after the hypertrophy process has progressed to overt heart failure, cardiac normality can no longer be restored (36). Indeed, a severe, acute after-load increase produces largely irreversible hypertrophy, even before the appearance of heart failure (160).

LEFT VENTRICLE   For the left ventricle of larger mammals exposed to a moderate, abrupt pressure overload, the data generally indicate that ventricular contractile performance is not compromised (121, 122, 127). However, one report shows that contractile performance measured in a segment of the in situ dog left ventricle is depressed with more pronounced pressure overloading and hypertrophy (98). Similarly, a chronic, progressive pressure overload of the dog left ventricle that produced moderate hypertrophy did not result in ventricular dysfunction (18). When the pig left ventricle was subjected to a chronic, progressive pressure overload that produced quite substantial myocardial hypertrophy, normal contractile performance was maintained, except in those animals in which left ventricular mass had more than doubled (159). These studies did not allow the assessment of contractile performance per unit mass of isolated muscle segments removed from pressure-hypertrophied left ventricles under well-defined in vitro conditions, as had most of the studies of pressure-hypertrophied right ventricles, so definite information about intrinsic muscle function as opposed to ventricular pump function is lacking. It nevertheless appears that the left ventricle is better able to tolerate a pressure overload without decremental contractile performance than is the right ventricle.

These contrasting responses of the right and left ventricles to pressure overloading may be related to the fact that the coronary vasculature is usually included in the hypertensive circuit in the left ventricular pressure-overload models, so ventricular wall stress and coronary perfusion pressure increase together. In contrast it is excluded in the right ventricular models, so ventricular wall stress increases, but coronary perfusion pressure does not. However, this potentially favorable situation with respect to myocardial perfusion in the left ventricular models probably does not entirely account for the contractile abnormalities being largely confined to the right ventricular models. Abnormal coronary blood flow is described in hypertensive left ventricular hypertrophy, both when the pressure overload includes (1, 5, 90, 117) and excludes (14) the coronary arteries, while coronary blood flow is normal in hypertensive right ventricular hypertrophy (81, 92), unless marked hypertrophy is combined with a severe acute hemodynamic stress (93) to elicit a transient perfusion defect. The contrasting right and left ventricular responses to pressure overloading may also be related to the very different normal anatomy and function of these two chambers in the adult. The right ventricle operates as a thin-walled volume pump, and the left ventricle acts as a thick-walled pressure pump. Thus a pressure overload constitutes a qualitative change in loading conditions for the right ventricle as opposed to a quantitative change in loading conditions for the left ventricle. Given these differences in anatomy and function before the imposition of a pressure overload, it may well be that the left ventricle is able to accommodate a greater degree of hypertrophy induced by a pressure overload than is the right ventricle before the onset of dysfunction.

For the left ventricle of rats subjected to a pressure overload, most early studies suggested that contractile function is well maintained initially (48, 65). A number of more recent studies, with two exceptions (1, 11), tend to support this view. However, while the rat left ventricle accommodates a sustained pressure overload without a significant early deterioration of contractile performance, there is evidence for an eventual functional deterioration (112, 113), and a longitudinal study of the left ventricle of the spontaneously hypertensive rat has demonstrated increased stiffness and decreased contractile function as these animals reach senescence (88).

As discussed in a recent review (141), in gradual pressure overload of the rat left ventricle (17) and in pressure overload of the rabbit left or right ventricle (3, 103), the major change in contractile function is an increase in twitch duration, and there is little if any effect on either external work or active tension generation per unit mass of myocardium. However, the speed of contraction is normal in very young rats under conditions of chronic, progressive pressure-overload hypertrophy of the right ventricle (61). Given that a hallmark of rat and rabbit ventricular hypertrophy is a reduced speed of cardiac contraction, it is of interest that in these animals this variable is subject to major modification through the genetic expression of different isoenzymic forms of a catalytic protein that regulates the kinetics of muscle cross-bridge activity. The initial demonstration of this genetic plasticity of myosin ATPase isoforms during rat cardiac hypertrophy (75) has since been confirmed by a number of workers (141). In the rat and rabbit, cardiac pressure overload in the adult results in a shift toward a greater proportion of the slower, V_3 isoform of this enzyme. This isoenzymic shift correlates well with the reduced rate of time-dependent events, measured either as cardiac mechanics or cardiac energetics. This change has been viewed as a favorable, compensatory response to a pressure overload (3, 74).

At present, this elegant and satisfying correlation unfortunately appears to be confined to the rat and rabbit (34). In the cat (160), the ferret (52), the pig (159), and the human (85), the cardiac myosin ATPase isoenzyme present in the normal adult consists primarily of the V_3 isoform. In these species an isoenzymic shift does not occur in response to a pressure overload of the heart. This seems to preclude the possibility that compensation for a cardiac pressure overload can occur in a number of mammalian species, including humans, through the mechanism of an isoenzymic shift of myosin ATPase isoforms and activity.

Volume Overloading

RIGHT VENTRICLE   Careful longitudinal analysis of clinical data shows that a pure right ventricular volume overload of substantial degree is well tolerated for decades, whereas a volume overload upon which a pressure overload is superimposed is poorly tolerated (72). Right ventricular function remains normal in the former instance, but irreversible abnormalities of right ventricular function develop in the latter instance. It is therefore not surprising that normal contractile function has been found in papillary muscles excised from the right ventricles of cats subjected to a chronic atrial septal defect (29). This study found normal myocardial contractile function under hypertrophy conditions comparable in degree and duration to those employed in previous studies (30, 35) of the cat right ventricle, in which a pressure overload from pulmonary artery banding was responsible for distinctly abnormal contractile behavior. Structural analysis of these two models showed that the volume density of cardiocytes from pressure-overloaded myocardium was decreased significantly from that observed in volume-overloaded myocardium, with a proportional increase in connective tissue (83). This finding provides a structural basis for at least some of the contractile abnormalities observed in pressure- but not volume-overload hypertrophy of the right ventricle. In any case, the nature of the inducing stress rather than the hypertrophy process itself is clearly responsible for the abnormalities observed in the pressure-overloaded cat right ventricle.

LEFT VENTRICLE   Studies employing various circulatory fistulae to produce left ventricular volume overloads (9, 59, 143), or studies employing heart block for this purpose (96, 151), have generally demonstrated normal contractile function, even in the face of developing heart failure. However, more systematic studies (97, 99) have demonstrated depressed left ventricular function following a chronic arteriovenous fistula which had resulted in heart failure; the contractile defect did not resolve when the fistula was closed. A possible basis for such myocardial damage was suggested by a study (6) showing that subendocardial blood flow is compromised during hemodynamic stress in the presence of such a fistula.

In left ventricular volume overloads of more significant clinical import than those just discussed, it has been found (144) that experimental aortic regurgitation does not produce myocardial dysfunction until the lesion has been present for some time. However, it has been shown (161) that hemodynamically important aortic regurgitation constitutes both a pressure overload and a volume overload of the left ventricle, whereas mitral regurgitation of a similar degree appears to be a relatively pure volume overload. Although left ventricular dysfunction may be present with either lesion, favorable loading conditions may mask such dysfunction with mitral regurgitation if ejection phase indices of ventricular function are the sole measurement employed. An intriguing preliminary report (68) shows that in an experimental model of mitral regurgitation, a decrement in the ratio of end systolic pressure to left ventricular volume may indicate declining ventricular function in the presence of a normal left ventricular ejection fraction. Since surgical correction of aortic regurgitation immediately reduces left ventricular wall stress, whereas correction of mitral regurgitation has the obverse effect, this finding may have considerable practical import.

Decompensation of Hypertrophied Myocardium

The quest for the basic etiology of cardiac dysfunction and eventual failure has been quite extensive, but as has been noted in recent reviews (49, 157), no single answer has been forthcoming. Given the amount of effort already devoted to this subject, it now appears unlikely that a single, central etiology will ever be identified. Cardiac contributions to this syndrome may arise both from primary defects of the cardiocyte and from myocardial defects extrinsic to the muscle cell.

CARDIOCYTE DEFECTS   Observed changes in excitation-contraction coupling, which translate most importantly into changes in calcium metabolism, have focused attention on the electrophysiology of hypertrophied myocardium. Prolongation of the action potential is the most obvious electrophysiological change in hypertrophied myocardium (4, 8, 50, 56, 150). Such a change may be compensatory in the sense of providing an increased level of activation for contraction, but there is the potential liability of impaired cardiac relaxation via myoplasmic calcium overload, although this has not been demonstrated directly (116). In addition, it has been suggested that cardiocyte enlargement, through a decrease in the surface-to-volume ratio of the cell, leads to a decrease in the proportion of electrically effective cell surface for calcium entry per unit cell volume (63), and there are further data to support this point (66). Biochemical studies of calcium metabolism in hypertrophied myocardium have led to the conclusion that there is a primary defect in calcium uptake by the sarcoplasmic reticulum (136), with a compensatory increase in calcium sequestration by the mitochondria (30), that correlates with increased contraction duration (119). Direct measurements of the calcium transient in hypertrophied myocardium (52) have shown a relationship between prolongations both of this transient and of twitch contractions.

Largely because catecholamines are a major endogenous regulator of inotropic state, changes in β-adrenoceptor function in hypertrophied and failing myocardium are of interest. Decreased norepinephrine stores in failing hearts have been found in humans (20) and experimental animals (21, 138). An increased plasma catecholamine concentration and a decreased number and responsiveness of β-adrenoceptors in peripheral lymphocytes have also been found during clinical heart failure (146), and similar findings have been reported for failed myocardium itself (15). These changes may be the result either of β-adrenoceptor "down regulation" in response to high levels of circulating catecholamines (157) or of altered coupling of activated cardiac β-adrenoceptors to cyclic AMP generation (25). However, these changes in β-adrenoceptor function appear more likely to be the effect rather than the cause of heart failure: During pressure overload hypertrophy (73) and early heart failure (62), cardiac β-adrenoceptor density is actually increased.

Because of the direct relationship between myocardial energetics and function, early reports that energy production (123) and utilization (2) are abnormal in failing myocardium generated interest in a potential energetic basis for the transition from cardiac hypertrophy to cardiac failure. In hypertrophied myocardium in the absence of failure, energy production via phosphorylating mitochondrial respiration is normal (29, 30). The rate of energy utilization was abnormally increased in some studies of acute pressure-overload hypertrophy (30, 51), but in other such studies (3, 128) there was decreased myosin ATPase activity, which was associated with a decreased net energy utilization. A similar decrement in the rate of energy utilization was found for a model of chronic, progressive pressure overload (35). As noted above, decreases in myofibrillar or myosin ATPase activity have been related in some species to an isoenzymic shift to the V_3 ATPase isoform (75). This adaptation can be viewed as favorably shifting the myothermal economy of hypertrophied myocardium (3, 141) rather than as leading to cardiac failure. Furthermore, in many species such a change in myosin isoenzymes does not occur during hypertrophy. Thus, no definite contribution of abnormal energetics to the decompensation of hypertrophied myocardium has been uncovered.

MYOCARDIAL DEFECTS   The increased cardiac mass and work load that accompany hypertrophy, together with findings indicating that the growth of the coronary vasculature may not be commensurate with that of the hypertrophying myocardium (5, 76, 90, 104), have prompted the thought that coronary blood flow may be deficient in hypertrophied myocardium. In experimental left ventricular pressure overload causing substantial hypertrophy, myocardial blood flow is usually normal at rest but is abnormal during hemodynamic stress, especially in the subendocardial layer (5, 14, 109, 117, 156). This also holds true for pressure overload of the right ventricle (81, 93), volume overload of either ventricle (6), and clinical left ventricular pressure overload (82, 114, 140). Over time, such episodic underperfusion could lead to myocardial damage. (See the review by Marcus & Chilian in this section for a complete account of changes in the coronary circulation associated with ventricular hypertrophy.)

In view of the abnormal cardiac systolic function seen when diastolic stiffness is increased, as in angina pectoris (80), alterations in muscle and chamber compliance during cardiac hypertrophy have been investigated as a potential source of decreased contractile function (49). Myocardial stiffness is usually normal in experimental volume-overload hypertrophy and is usually increased in experimental pressure-overload hypertrophy (87). Such increased stiffness may be based on increases both in cardiocyte size (86, 124) and in interstitial connective tissue (39, 145). However, increased connective tissue is the only one of these two structural changes found in pressure-overload hypertrophy but not in volume-overload hypertrophy (83). The possibility that such fibrosis and abnormal compliance are an artifact of acute pressure overloading (12) seems to be obviated by the finding of interstitial fibrosis (35, 145) and increased myocardial stiffness (88) in models of chronic, progressive pressure overloading, although myocardial stiffness is normal when such a pressure overload produces only a modest degree of hypertrophy (127). While increased myocardial stiffness is not usually observed in clinical situations unless the hemodynamic overload is severe (58, 87), such changes may then contribute to abnormal contractile function (49).

CARDIAC UNDERLOADING

The major impetus for the study of cardiac underloading has been the hypothesis that the alterations seen during cardiac hypertrophy are only rather restricted examples of a more generalized phenomenon of cardiac load regulation that is important both for cardiac growth and development and for the maintenance of cardiac normality in the adult. In this view, adult myocardium is not static but instead is a dynamic tissue whose characteristics are defined continuously by a narrow normal range of hemodynamic forces within a broad potential spectrum including both excessive and reduced loads. A particular advantage of using underloading to study cardiac load regulation was that it proved possible to generate a model (32) in which the load on a segment of ventricular myocardium could be reduced without altering the blood supply, innervation, or frequency of contraction of that segment and without significantly altering the hemodynamics either of the ventricle of which the segment comprises a part or of the organism as a whole. This rather straightforward in vivo reduction in cardiac load was achieved by transection of the chordae tendinae of a single right ventricular papillary muscle.

In a series of studies of this model (33, 64, 147, 149), the changes in cardiac structure, function, and biochemistry that resulted from this load reduction were defined at specified times after chordal transection. Structurally, it was found that the cardiocyte is critically dependent on a normal load. Unloading results in rapid and marked cellular dedifferentiation that exceeds that observed in skeletal muscle following either disuse or denervation. Functionally, the major changes were decreased strength and rapidity of contraction and increased passive stiffness. This finding has since been confirmed independently in a different model of cardiac unloading (78). Biochemically, the loss of differentiated cardiocyte properties was not limited to, but was most pronounced in the contractile proteins. Each of these changes was fully reversible when the papillary muscle was reloaded during a second operation. Thus, when load is varied without associated variations in other factors, the removal of load results in prompt cardiocyte dedifferentiation and atrophy, and the reimposition of load leads to equally prompt cardiocyte growth and redifferentiation.

CARDIAC LOAD REGULATION

Myocardium

The view that increased load itself may be a sufficient or even the primary factor responsible for cardiac hypertrophy following hemodynamic overloads is suggested by three lines of evidence. First, increases in the length of isolated, denervated cardiac tissue immediately cause increased protein synthesis (111), and this stimulatory effect has been dissociated from other potential contributors to this process (67). Second, either during β-adrenoceptor blockade (40) or after sympathectomy (154), chronic hypoxia, which may result in pulmonary hypertension, causes right ventricular hypertrophy. Third, reduction of myocardial load without selective changes in either cardiac innervation or catecholamine content results in marked, reversible alterations in cardiac structure and function (33, 147).

The studies suggesting that the adrenoceptor activation accompanying a hemodynamic challenge might be the primary factor initiating and maintaining cardiac hypertrophy have been reviewed recently, both in terms of increased cardiac sympathetic nerve activity (106, 107) and in terms of elevated levels of circulating adrenal catecholamines (69, 165). One line of investigation suggesting a role for catecholamines in cardiac hypertrophy utilized primarily the spontaneously hypertensive rat model. In this genetic variant it has been suggested that adrenergic factors play an important role in modulating cardiac hypertrophy in response to increased systemic arterial pressure (126). However, several other lines of evidence suggest that this may not be the case. When 6-hydroxydopamine was used to denervate the heart in another rat strain prior to induced renal hypertension, the development of cardiac hypertrophy in response to this hemodynamic challenge was not prevented (24). Furthermore, both central and peripheral sympathectomy in the spontaneously hypertensive rat may serve to prevent the development of hypertension but not the development of cardiac hypertrophy (38, 105, 148). Thus, it seems that the spontaneously hypertensive rat has a genetic hypertrophic cardiomyopathy that is not strictly dependent on either catecholamines or systemic hypertension, whereas in a genetically distinct rat strain without spontaneous cardiac hypertrophy, cardiac enlargement can be induced by systemic hypertension, even in the absence of cardiac sympathetic nerves.

Another line of investigation in support of the role of catecholamines in cardiac hypertrophy is derived from direct infusions of β-adrenoceptor agonists into the circulation. For instance, it has been suggested (71) that an infusion of norepinephrine that does not cause systemic hypertension is sufficient to produce cardiac hypertrophy in the dog. However, in the absence of continuous concurrent measurements of heart rate and systemic arterial pressure during the time that hypertrophy was occurring, it is difficult to support the contention that the increase in cardiac mass is unrelated to an increase in some net measurement of active ventricular wall stress, such as the tension-time index. Indeed, in a different study in the dog (162), it was found that the adrenal catecholamine released in response to a pressure overload was predominantly epinephrine rather than norepinephrine, and it has been found in the rat that the catecholamines produced by the adrenal medulla are not necessary for the development of cardiac hypertrophy (100). Studies of chronic hypoxia, albeit with an undefined hemodynamic load, have shown that right ventricular hypertrophy, at least in terms of organ weight, occurs despite either β-adrenoceptor blockade (40) or chemical sympathectomy (154). Finally, another study in dogs (84) showed that denervated hearts actually exhibit an accelerated hypertrophic response to pressure overloads.

It has also been suggested that another, unknown trophic factor initiates cardiac hypertrophy (53). Actively hypertrophying cardiac tissue is thought to synthesize a water-soluble, extractable molecule that causes increased RNA and protein synthesis when introduced into the coronary circulation of other hearts, even when these other hearts are mechanically unloaded. In addition, a number of other circulating substances, such as insulin, thyroxine, adrenocorticoids, and growth hormone, may increase the rate of protein synthesis (129) and thus may be of variable importance as cofactors for cardiac hypertrophy (165). However, there is no evidence either that any of these substances initiates cardiac hypertrophy following a hemodynamic overload or that any of them causes load-independent cardiac hypertrophy, even when the blood level of such factors is increased during a primary disease of the organ of origin.

One recent study (26) directly tested the hypothesis that increased load itself, rather than such secondary factors as sympathetic activation, may be responsible for cardiac hypertrophy in response to hemodynamic overloads. This hypothesis was tested in two ways: First, to dissect the specific local effect of load on the initiation and maintenance of hypertrophy from the general effect of neural or circulating agents on the hypertrophy of an entire stressed chamber, cardiocyte size was measured in an unloaded papillary muscle either during or following overloading of the ventricle as a whole; second, the possibility that activation of either the α- or β-adrenoceptors in a stressed chamber may mediate hypertrophy was tested in terms of cell and chamber size by imposing a ventricular pressure overload either after ventricular denervation or during the chronic blockade of each of these adrenoceptors. In the first type of test, locally appropriate load responses caused ventricular hypertrophy with papillary muscle atrophy, both when each aspect of differential loading was simultaneous and when a previously hypertrophied papillary muscle was unloaded in a pressure-overloaded right ventricle. In the second approach, the degree of hypertrophy caused by these procedures was the same as that caused by isolated pressure overloading. This study demonstrated that cardiac hypertrophy is a local response to increased load, so any factor mediating this response must be generated locally or active only in those cardiocytes in which stress and/or strain are increased. This study also showed that catecholamines do not mediate this response since adrenergic activation is neither necessary for, nor importantly modifies, the cardiac hypertrophic load response.

Cardiocyte

The major limitations of chronic in vivo studies of cardiac load regulation are twofold. First, it is extremely difficult in the intact animal to isolate and evaluate unequivocally the role of any single factor in controlling the biology of heart muscle. Second, cardiac tissue consists of striated muscle cells embedded in a complex of neural, vascular, and interstitial cells; the interaction of these tissue components with the cardiocytes in response to varying hemodynamic input is difficult to characterize fully. Short-term in vitro studies of cardiac tissue address the first but not the second of these problems; additionally, they do not permit the study over time of the regulation of cardiocyte growth in a stable preparation.

For these reasons, a long-term in vitro study of load effects on cultured cardiocytes maintained in serum-free medium was recently undertaken (28). The established concept that cellular stress and/or strain is an important determinant of the properties of striated muscle formed the experimental basis for this study. For quiescent skeletal muscle in vivo, it has been known for some time (42) that increased length has a primary stimulatory effect on metabolism. More recently, passive stretch of inactive skeletal muscle has been shown to cause increased growth and protein synthesis, even following denervation (46, 47, 135). In simpler in vitro studies of cultured skeletal muscle, it was found that morphogenesis depends on mechanical stretch of embryonic cells (152, 153), while growth in adult cells occurs in those areas adhering to a substrate (45). Finally, acute and chronic studies of myocardium (64, 89, 111) show that stress and/or strain is an important determinant of protein synthesis and growth.

It is clear that cell shape plays a fundamental role in the control of cell growth for a variety of normal mammalian cell types (43). It is equally clear that cell shape and growth are the combined result of forces actively exerted by the cells themselves (55) and of external forces to which the cells are subjected (94). The way in which these factors may operate on isolated cardiocytes is suggested by three observations. First, adult cardiac cells in culture that are not confluently adherent to a substrate soon become round (125). Second, cultured Purkinje cells show structural evidence of myofilament formation which is localized to cytoplasmic extensions (16), wherein a stress axis is presumably present. Third, myofibril formation, which involves the incorporation of α-actinin into nascent Z-lines, is localized to the growing pseudopods and spreading borders of embryonic cardiocytes (120).

These observations, together with the observations of hypertrophy in response to increased loads and atrophy in response to decreased loads, led to a comparison between terminally differentiated quiescent adult cat ventricular cardiocytes cultured either as nonadherent unloaded cells or as substrate-adherent loaded cells (28). Adult cardiocytes loaded via substrate adhesion were found to retain their differentiated features for up to two weeks in culture; unattached and thus unloaded cardiocytes quickly dedifferentiated. On the levels of structure, function, and composition, there were striking parallels between the findings of previous studies of unloaded cardiac tissue and those of this study. Structurally, unloaded cardiocytes in tissue (64) are virtually indistinguishable from unloaded cardiocytes in culture. Functionally, the rapid loss of effective contraction in response to electrical stimulation observed for unloaded myocardium (33) was also observed in unloaded cardiocytes. The protein loss seen in unloaded myocardium (64) likewise occurred in unloaded cardiocytes.

Thus, in this study, although growth during culture was not induced in these cells at their normal diastolic rest length in a simple culture medium, a variety of differentiated features, and at least some of the synthetic activity to support them, were well maintained in adherent cells but were rapidly lost in nonadherent cells. In addition, neither hyperplasia nor hypertrophy of adult feline cardiocytes occurred in response to adrenergic stimulation or other interventions that caused a modest amount of spontaneous contractile activity. Finally, a further recent study (79) under the same culture conditions demonstrated increased RNA synthesis when cardiocytes adherent to a deformable substrate were stretched past their diastolic resting length. This observation indicates that increased load may indeed be a primary cardiocyte growth stimulus.

These results are in distinct contrast to the results of several recent studies of neonatal rat cardiocytes (13, 130, 131, 133, 134). In the latter studies, hypertrophy was induced by an α_1-specific effect of catecholamines on ventricular cardiocytes isolated from one-day-old rats. There were definite α_1 effects on the cell size, cell protein content, and RNA content of these cardiocytes, which were documented by the use of specific adrenergic agonists and antagonists. However, these effects may not be directly applicable to an understanding of the control of growth in adult mammalian cardiocytes. Neither hyperplastic nor hypertrophic growth in response to norepinephrine was seen in adult cardiocytes (28).

At least two factors may be relevant to differences in the basic biological properties of adult feline cardiocytes and neonatal rat cardiocytes. First, the α_1-adrenergic effects observed in neonatal rat cardiocytes may not generally apply to cardiocytes derived from other species or older rats. It has been shown that the number of α_1-adrenoceptors in rat myocardium is far greater than that in canine myocardium and that the receptors may differ biochemically (91). In addition, isolated neonatal rat cardiocytes exhibit a catecholamine sensitivity more than 100 times that seen in the intact neonatal rat heart (57), and there is evidence that the density of rodent cardiac α-adrenoceptors peaks in the neonatal period and declines thereafter (163). Second, the question of whether growth stimulation is a primary and specific α_1-adrenergic effect on spontaneously beating neonatal rat cardiocytes (130) may well be made irrelevant by the inotropic (10, 41) and chronotropic (57) effects of α_1-adrenoceptor stimulation in this particular experimental preparation. These two effects, which may be related to the increase in Ca^{2+} fluxes and resultant rise in cytosolic Ca^{2+} caused by α_1-adrenergic activation (10, 41), should lead to increases in the force and frequency of contraction. These, in turn, would sum as increased cardiac systolic load. Thus, despite evidence that there may be independent regulation of growth and beating in this preparation (131), it is difficult to distinguish between a primary, α_1-adrenoceptor-dependent growth-stimulating effect and a secondary, load-dependent growth-stimulating effect in spontaneously beating neonatal cardiocytes.

There is an even more basic distinction between the study of cat cardiocytes and of rat cardiocytes: in the former, terminally differentiated adult cardiocytes were employed; in the latter, neonatal cardiocytes which may still divide (23) were employed. There is evidence that in lower vertebrates, such as urodele (102) and anuran (118) amphibians, the adult ventricular cardiocytes may be in the G_0 state of the cell cycle, such that the induction of cardiocyte proliferation is possible. However, the available evidence clearly shows that adult mammalian ventricular cardiocytes are terminally differentiated (164). Both because juvenile cardiac cells may undergo karyokinesis without cytokinesis (23) and because cell number rather than DNA synthesis was measured in the studies of rodent cardiocytes, the effects of α_1 stimulation on the cycling of these neonatal cells is not well defined. However, in view of the very basic difference between neonatal and adult mammalian cardiocytes with respect to growth regulation, it is not surprising that growth control in adult cardiocytes was found to differ from that reported for neonatal cardiocytes.

NEONATAL VERSUS ADULT CARDIOCYTE GROWTH REGULATION α_1-adrenergic stimulation causes, in addition to increased Ca^{2+} fluxes, a concurrent but probably independent increase in the turnover of phosphatidylinositol (41). This, in turn, leads to cell proliferation by the induction of the Ca^{2+}-phospholipid dependent protein kinase, protein kinase C (101). The way in which activation of protein kinase C leads to DNA synthesis (a marker for cell division) or RNA synthesis (a marker for cell growth) is unclear (142). For example, it has been shown recently that differentiated mammalian cells such as hepatocytes, which can be induced to re-enter the cell cycle from the G_0 state, respond to α_1-adrenergic stimulation by synthesizing DNA (37). Further, there is evidence that certain phorbol esters, which directly stimulate protein kinase C formation (155), are capable of causing growth in neonatal rat cardiocytes (132).

It has been known for some time that β_1-adrenoceptor stimulation induces cAMP formation, which is related to inhibition of cellular proliferation. This cyclic nucleotide inhibits the stimulation of protein kinase C by inositol phospholipid breakdown (101, Figure 25). There is also evidence that, in addition to the neonatal peak in the density of cardiac α-adrenoceptors, there is a similar peak in the density of cardiac β-adrenoceptors in neonatal rodents (19). In view of the similarity of cardiocyte and vascular α-adrenoceptors (10), it is of interest that vascular β_1-adrenoceptor stimulation blocks another effector of the protein kinase C pathway, ornithine decarboxylase, and blocks the usual α_1-adrenoceptor induction of this enzyme (77). A further recent finding is that ornithine decarboxylase inhibition leads to simultaneous, but not causally linked, cessation of cell division and induction of differentiation in embryonal carcinoma cells (60). In addition, skeletal myoblasts in cell culture can be induced to cease DNA synthesis and initiate differentiation when transferred to a simple, serum-free medium (115). Finally, of a number of tissues assayed in the adult rat, protein kinase C activity is lowest in the terminally differentiated cells of the heart (70). It is now clear that although pathways that lead to protein kinase C formation can be activated in adult cardiocytes, such activation is not required for either normal growth or hypertrophy (7, 110).

This information now may be integrated, at least speculatively, with the apparent induction of cardiocyte growth in neonatal rat cardiocytes by norepinephrine, a catecholamine with α_1- and β_1-adrenoceptor activity, and the demonstrated lack of effect of norepinephrine on terminally differentiated adult cardiocytes, both in vivo (26) and in vitro (28). As suggested before (22), functional adrenergic innervation of the neonatal heart may inhibit DNA synthesis, primarily through the induction of cAMP synthesis. Differentiation and hypertrophy rather than hyperplasia would then become the primary form of growth, possibly stimulated further by the load effects of norepinephrine-related inotropism and chronotropism, as well as by the increasing circulatory load. Thus, it is possible to envision a role for α_1-adrenergic stimulation of protein kinase C synthesis in the induction of growth and replication by neonatal rat cardiocytes, with a transition during ontogeny to differentiation and hypertrophic growth during the onset of functional adrenergic innervation and increasing hemodynamic loads. Finally, in the adult cardiocyte, further hypertrophic growth may well be a primary load response.

ACKNOWLEDGMENTS

Support during the preparation of this review was provided by Grants HL29146, HL29351, and HL29718 from the National Institutes of Health and by Veterans Administration research funds.

Literature Cited

1. Alfaro, A., Schaible, T. F., Malhotra, A., Yipintsoi, T., Scheuer, J. 1983. *Cardiovasc. Res.* 17:553–61
2. Alpert, N. R., Gordon, M. S. 1962. *Am. J. Physiol.* 202:940–46
3. Alpert, N. R., Mulieri, L. A. 1982. *Circ. Res.* 50:491–500
4. Aronson, R. S. 1980. *Circ. Res.* 47:443–54
5. Bache, R. J., Vrobel, T. R., Arentzen, C., Ring, W. S. 1981. *Circ. Res.* 49:742–50
6. Badke, F. R., White, F. C., Le Winter, M., Covell, J., Andres, J., et al. 1981. *Am. J. Physiol.* 241:H564–70
7. Bartolome, J., Huguenard, J., Slotkin, T. A. 1980. *Science* 210:793–94
8. Bassett, A. L., Gelband, H. 1973. *Circ. Res.* 32:15–26
9. Belenkie, I., Baumber, J. S., Rademaker, A. 1983. *Can. J. Physiol. Pharmacol.* 61:1274–80
10. Benfey, B. G. 1982. *Life Sci.* 31:101–12
11. Bing, O. H. L., Matsushita, S., Fanburg, B. L., Levine, H. J. 1971. *Circ. Res.* 28:234–45
12. Bishop, S. P., Melsen, L. R. 1976. *Circ. Res.* 39:238–45
13. Bishopric, N., Ordahl, C., Simpson, P. 1985. *Clin. Res.* 33:170 (Abstr.)
14. Borkon, A. M., Jones, M., Bell, J. H., Pierce, J. E. 1982. *J. Thorac. Cardiovasc. Surg.* 84:876–85
15. Bristow, M. R., Ginsburg, R., Minobe, W., Cubicciotti, R. S., Sageman, W. S., et al. 1982. *N. Engl. J. Med.* 307:205–11
16. Canale, E., Campbell, J., Campbell, G. R. 1983. *J. Mol. Cell. Cardiol.* 15:197–206
17. Capasso, J. M., Strobeck, J., Sonnenblick, E. H. 1981. *Am. J. Physiol.* 241:H435–41
18. Carabello, B. A., Mee, R., Collins, J. J., Kloner, R. A., Levin, D., et al. 1981. *Am. J. Physiol.* 240:H80–H86
19. Chen, F. M., Yamamura, H. I., Roeske,

W. R. 1979. *Eur. J. Pharmacol.* 58:
255–64

20. Chidsey, C. A., Braunwald, E., Morrow, A. G., Mason, D. T. 1963. *N. Engl. J. Med.* 269:653–8

21. Chidsey, C. A., Kaiser, G. A., Sonnenblick, E. H., Spann, J. F., Braunwald, E. 1964. *J. Clin. Invest.* 43:2386–93

22. Claycomb, W. C. 1977. *Biochem. J.* 168:599–601

23. Clubb, F. J., Bishop, S. P. 1984. *Lab. Invest.* 50:571–77

24. Cohen, J. 1974. *Circ. Res.* 34/35:49–57 (Suppl. II)

25. Cooper, G., Kent, R. L., McGonigle, P., Watanabe, A. M. 1986. *J. Clin. Invest.* 77:441–55

26. Cooper, G., Kent, R. L., Uboh, C. E., Thompson, E. W., Marino, T. A. 1985. *J. Clin. Invest.* 75:1403–14

27. Cooper, G., Marino, T. A. 1984. *Circ. Res.* 54:323–31

28. Cooper, G., Mercer, W. E., Hoober, J. K., Gordon, P. R., Kent, R. L., et al. 1986. *Circ. Res.* 58:692–705

29. Cooper, G., Puga, F. J., Zujko, K. J., Harrison, C. E., Coleman, H. N. 1973. *Circ. Res.* 32:140–48

30. Cooper, G., Satava, R., Harrison, C. E., Coleman, H. N. 1973. *Circ. Res.* 33:213–23

31. Cooper, G., Satava, R. M., Harrison, C. E., Coleman, H. N. 1974. *Am. J. Physiol.* 226:1158–65

32. Cooper, G., Tomanek, R. J. 1979. *Clin. Res.* 27:160 (Abstr.)

33. Cooper, G., Tomanek, R. J. 1982. *Circ. Res.* 50:788–98

34. Cooper, G., Tomanek, R. J. 1986. *Cardiovasc. Res.* In press

35. Cooper, G., Tomanek, R. J., Ehrhardt, J., Marcus, M. L. 1981. *Circ. Res.* 48:488–97

36. Coulson, R. L., Yazdanfar, S., Rubio, E., Bove, A. A., LeMole, G. M., et al. 1977. *Circ. Res.* 40:41–49

37. Cruise, J. L., Houck, K. A., Michalopoulos, G. K. 1985. *Science* 227:749–51

38. Cutilletta, A. F., Erinoff, L., Heller, A., Low, J., Oparil, S. 1977. *Circ. Res.* 40:424–34

39. Dammrich, J., Pfeifer, U. 1983. *Virchows Arch. B* 43:265–86

40. Dennis, P., Vaughan Williams, E. M. 1982. *J. Physiol.* 324:365–74

41. Exton, J. H. 1981. *Mol. Cell. Endocrinol.* 23:233–64

42. Feng, T. P. 1932. *J. Physiol. London* 74:441–54

43. Folkman, J., Moscona, A. 1978. *Nature* 273:345–49

44. Geha, A. S., Duffy, J. P., Swan, H. J. C. 1966. *Circ. Res.* 19:255–59

45. Glavinovic, M. I., Miledi, R., Nakajima, Y. 1983. *Proc. R. Soc. London Ser. B* 219:91–101

46. Goldspink, D. F. 1977. *J. Physiol. London* 264:267–82

47. Goldspink, D. F. 1978. *Biochem. J.* 174:595–602

48. Grimm, A. F., Kubota, R., Whitehorn, W. V. 1963. *Circ. Res.* 12:118–24

49. Grossman, W. 1980. *Am. J. Med.* 69:576–84

50. Gulch, R. W., Baumann, R., Jacob, R. 1979. *Basic Res. Cardiol.* 74:69–82

51. Gunning, J. F., Coleman, H. N. 1973. *J. Mol. Cell. Cardiol.* 5:25–38

52. Gwathmey, J. K., Morgan, J. P. 1985. *Circ. Res.* 57:836–43

53. Hammond, G. L., Lai, Y. K., Markert, C. L. 1982. *Science* 216:529–31

54. Hamrell, B. B., Alpert, N. R. 1977. *Circ. Res.* 40:20–25

55. Harris, A. K., Wild, P., Stopak, D. 1980. *Science* 208:177–79

56. Hayashi, H., Shibata, S. 1974. *Eur. J. Pharmacol.* 27:355–59

57. Hermsmeyer, K., Mason, R., Griffen, S., Becker, P. 1982. *Circ. Res.* 51:532–37

58. Hess, O. M., Schneider, J., Koch, R., Bamert, C., Grimm, J., et al. 1981. *Circulation* 63:360–71

59. Hultgren, P. B., Bove, A. A. 1981. *Cardiovasc. Res.* 15:522–28

60. Jetten, A. M., Shirley, J. E. 1985. *Exp. Cell. Res.* 156:221–30

61. Julian, F. J., Morgan, D. L., Moss, R. L., Gonzalez, M., Dwivedi, P. 1981. *Circ. Res.* 49:1300–10

62. Karliner, J., Barnes, P., Brown, M., Dollery, C. 1980. *Eur. J. Pharmacol.* 67:115–18

63. Kaufmann, R. L., Homburger, H., Wirth, H. 1971. *Circ. Res.* 28:346–57

64. Kent, R. L., Uboh, C. E., Thompson, E. W., Gordon, S. S., Marino, T. A., et al. 1985. *J. Mol. Cell. Cardiol.* 17:153–65

65. Kerr, A., Winterberger, A. R., Giambattista, M. 1961. *Circ. Res.* 9:103–5

66. Keung, E. C. H., Keung, C., Aronson, R. S. 1982. *Am. J. Physiol.* 243:H917–26

67. Kira, Y., Kochel, P. J., Gordon, E. E., Morgan, H. E. 1984. *Am. J. Physiol.* 246:C247–58

68. Kleaveland, J. P., Kussmaul, W. G., Carabello, B. A. 1985. *J. Am. Coll. Cardiol.* 5:486 (Abstr.)

69. Kolbel, F., Schreiber, V. 1983. *Basic Res. Cardiol.* 78:351–63

70. Kuo, J. F., Andersson, R. G. G., Wise,

B. C., Mackerlova, L., Salomonsson, I., et al. 1980. *Proc. Natl. Acad. Sci. USA* 77:7039–43
71. Laks, M. M., Morady, F., Swan, H. J. C. 1973. *Chest* 64:75–78
72. Liberthson, R. R., Boucher, C. A., Strauss, H. W., Dinsmore, R. E., McKusick, K. A., et al. 1981. *Am. J. Cardiol.* 47:56–60
73. Limas, C. J. 1979. *Biochim. Biophys. Acta* 588:174–78
74. Litten, R. Z., Martin, B. J., Low, R. B., Alpert, N. R. 1982. *Circ. Res.* 50:856–64
75. Lompre, A. M., Schwartz, K., d'Albis, A., Lacombe, G., Thiem, N. V., et al. 1979. *Nature* 282:105–7
76. Lund, D. D., Tomanek, R. J. 1978. *Am. J. Anat.* 152:141–52
77. Majesky, M. W., Yang, H. L., Juchau, M. R. 1985. *Life Sci.* 36:153–59
78. Manciet, L., Burt, J. M. 1985. *Fed. Proc.* 44:1379 (Abstr.)
79. Mann, D. L., Kent, R., Thompson, R., Cooper, G. 1986. *Circulation* In press (Abstr.)
80. Mann, T., Goldberg, S., Mudge, G. H., Grossman, W. 1979. *Circulation* 59:14–20
81. Manohar, M., Bisgard, G. E., Bullard, V., Rankin, J. H. G. 1981. *Am. J. Physiol.* 240:H881–88
82. Marcus, M. L., Doty, D. B., Hiratzka, L. F., Wright, C. B., Eastham, C. L. 1982. *N. Engl. J. Med.* 307:1362–67
83. Marino, T. A., Kent, R. L., Uboh, C., Fernandez, E., Thompson, E. W., Cooper, G. 1985. *Am. J. Physiol.* 249:H371–79
84. Matoba, T., Adachi, K., Ito, T., Yamashita, Y., Chiba, M., et al. 1984. *Experientia* 40:73–75
85. Mercadier, J., Bouveret, P., Gorza, L., Schiaffino, S., Clark, W. A., et al. 1983. *Circ. Res.* 53:52–62
86. Mirsky, I., Laks, M. M. 1980. *Circ. Res.* 46:530–42
87. Mirsky, I., Pasipoularides, A. 1980. *Fed. Proc.* 39:156–61
88. Mirsky, I., Pfeffer, J., Pfeffer, M. A., Braunwald, E. 1983. *Circ. Res.* 53:767–78
89. Morgan, H. E., Gordon, E. E., Kira, Y., Siehl, D. L., Watson, P. A., et al. 1985. *Physiologist* 28:18–27
90. Mueller, T. M., Marcus, M. L., Kerber, R. E., Young, J. A., Barnes, R. W., et al. 1978. *Circ. Res.* 42:543–49
91. Mukherjee, A., Haghani, Z., Brady, J., Bush, L., McBride, W., et al. 1983. *Am. J. Physiol.* 245:H957–61
92. Murray, P. A., Baig, H., Fishbein, M.

C., Vatner, S. F. 1979. *J. Clin. Invest.* 64:421–27
93. Murray, P. A., Vatner, S. F. 1981. *J. Clin. Invest.* 67:1314–23
94. Nakatsuji, N., Johnson, K. E. 1984. *Nature* 307:453–55
95. Natarajan, G., Bove, A. A., Coulson, R. L., Carey, R. A., Spann, J. F. 1979. *Am. J. Physiol.* 237:H676–80
96. Newman, W. H. 1978. *Am. J. Physiol.* 234:H88–H93
97. Newman, W. H. 1978. *Am. J. Physiol.* 235:H690–H700
98. Newman, W. H., Webb, J. G. 1980. *Am. J. Physiol.* 238:H134–43
99. Newman, W. H., Webb, J. G., Privitera, P. J. 1982. *Am. J. Physiol.* 243:H876–83
100. Nichols, J. R., Clancy, R. L., Gonzalez, N. C. 1983. *Am. J. Physiol.* 244:H234–38
101. Nishizuka, Y., Takai, Y., Kishimoto, A., Kikkawa, U., Kaibuchi, K. 1984. *Recent Prog. Horm. Res.* 40:301–45
102. Oberpriller, J. O., Oberpriller, J. C. 1971. *J. Cell Biol.* 49:560–63
103. Okada, T., Okuyama, H., Mashima, H., Sato, H., Kitamura, K. 1984. *J. Physiol.* 247:H699–H708
104. O'Keefe, D. D., Hoffman, J. I. E., Cheitlin, R., O'Neill, M. J., Allard, J. R., et al. 1978. *Circ. Res.* 43:43–51
105. Oparil, S., Cutilletta, A. F. 1979. *Am. J. Cardiol.* 44:970–78
106. Ostman-Smith, I. 1979. *Acta Physiol. Scand.* 108:1–118 (Suppl. 477)
107. Ostman-Smith, I. 1981. *Clin. Sci.* 61:265–72
108. Pannier, J. L. 1971. *Arch. Int. Physiol. Biochem.* 79:743–52
109. Parrish, D. G., Ring, W. S., Bache, R. J. 1985. *Am. J. Physiol.* 249:H534–39
110. Pegg, A. E. 1981. *J. Mol. Cell. Cardiol.* 13:881–87
111. Peterson, M. B., Lesch, M. 1972. *Circ. Res.* 31:317–27
112. Pfeffer, J. M., Pfeffer, M. A., Fishbein, M. C., Frohlich, E. D. 1979. *Am. J. Physiol.* 237:461–68
113. Pfeffer, M. A., Pfeffer, J. M., Frohlich, E. D. 1976. *Circ. Res.* 38:423–29
114. Pichard, A. D., Gorlin, R., Smith, H., Ambrose, J., Meller, J. 1981. *Am. J. Cardiol.* 47:547–54
115. Pinset, C., Whalen, R. G. 1985. *Dev. Biol.* 108:284–89
116. Polimeni, P. I., Cutilletta, A. F., Otten, M. D. 1983. *Cardiovasc. Res.* 17:170–76
117. Rembert, J. C., Kleinman, L. H., Fedor, J. M., Wechsler, A. S., Greenfield, J. C. 1978. *J. Clin. Invest.* 62:379–86

118. Rumyantsev, P. P. 1973. *Z. Zellforsch.* 139:431–50
119. Sack, D. W., Cooper, G., Harrison, C. E. 1977. *Basic Res. Cardiol.* 72:268–73
120. Sanger, J. W., Mittal, B., Sanger, J. M. 1984. *Cell. Motil.* 4:405–16
121. Sasayama, S., Franklin, D., Ross, J. 1977. *Am. J. Physiol.* 232:H418–25
122. Sasayama, S., Ross, J., Franklin, D., Bloor, D. M., Bishop, S., et al. 1976. *Circ. Res.* 38:172–78
123. Schwartz, A., Sordahl, L. A., Entman, M. L., Allen, J. C., Reddy, Y. S., et al. 1973. *Am. J. Cardiol.* 32:407–22
124. Schwarz, F., Flameng, W., Schaper, J., Hehrlein, F. 1978. *Am. J. Cardiol.* 42:895–903
125. Schwarzfeld, T. A., Jacobson, S. L. 1981. *J. Mol. Cell. Cardiol.* 13:563–75
126. Sen, S., Tarazi, R. C. 1983. *Am. J. Physiol.* 244:H97–H101
127. Serizawa, T., Mirsky, I., Carabello, B. A., Grossman, W. 1982. *Am. J. Physiol.* 242:H633–37
128. Shiverick, K. T., Hamrell, B. B., Alpert, N. R. 1976. *J. Mol. Cell. Cardiol.* 8:837–51
129. Siehl, D., Chua, B. H. L., Lautensack-Belser, N., Morgan, H. E. 1985. *Am. J. Physiol.* 248:C309–19
130. Simpson, P. 1983. *J. Clin. Invest.* 72:732–38
131. Simpson, P. 1985. *Circ. Res.* 56:884–94
132. Simpson, P., Karliner, J. S. 1985. *Clin. Res.* 33:229 (Abstr.)
133. Simpson, P., McGrath, A., Savion, S. 1982. *Circ. Res.* 51:787–801
134. Simpson, P., Savion, S. 1982. *Circ. Res.* 50:101–16
135. Sola, O. M., Christensen, D. L., Martin, A. W. 1973. *Exp. Neurol.* 41:76–100
136. Sordahl, L. A., McCollum, W. B., Wood, W. G., Schwartz, A. 1973. *Am. J. Physiol.* 224:497–502
137. Spann, J. F., Buccino, R. A., Sonnenblick, E. H., Braunwald, E. 1967. *Circ. Res.* 21:341–54
138. Spann, J. F., Chidsey, C. A., Pool, P. E., Braunwald, E. 1965. *Circ. Res.* 17:312–21
139. Spann, J. F., Covell, J. W., Eckberg, D. L., Sonnenblick, E. H., Ross, J., et al. 1972. *Am. J. Physiol.* 223:1150–57
140. Strauer, B. 1979. *Am. J. Cardiol.* 44:999–1006
141. Swynghedauw, B., Schwartz, K., Apstein, C. S. 1984. *Am. J. Cardiol.* 54:437–40
142. Tabor, C. W., Tabor, H. 1984. *Ann. Rev. Biochem.* 53:749–90
143. Taylor, R. R., Covell, J. W., Ross, J. 1968. *J. Clin. Invest.* 47:1333–42
144. Taylor, R. R., Hopkins, B. E. 1972. *Cardiovasc. Res.* 6:404–14
145. Thiedemann, K. U., Holubarsch, C., Medugorac, I., Jacob, R. 1983. *Basic Res. Cardiol.* 78:140–55
146. Thomas, J. A., Marks, B. H. 1978. *Am. J. Cardiol.* 41:233–43
147. Thompson, E. W., Marino, T. A., Uboh, C. E., Kent, R. L., Cooper, G. 1984. *Circ. Res.* 54:367–77
148. Tomanek, R. J., Bhatnagar, R. K., Schmid, P., Brody, M. J. 1982. *Am. J. Physiol.* 242:H1015–21
149. Tomanek, R. J., Cooper, G. 1981. *Anat. Rec.* 200:271–80
150. Tritthart, H., Leudcke, H., Bayer, R., Stierle, H., Kaufmann, R. 1975. *J. Mol. Cell. Cardiol.* 7:163–74
151. Turina, M., Bussmann, W. D., Krayenbuhl, H. P. 1969. *Cardiovasc. Res.* 3:486–95
152. Vandenburgh, H. 1982. *Dev. Biol.* 93:438–43
153. Vandenburgh, H., Kaufman, S. 1979. *Science* 203:265–68
154. Vaughan Williams, E. M., Dukes, I. D. 1983. *Cardiovasc. Res.* 17:379–89
155. Weinstein, I. B. 1983. *Nature* 302:750
156. White, F. C., Sanders, M., Peterson, T., Bloor, C. M. 1979. *Am. J. Pathol.* 97:473–88
157. Willerson, J. T. 1982. *N. Engl. J. Med.* 307:243–45
158. Williams, J. F., Potter, R. D. 1974. *J. Clin. Invest.* 54:1266–72
159. Wisenbaugh, T., Allen, P., Cooper, G., Holzgrefe, H., Beller, G., et al. 1983. *Circ. Res.* 53:332–41
160. Wisenbaugh, T., Allen, P., Cooper, G., O'Connor, W. N., Mezaros, L., et al. 1984. *Am. J. Physiol.* 247:H146–54
161. Wisenbaugh, T., Spann, J. F., Carabello, B. A. 1984. *J. Am. Coll. Cardiol.* 3:916–23
162. Womble, J. R., Haddox, M. K., Russell, D. H. 1978. *Life Sci.* 23:1951–58
163. Yamada, S., Yamamura, H. I., Roeske, W. R. 1980. *Eur. J. Pharmacol.* 68:217–21
164. Zak, R. 1974. *Circ. Res.* 34/35:17–26 (Suppl. II)
165. Zak, R. 1984. *Growth of the Heart in Health and Disease,* pp. 165–85. New York: Raven

Ann. Rev. Physiol. 1987. 49:519–31

CARDIAC MUSCLE CHANGES IN SENESCENCE[1]

Edward G. Lakatta

Laboratory of Cardiovascular Science, Gerontology Research Center, National Institute on Aging, National Institutes of Health, Baltimore, Maryland 21224

INTRODUCTION

The biophysical and biochemical mechanisms that govern cardiac muscle function change with age resulting in characteristic alterations in muscle function (22). This chapter reviews our present understanding of how the excitation, activation, and contraction mechanisms in cardiac muscle change with senescence. Many of the studies discussed here measured cardiac muscle function in thin trabeculae or papillary muscles that had been removed from the heart and superfused in physiologic saline. In these preparations the cardiac systole is simulated as a twitch or contraction elicited by an action potential that occurs in response to external electrical stimulation. A brief summary of the mechanisms that underlie the coupling of cardiac excitation, activation, and contraction is useful for an integrated interpretation of studies that have examined the impact of age on these mechanisms.

A GENERAL EXCITATION-ACTIVATION-CONTRACTION MODEL FOR CARDIAC MUSCLE

A simplified schema of excitation-contraction coupling is depicted in Figure 1. The depolarization itself or the Ca^{2+} influx that results from it (7) triggers Ca^{2+} release from the sarcoplasmic reticulum (SR) and causes the $[Ca^{2+}]$ of the myofibrillar space to increase from about 150 nM to micromolar levels.

The myofilaments (actin, myosin, troponin, tropomyosin) within each myofibril are arranged in serial units referred to as sarcomeres. These can vary in length from about 2.4 μm in the unstimulated state to about 1.6 μm during a contraction. Ca^{2+} binding to troponin results in actomyosin interaction followed by displacement of actin relative to myosin (sarcomere shortening) and force production. Then, as the $[Ca^{2+}]$ in the myoplasm is reduced, due in large measure to SR pumping, Ca^{2+} dissociates from the myofilaments, sarcomeres elongate, and relaxation of force ensues. Following a twitch, the excitation-contraction coupling mechanisms require time for optimal operation during a subsequent stimulation. The duration of this restitution time differs for different mechanisms, e.g. sarcolemmal ionic conductances, SR Ca^{2+} recycling, as depicted in Figure 1. In the steady state the Ca^{2+} influx into myocytes with depolarization is balanced by Ca^{2+} extrusion via a sarcolemmal Na-Ca exchanger and an adenosine triphosphate (ATP)-dependent Ca^{2+} pump.

The sarcomere length during a given contraction depends in part on its length prior to contraction, which is determined by the extent of stretch placed upon the tissue and by how much shortening occurs following myofilament Ca^{2+} activation. The velocity and extent of sarcomere shortening is determined by the extent and duration of Ca^{2+} binding to troponin. The extent of Ca^{2+} binding at the onset of contraction depends on the magnitude of the Ca^{2+} release from the SR and on the resting myofilament or sarcomere length (13). The extent to which Ca^{2+} remains bound during contraction depends on

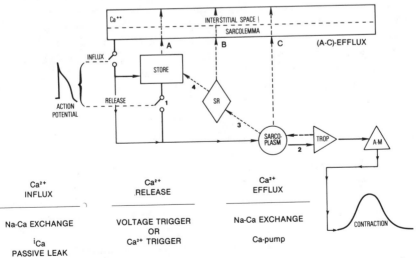

Figure 1 A general schematic model of excitation coupling in cardiac muscle (see text for details). (Modified from References 12 and 17.)

how fast and how much the sarcomeres shorten during a given contraction (16). Thus, the duration of Ca^{2+} myofilament activation is regulated not only by the duration of the transient increase in myoplasmic $[Ca^{2+}]$ elicited by excitation but by the shortening characteristics of sarcomeres during contraction. The precise molecular mechanisms of the length-dependence of Ca^{2+} binding remain to be elucidated.

The rate and extent of sarcomere shortening and the resultant increase in tissue stiffness and force production are dependent on (a) the rate at which ATP is hydrolyzed by myofilament ATPase (ATPase activation is modulated in part by the myosin isozyme composition); and on (b) the forces present within the tissue that are sometimes referred to as the "load" borne by the sarcomeres. The sarcomere load depends on the length of the sarcomeres and other structures within and among the cells that compose the myocardial tissue. The types of load are often classified as those present prior to excitation ("preload") and those present during the contraction itself ("afterload"). An unloaded cardiac cell, i.e. one that is unstretched and not stimulated to contract, maintains a sarcomere length of about 1.85 μm (12). This is referred to as the slack length. Thus following a contraction in an unstretched cell, sarcomeres are restored to this length; the forces (the precise nature of which remains to be elucidated) that cause this are referred to as restoring forces. During contractions in which sarcomere length drops below the slack length these restoring forces oppose shortening of sarcomeres. The preload is determined by the extent to which the isolated cardiac preparation is stretched by the experimenter. The afterload is determined by the extent to which the sarcomeres shorten, the range of sarcomere lengths over which the shortening occurs, by whatever preload persists during the contraction, and by restoring forces, if the sarcomeres shorten to less than slack length. As noted above, when sarcomeres shorten during contraction, their myofilament Ca^{2+} affinity is reduced. It is evident from the foregoing considerations that while myofilament Ca^{2+} activation, length, and load each are important determinants of the cardiac contraction, these factors cannot be considered to be independent of each other. Rather, they must be considered to be totally interdependent (18).

CARDIAC MUSCLE CHANGES IN SENESCENCE

The vast majority of studies of the changes that occur within the myocardium with senescence have employed the rat model (19). Rats in captivity are commonly referred to as "senescent" at that age at which approximately 50% mortality occurs, which in many strains is approximately two years (22). Many of the steps in the excitation-contraction scheme depicted in Figure 1 in cardiac muscle isolated from senescent rats differ quantitatively from those in muscle from younger adult rats. Generally, many of the events depicted in

Figure 1 occur at a slower rate in senescent than in younger adult muscle. Specifically, in an isometric contraction, i.e. one in which the ends of the muscle are fixed, the transmembrane action potential (TAP) that excites the cell (4, 28) and the myoplasmic $[Ca^{2+}]$ transient (25) and contractions (1, 3, 4, 8, 17, 25) that ensue are longer in duration. In isotonic contractions, i.e. those in which one of the muscle ends is not fixed and in which macroscopic muscle shortening is permitted to occur, the speed and extent of shortening are less in cardiac muscle from senescent versus younger adult rats (1,4). With senescence the myosin isozyme composition shifts from predominately V_1, a rapid ATPase, to predominately V_3, a slower ATPase (2, 5). The time required for restitution of the excitation-contraction coupling cycle is longer in senescence, as evidenced by the relative inability to produce a contraction in response to premature stimuli (20). These changes in excitation, activation, and contraction in senescence are discussed in more detail below.

Action Potential, Myoplasmic $[Ca^{2+}]$ Transient, and Twitch

Representative examples of TAP, force, and myoplasmic $[Ca^{2+}]$ transients of adult and senescent muscles are given in Figure 2. The resting membrane potential is unaltered with adult aging (4, 28). The magnitude of the prolongation of repolarization of the TAP in senescent muscle is striking, i.e. about twofold. This has been observed in two separate studies using different rat strains [Wistar (28) and Fischer 344 (4)] in pseudoisometric (auxotonic) right ventricular (28) and left ventricular (4) papillary muscles. In the Wistar strain, the action potential amplitude is also greater in senescent than in adult muscle in both high and low Ca^{2+} loading conditions (28). The TAP amplitude above zero millivolts ("overshoot") in rat cardiac muscle is Ca^{2+} dependent and appears to reflect Ca^{2+} conductance via "slow" Ca^{2+} channels. [These channels were recently shown to be fully activated within 3 msec following the onset of depolarization (24).] Influx of Ca^{2+} via this channel may trigger Ca^{2+} release by the SR (7). Thus, if the greater TAP overshoot in senescent muscle does indeed represent a Ca^{2+} current of greater magnitude, it might be concluded that the trigger for Ca^{2+} release or Ca^{2+} influx with each contraction in senescent muscle is greater than that in younger adult muscle.

The dramatic prolongation of the TAP observed in preloaded contractions in the senescent heart depicted in Figure 2A has not been observed to occur in unloaded preparations (22). Thus, the age differences observed in the TAP in Figure 2 may involve an age difference in response to stretch. However, the precise mechanisms that underlie the altered TAP in senescent muscle remain unknown, in large part, because of the problems inherent in voltage clamping multicellular ventricular muscle preparations. In this regard the recent advent of Ca^{2+}-tolerant single adult myocytes that permit measurements of specific

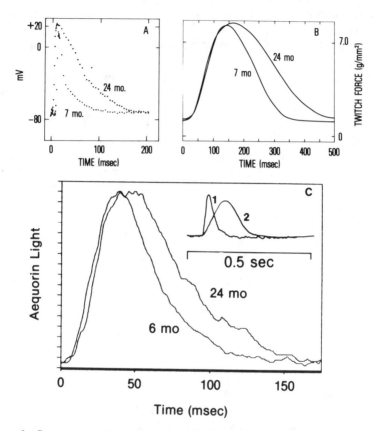

Figure 2 Computer resynthesis of simultaneously measured transmembrane action potentials (A) and contractions (B) from representative right ventricular papillary muscles of adult and senescent hearts. Muscles were stimulated to contract isometrically 24 times per minute at 29°C. Muscle length was that at which twitch force was maximal and bath $[Ca^{2+}]$ was 2.5 mM. (From Reference 28.) (C) Aequorin luminescence in representative cardiac muscles from adult (6 mo.) and senescent (24 mo.) rats. Aequorin was injected into 30–100 cells of a right ventricular papillary muscle from a 6- and a 24-month-old Wistar rat. The muscles were bathed in 2-mM Ca^{2+}. The luminescence transient is the average of 100 consecutive steady-state contractions at .33 Hz at 30°C at L_{max}. Note that the light transient is prolonged in the muscle from the 24 month old. The average time for aequorin luminescence to decay 50% in 11 young and 7 senescent muscles was 21.3 ± 1.5 and 32.9 ± 4.3 msec, respectively. Time to peak force in those same muscles in which light was measured was 88.8 ± 3.1 and 110.4 ± 6.8 msec, and half relaxation time was 54.9 ± 2.3 and 73.4 ± 4.4 msec in young and senescent muscles, respectively. The figure inset shows the time course of aequorin light, 1, relative to that of the concomitant isometric twitch, 2. (From Reference 25.)

ionic currents and their underlying channel kinetics represents a significant new opportunity for studies to elucidate the mechanism(s) of the prolonged TAP in senescence.

The myoplasmic [Ca^{2+}] transient that follows sarcolemmal depolarization in cardiac muscle has been monitored by injecting the chemiluminescent protein aequorin into multiple cells of that tissue and measuring the light transient that precedes contraction (25). The amplitude of the twitch (Figure 2B) and aequorin luminescence (Figure 2C) does not decline in senescent muscles when the [Ca^{2+}] in the superfusate is in the physiologic range and the rate of stimulation is low. The myofilament response to Ca^{2+} is not altered with age (3). This was demonstrated in studies in which cell and organelle membranes within thin papillary muscle were digested by detergent (Triton X) treatment to permit the buffering of [Ca^{2+}] within the myofilament space. Neither the maximum force nor the shape of the relationship between force and [Ca^{2+}] differ with age (3).

Peak twitch force at relatively low rates of stimulation (6–48 min^{-1}) also does not differ across a broad range of bathing [Ca^{2+}] or resting lengths (1, 4, 8, 10, 20–22, 28). However, note that the relatively low rates of stimulation required for studies in papillary muscles do not permit assessment of the extent of Ca^{2+} release at rates approaching those in the rat in vivo, e.g. 5 Hz and above. Additionally, the stability of isolated bulk muscle preparations requires that the studies be conducted at low temperatures, typically of 30°C or less, as depicted in Figure 2. Studies of the sort depicted in Figure 2 in single cardiac myocytes that can be stimulated at higher rates at 37°C may prove instructive. The post-extrasystolic twitch potentiation during continual paired stimulation is also preserved in senescent muscles bathed in a medium of low [Ca^{2+}] and stimulated at 24 pair/min (9). The maintenance of peak twitch force at low stimulation frequencies in senescent muscles may in part result from the prolonged myoplasmic Ca^{2+} transient (Figure 2C). The time for the aequorin luminescence to decay 50% from its peak is 30–50% longer in senescent than in younger adult muscles. In rat muscles bathed in physiologic [Ca^{2+}] in the absence of drugs, the amplitude of Ca^{2+} release and twitch force decline as the stimulation frequency is increased from .20 to 66 Hz, and the magnitude of the decline is not different in senescent and young adult muscles (25). In higher bathing [Ca^{2+}], muscles from younger adults are able to produce the same Ca^{2+} release and twitch force at the higher stimulation frequency, but senescent muscles cannot (25). In physiologic bathing [Ca^{2+}] when the coupling interval of paired stimulation is decreased from 200 to 100 msec, senescent but not adult muscles fail to generate a twitch response to the second stimulus (20). These deficits of the senescent muscle may be related in part to the diminished Ca^{2+} pumping rate by SR in senescent muscle (see below).

Sarcoplasmic Reticulum Function

The duration of the myoplasmic Ca^{2+} transient is prolonged in senescent muscles (Figure 2C). Although any mechanism that can alter the flux of Ca^{2+} into or out of the myoplasmic space might affect the duration of the myoplasmic $[Ca^{2+}]$, the decay of the Ca^{2+} transient is thought to largely depend upon the rate of Ca^{2+} removal by the SR Ca^{2+} pump (25). Earlier studies demonstrated that the rate of Ca^{2+} uptake into SR vesicles isolated from senescent Wistar rat hearts is less than that found for vesicles from younger adult hearts (8). The rate of SR Ca^{2+} pumping into the SR depends upon the myoplasmic $[Ca^{2+}]$ [or in isolated vesicles, on the $[Ca^{2+}]$ of the medium (8)]. The age difference in the SR Ca^{2+} uptake rate applies to the entire range of myoplasmic Ca^{2+} concentrations that occur in cardiac cells from diastole to systole (Figure 3A).

More recent studies (23) in another rat strain (Fischer 344) produced very similar results (Figure 3B). However, although the Ca^{2+} uptake rate in this study was found to be depressed, Ca^{2+} stimulation of the SR pump enzyme (i.e. the SR Ca^{2+}-ATPase) was not found to be age related. One possible explanation for this result is an age difference in the efficiency of coupling between ATP splitting and Ca^{2+} pumping (23). However, the net Ca^{2+} uptake in studies of this sort depends upon the Ca^{2+} pumped into vesicles and any Ca^{2+} efflux that may occur during the experiment. The latter can result from a passive, nonspecific leak or an efflux via Ca^{2+} channels through which

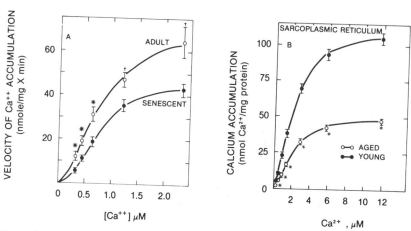

Figure 3 (A) The velocity of Ca^{2+} accumulation in sarcoplasmic reticulum isolated from the hearts of 6- to 8-month-old and 24- to 25-month-old Wistar rat. (From Reference 8.) (B) Effects of varying Ca^{2+} concentrations on ATP-supported Ca^{2+} accumulation by cardiac sarcoplasmic reticulum from 9 young and 9 aged Fischer 344 rat hearts. (From Reference 23.) See text for details.

Ca^{2+} release occurs in the cell in situ. Although the passive leaking of Ca^{2+} out of loaded SR vesicles did not differ with age (23), an age difference in spontaneous Ca^{2+} release via the Ca^{2+} channel in isolated SR vesicles has not been ruled out. The possibility that there are age differences in the conditions required for spontaneous SR Ca^{2+} release, which has been shown to be prominent in intact rat preparations, is an important issue because of the functional implications of spontaneous SR Ca^{2+} release when it occurs within cardiac cells that comprise bulk muscles (19). The diminution in the rate of net Ca^{2+} uptake into the SR is the most obvious mechanism to explain the prolonged Ca^{2+} transient in the senescent heart (Figure 2B).

Stiffness

A prolonged Ca^{2+} transient may cause a prolonged TAP since Ca^{2+} modulation of the Na-Ca exchanger or the nonspecific cation conductance referred to as the transient inward current (TI), produces a depolarization (24). The prolonged time course of the myoplasmic $[Ca^{2+}]$ transient may also affect other aspects of the cardiac contractions that depend on Ca^{2+}-myofilament interactions, including the time to peak force, the relaxation time (Figure 2B), and the ability of the myofilaments to shorten and stiffen at differing times following excitation. Muscle stiffness is measured as the ratio of the change in force in response to a change in muscle length. "Active dynamic" stiffness is that measured in response to small sinusoidal changes in muscle length made during the contraction (Figure 4, inset). It has been experimentally determined that as force increases with time during a contraction so too does the active dynamic stiffness (26, 27, 30), and that this stiffness is a linear function of the force (Figure 4). The slope coefficient (α) of the active stiffness force relationship increases in senescence but the intercept of the relationship does not (Figure 4).

The time to peak stiffness and to half-relaxation of peak stiffness are also prolonged in senescent versus younger adult cardiac muscle (26, 27, 30). The greater dynamic stiffness in senescent muscle is present only during contractile Ca^{2+} activation since the slope coefficient measured across a range of resting lengths (and therefore over a range of resting forces in unstimulated muscles) does not change with age (26, 27, 30). Thus, age differences in passive viscoelastic properties (17) cannot account for the increased dynamic stiffness during the contraction in senescent muscles as shown in Figure 4B. A possible explanation for the increase in the slope coefficient (α) of stiffness during contraction is as follows: At times during the contraction when force is still increasing and myoplasmic $[Ca^{2+}]$ (Ca_i) is decreasing (see Figure 2C, inset), Ca_i remains higher in senescent than in younger adult muscles (Figure 2C). This results in a relative increase in Ca^{2+}-myofilament interaction in senescent muscles at these later times, but not at earlier times during the

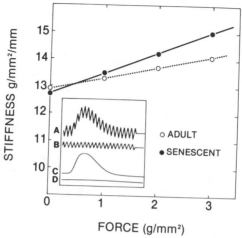

Figure 4 The active dynamic stiffness derived from the relationship of stiffness to force measurements made during the twitch in adult and senescent muscles. Inset shows how dynamic stiffness measurements are made. Twitch and resting force in two sequential contractions in the presence (*upper*) and absence (*lower*) of 17-Hz sinusoidal length perturbations (< 1% of muscle length). When the unperturbed signal is subtracted from the perturbed signal an approximation of force development due only to the length perturbation throughout the time course of the muscle contraction is derived. Stiffness is the change in force per change in length. Dynamic stiffness in resting muscle is independent of age. Active dynamic stiffness, i.e. the stiffness measured during contraction, is a linear function of force (stiffness = $\alpha F + B$) and is shown for both age groups. An age difference is note in α (the slope) (0.41 ± 0.14 in the adult muscles, $n = 8$, versus $0.76 \pm$ in the senescent muscles, $n = 17$, $p<0.03$) but not B (the intercept) (12.9 ± 0.14 in the adult versus 12.7 ± 1.3 in the senescent muscles). (Redrawn from Reference 27.)

contraction. This accounts for the increase in dynamic stiffness at later but not earlier times. Thus, the slope coefficient, α, but not the intercept of the stiffness force relation, increases in senescent versus younger muscles.

ATPase Activity

The myofibrillar ATPase activity in preparations prepared using detergents exhibits the identical Ca^{2+}-dependence ($K_m \approx 6.1$–6.2 μm and the Hill coefficient is ~ 4.5) as force (3). Although the Ca^{2+} sensitivity of myofibrillar ATPase does not change with age, peak ATPase activity declines during maturation and then remains stable from age 6 mo. through senescence (3, 22). The Ca^{2+}-activated ATPase activity in actomyosin preparations (actin plus myosin devoid of troponin and tropomyosin) declines during maturation but also shows a further decline with advancing adult age (5, 6). The ATPase activity of purified isolated myosin preparations when activated by Ca^{2+} declines progressively throughout the entire age range of 1–24 mo. (2, 5). This ATPase activity is determined by the myosin isozyme composition (11).

The fast isozyme content decreases progressively with age (Figure 5A). The lower level of V_1 isomyosin in preparations isolated from senescent hearts results in decreased ATPase activity. This effect is apparently related to the decline in the velocity of shortening in lightly loaded isotonic contractions (1, 5) and may be related to the prolongation of time to peak tension in isometric contractions (Figure 5B) and prolonged time to peak shortening in isotonic contractions (5).

The interpretation of age differences in shortening velocity may be confounded by the prolonged decay time of myoplasmic $[Ca^{2+}]$ in senescent muscle since these measurements are made by allowing the muscle to shorten as the Ca^{2+} decay is occurring. (Compare the timing of the aequorin transient with that of the contraction in Figure 2C, inset.) Thus, the effects of the myoplasmic $[Ca^{2+}]$ transient and the myosin ATPase activity on sarcomere shortening velocity are difficult to sort out. Specifically, it cannot be determined whether the measured diminution of shortening velocity or prolongation of shortening in senescent muscles is solely due to the change in isozyme composition, per se, or results in part from the change in SR function that appears to underlie the prolongation of the myoplasmic $[Ca^{2+}]$ transient.

Responses to Inotropic Drugs

The relative increase in twitch force in response to ouabain (9) or to catecholamines (10, 21) is substantially reduced (by greater than 50%) in the senescent heart. Dibutyryl adenosine 3',5'-cyclic phosphate (cAMP) mimics catecholamine agonists in producing a greater increase in contractile performance in

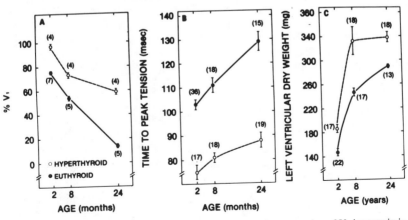

Figure 5   The effect of age and thyroid status on (A) the relative proportion of V_1 isomyosin in isolated myosin preparations, (B) time to peak force in isometric contractions, and (C) heart weight. Rats were injected with 0.6 mg thyroxine per kg IM for 7 days and studied on day 8. Note the marked decline in the percent of the V_1 isomyosin, as well as the prolongation of time to peak tension, that occurs with aging can be markedly attenuated by thyroxine. (From Reference 2.)

younger adult than in senescent myocardium (10). This observation, coupled with the finding of equal measured increments in cAMP and activation of cAMP-dependent protein kinase following receptor stimulation by catecholamines, suggests that the mechanism for the reduction in the contractile response to catecholamines in the senescent myocardium is at the level of, or distal to, the change in cellular protein phosphorylations that mediate the response. It is noteworthy that the response to augment contractile strength is diminished, but the relative relaxant effect of catecholamines is preserved in the senescent heart (10, 21). This observation suggests that the cellular mechanisms through which beta-adrenergic modulation of cardiac myocyte function causes enhanced relaxation are preserved in the senescent heart. Enhanced SR Ca^{2+} transport is thought to be a major factor in this relaxant effect (15). In SR isolated from adult and senescent hearts, the addition of cAMP and protein kinase produces equal increments in the Ca^{2+} uptake rate (14).

Similarities Between Effects of Aging and Experimental Cardiac Overload in Younger Animals

The multiple changes in cardiac excitation, activation, and contraction that occur with aging are all interrelated. Many of these changes can be interpreted as adaptive in nature. Many of these changes that occur with senescence in the normotensive rat also occur in the myocardium of younger animals in which experimentally induced hypertension has caused cardiac hypertrophy (5, 17,

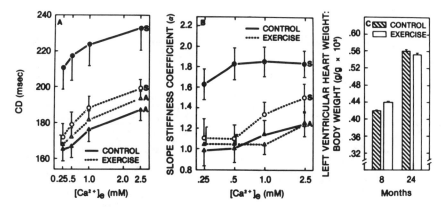

Figure 6   The effect of chronic (4 months, 5 days/week) mild, wheel exercise on (A) contraction duration (time to peak force plus time from peak to 50% force decay); (B) the active stiffness slope coefficient α (measured as in Figure 4) in isometric muscle stimulated at L_{max} at 29°C at 24 times per minute across a range of bathing $[Ca^{2+}]$ [Circles = senescent (24–26 mo.); triangles = adult (6–8 mo.)]; and (C) relative heart mass in adult (8 mo.) and senescent (24 mo.) rats. (From Reference 26.)

22). Thus, cardiac overload in younger hearts affects cardiac muscle in a manner that might be referred to as "accelerated aging." This finding raises the issue of whether the changes in cardiac muscle as reviewed above are due to the concomitant myocardial hypertrophy that accompanies senescence (29, 30). The extent of left heart hypertrophy from adulthood to senescence is moderate, however (29, 30; Figure 4B). Furthermore, the hypertrophy itself does not appear to be a *cause* of the changes in senescence (Figures 2 and 4), since these were measured in papillary muscles from the right ventricle, which does not hypertrophy with age (29). Additionally, Figure 4 shows that the decrease in V_1 myosin isozyme in the senescent muscle can be reversed by thyroxine, which causes further hypertrophy. Finally, chronic mild treadmill exercise that is insufficient to alter left ventricular mass reduces the contraction duration and active stiffness slope coefficient in the senescent heart to those levels measured in younger hearts (Figure 6). The striking results in Figures 5 and 6 indicate that at least some of the changes that occur in cardiac contraction with senescence are not fixed but are subject to modulation by hormones or physical activity.

Literature Cited

1. Alpert, N. R., Gale, H. H., Taylor, N. 1967. The effect of age on contractile protein ATPase activity and the velocity of shortening. In *Factors Influencing Myocardial Contractility,* ed. R. D. Tanz, F. Kavaler, J. Roberts, pp. 127–33. New York: Academic

2. Bhatnagar, G. M., Effron, M. B., Ruano-Arroyo, G., Spurgeon, H. A., Lakatta, E. G. 1985. Dissociation of myosin Ca^{2+}-ATPase activity from myosin isoenzymes and contractile function in rat myocardium. *Fed. Proc.* 44:826 (Abstr.)

3. Bhatnagar, G. M., Walford, G. D., Beard, E. S., Humphreys, S. H., Lakatta, E. G. 1984. ATPase activity and force production in myofibrils and twitch characteristics in intact muscle from neonatal, adult, and senescent rat myocardium. *J. Mol. Cell. Cardiol.* 16:203–18

4. Capasso, J. M., Malhotra, A., Remily, R. M., Scheuer, J., Sonnenblick, E. H. 1983. Effects of age on mechanical and electrical performance of rat myocardium. *Am. J. Physiol.* 245:H72–H81

5. Capasso, J. M., Malhotra, A., Scheuer, J., Sonnenblick, E. H. 1986. Myocardial biochemical, contractile and electrical performance following imposition of hypertension in young and old rats. *Circ. Res.* 58:445–60

6. Chesky, J. A., Rockstein, M. 1977. Reduced myocardial actomyosin adenosine triphosphatase activity in the ageing male Fischer rat. *Cardiovas. Res.* 11:242–46

7. Fabiato, A. 1982. Calcium release in skinned cardiac cells: Variations with species, tissues, and development. *Fed. Proc.* 41:2238–44

8. Froehlich, J. P., Lakatta, E. G., Beard, E., Spurgeon, H. A., Weisfeldt, M. L., et al. 1978. Studies of sarcoplasmic reticulum function and contraction duration in young adult and aged rat myocardium. *J. Mol. Cell. Cardiol.* 10:427–38

9. Gerstenblith, G., Spurgeon, H. A., Froehlich, J. P., Weisfeldt, M. L., Lakatta, E. G. 1979. Diminished inotropic responsiveness to ouabain in aged rat myocardium. *Circ. Res.* 44:517–23

10. Guarnieri, T., Filburn, C. R., Zitnik, G., Roth, G., Lakatta, E. G. 1980. Contractile and biochemical correlates of β-adrenergic stimulation of the aged heart. *Am. J. Physiol.* 239:H501–8

11. Hoh, J. F. Y., McGrath, P. A., Hale, P. T. 1977. Electrophoretic analysis of multiple forms of rat cardiac myosin: Effects of hypophysectomy and thyroxine replacement. *J. Mol. Cell. Cardiol.* 10:1053–76

12. Jewell, B. R. 1977. A reexamination of

the influence of muscle length on myocardial performance. *Circ. Res.* 40:221–30

13. Jewell, B. R. 1982. Activation of contraction in cardiac muscle. *Mayo Clin. Proc.* 57:6–13 Suppl.

14. Kadoma, M., Sacktor, B., Froehlich, J. P. 1980. Stimulation by cAMP and protein kinase of calcium transport in sarcoplasmic reticulum from senescent rat myocardium. *Fed. Proc.* 39:2040 (Abstr.)

15. Kirchberger, M. A., Tada, M., Katz, A. M. 1974. Adenosine 3'-5'-monophosphate-dependent protein kinase–catalyzed phosphorylation reaction and its relationship to calcium transport in cardiac sarcoplasmic reticulum. *J. Biol. Chem.* 249:666–75

16. Lab, M. J. 1982. Contraction-excitation feedback in myocardium. Physiological basis and clinical relevance. *Circ. Res.* 40:757–66

17. Lakatta, E. G. 1987. Do hypertension and aging similarly affect the myocardium? *Circulation* In press

18. Lakatta, E. G. 1986. Length modulation of muscle performance: Frank-Starling law of the heart. In *The Heart and Cardiovascular System*, Vol. 2, pp. 819–43, ed. H. M. Fozzard, E. Haber, R. B. Jennings, A. M. Katz, H. E. Morgan. New York: Raven

19. Lakatta, E. G., Capogrossi, M. C., Kort, A. A., Stern, M. D. 1985. Spontaneous myocardial Ca oscillations: An overview with emphasis on ryanodine and caffeine. *Fed. Proc.* 44:2977–83

20. Lakatta, E. G., Gerstenblith, G., Angell, C. S. 1975. Prolonged contraction duration in aged myocardium. *J. Clin. Invest.* 55:61–68

21. Lakatta, E. G., Gerstenblith, G., Angell, C. S., Shock, N. W., Weisfeldt, M. L. 1975. Diminished inotropic response of aged myocardium to catecholamines. *Circ. Res.* 36:262–69

22. Lakatta, E. G., Yin, F. C. P. 1982. Myocardial aging: Functional alterations and related cellular mechanisms. *Am. J. Physiol.* 242:H927–41

23. Narayanan, N. 1981. Differential alterations in ATP-supported calcium transport activities of sarcoplasmic reticulum and sarcolemma of aging myocardium. *Biochim. Biophys. Acta* 678:442–59

24. Noble, D. 1984. The surprising heart: A review of recent progress in cardial electrophysiology. *J. Physiol. London* 353:1–50

25. Orchard, C. H., Lakatta, E. G. 1985. Intracellular calcium transients and developed tensions in rat heart muscle. A mechanism for the negative interval-strength relationship. *J. Gen. Physiol.* 86:637–51

26. Spurgeon, H. A., Steinbach, M. F., Lakatta, E. G. 1983. Chronic exercise prevents characteristic age-related changes in rat cardiac contraction. *Am. J. Physiol.* 244:H513–18

27. Spurgeon, H. A., Thorne, P. R., Yin, F. C. P., Shock, N. W., Weisfeldt, M. F. 1977. Increased dynamic stiffness of trabeculae carneae from senescent rats. *Am. J. Physiol.* 232:H373–80

28. Wei, J. Y., Spurgeon, H. A., Lakatta, E. G. 1984. Excitation-contraction in rat myocardium: Alterations with adult aging. *Am. J. Physiol.* 246:H784–91

29. Yin, F. C. P., Spurgeon, H. A., Rakusan, K., Weisfeldt, M. L., Lakatta, E. G. 1982. Use of tibial length to quantify cardiac hypertrophy: Application in the aging rat. *Am. J. Physiol.* 243:H941–47

30. Yin, F. C. P., Spurgeon, H. A., Weisfeldt, M. L., Lakatta, E. G. 1980. Mechanical properties of myocardium from hypertrophied rat hearts. A comparison between senescence and by aortic banding. *Circ. Res.* 46:292–300

Ann. Rev. Physiol. 1987. 49:533–43
Copyright © 1987 by Annual Reviews Inc. All rights reserved

BIOCHEMICAL MECHANISMS OF CARDIAC HYPERTROPHY

H. E. Morgan, E. E. Gordon, Y. Kira, B. H. L. Chua, L. A. Russo, C. J. Peterson, P. J. McDermott, and P. A. Watson

Department of Physiology, The Pennsylvania State University, Hershey, Pennsylvania 17033

INTRODUCTION

To identify the biochemical mechanisms regulating cardiac hypertrophy we must (*a*) determine which of the reaction(s) in the synthesis of whole heart protein, and particularly contractile protein, generate flux; (*b*) isolate the enzymes and/or cellular organelles that catalyze the flux-generating reaction(s); and (*c*) identify the biochemical signal(s) that link the stimulus for hypertrophy to greater catalytic activity of the flux-generating step(s). In cardiac hypertrophy, these reactions involve expression of a wide variety of genes through synthesis of various species of RNA, as encoded in ribosomal DNA (rDNA) and genes for specific messenger RNAs (mRNAs); transport of these molecules to the cytoplasm; and use of these RNA components for synthesis of protein. The control of gene expression in heart is largely unexplored, although excellent progress has been made in understanding the mechanisms by which the initial transcripts of contractile protein genes are processed, and the sequences of the mRNA products have been determined (8, 15a, 17a, 21, 22, 23a). It is not known whether processing of pre-ribosomal RNA (pre-rRNA), in addition to transcription of rDNA, is an important determinant of the rRNA content of muscle cells. The transport of ribosomal proteins from the cytoplasm to the nuclear compartment and of ribosomal subunits and mRNA through the nuclear membrane to the cytoplasm has not been studied. Initiation of peptide chains, the first step in protein synthesis, is catalyzed by a series of initiation factors and is influenced by the availability of mRNA and initiator methionyl transfer RNA (tRNA) (see Reference 26 for a review). Elongation of peptide chains is determined by the activity of the elongation factors and the availability of amino-acyl tRNA. These enzymatic components have not been purified from heart or skeletal muscle. In addition, the availability of total mRNA and mRNAs for specific contractile proteins has been assessed in only a few instances (8, 43), and the tissue content of initiator methionyl tRNA and overall amino-acyl tRNAs has not been measured. However, the relative rates of peptide chain initiation and elongation have been evaluated by measuring the tissue content of ribosomal subunits and polysomes along with rates of protein synthesis (26). Due to space limitations, this review is restricted to studies of intact heart and does not include growth control in isolated cultured cells from heart or skeletal muscle.

The mechanisms of cardiac hypertrophy are not known because ventricular weight, total protein synthesis, and total RNA synthesis were measured rather than rates of flux through specific enzymatic reactions together with substrate and product concentrations of these reactions.

The rates of synthesis of total RNA, total proteins, specific RNA, or specific proteins have been determined by introducing radioactive precursors following application of a stimulus for hypertrophy, such as pressure overload or thyroid hormone injection (34). Generally, measurements of these rates have not been based upon a rigorous determination of the specific radioactivity of the precursor pool, and thus the validity of the measured values remains in question. Numerous attempts have been made to identify the biochemical signal linking a stimulus for growth to hypertrophy of the heart by measuring ventricular weight or rates of synthesis of total or specific heart proteins. These measurements involve activities of all enzymatic components, and substrate and cofactor availability for all steps in RNA and protein synthesis, and they preclude direct assessment of the effects of the stimulus on the flux-generating step(s). A determination of whether existing components, such as rRNA and mRNA, are used more efficiently or whether the capacity for synthesis increases as a result of higher tissue contents of these components has been made during rapid cardiac growth (34, 43). An increase in capacity for synthesis is a common finding. Frequently, inhibitors of the synthesis of putative signals for hypertrophy, such as prostaglandins and polyamines, have been employed to determine whether the rate of growth was affected (9, 30, 36). In other experiments, the tissue contents of such signal compounds, such as polyamines, have been correlated with rates of protein synthesis (9). Finally, perfusate concentrations of calcium have been varied to assess whether calcium availability is the signal linking the stimulus and response (13). These approaches to signal identification are insensitive because they measure the activity of the entire pathway rather than that of the flux-generating step. In these circumstances, a significant time delay occurs between the application of stimulus and the change in the overall rates of protein synthesis, and a rigorous determination of signal identity and molecular mechanism of action cannot be achieved. An early event following banding of the aorta in rats is induction of stress-protein synthesis. The role of these proteins in the subsequent hypertrophy of the heart is not understood (15).

ANIMAL MODELS OF RAPID CARDIAC GROWTH

Rapid growth of the heart is required to obtain a sensitive assessment of net protein accumulation. When all of the increase in cardiac mass is due to faster protein synthesis (i.e. protein degradation is unchanged), the synthesis rate generally must increase by at least 15% to be statistically significant relative to control (26). If one assumes a half-life for whole heart protein of 5 days (23, 26, 44), a 15% increase in the rate of protein synthesis would result in an 11% hypertrophy after 1 week and a 56% increase in mass after 1 month, which is a rapid rate of cardiac growth. This rate of growth has been observed (a) during the neonatal period in pigs, when growth of the left-ventricular free wall is approximately three times faster than that of the right-ventricular free wall (41); (b) after injection of replacement doses of thyroid hormone into hypothyroid rats or rabbits or after thyrotoxic doses to normal animals (28); and (c) in female rats swimming 6 hr/day (16). These conditions do not lead to depletion of the adenine nucleotide pool, impaired contractility of the heart, or focal necrosis of the ventricular wall, as occurs when banding of the aorta is tight enough to induce severe pressure overload and a rapid rate of growth (2, 35, 45). Aortic banding causes some portions of the heart muscle to die and their proteins to be rapidly degraded, while the bulk of the ventricular wall grows rapidly. The cellular heterogeneity that results from focal necrosis, when imposed upon that initially existing in the heart, prevents a rigorous assessment of the roles of protein synthesis and degradation in muscle cell hypertrophy. In an extreme case, thymidine incorporation into the heart of adult animals is confined to nonmuscle cells because the muscle cells do not divide (27). In general, pressure-overload models of cardiac hypertrophy associated with rapid growth are not suitable experimental systems for studies of the biochemical mechanisms of hypertrophy (2, 35). Likewise, volume-overload hypertrophy is too slow to provide a sensitive experimental model.

ROLE OF PROTEIN SYNTHESIS IN RAPID GROWTH

All studies of cardiac hypertrophy in vivo and in isolated heart preparations report that the rate of protein synthesis is increased above normal levels. As discussed below (see section on the role of protein degradation in rapid growth), the main question is whether the rate of synthesis increases more than is required to account for the rate of growth, which would suggest that protein degradation is also accelerated.

Increased Efficiency of Synthesis

The faster growth rate could be due to greater efficiency of, and/or capacity for, protein synthesis. The efficiency of synthesis is defined as the moles of amino acid incorporated per milligram of cellular RNA per hour. Capacity for synthesis is usually assessed by determining the milligrams of RNA per gram of tissue. In regard to changes in efficiency of synthesis, the extent to which heart RNA is found in ribosomal subunits indicates whether the catalytic activity of peptide chain initiation factors and the availability of mRNA and initiator methionyl tRNA are sufficient to result in only a small fraction of the total RNA in 40S and 60S subunits (26). In adult rats, 10–12% of the total RNA is found in ribosomal subunits in both control and rapidly growing hearts of thyroxine-injected rats. This observation indicates that peptide chain initiation is sufficiently rapid to shift the rate-controlling step to peptide chain elongation (34). Elongation rates when expressed per gram of heart are controlled by the catalytic activity of elongation factors, the availability of amino-acyl tRNA, and the number of ribosomes.

When hearts are removed from control and thyroxine-injected rats and perfused in vitro with buffer containing glucose, lactate, amino acids, insulin, and glucagon in physiological concentrations, the faster rates of protein synthesis in rapidly growing hearts are accounted for by greater numbers of ribosomes, as reflected by their greater RNA content (34). These findings suggest that a change in the efficiency of protein synthesis is not a prominent mechanism to increase cardiac mass in adult rats in vivo. However, in isolated beating rat hearts, beating hearts containing a ventricular drain, and tetrodotoxin arrested-drained preparations (18, 25, 37, 42) increased aortic pressure accelerates protein synthesis. These manipulations have one mechanical factor in common, namely stretch of the ventricular wall. The importance of wall stretch in vivo in induction of growth by exercise or thyroxine injection has not been rigorously examined.

In neonatal pigs, the free wall of the left ventricle (LVFW) grows approximately 3 times faster than the free wall of the right ventricle (RVFW) during the first 10 days of life (31, 41). In the LVFW of the neonatal pig, approximately 16% of total RNA is found in ribosomal subunits, whereas in the RVFW this value is 20%. These findings suggest that the efficiency of protein synthesis is increased in the more rapidly growing muscle due to more efficient peptide chain initiation. However, in both ventricles of the pig initiation is more of a limitation on protein synthesis than it is in adult rats. It is unknown whether the more rapid initiation of peptide chains in the LVFW as compared to the RVFW results from greater catalytic activity of the initiation factors or greater availability of mRNA or initiator methionyl tRNA. Injection of insulin and glucose into neonatal pigs 1 hr prior to death resulted in a decrease in the percent of RNA in ribosomal subunits to 10% of the total RNA, in both LVFW and RVFW (31), which is equivalent to the value found in adult rats. These findings suggest that synthesis of new components, such as mRNA or initiation factors, is not required to correct the restraint on peptide chain initiation in neonatal hearts.

Increased Capacity for Synthesis

An increase in total RNA content is a prominent feature of rapidly growing tissues, including the heart. Following imposition of a pressure overload, injection of thyroxine, or a regimine of swimming exercise, total RNA increases within 1–3 days in adult rats (16, 29, 34). rRNA and mRNA content increases in response to thyroxine-induced hypertrophy by 29 and 58%, respectively (43). Incorporation of radioactive precursors into the RNA of rat hearts indicates that all species of RNA are synthesized at a faster rate in rapidly growing tissue (19). In neonatal pig hearts, the RNA content of the LVFW is approximately 35% greater than that of the RVFW (31, 41). The relative amounts of rRNA and mRNA in these tissues of neonatal pigs have not been measured. Thus, increased capacity for protein synthesis, as evidenced by greater tissue contents of rRNA and mRNA, is an important factor in rapid growth.

Thus far, measurement of absolute rates of synthesis of mRNA and rRNA has been complicated by the rapid degradation of the nucleoside precursor in endothelial cells and by the compartmentation of the nucleotide pool between muscle and nonmuscle cells and among the cytosol, mitochondria, and nuclei of both cell types (5). Destruction of nucleoside precursors can be partially blocked with inhibitors of uridine phosphorylase, and the specific activities of the UTP pool in muscle cells as compared to whole heart can be obtained by measuring the UTP content of isolated muscle cells following pulse-labelling with radioactive uridine (5). Whether there is functional compartmentation of UTP between nuclei and other cellular compartments can then be determined by comparing the specific radioactivities of the UTP pool with UMP residues in pre-rRNA. Now that the base compositions of the 5' external spacer, 28S, and 18S segments of the rDNA are known (4, 14, 38) and complementary RNA probes are available to specifically isolate these segments, this comparison is underway (P. A. Watson, unpublished observations). Measurements of the pool size of pre-rRNA together with the UMP specific radioactivity of this molecule allow for estimation of the efficiency of rRNA processing and determination of whether processing, in addition to rDNA transcription, is a rate-controlling reaction for new ribosome synthesis.

Effects on new ribosome formation can also be assessed by measuring the rates of synthesis and of incorporation of ribosomal proteins (r-proteins) into cytoplasmic ribosomes (34). Formation of a new ribosome involves synthesis of approximately 70 r-proteins on cytoplasmic ribosomes, followed by migration of these proteins into the nucleus, where they bind to newly made pre-rRNA (40). The 40S and 60S ribosomal subunits appear in the cytoplasm after approximately 10–30 min. The pool of free r-proteins in the cytosol is quite small, and exchange of free and ribosome-bound proteins is very slow. In support of these observations, inhibition of RNA synthesis with actinomycin D prevents incorporation of r-proteins into cytoplasmic ribosomes but has no effect on synthesis of whole heart protein (34).

Stimuli that result in greater RNA content and rapid cardiac growth, including thyroxine injection and exposure to high aortic pressures, result in accelerated synthesis of new ribosomal subunits within 2–4 hr (34; B. H. L. Chua, unpublished observations). When thyrotoxic doses of thyroxine are injected into adult rats and their hearts are removed and perfused in vitro under simulated in vivo conditions, accelerated ribosome synthesis is observed within 4 hr (34). When new ribosome formation is measured in hearts from normal rats perfused with a buffer that contains glucose and insulin, an increase in aortic pressure from 60 to 120 mm Hg results in a 50% increase in incorporation of newly made r-proteins into cytoplasmic ribosomes, whereas whole heart protein synthesis is unaffected (B. H. L. Chua, unpublished observations). These experiments indicate that preferential synthesis of new ribosomes is an early event in hypertrophy of rat heart.

THE ROLE OF PROTEIN DEGRADATION IN RAPID GROWTH

One of the difficulties in assessing the role of proteolysis in rapid cardiac growth is the lack of methods for direct measurement of its rate in vivo (10, 24). Instead, protein degradation must be calculated from the rates of growth and protein synthesis. Growth rates are estimated over a period of days; rates of protein synthesis are measured at specific times during the growth period and are assumed to be constant throughout. The rates of protein synthesis are generally calculated using the specific radioactivity of plasma leucine or phenylalanine, but in some instances the specific activities of tRNA-bound amino acids have been used (7). Experiments of this type in rapidly growing heart and skeletal muscle indicate that the rate of protein synthesis increases more than is needed to account for the rate of growth and that proteolysis also is accelerated (2a, 24). Protein breakdown is probably accelerated because tissue remodeling is required during rapid growth.

Protein breakdown can be measured directly in muscle preparations in vitro by measuring the release of a nonmetabolized amino acid, such as phenylalanine or tyrosine, in the presence of an inhibitor of protein synthesis, e.g. cycloheximide (12, 33). Alternatively, the rate of proteolysis can be calculated from rates of net amino acid release and protein synthesis. The problem with these measurements is that the rate of proteolysis may be different in vitro than in vivo, despite attempts to simulate oxidative substrate, amino acid, and hormone availability, and the work of the heart (25, 34). In isolated hearts from control rats that are perfused under these simulated in vivo conditions, the rate of protein breakdown is equal to that of protein synthesis, which indicates that the tissue is in nitrogen balance, as expected (25). When rapidly growing hearts are removed from rats injected for 3–4 days with thyrotoxic doses of thyroxine, the rate of proteolysis measured in vitro in Langendorff preparations or working hearts is the same as in control hearts. This finding suggests that the rate of proteolysis does not change in the transition to rapid growth (33a, 34). In hearts from rats subjected to aortic banding 3–4 days earlier, the rate of proteolysis is increased during in vitro perfusion. However, the meaning of these findings is uncertain because of the tissue heterogeneity induced by focal necrosis in the ventricular wall (2, 35). In neither the thyrotoxic nor pressure-overload models of hypertrophy in rats have rates of protein synthesis been measured with sufficient frequency over the course of growth to indicate whether protein synthesis is more rapid than required for the observed rate of growth. The effects of cardiac work and increased aortic pressure on proteolysis have been explored in vitro in rat hearts (12). When hearts are supplied glucose or pyruvate as substrate without addition of insulin, the rate of proteolysis is more rapid than the rate of protein synthesis. Induction of cardiac work or exposure to high aortic pressure inhibits proteolysis in these circumstances. Exposure to high aortic pressure also inhibits proteolysis in hearts arrested with tetrodotoxin and containing a ventricular drain (12). These findings, as well as those from experiments with isolated skeletal muscle, suggest that stretch is the mechanical effect most closely linked to slower proteolysis (3, 11). Whether inhibition of proteolysis by stretch of the ventricular wall contributes to faster growth during pressure overload in vivo is unknown. In isolated rat hearts, inhibition of protein degradation during exposure to high aortic pressure does not appear to depend upon changes in energy availability, extracellular calcium concentration, prostaglandin synthesis, or change in rate of oxygen consumption (12).

MECHANICAL FACTORS ASSOCIATED WITH RAPID CARDIAC GROWTH

Studies of this topic have addressed two questions. *(a)* What mechanical parameter(s) appear to be linked to induction of rapid growth following an increase in cardiac work? And *(b)* does thyroxine accelerate growth directly by affecting the muscle cells or indirectly by changing mechanical activity? Induction of cardiac work in vitro, exposure of Langendorff preparations to high aortic pressure, and an increase in aortic pressure or intraventricular pressure in arrested-drained Langendorff hearts accelerate synthesis of whole heart protein during the second hour of perfusion (18, 25, 37, 42). Accelerated synthesis of cytoplasmic ribosomes occurs in the first and second hours of exposure of Langendorff preparations to high aortic pressure (B. H. L. Chua, unpublished observations). Acceleration of protein synthesis in arrested-drained hearts by exposure to high aortic pressure appears to exclude cardiac work, intraventricular pressure development, cardiac contraction, and accelerated oxygen consumption as obligatory mechanical or metabolic determinants of more rapid protein synthesis (18). Other studies have also ruled out faster coronary flow as the determining factor (1, 17, 18). The mechanical factor common to all of the interventions that accelerate protein synthesis is stretch of the ventricular wall. Peterson & Lesch (32) were the first to find that stretch of quiescent papillary muscles accelerates protein synthesis. Stretch also accelerates protein synthesis in isolated skeletal muscle and cultured muscle cells (3, 39). As indicated above, the biochemical signal that links stretch to faster protein synthesis has not been identified.

Thyroid hormone has a direct anabolic effect on cultured fetal mouse hearts (6). When administered to intact animals, however, the hormone increases heart rate, cardiac output, and cardiac contractility (28). Zimmer & Peffer (46) report that blockade of the hemodynamic effects of triodothyronine (T_3) by a constant infusion of metoprolol over a period of 3 days has no effect on cardiac growth. These studies suggest that T_3-induced hemodynamic alterations can be dissociated from the metabolic changes and that cardiac hypertrophy occurs independently of functional alterations. In contrast, when heterotopic hearts from adult hypothyroid rats are isotransplanted into hypothyroid recipients, injection of T_3 into the recipient results in the same time course of shift in V3 to V1 isomyosin in the transplanted and recipient heart (20). However, only the recipient heart carrying the full hemodynamic load increases in size as a result of hormone injection (B. Korecky, personal communication). These findings suggest that hemodynamic alterations may be important in T_3-induced growth. Further studies are needed to localize the effects of T_3 to specific reactions in RNA and protein synthesis and to determine the molecular mechanism of action of the hormone on the flux-generating reactions (17a). (See the accompanying chapter by Morkin for further information on this topic.)

SUMMARY

Rapid cardiac growth in adult rats and neonatal pigs involves more efficient use of existing components of the protein synthesis pathway and synthesis of new ribosomes and mRNA to increase the capacity for protein synthesis. Greater efficiency of synthesis can be induced by mechanical perturbations that stretch the ventricular wall, including increased cardiac work and increased ventricular pressure development in beating hearts, and increased aortic and intraventricular pressure in arrested-drained hearts. The biochemical signal linking stretch to more efficient protein synthesis has not been identified. Preferential synthesis of new ribosomes occurs in the first two hours of exposure of Langendorff preparations to high aortic pressure or within four hours after injection of thyroid hormone into normal rats. The rate of protein degradation is either accelerated or unchanged in hypertrophing hearts but is inhibited by induction of cardiac work or high aortic pressure in Langendorff preparations. Overall, increased capacity for, and efficiency of, protein synthesis are the major factors accounting for cardiac growth.

ACKNOWLEDGMENT

This work is supported by grants from the National Institutes of Health (HL-20388, HL-35289, HL-18258, and HL-07223). We wish to thank Maxine L. Gerberich for typing of the manuscript.

Literature Cited

1. Arnold, G., Kosche, F., Miessner, E., Neitzert, A., Lochner, W. 1968. The importance of the perfusion pressure in coronary arteries for the contractility and oxygen consumption of the heart. *Pflüg. Arch.* 299:339–56
2. Bishop, S. P., Melsen, L. R. 1976. Myocardial necrosis, fibrosis and DNA synthesis in experimental hypertrophy induced by sudden pressure overload. *Circ. Res.* 39:238–45
2a. Bonnin, C. M., Sparrow, M. P., Taylor, R. T. 1983. Increased protein synthesis and degradation in the dog heart during thyroxine administration. *J. Mol. Cell. Cardiol.* 15:245–50
3. Booth, F. W., Nicholson, W. F., Watson, P. A. 1982. Influence of muscle use on protein synthesis and degradation. In *Exercise and Sports Sciences Reviews*, ed. R. L. Terjung, pp. 27–48. New York: Franklin Inst. Press
4. Chikaraishi, D. M., Buchanon, L., Danna, K. L., Harrington, C. A. 1983. Genomic organization of rat rRNA. *Nucl. Acids Res.* 11:6437–52
5. Chua, B. H. L., Watson, P. A., Kleinhans, B., Morgan, H. E. 1985. Effect of 5-benzyloxybenzylacyclouridine on the labeling of UTP and RNA in perfused rat heart. *Fed. Proc.* 44:1773 (Abstr.)
6. Crie, J. S., Wakeland, J. R., Mayhew,

B. A., Wildenthal, K. 1983. Direct anabolic effects of thyroid hormone on isolated mouse heart. *Am. J. Physiol.* 245:C328–33
7. Everett, A. W., Prior, G., Zak, R. 1981. Equilibration of leucine between the plasma compartment and leucyl-tRNA in the heart, and turnover of cardiac myosin heavy chain. *Biochem. J.* 194:365–68
8. Everett, A. W., Sinha, A. N., Umeda, P. K., Jakovcic, S., Rabinowitz, M., Zak, R. 1984. Regulation of myosin synthesis by thyroid hormone: Relative change in the α- and β-myosin heavy chain mRNA levels in rabbit hearts. *Biochemistry* 23:1596–99
9. Flamigni, F., Rossoni, C., Stefanelli, C., Caldarera, C. M. 1986. Polyamine metabolism and function in the heart. *J. Mol. Cell. Cardiol.* 18:3–11
10. Garlick, P. J., McNurlan, M. A., Preedy, V. R. 1980. A rapid and convenient technique for measuring the rate of protein synthesis in tissues by injection of [³H]phenylalanine. *Biochem. J.* 192:719–23
11. Goldspink, D. F. 1977. The influence of immobilization and stretch on protein turnover of rat skeletal muscle. *J. Physiol.* 264:267–82
12. Gordon, E. E., Kira, Y., Demers, L. M., Morgan, H. E. 1986. Aortic pres-

sure as a determinant of cardiac protein degradation. *Am. J. Physiol.* 250:C932–38

13. Gordon, E. E., Kira, Y., Morgan, H. E. 1985. Dependence of protein synthesis on aortic pressure and calcium availability. In *Advances in Myocardiology*, ed. P. Harris, P. A. Poole-Wilson, pp. 145–56. New York: Plenum

14. Hadjiolov, A. A., Georgiev, O. I., Nosikov, V. V., Yavacher, L. P. 1984. Primary and secondary structure of rat 28S ribosomal RNA. *Nucl. Acid Res.* 12:3677–93

15. Hammond, G. L., Lai, Y. K., Markert, C. L. 1982. Diverse forms of stress lead to new patterns of gene expression through a common and essential metabolic pathway. *Proc. Natl. Acad. Sci. USA* 70:3485–88

15a. Hastings, K. E. M., Bucher, E. A., Emerson, C. P. 1985. Generation of troponin T isoforms by alternative RNA splicing in avian skeletal muscle. *J. Biol. Chem.* 260:13699–13703

16. Hickson, R. C., Hammons, G. T., Holloszy, J. O. 1979. Development and regression of exercise-induced cardiac hypertrophy in rats. *Am. J. Physiol.* 236:H268–72

17. Hjalmarson, A., Isaksson, O. 1972. In vitro workload and rat heart metabolism. I. Effect on protein synthesis. *Acta Physiol. Scand.* 86:126–44

17a. Izumo, S., Nadal-Ginard, B., Mahdavi, V. 1986. All members of the MHC multigene family respond to thyroid hormone in a highly tissue-specific manner. *Science* 231:597–99

18. Kira, Y., Kochel, P. J., Gordon, E. E., Morgan, H. E. 1984. Aortic perfusion pressure as a determinant of cardiac protein synthesis. *Am. J. Physiol.* 246:C247–58

19. Koide, T., Rabinowitz, M. 1969. Biochemical correlates of cardiac hypertrophy. II. Increased rate of RNA synthesis in experimental cardiac hypertrophy in the rat. *Circ. Res.* 24:9–18

20. Korecky, B., Zak, R., Schwartz, K. 1986. Role of thyroid hormone on selective synthesis of cardiac isomyosins. *J. Mol. Cell. Cardiol.* 18 (Suppl. I):161 (Abstr.)

21. Lompré, A. M., Nadal-Ginard, B., Mahdavi, V. 1984. Expression of cardiac ventricular α- and β-myosin heavy chain genes is developmentally and hormonally regulated. *J. Biol. Chem.* 259:6437–46

22. Mahdavi, V., Chambers, A. P., Nadal-Ginard, B. 1984. Cardiac α- and β-

myosin heavy chain gene are organized in tandem. *Proc. Natl. Acad. Sci. USA* 81:2626–30

23. Martin, A. F., Rabinowitz, M., Blough, R., Prior, G., Zak, R. 1977. Measurements of half-life of rat cardiac myosin heavy chain with leucyl-tRNA used as precursor pool. *J. Biol. Chem.* 252:3422–29

23a. Medford, R. M., Nguyen, H. T., Destree, A. T., Summers, E., Nadal-Ginard, B. 1984. A novel mechanism of alternative RNA splicing for the developmentally regulated generation of troponin T isoforms from a single gene. *Cell* 38:409–21

24. Millward, D. J. 1980. Protein turnover in skeletal and cardiac muscle during normal growth and hypertrophy. In *Degradative Processes in Heart and Skeletal Muscle*, ed. K. Wildenthal, pp. 161–96. Amsterdam: Elsevier/North-Holland Biomed.

25. Morgan, H. E., Chua, B. H. L., Fuller, E. O., Siehl, D. L. 1980. Regulation of protein synthesis and degradation during in vitro cardiac work. *Am. J. Physiol.* 238:E431–42

26. Morgan, H. E., Rannels, D. E., McKee, E. E. 1979. Protein metabolism of the heart. In *Handbook of Physiology. The Cardiovascular System I*, ed. R. M. Berne, N. Sperelakis, pp. 845–71. Bethesda, Maryland: Am. Physiol. Soc.

27. Morkin, E., Ashford, T. P. 1968. Myocardial DNA synthesis in experimental cardiac hypertrophy. *Am. J. Physiol.* 215:1409–13

28. Morkin, E., Fink, I. L., Goldman, S. 1983. Biochemical and physiologic effects of thyroid hormone on cardiac performance. *Prog. Cardiovasc. Res.* 25:435–64

29. Nair, K. G., Cutilletta, A. F., Zak, R., Koide, T., Rabinowitz, M. 1968. Biochemical correlates of cardiac hypertrophy. I. Experimental model, changes in heart weight, RNA content, and nuclear RNA polymerase activity. *Circ. Res.* 23:451–62

30. Palmer, R. M., Reeds, P. J., Atkinson, T., Smith, R. H. 1983. The influences of changes in tension on protein synthesis and prostaglandin release in isolated rabbit muscles. *Biochem. J.* 214:1101–14

31. Peterson, C. J., Morgan, H. E., Whitman, V., Klinger, M. H. 1986. Control of myocardial growth in the neonatal heart. *Fed. Proc.* 45:1040

32. Peterson, M. B., Lesch, M. 1972. Protein synthesis and amino acid transport in the isolated rabbit right ventricular

papillary muscle. Effect of isometric tension development. *Circ. Res.* 31:317–27

33. Rannels, D. E., Kao, R., Morgan, H. E. 1975. Effect of insulin on protein turnover in heart muscle. *J. Biol. Chem.* 250:1694–1701

33a. Sanford, C. F., Griffin, E. E., Wildenthal, K. 1978. Synthesis and degradation of myocardial protein during development and regression of thyroxine-induced cardiac hypertrophy in rats. *Circ. Res.* 43:688–94

34. Siehl, D., Chua, B. H. L., Lautensack-Belser, N., Morgan, H. E. 1985. Faster protein and ribosome synthesis in thyroxine-induced hypertrophy of rat heart. *Am. J. Physiol.* 248:C309–19

35. Siehl, D. L., Gordon, E. E., Kira, Y., Chua, B. H. L., Morgan, H. E. 1987. Protein degradation in the hypertrophic heart. In *Lysosomes: Their Role in Protein Breakdown*, ed. H. Glaumann, F. J. Ballard. London: Academic. In press

36. Smith, R. H., Palmer, R. M., Reeds, P. J. 1983. Protein synthesis in isolated rabbit forelimb muscles. The possible role of metabolites of arachidonic acid in the response to intermittent stretching. *Biochem. J.* 214:153–61

37. Takala, T. 1981. Protein synthesis in the isolated perfused rat heart. Effects of mechanical workload, diastolic ventricular pressure, and coronary flow on amino acid incorporation and its transmural distribution into left ventricular protein. *Basic Res. Cardiol.* 76:44–61

38. Torczynski, R., Bolton, A. P., Fuke, M. 1984. The complete nucleotide sequence of the rat 18S ribosomal RNA gene and comparison with the respective yeast and frog genes. *Nucl. Acids Res.* 11:4879–90

39. Vandenburgh, H. H. 1983. Cell shape and growth regulation in skeletal muscle: exogenous versus endogenous factors. *J. Cell. Physiol.* 116:363–71

40. Warner, J. R. 1974. The assembly of ribosomes in eukaryotes. In *Ribosomes,* ed. H. Nomura, A. Tissieres, P. Lengel, pp. 461–68. Cold Spring Harbor, NY: Cold Spring Harbor Lab.

41. Whitman, V., Schuler, H. G., Fripp, R. R. 1985. Cardiac development in the perinatal period. *Fed. Proc.* 44:467 (Abstr.)

42. Xenophontos, X. P., Morgan, H. E. 1986. Effect of intraventricular pressure on protein synthesis in arrested rat hearts. *Am. J. Physiol.* 251:C95–C98

43. Zähringer, J., Klaubert, A. 1982. The effect of triiodothyronine on the cardiac mRNA. *J. Mol. Cell. Cardiol.* 14:559–71

44. Zak, R., Martin, A. F., Reddy, M. K., Rabinowitz, M. 1976. Control of protein balance in hypertrophied cardiac muscle. *Circ. Res.* 38 (Suppl. 1):I145–50

45. Zimmer, H. G., Ibel, H., Gerlach, E. 1980. Significance of the hexose monophosphate shunt in experimentally induced cardiac hypertrophy. *Basic Res. Cardiol.* 75:207–13

46. Zimmer, H. G., Peffer, H. 1986. Dissociation of the hemodynamic from metabolic effects of triiodothyronine by metoprolol. *J. Mol. Cell. Cardiol.* 18 (Supp. I):301 (Abstr.)

Ann. Rev. Physiol. 1987. 49:545–54

CHRONIC ADAPTATIONS IN CONTRACTILE PROTEINS: GENETIC REGULATION

Eugene Morkin

Departments of Internal Medicine and Pharmacology, University of Arizona, Tucson, Arizona 85724

INTRODUCTION

Adaptive changes in contractile proteins are thought to underlie important alterations in the performance of cardiac and skeletal muscles. Changes at the protein level during development and in many types of physiological adaptations have been reviewed recently (21, 28, 36). Since these publications appeared, significant new information has emerged relating to the genetic mechanisms that regulate these responses, and further progress in this field is now likely to be rapid.

The genes with which we are concerned here are those that encode isoforms of myosin, α-actin, α-tropomyosin (TM), and troponin (TN) in mammalian cardiac and skeletal muscles. Genes encoding proteins that are accessible for transcription within these tissues are subject to three types of genetically programmed control systems, one usually "static" and the other two active. In static control, the gene is permanently "switched" on, that is, constitutively expressed within a tissue. However, rates of RNA and protein production nevertheless are subject to some degree of control, which is expressed particularly in association with changes in cell volume (14, 32). One form of active regulation involves the switching on and off of particular genes in response to specific physiological signals. This adaptive response acts at the phenotypic level rather than causing a change in the genetic material itself. It both activates gene expression and regulates the rate of RNA production within a multigene family encoding protein isoforms. The other active mechanism, referred to as alternative RNA processing, produces mRNAs coding for

545

0066-4278/87/0315-0545$02.00

different isoforms from a single gene. In the examples to be discussed, there are variations in the pattern of intron and exon splicing, initiation of transcription from different start sites, and the use of alternative termination sites.

REGULATION OF MYOSIN HEAVY-CHAIN GENE EXPRESSION

At least seven myosin heavy chains (MHCs) are known to be expressed in striated muscles of the rat, including one encoding a myosin form found only in extraocular muscles, embryonic and neonatal skeletal muscle forms, fast oxidative-glycolytic (Fast IIa) and fast glycolytic (Fast IIb) skeletal muscle forms, and two cardiac muscle types, α and β (20). The β form also is expressed in slow skeletal muscles in the rat (17), but a separate slow myosin form may be present in avian muscle (16).

Multigene families similar to that described in rat encode sarcomeric MHC forms in man (31), mouse (38), and rabbit (10, 34). The organization of the MHC genes is unusual and may provide some clues to the selective expression of different myosin forms (38). The genes expressed exclusively in mouse skeletal muscle are clustered on chromosome 11, and the human skeletal muscle MHC genes have been localized to chromosome 17. The cardiac α-MHC genes are separate from the skeletal MHC cluster; they are located on chromosome 14 in mouse and man.

In the rat, the α- and β-MHC genes are located about 4 kilobases (kb) apart and arranged in a 5' to 3' orientation that corresponds to the order of their developmental expression in ventricular myocardium, that is, the β-MHC gene is located upstream to the α-MHC gene (18). Restriction analysis suggests that α- and β-MHC genes are not linked to the skeletal MHC genes, but the embryonic, neonatal, and adult skeletal muscle MHC genes also are organized in a head-to-tail fashion that reflects the order of their developmental expression (19). Interestingly, the genes encoding the myosin light-chains (MLCs) are distributed among six chromosomes (1).

In heart and skeletal muscles, individual members of the relatively large MHC multigene family are expressed not only at different times during development but in response to different hormonal (8, 13, 14, 17), dietary (33), physiological (5), and innervational stimuli (28). Alterations in myosin gene expression in various muscle types may be functionally important, since the relative proportions of the isoforms are directly related to the intrinsic speed of contraction (21, 28, 36).

Control Mechanisms for MHC Gene Switching

The molecular mechanisms responsible for control of MHC gene expression are poorly understood. However, studies of gene expression in other systems have shown that the sequences in the flanking region located 5' to the coding sequences are important to the regulation of transcription. In addition to consensus "TATA" and "CAAT" boxes, which serve as RNA polymerase II recognition sites (2), two types of sequence elements are found frequently. One sequence type, termed enhancers, may stimulate transcription over considerable distances at positions either upstream or downstream from the promoter. The other type of effector element is located a variable distance upstream, generally within a few hundred base pairs, from the transcriptional initiation site. This second type of element may have either positive or negative effects on transcription. Elements of each type are thought to be recognized by DNA binding factors, which probably are proteins. The promoter elements may be cell type specific and may bind more than one factor.

Certain other conserved DNA sequences may be important in controlling the activation of gene families (9, 25). Homologous sequences in the 5' untranslated region have been identified in two MHC skeletal muscle genes both immediately upstream from the CAAT box and in the nucleotides between the CAAT and TATA promoter elements (11). The positions of the first two introns at the 5' terminus of MHC genes also are conserved (35). A 17-nucleotide element recently has been identified in the 5' flanking sequences of several muscle-specific genes (15a). Such conserved sequences may serve as sites of DNA-protein interactions that coordinate the expression of multigene families.

Actions of Thyroid Hormone on MHC Genes

Initially, thyroid hormone was found to stimulate transcription of α-MHC and inhibit expression of β-MHC (8, 17). Subsequently, it has been found to affect other members of this gene family in a highly muscle-specific manner (13–15). Because of the possibility of multiple hormonal interactions within intact animals, muscle cell culture systems have been sought that would permit the study of MHC regulation under more defined conditions. Suitable permanent cell lines derived from heart muscle are not available, but Nag & Cheng (23) have reported success in changing the predominant myosin isoform pattern in primary fetal heart cultures from the fetal (V_3) to adult (V_1) type with thyroid hormone treatment. Since the cells were grown in a medium containing fetal calf serum and high concentrations of several growth factors, it was not possible to determine whether these factors were required for the actions of thyroxine.

Recent data indicate that similar effects on cardiac MHC genes can be obtained in a defined medium (12). Supplementation of the medium with epithelial growth factor, endothelial cell growth supplement, insulin, selenium, and transferrin was found to increase RNA yields, but these factors were not required for switching from α- to β-MHC production. No effects on these genes were observed when a number of other cardioactive agents, including norepinephrine, isoproterenol, dibutryl cAMP, glucagon, and carbachol were added to the medium in the presence or absence of thyroid hormone.

Definition of DNA Sequence Requirements

To study the DNA sequence requirements for MHC control, synthetic α-MHC genes have been introduced into fetal heart cell cultures (14a). Chimeric genes were constructed using a restriction fragment of α-MHC that contains about 2.6 kb of 5' promoter region and 0.4 kb of coding sequence. The α-MHC fragment was ligated into the plasmid pSVO-CAT, which contains the gene coding for chloramphenicol acetyltransferase (CAT). Another chimeric gene was constructed using pSV2-CAT, which includes simian virus 40 (SV40) enhancer sequences in addition to the CAT gene. Since the CAT gene is found only in prokaryotes, measurement of CAT activity in cell homogenates provides a sensitive assay for the successful introduction of the chimeric gene and its hormonal responsiveness.

Surprisingly, both chimeric genes exhibited responses to thyroid hormone that closely mimicked those of the endogenous α-MHC gene. The level of CAT activity was greater when the α-MHC sequences were fused to pSV2-CAT rather than to pSVO-CAT, which reflects the presence of the SV40 enhancer sequence, but the degree of stimulation by thyroid hormone was comparable in both constructs. The α-MHC fusion gene showed a time course of activation and dose-response characteristics for triiodothyronine (T_3) that resembled those of the endogenous gene, which suggests that both genes may be regulated by similar factors.

The tissue specificity of thyroid hormone responsiveness was demonstrated by introducing these synthetic α-MHC genes into cultures of L_6E_9, a permanent skeletal muscle cell line, and rat R1 cells. Expression of the chimeric genes could be demonstrated in these cells, but no change in CAT activity was seen after addition of the hormone.

Synthetic α-actin (20) and myosin genes (Y. Mahdavi, unpublished observation) also have been found to be correctly expressed and developmentally regulated when transfected into rat myogenic cells lines. In all cases, sequences in the 5' flanking region seemed sufficient to regulate the rate of transcriptional initiation, but the exact binding sites, the nature of the binding factors, and many other important details of the protein-DNA interaction remain to be determined.

A minimum model for regulation of α- and β-MHC genes is represented in Figure 1. According to this diagram, the promoter region of the α-MHC gene contains a T_3-responsive element, possibly the nuclear T_3 receptor, followed by canonical CAAT and TATA sequences. Formation of a ternary complex of

T_3, its receptor, and a specific DNA binding site is postulated to activate transcription of the gene. In contrast, the β-MHC gene is constitutively expressed in the absence of the hormone, which suggests that a DNA sequence is present that has strong promoter activity independent of any interaction with the T_3-receptor complex. The different sensitivity of the β-MHC gene in various tissues could be explained by binding of tissue-specific factors to this positive effector element. In response to thyroid hormone, either the same factor that is responsible for α-MHC activation or a different one must bind to this element and cause its inactivation.

ALTERNATIVE RNA PROCESSING

Multiple genes for TN, MLC 1/3, and TM can only partially account for the heterogeneity of these proteins. Additional isoforms have been shown to result from variations in the splicing patterns of exons and introns from single genes (1, 3, 27, 29). Rearrangement of exons also makes possible the use of alternative transcriptional initiation and termination sites. The complexity of the gene splicing patterns now appears to be much greater than expected from protein sequence determinations. In principle, alternative RNA splicing may provide an important mechanism for regulating contractile protein interactions.

Troponin

The molecular basis for some of the TN-T heterogeneity was established by showing that a minimum of 10, and potentially 64, distinct mRNAs encoding TN-T isoforms are derived from a single gene (1, 3). As shown Figure 2 *(top)*, the production of these mRNAs is accomplished by a novel mechanism of alternative gene splicing among a number of 5' exons and two 3' exons which are used interchangeably. An unusual feature is that the splice is not

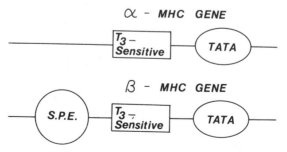

Figure 1 A minimum model for regulation of α- and β-MHC genes (S.P.E. = strong promoter element).

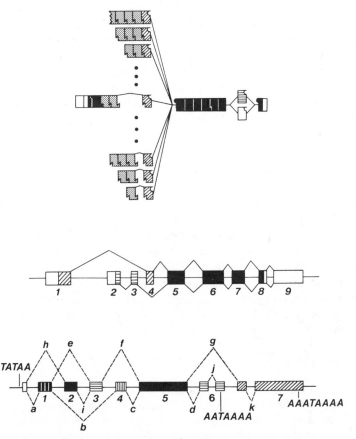

Figure 2 Diagram of the mechanisms involved in production of isoforms of TN-T, MLC 1/3, and TM. *(top)* Alternative joining of exons is theoretically capable of producing 64 distinct mRNAs from a single TN-T gene. (Modified from Reference 3.) *(center)* Splicing of transcripts from nine exons in MLC 1/3 gene produces two mRNAs by use of alternative initiation sites and alternative joining of exons. (Modified from Reference 1.) *(bottom)* Coding regions of α-TM mRNAs drawn tentatively as single exons. The splicing pattern produces two skeletal muscle transcripts (α_1 - TM = a + b + c + d + j; α_2 - TM = h + i + f + d + j) and one smooth muscle TM transcript (a + e + f + g + k). The 3' untranslated regions of skeletal transcripts (regions 6 and 7) are depicted as split by an intron, which is unusual in this location. (Redrawn from Reference 20.)

always made between codons but may transect codons, such that the three bases comprising the codon are provided from adjoining exons.

Different TN-T isoforms have been identified in slow skeletal muscle, heart, and embryonic muscles (4, 37). Also, there is evidence of additional heterogeneity of TN components, which may arise by gene switching in response to changes in thyroid status or cross innervation (6, 7).

Myosin Light Chains

It has been demonstrated in chicken, rat, and mouse that the skeletal MLC 1 and MLC 3 mRNAs originate from a single gene by differential transcription (1, 27). The gene is 18 kb in size and has two transcription initiation sites from which a 17.5-kb and an 8-kb precursor mRNA are transcribed. As depicted in Figure 2 (*center*), these two mRNAs are processed by different modes of splicing: They both use the same 3' exons, but each has two additional 5' exons, one of which is the initiation site specific for that message.

MLCs in other tissues are encoded by a large multigene family, which is distributed among at least six chromosomes (1). Many of these MLC forms are known to be subject to developmental and innervational regulation (28, 36).

Tropomyosin

TM is found in both muscle and nonmuscle cell types as are many other contractile proteins. Generally, these forms are products of separate genes. In the case of TM, however, three forms have been identified: two are abundant in skeletal muscle, and the third is the predominant form found in smooth muscle (22, 29). All three mRNAs are produced by alternative splicing of a single gene, as shown in Figure 2 (*bottom*), in a complex pattern of splicing that could, in principle, generate as many as eight separate mRNAs. The existence of the other five possible mRNAs has not yet been confirmed, however.

The production of both skeletal and smooth muscle forms from a single gene is particulary interesting since the TM forms interact differently with the other components of the contractile system in striated and smooth muscles (26). The differences in sequence found between the smooth and striated muscle forms may define the sites of TM interaction with TN-I and TN-T binding domains.

Mechanisms of RNA Processing

Splicing of mRNAs has been under intensive investigation during the last few years. Recent studies using in vitro mammalian splicing systems have provided an outline of the splicing process (24, 30). An unresolved question is how alternatively spliced exons are recognized. No characteristic DNA sequences have been found in the exons or flanking introns, and it has been postulated that other factors, such as proteins or small RNAs, must be involved in the exon selection and alignment steps. Also, the relationship, if any, between the factors that regulate gene switching and those responsible for alternative RNA processing has not yet been defined.

WHY SO MANY CONTRACTILE PROTEIN ISOFORMS?

Two basic hypotheses have been advanced to explain the astonishing number of contractile protein isoforms that now have been identified (see discussion in Reference 4). The first proposal, simply stated, is that the diversity of gene structure arises because the isoforms provide a slight functional advantage. An alternative hypothesis places the diversity at the level of the gene. In this model, duplication of contractile protein genes would allow them to be placed under different, tissue-specific, developmental, and adaptive regulatory programs. Isoform diversity would be secondary to duplication of genes and would reflect mutational drift. The fact that these genes have evolved over millions of years suggests that elements of both proposals may have played some role.

SUMMARY AND CONCLUSIONS

The pleiotropic alterations in contractile protein isoforms can be explained by the interaction of only a few molecular mechanisms with the basic genotype of the muscle cell. Rapid advances in delineating the details of these mechanisms can be expected to provide greater insight into the genetic control of contractile protein expression than might have been anticipated only a few years ago.

ACKNOWLEDGMENT

Original investigations by the author cited in this work were supported by grants from the National Institutes of Health (HL20984, HL35751) and the Gustavus and Louise Pfeiffer Research Foundation.

Literature Cited

1. Barton, P. J. R., Buckingham, M. E. 1985. The myosin alkali light chain proteins and their genes. *Biochem. J.* 231:249–61
2. Breathnach, R., Chambon, P. 1981. Organization and expression of eucaryotic split genes coding for proteins. *Ann. Rev. Biochem.* 50:349–83
3. Breitbart, R. E., Nguyen, H. T., Medford, R. M., Destree, A. T., Mahdavi, V., Nadal-Ginard, B. 1985. Intricate combinatorial patterns of exon splicing generate multiple regulated troponin T isoforms from a single gene. *Cell* 41:67–82
4. Cooper, T. A., Ordahl, C. P. 1984. A single troponin T gene regulated by different programs in cardiac and skeletal

muscle development. *Science* 226:979–82
5. Delaney, P., Vitek, S., Cribbs, L., Siddiqui, M. A. Q. 1985. Increased levels of myosin mRNAs in spontaneously hypertensive rat heart. *Biochem. Biophys. Res. Commun.* 132:820–28
6. Dhoot, G. K., Perry, S. V. 1981. Effect of thyroidectomy on the distribution of the fast and slow forms of troponin-I in rat soleus muscle. *FEBS Lett.* 133:225–29
7. Dhoot, G. K., Perry, S. V., Vrbova, G. 1981. Changes in the distribution of the components of the troponin complex in muscle fibres after cross-innervation. *Exp. Neurol.* 72:513–30
8. Everett, A. W., Sinha, A. M., Umeda,

P., Jakovcic, S., Robinowitz, M., Zak, R. 1984. Regulation of myosin synthesis by thyroid hormone: Relative change in the alpha- and beta-myosin heavy chain mRNA levels in rabbit heart. *Biochemistry* 23:1596–99

9. Fowlkes, D. M., Mulis, N. T., Comeau, C. M., Crabtree, G. R. 1984. Potential basis for regulation of the coordinately expressed fibrinogen genes: Homology in the 5' flanking regions. *Proc. Natl. Acad. Sci. USA* 81:2313–16

10. Friedman, D. J., Umeda, P. K., Sinha, A. M., Hsu, H. J., Jakovcic, S., Rabinowitz, M. 1984. Characterization of genomic clones specifying rabbit alpha- and beta-ventricular myosin heavy chains. *Proc. Natl. Acad. Sci. USA* 82:3044–48

11. Gulick, J., Kropp, K., Robbins, J. 1985. The structure of two fast-white myosin heavy chain promoters. A comparative study. *J. Biol. Chem.* 260:14513–20

12. Gustafson, T. A., Bahl, J. J., Markham, B. E., Morkin, E. 1986. Analysis of thyroid hormone control of myosin heavy chain (MHC) gene expression in cultured fetal rat heart cells using synthetic oligonucleotide probes. *Fed. Proc.* 45:787

13. Gustafson, T. A., Markham, B. E., Morkin, E. 1985. Analysis of thyroid hormone effects on myosin heavy chain gene expression in cardiac and soleus muscles using a novel dot-blot mRNA assay. *Biochem. Biophys. Res. Commun.* 130:1161–67

14. Gustafson, T. A., Markham, B. E., Morkin, E. 1986. Effects of thyroid hormone on α-actin and myosin heavy chain expression in cardiac and skeletal muscles of the rat: Measurement of mRNA content using synthetic oligonucleotide probes. *Circ. Res.* 59:194–201

14a. Gustafson, T. A., Markham, B. E., Bahl, J. J., Morkin, E. 1986. 5' Nucleotide sequences of the rat alpha myosin heavy chain gene mediate thyroid hormone regulated expression. *Circulation* 74(Suppl. II):II–620

15. Izumo, S., Nadal-Ginard, B., Mahdavi, V. 1986. All members of the MHC multigene family respond to thyroid hormone in a highly tissue specific manner. *Science* 231:597–60

15a. Jaynes, J. B., Chamberlain, J. S., Buskin, J. N., Johnson, J. E., Hauschka, S. D. 1986. Transcriptional regulation of the muscle creatine kinase gene and regulated expression in transfected mouse myoblasts. *Mol. Cell Biol.* 6:2855–64

16. Kennedy, J. M., Kamel, S., Tambone, W. W., Vrbova, G., Zak, R. 1986. The expression of myosin heavy chain isoforms in normal and hypertrophied chicken slow muscle. *J. Cell Biol.* 103:977–83

17. Lompre, A. M., Nadal-Ginard, B., Mahdavi, V. 1984. Expression of the cardiac ventricular alpha- and beta-myosin heavy chain genes is developmentally and hormonally regulated. *J. Biol. Chem.* 259:6437–46

18. Mahdavi, V., Chambers, A. O., Nadal-Ginard, B. 1984. Cardiac alpha- and beta-myosin heavy chain genes are organized in tandem. *Proc. Natl. Acad. Sci. USA* 81:2626–30

19. Mahdavi, V., Strehler, E. E., Periasamy, M., Wieczorek, D., Izumo, S., et al. 1986. Sarcomeric myosin heavy chain gene family: Organization and pattern of expression. In *Molecular Biology of Muscle Development, UCLA Symp. Mol. Cell. Biol. New Ser.* ed. C. Emerson, D. Fischman, B. Nadal-Ginard, M. A. Q. Siddiqui, Vol. 29, pp. 345–61. New York: Liss

20. Melloul, D., Aloni, B., Calvo, J., Yaffe, D., Nudel, U. 1984. Developmentally regulated expression of chimeric genes containing muscle actin DNA sequences in transfected myogenic cells. *EMBO J.* 3:983–90

21. Morkin, E., Flink, I. L., Goldman, S. 1983. Biochemical and physiologic effects of thyroid hormone on cardiac performance. *Prog. Cardiovasc. Dis.* 25:435–64

22. Nadal-Ginard, B., Breitbart, R. E., Strehler, E. E., Ruiz-Opazo, N., Periasamy, M., Mahdavi, V. 1986. Alternative splicing: A common mechanism for the generation of contractile protein diversity from single genes. See Ref. 19, pp. 387–410

23. Nag, A. C., Cheng, M. 1984. Expression of myosin isoforms in cardiac muscle cells in culture. *Biochem. J.* 221:21–26

24. Padgett, R. A., Konarska, M. M., Grabowski, P. J., Hardy, S. F., Sharp, P. A. 1984. Lariat RNAs as intermediates and products in the splicing of messenger RNA precursors. *Science* 225:898–903

25. Parslow, T. G., Blair, D. L., Murphy, W. J., Granner, D. K. 1984. Structure of the 5' ends of immunoglobulin genes: A novel conserved sequence. *Proc. Natl. Acad. Sci. USA* 81:2650–54

26. Pearlstone, J. R., Smillie, L. B. 1982. Binding of troponin T fragments to several types of tropomyosin. *J. Biol. Chem.* 257:10587–92

27. Periasamy, M., Strehler, E. E., Garkinkel, L. I., Gubits, R. M., Ruiz-Opazo, N., Nadal-Ginard, B. 1984. Fast skeletal muscle myosin light chains 1 and 3 are produced from a single gene by a combined process of differential RNA transcription and splicing. *J. Biol. Chem.* 259:13595–13604

28. Pette, D., Vrbova, G. 1985. Invited review: Neural control of phenotypic expression in mammalian muscle fibers. *Muscle Nerve* 8:676–89

29. Ruiz-Opazo, N., Weinberger, J., Nadal-Ginard, B. 1985. Comparison of α-tropomyosin sequences from smooth and striated muscle. *Nature* 315:67–70

30. Ruskin, B., Krainer, A. R., Maniatis, T., Green, M. R. 1984. Excision of an intact intron as a novel lariat structure during pre-mRNA splicing in vitro. *Cell* 38:317–31

31. Saez, L., Leinwand, L. 1986. Characterization of diverse forms of myosin heavy chain expressed in adult human skeletal muscle. *Nucl. Acids Res.* 14:2951–69

32. Schwartz, K., Bastie, D., Bouveret, P., Oliviero, P., Alonso, S., Buckingham, M. 1986. α-Skeletal muscle actin mRNAs accumulate in hypertrophied adult rat hearts. *Circ. Res.* In press

33. Sheer, D., Morkin, E. 1984. Myosin isoenzyme expression in rat ventricle: Effects of thyroid hormone analog, catacholamines, glucocorticoids and high carbohydrate diet. *J. Pharmacol. Exp. Ther.* 229:872–79

34. Sinha, A. M., Friedman, D. J., Nigro, J. M., Jakovcic, S., Rabinowitz, M., Umeda, P. K. 1984. Expression of rabbit ventricular alpha-myosin heavy chain messenger RNA sequences in atrial muscle. *J. Biol. Chem.* 259:6674–80

35. Strehler, E. E., Mahdavi, V., Perisamy, M., Nadal-Ginard, B. 1985. Intron positions are conserved in the 5' end region of myosin heavy chain genes. *J. Biol. Chem.* 260:468–71

36. Swynghedauw, B. 1986. Developmental and functional adaptation of contractile proteins in cardiac and skeletal muscles. *Physiol. Rev.* In press

37. Toyota, N., Shimada, Y. 1981. Differentiation of troponin in cardiac and skeletal muscles in chicken embryos as studied by immunofluorescence microscopy. *J. Cell Biol.* 91:497–504

38. Weydert, A., Daubas, P., Lazaridis, I., Barton, P., Garner, I., et al. 1985. Genes for skeletal muscle myosin heavy chains are clustered and are not located on the same mouse chromosome as a cardiac myosin heavy chain gene. *Proc. Natl. Acad. Sci. USA* 82:7183–87

RESPIRATORY PHYSIOLOGY

INNERVATION OF AIRWAY SMOOTH MUSCLE

Introduction, Robert E. Forster, II, *Section Editor*

Our understanding of the control of airway smooth muscle contraction, a topic of great practical importance, has been significantly advanced in the recent past. Particular aspects of the anatomy and physiology of this system are summarized in this section.

The macroscopic and microscopic circuitry of the nerve supply to the smooth muscle of the larger airways is discussed in the article by Gabella. Most afferent fibers are vagal ones that originate in the nodose ganglion, whereas most efferent fibers arise from ganglia in the walls of the large airways. While the principal output to the muscle fibers is cholinergic and excitatory, there are also adrenergic fibers, as well as nonadrenergic, noncholinergic fibers. The precise course and site of terminal synapses of the nerves from the sympathetic and parasympathetic systems are not clear; for example, it is not known how many sympathetic fibers synapse in the paratracheal ganglia and how many pass through these ganglia.

In his article, Coburn describes the function of the paratracheal ganglia in the airway. These ganglia integrate inputs from parasympathetic, sympathetic, and nonadrenergic/noncholinergic nerves and provide local control of airway smooth muscle to a much greater degree than was appreciated until recently.

Kalia first summarizes the microcircuitry of the motor outflow from the brain stem nuclei to the smooth musculature via the ganglionic network of the airways. Afferents from the trachea terminate on central sensory nuclei, and the ultrastructure of these synapses is described and their function discussed. Finally, she considers the performance of the neural networks and the relationships between bronchomotor tone and central respiratory control.

The article by Sant'Ambrogio concentrates on the nervous receptors in the tracheobronchial tree: the slowly adapting receptors, the rapidly adapting receptors, and the nonmyelinated C fibers, which include the J fibers of the lung parenchyma.

The chapter by Lundberg considers the action of humoral transmitting agents on airway smooth muscle, particularly the recent findings that certain peptides, such as vasoactive intestinal polypeptide, can act as neuronal mediators.

As these reviews show, the control of airway smooth muscle is much more complicated than previously thought, involving many levels of the nervous system and a battery of transmitting agents.

Ann. Rev. Physiol. 1987. 49:557–72

POLYPEPTIDE-CONTAINING NEURONS IN AIRWAY SMOOTH MUSCLE

J. M. Lundberg

Department of Pharmacology, Karolinska Institute, Box 60400, S-104 01 Stockholm, Sweden

A. Saria

Department of Experimental and Clinical Pharmacology, University of Graz, A-8010 Graz, Austria

INTRODUCTION

Acetylcholine and noradrenaline have long been the only identified neuronal mediators in the bronchial smooth muscle of the airways. However, increasing evidence suggests that several biologically active polypeptides are also present in nerves of the respiratory tract. In the present review we concentrate on peptides in parasympathetic and sensory nerves that have been most thoroughly characterized with regard to functional aspects.

PEPTIDES IN PARASYMPATHETIC NERVES

Vasoactive Intestinal Polypeptide

VIP is a 28-amino-acid peptide (76) that was discovered to act as a vasodilator in lung extracts (88, see 87). VIP-like immunoreactivity (-LI) has been localized by immunohistochemistry in a variety of species, including man, to local ganglion cells and nerve fibers in, for instance, the tracheobronchial smooth muscle layer and around blood vessels (22, 104). Many VIP-immunoreactive (-IR) nerves are present in the smooth muscle layer of the

557

0066-4278/87/0315-0557$02.00

trachea and bronchi. The density of VIP-IR nerves generally diminishes in the small airways (22), and such nerves are absent in the distal bronchi of guinea pig (60). It remains to be established, using specific histochemical techniques, whether VIP is present in cholinergic nerves or in a separate population of local ganglion cells.

VIP exerts potent bronchodilator activity (Figure 1) (87, see 37) and may be a transmitter of the nonadrenergic inhibitory nerves in tracheobronchial smooth muscle (12, 14, 15). Electrical field stimulation of tracheobronchial preparations in vitro causes overflow of VIP-LI into the superfusion medium in a tetrodotoxin-sensitive manner (74). Furthermore, the amount of VIP-LI in the incubation medium after electrical field stimulation is correlated to the magnitude of the nonadrenergic relaxation of the specimens.

VIP causes a long-lasting relaxation of airway smooth muscle in vitro, which is unaffected by adrenergic blocking agents or indomethacin (2, 12, 37). This long-lasting effect of VIP is similar to the nonadrenergic muscle relaxation evoked by nerve stimulation. In vivo VIP reverses the serotonin-

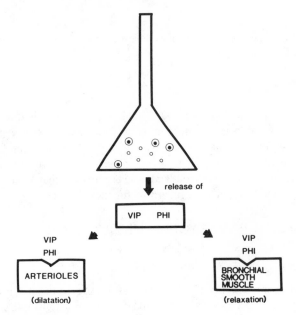

Figure 1   Schematic illustration of hypothetical events occurring upon activation of nonadrenergic local neurons in lower airways containing VIP and peptide (P) with N-terminal histidine (H) and C-terminal isoleucine (I) or methionine (M). These two peptides are likely to induce relaxation of tracheobronchial smooth muscle, an increase in local blood flow, and possibly venular relaxation. It remains to be established whether VIP and PHI act on the same or different types of receptors. The possible corelease of acetylcholine or other additional mediators from VIP/PHI nerves has not yet been established.

induced bronchoconstriction upon systemic administration in the cat. This response is similar to that induced by preganglionic vagal stimulation in the presence of adrenergic and cholinergic blocking agents (23, 24). One general problem in investigating bronchial VIP effects in vivo is the potent vasodilator action of VIP, which secondarily induces sympathetic activation due to the fall in systemic vascular resistance. This associated effect may explain why VIP has little or no effect on airway conductance in man (4, 80). In vitro, however, human bronchial smooth muscle is relaxed by VIP (79).

Specific binding sites with high affinity for VIP have been demonstrated in homogenates of lung membranes using radioligand binding techniques (84). Recent autoradiographic studies have indicated that VIP binding sites are present in the airway smooth muscle layer (6). VIP receptor activation is coupled to adenylate cyclase and thereby increases the intracellular concentration of cyclic AMP (84).

Several methods have been employed to antagonize pharmacologically VIP effects. Prolonged incubation of cat airway smooth muscle with high concentrations of VIP in vitro has been reported to reduce the nonadrenergic, relaxatory response to nerve stimulation (37). In contrast, presence of a supramaximal concentration of VIP did not reduce the smooth muscle relaxation to subsequent nerve stimulation in the guinea pig trachea (44, 45). Furthermore, in this latter species the relaxant effect of exogenous VIP was unaffected during a sustained inhibition of the airway muscle tone induced by field stimulation (45). These findings can be interpreted as evidence against a role for VIP in the nerve-mediated, nonadrenergic relaxation of the airway smooth muscle, since occupancy of VIP receptors by exogenous peptide did not modify the effect of the endogenously released, nonadrenergic, inhibitory transmitter. However, preincubation with VIP antibodies was reported to reduce the nerve-evoked, nonadrenergic relaxation of the guinea pig trachea (74). These partly conflicting data should also be considered in light of the recent finding that at least one additional peptide with relaxant activity on tracheobronchial smooth muscle may be coreleased with VIP upon nerve stimulation (Figure 1; see below).

Peptide Histidine Isoleucine (PHI)

Peptide with N-terminal histidine and C-terminal isoleucine amide (PHI) is a 27-amino-acid peptide with marked structural similarities to VIP (100). The C-terminal amino acid of the human form of PHI is methionine rather than isoleucine as in the pig, so the human form of PHI is termed PHM (38). Both VIP and PHM are expressed on the same precursor gene, which suggests that they are synthesized in the same prohormone (38). Immunohistochemical studies have shown that most likely VIP- and PHI-IR coexist in nerves of the airway smooth muscle (13, 60). Based on studies from the submandibular salivary gland of the cat, it can be assumed that parasympathetic nerve stimulation induces corelease of both VIP- and PHI-LI in a 1 : 1 ratio (Figure 1) (61). Like VIP, PHI binds to receptors in the lung (85) and induces cyclic AMP production. PHI is slightly less potent than VIP as a bronchodilator in vitro and in inhibiting the vagally induced bronchoconstriction in vivo (60). PHM also acts as a potent smooth muscle–relaxing agent in isolated human bronchi in vitro (79). Thus, the efforts to antagonize pharmacologically the nonadrenergic relaxation evoked by field stimulation using VIP tolerance or VIP antisera should be extended to take PHI into account, provided that VIP and PHI activate separate receptors and that VIP antisera do not crossreact with and immunoneutralize PHI. Both VIP and PHI are potent vasodilator agents (see 5, 60), so in addition to nonvascular smooth muscle relaxation, these peptides may be involved in the noncholinergic (atropine-resistant), vagal control of blood flow in the tracheobronchial smooth muscle layer and mucosa (Figure 1) (71).

PEPTIDES IN SENSORY NERVES

Biochemical Identification and Characterization of Tachykinins and Calcitonin Gene–Related Peptide in Sensory Nerves

Substance P (SP)-LI has been demonstrated in nerves of the airways in several species including man (54, 62, 77, 103, 106). Recent evidence suggests that a whole family of structurally related tachykinins is present in the airway neurons. It has been demonstrated that SP, neurokinin A (NKA, initially called substance K), neuropeptide K (NPK; Ref. 101)-like immunoreactivities (-LI), and an eledoisin (ELE)-related peptide (not yet fully identified) are present in nerves of the lung (Figure 2) (36). The simultaneous occurrence of SP, NKA, and NPK can be related to a common tachykinin precursor gene (see 36, 101).

Calcitonin gene-related peptide (CGRP) is composed of 37 amino acid residues (86) and CGRP-LI is also present, presumably in sensory nerves in the airways (11, 63, 72). CGRP has no structural similarity to tachykinins. The possible molecular heterogeneity of the CGRP-LI in airway nerves, however, has yet to be established.

Using immunohistochemistry, it has been shown that both tachykinin-LI (initially demonstrated using antibodies raised against SP) and CGRP-LI are present in sensory ganglion cells and axons known to project to the trachea and lower airways. Thus, cell bodies in the jugular and nodose ganglia, as well as axons in the vagal nerves, are tachykinin and CGRP immunoreactive (11, 63, 72). Histochemical techniques have revealed that CGRP-LI coexists with the newly identified tachykinins both in cell bodies in sensory ganglia

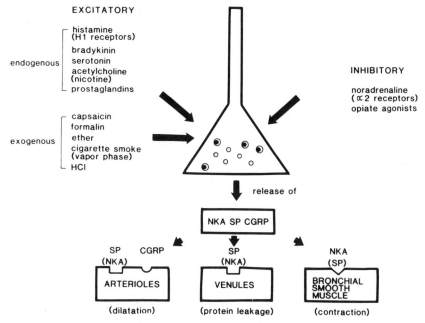

Figure 2   Schematical illustration of hypothetical events occurring following release of multiple peptides from the same peripheral endings of tracheobronchial, capsaicin-sensitive sensory neurons. There is evidence that endogenous as well as exogenous substances may modulate or induce the release of peptides. It is assumed that substance P (SP), neurokinin A (NKA), and calcitonin gene related peptide (CGRP) can be released simultaneously upon neuronal activation. SP and NKA may act on "SP-P" receptors (where NKA has a weaker activity, as indicated by parentheses) on arterioles causing vasodilatation and on venules inducing plasma protein leakage. Tachykinin-induced contraction of tracheobronchial smooth muscle seems to be mediated via "SP-E" or "SP-K" receptors, which would explain why NKA is a much more potent bronchoconstrictor than SP. CGRP is a vasodilating agent that acts by relaxing the arterioles; no clear-cut plasma protein leakage or bronchoconstrictive effects of CGRP have been demonstrated in vivo. There is also evidence for an inhibition of peptide release from peripheral sensory neurons by the alpha$_2$-adrenoceptor agonist clonidine and opiate receptor agonists.

and in terminal areas in the airways (Figure 2) (63, 72). SP-IR neurons projecting in the right vagus nerve innervate the lower trachea, both stem bronchi, and the right lung; SP-IR fibers in the left vagus nerve mainly project to the left stem bronchi and lung of the guinea pig (54). There is a similar unilateral innervation by CGRP-IR fibers of the right vagus nerve of the lower trachea in the rat (11). About 50% of the SP-IR in the guinea-pig lung seem to have a nonvagal origin. Thus functional, histochemical, and biochemical evidence suggests that tachykinin-containing sensory ganglion cells of the upper thoracic spinal ganglia project to the lower airways via sympathetic pathways (19, 54, 93).

Peripheral branches of tachykinin- and CGRP-containing sensory nerves can be found around local tracheobronchial ganglion cells, around blood vessels, within the tracheobronchial smooth muscle layers, and under and within the epithelium lining the respiratory tract (11, 62, 63, 72). Although it has been proposed that axon reflexes within the airways can account for a variety of local reactions (see below), it remains to be established that intraepithelial and perivascular nerves, as well as nerves in the bronchial smooth muscle layer, actually represent branches of the same sensory neuron.

Capsaicin, the pungent agent in hot peppers, has been extensively used as an experimental tool in studies on peptide-containing sensory nerves (40, 41, 96). Capsaicin is known to selectively activate a population of vagal C-fiber afferents in the airways (see 17, 107) and to initiate a cascade of both central reflexes and local release of bioactive peptides (see below). After exposure to a high dose of capsaicin, tachykinin- (54, 62) and CGRP-IR nerves (11, 63, 72) disappear to a very large extent from the airways. Histochemical and biochemical evidence, however, suggest that cholinergic, VIP-ergic, and sympathetic nerves seem to remain after capsaicin treatment (41, 66, 72). The selective action of capsaicin treatment on tachykinin- and CGRP-IR nerves suggests that these peptides are present in chemosensitive C-fiber afferents. Ultrastructural analysis has shown that intraepithelial, presumably sensory, tracheal nerve fibers degenerate after capsaicin treatment (33). To damage the sensory nerves selectively, capsaicin treatment can be performed either systemically or locally on the vagal nerves (54, 93). Systemic capsaicin treatment leads to an almost total depletion of SP- and CGRP-IR in the airways (54); application of local capsaicin on the cervical vagal nerves seems to leave SP-IR fibers, of presumably spinal origin, uninfluenced (54, 93).

CGRP- and tachykinin-LI are also present in cell bodies of the vagal and spinal sensory ganglia, as well as in terminals in the lower airways of man (62, 65, 72). However, the tachykinin- and CGRP-IR nerves in human trachea and bronchi are relatively sparse (72), and the peptide content is considerably lower compared to that in the guinea pig (72, 73).

Release of Peptides from Sensory Nerves

The isolated, perfused guinea pig lung has been used as an in vitro model to study the release of peptides from the peripheral branches of sensory neurons. Thus, SP-, NKA- (92), and ELE-related material (94), as well as CGRP-LI (72), has been found to be released from the lung upon exposure to high concentrations of K^+ and capsaicin. Furthermore, agents known to activate sensory nerves, such as the nicotine analogue dimethylphenyl piperazine (DMPP), histamine, and bradykinin (see 107), release tachykinin-LI from the lung (Figure 2) (94). In addition, electrical stimulation of the distal end of cut vagal nerves causes a release of multiple tachykinins in the perfused lung

(94). The capsaicin-induced release of tachykinins from sensory nerves (89) and the contractions of the tracheobronchial smooth muscle in vitro (59, 97) are resistant to tetrodotoxin. These observations suggest an action of capsaicin independent of nerve-impulse propagation. Thus, capsaicin probably releases mediators directly from sensory nerve terminals at the site of exposure (see 65, 96). In vivo, however, inhalation of capsaicin may be associated with a release of sensory neuropeptides partly via axon reflexes since, for instance, the protein extravasation response in the tracheal mucosa induced by application of intraluminal capsaicin can be reduced by treatment with lidocaine, a local anesthetic (53).

Comparison of Local Reactions Due to Sensory Nerve Irritation and Effects of Neuropeptides

Several local reactions in the airways can be elicited by irritation of capsaicin-sensitive C-fiber afferents. Capsaicin causes increased local mucosal blood flow (Figure 2) (67, 71). A vasodilatation response, as studied in the nasal mucosa (67) and recently in the trachea (71), can also be induced by tachykinins and CGRP. Vagal nerve stimulation in the presence of a ganglionic blocking agent meant to abolish parasympathetic vasodilator mechanisms still induces some vasodilatation in the tracheal mucosa (71). This result may be related to an antidromic stimulation of sensory nerves resulting in release of multiple peptides with vasodilator activity. The relative importance of individual peptides for the vagally evoked tracheal vasodilator response, however, remains to be established using specific antagonists.

Another important local reaction in the airway mucosa is protein extravasation, which occurs upon antidromic nerve stimulation of sensory nerves or irritation by chemicals (Figure 2). Tachykinins, especially SP, are very potent inducers of protein extravasation via increased permeability of postcapillary venules (50, 51, 53, 82). CGRP, however, does not cause detectable protein extravasation in the airway mucosa (63). In addition, CGRP can enhance protein extravasation by tachykinins, most likely due to its potent vasodilator activity (10, 28). Experiments with SP analogues with tachykinin-antagonistic activity suggest that most of the protein extravasation response in the trachea induced by vagal nerve stimulation (57) or cigarette-smoke irritation (56) is due to tachykinins rather than CGRP. The protein-extravasation reaction seen upon excitation of capsaicin-sensitive sensory nerves is particularly pronounced in the airways of the rat and guinea pig. Species differences, however, seem to exist: Vagal nerve stimulation or application of capsaicin on the tracheal mucosa of cat and dog does not induce detectable protein extravasation in the airway mucosa, as indicated by Evans blue leakage (65).

One major effect of tachykinins is contraction of tracheobronchial smooth muscle (Figure 2). SP is a well-known bronchoconstrictor both in vivo and in vitro (3, 52, 77) in a variety of species including man (25, 55). However, other tachykinins, especially NKA and ELE, are much more potent bronchoconstrictors than is SP in the guinea pig (35) or in isolated human bronchi in vitro (46, 64, 73). Tachykinins are considered to exert their effects on target cells via different types of receptors (Figure 2) (see 39). The fact that ELE and NKA are much more potent than SP in inducing bronchoconstriction suggests that activation of an "SP-E" or "SP-K" receptor is involved. However, when tachykinins have a similar biological activity, such as relaxation of vascular smooth muscle, these peptides are considered to act on an "SP-P" receptor (see 39). The bronchoconstrictor effects of tachykinins in the guinea pig (52) and man (73) are resistant to atropine, which suggests a noncholinergic mechanism of action independent of muscarinic receptor activation.

Systemic administration of capsaicin (52, 70, 75) or vagal nerve stimulation (9, 52, 70) induces noncholinergic bronchoconstriction in the guinea pig in vivo. Experiments using electrical field stimulation of guinea pig bronchi in vitro have also revealed a long-lasting, mainly atropine-resistant, contractile component (31, 52) that is sensitive to capsaicin treatment (52, 97) and is blocked by SP analogues with general tachykinin-antagonistic activity (43, 49, 57). Nonadrenergic, dilatory mechanisms are obvious in the smooth muscle of the trachea but seem to be of minor importance in the peripheral airways of the guinea pig. A noncholinergic bronchoconstriction induced by field stimulation of capsaicin-sensitive sensory nerves is therefore easy to demonstrate in guinea pig bronchi but not in the trachea (see 57). Capsaicin-induced bronchoconstriction in vivo is markedly enhanced by propranolol treatment in the guinea pig (34). This suggests that capsaicin, in addition to local release of sensory neuropeptides with bronchoconstrictor activity, also induces bronchodilator reflexes via beta-adrenergic mechanisms. Capsaicin is known to release catecholamines via reflexogenic activation of the adrenal medulla (1). Thus, circulating adrenaline may represent an important mechanism to counteract the bronchoconstrictor response to capsaicin, since inhibition of noradrenaline release from sympathetic nerve terminals did not significantly enhance the capsaicin-induced bronchoconstriction (9).

Species differences also seem to exist with regard to both the existence and mechanisms of capsaicin- or tachykinin-induced bronchoconstriction. Vagal noncholinergic bronchoconstriction is not prominent in the rat, and tachykinins have relatively poor bronchoconstrictor effects in this species (42). For comparison, it should be emphasized that even in very low doses SP induces a marked protein extravasation in the airway mucosa of the rat (90). In the rat (42) and to some extent in the rabbit (29, 98, 99), tachykinins induce bronchoconstriction partly via cholinergic mechanisms. Capsaicin causes contraction of human bronchi in vitro (55), while SP in this preparation has a rather weak bronchoconstrictor activity (55, 64, 73). However, as in the guinea pig, other tachykinins such as NKA (46, 64, 73) are much more potent bronchoconstrictors than is SP on human bronchi. In man, however, no consistent atropine-resistant bronchial contraction has been obtained upon electrical field stimulation in vitro (see 21, 83, 102). This observation does not exclude a role for sensory neuropeptides in the control of bronchial smooth muscle tone in man, since powerful opposing bronchodilatory mechanisms, as in the guinea pig trachea (see above), may dominate during field stimulation in atropinized human preparations (83, 102). Inhalation of capsaicin aerosol in humans has been reported to induce cough (18) and retrosternal discomfort but only a transient, mainly cholinergic, bronchoconstriction (26). However, the existence of capsaicin-activated, adrenergic bronchodilator reflexes has not yet been clearly shown in man. Furthermore, powerful protective reflexes, including coughing, may prevent the spread of inhaled capsaicin to the lower airways.

No bronchoconstrictor effect of CGRP has been observed in the guinea pig in vivo (34, 63) or in vitro (72). However, CGRP caused a marked inhibition of spontaneous or tachykinin-induced ureteric smooth muscle contractions in this species (34). It has been reported that CGRP is a very potent bronchoconstrictor in human bronchi in vitro (78, 81). In contrast, other investigators did not obtain any effect of CGRP on smooth muscle tone of isolated human bronchi in vitro; whereas in the same experiments CGRP potently relaxed human pulmonary arteries (72).

CNS-Mediated Reflexes via Capsaicin-Sensitive Afferents

Irritation of capsaicin-sensitive sensory nerves in the lower airways is followed by rapid protective reflexes and autonomic activation. Thus, capsaicin produces powerful coughing upon inhalation by humans (18, 26). Capsaicin also induces exocrine secretion in the tracheal mucosa of experimental animals (20) and bronchoconstriction in man (26) via cholinergic parasympathetic reflexes. In the guinea pig, however, the vagovagal reflexes do not seem to contribute to the bronchoconstrictor effects of iv capsaicin (9). Instead, as mentioned above, capsaicin may actually initiate adrenergic bronchodilator reflexes in the latter species (34).

Functional and Pathophysiological Significance of Tracheobronchial Capsaicin-Sensitive Afferents

Capsaicin-sensitive C-fiber afferents are markedly excited upon local irritation of the airway mucosa either by toxic chemicals or upon mediator release during allergic reactions. Several stimuli have been shown to activate capsaicin-sensitive nerves in studies using electrophysiological techniques (17, 107) or as indirectly suggested by the absence of protein extravasation and bronchoconstrictor responses in capsaicin-pretreated animals (Figure 2) (51,

52, 70, 90). Several irritant chemicals including cigarette smoke excite capsaicin-sensitive nerves. It seems clear that nicotine (and the stable nicotine analogue, DMPP) can induce bronchoconstriction (48) and protein extravasation in the trachea (58), as well as release tachykinins from sensory nerves (48, 94). The cigarette-smoke-induced protein extravasation in rat airways, however, depends mainly on irritants in the vapor phase of the smoke, rather than the particulate phase, which contains nicotine (53, 56). This suggests that the local nicotine concentration obtained upon inhalation of cigarette smoke is not sufficient to activate capsaicin-sensitive nerves.

Several lines of evidence suggest that capsaicin-sensitive nerves are activated by mediators released upon mast-cell degranulation, such as histamine (via histamine 1 receptors) and serotonin (Figure 2). The histamine-induced protein extravasation response in the rat trachea (53) and bronchoconstriction in the guinea pig (52, 70) are significantly reduced after capsaicin treatment. Furthermore, histamine has been found to induce release of tachykinin-LI from the guinea pig lung in vitro (94). The mainly histamine-mediated protein extravasation response in the trachea and bronchoconstriction upon antigen challenge in sensitized guinea pigs were reduced after capsaicin treatment (90). Furthermore, the flare response, which probably reflects vasodilatation in the human skin, induced by local histamine injection (8) or by challenge with antigen in allergic patients is absent after local capsaicin treatment (68, 69). In contrast, the protein extravasation in the tracheobronchial mucosa and the bronchoconstriction induced by leukotriene C_4 do not seem to be influenced by capsaicin treatment (65).

Bradykinin, which is produced upon, for instance, local tissue damage, is a very potent activator of C-fiber afferents in the airways (47, see 107). Furthermore, the protein extravasation in the rat trachea induced by bradykinin can, to a large extent, be inhibited by capsaicin treatment (53). In addition, bradykinin has been demonstrated to release tachykinin-LI from capsaicin-sensitive lung afferents (94), and the contractile response to bradykinin, at least in the eye, can be blocked by SP antagonists (105). Bradykinin has potent bronchoconstrictor effects when inhaled by asthmatic subjects but has very little effect in normal persons (95). Furthermore, bradykinin has only minor contractile effects on isolated human bronchi in vitro. This finding suggests an indirect bronchoconstrictor action in vivo, which may be mediated via activation of C-fiber afferents (27). It is known that certain prostaglandins activate vagal C-fiber afferents (Figure 2) (16). As discussed above, activation of capsaicin-sensitive C-fiber afferents in the rat trachea is usually associated with plasma protein leakage. However, prostaglandin E or $F_{2\alpha}$ alone does not induce protein extravasation, although they potentiate the effect of capsaicin (91).

Some agents are likely to inhibit the local release of mediators from sensory nerves (Figure 2). The noncholinergic, vagal bronchoconstriction in the guinea pig can be attenuated by treatment with clonidine (30, 32). This indicates that alpha$_2$-adrenoceptor activation can inhibit peptide release from capsaicin-sensitive sensory nerves. Inhibition of noncholinergic bronchial contractions was also demonstrated with the stable enkephalin analogue D-Pro^2, Met^5-enkephalinamide in a naloxone-reversible manner (7). This result suggests the presence of opiate receptors on peripheral branches of airway sensory nerves. However, since the opiate antagonist naloxone neither influenced the basal tone nor the bronchoconstriction responses obtained by vagal (9) or electrical field stimulation (7), the possible physiological role for opioid receptors on sensory nerves in the guinea pig lung remains to be established.

In conclusion, capsaicin-sensitive C-fiber afferents in the airways have been characterized both with regard to the release of local bioactive peptides and their importance in local and reflexogenic responses to irritant chemicals and as mediators of the allergic reaction. It seems likely that a more complete understanding of the functional importance of these nerves will also help to reveal the pathophysiology of airway disorders.

ACKNOWLEDGMENTS

The present studies have been supported by grants from the Swedish Medical Research Council (14X-6554), the American Council for Tobacco Research, the Swedish Tobacco Company, Petrus och Augusta Hedlunds Stiftelse, the Swedish Work Environmental Fund, funds from the Karolinska Institute, and the Austrian Scientific Research Funds (5605 and 6166). For expert secretarial help we thank Mrs. Hilka Lindberg.

Literature Cited

1. Allison, D. J., Powis, D. A. 1971. Adrenal catecholamine secretion during stimulation of the nasal mucous membrane in the rabbit. *J. Physiol.* 217:327–39

2. Altiere, R. J., Diamond, L. 1984. Comparison of vasoactive intestinal peptide and isoproterenol relaxant effects in isolated cat airways. *J. Appl. Physiol.* 56:986–92

3. Andersson, P., Persson, H. 1977. Effect of substance P on pulmonary resistance and dynamic pulmonary compliance in the anaesthetized cat and guinea-pig. *Acta Pharmacol. Toxicol.* 41:444–48

4. Barnes, P. J., Dixon, C. M. S. 1984. The effect of inhaled vasoactive intestinal peptide on bronchial hyperreactivity in man. *Am. Rev. Respir. Dis.* 130:162–66

5. Barnes, P. J., Cadieux, A., Carstairs, J. R., Greenberg, B., Polak, J. M., Rhoden, K. 1986. VIP in bovine pulmonary artery: Localization, function and receptor autoradiography. *Br. J. Pharmacol.* In press

6. Barnes, P. J., Carstairs, J. R. 1986. Autoradiographic distribution of VIP receptors in guinea-pig and human lung. *J. Pharmacol. Exp. Ther.* In press

7. Bartho, L., Amann, R., Saria, A., Szolcsányi, J., Lembeck, F. 1986. Effects of opioid drugs on peripheral capsaicin-sensitive neurones of the guinea-pig bronchus and rabbit ear. *Naunyn-Schmiedebergs Arch. Pharmacol.* In press

8. Bernstein, J. E., Swift, R. M., Soltani, K., Lorincz, A. L. 1981. Inhibition of axon reflex vasodilatation by topically

568   LUNDBERG & SARIA

applied capsaicin. *J. Invest. Derm.*
76:394–95

9. Biggs, D. F., Goel, V. 1985. Does capsaicin cause reflex bronchospasm in guinea-pigs? *Europ. J. Pharm.* 115:71–80

10. Brain, S. D., Williams, T. J. 1985. Inflammatory oedema induced by synergism between calcitonin gene-related peptide (CGRP) and mediators of increased vascular permeability. *Br. J. Pharmacol.* 86:855–60

11. Cadieux, A., Springall, D. R., Mulderry, P. K., Rodrigo, J., Ghatei, M. A., et al. 1986. Occurrence, distribution and ontogeny of CGRP-immunoreactivity in the rat lower respiratory tract: Effect of capsaicin treatment and surgical denervations. *Neuroscience* In press

12. Cameron, A. C., Johnson, C. F., Kirkpatrick, C. T., Kirkpatrick, M. C. A. 1983. The quest for the inhibitory neurotransmitter in bovine tracheal smooth muscle. *Q. J. Exp. Physiol.* 68:413–26

13. Christofides, N. D., Yiangou, Y., Piper, P. J., Ghatei, M. A., Sheppard, M. N., et al. 1984. Distribution of peptide histidine isoleucine in the mammalian respiratory tract and some aspects of its pharmacology. *Endocrinology* 115:1958–63

14. Coburn, R. F., Tomita, T. 1973. Evidence for nonadrenergic inhibitory nerves in the guinea-pig trachealis muscle. *Am. J. Physiol.* 224:1072–80

15. Coleman, R. A., Levy, G. P. 1974. A non-adrenergic inhibitory nervous pathway in the guinea-pig trachea. *Br. J. Pharmacol.* 52:167–74

16. Coleridge, H. M., Coleridge, J. C., Ginzel, K., Baker, D., Banzett, R., Morrison, M. 1976. Stimulation of irritant receptors and afferent C-fibres in the lungs by prostaglandins. *Nature* 5585:451–53

17. Coleridge, J. C. G., Coleridge, H. M. 1984. Afferent vagal C-fibre innervation of the lung and airways and its functional significance. *Rev. Physiol. Biochem. Pharmacol.* 99:1–110

18. Collier, J. G., Fuller, R. W. 1984. Capsaicin inhalation in man and the effects of sodium chromoglycate. *Br. J. Pharmacol.* 81:113–17

19. Dalsgaard, C.-J., Lundberg, J. M. 1984. Vagal and spinal afferent innervation of the guinea-pig lower respiratory tract as studied by the HRP-technique. *Neurosci. Lett.* 45:117–22

20. Davies, B., Roberts, A. M., Coleridge, H. M., Coleridge, J. C. G. 1982. Reflex tracheal gland secretion evoked by stimulation of bronchial C-fibres in dogs. *J. Appl. Physiol. Respir. Environ. Exercise Physiol.* 53:985–91

21. Davis, C., Kannan, M. S., Jones, T. R., Daniel, E. E. 1982. Control of human airway smooth muscle in in vitro studies. *J. Appl. Physiol.* 53:1080–87

22. Dey, R. D., Shannon, W. A. Jr., Said, S. I. 1981. Localization of VIP-immunoreactive nerves in airways and pulmonary vessels of dogs, cats and human subjects. *Cell Tiss. Res.* 220:231–38

23. Diamond, L., O'Donnell, M. 1980. A non-adrenergic vagal inhibitory pathway to feline airways. *Science* 208:185–88

24. Diamond, L., Szarek, J. L., Gillespie, M. N., Altiere, R. J. 1983. In vivo bronchodilator activity of vasoactive intestinal peptide in the cat. *Am. Rev. Respir. Dis.* 128:827–32

25. Finney, M. J. B., Karlsson, J.-A., Persson, C. G. A. 1985. Effects of bronchoconstrictors and bronchodilators on a novel small airway preparation. *Br. J. Pharmacol.* 85:29–36

26. Fuller, R. W., Dixon, C. M. S., Barnes, P. J. 1985. The bronchoconstrictor response to inhaled capsaicin in humans. *J. Appl. Physiol.* 85:1080–84

27. Fuller, R. W., Dixon, C. M. S., Cuss, F., Barnes, P. J. 1986. In vivo and in vitro assessment of bradykinin induced bronchoconstriction in humans. *Am. Rev. Respir. Dis.* In press

28. Gamse, R., Saria, A. 1985. Potentiation of tachykinin-induced plasma protein extravasation by calcitonin gene-related peptide. *Eur. J. Pharmacol.* 114:61–66

29. Grunstein, M. M., Tanaka, D. T., Grunstein, J. S. 1984. Mechanisms of substance P induced bronchoconstriction in maturing rabbit. *J. Appl. Physiol.* 57:1238–46

30. Grundström, N., Andersson, R. G. G. 1985. In vivo demonstration of alpha₂-adrenoceptor-mediated inhibition of the excitatory non-cholinergic neurotransmission in guinea-pig airways. *Naunyn-Schmiedeberg's Arch. Pharmacol.* 328:236–40

31. Grundström, N., Andersson, R. G. G., Wikberg, J. E. S. 1981. Pharmacological characterization of the autonomous innervation of the guinea-pig tracheobronchial smooth muscle. *Acta Pharmacol. Toxicol.* 49:150–57

32. Grundström, N., Andersson, R. G. G., Wikberg, J. E. S. 1984. Inhibition of the excitatory non-adrenergic, non-cholinergic neurotransmission in the guinea-pig tracheo-bronchial tree mediated

by alpha$_2$-adrenoceptors. *Acta Pharmacol. Toxicol.* 54:8–14

33. Hoyes, A. P., Barber, P., Jagessar, H. 1981. Effect of capsaicin on the intraepithelial axons of the rat trachea. *Neurosci. Lett.* 26:329–34

34. Hua, X.-Y., Lundberg, J. M. 1986. Dual capsaicin effects on ureteral motility: Low dose inhibition mediated by calcitonin gene-related peptide and high dose stimulation by tachykinins? *Acta Physiol. Scand.* 128:453–65

35. Hua, X.-Y., Lundberg, J. M., Theodorsson-Norheim, E., Brodin, E. 1984. Comparison of cardiovascular and bronchoconstrictor effects of substance P, substance K and tachykinins. *Naunyn-Schmiedeberg's Arch. Pharmacol.* 328:196–201; 1985. Erratum 328: 361

36. Hua, X.-Y., Theodorsson-Norheim, E., Brodin, E., Lundberg, J. M. 1985. Multiple tachykinins (neurokinin A, neuropeptide K and substance P) in capsaicin-sensitive sensory neurons in the guinea-pig. *Regul. Peptides* 13:1–19

37. Ito, Y., Takeda, K. 1982. Nonadrenergic inhibitory nerves and putative transmitters in the smooth muscle of cat trachea. *J. Physiol.* 330:497–511

38. Itoh, N., Obata, K., Yanaihara, N., Okamoto, H. 1983. Human preprovasoactive intestinal polypeptide contains a novel PHI-27-like peptide, PHM-27. *Nature* 304:547–49

39. Iversen, L. L. 1982. Substance P. *Br. Med. Bull.* 38:277–82

40. Jancsó, G., Király, E., Jancsó-Gábor, A. 1977. Pharmacologically induced selective degeneration of chemosensitive primary sensory neurons. *Nature* 270: 741–43

41. Jancsó, N., Jancsó-Gábor, A., Szolcsanyi, I. 1968. The role of sensory nerve endings in neurogenic inflammation induced in human skin and in the eye and paw of the rat. *Br. J. Pharmacol. Chemother.* 32:32–41

42. Joos, G., Kips, J., Pauwels, R., Van der Straeten, M. 1986. The effect of tachykinins on the conducting airways of the rat. *Arch. Int. Pharmacodyn.* 280:176–90 (Suppl.)

43. Karlsson, J.-A., Finney, M. J. B., Persson, C. G. A., Post, C. 1984. Substance P antagonists and the role of tachykinins in non-cholinergic bronchoconstriction. *Life Sci.* 35:2681–91

44. Karlsson, J.-A., Persson, C. G. A. 1983. Evidence against vasoactive intestinal polypeptide (VIP) as a dilator and in favour of substance P as a constrictor in airway neurogenic responses. *Br. J. Pharmacol.* 79:634–36

45. Karlsson, J.-A., Persson, C. G. A. 1984. Neither vasoactive intestinal peptide (VIP) nor purine derivatives may mediate non-adrenergic tracheal inhibition. *Acta Physiol. Scand.* 122:589–98

46. Karlsson, J.-A., Persson, C. G. A. 1985. Effects of different substance P analogues on tachykinin-induced contraction of airway smooth muscle. In *Tachykinin Antagonists*, ed. R. Håkanson, F. Sundler, pp. 181–88. Amsterdam: Elsevier

47. Kaufman, M. P., Coleridge, H. M., Coleridge, J. C. G., Baker, D. G. 1980. Bradykinin stimulates afferent vagal C-fibres in intrapulmonary airways of dogs. *J. Appl. Physiol.* 48:511–17

48. Kizawa, Y., Takayanagi, I. 1985. Possible involvement of substance P-immunoreactive nerves in the mediation of nicotine-induced contractile responses in isolated guinea-pig bronchus. *Eur. J. Pharmacol.* 113:319–24

49. Leander, S., Grundström, N., Andersson, R. G. G., Håkanson, R. 1984. Neuronally mediated non-cholinergic contraction of guinea-pig bronchial smooth muscle is inhibited by a substance P antagonist. *Agents Actions* 14: 315–18

50. Lembeck, F., Holzer, P. 1979. Substance P as neurogenic mediator of antidromic vasodilatation and neurogenic plasma extravasation. *Naunyn-Schmiedebergs Arch. Pharmacol.* 310:175–83

51. Lundberg, J. M., Saria, A. 1982. Capsaicin-sensitive vagal neurons involved in control of vascular permeability in rat trachea. *Acta Physiol. Scand.* 115:521–23

52. Lundberg, J. M., Saria, A. 1982. Bronchial smooth muscle contraction induced by stimulation of capsaicin-sensitive vagal sensory neurons. *Acta Physiol. Scand.* 116:473–76

53. Lundberg, J. M., Saria, A. 1983. Capsaicin induced desensitization of the airway mucosa to cigarette smoke, mechanical and chemical irritants. *Nature* 302:251–53

54. Lundberg, J. M., Brodin, E., Saria, A. 1983. Effects and distribution of vagal capsaicin-sensitive substance P neurons with special reference to the trachea and lungs. *Acta Physiol. Scand.* 119:243–52

55. Lundberg, J. M., Martling, C.-R., Saria, A. 1983. Substance P and capsaicin induced bronchial smooth muscle contraction in human airways. *Acta Physiol. Scand.* 119:49–53

56. Lundberg, J. M., Martling, C.-R., Saria, A., Folkers, K., Rosell, S. 1983. Cigarette smoke induced oedema due to activation of capsaicin-sensitive vagal afferents and substance P release. *Neuroscience* 10:1361–68

57. Lundberg, J. M., Saria, A., Brodin, E., Rosell, S., Folkers, K. 1983. A substance P antagonist inhibits vagally induced increase in vascular permeability and bronchial smooth muscle contraction in the guinea-pig. *Proc. Natl. Acad. Sci. USA* 80:1120–24

58. Lundberg, J. M., Saria, A., Martling, C.-R. 1983. Capsaicin pretreatment abolishes cigarette smoke-induced oedema in rat tracheobronchial mucosa. *Eur. J. Pharmacol.* 86:317–18

59. Lundberg, J. M., Brodin, E., Hua, X.-Y., Saria, A. 1984. Vascular permeability changes and smooth muscle contraction in relation to capsaicin-sensitive substance P afferents in the guinea-pig. *Acta Physiol. Scand.* 120:217–27

60. Lundberg, J. M., Fahrenkrug, J., Hökfelt, T., Martling, C.-R., Larsson, O., et al. 1984. Coexistence of peptide HI (PHI) and VIP in nerves regulating blood flow and bronchial smooth muscle tone in various mammals including man. *Peptides* 5:593–606

61. Lundberg, J. M., Fahrenkrug, J., Larsson, O., Änggård, A. 1984. Co-release of vasoactive intestinal polypeptide and peptide histidine isoleucine in relation to atropine-resistant vasodilatation in cat submandibular salivary gland. *Neurosci. Lett.* 52:37–42

62. Lundberg, J. M., Hökfelt, T., Martling, C.-R., Saria, A., Cuello, C. 1984d. Sensory substance P-immunoreactive nerves in the lower respiratory tract of various mammals including man. *Cell Tiss. Res.* 235:251–61

63. Lundberg, J. M., Franco-Cereceda, A., Hua, X.-Y., Hökfelt, T., Fischer, J. 1985a. Co-existence of substance P and calcitonin gene-related peptide immunoreactivities in sensory nerves in relation to cardiovascular and bronchoconstrictor effects of capsaicin. *Eur. J. Pharmacol.* 108:315–19

64. Lundberg, J. M., Saria, A., Theodorsson-Norheim, E., Brodin, E., Hua, X.-Y., et al. 1985b. Multiple tachykinins in capsaicin-sensitive afferents: Occurrence, release and biological effects with special reference to irritation of the airways. In *Tachykinin Antagonists,* ed. R. Håkanson, F. Sundler, pp. 159–69. Amsterdam: Elsevier

65. Lundberg, J. M., Saria, A., Lundblad, L., Änggård, A., Martling, C.-R., et al.

66. Lundblad, L., Lundberg, J. M., Brodin, E., Änggård, A. 1983. Origin and distribution of sensory substance P nerves in the nasal mucosa. *Acta Otolaryngol.* 96:485–93

67. Lundblad, L., Änggård, A., Lundberg, J. M. 1984. Effects of antidromic trigeminal nerve stimulation in relation to parasympathetic vasodilatation in cat nasal mucosa. *Acta Physiol. Scand.* 119:7–13

68. Lundblad, L., Lundberg, J. M., Änggård, A., Zetterström, O. 1985. Capsaicin pretreatment inhibits the flare component of the cutaneous allergic reaction in man. *Eur. J. Pharmacol.* 113:461–62

69. Lundblad, L., Lundberg, J. M., Änggård, A., Zetterström, O. 1986. Capsaicin-sensitive nerves and the cutaneous allergy reaction in man: Possible involvement of sensory neuropeptides in the flare reaction. *Allergy* In press

70. Martling, C.-R., Saria, A., Andersson, P., Lundberg, J. M. 1984. Capsaicin pretreatment inhibits vagal cholinergic and non-cholinergic control of airway mechanics in the guinea-pig. *Naunyn-Schmiedebergs Arch. Pharmacol.* 325:343–48

71. Martling, C.-R., Gazelius, B., Lundberg, J. M. 1987. Nervous control of blood flow in the cat trachea. *Acta Physiol. Scand.*

72. Martling, C.-R., Saria, A., Yan, Z., Lundberg, J. M., Fischer, J., Hökfelt, T. 1986. Calcitonin gene-related peptide and the lung: Co-existence with substance P, release by capsaicin and vasodilatory effects. *Thorax* Submitted

73. Martling, C.-R., Theodorsson-Norheim, E., Lundberg, J. M. 1987. Occurrence and effects of multiple tachykinins (substance P, neurokinin A and neuropeptide K) on human bronchi. *Life Sci.* In press

74. Matsuzaki, Y., Hamasaki, Y., Said, S. I. 1980. Vasoactive intestinal peptide: a possible transmitter of nonadrenergic relaxation of guinea-pig airways. *Science* 210:1252–53

75. Molnár, J., Mahara, G., György, L., Unyi, G. 1969. The bronchoconstrictor action of capsaicin in the guinea-pig. *Acta Physiol. Acad. Sci. Hung.* 36:413–420

76. Mutt, V., Said, S. I. 1974. Structure of

1986. Bioactive peptides in capsaicin-sensitive C-fibre afferents of the airways—Functional and pathophysiological implications. In *Lung Biology in Health and Disease,* ed. M. Kaliner, P. Barner. New York: Dekker In press the porcine vasoactive intestinal octapeptide. The amino acid sequence. Use of kallikrein in its determination. *Eur. J. Biochem.* 42:531–89

77. Nilsson, G., Dahlberg, K., Brodin, E., Sundler, F., Strandberg, K. 1977. Distribution and constrictor effects of substance P in guinea-pig tracheobronchial tissue. In *Substance P*, ed. U. S. von Euler, B. Pernow, pp. 57–61. New York: Raven

78. Palmer, J. B., Cuss, F. M., Mulderry, P. K. 1985. Calcitonin gene-related peptide is localized to human airway nerves and potently constricts human airway smooth muscle. *Thorax* 40:713

79. Palmer, J. B., Cuss, F. M. C., Barnes, P. J. 1986a. Responses to vasoactive intestinal peptide, peptide histidine methionine and their role in nonadrenergic inhibitory responses in isolated human airways. *J. Appl. Physiol.* In press

80. Palmer, J. B., Cuss, F. M. C., Warren, J. B., Barnes, P. J. 1986b. The effect of infused vasoactive intestinal peptide on airway function in normal subjects. *Thorax* In press

81. Palmer, J. B., Cuss, F. M. C., Mulderry, P. K., Ghatei, M. A., Springgall, D. R., et al. 1986. Calcitonin gene-related peptide is localized to human airway nerves and potently constricts human airway smooth muscle. *Br. J. Pharmacol.* In press

82. Persson, C. G. A., Erjefält, I., Karlsson, J.-A. 1985. Effects of tachykinins and tachykinin antagonists on the tracheobronchial microcirculation. In *Tachykinin Antagonists*, ed. R. Håkanson, S. Sundler, pp. 171–79. Amsterdam: Elsevier

83. Richardson, J. B., Beland, J. 1976. Nonadrenergic inhibitory nervous system in human airways. *J. Appl. Physiol.* 41:764–71

84. Robberecht, P., Chatelain, P., De Neef, P., Camus, J.-C., Waelbroeck, M., Christophe, J. 1981. Presence of vasoactive intestinal peptide receptors coupled to adenylate cyclase in rat lung membranes. *Biochem. Biophys. Acta* 678:76–82

85. Robberecht, P., Tatemoto, K., Chatelain, P., Waelbroek, M., Delhaye, M., et al. 1982. Effects of PHI on vasoactive intestinal peptide receptors and adenylate cyclase activity in lung membranes. A comparison in man, rat, mouse and guinea-pig. *Regul. Peptides* 4:241–50

86. Rosenfeld, M. G., Mermod, J.-J., Amara, S. G., Swanson, L. W., Sawchenko, P. E., et al. 1983. Production of

a novel neuropeptide encoded by the calcitonin gene via tissue-specific RNA processing. *Nature* 304:129–35

87. Said, S. I. 1982. Vasoactive peptides in the lung, with special reference to vasoactive intestinal peptide. *Exp. Lung Res.* 3:343–48

88. Said, S. I., Kitamura, S., Yoshida, T., Preskitt, J., Holden, L. D. 1974. Humoral control of airways. *Ann. NY Acad. Sci.* 221:103–14

89. Saria, A., Lundberg, J. M., Hua, X.-Y., Lembeck, F. 1983. Capsaicin-induced substance P release and sensory control of vascular permeability in the guinea-pig ureter. *Neurosci. Lett.* 41:167–72

90. Saria, A., Lundberg, J. M., Skofitsch, G., Lembeck, F. 1983b. Vascular protein leakage in various tissues induced by substance P, capsaicin, bradykinin, serotonin, histamine and by antigen challenge. *Naunyn-Schmiedebergs Arch. Pharmacol.* 324:212–18

91. Saria, A., Lundberg, J. M. 1984a. Activation of sensory substance P neurons in the respiratory tract by cigarette smoke, mechanical and chemical irritants. In *Frontiers in Hormone Research*, ed. M. Ratzenhofer, Vol. 12, pp. 123–26. Basel: Karger

92. Saria, A., Theodorsson-Norheim, E., Gamse, R., Lundberg, J. M. 1984b. Release of substance P and substance K-like immunoreactivities from the isolated perfused guinea-pig lung. *Eur. J. Pharmacol.* 106:207–8

93. Saria, A., Martling, C.-R., Dalsgaard, C.-J., Lundberg, J. M. 1985. Evidence for substance P-immunoreactive spinal afferents that mediate bronchoconstriction. *Acta Physiol. Scand.* 125:407–14

94. Saria, A., Martling, C.-R., Yan, Z., Theodorsson-Norheim, E., Lundberg, J. M. 1986. Release of multiple tachykinins from sensory nerves in the lung by bradykinin, histamine, nicotine and vagal nerve stimulation. *Am. Rev. Respir. Dis.* Submitted for publication

95. Simonsson, B. G., Skoogh, B. F., Bergh, N. P., Andersson, R., Svedmyr, N. 1973. In vivo and in vitro effects of bradykinin on bronchial motor tone in normal subjects and in patients with airway obstruction. *Respiratory* 30:377–88

96. Szolcsanyi, J. 1984. Capsaicin and neurogenic inflammation: History and early findings. In *Antidromic Vasodilatation and Neurogenic Inflammation*, ed. L. A. Chahl, J. Szolcsanyi, F. Lembeck, pp. 27–55. Hung. Acad. Scipp.

97. Szolcsanyi, J., Barthó, L. 1982. Cap-

saicin-sensitive non-cholinergic excitatory innervation of the guinea-pig tracheobronchial smooth muscle. *Neurosci. Lett.* 34:247–52

98. Tanaka, D. T., Grunstein, M. M. 1984. Mechanisms of substance P-induced contraction of rabbit airway smooth muscle. *J. Appl. Physiol.* 57:1551–57

99. Tanaka, D. T., Grunstein, M. M. 1985. Substance P augments electrically-induced contraction of isolated rabbit tracheal smooth muscle. *Am. Rev. Respir. Dis.* 131:285

100. Tatemoto, K., Mutt, V. 1981. Isolation and characterization of the intestinal porcine PHI (PHI-27), a new member of the glucagon-secretion family. *Proc. Natl. Acad. Sci. USA* 78:6603–7

101. Tatemoto, K., Lundberg, J. M., Jörnwall, H., Mutt, V. 1985. Neuropeptide K: Isolation, structure and biological activities of a novel brain tachykinin. *Biochim. Biophys. Res. Commun.* 128:947–53

102. Taylor, S. M., Paré, P. D., Schellenerg, R. 1984. Cholinergic and nonadrenergic mechanisms in human and guinea-pig airways. *J. Appl. Physiol.* 56:958–65

103. Terenghi, G., McGregor, G. P., Bhuttarcharji, J., Wharton, J., Bloom, S. R., Polak, J. M. 1983. Vagal origin of substance P-containing nerves in the guinea-pig lung. *Neurosci. Lett.* 36:229–36

104. Uddman, R., Alumets, J., Densert, O., Håkanson, R., Sundler, F. 1978. Occurrence and distribution of VIP nerves in the nasal mucosa and tracheobronchial wall. *Acta Otolaryngol.* 86:443–48

105. Wahlestedt, C., Bynke, G., Håkanson, R. 1984. Pupillary constriction by bradykinin and capsaicin: Mode of action. *Eur. J. Pharmacol.* 106:577–83

106. Wharton, J., Polak, J. M., Bloom, S. R., Will, J. A., Brown, M. R., Pearse, A. G. E. 1979. Substance P-like immunoreactive nerves in mammalian lung. *Invest. Cell Pathol.* 2:3–10

107. Widdicombe, J. 1981. Nervous receptors in the respiratory tract and lungs. In *Lung Biology in Health and Disease*, ed. T. Hornbein. 17:429–72

Ann. Rev. Physiol. 1987. 49:573–82

PERIPHERAL AIRWAY GANGLIA

Ronald F. Coburn

Department of Physiology, University of Pennsylvania School of Medicine, Philadelphia, Pennsylvania 19104

INTRODUCTION

The study of the control of airway smooth muscle exerted at the level of the parasympathetic ganglia is in its infancy. Early anatomical studies established the existence and location of these ganglia (25, 26, 35). In the last decade research has emphasized identifying neural inputs to airway smooth muscle, and more recently, attention has been turned to questions of the roles of peripheral ganglia. The first reports of the electrophysiological properties of neurons within these ganglia appeared only five years ago (7, 11). The rapidly developing area of polypeptide investigation (31, 34, 58) further stimulated interest in neurotransmission in airway ganglia. Peripheral airway ganglia appear to function to process signals directed at smooth muscle, secretory cells, vascular smooth muscle, and epithelial cells. This review concentrates on recent studies of peripheral airway ganglia and emphasizes electrophysiological properties and the state of our knowledge of how neuronal inputs may be directed to control airway smooth muscle.

GENERAL PROPERTIES OF AIRWAY PARASYMPATHETIC GANGLIA

Neural Inputs to Airway Smooth Muscle

It is evident that in both humans and most animal species control of airway smooth muscle tension is dominated by excitatory neural inputs transmitted via cholinergic motor nerves (15, 50, 60). Preganglionic cholinergic motor neurons synapse on neurons in peripheral airway ganglia that provide axons innervating smooth muscle cells. Prior to 1972, airway tone was thought to be a function of the relative activities of cholinergic excitatory and sympathetic inhibitory inputs (10, 60). However, adrenergic innervation within smooth

573

muscle is scanty and is variable in different species (21, 46, 49, 59). Since adrenergic terminals are seen in close apposition to neurons in the peripheral parasympathetic ganglia (37), sympathetic input can probably influence ganglionic processing of signals directed to smooth muscle. In the dog, in which nonadrenergic, noncholinergic inhibitory innervation to smooth muscle is minimal or absent (52), sympathetic nerves may directly innervate smooth muscle and function as the major inhibitory mechanism (10, 43). Some of the data seem contradictory: In human bronchi, the lack of catecholamine fluorescence (59) appears to indicate the absence of adrenergic nerves, but electron microscopic findings show the presence of typical adrenergic terminals (40); the adrenergic innervation to the guinea pig trachealis muscle seems scanty (21, 49), but direct stimulation of sympathetic nerve trunks evokes a strong relaxation that is inhibited more than 95% by adrenergic antagonists (62).

There is evidence for a strong nonadrenergic, noncholinergic inhibitory nervous system directed to airway smooth muscle. Field stimulations of isolated airway muscle strips from guinea pig, cat, baboon, and human airways evoke relaxations that are not due to release of norepinephrine (21, 22, 47, 51). The nonadrenergic, noncholinergic inhibitory system can also be activated by vagal stimulation (16, 24, 36, 62) and a reflex evoked by stimulation of laryngeal mucosa (55). Hexamethonium inhibits such responses (24, 62), which suggests that vagal inhibitory fibers may synapse in peripheral airway ganglia rather than directly innervate smooth muscle cells. Little is known about postganglionic inhibitory motor neurons. There may be discrete inhibitory and excitatory neurons to smooth muscle, or a single nerve fiber may contain acetylcholine and an inhibitory neurotransmitter(s) that are released as cotransmitters (9). Whether VIP is an inhibitory neurotransmitter present in postganglionic inhibitory motor nerves is still controversial (1, 14, 23, 28). Nonadrenergic relaxations are not dependent on the presence of epithelia (57), are not due to stimulation of sensory neurons (2), and occur independently of cholinergic mechanisms (4). The inhibitory innervation to airway smooth muscle has not been studied using microelectrode techniques, and an inhibitory junction potential in smooth muscle cells has not yet been recorded.

A working hypothesis is that peripheral airway ganglia process neural inputs, including cholinergic excitatory and sympathetic and nonadrenergic inhibitory inputs. There is no evidence, at present, that peripheral airway ganglion neurons can generate signals independent of input from the central nervous system, as occurs in the myenteric plexus (61), where central input appears to modulate rather than control. Afferent input, from the epithelium or from stretch receptors, may influence ganglionic integration of neural inputs, but there is as yet no convincing evidence of this. Some observations made on field-stimulated muscle preparations suggest there may be non-cholinergic excitory neurons that release substance P (5, 44, 45). However, these results can probably be explained by stimulation of sensory or "sensory-motor" nerve terminals within muscle, rather than stimulation of peripheral ganglia.

Characteristics of Airway Ganglion Neurons

Research on peripheral airway ganglia did not proceed from extracellular to intracellular electrodes, as did the work on other peripheral mammalian ganglia. The only studies currently available utilized intracellular electrode data to classify various types of neurons. It should be noted that the classifications of various ganglion cells in the myenteric plexus varied depending on whether extracellular or intracellular electrodes were utilized (61). In this case, at least six patterns of responses were seen using extracellular electrodes, whereas with intracellular electrodes only four types of different cells were identified. Ganglion cell classifications have also been based on the types of neuropeptides or neurotransmitters present in various cells or on cell morphology (61).

The ferret paratracheal ganglia was the first preparation adapted for the study of the electrophysiological characteristics of peripheral airway ganglia (7, 11). This preparation was used because of the easy access to ganglion cells and easy visability of the cells in the absence of staining (13). The architecture of the plexus has been adequately described (8, 13, 19, 29). There are superficial ganglia that appear to lie in fascia posterior to the muscle and a nerve-ganglion plexus running on the muscle surface that shows a highly structured arrangement of chains of ganglia running parallel to the axis of the trachea (i.e. the ganglia are separated by nerve trunks, which have been called interganglionic nerve trunks). Several branches of the laryngeal nerves enter the nerve-ganglion plexus. Nerves extend from the plexus into smooth muscle and probably to secretory cell and epithelial targets. Studies of the nerve-ganglion plexus using acetylcholinesterase histochemistry (8) show a more dense plexus than is seen using a silver stain (19). Electron microscopic (EM) sections of ganglion cells show a dense neuropil that includes two different types of nerve endings: those with mainly round, agranular vesicles and those with large, dense-cored vesicles with an electrolucent halo around the core (13). EM sections of the interganglionic nerve trunk show that most fibers are nonmyelinated, though a small proportion are myelinated (13).

Cameron & Coburn (13) studied the characteristics of neurons utilizing somal microelectrode penetration of cells in ganglia located in the plexus running on the surface of the ferret trachealis muscle. These studies revealed two different types of neurons, which were classified on the basis of (a) their responses to an applied intracellular current and (*b*) the characteristics of the postsynaptic potentials evoked from them via preganglionic electrical stimulation.

One cell type is characterized by a single action potential followed by a very large, long-lasting after-hyperpolarization. Only rarely can more than one action potential be evoked, even with extended cathodal pulses. Action potentials are inhibited by tetrodotoxin. Current-voltage plots indicated that most of these cells exhibit outward rectification. Single preganglionic nerve stimulations always evoked a fast excitatory postsynaptic potential (EPSP) and, rarely, a fast inhibitory postsynaptic potential (IPSP). The fast EPSP is graded, is inhibited by hexamethonium, and frequently triggers a single action potential. This cell, which was called an AH cell because of the prominent post–action potential after-hyperpolarization, seems similar to the type II/AH cells described in the myenteric plexus (61). Tracheal ganglion AH cells (studied using horseradish peroxidase injections) are all multipolar (38, 39). There are processes within the ganglion capsule that appear to be dendrites. In addition, there are single to multiple processes that run unidirectionally or bidirectionally for long distances in interganglionic nerve trunks. These processes often appear to come into close contact with neighboring ganglia. Processes are also seen extending into smooth muscle. AH cells in the ferret paratracheal ganglion differ from AH cells in the myenteric plexus (61) in that they have very long axons.

The second type of cell found by Cameron & Coburn in this structure shows no action potential when cathodal current is injected intrasomally (13). Sixty to seventy percent of the cells are of this type. Voltage-current studies often showed anomalous rectification. The resting membrane potential in these cells is consistently greater than that seen in AH cells. A slow EPSP (32) is evoked in these cells by stimulation of the interganglionic nerve trunks or inlet nerves. At least some of these cells are neurons that have a similar morphology as AH cells, as visualized by horseradish peroxidase injections (39). The lack of an evoked action potential in response to cathodal current injection or stimulation of an interganglionic nerve trunk is probably explained by action potential–generating sites distant from the soma.

Baker and associates (6) also described a cell type in the ferret paratracheal ganglia that show single action potentials followed by a prominent after-hyperpolarization and the presence of fast EPSPs. In a more recent publication from this group (8), all ten of the cells studied showed multiple action potentials with cathodal current injection. Horseradish peroxidase injections into these cells showed that their morphology is similar to that of AH cells (38, 39). Specifically, they have multiple processes within the ganglia, which are presumed to be dendrites; single or multiple axons that course through the interganglionic nerve trunk; and processes that are directed into smooth muscle.

The cat paratracheal ganglia has been studied using an in vivo preparation (48). This preparation revealed three populations of neurons, which were classified on the basis of their spontaneous action potentials: (a) Some cells showed inspiratory spikes that were inhibited by lung inflation; (b) other cells fired during expiration; and (c) a third group of cells fired randomly. To our knowledge, this preparation has yet to be studied in vitro.

In rabbit paratracheal ganglia (27), two cell types have been identified on the basis of whether the repetitive discharge during a prolonged current injection accommodated (type II) or was inactivated (type I). Type I cells were studied to determine the basis of repetitive action potentials. Post–action potential hyperpolarizations were observed in both cell types. The nature of postsynaptic potentials in this preparation has yet to be studied.

Neurotransmission in Peripheral Airway Ganglia

A goal in studies of peripheral airway ganglia is to determine how information reaching these structures is processed into signals aimed at smooth muscle cells and other effector cells. There were several approaches to the study of integration of neuronal inputs to airway smooth muscle before the electro-physiological properties of peripheral airway ganglia could be studied. Yip et al (62) developed an in vivo approach in which they compared the effects of field stimulation and vagal nerve stimulation on the tension responses of trachealis muscle. Data obtained from studies of the guinea pig trachea suggested that peripheral airway ganglia filter inhibitory input to trachealis muscle. Recently, using a similar approach Skoogh examined excitatory input in anesthetized ferrets (54). It was shown that peripheral ganglia can filter excitatory input, as well. These preparations show promise as useful ways to study neurotransmission and integration of neural inputs. However, field stimulation and nerve stimulation may generate different patterns of neuro-transmitter release and give different tension responses that are not due to "filtering."

An experimental preparation for studying neurotransmission in the isolated ferret paratracheal ganglion is illustrated in Figure 1. Preganglionic nerve fibers are stimulated and evoked EPSPs and action potentials are recorded in AH cells. The data shown in this figure emphasize the effects of post–action potential after-hyperpolarizations on neurotransmission (for further discussion, see below). This approach allows the experimenter to stimulate different inputs simultaneously and to study the classical mechanisms of neurointegration and the effects of various neuropeptides or other agents on neurotransmission.

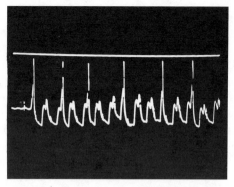

20 mV |—
50 mS

Figure 1   Filtering of input to an AH cell in the ferret paratracheal ganglia. An interganglionic nerve trunk was electrically stimulated at 30 Hz. A microelectrode was present in an AH cell body located 1 cm from the stimulating electrode. Note that post–action potential after-hyperpolarizations inhibited the trigger of action potentials by evoked EPSPs. (From Reference 20.)

Prejunctional Inhibition and Post–Action Potential After-Hyperpolarizations

Baker et al (6, 7) studied the effects of norepinephrine on prejunctional release of acetylcholine in the ferret paratracheal ganglion. This study is important because it was the first to demonstrate apparent presynaptic inhibition of neurotransmission in an airway peripheral ganglion. Baker et al showed that administration of micromolar concentrations of norepinephrine into the bathing solution resulted in a slow fall in the amplitude of the EPSPs evoked by electrical interganglionic nerve trunk stimulation. The study was performed on ganglion cells that exhibited single action potentials during application of cathodal current, i.e. apparent AH cells. Following removal of norepinephrine from the bath, the amplitude of the EPSPs did not rise again; however, a nonspecific α-adrenergic blocking agent, phentolamine, did cause an increase in the depressed amplitude of evoked EPSPs. This study demonstrated an effect on neurotransmission, as implied by decreases in EPSP, but did not rigorously exclude a postsynaptic effect. The adrenergic inhibition of impulse transmission has been confirmed with studies of neurotransmission using a more intact preparation (54). Modulation of neurotransmitter release appears to be a common mechanism in many different preparations, and many examples of this phenomenon have now been observed in other peripheral ganglia (17, 61) and at the airway smooth muscle myoneural junction (30, 53, 56).

The post–action potential after-hyperpolarization seen in ferret paratracheal AH cells appears to be an important mechanism controlling neurotransmission. Studies of the ferret paratracheal ganglion show that action potentials evoked by short cathodal pulses are inhibited during the post–action potential after-hyperpolarization. These after-hyperpolarizations are not seen following current-evoked depolarizations that do not evoke action potentials or after EPSPs that do not evoke action potentials. Increases in the ratio of Mg^{2+} to Ca^{2+} in the bathing solution and displacement of the resting membrane potential to -90 mV, the presumed equilibrium potential of K^+, inhibit the post–action potential hyperpolarization (12). Thus, the mechanism may involve Ca^{2+} activation of a K^+ conductance. The K^+ channel involved is not inhibited by tetraethylammonium ion or 4-aminopyridine. The amplitude and duration of the evoked after-hyperpolarization may be related to the amplitude of the preceding action potential. This is expected to be true if the inward calcium current occurs via a potential-dependent calcium channel. Post–action potential after-hyperpolarizations have been observed in both cell types found in rabbit paratracheal ganglion. The duration of the after-hyperpolarization was longer in nonaccommodating (type I) cells than in accommodating (type II) cells.

Wood (61) has suggested that the after-hyperpolarization that follows action potentials in type II/AH cells in the myenteric plexus may be under the control of neurotransmitters via receptor-coupled Ca^{2+} channels. This hypothesis, if it applies to peripheral airway AH cells, suggests that transmission of inputs to these cells could be partially controlled by transmitters or mediators acting on the after-hyperpolarization mechanism.

Circuitry in Peripheral Airway Ganglia

It seems important to elucidate the microcircuitry within individual ganglia and the circuitry within the nerve-ganglion plexus. In the myenteric plexus, studies combining immunocytochemistry, electrophysiology, and morphology have proven feasible and are yielding valuable information (61). Such studies can be done in peripheral airway ganglia. Some information is available about the circuitry of the paratracheal nerve-ganglion plexus in the ferret. Coburn investigated the spread of electrical signals to AH ganglion cells and smooth muscle cells following an electrical stimulation of a single inlet nerve or interganglionic nerve trunk (18). He found that the circuitry is such that stimulation at any point in the preparation results in transmission of the signal to AH cells and smooth muscle cells throughout the preparation. Analyses of the conduction velocities obtained with various types of stimulation suggested that the signal is carried by populations of myelinated neurons that run in inlet nerves and project into the interganglionic nerve trunks and by postjunctional, nonmyelinated neurons. In addition, there appear to be extensive connections between AH cells in different ganglia. Transmission of the electrical signal could not be explained by transmission in a smooth muscle syncytium. It was concluded that the circuitry is divergent and may coordinate neural input to different smooth muscle cells. These data are consistent with the functional

580   COBURN

organization of autonomic innervation observed in other tissue (33) and with
Langely's views of the function of postganglionic nerve plexuses (41). This
first "functional" study of circuitry will probably be extended to the interactions of different types of neurons in this nerve-ganglion plexus.

CONCLUSIONS

Peripheral parasympathetic airway ganglia function to integrate and coordinate neural inputs to airway smooth muscle and other airway cells. Most
questions about how these structures function are unanswered. Preparations
are now available for study of peripheral airway ganglia, and a better understanding of their roles should be forthcoming.

Literature Cited

1. Altiere, R. J., Diamond, L. 1985. Effect
   of alfa chymotrypsin on the nonadrenergic noncholinergic inhibitory
   system in cat airways. *Eur. J. Pharmacol.* 114:75–78
2. Altiere, R. J., Diamond, L. 1986. Role
   of vagal sensory fibers in nonadrenergic
   noncholinergic inhibitory responses in
   cat airways. *Am. Rev. Respir. Dis.*
   133:1159–62
3. Altiere, R. J., Szarek, J. L., Diamond,
   L. 1984. Neural control of relaxations in
   cat airways smooth muscle. *J. Appl.
   Physiol.* 57:1536–48
4. Altiere, R. J., Szarek, J. L., Diamond,
   L. 1985. Neurally mediated nonadrenergic relaxation in cat airways
   occurs independent of cholinergic mechanisms. *J. Pharmacol. Exp. Ther.*
   234:590–97
5. Andersson, R. G. G., Grundstrom, N.
   1983. The excitatory non-cholinergic,
   non-adrenergic nervous system of the
   guinea-pig airways. *Eur. J. Respir. Dis.*
   131:141–57 (Suppl.)
6. Baker, D. G., Basbaum, C. B., Herbert,
   D. A., Mitchell, R. A. 1983. Transmission of airway ganglia of ferrets: Inhibition by norepinephrine. *Neurosci. Let.*
   41:139–143
7. Baker, D. G., Herbert, D. A., Mitchell,
   R. A. 1982. Cholinergic neurotransmission in airway ganglia: Inhibition by
   norepinephrine. *Physiologist* 25:225
8. Baker, D. G., McDonald, D. M., Basbaum, C. B., Mitchell, R. A. 1986. The
   architecture of nerves and ganglia of the
   ferret trachea as revealed by acetylcholinesterase histochemistry. *J. Comp.
   Neurol.* 246:513–26
9. Burnstock, G. 1976. Do some cells re-

lease more than one transmitter? *Neurosci.* 1:239–48
10. Cabezas, G. A., Graf, P. D., Nadel, J.
    A. 1971. Sympathetic versus parasym-
    pathetic nervous regulation of airways in
    dogs. *J. Appl. Physiol.* 31:651–65
11. Cameron, A. R., Coburn, R. F. 1981.
    Electrical properties of the cells of the
    ferret paratracheal ganglion. *Physiolo-
    gist* 24:84
12. Cameron, A. R., Coburn, R. F. 1982.
    Calcium dependence of the after
    hyperpolarization of type A cells of the
    ferret paratracheal ganglion. *Fed. Proc.*
    41:1356
13. Cameron, A. R., Coburn, R. F. 1984.
    Electrical and anatomic characteristics
    of cells of ferret paratracheal ganglion.
    Am. J. Physiol. 246:C450–58
14. Cameron, A. R., Johnston, C. F., Kirk-
    patrick, C. T., Kirkpatrick, M. C. A.
    1983. The quest for the inhibitory
    neurotransmitter in bovine tracheal
    smooth muscle. *Q. J. Exp. Physiol.*
    68:413–26
15. Cameron, A. R., Kirkpatrick, C. T.
    1977. A study of excitatory neuro-
    muscular transmission in the bovine
    trachea. *J. Physiol. London* 270:733–
    45
16. Chesrown, S. E., Venugopalan, C. S.,
    Gold, W. M., Drazen, J. M. 1980. In
    vivo demonstration of nonadrenergic in-
    hibitory innervation of the guinea pig
    trachea. *J. Clin. Invest.* 65:314–20
17. Christ, D. D., Nishi, S. 1969. Presynap-
    tic action of epinephrine on sympathetic
    ganglia. *Life Sci.* 8:1235–38
18. Coburn, R. F. 1984. Neural coordina-
    tion of excitation of ferret trachealis
    muscle. *Am. J. Physiol.* 246:C459–66

19. Coburn, R. F. 1984. The anatomy of the ferret paratracheal parasympathetic nerve-ganglion plexus. *Exp. Lung Res.* 7:1–9
20. Coburn, R. F. 1986. Cholinergic neuroeffector mechanisms in airway smooth muscle. In *Lung Biology in Health and Disease,* ed. M. Kaliner, P. Barnes. New York:Dekker. In press
21. Coburn, R. F., Tomita, T. 1973. Evidence for nonadrenergic inhibitory nerves in the guinea pig trachealis muscle. *Am. J. Physiol.* 224:1072–80
22. Coleman, R. A., Levy, G. P. 1974. A non-adrenergic inhibitory nervous pathway in guinea pig trachea. *Br. J. Pharmacol.* 52:167–74
23. Dey, R. D., Shannon, J. W. A., Said, S. I. 1981. Localization of VIP immunoreactive nerves in airway and pulmonary vessels of dogs, cats and human subjects. *Cell Tissue Res.* 222:231–39
24. Diamond, L., O'Donnell, M. 1980. A nonadrenergic vagal inhibitory pathway to feline airways. *Science* 208:185–88
25. Elfman, A. G. 1943. The afferent and parasympathetic innervations of the lung and trachea of the dog. *Am. J. Anat.* 72:1–28
26. Fisher, A. W. 1964. The intrinsic innervation of the trachea. *J. Anat.* 98:117–24
27. Fowler, J. C., Weinreich, D. 1986. Electrophysiological membrane properties of paratracheal ganglion neurons of the rabbit. *Neurosci. Abstr.* 11:1182
28. Goyal, R. K., Rattan, S., Said, S. I. 1980. VIP as a possible neurotransmitter of non-cholinergic non-adrenergic inhibitory neurones. *Nature* 288:378–80
29. Grillo, M. A., Nadel, J. A. 1980. Vital staining of tracheal ganglia. *Physiologist* 23:77
30. Hahn, H. L., Wilson, A. G., Graf, P. D., Fischer, S. P., Nadel, J. A. 1978. Interaction between serotonin and efferent vagal nerves in dog lungs. *J. Appl. Physiol.* 44:144–49
31. Hakanson, R., Sundler, F., Moghimzadeh, E., Leander, S. 1983. Peptide-containing nerve fibres in the airways: Distribution and functional implications. *Eur. J. Respir. Dis.* 131:115–39 (Suppl.)
32. Hartzell, H. C. 1981. Mechanisms of slow postsynaptic potentials. *Nature* 291:539–44
33. Hillarp, N. A. 1959. The construction and functional organization of the autonomic innervation apparatus. *Acta Physiol. Scand. Suppl.* 157:1–38
34. Hokfelt, T., Johansson, O., Ljungdahl, A., Lundberg, J. M., Schultzberg, M.

1980. Peptidergic neurones. *Nature* 284:515–21
35. Honjin, R. 1954. On the ganglia and nerves of the lower respiratory tract of the mouse. *J. Morphol.* 95:263–88
36. Irvin, C. G., Boileau, R., Tremblay, J., Martin, R. R., Macklem, P. T. 1980. Bronchodilation: Noncholinergic, nonadrenergic mediation demonstrated in vivo in the cat. *Science* 207:791–92
37. Jacobowitz, D., Kent, K. M., Fleisch, J. H., Cooper, T. 1973. Histofluorescent study of catecholamine-containing elements in cholinergic ganglion from the calf and dog lung. *Proc. Soc. Exp. Biol. Med.* 144:464–66
38. Kalia, M., Cameron, A. R., Coburn, R. F. 1983. Morphological characteristics of physiologically identified parasympathetic nerve fibers in ferret trachealis muscle. *Fed. Proc.* 42:999
39. Kalia, M., Coburn, R. F. 1986. The morphology of spiking and non-spiking neurons in the ferret paratracheal ganglia. *Fed. Proc* 45:315
40. Laitinen, A., Partanen, M., Hervonen, A., Laitinen, L. A. 1985. Electron microscopic study on the innervation of the human lower respiratory tract: Evidence of adrenergic nerves. *Eur. J. Respir. Dis.* 67:209–15
41. Langely, J. N. 1904. On the question of commissural fibres between nerve-cells having the same function and situated in the same sympathetic ganglion, and on the function of post-ganglionic nerve plexuses. *J. Physiol. London* 31:244–59
42. Leff, A. R., Munoz, N. M. 1981. Selective autonomic stimulation of canine trachealis with dimethylphenylpiperazinium. *J. Appl. Physiol.* 51:428–37
43. Leff, A. R., Munoz, N. M., Hendrix, S. G. 1983. Parasympathetic and adrenergic contractile responses in canine trachea and bronchus. *J. Appl. Physiol.* 55:113–20
44. Lundberg, J. M., Saria, A. 1982. Bronchial smooth muscle contraction induced by stimulation of capsaicin-sensitive sensory neurons. *Acta Physiol. Scand.* 116:473–76
45. Lundberg, J. M., Saria, A., Brodin, E., Rosell, S., Folkers, K. 1983. A substance P antagonist inhibits vagally induced increase in vascular permeability and bronchial smooth muscle contraction in the guinea pig. *Proc. Natl. Acad. Sci. USA* 80:1120–24
46. Mann, S. 1971. The innervation of mammalian bronchial smooth muscle: The localization of catecholamines and cholinesterases. *Histochem. J.* 3:319–31

47. Middendorf, W. F., Russell, J. A. 1980. Innervation of airway smooth muscle in the baboon: Evidence for a nonadrenergic inhibitory system. *J. Appl. Physiol.* 48:947–56

48. Mitchell, R. A., Baker, D. G., Basbaum, C. B., Herbert, D. A. 1984. In vivo recording from tracheal parasympathetic ganglia. *Physiologist* 26:A–37

49. O'Donnell, S. R., Saar, N. 1973. Histochemical localization of adrenergic nerves in the guinea-pig trachea. *Br. J. Pharmacol.* 47:707–10

50. Olsen, C. R., Colebatch, H. J. H., Mebel, P. E., Nadel, J. A., Staub, N. C. 1965. Motor control of pulmonary airways studied by nerve stimulation *J. Appl. Physiol.* 20:202–14

51. Richardson, J., Beland, J. 1976. Nonadrenergic inhibitory nerves in human airways. *J. Appl. Physiol.* 41:764–71

52. Russell, J. A. 1978. Responses of isolated canine airways to electrical stimulation and acetylcholine. *J. Appl. Physiol.* 45:690–98

53. Russell, J. A., Simons, E. J. 1985. Modulation of cholinergic neurotransmission in airways by enkephalin. *J. Appl. Physiol.* 58:853–58

54. Skoogh, B. E. 1983. Transmission through airway ganglia. *Eur. J. Respir. Dis.* 131:159–70 (Suppl.)

55. Szarek, J. L., Gillespie, M. N., Altiere, R. J., Diamond, L. 1986. Reflex activation of the nonadrenergic noncholinergic inhibitory nervous system in feline airways. *Am. Rev. Respir. Dis.* 131:A278

56. Tanaka, D. T., Grunstein, M. M. 1986. Effect of substance P on neurally mediated contraction of rabbit airway smooth muscle. *J. Appl. Physiol.* 60:458–64

57. Thompson, D. C., Wells, J. L., Altiére, R. J., Diamond, L. 1985. The effect of epithelium removal on nonadrenergic, noncholinergic inhibitory responses in the isolated central airways of the cat and guinea pig. *Am. Rev. Respir. Dis.* 133:A172

58. Uddman, R., Alumets, J., Densert, O., Hakanson, R., Sundler, F. 1978. Occurrence and distribution of VIP nerves in the nasal mucosa and tracheobronchial wall. *Acta Otolaryngol.* 86:443–48

59. Weiner, N. 1967. Adrenergic innervation of bronchial muscle. *Aspen Emphysema Conf.* 10:157–266

60. Widdicombe, J. G. 1963. Regulation of tracheobronchial smooth muscle. *Physiol. Rev.* 43:1–37

61. Wood, J. D. 1984. Enteric neurophysiology. *Am. J. Physiol.* 247:G585–98

62. Yip, P., Palombini, B., Coburn, R. F. 1981. Inhibitory innervation to the guinea pig trachealis muscle. *J. Appl. Physiol.* 50:374–82

Ann. Rev. Physiol. 1987. 49:583–94

INNERVATION OF AIRWAY SMOOTH MUSCLE: FINE STRUCTURE

Giorgio Gabella

Department of Anatomy, University College London, Gower Street, London, WC1E 6BT, England

Introduction

In what are clearly early days in the study of the innervation of airways, it is possible to identify a set of structural parameters in muscle that determine the contractile behavior of the apparatus. A few of these parameters are examined in this article.

Sources of Nerve Fibers

Nerve fibers of various origins run within the musculature of the trachea and bronchi. Their sources are varied and not well characterized. The main source of afferent fibers to trachea and bronchi is the vagus nerves (with nerve cell bodies in the nodose ganglion); whether there are also some afferent fibers from dorsal root ganglia remains to be proven. The vagal (afferent) fibers represent the largest nerve supply to the bronchial and tracheal muscles of the mouse, as judged from the extent of the loss of intramuscular nerve endings after vagotomy (46). The majority of efferent fibers originate from cell bodies in the tracheal and bronchial ganglia (see chapter by R. Coburn in this volume) (and possibly in some other of the many ganglia associated with mediastinal organs). These neurones are mainly driven by vagal nerve fibers and are part of the parasympathetic outflow; they include excitatory and inhibitory neurones. Axons projecting from these ganglion cells to the tracheal muscle of the ferret have been traced after intracellular injection of horseradish peroxidase (31).

0066-4278/87/0315-0583$02.00

Nerve-Mediated Responses

A nerve-mediated excitatory cholinergic response is present in the airways of all the species investigated (23, 59). Cholinergic fibers, issued by tracheal and bronchial ganglion neurones (parasympathetic postganglionic fibers) and operating via muscarinic receptors, are the principal nerve input to the tracheobronchial muscles.

A small but distinct alpha-adrenergic excitatory response is present in the trachea of the dog (55), man (33), and rat (57), but is absent in the guinea pig trachea (60). A marked contraction of the cervical trachea, mediated by alpha-adrenoceptors, occurs upon stimulation of the sympathetic trunk or administration of an adrenergic agonist in the rabbit in vivo (43). A noncholinergic, nonadrenergic excitatory nerve response is recorded from the musculature in the guinea pig bronchi and trachea (56).

Two nerve-mediated inhibitory responses have been uncovered. The more conspicuous one is mediated by adrenergic nerve endings acting on beta-adrenergic receptors (23). This response is well documented in vitro (22, 55). It can also be elicited in vivo from the cervical trachea of the guinea pig by transmural stimulation (in the presence of atropine); this response is markedly inhibited by beta-blockers (60). A relaxation of lesser extent but of similar time course is obtained by stimulation of the sympathetic trunks and is abolished by hexamethonium. This result indicates that the trunk contains preganglionic fibers that synapse within ganglia (mainly the stellate ganglion) (60).

The second inhibitory response is insensitive to adrenergic and cholinergic blockers and has been demonstrated in vitro in the trachea of several species (11, 12, 49). It is absent in the trachea of the dog (55). More recently this response was observed in vivo in the cat bronchi (16, 28) and the guinea pig trachea (9, 60). In the latter species the relaxation can be achieved with much greater ease in the thoracic than in the cervical portion of the trachea (60). Moreover, it can also be obtained with a prolonged stimulation of the vagus nerve (28, 60), and it is inhibited by hexamethonium (60). This finding indicates that the neural structures in question are not the vagal fibers themselves, but fibers that originate from local (tracheal) ganglion cells that are synaptically driven by vagal fibers. The existence within the vagus nerve of bronchodilator fibers (in addition to the principal, bronchoconstrictor, fibers) has often been noted (59).

Afferent mechanisms involving mainly afferent fibers of the vagus nerve are well established (51). The sensory receptors include chemoreceptors, mechanoreceptors, and stretch receptors [the so-called rapidly adapting receptors and slowly adapting receptors; the latter outnumber the former by a factor of 10 (58)]. In the trachea of the dog, cat, and rabbit the slowly adapting stretch receptors are probably entirely located within the trachealis muscle itself (3, 42). Other afferent mechanisms are mediated by nerve fibers traveling in the sympathetic nerves and the stellate ganglion (26, 35).

Finally, there are efferent responses that are mediated not by efferent nerves but by afferent fibers, through a mechanism known as the axon reflex. In the trachea of the guinea pig and rat, axon reflexes involving vagal afferent axons enhance vascular permeability and produce smooth muscle contraction (37, 39); the latter response can also be induced in human bronchi in vitro (38).

Distribution of Intramuscular Nerve Fibers

Nerve fibers penetrate the muscle mainly from its adventitial side and are gathered into small bundles. These nerve bundles are connected to meshes of the tracheal ganglionated plexus and to perivascular nerves. Histochemistry and electron microscopy indicate that these nerve bundles contain an admixture of nerve fibers of different type (e.g. cholinergic and adrenergic). How exactly the sympathetic and the parasympathetic inputs merge into these bundles is not clear. It remains to be established, for example, to what extent or in what proportion adrenergic fibers traverse tracheal ganglia before reaching the muscle. The admixture of fibers of different nature within the same bundle (i.e. wrapped by the same Schwann cell) is common to all autonomic nerves. The closeness of, for example, adrenergic and cholinergic axons offers the possibility of a direct chemical interaction between the two pathways, a possibility that has often been commented upon.

The main muscular component of the trachea runs transversely to the length of the organ. It forms a continuous lamina that is as long as the trachea and measures about 1.5 mm in width in the mouse and about 10 mm in man. At the microscopic level the muscular lamina is interrupted by slender septa of connective tissue (chiefly collagen), which create discrete bundles of muscle cells. The lateral continuity of the muscle is maintained by the repeated splitting and merging of the bundles with one another. A few elastic fibers are found within the muscle, but the main elastic component of the trachea is a conspicuous layer of elastic fibers running longitudinally between the muscle and the lamina propria. [The histochemistry of this elastic lamina has recently been investigated (6).] In silver-impregnated preparations of the trachea of primates, Fisher (21) noted a rich meshwork of longitudinally arranged nerve fibers close to the elastic lamina.

Many authors have noted that nerve bundles are found mostly within the intramuscular septa, rather than inside muscle bundles. The nerve bundles lie approximately parallel to the muscle (and this is true of the bronchial musculature too, where the orientation of the muscle is more variable), and they branch and merge, forming a fine-meshed net. The pattern of this arborization is not known. It is unlikely that it resembles a tree, because the bundles appear to form a "closed" mesh [which in the days of silver-impregnation studies used to be called autonomic ground plexus (21)], and the true anatomical endings are only short projections emerging from the meshwork. Many of the endings (in a functional sense, i.e. the sites of transmitter release) are varicosities of axons that do not leave the nerve bundle they inhabit.

Nerve bundles do not show a preferential distribution across the thickness of the tracheal muscle. However, in the ferret it has been found that the great majority of axons lie at the adventitial surface of the muscle or within the first 5 μm from this surface (4), an arrangement of the innervation that more closely resembles that of blood vessels than that of viscera. When longitudinal musculature is present [a regular occurrence in man (19) and not an unusual one in laboratory animals such as the rat], it is not known whether it has the same pattern of innervation as the adjacent transverse musculature.

Histochemical Types of Nerve Fiber

Cholinergic fibers in the airways have only been localized in an indirect and tentative way by acetylcholinesterase histochemistry. Positive fibers have been localized in the bronchial muscle of several species (2, 18, 20, 54). The acetylcholinesterase reaction is positive in the ganglion neurones of the plexus of trachea and bronchi (2, 20).

There are abundant adrenergic fibers in the bronchial muscles of the cat (13, 53), goat, sheep, pig, calf (41), and dog (35), whereas few are found in the bronchial muscles of the rabbit (41) and man (47). The trachea of the rabbit (41) and the dog (55) have few fluorescent fibers, and most of these are perivascular. No fluorescent fibers are found in the bovine tracheal muscle (8), whereas in the cat trachea the adrenergic innervation is well developed (53). In the guinea pig tracheal muscle, adrenergic fibers are readily found (by fluorescence microscopy) in the cervical portion, whereas they are scanty in the thoracic portion (11, 44, 45) and are rare in the bronchiole muscles (45). The uptake of tritiated norepinephrine by the guinea pig trachea has a similar gradient (24), and the pharmacological effect of beta-blockers on the relaxation elicited by transmural stimulation is markedly greater in the cervical than in the thoracic trachea of the guinea pig (11). [However, no differences were noted in the electron microscope in the frequency of adrenergic endings in the two parts of the trachea (27, 30; see section on types of nerve endings).] Histochemically, adrenergic fibers are always less numerous than the fibers interpreted as cholinergic, although their distribution is the same (53). There are, however, no quantitative studies of this discrepancy, and it is surprising that the question of adrenergic innervation has not been studied in greater detail, either by fluorescence histochemistry or by immunofluorescence.

Adrenergic fibers originate from neurones in the sympathetic chain, whereas adrenergic neurones are not found in the ganglia near the trachea and bronchi (20, 29). Interestingly, however, in some animals, such as the calf, some adrenergic fibers are seen by fluorescence microscopy to be closely associated with a proportion of the bronchial ganglion neurones (29). Knight (34) has made a similar observation in the cat and has extended it to the electron microscope level. The adrenergic endings were described as forming numerous synaptic complexes with dendrites of ganglion neurones. The possibility of adrenergic modulation of the parasympathetic transmission to the airways has been discussed by many authors, and recently, in yet another animal species, the ferret, it has been shown that noradrenaline inhibits cholinergic (nicotinic) transmission in tracheal ganglia by acting on alpha-adrenoceptors (1).

Other chemical classes of nerve fibers are recognized by immunohisto-chemistry for peptides, which include substance P (6b) and calcitonin gene–related peptide (37b) [both these substances are probably associated with afferent vagal fibers and vasoactive intestinal peptide (15b, 41b)]. Other chemicals localized in airway ganglia and intramuscular nerves include the enzyme neurone-specific enolase and the calcium binding protein S-100 (52). The latter substance occurs in satellite cells of the ganglia and in the Schwann cells of intramuscular nerve bundles.

Density of Innervation

The concept of innervation is rather vague. Although the presence of nerves within a muscle constitutes "innervation" in a broad sense, the relevant parameters are the distribution and spatial density of intramuscular axons that are in a position to be influenced by, or to influence, muscle behavior. So it seems useful, for example, to distinguish between intrafascicular and in-terfascicular nerve bundles, as Hoyes & Barber (27) have done; however, a precise distinction is generally difficult to make. Although it is not clear how close a varicosity must be to a muscle cell to be able to influence it, it is unlikely that varicosities embedded in collagen and lying many micrometers away from the nearest muscle cell (as has been found) can succeed in nerve-muscle transmission. There are little firm data [except for the fluores-cence microscopy observations in the adrenergic fibers in organs such as the iris (40)] on the frequency of varicosities along an axon, on the uniformity of size and shape of varicosities along an axon, etc. If the pattern of varicosities is as regular as it appears in the adrenergic fibers of the iris, then it could be argued that the varicosities develop as an intrinsic feature of the terminal part of an axon and not exclusively in those portions of an axon where a postjunc-tional structure is present. The density of innervation is usually expressed as number of nerve bundles, axons, varicose axons, and muscle cells on trans-verse sections of a muscle (i.e. the ratio of axon profiles to muscle cell profiles). It should be borne in mind that this value gives only a rough estimate of the true extent of the nerve supply.

The density of innervation of the tracheal muscle varies considerably among animal species. In man there is less than one axon per 100 muscle cell profiles (15); whereas in the dog the ratio is 3.5 to 100 (and the ratio for varicose axons is 1.9 to 100) (32). In the guinea pig there are 19.2 varicosities per 100 muscle cell profiles in the cervical trachea and 12.7 per 100 in the thoracic trachea (30). Lower values (6.7 and 7.0, respectively) were obtained by Hoyes & Barber (27); this difference is partly accounted for by the fact that these authors counted only intrafascicular axons. Further differences among species are shown in Table 1 (G. Gabella & C.-H. Chiang, unpublished results). The range of the axonal densities in the tracheal muscles of mouse, rat, rabbit, and sheep spans more than one order of magnitude. As the volume of the muscle increases, its innervation tends to become sparser. Interestingly, nerve density also varies along the length of the airways. Whereas there is little or no variability along the trachea of the few other species studied, in man the density of innervation of the muscles of the bronchi of the 4th to 7th order is 18 axons per 100 muscle cells, i.e. about 20 times greater than in the trachea (15).

Types of Nerve Ending

Some nerve endings occur singly and are almost completely devoid of Schwann cell wrapping. However, the majority of varicosities (which, by definition, are regarded as nerve endings because they contain "synaptic" vesicles and are thus sites of transmitter release) lie within small nerve bundles comprised of two or more varicose axons and a Schwann cell. At least cholinergic and adrenergic nerve endings of airway musculature have

Table 1 Density of innervation and frequency of gap junctions in the trachealis muscle of mouse, rat, rabbit, and sheep

Animal	No. of muscle cell profiles examined	No. of axons	No. of varicose axons	No. of gap junctions
		(per 100 muscle cell profiles)		
Mouse 1	280	35	15	10.7
	332	49	21	10.3
Rat 1	318	74	27	6.3
	225	43	21	9.8
Rabbit 1	621	17	5	11.9
	636	15	8	8.3
Sheep 1	1085	4	1	1.8

been classified with confidence by many investigators. Cholinergic endings mainly contain agranular vesicles ranging in size from 40 to 70 nm; these vesicles are accompanied by a few large granular vesicles, mitochondria, and microtubules. In all respects these endings do not differ from endings interpreted as cholinergic in other visceral muscle. However, their quantitative characterization is currently very limited. It is doubtful that all the endings containing a high proportion of small agranular vesicles are actually cholinergic.

Adrenergic endings mainly contain small agranular vesicles (the granularity is usually apparent only after injection of the adrenergic false transmitter 5-hydroxydopamine) plus a small number of large granular vesicles, mitochondria, and microtubules (15, 30, 35, 53). Endings of this type are absent in the bovine tracheal muscle (8).

Other "types" of nerve ending have been observed: For example, Knight (34, 35) reported "type II" axons containing small, round or irregular vesicles of 20–60 nm in diameter, small flat agranular vesicles, and a few large dense-core vesicles of 70–100 nm in diameter. Whether these structures represent a separate type of ending awaits confirmation. A type 2 nerve ending described by Hoyes & Barber (27) in the guinea pig tracheal muscle contains mainly large, dense-core vesicles. These endings are much fewer in number than the type 1 (cholinergic and adrenergic) endings reported by the same authors and are interpreted as releasing a nonadrenergic noncholinergic inhibitory transmitter (27).

The ultrastructural identification of afferent nerve endings is extremely difficult in all viscera, and the airways are no exception. However, the endings of the vagal fibers in the airways contain the peptide substance P (39), and it should therefore be possible to identify these endings by immunocytochemistry. In the guinea pig trachea, intramuscular nerve endings containing numerous mitochondria and only small numbers of vesicles have been regarded as afferent endings (27). These endings are relatively few in number compared with the other types, and they are more numerous within muscle bundles than between muscle bundles. In the bronchial walls of the rat, including their musculature, there are nerve endings that are very elongated, devoid of Schwann cell covering, and rich in mitochondria (17). Endings of this type have been labelled free lanceolate terminals and are thought to be specialized sensory endings that are in contact with the basal lamina of muscle cells or with elastic and collagen fibers (17).

Neuromuscular Junctions

Close contacts between nerve endings (varicosities) and muscle cells are rare in the airway muscles of all species studied. These contacts should not be called synapses, and the question of to what extent they can be regarded as neuromuscular junctions is open to discussion. In the dog trachea the closest approach of a nerve ending to a muscle cell is 140 nm (32); in man it is 100 nm, but most of the endings lie more than 1 μm away from the nearest muscle cell (15). In animal species such as the mouse and the rat the neuromuscular cleft is less than 50 nm in about 5% of all the nerve endings (G. Gabella & C.-H. Chiang, unpublished results). A few close neuromuscular contacts (with a cleft of less than 20 nm) were seen in the tracheal muscle of the guinea pig (30) and monkey (35).

Gap Junctions

Nexuses or gap junctions provide a mechanism for free and direct flow of ions between cells and therefore electrically couple the cells. Electrical coupling is a crucial electrophysiological characteristic of smooth muscles, but a precise correlation of the occurrence and extent of electrical coupling with the occurrence and density of gap junctions has not been demonstrated. Some smooth muscles are devoid of gap junctions (14, 25), and it is possible that other structures, in addition to gap junctions, support electrical coupling. This uncertainty is increased by the fact that gap junctions may serve other roles by providing other chemical couplings in addition to ionic coupling.

Gap junctions are observed between muscle cells in the tracheal muscle. In man 2.7 gap junctions per 100 muscle cell profiles were counted (15); in the cow there are about 8 gap junctions per 100 muscle cells (7). Other quantitative values on the frequency of gap junctions in mouse, rat, rabbit, and sheep are shown in Table 1. Gap junctions are described as rare in the trachea of the dog (55) and the guinea pig (30, 50). There is clearly a great variation in this parameter among species, and from the little evidence at hand it seems that gap junctions are not more abundant when innervation is less dense.

Distribution of Receptors

The presence of certain receptors in airway musculature is generally established by pharmacological means (see section on nerve-mediated responses). The localization and density of muscarinic receptors in the tracheal muscle of the ferret have been studied by means of tritiated propylbenzylcholine mustard ([^{3}H]PrBCM) binding (4). Light microscopy autoradiography shows a high concentration of grains over the muscle cells ($\sim$21 receptor sites per square micrometer of muscle cell membrane). The density appears to be higher over the muscle cells near the adventitia than over those near the mucosa. This observation matches receptor distribution with the position of axons (see section on the distribution of intramuscular nerve fibers). In this study there was no evidence of a concentration of grains over discrete areas of the cell surface ("hot spots") (4). This observation is in agreement with observations in other smooth muscles but awaits confirmation at the ultrastructural level.

Studies of localization of receptors get to the very core of the process of neurotransmission. The technical difficulties, however, are almost insurmountable; variable access to exogenous ligands and the transient nature of their physiological binding, the complex nature of the receptor molecule, and membrane fluidity severely limit one's ability to determine the site of ligand receptors.

Vascularization

The type and density of vascularization are important parameters in muscles, in that blood vessels supply nutrient to the tissue. They also provide a mechanism for removing transmitters and bringing regulatory substances to muscle cells and nerves. Blood vessels also provide a route or a preferred path along which nerve bundles grow. The blood vessels to the tracheal and bronchial muscle arise from the laryngeal and the bronchial arteries and not from the pulmonary vessels (5), but the details of this microcirculatory tree are not known. The tracheal musculature is generally poorly vascularized. In mice, rats, guinea pigs, rabbits, and sheep, very few blood vessels (capillaries, arterioles, venules) are found within muscle bundles. More often, blood vessels run within the connective tissue septa, but most of the vessels are found at the adventitial or the mucosal surface of the muscle (G. Gabella & C.-H. Chiang, unpublished observations). The tracheal ganglia, which are well encapsulated by a perineurium, contain numerous blood vessels, mainly capillaries (10).

Conclusions

Although little evidence is available, the innervation of airway musculature seems to show no marked differences from that of other visceral muscles or any unique features. There are, however, wide differences among animal species (48). These differences are probably more extensive than those found in the gut but are similar to those known to occur in other smooth muscles, especially in blood vessels. Species differences are, however, generally not well documented, and the full benefit of rigorous comparative studies has not yet been obtained in this field. Many other areas related to the innervation have attracted little interest, such as those of development, the trophic interactions between nerves and airway musculature, hypertrophic growth, and the general dynamic structural aspects of the tissues that make up the airways.

Literature Cited

1. Baker, D. G., Basbaum, C. B., Herbert, D. A., Mitchell, R. A. 1983. Transmission in airway ganglia of ferrets: Inhibition by norepinephrine. *Neurosci. Lett.* 41:139–43

2. Baker, D. G., McDonald, D. M., Basbaum, C. B., Mitchell, R. A. 1986. The architecture of nerves and ganglia of the ferret trachea as revealed by acetylcholinesterase histochemistry. *J. Comp. Neurol.* 246:513–26

3. Bartlett, D. Jr., Jefferey, P., Sant'Ambrogio, G., Wise, J. C. M. 1976. Location of stretch receptors in the trachea and bronchi of the dog. *J. Physiol. London* 258:409–20

4. Basbaum, C. B., Grillo, M. A., Widdicombe, J. H. 1984. Muscarinic receptors: Evidence for a nonuniform distribution in tracheal smooth muscle and exocrine glands. *J. Neurosci.* 4:508–20

5. Berry, J. L. 1935. The relation between bronchial and pulmonary circulation in the human lung, investigated by radiopaque injections. *J. Physiol. London* 24:305–14

6. Böck, P., Stockinger, L. 1984. Light and electron microscopic identification of elastic, elaunin and oxytalan fibers in human tracheal and brochial mucosa. *Anat. Embryol.* 170:145–53

6b. Cadieux, A., Springall, D. R., Mulderry, P. K., Rodrigo, J., Ghatei, M. A., et al. 1986. Occurrence, distribution and ontogeny of CGRP immunoreactivity in the rat lower respiratory tract: Effect of capsaicin treatment and surgical denervations. *Neuroscience* 19:605–27

7. Cameron, A. R., Bullock, C. G., Kirkpatrick, C. T. 1982. The ultrastructure of bovine tracheal smooth muscle. *J. Ultrastruct. Res.* 81:290–305

8. Cameron, A. R., Johnston, C. F., Kirkpatrick, C. T., Kirkpatrick, M. C. A. 1983. The quest for the inhibitory neurotransmitter in bovine tracheal smooth muscle. *Q. J. Exp. Physiol.* 68:413–26

9. Chesrown, S. E., Venugopalan, C. S., Gold, W. M., Drazen, J. M. 1980. In vivo demonstration of nonadrenergic inhibitory innervation of the guinea pig trachea. *J. Clin. Invest.* 65:314–20

10. Chiang, C.-H., Gabella, G. 1986. Quantitative study of the ganglion neurons of the mouse trachea. *Cell Tiss. Res.* 246:243–52

11. Coburn, R. F., Tomita, T. 1973. Evidence for noradrenergic inhibitory nerves in the guinea pig trachealis muscle. *Am. J. Physiol.* 224:1072–80

12. Coleman, R. A., Levy, G. P. 1974. A non-adrenergic inhibitory nervous pathway in guinea-pig trachea. *Br. J. Pharmacol.* 52:167–74

13. Dahlstrom, A., Fuxe, K., Hokfelt, T., Norberg, K.-A. 1966. Adrenergic innervation of the bronchial muscle of the cat. *Acta Physiol. Scand.* 66:507–8

14. Daniel, E. E., Daniel, V. P., Duchon, G., Garfield, R. E., Nichols, M., et al. 1976. Is the nexus a necessary for cell-to-cell coupling in smooth muscle? *J. Membr. Biol.* 208:207–39

15. Daniel, E. E., Kannan, M., Davis, C., Posey-Daniel, V. 1986 Ultrastructural studies on the neuromuscular control of human tracheal and bronchial muscle. *Respir. Physiol.* 63:109–28

15b. Dey, D. D., Shannon, W. A., Said, S. I. 1981. Localization of VIP-immunoreactive nerves in airways and pulmonary vessels of dogs, cats, and human subjects. *Cell Tiss. Res.* 220:231–38

16. Diamond, L., O'Donnell, M. 1980. A nonadrenergic vagal inhibitory pathway to feline airways. *Science* 208:185–88

17. Düring, V. M., Andres, K. H., Iravani, J. 1974. The fine structure of the pulmonary stretch receptor in the rat. *Z. Anat. Entwicklungsgesch.* 143:215–22

18. El-Bermani, A.-W., Grant, M. 1975. Acetylcholinesterase-positive nerves of the rhesus monkey bronchial tree. *Thorax* 30:162–70

19. Ferner, H., Müller, I. 1961. Mikroskopische Anatomie und Architektonik der membranösen Trachealwand der Menschen. *Z. Mikrosk. Anat. Forsch.* 67:571–91

20. Fillenz, M. 1970. Innervation of pulmonary and bronchial blood vessels of the dog. *J. Anat.* 106:449–61

21. Fisher, A. W. F. 1964. The intrinsic innervation of the trachea. *J. Anat.* 98:117–24

22. Fleisch, J. H., Maling, H. M., Brodie, B. B. 1970. Evidence for existence of alpha-adrenergic receptors in the mammalian trachea. *Am. J. Physiol.* 218:596–99

23. Foster, R. W. 1964. A note on the electrically transmurally stimulated isolated trachea of the guinea-pig. *J. Pharm. Pharmacol.* 16:125–28

24. Foster, R. W., O'Donnell, S. R. 1972. Some evidence of the active uptake of

noradrenaline in the guinea-pig isolated trachea. *Br. J. Pharmacol.* 45:71–82

25. Gabella, G. 1981. Structure of smooth muscles. In *Smooth Muscle: An Assessment of Current Knowledge*, ed. E. Bulbring, A. F. Brading, A. W. Jones, T. Tomita, pp. 1–46. London: Arnold. 563 pp.

26. Holmes, R., Torrance, R. W. 1959. Afferent fibres of the stellate ganglion. *Q. J. Exp. Physiol.* 44:271–81.

27. Hoyes, A. D., Barber, P. 1980. Innervation of the trachealis muscle in the guinea-pig: A quantitative ultrastructural study. *J. Anat.* 130:789–800

28. Irvin, C. G., Boileau, R., Tremblay, J., Martin, R. R., Macklem, P. T. 1980. Bronchodilatation: Noncholinergic, nonadrenergic mediation demonstrated in vivo in the cat. *Science* 207:791–92

29. Jacobowitz, D., Kent, K. M., Fleisch, J. H., Cooper, T. 1973. Histofluorescence study of catecholamine-containing elements in cholinergic ganglia from the calf and dog lung. *Proc. Soc. Exp. Biol. Med.* 144:464–66

30. Jones, T. R., Kannan, M. S., Daniel, E. E. 1980. Ultrastructural study of guinea pig tracheal smooth muscle and its innervation. *Can. J. Physiol. Pharmacol.* 58:974–83

31. Kalia, M., Cameron, A. R., Coburn, R. F. 1983. Morphological characteristics of physiologically identified parasympathetic nerve fibers in ferret trachealis muscle. *Fed. Proc.* 42:999

32. Kannan, M. S., Daniel, E. E. 1980. Structural and functional study of canine tracheal smooth muscle. *Am. J. Physiol.* 238:C27–C33

33. Kneussl, M. P., Richardson, J. P. 1978. Alpha-adrenergic receptors in human and canine trachael and bronchial smooth muscle. *J. Appl. Physiol.* 45:307–11

34. Knight, D. S. 1980. A light and electron microscopic study of feline intrapulmonary ganglia. *J. Anat.* 131:413–28

35. Knight, D. S., Hyman, A. L., Kadowitz, P. J. 1981. Innervation of intrapulmonary airway smooth muscle of the dog, monkey and baboon. *J. Autonomic Nerv. Syst.* 3:31–43

36. Kostreva, D. R., Zuperku, E. J., Hess, G. L., Coon, R. L., Kampine, J. P. 1975. Pulmonary afferent activity recorded from sympathetic nerves. *J. Appl. Physiol.* 39:37–40

37. Lundberg, J. M., Brodin, E., Hua, X., Saria, A. 1984. Vascular permeability changes and smooth muscle contraction in relation to capsaicin-sensitive substance P afferents in the guinea-pig. *Acta Physiol. Scand.* 120:217–27

37b. Lundberg, J. M., Hokfelt, T., Martling, C. R., Saria, A., Cuello, C. 1984. Substance P–immunoreactive sensory nerves in the lower respiratory tract of various mammals including man. *Cell Tiss. Res.* 235:251–61

38. Lundberg, J. M., Martling, C.-R., Saria, A. 1983. Substance P and capsaicin-induced contraction of human bronchi. *Acta Physiol. Scand.* 119:49–53

39. Lundberg, J. M., Saria, A. 1982. Bronchial smooth muscle contraction induced by stimulation of capsaicin-sensitive sensory neurons. *Acta Physiol. Scand.* 116:473–76

40. Malmfors, T. 1965. The adrenergic innervation of the eye as demonstrated by fluorescence microscopy. *Acta Physiol. Scand.* 64:Suppl. 248

41. Mann, S. P. 1971. The innervation of mammalian bronchial smooth muscle: The localization of catecholamines and cholinesterases. *Histochem. J.* 3:319–31

41b. Matsuzaki, Y., Hamasaki, Y., Said, S. I. 1980. Vasoactive intestinal peptide: A possible transmitter of adrenergic relaxation of guinea pig airways. *Science* 210:1252–53

42. Mortola, J. P., Sant'Ambrogio, G. 1979. Mechanics of the trachea and behaviour of its slowly adapting stretch receptors. *J. Physiol. London* 286:577–90

43. Mustafa, K. Y., Elkhawad, A. O., Bicik, V., Mardini, I. A., Thulesius, O. 1982. Adrenergic and cholinergic induced contractions of tracheal smooth muscle in the rabbit as demonstrated by a new in vivo method. *Acta Physiol. Scand.* 114:129–34

44. O'Donnell, S. R., Saar, N. 1973. Histochemical localization of adrenergic nerves in the guinea-pig trachea. *Br. J. Pharmacol.* 47:707–10

45. O'Donnell, S. R., Saar, N., Wood, L. J. 1978. The density of adrenergic nerves at various levels in the guinea-pig lung. *Clin. Exp. Pharmacol. Physiol.* 5:325–32

46. Pack, R. J., Al-Ugaily, L. H., Widdicombe, J. G. 1984. The innervation of the trachea and extrapulmonary bronchi of the mouse. *Cell Tiss. Res.* 238:61–68

47. Pack, R. J., Richardson, P. S. 1984. The aminergic innervation of the human bronchus: A light and electron microscopic study. *J. Anat.* 138:493–502

48. Richardson, J. B. 1979. Nerve supply to

the lungs. *Am. Rev. Respir. Dis.* 119:785–802

49. Richardson, J. B., Beland, J. 1976. Nonadrenergic inhibitory nervous system in human airways. *J. Appl. Physiol.* 41:764–71

50. Richardson, J. B., Ferguson, C. C. 1979. Neuromuscular structure and function in the airways. *Fed. Proc.* 38:202–8

51. Sant'Ambrogio, G. 1982. Information arising from the tracheobronchial tree of mammals. *Physiol. Rev.* 62:531–69

52. Sheppard, M. N., Kurian, S. S., Henzen-Longmans, S. C., Michetti, F., Cocchia, D., et al. 1983. Neurone-specific enolase and S-100: New markers for delineating the innervation of the respiratory tract in man and other mammals. *Thorax* 38:333–40

53. Silva, D. G., Ross, G. 1974. Ultrastructural and fluorescence histochemical studies on the innervation of the tracheobronchial muscle of normal cats and cats treated with 6-hydroxydopamine. *J. Ultrastruct. Res.* 47:310–28

54. Smith, R. B., Taylor, I. M. 1971. Observations on the intrinsic innervation of trachea, bronchi and pulmonary vessels in the sheep. *Acta Anat.* 80:1–13

55. Suzuki, H., Morita, K., Kuriyama, H. 1976. Innervation and properties of the smooth muscle of the dog trachea. *Jap. J. Physiol.* 26:303–20

56. Szolcsányi, J., Barthó, L. 1982. Capsaicin-sensitive non-cholinergic excitatory innervation of the guinea-pig tracheobronchial smooth muscle. *Neurosci. Lett.* 34:247–51

57. Vornanen, M. 1982. Adrenergic responses in different sections of rat airways. *Acta Physiol. Scand.* 114:587–91

58. Widdicombe, J. G. 1954. Receptors in the trachea and bronchi of the cat. *J. Physiol. London* 123:71–104

59. Widdicombe, J. G. 1963. Regulation of tracheobronchial smooth muscle. *Physiol. Rev.* 43:1–37

60. Yip, P., Palomini, B., Coburn, R. F. 1981. Inhibitory innervation to the guinea pig trachealis muscle. *J. Appl. Physiol.* 50:374–82

Ann. Rev. Physiol. 1987. 49:595–609

ORGANIZATION OF CENTRAL CONTROL OF AIRWAYS

Madhu P. Kalia

Department of Pharmacology, Jefferson Medical College of Thomas Jefferson University, Philadelphia, Pennsylvania 19107

INTRODUCTION

This review discusses the major aspects of brain stem microcircuitry that relate to control of airway smooth muscle and draws upon material gathered from neuroanatomical and electrophysiological studies. Until recently, the enigma of how the central nervous system (CNS) communicates with the ganglion cells in the walls of airways that ultimately control smooth muscle function was to a large extent unresolved. The use of sensitive tracers and careful anatomical mapping has revealed the existence of a well-organized system of motor and sensory connections between the airways and the brain stem. This information could lead to a better understanding of the morphological, neurochemical, and functional correlates of the neural control of airway smooth muscle. The questions we can now begin to answer include: How is the CNS organized to produce continuous alterations in airway caliber in response to a variety of visceral and somatic afferent inputs? How are the sensory and motor mechanisms integrated in the control of airway smooth muscle? What is the neurochemical basis for central and peripheral neural control of airway smooth muscle? To what extent are local neuronal circuits in airway smooth muscle capable of independent adjustments in air flow through the tracheobronchial tree?

BRAIN STEM NUCLEI THAT PROVIDE MOTOR CONTROL OF AIRWAY SMOOTH MUSCLE

Conclusions regarding the organization of connections between motor nuclei in the brain stem and the various regions of the tracheobronchial tree have

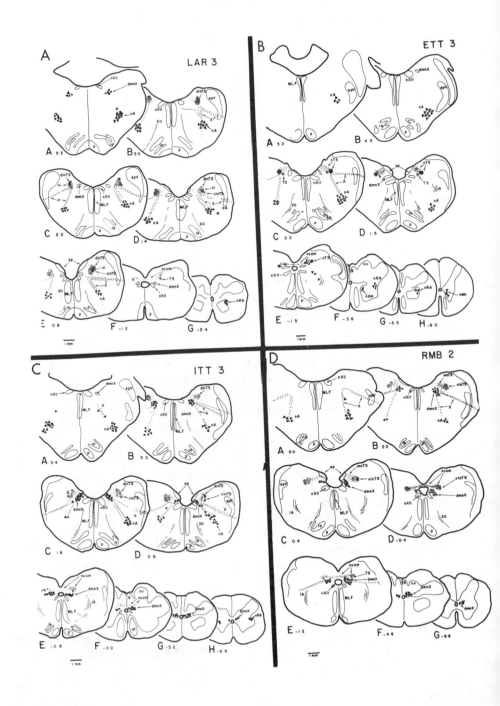

been reevaluated recently (15, 18) in light of experiments in which the location of labeled medullary neurons was correlated with the location of injections of horseradish peroxidase (HRP) into airways in various locations (Figure 1). A rather striking overall finding in these studies was the absence of discernible topographic representation of the thoracic and abdominal visceral organs within the dorsal motor nucleus of the vagus (dmnX) and the nucleus ambiguus (nA). Earlier studies (11) on the degeneration of perikarya following peripheral nerve section had led to the conclusion that there was topographic organization in the dmnX of the rabbit and that the trachea and bronchi were innervated by the caudal part of the dmnX. This could not be confirmed in the cat (18, 30). There is preferential innervation of a given viscus by a particular vagal nucleus, i.e. the dmnX of the nA. The most striking example of this preference is the larynx and the extrathoracic trachea, where practically no contribution by the dmnX is made to their motor innervation. In addition, the trachea, bronchi, and lungs, which were previously considered to be innervated almost exclusively by the dmnX (6, 11, 24, 26, 28, 31, 39), were found to be innervated also by the nA (18).

The Dorsal Motor Nucleus of the Vagus

The extrathoracic trachea (ETT) in the cat is not innervated by the dmnX (18), whereas the intrathoracic trachea (ITT) receives a substantial contribution from the dmnX. It is hypothesized that the ITT, due to its location inside the thorax where it is exposed to a negative intrapleural pressure, requires different central control than the ETT, which is located in the neck and is exposed to atmospheric pressure. Since these two regions of the airways serve as conduits for airflow, different central control mechanisms could provide the basis for an uninterrupted airflow. Bronchi receive innervation from both vagus nerves (18) by virtue of the crossing of vagal fibers in the posterior pulmonary plexus (13, 25, 32) and are innervated by the dmnX. However, contrary to earlier beliefs (3, 11, 23), the entire length of the dmnX contributes fibers to the main bronchi. Both sides of the medulla oblongata control bronchial caliber. In addition to the crossing of vagal fibers in the posterior pulmonary plexus, which results in a bilateral representation of

←―――

Figure 1   Projection drawings of coronal sections through the medulla of the cat following application of HRP into the (A) larynx (LAR), (B) extrathoracic trachea (ETT), (C) intrathoracic trachea (ITT), and (D) right main bronchus (RMB). Levels of sections in number of millimeters rostral or caudal to the obex are indicated in the lower left corner of each section. Interrupted lines indicate the position of sensory and motor fibers of the vagus nerve (X) labeled with HRP reaction product. Dots represent the presence of HRP-labeled afferent terminals within the various subnuclei of the nTS. Solid triangles indicate the location of perikarya retrogradely labeled with HRP. (From Reference 18.)

bronchi in the brain stem, elaborate reciprocal connections exist across the midline in the brain stem connecting the dorsal and ventral respiratory groups. (See Reference 14 for a complete review on the subject.)

The Nucleus Ambiguus

Bronchi are innervated by the rostral portion of the nA, while the cardiac and pulmonary fibers originate from its caudal region. Stimulation of the peripheral end of the cut vagus nerve in the dog and cat causes either bronchodilation or bronchoconstriction (9). The nA may be involved in mediating this inhibitory effect on airways.

The Nucleus Retroambigualis

Neurons located in the nucleus retroambigualis (nRA) project to the ETT (18). The nRA is considered to be the rostral extension of the intermediolateral cell column. It should be noted that the nRA is also the location of expiratory neurons. The relationship between true "respiratory" neurons, i.e. bulbo-spinal or interneurons that form part of the central respiratory pattern generator, and motoneurons to the ETT is unresolved.

The Nucleus Dorsomedialis

The nucleus dorsomedialis (ndm) is located in Lamina VIII of the cervical spinal cord and contributes to the innervation of the ETT (18). The functional significance of this innervation is, at present, unknown.

BRAIN STEM NUCLEI THAT RECEIVE AFFERENTS ORIGINATING IN THE AIRWAYS

The Nucleus of the Tractus Solitarius

Visceral afferents terminate in the caudal region of the nucleus of the tractus solitarius (nTS). Central sensory projections of airways were difficult to investigate with previously available degeneration methods because sensory rootlets are not distinct from motor fibers and because transganglionic degeneration is incomplete and unreliable. The transganglionic transport of horseradish peroxidase (HRP) has provided an effective way of determining afferent connections (12, 16, 21, 22). A topographical organization exists within subnuclei of the nTS and the airways (Figure 2).

Extrathoracic Trachea

The ETT is innervated by the recurrent and superior laryngeal nerves. The principal sensory receptors in the extrathoracic trachea are the stretch and irritant receptors (10). The stretch receptors are located within the trachealis muscle; the irritant receptors are found in the lining of the trachea (2, 33, 37). After HRP was injected into ETT, afferents from the ETT were found to terminate in a number of regions of the nTS (Figure 2B).

Intrathoracic Trachea

Significant differences in the distribution of central sensory projections of the ITT as compared to the ETT have been found (18) (Figure 2C). However, while sensory nerve terminals were found to be distributed to the medial third of the dmnX among large numbers of HRP-labeled neurons following injection of HRP into the ITT, this was not observed upon injection into the ETT. The functional significance of sensory nerve terminals surrounding motoneuron cell bodies that innervate the same viscus is not entirely obvious. It is possible that the ITT, due to its intrathoracic location, needs to have parasympathetic bronchodilator (purinergic) fibers activated during inspiration to oppose the negative intrapleural pressures exerted in the thorax.

Main Bronchi

Sensory endings in the main bronchi (MB) resemble those in the ETT and ITT, i.e. the main sensory receptors are the pulmonary stretch and irritant receptors, which are located in positions similar to those described for the ETT. However, the main bronchus is innervated by pulmonary branches of the vagus nerve, unlike the ETT and ITT, which are innervated by laryngeal branches. Significant differences between the central representation of sensory fibers from the main bronchus and the trachea have been found (Figure 2D). No sensory fibers project to the dmnX. Furthermore, although nearly all subdivisions of the nTS receive sensory fibers from the right MB (RMB), the heaviest projection is to the ventrolateral nTS (vlnTS) (Figure 2D).

It has already been noted that the MB are connected to the nTS and the motor nuclei (dmnX and nA) bilaterally. The bilateral innervation of the lungs and larger airways has been known to anatomists since 1921, when Larsell & Mason (25) first pointed out that sensory nerve fibers in both lungs degenerate following unilateral vagotomy. Later, Honjin (13) studied end formations in the hilus of the opposite lung and showed that the degeneration phenomenon could be traced to afferent endings. This bilateral innervation of the lung is derived from communicating branches between the two vagus nerves in the pulmonary plexus. These anatomical studies have escaped attention in recent studies on pulmonary reflexes, as it is currently held that each vagus nerve is involved in innervating the lung of the ipsilateral side (7, 35, 38). This has led to a series of studies that assume that unilateral vagotomy is an acceptable means for denervating a lung (5, 8). In such studies mechanical manipulations of this so-called denervated lung are not considered to be registered in the central medullary respiratory apparatus. However, based on HRP studies (18)

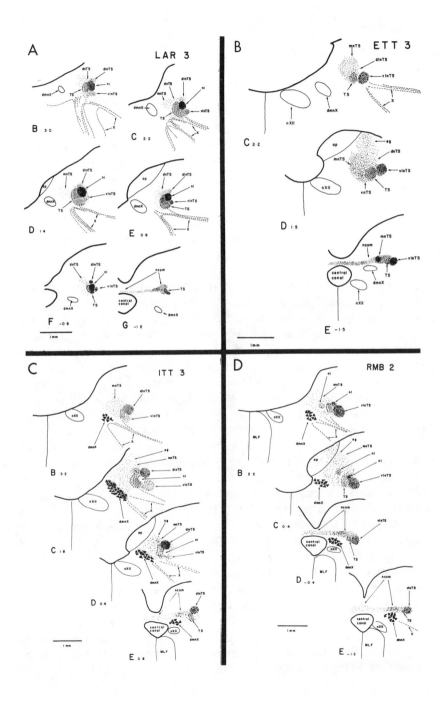

and earlier degeneration studies (13, 25), unilateral vagotomy does not lead to sensory or motor denervation of either lung. Thus conclusions based on such experiments should be interpreted with extreme caution.

CENTRAL TERMINATIONS OF SLOWLY ADAPTING RECEPTOR STRETCH AFFERENTS

Light Microscopic Evaluation

The arborization of functionally identified slowly adapting receptor (SAR) stretch afferents that originate in the lungs and airways was studied in the medulla oblongata of the cat following intra-axonal labeling with a conjugate of wheat germ agglutinin and horseradish peroxidase (WGAHRP) (19). SAR afferents were identified on the basis of their stimulation by lung inflation, inhibition by noninflation, and demonstration of constant-latency orthodromic responses to electrical stimulation of the ipsilateral vagus nerve (Figures 3 and 4). Spontaneous firing in phase with inspiration was characteristic of these afferent fibers. The typical steep, rising phase of the action potentials of the afferents confirmed the intra-axonal location of the microelectrode. Horseradish peroxidase histochemistry of the brain stem revealed details of the distribution and morphology of the lung stretch afferent fibers as they arborized in the various subnuclei of the nucleus of the tractus solitarius (nTS) and adjacent medulla.

A number of significant findings resulted from this study: (*a*) A single lung SAR stretch afferent fiber arborized over a considerable distance rostro-caudally in the brain stem (1700–2100 μm). (*b*) A single lung SAR stretch afferent fiber terminated in hundreds of bouton terminals (650–1180). (*c*) There was a remarkably consistent pattern of distribution of these terminal arborizations of SAR afferents in the subnuclei of the nucleus of the tractus solitarius (nTS). (*d*) The ventral (vnTS), intermediate (nI), ventrolateral (vlnTS), and interstitial (ni) subnuclei of the nTS were the only regions of the nTS that received bouton terminals of SAR afferent fibers. (*e*) Under the light microscope the pattern of termination of SAR afferents was similar in all the axons studied in this series. (*f*) The remarkable similarity in the central distribution of different lung SAR stretch afferents (which must have origin-

←

Figure 2   High-power projection drawings through the dorsomedial region of the medulla of the right side, showing the nTS-dmnX complex following application of HRP into the (A) larynx (LAR), (B) extrathoracic trachea (ETT), (C) intrathoracic trachea (ITT), and (D) right main bronchus (RMB). Interrupted lines, dots, and filled triangles symbolize the same structures as in Figure 1. The appropriate rostrocaudal levels are indicated in each section (lower left corner). (From Reference 18.)

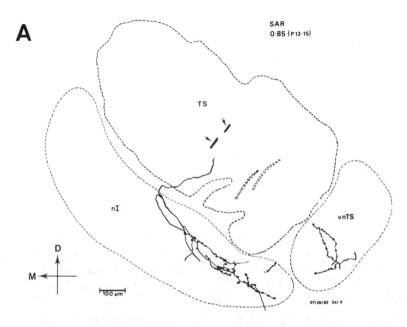

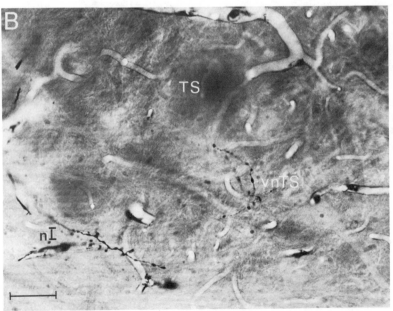

ated from different regions of the tracheobronchial tree) indicates that their localization is modality specific rather than topographic in the CNS. (*g*) The injected parent axon in each case could be followed in the TS at all levels, and its position and orientation remained consistent. This parent axon could be traced to levels as far as 3.5 mm rostral to the obex, whereas the region of terminal arborization was located ~1.7–2.1 mm rostral to the obex. This pattern indicates that a single lung SAR stretch afferent fiber descends caudally upon entering the nTS. In the cat, vagal afferent fibers are known to enter the medulla at levels between 0.5 mm and 3.2 mm rostral to the obex (17). The parent axon branches many times at a number of different rostro-caudal levels, and each preterminal segment of the fiber has 2–5 terminal boutons. Frequently, the axonal branches projected towards the medial side of the TS, and upon entering the nI, the fibers branched and coursed dorsally and ventrally, giving off local branches that terminated within 50–100 μm in the nI and vnTS. The part of the parent axon that was located lateral to the TS bifurcated at the lateral border of the TS, and branches coursed dorsally and ventrally, giving off terminals to the ni, vlnTS, and vnTS. Thus, the vnTS received branches from both lateral and medial branches of the parent axon and contained as many as 649 bouton terminals.

Ultrastructural differences in the bouton terminals in the different subnuclei of the nTS were found (18) and provide structural evidence for functional differences of SAR terminals in the various regions of the medulla. SAR afferents from the lungs and tracheobronchial tree have distinct patterns of distribution in the nTS. In addition, these findings support the concept that representation of pulmonary afferents in the medulla is constituted by a differentiated distribution of nerve terminals in the various subnuclei of the nTS. Modality-specific localization (of SAR afferents in this case) appears to predominate in the nTS. The widespread rostrocaudal distribution of a single lung SAR stretch afferent demonstrates the remarkable degree of divergence of a single afferent fiber. In contrast, the finding that the terminals of different SAR afferents are localized in only a few subnuclei of the nTS suggests a high degree of specificity, which could provide the morphological basis for highly focused physiological effects.

Figure 3 (A) Reconstruction in the coronal plane of an axon collateral from a slowly adapting lung stretch afferent fiber injected intra-axonally with wheat germ agglutinin and horseradish peroxidase (WGAHRP). The level of the section is 0.85 mm rostral to the obex, and according to the plane of Berman (4), it is P 13.15, as indicated in parentheses. Arrows indicate the location of the injected axon in the tractus solitarius (TS). This collateral arborized predominantly in the intermediate (nI) and ventral (vnTS) subnuclei of the nTS. Note the large numbers of *en passant* swellings in the arborization of this axon collateral. (B) Brightfield photomicrograph of the collateral arborization at one focal plane showing arborization in the nI and the nTS. Orientation of the section is the same as in A. Bar = 100 μm. (From Reference 19.)

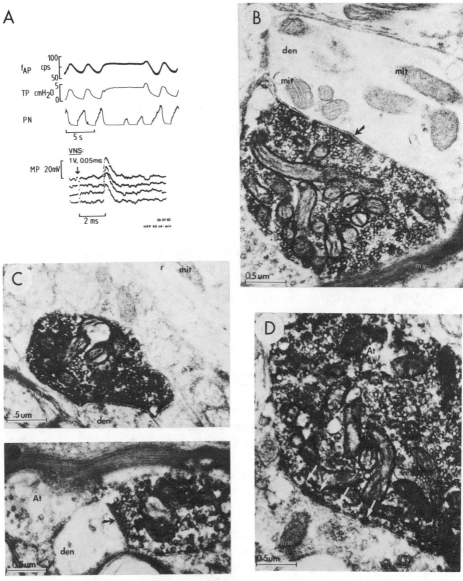

Figure 4 (A) Responses of a slowly adapting lung stretch receptor (SAR) afferent recorded intra-axonally prior to the intra-axonal application of WGAHRP conjugate. *(Upper panel)* Frequency of action potentials (FAP), tracheal pressure (TP), and the integrated record of the phrenic nerve activity (PN). This SAR afferent became tonically active (frequency of discharge over 50 Hz) following the microelectrode impalement, and its discharge increased at the end of

Ultrastructure

The synaptic profiles formed by the bouton terminals of SAR afferents contain round synaptic vesicles. Synaptic boutons (1.0–3.0 μm in diameter) were usually of the *en passant* variety and made contact with different structures depending upon the subnucleus examined. In the ventral and the ventrolateral subnuclei of the vnTS and vlnTS, symmetrical (Type I) synaptic contacts containing round, clear synaptic vesicles of 35–50 μm in diameter were found. These contacts were made with: (*a*) the soma of cell bodies in the subnucleus; (*b*) spiny dendrites in the nucleus; (*c*) vesicle-containing axon terminals that were presynaptic to the HRP-labeled bouton terminal; and (*d*) vesicle-containing dendrites in which the HRP profile was located presynaptically. The terminal axon remained myelinated until the last micrometer before the bouton terminal. The synaptic bouton received axon-axonal contacts from unlabeled bouton terminals containing round, clear vesicles.

In the intermediate (nI) and interstitial (ni) subnuclei of the TS, the pattern of contact was remarkably different from that observed in the ventrally located subnuclei. In the nI and ni subnuclei, contacts were made almost exclusively with dendrites, and most of the contacts were of the *en passant* variety. No axon-axonal contacts were seen in these subnuclei.

These regional variations in the ultrastructure of lung stretch afferent fiber terminations in the nucleus of the TS of the cat indicate that the processing of the information conveyed by these afferent fibers is remarkably different in the different subnuclei of the nTS.

←───

each lung inflation (see tracheal pressure trace). A long-lasting lung inflation test produced an increase in the tonic discharge of the axon to 80 Hz. *(Lower panel)* Four intra-axonal recordings at fast sweep speeds from the unit. The orthodromically activated action potentials are shown following four separate stimuli of 1.0-V intensity and 0.05-ms duration applied to the vagus nerve. Note the constant latency in the response in all four recordings. The steep rising phase of the action potentials indicates the intra-axonal location of the microelectrode. This axon was located at a level 0.15 mm rostral to the obex. (B) High-magnification photomicrograph of a bouton terminal in the ventrolateral subnucleus (vl) of the nTS making synaptic contact with the vesicle-containing dendrite. Curved arrow points to a group of clear vesicles and straight arrow points to the synaptic contact. This bouton terminal is densely packed with large, clear vesicles. Bar = 0.5 μm. (C) *(Upper panel)* High-magnification electron micrograph of a WGAHRP-filled bouton terminal in the interstitial subnucleus of the nTS (nI) making synaptic contact *(arrow)* with a dendrite (den). The bouton terminal contains clear vesicles. *(Lower panel)* Higher magnification of another bouton terminal in the nI. This terminal made a large Type 1 asymmetrical contact with a dendrite, which is marked with an arrow. (mit=mitochondrion, my=myelin.) Bar = 0.5 μm. (D) An HRP-filled bouton terminal in the nI, showing the presence of an array of presynaptic densities marked by white arrows. At this junction, no postsynaptic density could be distinguished. Bar = 0.5 μm. (From Reference 20.)

Respiratory Modulation of Airway Smooth Muscle and Changes in Sensitivity of Lung Stretch Receptors in Airways

The intrathoracic airway smooth muscle contracts with inspiration, and SAR afferent discharge is modified by mechanical interaction with airway smooth muscle (36). Vagal motoneurons in the nucleus ambiguus fire in synchrony with inspiration (27, 40). Tracheal smooth muscle contracts and relaxes synchronously with inspiration and expiration, respectively (1). In addition, transpulmonary pressure, which has been considered to be an index of airway resistance, has been shown to increase with inspiration. Nadel & Widdicombe (34) previously demonstrated that increased tracheal volume and lower airway resistance produce reflexes that parallel in magnitude the level of breathing (34). The effect of natural contraction of airway smooth muscle on pulmonary receptors, i.e. alterations in their sensitivity or their responses, has not been investigated. Most investigators have studied afferent fibers from receptors after cutting the vagus nerve, and thus both afferent and efferent connections of the airways have been determined.

The effects of inspiratory contraction of airway smooth muscles on pulmonary receptors was recently reported by Richardson et al (36), who recorded afferent activity with electrodes placed on the intact vagus nerve. These in vivo studies in the cat revealed two populations of neurons that showed different firing patterns during lung inflation. One population of neurons responds to lung inflation by an increase in cell firing. These neurons project to airway smooth muscle. A second set of neurons decrease their activity during lung inflation. These neurons project to nonmuscle effector organs. These studies indicate that an elaborate organization of postganglionic neurons exists in airways.

RELATIONSHIP BETWEEN CONTROL OF AIRWAYS AND CONTROL OF RESPIRATION

The presence of reciprocal connections between the central respiratory pattern generator, bilateral innervation of the bronchi, and the involvement of the entire dmnX in the innervation of this region indicate the complexity of the CNS control exerted on the bronchi. This complex system may provide the anatomical substrate for accurate and well-integrated control of airway caliber.

Bronchomotor Tone and Central Respiratory Control

The question of whether bronchomotor tone can be considered to be independent of the state of the central respiratory pattern generator has been raised (36). What predictions can be made regarding respiratory reflexes and the direction of change in airway resistance? The recent finding that respiratory output itself can modulate stretch receptor afferent firing rate through the link with smooth muscle is a very important and exciting concept since it was previously presumed that these stretch receptor afferents were sensitive only to lung volume. Mitchell et al (29) investigated the interaction of arterial CO_2 and lung inflation by denervating one lung, occluding the pulmonary artery, and performing manipulations on each lung independently. They found that the apparently simple effect of airway pressure and P_{CO_2} on ventilation were actually more complex. There may be a link between Pa_{CO_2} and pulmonary stretch receptors in the innervated lung. Again, it must be emphasized that a number of investigators continue to consider ipsilateral vagotomy as a means of denervating one lung, even though a considerable number of fibers have already crossed to the other side in the pulmonary plexus (13).

Relationship Between Airway Tone and Breathing

Nadel & Widdicombe (34) found that increased tracheal pressure decreased airway resistance and increased both hypoxic and hypercapnic stimulation of breathing. Richardson et al (36) suggested that the major neural traffic to airways arises from the central pattern generator. Baker & Mitchell (1) recently demonstrated that a major part of airway smooth muscle tone is regulated by parasympathetic fibers that probably originate from the regions in the ventral respiratory group. It is extremely important to distinguish between the ventral respiratory group, which is a group of neurons located in the vicinity of the nucleus retroambigualis, and the vagal preganglionic motor neurons, which innervate the airway smooth muscle. Are these two populations the same group of neurons with collaterals in different directions, or do they represent two different populations of neurons that are intermixed in the same region, or are they two distinct populations of neurons with no intermixing? Questions such as these must be resolved before we can ultimately determine how airway smooth muscle is controlled.

ACKNOWLEDGMENTS

This work was supported by USPHS grants HL 30991, HL 31997, and HL 33632 from the National Institutes of Health. A number of the studies reported were done in collaboration with Marsel Mesulam and Diethelm Richter. The assistance of Sue DiIenno in the preparation of this manuscript is greatly appreciated.

Literature Cited

1. Baker, D. G., Mitchell, R. A. 1981. Parasympathetic bronchoconstrictor fibers fire with an inspiratory rhythm to evoke rhythmic fluctuations in airway smooth muscle tone. *Physiologist* 24: 101 (Abstr.)
2. Bartlett, D., Jeffrey, P., Sant'Ambrogio, G., Wise, J. C. M. 1976. Location of stretch receptors in the trachea and bronchi of the dog. *Int. Physiol.* 258: 409–20
3. Bell, F. R. 1960. The localization within the dorsal motor nucleus of the vagus of the efferent fibers of the ruminant stomach. *J. Anat.* 94:410–17
4. Berman, A. L. 1968. The Brain Stem of the Cat. In *A Cytoarchitectonic Atlas with Stereotaxic Coordinates.* Madison, Wisc.: Univ. Wisc. Press
5. Bouverot, P., Flandrois, R., Puccinelli, R., Dejours, P. 1965. Etude du role des chemorecepteurs arteriels dans la regulation de le respiration pulmonaire chez le chien eveille. *Arch. Int. Parmacodyn.* 157:253–71
6. Cajal, S. R. 1909. *Histologie due Systeme Nerveux de l'Homme et des Vertebres,* Vol. 1. Paris: Maloine
7. Coleridge, H. M., Coleridge, J. C. G., Luck, J. C. 1965. Pulmonary afferent fibers of small diameter stimulated by capsaicin and by hyperinflation of the lungs. *J. Physiol.* 179:248–62
8. Dejours, P. 1970. In *Breathing: Hering-Breuer Centenary Symp.,* ed. R. Porter, pp. 48–49. London: Churchill
9. Dixon, W. E., Brodie, T. G. 1903. Contributions to the physiology of the lungs. Part I. The bronchial muscles, their innervation and the action of drugs upon them. *J. Physiol.* 29:97–173
10. Fillenz, M., Widdicombe, J. G. 1971. Receptors of the lungs and airways. In *Handbook of Sensory Physiology,* ed. E. Neil, 3:81–112. Heidelberg: Springer-Verlag
11. Getz, B., Sirnes, T. 1949. The localization within the dorsal motor vagal nucleus—an experimental investigation. *J. Comp. Neurol.* 90:95–110
12. Gwyn, D. G., Leslie, R. A., Hopkins, D. A. 1979. Gastric afferents to the nucleus of the solitary tract in the cat. *Neurosci. Lett.* 13:13–17
13. Honjin, R. 1956. On the nerve supply of the lung of the mouse with special reference to the structure of the peripheral vegetative nervous system. *J. Comp. Neurol.* 105:587–625
14. Kalia, M. 1981. Anatomical organiza-

tion of central respiratory neurons. *Ann. Rev. Physiol.* 43:105–20
15. Kalia, M. 1981. Brain stem localization of vagal preganglionic neurons. *J. Auton. Nerv. Syst.* 3:451–81
16. Kalia, M., Mesulam, M. M. 1979. Intramedullary course of afferent and efferent fibers of the vagus: A study using the tetramethyl benzidine reaction for horseradish peroxidase. In *Central Nervous Control Mechanisms in Breathing,* ed. C. von Euler, H. Lagercrantz, pp. 273–85. Oxford: Pergamon
17. Kalia, M., Mesulam, M. M. 1980. Brain stem projections of sensory and motor components of the vagus complex in the cat: I. The cervical vagus and nodose ganglion. *J. Comp. Neurol.* 193:435–65
18. Kalia, M., Mesulam, M. M. 1980. Brain stem projections of sensory and motor components of the vagus complex in the cat: II. Laryngeal, tracheobronchial, cardiac, and gastrointestinal branches. *J. Comp. Neurol.* 193:467–508
19. Kalia, M., Richter, D. 1985. Morphology of physiologically identified slowly adapting lung stretch receptor afferents stained with intra-axonal horseradish peroxidase in the nucleus of the treactus solitarius of the cat. I. A light microscopic analysis. *J. Comp. Neurol.* 241:503–20
20. Kalia, M., Richter, D. 1985. Morphology of physiologically identified slowly adapting lung stretch receptor afferents stained with intra-axonal horseradish peroxidase in the nucleus of the tractus solitarius of the cat. II. An ultrastructural analysis. *J. Comp. Neurol.* 241:521–35
21. Kalia, M., Welles, R. V. 1980. Brain stem projections of the aortic nerve in the cat: A study using tetramethyl benzidine as the substrate for horseradish peroxidase. *Brain Res.* 188:23–32
22. Katz, D. M., Karten, H. J. 1979. The discrete anatomical localization of vagal aortic afferents within a catecholamine-containing cell group in the nucleus solitarius. *Brain Res.* 171:187–95
23. Kerr, F. W. L. 1967. Function of the dorsal motor nucleus of the vagus. *Science* 157:451–52
24. Kerr, F. W. L. 1969. Preserved vagal visceromotor function following destruction of the dorsal motor nucleus. *J. Physiol.* 202:755–69

25. Larsell, O., Mason, M. L. 1921. Experimental degeneration of the vagus nerve and its relation to the terminations in the lung of the rabbit. *J. Comp. Neurol.* 33:509–16
26. Marinesco, M. G. 1897. Les noyaux musculo-stries et musculo-lisses du pneumogastrique. *C. R. Seanc. Soc. Biol.* 49:168–69
27. McAllen, R. M., Spyer, K. M. 1978. Two types of vagal preganglionic motoneurons projecting to the heart and lungs. *J. Physiol.* 282:353–64
28. Mitchell, G. A. G., Warwick, R. 1955. The dorsal vagal nucleus. *Acta Anat.* 23:371–95
29. Mitchell, G. S., Cross, B. A., Hiramoto, T., Scheid, P. 1982. Interactions between lung stretch and Pa(CO2) in modulating ventilatory activity in dogs. *J. Appl. Physiol.* 53:185–91
30. Mohiuddin, A. 1953. Vagal preganglionic fibers to the alimentary canal. *J. Comp. Neurol.* 99:289–317
31. Molhant, M. 1910. Les connexions anatomiques et la valeur functionelle du noyau dorsal du vague. *Nevraxe* 11:137–244
32. Molhant, M. 1913. Le nerf vague: Etude anatomique et experimentale: les ganglions peripheriques du vague. *Nevraxe* 15:521–79
33. Mortola, J. P., Sant'Ambrogio, G.,

34. Clement, M. G. 1975. Localization of irritant receptors in the airways of the dog. *Respir. Physiol.* 24:107–14
34. Nadel, J. A., Widdicombe, J. G. 1962. Effect of changes in blood gas tensions and carotid sinus pressure on tracheal volume and total lung resistance to airflow. *J. Physiol.* 163:13–33
35. Paintal, A. S. 1963. Vagal afferent fibers. *Ergeb. Physiol.* 52:74–156
36. Richardson, C. A., Herbert, D. A., Mitchell, R. A. 1984. Modulation of pulmonary stretch receptors and airway resistance by parasympathetic efferents. *J. Appl. Physiol.* 57:1842–49
37. Sant'Ambrogio, G., Remmers, J. E., DeGroot, W. J., Callas, G., Mortola, J. P. 1978. Localization of rapidly adapting receptors in the trachea and main stem bronchus of the dog. *Respir. Physiol.* 33:359–66
38. Sellick, H., Widdicombe, J. G. 1970. Vagal deflation and inflation reflexes initiated by lung irritant receptors. *Q. J. Exp. Physiol.* 55:153–63
39. Szentagothai, J. 1943. Die lokalisation der Kehlkopf muskulatur in den vaguskernen. *Z. Anat. Entw. Gesch.* 112:704–10
40. Widdicombe, J. G. 1966. Action potentials in parasympathetic and sympathetic efferent fibres to the trachea and lungs of dogs and cats. *J. Physiol.* 186:56–88

Ann. Rev. Physiol. 1987. 49:611–27
Copyright © 1987 by Annual Reviews Inc. All rights reserved

NERVOUS RECEPTORS OF THE TRACHEOBRONCHIAL TREE

Giuseppe Sant'Ambrogio

Department of Physiology and Biophysics, The University of Texas Medical Branch, Galveston, Texas 77550

AFFERENT SUPPLY TO THE TRACHEOBRONCHIAL TREE

A recent study on the cat vagus nerve (43), which used light and electron microscopy, found a total of 5558 afferent fibers entering the lobes of the left lung. Of these fibers, 471 were myelinated and 5087 were unmyelinated, i.e. the unmyelinated component is 10.8 times greater than its myelinated counterpart. Comparable data are not available for the vagal branches and nerves supplying the extrapulmonary airways.

The vagus nerve and its branches undergo considerable change during development. An extreme case is that of the opossum, which up to 20 days from birth does not have any myelinated fibers (54). Newborn kittens have only 10% of the number of myelinated fibers found in adult cats (59).

SLOWLY ADAPTING STRETCH RECEPTORS

Most of the slowly adapting stretch receptors (SARs) are located in intrathoracic airways. These receptors regularly increase their rate of discharge in the course of inspiration. SARs located in the extrathoracic trachea increase their activity during the period of expiratory flow (92). A sizable proportion of SARs [between 27% and 63% in the various species studied (29, 50, 66, 74, 80)] maintain a discharge at functional residual capacity (FRC). Most of those active at FRC with a transpulmonary pressure of 3–5 cm H_2O remain active even at zero transmural pressure and are located in the trachea (7). The fibers of these endings have conduction velocities characteristic of myelinated axons (74).

611

SARs have a long-lasting discharge in response to a maintained lung inflation: There is a rapid decline in activity immediately after the inflation that slows progressively into a sustained firing. This behavior identifies these endings as slowly adapting receptors. These adaptive processes have been found to be related to the viscoelastic properties of the tissue containing the SARs (22).

A particular category of slowly adapting receptors has an expiratory discharge during spontaneous ventilation (57, 103) and artificial ventilation (57, 101) has been described in rabbits (57), cats (103), monkeys (103), and rats (101). These receptors have myelinated fibers and are localized in both intrapulmonary and extrapulmonary intrathoracic airways (57). The circumstances of activation of these receptors are obscure.

There are SARs along the tracheobronchial tree down to the terminal bronchioles (65). Most of the localization experiments indicate a higher concentration of SARs in the larger, more proximal airways with a progressive decline toward the periphery (29, 49, 64, 65, 82, 90). Several observations indicate a more important role of intrapulmonary SARs for the inflation reflex (56, 70), whereas other reflex responses have been attributed to SARs of the extrapulmonary tracheobronchial tree (1, 77, 88, 105).

Tracheal SARs are only found in the membraneous posterior wall; removal of the tunica fibrosa overlying the receptor field does not substantially affect receptor function (5, 67). This finding suggests these SARs are located within the trachealis muscle. Similar evidence exists for SARs located in the main stem bronchus and lobar bronchus (5). There is also ample indirect evidence based on reflex studies and recording from SARs (5, 11) that these endings are associated with the smooth muscle.

Proper Stimulus and Response to Transmural Pressure

Although there is a relationship between respiratory volume and SAR discharge rate, it is clear (23, 48, 106) that the response of these receptors is more closely associated with transpulmonary pressure and even more directly with circumferential tension (5).

SARs vary in their response to transmural pressure in several ways. (a) Most of the extrapulmonary receptors are active at FRC [a distending pressure of 3–5 cm H_2O for intrathoracic airways and zero transmural pressure in the extrathoracic trachea (66)]. (b) Most of the intrapulmonary SARs have a higher transpulmonary pressure threshold within the tidal volume range (66). (c) Extrapulmonary SARs also respond to collapsing pressure in a proportional way, once a given value is exceeded (5, 67, 106). (d) Two different responses to steady-state transpulmonary pressure have been identified (66): a Type I receptor with a response that tends to saturate above 10 cm H_2O and a Type II with a more linear response. Type I receptors prevail in the larger, more proximal airways, while Type II are more common in distal airways (66). Very recently Pack et al (72) reexamined these properties of SARs in the dog and "found a continuum of responses which approximated a normal distribution." In another species, the opossum, the two types of receptor were not seen; all SARs showed a fairly linear response to changes in transmural pressure (29).

Most SARs, in addition to responding to a maintained transmural pressure, respond to its rate of change (7, 23, 72). Direct measurements of applied forces and discharge rates have been conducted on segments of the posterior wall of extrathoracic trachea isolated either in vitro (11) or in vivo (67). SARs can respond to both the amount (static response) and the rate (dynamic response) of inflation. The receptor fires at a higher rate while the pressure is changing than when it is at any given steady transmural pressure; the higher the rate of inflation, the higher the increase in receptor discharge (7, 23, 72). In addition to the increase in receptor activity, an increase in inflation rate lowers the transmural pressure at which the receptor is recruited: the faster the inflation the lower the threshold (72). Another feature of the dynamic responsiveness is its dependence on the degree of inflation. There is a greater increase in firing rate with a given inflation rate at a higher than at a lower transpulmonary pressure (7, 67, 72). A force-transducing element in series with both a viscous element and an elastic element arranged in parallel was proposed as a model of SARs. The elastic element would account for the static response of the SARs and the viscous element would account for their dynamic sensitivity (89).

Other Mechanical Factors Relevant to SAR Stimulation

The extrapulmonary airways are composed of a series of U-shaped cartilaginous rings that support a membranous posterior wall. At zero transmural pressure neither structure (cartilage nor posterior wall) is at its resting position. The cartilage, because it tends to expand, exerts a transverse stretch on the posterior wall keeping it extended beyond its resting length. The mechanical coupling between these two structures explains most of the properties of the SARs in the extrapulmonary airways (5, 67). Most SARs are active at zero transmural pressure, respond to both distending and collapsing pressures (when the posterior wall is stretched either outward or inward), and show the least activity at low collapsing pressure (67, 92). This behavior results in an asymmetric response curve of tracheal SARs to positive and negative pressures. The asymmetry of the response of these receptors to positive and negative pressure can be understood considering that with negative pressure the tension of the posterior wall depends on the balance between two conflicting factors: inward stretching of the posterior wall and the closing of the rings, which tends to decrease the radius of curvature and therefore posterior wall tension. With higher negative pressures the inward stretching of the posterior wall prevails because the cartilage becomes increasingly stiffer (67) and thus SAR activity increases. With lower negative pressures the inward motion of the cartilaginous rings prevails, leading to a decrease of the radius of curvature which, despite the increase in transmural negative pressure, lowers the tension of the posterior wall and hence the discharge of the receptors (67).

This characteristic response has significant physiological implications. Half of the trachea is outside the thorax, and the corresponding changes in transmural pressure during the breathing cycle differ from those in the intrathoracic trachea and bronchi. In these latter airways the transmural pressure at end expiration is $+4$ to $+5$ cm H_2O and increases to a higher value at end inspiration. This leads to a corresponding increase in the SAR activity, which can be predicted from the response curve. In the extrathoracic trachea the transmural pressure is zero at both end expiration and end inspiration but becomes negative with inspiratory airflow and positive in the presence of expiratory airflow. Since there is an asymmetric response curve to transmural pressure, there is a decrease in the discharge by SARs during inspiration and an increase during expiration in the extrathoracic trachea. Both intrathoracic and extrathoracic SARs send signals related to transmural pressure, but those inside the thorax can signal both flow and volume, whereas those in the extrathoracic trachea can only send information related to airflow and its rate of change (89, 92). Activation of extrathoracic and intrathoracic airway SARs during a breathing cycle is thus out of phase, i.e. during inspiration, activity in the intrathoracic SARs increases but decreases in the extrathoracic trachea SARs, and the reverse occurs during expiration.

The mechanical characteristics of the cartilaginous rings, which have a greater compliance at low collapsing pressures, provide the proper set point for the extrapulmonary SARs within the physiological pressure range. If the cartilage were completely rigid, there would be a symmetrical response to negative and positive transmural pressures, and in this case equally increasing signals would originate from the extrathoracic trachea during each of the two phases of the breathing cycle (89).

Cooling of the tracheal lumen depresses both the static and dynamic responses of tracheal SARs. A decrease in temperature from 37 to 27°C caused a reduction in SAR activity of about 25% (87). This finding could partially explain the bronchoconstrictive action of inhaling cold air.

Response to Carbon Dioxide

Carbon dioxide can either stimulate or inhibit airway SARs. The change in bronchomotor tone has a well-documented influence on this response (5, 11). An inhibitory effect of CO_2 has been shown in rats (94), rabbits (69), dogs (6,

10, 17, 91), cats (55), and marsupials (12, 29). Generally, the inhibitory effect of CO_2 is particularly strong when CO_2 is administered at hypocapnic levels (10, 17, 69, 92); at or above normocapnic levels its influence becomes weaker.

Bronchial but not tracheal SARs are susceptible to inhibition by CO_2 inhalation (6). The bronchial endings are affected by CO_2 in the bronchial lumen but not by an increased CO_2 concentration in blood (6, 10). Recently, Green et al used a preparation in which pulmonary and systemic circulations were isolated and their CO_2 concentrations were independently controlled and found that increases in the pulmonary blood P_{CO_2} from 25 to 70 mm Hg depressed SAR activity in a relatively linear fashion. The systemic P_{CO_2} and lung mechanics apparently did not influence this response (38). It must be pointed out that in this preparation, in which ventilation was kept at a constant level, increases in CO_2 in pulmonary blood involved concomitant increases in the alveolar and dead-space air. The site of action of CO_2 on SARs (blood versus air) is relevant to discussions of exercise hyperpnea, during which the pulmonary arterial blood, but not the alveolar and dead-space air, has an elevated P_{CO_2}.

The possibility that the inhibitory effect of CO_2 is mediated by changes in the smooth muscle tone has been extensively explored and generally denied (10, 17, 69, 91). Hypocapnia in the air spaces, especially that accompanying occlusion of the pulmonary circulation, causes bronchoconstriction that could excite SARs; CO_2 administration could reduce smooth muscle contraction, which would account for the diminished SAR discharge. In most cases the depression of SAR activity could not be accounted for by a change in transmural pressure, and the use of bronchodilators did not prevent the CO_2 effect (10, 17, 69, 91). However, when hypercapnia could exert a broncho-constrictive effect through chemoreceptor stimulation, SARs increased their activity (32, 34, 79).

The SARs are generally insensitive to changes in blood and air oxygen tensions (104). However, when hypoxia, through its action on the peripheral chemoreceptors, causes a bronchoconstrictive reflex, SARs are readily stimulated (32, 34).

Characteristics of SARs in the Newborn

SARs have a similar distribution in the adult and the newborn and are more concentrated in the larger airways (32, 60). A major difference is that in the newborn there is little or no activity at FRC (32, 58, 60, 95). SARs in newborns have higher transpulmonary pressure thresholds and lower discharge rates at any given pressure (33), which leads to a reduced level of activity during the respiratory cycle. Various factors could be responsible for these differences: (a) In the adult, SARs and RARs (rapidly adapting receptors) have myelinated fibers, but in the newborn many fibers are un-myelinated. (*b*) In the newborn there is a different mechanical coupling between the back wall of the trachea and the more compliant cartilages that leads to a lower mechanical tension at the receptor site. (*c*) The smaller value of transpulmonary pressure (P_{tp}) at FRC in the newborn (31) is also likely to reduce SAR stimulation.

Hypercapnia exerts similar influences on SARs in newborns and adults. When efferent smooth muscle innervation is blocked or the CO_2 partial pressure is not allowed to rise in the arterial blood, inhaled CO_2 either has no effect or inhibits SARs, depending on their location (34). However, when hypercapnia stimulates peripheral and central chemoreceptors, causing an increase in airway smooth muscle tone, SAR discharge increases, as in the adult (32, 34).

Structure

A recent study using electron microscopy of small airways in the rat shows endings within the smooth muscle that extend toward the epithelium (27). Light and electron microscopy have been used to study presumptive afferent endings in smooth muscle of the trachea in the dog (28, 53). Serial thick sections demonstrated that medullated fibers running between fascicles of the muscle give rise to unencapsulated endings with features considered typical of mechanoreceptors. These features are large numbers of mitochondria, depos-its of glycogen, and direct attachment of parts of the cell membrane to the basal lamina. The relationship of nerve to muscle appears complex; these endings cannot be described as in series or in parallel. Each myelinated fiber and terminal complex has an associated group of unmyelinated fibers with regions that appear to be terminal but do not form synapses.

RAPIDLY ADAPTING RECEPTORS

Rapidly adapting receptors (RARs) show irregular and scant activity in eupnea, more often during inspiration; hyperpnea increases their discharge (3, 63, 68, 84, 97). Their respiratory modulation has been reported to be absent in some species (9).

Location Along the Tracheobronchial Tree and within Airway Wall

As is the case in SARs, RARs are found only in areas of lung parenchyma with bronchi or bronchioles (68). They are not evenly distributed along the tracheobronchial tree but are concentrated in the more proximal airways (68). In the extrapulmonary airways the concentration of RARs increases from the upper trachea to the main stem bronchus (93). The hilar airways are very accessible to chemical and mechanical irritants, and receptors in these airways can be readily activated, evoking protective reflex actions. Hence the RARs provide an effective defense. Together with SARs, these endings, due to their central location, are capable of monitoring mean lung compliance and possibly provide the reflex actions to maintain it within an appropriate range of values (37, 45, 97).

The RAR distribution along the circumference of the trachea and the main stem bronchus is entirely different from that of the SARs: RARs are found all along the circumference (93).

Rapidly adapting receptors are less numerous than SARs; the ratio of RARs to SARs is 1 : 4 in the rabbit (82) and 1 : 10 in the cat (106). Fibers containing RARs have conduction velocities similar to those containing SARs, although the mean velocity is somewhat lower (24, 48, 61, 73, 84).

Response to Local Probing and to Changes in Transpulmonary Pressure

RARs can be stimulated both by gross deformations introduced by large distending or collapsing transmural pressures and by discrete mechanical stimulation. The two mechanisms of stimulation can often be separated by a superficial lesion of the receptor field. The response to local probing is abolished by such a lesion but the responses to inflation and deflation are retained (93). This result may indicate that there is a multibranched neural supply for RARs distributed to both superficial (epithelial) and deeper layers of the airways.

RARs respond to transpulmonary pressure, as well as to its rate of change, with a pattern distinctly dissimilar from that of SARs. These receptors respond to a step change in pressure with a burst of action potentials at irregular intervals that subsides very rapidly. A mechanical model in which a force transducing element is attached to a purely viscous element would account for this behavior. Whether such a mechanical arrangement exists in the mucosal and submucosal layers remains entirely speculative.

The various factors involved in the response of RARs to lung inflation were evaluated in a recent study (71) in which lung inflations were performed at several constant flow rates. The results show that at a constant rate of inflation RARs increase their firing as lung volume (and transpulmonary pressure) increases. Receptor activity is also greatly dependent on flow rate, but this response tends to saturate. In contrast, it was recently reported (72) that SAR firing shows an increasing sensitivity to flow rates. As is the case for SARs, an increase in inflation rate lowers the volume (or transpulmonary pressure) threshold at which RARs are recruited.

As in the case of SARs, the stimulus appeared to be transpulmonary pressure more than volume: this is apparent when lung compliance is varied.

There is an inverse relationship between lung compliance and RAR activation (45, 97). This fact may explain the greater activation of RARs in conditions such as pulmonary congestion and edema (96). RARs are generally considered to provide a positive feedback mechanism to inspiration (37) that would trigger periodic augmented breaths that preserve lung compliance (97).

Response to Inhaled Irritants and Bronchomotor Agents

Many substances inhaled in the form of gas (ammonia, ethyl ether, sulfur dioxide), aerosols, or fumes activate RARs (63). The action of some of the inhaled irritants varies in different species. For instance, ammonia and cigarette smoke cause more reflex response in rabbits and guinea pigs than in dogs (9, 84). The stimulatory action of inhaled smoke, and even that of inhaled inert dust (63), cannot be attributed to a direct mechanical distortion of the receptor site and perhaps is mediated by the release of some active substance.

The activity of RARs (and that of SARs) is affected by variations in bronchomotor tone. Histamine stimulates RARs indirectly by causing a contraction of airway smooth muscle (9, 16, 63). Other evidence (102) indicates that histamine also acts directly: Its action persists after administration of isoproterenol, which prevents changes in lung mechanics. Dixon et al (26) have suggested that histamine sensitizes RARs to the action of bronchoconstriction.

The stimulatory action of acetylcholine on RARs is essentially dependent on its bronchoconstrictive effect (102). The activation observed with 5-hydroxytryptamine is mostly, but not entirely, attributed to increased bronchomotor tone (26).

Prostaglandins (PGs) are also of particular interest since, like histamine, they are released during anaphylaxis in the lung. When $PGF_{2\alpha}$ is given as an aerosol, RARs are stimulated even when the bronchoconstrictor effect of $PGF_{2\alpha}$ is blocked by isoproterenol (85). This observation supports the idea that $PGF_{2\alpha}$ has a "direct" action on RARs that is independent of local or diffuse changes in lung mechanics. However, the results of Coleridge et al (18) favor an indirect stimulatory action of $PGF_{2\alpha}$ on RARs mediated by changes in bronchomotor tone. These authors (18) found that prostaglandins of the E series, which have a strong bronchodilating action, do not excite RARs. They consider RARs primarily mechanoreceptors. Bradykinin, another substance released in the lung during asthma attacks and anaphylaxis, was found to have only a weak stimulatory effect on RARs in dogs (especially when injected in the systemic circulation). This effect was mainly attributed to sensitization of the receptor to changes in pulmonary mechanics (46).

Response to Carbon Dioxide

Coleridge et al (17) reported a marked increase in RAR activity in dogs when airway CO_2 diminished after ligation of the pulmonary artery to the corresponding lung. A reversal of this excitatory effect occurred when the CO_2 was raised to normocapnic levels. This inhibitory effect of CO_2 on RARs (as on SARs) seemed especially strong at low levels of hypocapnia. In rabbits (96) and dogs (84) that were artificially ventilated at constant rate and volume, increases in CO_2 concentration above normocapnic levels did not modify RAR activity, although a slight decrease in this activity was noticed in rabbits.

Properties of RARs in Newborns

Rapidly adapting receptors make up a smaller portion of the receptor population in newborns than in adults of the same species: 4% (of total SARs + RARs) versus 15%, respectively, in the dog (33) and 5% versus 18%, respectively, in the opossum (30).

The decreased sensitivity of the newborn to tracheobronchial irritation, as measured by the ability of this stimulation to induce coughing (51), is indeed consistent with sparse RAR activity. However, an apparent discrepancy exists between the higher frequency of sighs during early development (35) and the scant RAR activity found in newborn animals. The scarce RAR activity may be compensated by a particularly low lung compliance due to an end-expiratory volume within the closing volume range (31).

Structure

Das et al (21) compared the morphology of the nervous supply of the superficial layers of the airways of cats before and after unilateral vagotomy below the nodose ganglion. Most of the fibers within the epithelium on the vagotomized side degenerated, which establishes their afferent nature. These same authors found a greater concentration of these apparently afferent terminals in the larger airways of the cat. Similar results were obtained in the rat (44).

C-FIBER RECEPTORS

C-fiber afferents do not correspond to a homogenous group of receptors; they have been separated by both pharmacological and physiological criteria into two main categories: pulmonary C-fiber receptors (also called J receptors; 75) and bronchial C-fiber receptors (14). This nomenclature implies a different anatomical sites of the respective fiber endings. The pulmonary C fibers would be in the lung parenchyma, outside the bronchial and bronchiolar walls, and the bronchial C fibers enclosed within the tracheobronchial walls. These localizations are suggested by the preferential access to either the pulmonary or the bronchial circulation. However, this criterion, which undoubtedly separates two distinct groups of endings, seems inappropriate as a tool for determining the locations of the two fiber types. Fiber endings containing SARs and RARs that are located even in large intrapulmonary airways are affected by an active agent preferentially, or even uniquely, through the pulmonary circulation (86). C-fiber receptors that are accessible through both pulmonary and systemic circulations have been described in rabbits (100); in dogs, a few such receptors are not accessible through either route (47).

Bronchial C-fiber endings have been located directly in large intrapulmonary bronchi and other, smaller airways by probing the mucosal surface with a catheter or a bristle (14).

Although this review focuses on the tracheobronchial tree, we will discuss both bronchial and pulmonary C-fiber receptors to contrast their properties and because, in the reviewer's judgement, the pulmonary (alveolar) location remains an open proposition. Most of the reflex actions attributed to "bronchial" and "pulmonary" C fibers are essentially the same. They consist of (20): rapid and shallow breathing (often preceded by apnea), bronchoconstriction, cough, mucous secretion, bradycardia, and a decrease in total vascular peripheral resistance. No direct observations on C fiber activity in the newborn are available.

Mechanosensitivity of Pulmonary and Bronchial C-Fiber Receptors

A study that compared the responses of the various bronchopulmonary afferents to lung inflation showed that the transpulmonary pressure necessary to change activity was the lowest for SARs (5.8 ± 1.5 cm H_2O) and highest for bronchial C-fiber endings (26.5 ± 2.9 cm H_2O); these values were intermediate in RARs (13.5 ± 2.2 cm H_2O) and pulmonary C-fiber receptors (16.4 ± 1.8 cm H_2O) (47). During spontaneous breathing, pulmonary C-fiber endings show significant activity with a respiratory rhythmicity (1.9 ± 0.2 impulses/s) that decreases markedly under conditions of artificial ventilation with the chest open. The activity of bronchial C-fiber receptors is sparse and irregular during both spontaneous and artificial breathing (15).

A reduction in lung volume below FRC is an ineffective stimulus of both bronchial and pulmonary C-fiber receptor activity (14, 19). An increase of pressure in the pulmonary interstitium, such as that which occurs with pulmonary congestion or edema, is a strong stimulator of pulmonary C-fiber endings but has only a weak effect on bronchial C-fiber endings (15). According to Paintal (75), an increase in interstitial pressure is the most effective stimulator of J receptors. In general, pulmonary C-fiber receptors show a greater response to mechanical events and thus are more likely to be responsible for the corresponding reflex responses. Moderate to large pulmonary inflations, introduced while nervous conduction in myelinated fibers is blocked, cause a tonic inspiratory activation with a superimposed rapid, shallow breathing (20, 40), bronchoconstriction (81), bradycardia, and a decrease in vascular peripheral resistance (13).

Pisarri et al have suggested that pulmonary C-fiber receptors provide an excitatory input to the control of breathing rate that opposes the inhibitory input from SARs (76).

Considerable attention has been directed in recent years to pulmonary C fibers (J receptors) and to the fact that they respond to pulmonary congestion and edema. The suggestion (75) that these endings may be involved in limiting the intensity of exercise (the J reflex) has focused additional attention on them. The reflex responses of J receptors have mainly been characterized by stimulating J-receptor activity with phenyldiguanide (PDG) injected into the right heart. Recently, the pattern of breathing produced by excitation of J receptors with PDG has been compared with that induced by increases of pulmonary blood flow, which corresponds to that observed in moderate exercise (2). These respiratory responses consisted of a short period of apnea followed by breaths of smaller amplitude and shorter duration. This type of breathing pattern hardly corresponds to the ventilatory effect of exercise, even at the point of exhaustion. However, this breathing pattern does resemble that observed in diseases that involve the pulmonary vasculature (39).

Delpierre et al (24) reported that bronchial C fibers doubled their activity when tracheal temperature was raised from 29 to 33°C. In light of the bronchoconstrictive action attributed to these endings, this observation is relevant to discussions of postexercise bronchoconstriction.

Chemosensitivity of Pulmonary and Bronchial C-Fiber Receptors

Whereas pulmonary C-fiber receptors have a greater mechanosensitivity, bronchial C-fiber receptors have a higher chemosensitivity. This property of bronchial C-fiber is particularly evident in the responses to substances naturally present in, or released by, the lung. This finding is of great physiopathological interest. Coleridge & Coleridge (20) found that bronchial C fibers respond in a manner similar to that of the skin afferent C fibers upon stimulation by humoral mediators of inflammation; these include histamine (14, 16), prostaglandins (16, 18), serotonin (20), and bradykinin (46). These substances activate bronchial C fibers when injected into the systemic circulation or inhaled in the form of an aerosol. Pulmonary C fibers are stimulated by prostaglandins, especially those of the E series (16, 18), but remain virtually unaffected by histamine, serotonin, or bradykinin (20, 45a, 46).

Of physiological interest is the alleged CO_2 sensitivity of bronchopulmonary C fibers, especially when they are viewed as CO_2 mixed venous sensors, possibly implied in exercise hyperpnea. A short report advanced this possibility (25), but a later study disclosed that only a very small increase in both bronchial and pulmonary C-fiber activity occurred when CO_2 in the end tidal air of a vascularly isolated lung was raised from 19 to 30 mm Hg (17). Delpierre et al (24) found a transient increase in bronchopulmonary C-fiber activity at the beginning and end of an hypercapnic stimulus. (In this experiment CO_2 was added to the air mixture given to a passively ventilated cat.) In this study the activity increased in most of the receptors within a P_{CO_2} range of 14–28 mm Hg; there was no further change at higher P_{CO_2} levels. More recently, Trenchard et al (100) injected sodium dithionite (a reducing agent that releases CO_2 from the blood and thus raises CO_2 concentration in the end-tidal) air into the right atrium of rabbits and found a prompt and brisk activation of pulmonary C fibers.

It is well documented that CO_2, either inhaled (4, 8) or added to the mixed venous blood (98), evokes a vagally mediated hyperpnea. Recent data support a prominent role of C fibers in the tachypnea that occurs during CO_2 breathing; the tachypnea persists after anodal block of myelinated fibers (83). New evidence supporting a CO_2/H^+ sensitivity of pulmonary C-fiber receptors is derived from experiments in which injection of lactic acid and acetic acid into the right atrium caused a vagally mediated increase in breathing rate (99).

Morphology of C-Fiber Afferents

Electron microscopy of the alveolar wall in human (36) and rat lungs (62) has revealed a scant number of nonmyelinated fibers and few or no identifiable afferent terminals. In contrast, the mouse lung (41) has a good supply of nonmyelinated fibers and recognizable afferent terminals within its alveolar walls and alveolar ducts that are often associated with Type I pneumocytes.

Unmyelinated fibers with corresponding terminals have been found within the tracheal epithelium of humans (78). Similar observations have been made in the intrapulmonary airway of mice (42): These endings have structures identical to those of the alveolar wall.

SYMPATHETIC AFFERENT ACTIVITY

An irregular nervous activity with a clear respiratory modulation has been recorded in higher thoracic white rami communicants in dogs (52). The discharge rate is linearly related to transpulmonary pressure and has nonadapting characteristics. The nerve fibers involved have a conduction velocity ranging from 7 to 12 m/s. The location of these endings is uncertain; some seem to be associated with unidentified pulmonary structures and are also stimulated by mechanical probing in the pulmonary veins and arteries (52). There is evidence that the excitatory effects of some chemical and mechanical stimuli to airway and pulmonary structures are mediated by sympathetic afferents (77, 105).

Literature Cited

1. Agostoni, E., Citterio, G., Piccoli, S. 1985. Reflex partitioning of inputs from stretch receptors of bronchi and thoracic trachea. *Respir. Physiol.* 60:311–28
2. Anand, A., Paintal, A. S. 1980. Reflex effects following selective stimulation of J-receptors in the cat. *J. Physiol. London* 229:553–72
3. Armstrong, D. J., Luck, J. C. 1974. A comparative study of irritant and type J receptors in the cat. *Respir. Physiol.* 21:47–60
4. Banzett, R. B., Coleridge, H. M., Coleridge, J. C. G. 1978. Pulmonary CO_2 ventilatory reflex in dogs: Effective range of CO_2 and results of vagal cooling. *Respir. Physiol.* 34:121–34
5. Bartlett, D. Jr., Jeffery, P., Sant'Ambrogio, G., Wise, J. C. M. 1976. Location of stretch receptors in the trachea and bronchi of the dog. *J. Physiol. London* 258:409–20
6. Bartlett, D. Jr., Sant'Ambrogio, G. 1976. Effect of local and systemic hypercapnia on the discharge of stretch receptors in the airways of the dog. *Respir. Physiol.* 26:91–99
7. Bartlett, D. Jr., Sant'Ambrogio, G., Wise, J. C. M. 1976. Transduction properties of tracheal stretch receptors. *J. Physiol. London* 258:421–32
8. Bartoli, A., Cross, B. A., Guz, A., Jain, S. L., Noble, M. I. M., Trenchard, D. W. 1974. The effect of carbon dioxide in the airways and alveoli on ventilation: A vagal reflex studied in the dog. *J. Physiol. London* 240:91–109
9. Bergren, D. R., Sampson, S. R. 1982. Characterization of intrapulmonary rapidly adapting receptors of guinea pigs. *Respir. Physiol.* 47:83–95
10. Bradley, G. W., Noble, M. I. M., Trenchard, D. 1976. The direct effect on pulmonary stretch receptors discharge produced by changing CO_2 concentration in dogs on cardiopulmonary bypass and its action on breathing. *J. Physiol. London* 261:359–73
11. Bradley, G. W., Scheurmier, N. 1977. The transduction properties of tracheal stretch receptors in vitro. *Respir. Physiol.* 31:356–75
12. Bystrzycka, E. K., Nail, A. B. 1980. CO_2 sensitivity of stretch receptors in the marsupial lung. *Respir. Physiol.* 39:111–19
13. Cassidy, S. S., Eschenbacher, W. L., Johnson, R. L. 1979. Reflex cardiovascular depression during unilateral lung hyperinflation in the dog. *J. Clin. Invest.* 64:620–26
14. Coleridge, H. M., Coleridge, J. C. G. 1977. Impulse activity in afferent vagal C-fibers with endings in the intrapulmonary airways of the dogs. *Respir. Physiol.* 29:143–50
15. Coleridge, H. M., Coleridge, J. C. G. 1977. Afferent vagal C-fibers in the dog lung: Their discharge during spontaneous breathing and their stimulation by alloxan and pulmonary congestion. In *Krogh Centenary Symp. Respir. Adaptations, Capillary Exchange Reflex Mech.*, pp. 393–406. Dehli: Vallabhbhai Patel Chest Inst., Univ. Dehli
16. Coleridge, H. M., Coleridge, J. C. G., Baker, D. G., Ginzel, K. H., Morrison, M. A. 1978. Comparison of the effects of histamine and prostaglandin on afferent C-fiber endings and irritant receptors in the intrapulmonary airways. *Adv. Exp. Med. Biol.* 99:291–305
17. Coleridge, H. M., Coleridge, J. C. G., Banzett, R. B. 1978. Effect of CO_2 on afferent vagal endings in the canine lung. *Respir. Physiol.* 34:135–41
18. Coleridge, H. M., Coleridge, J. C. G., Ginzel, K. H., Baker, D. G., Banzett, R. B., Morrison, M. A. 1976. Stimulation of irritant receptors and afferent C-fibers in the lungs by prostaglandins. *Nature* 264:451–53
19. Coleridge, H. M., Coleridge, J. C. G., Luck, J. C. 1965. Pulmonary afferent fibres of small diameter stimulated by capsaicin and by hyperinflation of the

lungs. *J. Physiol. London* 179:248–62

20. Coleridge, J. C. G., Coleridge, H. M. 1984. Afferent vagal C fibre innervation of the lungs and airways and its functional significance. *Rev. Physiol. Biochem. Pharmacol.* 99:1–110

21. Das, R. M., Jeffery, P. K., Widdicombe, J. G. 1979. Experimental degeneration of intra-epithelial nerve fibers in cat airways. *J. Anat.* 128:259–67

22. Davenport, P. W., Sant'Ambrogio, F. B., Sant'Ambrogio, G. 1981. Adaptation of tracheal stretch receptors. *Respir. Physiol.* 44:339–49

23. Davis, H. L., Fowler, W. S., Lambert, E. H. 1956. Effect of volume and rate of inflation and deflation on transpulmonary pressure and response of pulmonary stretch receptors. *Am. J. Physiol.* 187:558–66

24. Delpierre, S., Grimaud, C., Jammes, Y., Mei, N. 1981. Changes in activity of vagal bronchopulmonary C-fibres by chemical and physical stimuli in the cat. *J. Physiol. London* 316:61–74

25. Dickinson, C. J., Paintal, A. S. 1970. Stimulation of type J pulmonary receptors in the cat by carbon dioxide. *Clin. Sci.* 38:33P

26. Dixon, M., Jackson, D. M., Richards, I. M. 1979. The effects of histamine, acetylcholine and 5-hydroxytryptamine on lung mechanics and irritant receptors in the dog. *J. Physiol. London* 287:393–403

27. During, M. von, Andres, K. H., Iravani, J. 1974. The fine structure of the pulmonary stretch receptor in the rat. *Z. Anat. Entwicklungsgesch.* 143:215–22

28. Elftman, A. F. 1943. The afferent and parasympathetic innervation of the lungs and trachea of the dog. *Am. J. Anat.* 72:2–28

29. Farber, J. P., Fisher, J. T., Sant'Ambrogio, G. 1983. Distribution and discharge properties of airway receptor in the opossum, didelphis marsupialis. *Am. J. Physiol.* 245:R209–14

30. Farber, J. P., Fisher, J. T., Sant'Ambrogio, G. 1984. Airway receptor activity in the developing opossum. *Am. J. Physiol.* 246:R756–58

31. Fisher, J. T., Mortola, J. P. 1980. Statics of the respiratory system in newborn mammals. *Respir. Physiol.* 41:155–72

32. Fisher, J. T., Sant'Ambrogio, F. B., Sant'Ambrogio, G. 1983. Stimulation of tracheal slowly adapting stretch receptors by hypercapnia and hypoxia. *Respir. Physiol.* 53:325–39

33. Fisher, J. T., Sant'Ambrogio, G. 1982. Location and discharge properties of respiratory vagal afferents in the newborn dog. *Respir. Physiol.* 50:209–20

34. Fisher, J. T., Sant'Ambrogio, G. 1982. Effects of inhaled CO_2 on airway stretch receptors in the newborn dog. *J. Appl. Physiol.* 53:1461–65

35. Fleming, P. J., Goncalves, A. L., Levine, M. R., Woollard, S. 1984. The development of stability of respiration in human infants: Changes in ventilatory responses to spontaneous sighs. *J. Physiol. London* 347:1–16

36. Fox, B., Bull, T. B., Guz, A. 1980. Innervation of alveolar walls in the human lung: An electron microscopic study. *J. Anat. London* 131:683–92

37. Glogowska, M., Richardson, P. S., Widdicombe, J. G., Winning, A. J. 1972. The role of the vagus nerves, peripheral chemoreceptors and other afferent pathways in the genesis of augmented breaths in cats and rabbits. *Respir. Physiol.* 16:179–96

38. Green, J. F., Schertel, E. R., Coleridge, H. M., Coleridge, J. C. G. 1986. Effect of pulmonary arterial P_{CO_2} on slowly adapting pulmonary stretch receptors. *J. Appl. Physiol.* 60:2048–55

39. Guz, A., Trenchard, D. W. 1971. The role of non-myelinated vagal afferent fibres from the lungs in the genesis of tachypnea in the rabbit. *J. Physiol. London* 213:345–71

40. Hammouda, M., Wilson, W. H. 1935. The presence in the vagus of fibres transmitting impulses augmenting the frequency of respiration. *J. Physiol. London* 83:292–312

41. Hung, K. S., Hertweck, M. S., Hardy, J. D., Loosli, C. G. 1972. Innervation of pulmonary alveoli of the mouse lung: An electron microscopic study. *Am. J. Anat.* 135:477–96

42. Hung, K. S., Hertweck, M. S., Hardy, J. D., Loosli, C. G. 1973. Ultrastructure of nerves and associated cells in bronchiolar epithelium on the mouse lung. *J. Ultrastruct. Res.* 43:426–37

43. Jammes, Y., Fornaris, E., Mei, N., Barrat, E. 1982. Afferent and efferent components of the bronchial vagal branches in cats. *J. Auton. Nerv. Syst.* 5:165–76

44. Jeffery, D., Reid, L. 1973. Intraepithelial nerves in normal rat airways: A quantitative electron microscopic study. *J. Anat.* 114:35–45

45. Jonzon, A., Pisarri, T. E., Coleridge, J. C. G., Coleridge, H. M. 1986. Rapidly adapting receptor activity in dogs is inversely related to lung compliance. *J. Appl. Physiol.* 61:1980–87

45a. Karczewski, W., Widdicombe, J. G. 1969. The role of the vagus nerve in the respiratory and circulatory responses to intravenous histamine and phenyl diguanide in rabbits. *J. Physiol. London* 201:271–92

46. Kaufman, M. P., Coleridge, H. M., Coleridge, J. C. G., Baker, D. G. 1980. Bradykinin stimulates afferent vagal C-fibers in intrapulmonary airways of dogs. *J. Appl. Physiol.* 48:511–17

47. Kaufman, M. P., Iwamoto, G. A., Ashton, J. H., Cassidy, S. S. 1982. Responses to inflation of vagal afferents with endings in the lungs of dogs. *Circ. Res.* 51:525–31

48. Knowlton, G. C., Larrabee, M. G. 1946. A unitary analysis of pulmonary volume receptors. *Am. J. Physiol.* 147:100–14

49. Kohl, J., Koller, E. A., Kuoni, J., Mokry, L. 1986. Location-dependent characteristics of pulmonary stretch receptor activity in the rabbit. *Pflüg. Arch.* 406:303–7

50. Koller, E. A., Ferrer, P. 1973. Discharge patterns of the lung stretch receptors and activation of deflation fibers in anaphylactic bronchial asthma. *Respir. Physiol.* 17:113–26

51. Korpas, J., Tomori, Z. 1979. *Cough and Other Respiratory Reflexes.* Basel: Karger

52. Kostreva, D. R., Zuperku, E. J., Hess, G. L., Coon, R. L., Kampine, J. P. 1975. Pulmonary afferent activity recorded from sympathetic nerves. *J. Appl. Physiol.* 39:37–40

53. Krauhs, J. M. 1984. Morphology of presumptive slowly adapting receptors in dog trachea. *Anat. Rec.* 210:73–85

54. Krous, H. F., Jordan, J., Wen, J., Farber, J. P. 1985. Developmental morphometry of the vagus in the opossum. *Dev. Brain Res.* 20:155–59

55. Kunz, A. L., Kawashiro, T., Scheid, P. 1976. Study of CO_2 sensitive vagal afferents in the cat lung. *Respir. Physiol.* 27:347–55

56. Lloyd, T. C. Jr. 1979. Effects of extrapulmonary airway distension on breathing in anesthetized dogs. *J. Appl. Physiol.* 46:890–96

57. Luck, J. C. 1970. Afferent vagal fibres with an expiratory discharge in the rabbit. *J. Physiol. London* 211:63–71

58. Marlot, D., Duron, B. 1979. Postnatal development of vagal control of breathing in the kitten. *J. Physiol. Paris* 75:891–900

59. Marlot, D., Duron, B. 1979. Postnatal maturation of phrenic, vagus, and intercostal nerves in the kitten. *Biol. Neonate* 36:264–72

60. Marlot, D., Mortola, J. P., Duron, B.

1982. Functional localization of pulmonary stretch receptors in the tracheobronchial tree of the kitten. *Can. J. Physiol. Pharmacol.* 60:1073–77

61. Mei, N. 1980. Disposition anatomique et propriétés électrophysiologiques des neurones sensitifs vagaux chez le chat. *Exp. Brain Res.* 11:465–79

62. Meyrick, B., Reid, L. 1971. Nerves in rat intraacinar alveoli: An electron microscopic study. *Respir. Physiol.* 11: 367–77

63. Mills, J. E., Sellick, H., Widdicombe, J. G. 1970. Epithelial irritant receptors in the lungs. In *Breathing: Hering-Breuer Centenary Symp.*, ed. R. Porter, pp. 77–99. London: Churchill

64. Miserocchi, G., Mortola, J., Sant'Ambrogio, G. 1973. Localization of pulmonary stretch receptors in the airways of the dog. *J. Physiol. London* 235:775–82

65. Miserocchi, G., Sant'Ambrogio, G. 1974. Distribution of pulmonary stretch receptors in the intrapulmonary airways of the dog. *Respir. Physiol.* 21:71–75

66. Miserocchi, G., Sant'Ambrogio, G. 1974. Responses of pulmonary stretch receptors to static pressure inflations. *Respir. Physiol.* 21:77–85

67. Mortola, J. P., Sant'Ambrogio, G. 1979. Mechanics of the trachea and behavior of its slowly adapting stretch receptors. *J. Physiol. London* 286:577–90

68. Mortola, J. P., Sant'Ambrogio, G., Clement, M. G. 1975. Localization of irritant receptors in the airways of the dog. *Respir. Physiol.* 24:107–14

69. Mustafa, M. E. K. Y., Purves, J. J. 1972. The effect of CO_2 upon discharge from slowly adapting stretch receptors in the lung of rabbits. *Respir. Physiol.* 16:197–212

70. Nilsestuen, J. O., Coon, R. L., Woods, M., Kampine, J. P. 1981. Localization of lung receptors mediating the breathing frequency response to pulmonary CO_2. *Respir. Physiol.* 45:343–55

71. Pack, A. I., Delaney, R. G. 1983. Response of pulmonary rapidly adapting receptors during lung inflation. *J. Appl. Physiol.* 55:955–63

72. Pack, A. I., Ogilvie, M. D., Davies, R. O., Galante, R. J. 1986. Responses of pulmonary stretch receptors during ramp inflations of the lung. *J. Appl. Physiol.* 61:344–52

73. Paintal, A. S. 1953. The conduction velocities of respiratory and cardiovascular afferent fibers in the vagus nerve. *J. Physiol. London* 121:341–59

74. Paintal, A. S. 1966. Re-evaluation of

respiratory reflexes. *Q. J. Exp. Physiol.* 51:151–63
75. Paintal, A. S. 1969. Mechanism of stimulation of Type J pulmonary receptors. *J. Physiol. London* 203:511–32
76. Pisarri, T. E., Yu, J., Coleridge, H. M., Coleridge, J. C. G. 1986. Background activity in pulmonary vagal C-fibers and its effect on breathing. *Respir. Physiol.* 64:29–43
77. Rao, S. V., Sant'Ambrogio, F. B., Sant'Ambrogio, G. 1981. Respiratory reflexes evoked by tracheal distension. *J. Appl. Physiol.* 50:421–27
78. Rhodin, J. A. G. 1966. Ultrastructure and function of the human tracheal mucosa. *Am. Rev. Respir. Dis.* 93:1–15
79. Richardson, C. A., Herbert, D. A., Mitchell, R. A. 1984. Modulation of pulmonary stretch receptors and airway resistance by parasympathetic efferents. *J. Appl. Physiol.* 57:1842–49
80. Richardson, P. S., Sant'Ambrogio, G., Mortola, J., Bianconi, R. 1973. The activity of lung afferent nerves during tracheal occlusion. *Respir. Physiol.* 18:273–83
81. Roberts, A. M., Coleridge, H. M., Coleridge, J. C. G. 1982. Reciprocal action of pulmonary stretch receptors and lung C-fibers on tracheal smooth muscle tone in dogs. *Fed. Proc.* 41:986
82. Roumy, M., Leitner, L. M. 1980. Localization of stretch and deflation receptors in the airways of the rabbit. *J. Physiol. Paris* 76:67–70
83. Russell, N. J. W., Raybould, H. E., Trenchard, D. 1984. Role of vagal C-fiber afferents in respiratory response to hypercapnia. *J. Appl. Physiol.* 56:1550–58
84. Sampson, S. R., Vidruk, H. 1975. Properties of "irritant" receptors in canine lung. *Respir. Physiol.* 25:9–22
85. Sampson, S. R., Vidruk, E. H. 1977. Chemical stimulation of rapidly adapting receptors in the airways. In *The Regulation of Respiration During Sleep and Anesthesia,* ed. R. S. Fitzgerald, H. Gautier, S. Lahiri, pp. 281–90. New York: Plenum
86. Sant'Ambrogio, F. B., Sant'Ambrogio, G. 1982. Circulatory accessibility of nervous receptors localized in the tracheobronchial tree. *Respir. Physiol.* 49:49–73
87. Sant'Ambrogio, F. B., Sant'Ambrogio, G., Mathew, O. P. 1986. Effect of cold airway cooling on tracheal stretch receptors. *Respir. Physiol.* In press
88. Sant'Ambrogio, F. B., Sant'Ambrogio, G., Mortola, J. P. 1977. Reflex influences from the extrathoracic trachea during airway occlusion. *Respir. Physiol.* 36:327–36
89. Sant'Ambrogio, G. 1982. Information arising from the tracheobronchial tree of mammals. *Physiol. Rev.* 62:531–69
90. Sant'Ambrogio, G., Miserocchi, G. 1973. Functional localization of pulmonary stretch receptors in the airways of the cat. *Arch. Fisiol.* 70:3–9
91. Sant'Ambrogio, G., Miserocchi, G., Mortola, J. 1974. Transient responses of pulmonary stretch receptors in the dog to inhalation of carbon dioxide. *Respir. Physiol.* 22:191–97
92. Sant'Ambrogio, G., Mortola, P. 1977. Behavior of slowly adapting stretch receptors in the extrathoracic trachea of the dog. *Respir. Physiol.* 31:377–85
93. Sant'Ambrogio, G., Remmers, J. E., DeGroot, W. J., Callas, G., Mortola, J. P. 1978. Localization of rapidly adapting receptors in the trachea and main stem bronchus of the dog. *Respir. Physiol.* 33:359–66
94. Schoener, E. P., Frankel, H. M. 1972. Effect of hyperthermia and $P_{A_{CO_2}}$ on the slowly adapting pulmonary stretch receptor. *Am. J. Physiol.* 222:68–72
95. Schwieler, G. H. 1968. Respiratory regulation during postnatal development in cats and rabbits and some of its morphological substrate. *Acta Physiol. Scand. Suppl.* 304:1
96. Sellick, H., Widdicombe, J. G. 1969. The activity of lung irritant receptors during pneumothorax, hyperpnea and pulmonary vascular congestion. *J. Physiol. London* 203:359–81
97. Sellick, H., Widdicombe, J. G. 1970. Vagal deflation and inflation reflexes mediated by lung irritant receptors. *Q. J. Exp. Physiol.* 55:153–63
98. Sheldon, M. I., Green, J. F. 1982. Evidence for pulmonary CO_2 chemosensitivity: Effects on ventilation. *J. Appl. Physiol.* 52:1192–97
99. Trenchard, D. 1986. CO_2/H^+ receptors in the lungs of anesthetized rabbits. *Respir. Physiol.* 63:227–40
100. Trenchard, D., Russell, N. J. W., Raybould, H. E. 1984. Non-myelinated vagal lung receptors and their reflex reflects on respiration in rabbits. *Respir. Physiol.* 55:63–79
101. Tsubone, H. 1986. Characteristics of vagal afferent activity in rats—three types of pulmonary receptors responding to collapse, inflation and deflation of the lung. *Exp. Neurol.* 92:541–52
102. Vidruk, E. H., Hahn, H. L., Nadel, J. A., Sampson, S. R. 1977. Mechanisms

by which histamine stimulates rapidly adapting receptors in dog lungs. *J. Appl. Physiol.* 43:397–402

103. Wei, J. Y., Shen, E. 1985. Vagal expiratory afferent discharges during spontaneous breathing. *Brain Res.* 355:213–19

104. Whitteridge, D., Bulbring, E. 1944. Changes in activity of pulmonary receptors in anaesthesia and their influence on respiratory behavior. *J. Pharmacol. Exp. Ther.* 81:340–59

105. Widdicombe, J. G. 1954. Respiratory reflexes from the trachea and bronchi of the cat. *J. Physiol. London* 123:55–70

106. Widdicombe, J. G. 1954. Receptors in the trachea and bronchi of the cat. *J. Physiol. London* 123:71–104

107. Widdicombe, J. G. 1954. The site of pulmonary stretch receptors in the cat. *J. Physiol. London* 125:336–51

SPECIAL TOPIC: MOLECULAR MECHANISM OF MUSCLE CONTRACTION

General Introduction

Y. E. Goldman, Section Editor

Department of Physiology, School of Medicine, University of Pennsylvania, Philadelphia, Pennsylvania 19104

B. Brenner

Institute of Physiology II, University of Tübingen, D-7400 Tübingen, West Germany

EXPERIMENTAL APPROACHES

Contraction of striated muscle occurs when actin and myosin filaments slide past each other (12, 15). It is generally accepted that this process is driven by parts of the myosin molecules, the cross-bridges, which protrude from the myosin-containing thick filaments and cyclically interact with the actin in the thin filaments as ATP is hydrolyzed (7, 10, 11, 14). In studying the detailed mechanism of the cyclic cross-bridge action, several approaches are available: biochemical studies of the isolated proteins in solution, physiological measurements of muscle fiber mechanics and energetics, and structural studies using electron microscopy, X-ray diffraction, and spectroscopic probes.

These methods allow us to specify the chemical identity, the mechanical properties, and the detailed structure of states in the cross-bridge cycle. Furthermore, the kinetics of the cycle, including the reaction steps, their rates, and how they are physiologically controlled, can be investigated. In order to form a complete hypothesis for the molecular mechanism of muscle contraction, we need to include a detailed description of each state and each reaction.

The elementary steps of the actomyosin ATPase have been extensively characterized in biochemical experiments on the isolated proteins (1, 3, 8, 25, 32, 33), and the resulting sequence of reaction steps leading to ATP hydrolysis serves as a common basis for discussing experiments on the organized contractile system. A reaction scheme for the ATPase in solution is discussed in the next section; however, some of the reaction rates, and possibly even the reaction pathway, are expected to differ in muscle fibers, as discussed in the following section.

THE ACTOMYOSIN ATPase IN SOLUTION

Figure 1 shows a scheme of elementary reaction steps for the pathway of the actomyosin ATPase (3, 8, 25, 32), where M represents a myosin head (subfragment 1) and A represents actin. In the absence of actin, myosin splits ATP slowly (bottom row of Figure 1). ATP binds very tightly to myosin ($K_1 \approx 10^{11}$ M^{-1}; K_i is the equilibrium constant of the ith reaction step) and is split rapidly ($k_{3d} > 150$ s^{-1}; k_i and k_{-i} are the rate constants for the elementary forward and backward reactions). The M·ADP·P_i complex thus formed has relatively high basic free energy because ADP and P_i are tightly bound to M·ADP·P_i and reformation of M·ATP occurs readily ($k_{-3d} \approx 15$ s^{-1}). P_i dissociates very slowly ($k_{+5d} \approx 0.06$ s^{-1}), then ADP dissociates and ATP binds again. In the presence of ATP, the states significantly populated are M·ATP and M·ADP·P_i.

Actin activates the myosin ATPase (4, 31) by binding to M·ADP·P_i (Figure 1, step 4), markedly accelerating P_i release (step 5a; reference 17). ADP release (step 9a) and ATP binding (step 1a) are rapid. ATP binding causes myosin to dissociate from actin because the affinity of M·ATP for actin is several orders of magnitude less than the affinity of M (without nucleotide) for actin. The hydrolysis step occurs both with myosin attached to actin (step 3a) and with dissociated myosin (step 3d; references 23, 29). At low actin concentrations ($<10^{-4}$ M) the reaction proceeds mainly through step 3d, so that on binding ATP myosin dissociates from actin before splitting the ATP. At high actin concentrations, especially at low ionic strength, step 3a is significant and steps 2 and 4 should be considered rapid equilibria. Since the actin affinity is low, the states in this part of the cycle are termed the "weak binding states" (29).

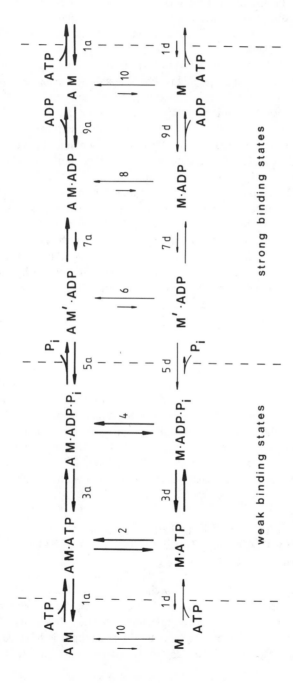

Figure 1 A kinetic scheme of the in vitro elementary steps of the actomyosin ATPase. "A" represents actin, "M" is myosin subfragment 1. The heavy solid arrows indicate the predominant cyclic reaction pathway in the presence of actin. The relative lengths of the forward and reverse arrows qualitatively indicate the change in free energy across the corresponding step. (Modified from references 3, 8, 25, and 32.)

On release of P_i, the myosin binding to actin becomes much stronger. In fact, myosin binding to actin becomes progressively stronger as the reaction proceeds from M·ATP toward M. The association constants for binding of the various myosin states to actin are approximately M·ATP, 10^4 M^{-1}; M·ADP·P_i, 10^4 M^{-1}; M·ADP, 10^6 M^{-1}; M, 10^7 M^{-1}. The equilibrium and rate constants quoted are appropriate to rabbit skeletal myosin and actomyosin at approximately 20°C, pH 7–8, and 20–100 mM ionic strength (3, 8, 25, 32).

The state AM'·ADP, which is capable of binding P_i, is formed preferentially during ATP hydrolysis. AM'·ADP is different from AM·ADP formed by adding ADP to AM in that AM·ADP cannot readily bind P_i (24). It is not clear whether AM·ADP is a state on the hydrolysis pathway. AM'·ADP might dissociate directly to AM without the intervening AM·ADP state. The AM'·ADP and M'·ADP states are often not included in the kinetic schemes when the results under consideration do not require these two states.

Which reactions within the cycle control the turnover rate is presently controversial (8). According to Rosenfeld & Taylor (23), the turnover rate is controlled by the ATP hydrolysis step (3d, 3a), whereas Stein et al (28, 29) propose that the rate-limiting step is an isomerization following hydrolysis. This isomerization is not explicitly shown in Figure 1 but is lumped in with the M·ADP·P_i and AM·ADP·P_i states.

The dominant pathway of ATP hydrolysis observed in vitro is indicated by the heavy arrows in Figure 1. It is natural to assume that the pathway for ATP hydrolysis in a muscle fiber corresponds to that in solution. If this hypothesis is correct, cross-bridge attachment would correspond to the association of M·ADP·P_i and actin (step 4); a structural change in the cross-bridge, leading to force generation or filament sliding, would correspond to product release (steps 5a, 7a, and/or 9a); and cross-bridge detachment would correspond to ATP binding and dissociation of M·ATP from actin (steps 1a and 2). These ideas were postulated by Lymn & Taylor in 1971 (17), and progress in this area was recently reviewed by Eisenberg & Hill (3) and Hibberd & Trentham (8). A major goal of current research is to determine how closely the ATPase reaction in muscle fibers corresponds to this scheme.

FACTORS THAT CAUSE DIFFERENCES BETWEEN THE ATPase REACTIONS IN VITRO AND IN MUSCLE FIBERS

Myosin is generally isolated by dissolving it in a medium of high ionic strength (~600 mM; reference 20) to disrupt the ionic bonds between the rod-shaped tail regions of adjacent myosin molecules that make up the backbone of the thick filaments (19). If the ionic strength is lowered again into the physiological range (~100–250 mM), myosin repolymerizes to form filaments (13). These filaments are difficult to use for rapid kinetic studies because they increase the solution viscosity and do not mix homogeneously with actin filaments. Therefore, proteolytic fragments of myosin that are soluble at physiological ionic strength and below are useful for studying actomyosin kinetics (16). Subfragment 1 (S-1) is the globular head portion of the myosin molecule that contains the binding sites for both ATP and actin. Heavy meromyosin (HMM) contains two S-1 heads plus part of the rod portion, but not the tail section (termed LMM) that causes polymerization at low ionic strength.

Actin can be isolated and purified by depolymerizing it at low ionic strength (~5 mM) to the globular form (G-actin) and then, in the presence of Mg^{2+} or Ca^{2+}, ATP, and higher ionic strength (>50 mM), repolymerizing it to the filamentous form (F-actin) (26). Only F-actin activates the myosin ATPase. Studying the actin-activated myosin ATPase, which is analogous to the energy-transducing reaction in a muscle fiber, requires the filamentous form of actin.

In considering the applicability of results from biochemical experiments to the events during muscle contraction we must accept that the isolation, purification, and fragmentation procedures modify the proteins significantly. The packing of the proteins into the normal thick filaments or the proximity of other myosin molecules in a fiber may also alter the ATPase reactions from those of the solubilized fragments (34).

The interactions between actin and myosin in solution are bimolecular in the sense that the frequency of collisions between them depends on both protein concentrations. The concept of protein concentration has an altered significance when applied to the contractile apparatus because in a muscle fiber the filaments are aligned in a nearly crystalline array. In vertebrate skeletal muscle, the filaments are hexagonally packed with two thin filaments per thick filament. Each thick filament has six nearest-neighbor thin filaments. Both sets of filaments are axially polarized so that the interfilament sliding force tends to cause muscle shortening. The helical arrangement of actin monomers in the thin filaments allows groups of actin monomers (so-called target zones) to be oriented appropriately for myosin attachment (27). These geometrical factors influence the likelihood of interaction between myosin and actin. Models of muscle contraction generally consider actomyosin interaction in the filament lattice to be a first-order process described by a probability per unit time rather than by a bimolecular rate constant (9).

Experiments on S-1 and HMM are often performed at an ionic strength (<50 mM) well below the physiological value because the affinity of myosin and myosin-nucleotide states for actin increases as the ionic strength is lowered (6, 35). This allows substantial actin-activation of the myosin

634

ATPase at actin concentrations (10–50 μM) low enough for rapid mixing experiments. The ionic-strength dependence of actomyosin affinity suggests that ionic bonds are involved in the actomyosin association (35). However, steps of the ATPase cycle other than myosin association and dissociation may be affected by reducing ionic strength.

Another reason the elementary chemical reactions of actomyosin in a muscle fiber may differ from those of the isolated proteins follows directly from the energy transduction process (9). Consider an attached cross-bridge state that contributes to sliding force between the filaments. Its basic free energy, $\mu_1(x)$, depends on tension according to the relation

$$\mu_1(x) = \mu_0 + \int F(x)dx, \qquad\qquad 1.$$

where $F(x)$ is the force as a function of strain. The equilibrium constant K between that state and one with free energy, μ_2, that produces no force is given by:

$$K = e^{[\mu_1(x) - \mu_2]/RT}. \qquad\qquad 2.$$

If the rate constant governing the transition from state 1 to state 2 is k_+, then the reverse transition has the rate constant k_-, given by:

$$k_- = k_+/K = k_+ e^{[\mu_2 - \mu_1(x)]/RT}. \qquad\qquad 3.$$

It is apparent that a change in μ_1 when the filaments slide will alter the equilibrium constant K and the kinetic parameters k_+ and/or k_-. This mechanical influence on the transition rates will not be present in the biochemical experiments because the isolated proteins are not subject to mechanical constraints that maintain a state away from its lowest-energy structural configuration.

An important example of reaction rates that depend on filament sliding is the "Fenn effect." Fenn (5) discovered that the heat produced by contracting frog muscles increases if they are allowed to shorten and produce external work. Although the molecular explanation of this "shortening heat" may be complex, the Fenn effect implies that some energy-liberating chemical reactions of the cross-bridge cycle depend on filament sliding or on mechanical stress or strain in the cross-bridges.

SCOPE OF THE ARTICLES

The contributors to this Special Topic section describe studies of the relationships between mechanical, chemical, energetic, and structural aspects of muscle contraction. Many recent experiments were performed on muscle fibers that had had their surface membranes removed mechanically (21) or made permeable by various chemical agents (2, 18, 22, 30). These "skinned" muscle fibers allow the biochemical milieu to be experimentally defined and varied, and they allow nucleotide analogs, isotopically labelled compounds, probe molecules, and photochemical compounds to readily diffuse into the filament lattice. Y. E. Goldman discusses some new techniques to resolve biochemical reaction rates in muscle fibers, including caged-ATP photolysis and ^{18}O exchange. B. Brenner tests predictions of the biochemical scheme using high-resolution mechanical techniques to characterize cross-bridge kinetics and X-ray diffraction to probe the structure of cross-bridge states. E. Homsher discusses thermal and chemical measurements on intact muscle that relate to the energetics of actomyosin. D. D. Thomas presents spectroscopic probes capable of detecting the orientation and mobility of cross-bridges in various states of the cycle.

Literature Cited

1. Adelstein, R. S., Eisenberg, E. 1980. Regulation of kinetics of the actin-myosin-ATP interaction. *Ann. Rev. Biochem.* 49:921–56
2. Eastwood, A. B., Wood, D. S., Bock, K. L., Sorenson, M. M. 1979. Chemically skinned mammalian skeletal muscle. I. The structure of skinned rabbit psoas. *Tissue Cell* 11:553–66
3. Eisenberg, E., Hill, T. L. 1985. Muscle contraction and free energy transduction in biological systems. *Science* 227:999–1006
4. Eisenberg, E., Moos, C. 1968. The adenosine triphosphatase activity of acto-heavy meromyosin. A kinetic analysis of actin activation. *Biochemistry* 7:1486–89
5. Fenn, W. O. 1923. A quantitative comparison between the energy liberated and the work performed by the isolated sartorius muscle of the frog. *J. Physiol.* 58:175–203
6. Greene, L. E., Sellers, J. R., Eisenberg, E., Adelstein, R. S. 1983. Binding of gizzard smooth muscle myosin subfragment 1 to actin in the presence and absence of adenosine 5'-triphosphate. *Biochemistry* 22:530–35
7. Hanson, J., Huxley, H. E. 1955. The structural basis of contraction in striated muscle. *Symp. Soc. Exp. Biol.* 9:228–64
8. Hibberd, M. G., Trentham, D. R. 1986. Relationships between chemical and mechanical events during muscular contraction. *Ann. Rev. Biophys. Biophys. Chem.* 15:119–61
9. Hill, T. L. 1974. Theoretical formalism for the sliding filament model of muscle contraction of striated muscle. Part I. *Prog. Biophys. Mol. Biol.* 28:267–340
10. Huxley, A. F. 1957. Muscle structure and theories of contraction. *Prog. Biophys. Biophys. Chem.* 7:255–318
11. Huxley, A. F. 1974. Muscular contraction (review lecture). *J. Physiol.* 243:1–43
12. Huxley, A. F., Niedergerke, R. 1954. Interference microscopy of living muscle fibres. *Nature* 173:971–73
13. Huxley, H. E. 1963. Electron microscope studies on the structure of natural and synthetic protein filaments from striated muscle. *J. Mol. Biol.* 7:281–308
14. Huxley, H. E. 1969. The mechanism of muscular contraction. *Science* 164:1356–66
15. Huxley, H. E., Hanson, J. 1954. Changes in the cross-striations of muscle during contraction and stretch and their structural interpretation. *Nature* 173:973–76
16. Lowey, S., Slayter, H. S., Weeds, A. G., Baker, H. 1969. Substructure of the myosin molecule. I. Subfragments of myosin by enzymic degradation. *J. Mol. Biol.* 42:1–29
17. Lymn, R. W., Taylor, E. W. 1971. Mechanism of adenosine triphosphate hydrolysis by actomyosin. *Biochemistry* 10:4617–24
18. Magid, A., Reedy, M. K. 1980. X-ray diffraction observations of chemically skinned frog skeletal muscle processed

by an improved method. *Biophys. J.* 30:27–40

19. McLachlan, A. D., Karn, J. 1982. Periodic charge distributions in the myosin rod amino acid sequence match crossbridge spacings in muscle. *Nature* 299:226–31

20. Mommaerts, W. F. H. M., Parrish, R. G. 1951. Studies on myosin. I. Preparation and criteria of purity. *J. Biol. Chem.* 188:545–52

21. Natori, R. 1954. The property and contraction process of isolated myofibrils. *Jikeikai Med. J.* 1:119–26

22. Orentlicher, M., Reuben, J. P., Grundfest, H., Brandt, P. W. 1974. Calcium binding and tension development in detergent-treated muscle fibers. *J. Gen. Physiol.* 63:168–86

23. Rosenfeld, S. S., Taylor, E. W. 1984. The ATPase mechanism of skeletal and smooth muscle acto-subfragment 1. *J. Biol. Chem.* 259:11908–19

24. Sleep, J. A., Hutton, R. L. 1980. Exchange between inorganic phosphate and adenosine 5'-triphosphate in the medium by actomyosin subfragment 1. *Biochemistry* 19:1276–83

25. Sleep, J. A., Smith, S. J. 1981. Actomyosin ATPase and muscle contraction. *Curr. Top. Bioenerg.* 11:239–86

26. Spudich, J. A., Watt, S. 1971. The regulation of rabbit skeletal muscle contraction. I. Biochemical studies of the interaction of the tropomyosin-troponin complex with actin and the proteolytic fragments of myosin. *J. Biol. Chem.* 246:4866–71

27. Squire, J. M. 1972. General model of myosin filament structure. II. Myosin filaments and cross-bridge interactions in vertebrate striated and insect flight muscles. *J. Mol. Biol.* 72:125–38

28. Stein, L. A., Chock, P. B., Eisenberg, E. 1984. The rate-limiting step in the actomyosin adenosinetriphosphatase cycle. *Biochemistry* 23:1555–63

29. Stein, L. A., Schwarz, R. P. Jr., Chock, P. B., Eisenberg, E. 1979. Mechanism of actomyosin adenosine triphosphatase. Evidence that adenosine 5'-triphosphate hydrolysis can occur without dissociation of the actomyosin complex. *Biochemistry* 18:3895–3909

30. Szent-Györgyi, A. 1949. Free-energy relations and contractions of actomyosin. *Biol. Bull.* 96:140–61

31. Szentkiralyi, E. M., Oplatka, A. 1969. On the formation and stability of the enzymically active complexes of heavy meromyosin with actin. *J. Mol. Biol.* 43:551–66

32. Taylor, E. W. 1979. Mechanism of actomyosin ATPase and the problem of muscle contraction. *CRC Crit. Rev. Biochem.* 6:103–64

33. Trentham, D. R., Eccleston, J. F., Bagshaw, C. R. 1976. Kinetic analysis of ATPase mechanisms. *Q. Rev. Biophys.* 9:217–81

34. Ueno, H., Harrington, W. F. 1986. Local melting in the subfragment-2 region of myosin in activated muscle and its correlation with contractile force. *J. Mol. Biol.* 190:69–82

35. White, H. D., Taylor, E. W. 1976. Energetics and mechanism of actomyosin adenosine triphosphatase. *Biochemistry* 15:5818–26

Ann. Rev. Physiol. 1987. 49:637–54

KINETICS OF THE ACTOMYOSIN Atpase IN MUSCLE FIBERS

Yale E. Goldman

Department of Physiology, School of Medicine, University of Pennsylvania, Philadelphia, Pennsylvania 19104

CROSS-BRIDGE CYCLING RATE

This chapter reviews some recent estimates of specific elementary rate constants of the actomyosin ATPase in muscle fibers. These values are compared to the corresponding rate constants obtained with myosin and actomyosin in solution to determine whether or not the packing of the proteins into the normal filament lattice influences the reaction rates and to determine which elementary reactions are modulated by mechanical stress and strain on the proteins. A biochemical scheme for the actomyosin ATPase in solution is given in the General Introduction to this Special Topic section and is hereafter referred to as Scheme 1. Reasons to expect important differences between the kinetics of the actomyosin ATPase in solution and in fibers are discussed in the General Introduction. The reaction rates in fibers for steps in the pathway are compared to the overall ATPase rate per myosin head; the reaction steps that are relatively fast typically follow states that are not highly populated during ATPase activity. Reaction steps that are fast in isometric contracting conditions are unlikely to be rate-limiting control points required to explain increased energy liberation during shortening. The discussion here is limited almost exclusively to glycerol-extracted skeletal muscle fibers from rabbit psoas muscle because the most detailed comparison of the biochemistry and physiology has been performed on that system. In addition to the remainder of this Special Topic section, related reviews by Eisenberg & Hill (21) and Hibberd & Trentham (44) have recently appeared.

The hypothesis presented in the introduction to this section, that the cross-bridge cycle follows the same reaction path as that of the actomyosin ATPase in solution, implies that each cycle corresponds to hydrolysis of one

0066-4278/87/0315-0637$02.00

637

ATP molecule. The steady ATPase rate during full Ca^{2+} activation is $3.2\ s^{-1}$ per myosin head in glycerol-extracted single fibers from rabbit psoas muscle at 20°C and an ionic strength of 200 mM (80). The ATPase rate was obtained by incubating single fibers held at a fixed length for 15 min to 1 hr in a small (45 μl) trough of activating solution with 15-mM ATP and then measuring the product ADP by high-performance liquid chromatography (HPLC).

The ATPase rate can also be measured in skinned muscle fibers by coupling ADP formation to oxidation of nicotinamide adenine dinucleotide (reduced form, NADH) using pyruvate kinase and lactate dehydrogenase. The reaction is followed by a decrease in fluorescence (40, 63, 77) or optical absorption (27) by NADH. Another method is to initiate ATP splitting abruptly by the photochemical means described below and to quench the reaction by suddenly freezing the fiber at later time points (26). ADP within the fiber is measured by liquid scintillation counting of radiolabelled nucleotide. Chemical methods to quantitate nucleotide levels and creatine/phosphocreatine after freezing (20, 46, 57) or nuclear magnetic resonance spectroscopy (18) are used in intact muscle fibers. These methods have given values for the ATPase rate during active contractions of 0.6–$3.1\ s^{-1}$ per myosin head in skinned fibers from rabbit muscle at 13–25°C (3, 26, 27, 55, 77) and from skinned or intact frog muscle at 0–15°C (13, 18, 61). These values were calculated with the assumption that all the heads participate in an active contraction, but this point has not been established.

When intact fibers shorten and produce maximal work during an active contraction, the ATPase rate increases about fivefold (46, 57). Maximal ATPase activity of the actin-activated myosin subfragment 1 ATPase in solution is also about 10–30 times faster than the rate in isometric contractions of muscle fibers (69, 82). In both of these cases, the force generated or maintained by the myosin cross-bridges is less than in isometric contractions when the ATPase rate is low. Thus mechanical factors like stress or strain on the force-producing cross-bridges probably limit the ATPase rate in the isometric cross-bridge cycle (47). As discussed below, several of the steps in isometric conditions have been determined to be much faster than the 1–$3\ s^{-1}$ overall turnover rate. This result makes it unlikely that these steps are rate limiting during steady contractions.

CAGED COMPOUNDS

Photochemical generation of ATP from a photolabile precursor molecule, termed caged ATP (51), has been particularly useful in studying actomyosin chemistry in muscle fibers. Caged ATP is inert when put in a skinned muscle fiber, but it can be split by an intense pulse of near-UV laser light to form ATP and a leaving group. The net effect of this photochemical reaction is a sudden (within milliseconds) increase in ATP concentration in the fiber (67), which abruptly initiates or perturbs the cross-bridge cycle. The mechanical and biochemical transients initiated by caged ATP photolysis have enabled us to estimate several reaction rates in the cross-bridge cycle.

Caged compounds and the pulse photolysis method are applicable to many biological systems in which diffusion delays limit the experimentally available kinetic information. J. W. Walker, G. P. Reid, and D. R. Trentham (personal communication) have developed a new synthesis route that significantly reduces the time required for preparation of caged derivatives of phosphate and thiophosphate compounds. Among the compounds that have been used in kinetic studies on muscle are the photolabile precursors of nucleotides ϵ-ATP (16), CTP (76), ATPγS, AMPPNP, ADP (30), cyclic AMP (72), cyclic GMP (72), inorganic phosphate, and inositol trisphosphate (33). Many other photolabile or photoisomerizable chemicals that have been used to study excitable membrane channels and receptors have been reviewed by Lester and colleagues (39, 60).

ATP BINDING AND CROSS-BRIDGE DETACHMENT

The use of photochemical production of ATP by caged ATP photolysis circumvents the diffusion-controlled limitation of time resolution in measuring ATP-induced cross-bridge detachment. In such experiments a skinned muscle fiber is soaked in a solution with no ATP, which causes virtually all the cross-bridges to attach (11, 62, 79) to form the nucleotide-free rigor complex, AM (Scheme 1). Caged ATP diffuses readily into skinned muscle fibers and before photolysis causes little or no cross-bridge detachment (31). Figure 1A of this chapter shows force records from such an experiment on a single glycerol-extracted fiber from rabbit psoas muscle. For the recording labelled (i) the fiber was held isometric at a sarcomere length of 2.6 μm. At the arrow a 50-ns pulse from a frequency-doubled ruby laser ($\lambda = 347$ nm) photolyzed 700 μM of the caged ATP to ATP, which initiated cross-bridge detachment, as indicated by the decrease in tension. Ca^{2+} was present, so the cross-bridges then reattached and produced active force, as indicated by the subsequent tension rise (30, 32). After the recording the fiber was relaxed in a Ca^{2+}-free solution.

Next, another rigor contraction was initiated by removing ATP and then adding caged ATP. For the trace labelled (s) in Figure 1 the muscle fiber was stretched by 0.53% to increase the strain on the cross-bridges one second before the laser pulse. Tension dipped further in this case because each rigor cross-bridge was supporting more force (32).

In the conditions of the experiment (20°C, pH 7.1) ATP is released exponentially after the laser pulse with a rate constant of 118 s^{-1} (31, 67).

A   B

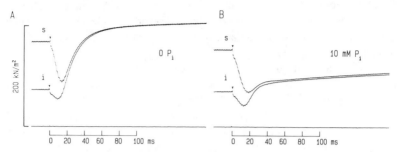

Figure 1 Tension transients initiated by photolysis of caged ATP within a single glycerol-extracted muscle fiber. At the start of each trace the fiber was in rigor with 10-mM caged ATP and 100-μM free Ca^{2+}. The arrowheads indicate the time of the laser pulse that photochemically released ATP (700 μM in A, 870 μM in B). The kinetics of cross-bridge detachment and reattachment are indicated by the time course of tension decline and redevelopment. The effect of a steady 10-mM concentration of P_i (B) is to reduce steady active tension and to increase the kinetically observed rate constant for force development.

This lag is significant, but it does not fully limit the observed rate of cross-bridge detachment (29), which is highly sensitive to the final ATP concentration. Several methods of analysis of mechanical records like those in Figure 1A yielded values of $0.2–1 \times 10^6$ $M^{-1}s^{-1}$ for the second-order rate constant of AM dissociation by ATP. This apparent second-order rate constant might correspond to k_{+1a} in Scheme 1 if k_{+2} is very fast, or it might correspond to the product $K_{1a} \cdot k_{+2}$ if k_{-1a} is comparable to k_{+2}. (K_i is the equilibrium constant of the ith reaction step; k_{+i} and k_{-i} are the rate constants for the forward and reverse reactions.) In the latter case the initial ATP binding (step 1) reaches an equilibrium early in the transient. In principle k_{+2} could be estimated if the detachment rate reached a plateau at high ATP concentrations, but no such plateau has been observed; the detachment rate increases with ATP concentration up to at least 1 mM (31, 32).

Ca^{2+} has little effect on the rate of ATP-induced cross-bridge detachment at free Ca^{2+} concentrations between 10^{-8} M and 3×10^{-5} M. This observation indicates that steps 1 and 2 are not controlled by the Ca^{2+} regulatory system (31, 32). When rigor fibers were stretched one second before the laser pulse to raise tension to the level maintained by actively contracting fibers, the rate of ATP-induced detachment increased ~50% (31). This relatively small effect may be due to a change of k_{+1a} or k_{+2}. Since the kinetics of ATP-induced detachment are partially limited by the rate of ATP release from caged ATP, the true effect of stretch on detachment rate may be greater than observed experimentally.

Many other estimates are available in the literature for the rate constant of ATP-induced cross-bridge dissociation in skinned muscle fibers (10, 23, 24, 27, 52, 53). The conditions and methods of these experiments varied extensively, but most of the studies focused on a mechanical parameter that decreases as ATP concentration is lowered. This approach to estimating detachment rate is based on the assumption that the observed mechanical parameter will be limited by the rate of ATP binding if the ATP concentration is sufficiently low. Shortening velocity (10, 24), steady-state ATPase rate (27), and the force response after step (23) or sinusoidal (52, 53) length perturbations all suggest apparent rate constants for ATP binding in the range 0.2–3×10^6 $M^{-1}s^{-1}$. This range of values is similar to that observed using caged ATP photolysis. The agreement of the results obtained with different methods strongly suggests that these experiments do measure cross-bridge detachment. The similarity of the results using shortening velocity (10, 24) and small length perturbations in fibers supporting maximum load (23, 52, 53) indicates that cross-bridge stress or strain and sliding velocity do not markedly affect ATP-induced detachment.

An unusually low value for ATP-induced dissociation of AM (4–8×10^3 $M^{-1}s^{-1}$) was obtained by Cooke & Bialek (10) from the decline of isometric tension as ATP concentration was raised from 50 μM to the millimolar range. This decline has been reported in many studies (3, 5, 24, 31), but its relationship to the rapid binding of ATP, inferred from photolysis experiments and the other mechanical studies, is not straightforward. Cooke & Bialek postulated a detailed model in which cross-bridges are detached rapidly by ATP only within a limited range of strain values.

In vitro, ATP-induced dissociation of AM is measured by a decrease of solution turbidity or fluorescence from pyrene-labelled actin when actomyosin subfragment 1 (S-1) or acto-heavy meromyosin is mixed with ATP in a rapid reaction apparatus. In solution, ATP dissociates the myosin heads from actin with a second-order rate constant of 1–3×10^6 $M^{-1}s^{-1}$ (68, 84); these values are only 2–5 times faster than the corresponding rates measured in muscle fibers. When the proteins are packed into the filament lattice of a muscle fiber, the rate of this step is not greatly affected.

The rate of dissociation of AM by ATP during a normal contraction can be estimated by multiplying the second-order rate constant for dissociation (2×10^5 $M^{-1}s^{-1}$) by the normal intracellular Mg-ATP concentration (5×10^{-3} M), which gives 10^3 s^{-1}. This value is much too great to be rate-limiting in the cross-bridge cycle in which a myosin head splits ATP once every 0.3–1.5 s. Each time the head reaches the AM state, ATP binds and dissociates the cross-bridge in approximately 1 ms ($1/10^3$ s^{-1}).

ATP HYDROLYSIS STEP

Ferenczi and coworkers measured the kinetics of ATP cleavage in muscle fibers (22, 26). In these experiments ATP was released from caged ATP within single fibers in rigor, as discussed above, but the reaction was quenched by freezing the fibers between liquid N_2–cooled copper blocks.

The caged ATP was radioactive, so the time course of ADP production within the fiber could be measured by liquid scintillation counting following HPLC separation of the nucleotides. This analysis showed that when ATP was released from caged ATP, it was initially cleaved at a rate much higher than the steady rate. The initial "burst" of ADP formation amounted to approximately one ADP molecule per myosin head in the fiber, which indicates that reactions 3d and/or 3a (Scheme 1) are much faster than the rate-determining step. A value of 40–60 s^{-1} was obtained at 12°C and no Ca^{2+}, which corresponds to the sum $(k_{+3d} + k_{-3d})$ or $(k_{+3a} + k_{-3a})$.

Whether the cleavage reaction proceeds while myosin is attached to actin (step 3a) or following detachment (steps 2 and 3d) is not presently known. In experiments with isolated actomyosin, both reaction paths are significant, particularly at high actin concentrations, which are analogous to the conditions within the filament lattice (8). An initial burst of ADP formation is also seen in studies with the isolated proteins. When ATPase activity is initiated abruptly, myosin and actomyosin cleave the first mole of ATP at a more rapid rate than the steady-state conditions (64).

Is ATP hydrolysis reversible? Reaction steps −3d and −3a (reformation of ATP from protein-bound ADP and P_i) can be probed by studying the exchange of oxygen atoms between $M \cdot ADP \cdot P_i$ and the solvent, as shown in Figure 2. An atom of solvent water is incorporated into the bound P_i on ATP

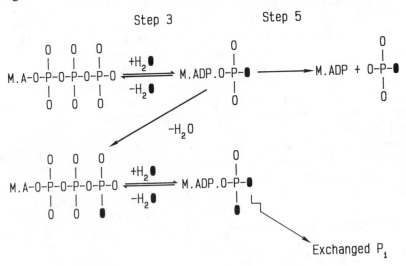

Figure 2 Mechanism of oxygen exchange between $M \cdot ADP \cdot P_i$ and solvent. The reaction numbers correspond to those of Scheme 1. On hydrolysis (step 3) a labelled solvent oxygen (●) is incorporated into protein-bound P_i. On reformation of ATP (−3) either the same oxygen atom (●) or an unlabelled oxygen (O; downward arrow) is lost to the solvent. Product P_i contains 1–4 labelled oxygen atoms, and the distribution among these isotopes depends on k_5/k_{-3}.

hydrolysis (step 3), but a different oxygen atom can be lost to the solvent on reformation of ATP (step -3, downward arrow). Although it is tightly bound, the P_i in M·ADP·P_i can apparently rotate in its binding site because all four oxygen atoms have a significant probability of being released. Further hydrolysis and ATP reformation steps incorporate more solvent oxygen atoms into the P_i that is finally released to the medium. If the reaction is carried out in solvent enriched in the stable water isotope, $H_2^{18}O$, mass spectrometry of the product P_i indicates the extent of oxygen exchange between solvent and P_i in the M·ADP·P_i intermediate. Numerically, a ratio (R) of the rate of P_i release to the rate of reformation of ATP is determined from the mass spectral distribution. For myosin in the absence of actin (lower line of Scheme 1) $R = k_{5d}/k_{-3d}$ (81). For Scheme 1 including actin, $R = k_{5a}·K_4/(k_{-3a}·K_4 + k_{-3d})$ (80).

Experiments on relaxed muscle fibers showed extensive oxygen exchange, which indicates that multiple reversals of the hydrolysis step occur before P_i release (45). The isotope distributions could not be explained by a single pathway (as in Figure 2) but could be adequately described by two components of product P_i with different values of R. The mechanism of this apparent multiplicity of oxygen exchange pathways is not clear, but in relaxed fibers, contaminating ATPases that undergo little oxygen exchange, such as sarcoplasmic reticulum Ca-ATPase or mitochondrial ATPase, possibly contribute. The major component (75%) of the ATPase flux, amounting to an ATPase rate of 0.1 s^{-1} per myosin head, had an R value of 0.015. If P_i release (step 5d) from M·ADP·P_i is assumed to be rate limiting for the overall ATPase, then $k_{-3d} = 0.1/0.015 = 7$ s^{-1}, a value very similar to that found in isolated myosin S-1 (81).

In Ca^{2+}-activated fibers the intermediate oxygen exchange was much less. This finding indicates that attachment of M·ADP·P_i to actin promotes P_i release during contraction (45). The major flux pathway had a high R value (approximately 2.3), which suggests that P_i is often released before steps 3d and 3a can reverse at all. A reversible hydrolysis step and acceleration of P_i release by actin occur in isolated myosin and actomyosin (81). The oxygen exchange experiments provide strong evidence that these events characterize the chemistry of the contractile proteins in muscle fibers as well.

FORCE GENERATION

The term driving stroke is used here as an abbreviation for "structural change in actomyosin leading to a force-generating state" without reference to whether or not external work is done. Although it is commonly assumed that a tilting motion of the myosin head stretches an elastic part of subfragment 2 in an isometric contraction, evidence for such a tilting motion is presently inconclusive. The accompanying chapter by Thomas (78) treats such structural questions in detail.

The nature of the coupling between chemical reactions and the structural change is not known either. The driving stroke may correspond directly to one or several of the chemical reactions. Alternatively, the relationship may be a reciprocal interaction in which a chemical step allows a mechanical event to proceed, which in turn allows the next chemical step to occur. A. F. Huxley (48) has discussed the latter possibility using an analogy to a clock escapement, in which a main spring powers the motions, but the remainder of the mechanical events regulate the rate of energy liberation. During muscle contractions the chemical events power the mechanical and structural changes; but the Fenn effect (increased energy liberation during active shortening) implies that energy liberation is regulated by cross-bridge stress or strain or filament sliding. Several lines of evidence discussed below link P_i release from $AM \cdot ADP \cdot P_i$ with the driving stroke. However, determining whether the mechanical and structural events alternate with biochemical reactions, like a clock escapement, or whether the chemical step corresponds directly to the structural change is a major challenge.

If a reaction model like:

$$rigor + ATP \rightarrow detached \rightarrow active$$

is fit to experimental traces such as those of Figure 1A, numerical values are obtained for cross-bridge detachment and reattachment with force generation. In rabbit psoas fibers at 20°C the rate of the latter reaction averages 80 s^{-1}(32), a value somewhat higher than that obtained using an abrupt mechanical stretch perturbation (7). In the caged ATP experiments, the rate of cross-bridge reattachment with force generation does not appreciably depend on ATP concentration (32), whereas detachment of cross-bridges from the rigor state is sensitive to ATP concentration, as discussed earlier. These features are consistent with the biochemical Scheme 1 detailed in the introduction. The experimentally observed reattachment and force generation presumably involve steps 3d, 4, and 5a and also depend on the rates of steps −5a and −4, as discussed below.

The rapidity of cross-bridge detachment from AM and reattachment into force-generating states might lead to the expectation that practically all of the cross-bridges would populate $AM' \cdot ADP$ or $AM \cdot ADP$ during active contractions. But x-ray diffraction (41, 66), mechanical stiffness (34, 85), and spectroscopic probe data (78) imply that a significant proportion (20–80%) of the cross-bridges are detached during contractions. These findings can be reconciled if reversibility of reactions 2, 3, 4, and 5a in Scheme 1 allows population of $M \cdot ATP$ and $M \cdot ADP \cdot P_i$ during steady contractions.

P_i RELEASE AND REBINDING

The rate of release of P_i from $M \cdot ADP \cdot P_i$ or $AM \cdot ADP \cdot P_i$ has not been directly measured in muscle fibers. The oxygen exchange experiments discussed above indicate that in relaxed muscle fibers the rate of P_i release is low compared to the rate of reversal of ATP hydrolysis. By analogy to isolated myosin, breakdown of $M \cdot ADP \cdot P_i$ to $M \cdot ADP$ is probably slow enough to determine the ATPase rate in relaxed fibers. k_{5d} would then be $\sim 0.1 \ s^{-1}$, which is consistent with the rate of step 5d in myosin. However, the metabolic rate of resting intact muscle indicates a much lower myosin ATPase rate than that of skinned muscle fibers or isolated myosin (58). Thus isolation of the myosin and skinning of the fibers do modify the ATPase reaction (25, 83). As discussed above, the intermediate oxygen exchange data suggest that in active contractions P_i release from $AM \cdot ADP \cdot P_i$ is faster than from $M \cdot ADP \cdot P_i$. Several observations from caged ATP experiments suggested to us that P_i release is closely linked to the driving stroke (43). When a fiber is switched from rigor to active contraction by photolysis of caged ATP, if a steady 10-mM concentration of P_i is included in the medium, the active force is reduced but the steady-tension value is reached earlier than in the absence of P_i (Figure 1B). This increase of the rate constant was a new observation, but the reduction of active force generation by P_i had been previously reported (4, 42) and has been confirmed by a number of groups (2, 12, 28, 54, 56).

Following perturbation of a dynamic system, the observed approach to a new distribution of intermediates generally indicates the *sum* of the forward and reverse rate constants of the elementary step leading to the observed state. The intermediate detected in a tension recording, such as that shown in Figure 1B, is the active force-generating state, so the faster approach to a lower tension value suggests that 10-mM P_i accelerates reversal of the driving stroke. If P_i binding to $AM' \cdot ADP$ (step $-5a$) reverses the driving stroke, then P_i release is linked, either directly or in the manner of a clock escapement, to the forward driving stroke. The approach to the steady-tension value (sum of forward and reverse reaction rates) would occur more rapidly in 10-mM P_i because the reverse reaction rate is increased.

Measurements of oxygen exchange between the solvent and ^{18}O-labelled P_i in the medium confirmed that P_i binds to the active site during contractions (80). P_i also decreases the steady ATPase rate, but this decrease is less than the decrease in force (55, 80, but see 2). The second-order rate constant for step $-5a$ estimated from the experiments using ^{18}O exchange ($\sim 5 \times 10^2$ $M^{-1}s^{-1}$) is less than that estimated from the caged ATP mechanical experiments ($1.5-10 \times 10^3 \ M^{-1}s^{-1}$). This apparent discrepancy may indicate an interesting stress or strain dependence of the reaction rates. The mechanical measurements reflect those cross-bridges producing the most force, whereas biochemical measurements of ^{18}O exchange and ATPase rate include cross-bridges under a wide range of strains (44, 80).

Another effect of adding P_i to the medium in photolysis experiments is a dramatic acceleration of relaxation from rigor when ATP is liberated from caged ATP in the absence of Ca^{2+} (43). Detachment of rigor cross-bridges does not seem to be affected by P_i, but some detached cross-bridges reattach to the thin filament and produce active force even in the absence of Ca^{2+} (30, 31). P_i may speed relaxation by binding to AM'·ADP (step −5a), reversing the driving stroke and allowing reversal of cross-bridge attachment (step −4). If this idea applies to intact muscle, relaxation after electrical stimulation may involve reversal of steps 4 and 5 instead of ADP release and binding of another ATP molecule. This mechanism would save a significant amount of energy for the cell and allow quick relaxation of a muscle twitch without requiring a rapid isometric cycling rate. However, this speculation remains to be tested.

The reduction of active isometric tension in skinned fibers by P_i is compatible with reversal of the driving stroke, and the reduction of force in fatigued skeletal muscle (12, 19, 28, 59) or ischemic heart muscle (1, 28) may be due partly to P_i accumulation. Shortening velocity does not seem to be influenced by P_i (12), which suggests that reactions at the end of the working stroke during filament sliding are not affected by changes of P_i concentration.

The dynamic mechanical state of muscle fibers can be characterized by imposition of small sinusoidal length changes and analysis of the resulting tension oscillations (52, 53). There is a characteristic frequency at which an activated muscle fiber produces net work during its cyclic length change. The optimum frequency for oscillatory work production and the magnitude of work per cycle are increased when P_i concentration is raised from 0 to 10 mM (42, 54, 55). This interesting result is not expected on the basis of Scheme 1 and has been discussed in terms of branched or alternative pathways for ATP hydrolysis when the filaments slide (55). This effect may be important if it elucidates a marked stress or strain dependence of the chemical and mechanical reaction pathway.

In isolated actomyosin, the free-energy drop associated with P_i release from AM·ADP·P_i is a substantial proportion (~50%) of the total free energy liberated by ATP hydrolysis; thus the postulated linkage of P_i release to the driving stroke is reasonable. In solution, the equilibrium of step 5a is far toward AM'·ADP + P_i. However, in a fiber if AM'·ADP bears more force than AM·ADP·P_i, then the mechanical component of free energy would shift K_{5a} toward AM·ADP·P_i. In that case P_i could bind to AM'·ADP more easily in a fiber than in solution. Oxygen exchange measurements support this prediction but the rate of P_i binding to AM'·ADP in actomyosin S-1 was only about fivefold lower than in fibers (87).

Comparison of mechanical and x-ray diffraction results between "weak" and "strong" binding actomyosin complexes, discussed in the accompanying chapter by Brenner (6), leads to a conclusion similar to that reached here: Strong binding states (AM'·ADP to AM) bear the force during steady contractions.

ADP RELEASE AND REBINDING

White and coworkers (75) noted a close correlation between the maximum shortening velocity (V_{max}) and the rate of ADP release from AM·ADP in muscle types that contract with a wide range of speeds. If V_{max} is given as relative sliding velocity between thick and thin filaments and the maximum attachment range of the cross-bridge is assumed to be 10 nm of filament sliding, the maximum duration (t_{max}) of attachment between a cross-bridge and a particular actin monomer is equal to 10 nm/V_{max}. Rabbit psoas fibers shorten at $V_{max} \approx 4$ μm/sec per half sarcomere (70), giving $t_{max} = 2.5$ ms. If Scheme 1 applies, then ADP release and ATP binding must occur within this time. In rabbit skeletal myosin S-1, ADP is released from AM·ADP (k_{9a}) faster than 400 s^{-1}, which is compatible with a 2.5-ms duration of attachment. In myosin from slower tissues such as cardiac and smooth muscle, k_{9a} is correspondingly lower. These findings raise the possibility that ADP release controls V_{max}.

The dissociation constant of ADP for AM ($1/K_{9a}$ in Scheme 1) is about 200 μM with rabbit skeletal actomyosin S-1 (38) or myofibrils (50). Measurements of the force-velocity curve in skinned psoas fibers indicate that shortening velocity decreases as the ADP concentration is raised (12). ADP acts as a competitive inhibitor of ATP-induced detachment with an inhibition constant of 200–300 μM (12). Mechanical analysis using sinusoidal length changes gave compatible results (54).

The rate of ADP binding to AM, k_{-9a} of Scheme 1, can be estimated from the product $k_{9a} \cdot K_{9a} = k_{-9a}$. Although this relationship may not be valid for ligands that induce muscle elongation (e.g. AMPPNP, pyrophosphate) (73), ADP causes little if any elongation (14). If k_{9a} is taken to be 500 s^{-1} and $1/K_{9a}$ to be 200 μM, k_{-9a} is 2.5×10^6 M^{-1}s^{-1}; this value is similar to the rate constant for ATP binding to AM. Note that AM·ADP may not be on the pathway of ATP hydrolysis if AM'·ADP can dissociate directly to AM (44).

The kinetics of ADP release can also be detected by measuring cross-bridge detachment upon photolysis of caged ATP in the presence of steady concentrations of ADP (17). Since there is only one nucleotide binding site per myosin head, ADP must dissociate before ADP binds. Experiments using a range of ADP concentrations in the presence of Ca^{2+} indicated the dissociation constant for ADP with AM is ~250 μM (17). This value agrees with that found in other mechanical studies. No major dependence on cross-bridge strain was detected. The shape of the transients following photolysis suggested that cross-bridges do not detach fully with ADP present. In contrast, a reduced ATP concentration yields transients that suggest slower but full detachment. This finding with ADP was unexpected and may indicate an interaction between the two heads of myosin. When one head has ADP bound, it may prevent normal ATP-induced detachment of the other. Another possibility is that the actin monomers available to a detached head for reattachment may be limited if its partner is in the AM·ADP state.

In the absence of Ca^{2+}, relaxation following caged ATP photolysis had a complex time course when ADP was present. Tension declined only slightly during the 50–70 ms period following ATP release. Tension then suddenly decreased to the relaxed level (15). Whether ADP was released from AM·ADP at the beginning or end of this 50–70 ms period is not known, but the experiments open the possibility that ADP release is controlled by the Ca^{2+} regulatory system. Relaxation of intact muscle after tetanic stimulation also shows a sharp break between slow and fast phases (9, 49), so these results with caged ATP may bear on the biochemical events during physiological relaxation.

P_i AND NUCLEOTIDE ANALOGS

These compounds have the potential to reveal structural, chemical, and kinetic aspects of the mechanism by imitating well-defined states in the normal mechanism. Two analogs that have been useful in kinetic studies on muscle fibers are discussed here: the nucleotide analog, ϵ-ATP, and the P_i analog, V_i.

ϵ-ATP is a fluorescent derivative of ATP that interacts with myosin and actomyosin like ATP, but the elementary hydrolysis step (3d and/or 3a) of the ATPase pathway is much slower with ϵ-ATP (74). When psoas muscle fibers are relaxed by photolysis of caged ϵ-ATP in the absence of Ca^{2+}, the initial tension rise observed with ATP (30, 31) is markedly suppressed, which suggests that following detachment, hydrolysis of the triphosphate normally precedes reattachment (16). Polarization of ϵ-ATP fluorescence has been used by Yanagida and coworkers (86 and references therein) to measure the angular orientation of nucleotide bound to myosin and actin in muscle fibers, as discussed in the accompanying chapter by Thomas (78).

Fluorescence intensities of related compounds, ϵ-2-aza-ATP and ϵ-2-aza-ADP, are enhanced $\sim$12-fold and $\sim$5-fold, respectively, on binding to heavy meromyosin (HMM) or acto-HMM (71). The fluorescence intensity from bound nucleotide is enhanced $\sim$12-fold in muscle fibers relaxed or contracting in the presence of ϵ-2-aza-ATP and is enhanced $\sim$5-fold in rigor with added ϵ-2-aza-ADP. These observations led to the conclusion that the predominant state of a force-generating cross-bridge is AM·ADP·P_i (71), which conflicts with the interpretation given above that AM'·ADP generates force. However, 10-mM P_i does not decrease steady, active tension in ϵ-ATP (with Ca^{2+}) or accelerate relaxation following photolysis of caged ϵ-ATP (in the absence of Ca^{2+}; 16) as occurs with ATP. A possible explanation of these different conclusions is that AM'·ϵ-ADP or AM'·ϵ-2-aza-ADP is not highly populated when ϵ-ATP or ϵ-2-aza-ATP is the substrate, in which case P_i would not bind. This situation points out a potential problem with analog studies: The cross-bridge cycle with an analog may not correspond exactly to the physiological reaction with ATP. However, such kinetic differences and unique properties of analogs can be used to advantage in probing particular reaction steps.

Orthovanadate (V_i) acts as an analog of P_i in solution, binding tightly to M·ADP or AM·ADP and forming a stable M·ADP·V_i complex (35). Experiments on skinned psoas fibers with isotopically labelled V_i and ADP showed that M·ADP·V_i is stable on the time scale of hours (14). V_i seemed to bind only during cross-bridge cycling, not in rigor, rigor with ADP, or relaxation. These observations indicate that V_i binds to AM'·ADP (14, 65). Earlier experiments in which insect muscle fibers in rigor were relaxed by ADP and V_i (36) might be explained if a low concentration of ATP contaminated the ADP stock. The experiments on rabbit fibers showing that V_i does not bind in the rigor condition with ADP suggest that AM·ADP formed from AM plus ADP is a different state from AM'·ADP formed during cross-bridge cycling. However, this conclusion is not definitive because the fiber supports more force during active contractions than in rigor, and it is possible that the mechanical strain would increase the free energy of AM·ADP enough to bind V_i or P_i. V_i binding to AM'·ADP during cross-bridge cycling provides strong evidence that in fibers, product dissociation from AM·ADP·P_i is ordered as in Scheme 1: P_i dissociates before ADP.

A review by Goody & Holmes (37) emphasized structural and biochemical results with the ATP analog, AMPPNP. The recent improvement of chemical synthetic techniques, mentioned above in the discussion of caged compounds, should enable determination of the interaction kinetics of actomyosin in fibers with AMPPNP (J. W. Walker, M. Yamakawa, D. R. Trentham, and Y. E. Goldman, unpublished data) or other nucleotide analogs.

SUMMARY

Many characteristics expected from the cyclic ATPase mechanism of Scheme 1 are apparent in reactions measured directly in muscle fibers. ATP detaches rigor cross-bridges rapidly. Reattachment and force generation are also rapid compared to the overall cycling rate, but reversibility of many of the reactions allows significant population of detached states during contraction. ATP hydrolysis shows rapid, "burst" kinetics and is also readily reversible. P_i is released before ADP in the cycle. P_i release is slow in relaxed fibers but is promoted by the interaction between myosin and actin during contraction.

Actomyosin kinetics differ in fibers from the ATPase reaction in solution in that P_i binds more readily to AM'·ADP in fibers, and complex, Ca^{2+}-dependent kinetics are evident for ADP release. These properties suggest that the mechanical driving stroke of the cross-bridge cycle and events during physiological relaxation are closely linked to the product release steps.

All of the reactions, except step 7a, in the main pathway for ATP hydrolysis, indicated in Scheme 1 by heavy arrows, are fast compared to the overall cycling rate in isometric contractions. Based on this finding, we expect step 7a (or isomerizations of the flanking states) to be relatively slow (~ 3 s^{-1}). But neither the rate-limiting reaction, nor the expected major dependence on mechanical load or shortening that would explain the Fenn effect, have actually been detected. Use of the pulse photolysis and oxygen exchange methods with structural and spectroscopic techniques and with perturbations of mechanical strain promise to reveal these aspects of the mechanism.

ACKNOWLEDGMENTS

I am grateful to Drs. R. Cooke, M. A. Greeves, A. P. Somlyo, and D. R. Trentham for helpful comments on the manuscript. This work was supported by the Muscular Dystrophy Association and National Institutes of Health grants HL15835 to the Pennsylvania Muscle Institute and AM26846.

Literature Cited

1. Allen, D. G., Morris, P. G., Orchard, C. H., Pirolo, J. S. 1985. A nuclear magnetic resonance study of metabolism in the ferret heart during hypoxia and inhibition of glycolysis. *J. Physiol. London* 361:185–204

2. Altringham, J. D., Johnston, I. A. 1985. Effects of phosphate on the contractile properties of fast and slow muscle fibres from an antarctic fish. *J. Physiol. London* 368:491–500

3. Arata, T., Mukohata, Y., Tonomura, Y. 1977. Structure and function of the two heads of the myosin molecule. *J. Biochem.* 82:801–12

4. Brandt, P. W., Cox, R. N., Kawai, M., Robinson, T. 1982. Regulation of tension in skinned muscle fibers: Effect of cross-bridge kinetics on apparent Ca^{2+} sensitivity. *J. Gen. Physiol.* 79:997–1016

5. Brandt, P. W., Reuben, J. P., Grundfest, H. 1972. Regulation of tension in the skinned crayfish muscle fiber II. Role of calcium. *J. Gen. Physiol.* 59:305–17

6. Brenner, B. 1987. Mechanical and structural approaches in correlating cross-bridge action in muscle with actomyosin ATPase in solution. *Ann. Rev. Physiol.* 49:655–72

7. Brenner, B., Eisenberg, E. 1986. Rate of force generation in muscle: Correlation with actomyosin ATPase activity in solution. *Proc. Natl. Acad. Sci. USA* 83:3542–46

8. Brenner, B., Yu, L. C., Greene, L. E., Eisenberg, E., Schoenberg, M. 1986. Ca^{2+}-sensitive crossbridge dissociation in the presence of MgPPi in skinned rabbit psoas fibers. *Biophys. J.* In press

9. Cannell, M. B. 1986. Effect of tetanus

duration on the free calcium during the relaxation of frog skeletal muscle fibres. *J. Physiol. London* 376:203–18

10. Cooke, R., Bialek, W. 1979. Contraction of glycerinated muscle fibers as a function of the ATP concentration. *Biophys. J.* 28:241–58

11. Cooke, R., Franks, K. 1980. All myosin heads form bonds with actin in rigor rabbit skeletal muscle. *Biochemistry* 19:2265–69

12. Cooke, R., Pate, E. 1985. The effects of ADP and phosphate on the contraction of muscle fibers. *Biophys. J.* 48:789–98

13. Curtin, N. A., Gilbert, C., Kretzschmar, K. M., Wilkie, D. R. 1974. The effect of the performance of work on total energy output and metabolism during muscular contraction. *J. Physiol. London* 238:455–72

14. Dantzig, J. A., Goldman, Y. E. 1985. Suppression of muscle contraction by vanadate: Mechanical and ligand binding studies on glycerol-extracted rabbit fibers. *J. Gen. Physiol.* 86:305–27

15. Dantzig, J. A., Hibberd, M. G., Goldman, Y. E., Trentham, D. R. 1984. ADP slows cross-bridge detachment rate induced by photolysis of caged ATP in rabbit psoas muscle fibers. *Biophys. J.* 45:8a

16. Dantzig, J. A., Trentham, D. R., Goldman, Y. E. 1985. Mechanics of muscle contraction and relaxation in ε-ATP and caged ε-ATP. *Biophys. J.* 47:25a

17. Dantzig, J. A., Trentham, D. R., Goldman, Y. E. 1986. Kinetics of activation of skeletal muscle fibers by photolysis of caged ATP in the presence of MgADP. *Biophys. J.* 49:268a

18. Dawson, M. J., Gadian, D. G., Wilkie, D. R. 1978. Muscular fatigue investigated by phosphorus nuclear magnetic resonance. *Nature* 274:861–66

19. Dawson, M. J., Smith, S., Wilkie, D. R. 1986. The $[H_2PO_4^{1-}]$ may determine cross-bridge cycling rate and force production in living fatiguing muscle. *Biophys. J.* 49:268a

20. Dydyńska, M., Wilkie, D. R. 1966. The chemical and energetic properties of muscles poisoned with fluordinitrobenzene. *J. Physiol. London* 184:751–69

21. Eisenberg, E., Hill, T. L. 1985. Muscle contraction and free energy transduction in biological systems. *Science* 227:999–1006

22. Ferenczi, M. A. 1986. Phosphate burst in permeable muscle fibers of the rabbit. *Biophys. J.* 50:471–77

23. Ferenczi, M. A., Goldman, Y. E., Ron-dinone, J. F., Simmons, R. M. 1980. Mechanical transients in frog skinned muscle fibers at low magnesium adenosine triphosphate concentrations. *Fed. Proc.* 39:1962

24. Ferenczi, M. A., Goldman, Y. E., Simmons, R. M. 1984. The dependence of force and shortening velocity on substrate concentration in skinned muscle fibres from *Rana temporaria*. *J. Physiol. London* 350:519–43

25. Ferenczi, M. A., Homsher, E., Simmons, R. M., Trentham, D. R. 1978. Reaction mechanism of the magnesium ion–dependent adenosine triphosphatase of frog muscle myosin and subfragment 1. *Biochem. J.* 171:165–75

26. Ferenczi, M. A., Homsher, E., Trentham, D. R. 1984. The kinetics of magnesium adenosine triphophate cleavage in skinned muscle fibres of the rabbit. *J. Physiol. London* 352:575–99

27. Glyn, H., Sleep, J. 1985. Dependence of adenosine triphosphatase activity of rabbit psoas muscle fibres and myofibrils on substrate concentration. *J. Physiol. London* 365:259–76

28. Godt, R. E., Fender, K. J., Shirley, G. C., Nosek, T. M. 1985. Contractile failure with fatigue or hypoxia: Studies with skinned skeletal and cardiac muscle fibers. *Biophys. J.* 47:293a

29. Goldman, Y. E. 1985. Laser pulsed release of ATP and other optical methods in the study of muscle contraction. In *Optical Methods in Cell Physiology*, ed. P. De Weer, B. M. Salzberg, pp. 397–415. New York: Wiley. 480 pp.

30. Goldman, Y. E., Hibberd, M. G., McCray, J. A., Trentham, D. R. 1982. Relaxation of muscle fibres by photolysis of caged ATP. *Nature* 300:701–5

31. Goldman, Y. E., Hibberd, M. G., Trentham, D. R. 1984. Relaxation of rabbit psoas muscle fibres from rigor by photochemical generation of adenosine 5'-triphosphate. *J. Physiol. London* 354:577–604

32. Goldman, Y. E., Hibberd, M. G., Trentham, D. R. 1984. Initiation of active contraction by photogeneration of adenosine 5'-triphosphate in rabbit psoas muscle fibres. *J. Physiol. London* 354:605–24

33. Goldman, Y. E., Reid, G. P., Somlyo, A. P., Somlyo, A. V., Trentham, D. R., Walker, J. W. 1986. Activation of skinned vascular smooth muscle by photolysis of "caged inositol trisphosphate" to inositol 1,4,5-trisphosphate $(InsP_3)$. *J. Physiol. London* 377:100P

34. Goldman, Y. E., Simmons, R. M.

1977. Active and rigor muscle stiffness. *J. Physiol. London* 269:55P–57P

35. Goodno, C. C., Taylor, E. W. 1982. Inhibition of actomyosin ATPase by vanadate. *Proc. Natl. Acad. Sci. USA* 79:21–25

36. Goody, R. S., Hofmann, W., Reedy, M. K., Magid, A., Goodno, C. 1980. Relaxation of glycerinated insect flight muscle by vanadate. *J. Musc. Res. Cell. Motil.* 1:198–99

37. Goody, R. S., Holmes, K. C. 1983. Cross-bridges and the mechanism of muscle contraction. *Biochim. Biophys. Acta* 726:13–39

38. Greene, L. E., Eisenberg, E. 1980. Dissociation of the actin·subfragment 1 complex by adenyl-5'-yl imidodiphosphate, ADP, and PP_i. *J. Biol. Chem.* 255:543–48

39. Gurney, A. M., Lester, H. A. 1986. Light-flash physiology with synthetic photosensitive compounds. *Physiol. Rev.* In press

40. Güth, K., Junge, J. 1982. Low Ca^{2+} impedes cross-bridge detachment in chemically skinned *Taenia coli. Nature* 300:775–76

41. Haselgrove, J. C., Huxley, H. E. 1973. X-ray evidence for radial cross-bridge movement and for the sliding filament model in actively contracting skeletal muscle. *J. Mol. Biol.* 77:549–68

42. Herzig, J. W., Peterson, J. W., Rüegg, J. C., Solaro, R. J. 1981. Vanadate and phosphate ions reduce tension and increase cross-bridge kinetics in chemically skinned heart muscle. *Biochim. Biophys. Acta* 672:191–96

43. Hibberd, M. G., Dantzig, J. A., Trentham, D. R., Goldman, Y. E. 1985. Phosphate release and force generation in skeletal muscle fibers. *Science* 228:1317–19

44. Hibberd, M. G., Trentham, D. R. 1986. Relationships between chemical and mechanical events during muscular contraction. *Ann. Rev. Biophys. Biophys. Chem.* 15:119–61

45. Hibberd, M. G., Webb, M. R., Goldman, Y. E., Trentham, D. R. 1985. Oxygen exchange between phosphate and water accompanies calcium-regulated ATPase activity of skinned fibers from rabbit skeletal muscle. *J. Biol. Chem.* 260:3496–3500

46. Homsher, E., Yamada, T., Wallner, A., Tsai, J. 1984. Energy balance studies in frog skeletal muscles shortening at one-half maximal velocity. *J. Gen. Physiol.* 84:347–59

47. Huxley, A. F. 1957. Muscle structure and theories of contraction. *Prog. Biophys.* 7:255–318

48. Huxley, A. F. 1980. *Reflections on Muscle*, pp. 91–96. Princeton: Princeton Univ. Press. 111 pp.

49. Huxley, A. F., Simmons, R. M., 1973. Mechanical transients and the origin of muscular force. *Cold Spring Harbor Symp. Quant. Biol.* 37:669–80

50. Johnson, R. E., Adams, P. H. 1984. ADP binds similarly to rigor muscle myofibrils and to actomyosin-subfragment one. *FEBS Lett.* 174:11–14

51. Kaplan, J. H., Forbush, B. III, Hoffman, J. F. 1978. Rapid photolytic release of adenosine 5'-triphosphate from a protected analogue: Utilization by the Na:K pump of human red blood cell ghosts. *Biochemistry* 17:1929–35

52. Kawai, M. 1979. Effect of MgATP on cross-bridge kinetics in chemically skinned rabbit psoas fibers as measured by sinusoidal analysis technique. In *Cross-Bridge Mechanism in Muscle Contraction*, ed. H. Sugi, G. H. Pollack, pp. 149–69. Baltimore: Univ. Park Press. 665 pp.

53. Kawai, M. 1982. Correlation between exponential processes and cross-bridge kinetics. In *Basic Biology of Muscles: A Comparative Approach. Soc. Gen. Physiol. Series*, ed. B. M. Trawog, R. J. C. Levine, M. M. Dewey, 37:109–30. New York: Raven. 406 pp.

54. Kawai, M. 1986. The role of orthophosphate in crossbridge kinetics in chemically skinned rabbit psoas fibres as detected with sinusoidal and step length alterations. *J. Musc. Res. Cell Motil.* 7:421–34

55. Kawai, M., Güth, K., Winnikes, K., Haist, C., Rüegg, J. C. 1986. The effect of inorganic phosphate on the ATP hydrolysis rate and the tension transients in chemically skinned rabbit psoas fibers. *Pflüg. Arch.* In press

56. Kentish, J. C. 1986. The effects of inorganic phosphate and creatine phosphate on force production in skinned muscles from rat ventricle. *J. Physiol. London* 370:585–604

57. Kushmerick, M. J., Davies, R. E. 1969. The chemical energetics of muscle contraction. II. The chemistry, efficiency and power of maximally working sartorius muscles. *Proc. R. Soc. London Ser. B* 174:315–53

58. Kushmerick, M. J., Paul, R. J. 1976. Aerobic recovery metabolism following a single isometric tetanus in frog sartorius muscle at 0°C. *J. Physiol. London* 254:693–709

59. Lacktis, J. W., Homsher, E. 1986. Inorganic phosphate inhibition of force in muscles. *Biophys. J.* 49:269a

60. Lester, H. A., Nerbonne, J. M. 1982. Physiological and pharmacological manipulations with light flashes. *Ann. Rev. Biophys. Bioeng.* 11:151–75

61. Levy, R. M., Umazume, Y., Kushmerick, M. J. 1976. Ca^{2+} dependence of tension and ADP production in segments of chemically skinned muscle fibers. *Biochim. Biophys. Acta* 430:352–65

62. Lovell, S. J., Knight, P. J., Harrington, W. F. 1981. Fraction of myosin heads bound to thin filaments in rigor fibrils from insect flight and vertebrate muscles. *Nature* 293:664–66

63. Loxdale, H. D., Tregear, R. T. 1985. Dissociation between mechanical performance and the cost of isometric tension maintenance in *Lethocerus* flight muscle. *J. Musc. Res. Cell Motil.* 6:163–75

64. Lymn, R. W., Taylor, E. W. 1971. Mechanism of adenosine triphosphate hydrolysis by actomyosin. *Biochemistry* 10:4617–24

65. Magid, A., Goodno, C. C. 1982. Inhibition of cross-bridge force by vanadate ion. *Biophys. J.* 37:107a

66. Matsubara, I., Yagi, N., Hashizume, H. 1975. Use of an X-ray television for diffraction of the frog striated muscle. *Nature* 255:728–29

67. McCray, J. A., Herbette, L., Kihara, T., Trentham, D. R. 1980. A new approach to time-resolved studies of ATP-requiring biological systems: Laser flash photolysis of caged ATP. *Proc. Natl. Acad. Sci. USA* 77:7237–41

68. Millar, N. C., Geeves, M. A. 1983. The limiting rate of the ATP-mediated dissociation of actin from rabbit skeletal muscle myosin subfragment 1. *FEBS Lett.* 160:141–48

69. Mornet, D., Bertrand, R., Pantel, P., Audemard, E., Kassab, R. 1981. Structure of the actin-myosin interface. *Nature* 292:301–6

70. Moss, R. L., 1986. Effects on shortening velocity of rabbit skeletal muscle due to variations in the level of thin filament activation. *J. Physiol. London* 377:487–505

71. Nagano, H., Yanagida, T. 1984. Predominant attached state of myosin crossbridges during contraction and relaxation at low ionic strength. *J. Mol. Biol.* 177:769–85

72. Nerbonne, J. M., Richard, S., Nargeot, J., Lester, H. A. 1984. New photoactivatable cyclic nucleotides produce intracellular jumps in cyclic AMP and cyclic GMP concentrations. *Nature* 310:74–76

73. Pate, E., Cooke, R. 1986. A model for the interaction of muscle cross-bridges with ligands which compete with ATP. *J. Theor. Biol.* 118:215–30

74. Rosenfeld, S. S., Taylor, E. W. 1984. Reactions of $1\text{-}N^6$-ethenoadenosine nucleotides with myosin subfragment 1 and acto-subfragment 1 of skeletal and smooth muscle. *J. Biol. Chem.* 259:11920–29

75. Siemankowski, R. F., Wiseman, M. O., White, H. D. 1985. ADP dissociation from actomyosin subfragment 1 is sufficiently slow to limit the unloaded shortening velocity in vertebrate muscle. *Proc. Natl. Acad. Sci. USA* 82:658–62

76. Somlyo, A. V., Somlyo, A. P., Goldman, Y. E., Fujimori, T., Bond, M., et al. 1986. Photolysis of caged nucleotides (ATP and CTP) for kinetic studies of vascular smooth muscle contraction. *J. Musc. Res. Cell Motil.* 7:380

77. Takashi, R., Putnam, S. 1979. A fluorimetric method for continuously assaying ATPase: Application to small specimens of glycerol-extracted muscle fibers. *Analyt. Biochem.* 92:375–82

78. Thomas, D. D. 1987. Spectroscopic probes of muscle cross-bridge action. *Ann. Rev. Physiol.* 49:691–709

79. Thomas, D. D., Cooke, R. 1980. Orientation of spin-labeled myosin heads in glycerinated muscle fibers. *Biophys. J.* 32:891–906

80. Webb, M. R., Hibberd, M. G., Goldman, Y. E., Trentham, D. R. 1986. Oxygen exchange between P_i in the medium and water during ATP hydrolysis mediated by skinned fibers from rabbit skeletal muscle: Evidence for P_i binding to a force-generating state. *J. Biol. Chem.* 261:15557–64

81. Webb, M. R., Trentham, D. R. 1981. The mechanism of ATP hydrolysis catalyzed by myosin and actomyosin, using rapid reaction techniques to study oxygen exchange. *J. Biol. Chem.* 256:10910–16

82. Weeds, A. G., Taylor, R. S. 1975. Separation of subfragment-1 isoenzymes from rabbit skeletal muscle myosin. *Nature* 257:54–56

83. Wells, C., Bagshaw, C. R. 1984. The Ca^{2+} sensitivity of the actin-activated ATPase of scallop heavy meromyosin. *FEBS Lett.* 168:260–64

84. White, H. D., Taylor, E. W. 1976. Energetics and mechanism of actomy-

osin adenosine triphosphatase. *Biochemistry* 15:5818–26

85. Yamamoto, T., Herzig, J. W. 1978. Series elastic properties of skinned muscle fibres in contraction and rigor. *Pflüg. Arch.* 373:21–24

86. Yanagida, T. 1984. Angles of fluorescently labelled myosin heads and actin monomers in contracting and rigor stained muscle fiber. In *Contractile*

Mechanisms in Muscle, ed. G. H. Pollack, H. Sugi, pp. 397–411. New York: Plenum. 921 pp.

87. Zimmerman, R., Webb, M. R., Trentham, D. R., Goldman, Y. E. 1986. Medium P_i-water oxygen exchange during ATP hydrolysis by actomyosin subfragment 1 from rabbit skeletal muscle: Reversible P_i binding to a bound ADP state. *Biophys. J.* 49:45a

Ann. Rev. Physiol. 1987. 49:655–72

MECHANICAL AND STRUCTURAL APPROACHES TO CORRELATION OF CROSS-BRIDGE ACTION IN MUSCLE WITH ACTOMYOSIN ATPase IN SOLUTION

Bernhard Brenner

Institute of Physiology II, University of Tübingen, D-7400 Tübingen, West Germany

INTRODUCTION AND SCOPE

Recent progress in analyzing the actomyosin ATPase with isolated proteins in solution has been summarized in kinetic schemes of this system (see the general introduction to this Special Topic section; 48, 52, 54, 56, 59). Eisenberg & Greene (19) and Eisenberg & Hill (20) applied the theoretical formalism of Hill (31) to correlate biochemical properties of the isolated proteins described in the kinetic schemes with physiological actomyosin cross-bridge properties like force and elasticity. This attempt to relate results of experiments in solution with cross-bridge action in muscle was based on the fundamental assumption that the properties of the isolated proteins in solution closely correlate with the behavior of cross-bridges in the organized contractile system.

In this article we review the results of mechanical and X-ray diffraction approaches that were used to test the assumption of a close correlation between the behavior of isolated actomyosin in solution and the behavior of cross-bridges in the organized contractile system. We also review experiments designed to test the implications of solution experiments for cross-bridge action in muscle. First, we summarize the experimental evidence that suggests there are two kinetically different groups of cross-bridge states in muscle fibers that have kinetic properties similar to those described for the

655

weak and strong binding states of the myosin fragments (subfragment 1, S-1, and heavy meromyosin, HMM) in solution. Second, we review evidence for structural differences between cross-bridges attached in the weak and strong binding states. Finally, we discuss the experiments designed to test the implications of the biochemical experiments on regulation of muscle and of the physiological significance of the rate-limiting step of the actomyosin ATPase.

Because of space limits, the scope of this review is confined to results of high-resolution mechanical experiments, used to characterize cross-bridge kinetics in muscle, and to X-ray diffraction experiments, used to examine cross-bridge attachment and the structure of different states of attached cross-bridges. For more comprehensive reviews of mechanical and X-ray diffraction experiments, the reader is referred to other articles on these subjects (e.g. 32, 33, 36, 53, 61). In this article we focus on results from skinned fibers from rabbit psoas muscle because most of the physiological experiments of interest were obtained on this preparation and actomyosin from rabbit fast skeletal muscle is the best characterized system for comparison with the physiological experiments.

PROPERTIES OF ISOLATED PROTEINS IN SOLUTION

Although some of the details are still under discussion (see the general introduction to this Special Topic section), all of the proposed kinetic schemes for the actomyosin ATPase cycle in solution have some common features: First, there are two groups of states. One group, the weak binding states (Figure 1 of the general introduction), is characterized by (a) low affinity of the myosin heads for actin (56), (b) a rapid equilibrium between association to and dissociation from actin (13, 56, 60), and (c) binding of the myosin heads to actin even in the absence of Ca^{2+} (13, 14, 57, 58). The other group, the strong binding states, is characterized by (a) a much higher affinity of the myosin heads for actin (23, 29, 39, 43, 60), (b) an equilibrium between association to and dissociation from actin but with a much slower rate of detachment than in the weak binding states (41, 60), and (c) Ca^{2+}-dependent, cooperative binding to actin (24). A second feature common to all of the biochemical kinetic schemes is that the rate-limiting reaction step occurs either before the transition (48, 54, 56) or is part of the transition from the weak binding states to the strong binding states (28, 59). Independent of its exact position in the pathway, the rate-limiting step controls the rate of the transition from the weak binding states to the strong binding states when the system is cycling. Third, a major mechanism of regulation appears to be the control of the rate of the transition from the weak binding states to the strong binding states since in the presence of MgATP and absence of Ca^{2+} S-1 and HMM bind to actin but do not show significant ATPase activity (13, 14, 57, 58).

Possible Implications for Cross-Bridge Action in Muscle

The assumption that the behavior of actomyosin in solution closely correlates with the behavior of cross-bridges in muscle has several implications for cross-bridge action (19, 20). In this regard, it was proposed that in muscle two groups of cross-bridge states exist, just as are found with myosin S-1 in solution, and that these two groups represent two different conformations of the myosin head. Furthermore, the cross-bridges were proposed to cycle between the two conformations while splitting ATP. It was suggested that in the myofilament lattice in muscle, the transition from the weak binding to the strong binding conformation, induced by phosphate release, causes deformation of the elastic cross-bridge, resulting in force generation or filament sliding. It was further suggested that rebinding of ATP induces the reverse transition and leads to negative force production for a brief period, which is followed by rapid detachment of deformed cross-bridges. According to this model, only the strong binding conformation significantly contributes to force generation and work production. Thus the mechanism that is rate limiting in solution and that determines the rate of the transition from the weak binding states to the strong binding states was postulated to control the rate of force generation in the cross-bridge cycle. Finally, based on the binding of S-1 or HMM to actin plus troponin and tropomyosin (regulated actin) under relaxing conditions (ATP, no Ca^{2+}), it was postulated that muscle is regulated not through cross-bridge attachment but rather through a subsequent kinetic step, possibly P_i release.

KINETIC PROPERTIES OF CROSS-BRIDGE STATES IN MUSCLE

Experimental Approaches

Using mechanical approaches, the extent of cross-bridge attachment to actin can be determined by studying the elastic properties (stiffness) of muscle fibers. Huxley & Simmons (34) and Ford et al (22) presented evidence that fiber stiffness, i.e. the instantaneous relation between force and relative filament sliding (Figure 1), is proportional to the number of attached cross-bridges. However, detachment, reattachment to less strained positions or transitions between different attached states possibly take place during the measurements and thereby affect the observed force and fiber stiffness. Thus, to determine the number of attached cross-bridges from fiber stiffness, the applied length changes have to be fast compared to the kinetics of detachment, reattachment, and transitions between attached states. If this condition is met, the observed fiber stiffness will not increase further when the speed of the applied length change is increased (7, 9, 21, 49).

There are two mechanical approaches to detection of rapid detachment and possible reattachment of cross-bridges. First, fiber stiffness can be measured as a function of the speed of the applied length change to determine over what range of speeds detachment and reattachment of cross-bridges can occur as the filaments slide (Figure 1; 7, 9, 50). Alternatively, when detachment is slow, e.g. in rigor or in the presence of MgPP$_i$ or AMPPNP, the decay of force following quick stretches can be used to characterize attachment and detachment kinetics (37, 51). In either of these approaches, the relative sliding of the filaments has to be measured at the level of the sarcomere. Significant differences between relative filament sliding and changes in overall fiber length might be introduced by elastic and nonelastic behavior of the fiber ends and, in fast measurements, by effects of the surrounding solution and fiber inertia.

As a second, independent method for obtaining information about the extent of cross-bridge attachment, X-ray diffraction patterns can be used. The mass associated with the actin filament, estimated from the equatorial reflections, was shown to provide information about cross-bridge attachment (10, 27, 35, 65). The equatorial reflections (12, 62, 64) and the actin- and myosin-based layer lines were recorded (44, 62) to study possible differences in the structure of attached cross-bridges in various states.

Evidence for Cross-Bridge States with Properties Similar to Those Described for the Weak Binding States in Solution

The weak binding states of S-1 or HMM in solution (see Figure 1 in the general introduction) are characterized by three major properties: (a) low affinity for actin (56), (b) binding to actin even in the absence of Ca^{2+} (13, 14, 57, 58), and (c) a rapid equilibrium between associated and dissociated states (13, 56). To test whether states with qualitatively similar properties can be found in muscle cross-bridges, the experimental conditions were choosen to give a pure population of such cross-bridge states with a significant fraction bound to actin. This approach allowed the characterization of actin affinity, attachment and detachment kinetics, and the structure of cross-bridges interacting with actin in the weak binding states. The work of Marston (40, 42) showed that in relaxed muscle fibers either ATP or the hydrolysis products (ADP + P$_i$) are bound to the cross-bridges. This suggests that the cross-bridge states in relaxed muscle are chemically equivalent to the weak binding states of the isolated proteins. Relaxed fibers were therefore used to characterize the kinetic properties of these chemical states in muscle.

EVIDENCE FOR CROSS-BRIDGE ATTACHMENT IN RELAXED FIBERS AT LOW IONIC STRENGTH   To optimize conditions for cross-bridge attachment in relaxed fibers, the first experiments were performed at an ionic strength of 0.02 M since in solution, the affinity of S-1 and HMM for regulated actin increases when ionic strength is lowered (14, 25).

Using single skinned rabbit psoas fibers, Brenner et al (9) showed that in the absence of Ca^{2+} these fibers are completely relaxed at 5°C and an ionic strength of 0.02 M; they do not develop active force, do not shorten actively, and have no unusual resting tension. However, when the fibers are stretched very rapidly under these conditions, they show 1/2 to 2/3 the stiffness observed in fully Ca^{2+}-activated fibers and up to about 1/2 the stiffness measured in rigor. Similar results, although initially interpreted differently, were reported by Yanagida et al (63). In addition, it was shown that the stiffness of relaxed fibers at low ionic strength is very closely proportional to the extent of filament overlap (9), i.e. it is proportional to the number of possible actin-myosin interactions. This finding suggests that the observed stiffness results from cross-bridge attachment.

Further independent evidence for cross-bridge attachment in relaxed fibers at low temperature and low ionic strength comes from equatorial X-ray diffraction patterns recorded from the same single skinned fiber preparation (12). Two-dimensional electron-density maps, reconstructed from the equatorial patterns recorded in relaxed fibers at low ionic strength (0.02 M), show much more mass associated with the actin filaments than can be accounted for by the actin filaments alone. The mass associated with the thin filaments in relaxed fibers is approximately as great as that in fully Ca^{2+}-activated fibers at the same temperature (12). Therefore, both stiffness and equatorial X-ray diffraction data are consistent with significant cross-bridge attachment in relaxed fibers at low ionic strength, which is analogous to the binding of S-1 or HMM to regulated actin under the same conditions.

ATTACHMENT AND DETACHMENT KINETICS IN RELAXED FIBERS AT LOW IONIC STRENGTH   The other typical feature of the weak binding states in solution is that the soluble myosin fragments rapidly achieve an equilibrium between association with and dissociation from actin (13, 56, 60).

To characterize the kinetics of cross-bridge detachment and reattachment, length changes of 5–10 nm per half-sarcomere were applied, and the effect of the speed of these length changes on fiber stiffness was determined (7, 9). Such measurements are illustrated in Figure 1. In fibers in rigor, stiffness

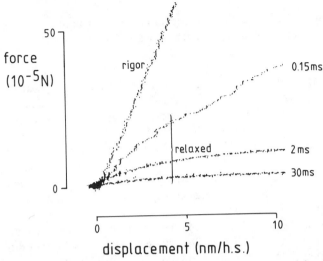

Figure 1   Stiffness of skinned rabbit psoas fibers when relaxed or in rigor and the effect of the speed of applied length changes. Force and changes in sarcomere length were recorded while the fiber was stretched from one end. Fiber stiffness is defined as the slope of each trace. Coordinates: the abscissa shows the amount of length change in nm half-sarcomere^{-1}; the ordinate shows the force in N. The temperature was 5°C and the ionic strength was 0.02 M for relaxed and 0.17 M for rigor conditions. The values shown next to the traces indicate the time required to stretch the fiber 5 nm/half-sarcomere beyond the resting length. Rigor stiffness was independent of the speed of stretch. (Reproduced from Reference 9.)

changed only by about 10–15% when the speed of the length change was varied over almost six orders of magnitude, up to about 5×10^4 nm half-sarcomere^{-1} s^{-1} (7). In contrast, relaxed fibers at low ionic strength showed a very significant effect of stretch speed on fiber stiffness over the whole range of speeds that could be attained, e.g. up to about 5×10^4 nm half-sarcomere^{-1} s^{-1} (7). The stiffness of relaxed fibers at low ionic strength is about 1/2 to 2/3 that of active stiffness when measured at the highest-speed stretches but only about 10% of the active fiber stiffness when measured using slower stretches of about 10^2 nm half-sarcomere^{-1} s^{-1}. Since cross-bridge attachment in relaxed fibers can only be detected with fast length changes, these attached cross-bridges cannot be the source of the short-range elasticity previously described by D. K. Hill (30).

A qualitative estimate of the underlying rate constants for detachment and reattachment can be obtained from the following considerations: First, a significant fraction, but very likely not all, of the cross-bridges are attached in relaxed fibers at low ionic strength. Thus the binding constant is around unity and the rate constants of attachment and detachment are about the same order of magnitude. Second, fiber stiffness increases with the speed of the applied stretch over more than two decades. Single rate constants for detachment and reattachment could account for about two decades of speed dependence of stiffness (49). For relaxed fibers at low ionic strength these rate constants should be around 5×10^4 s^{-1}. Since no speed-independent stiffness value was reached even with the fastest stretches, the speed dependence of relaxed fiber stiffness is wider than two decades and the cross-bridge detachment and reattachment are probably determined by a spectrum of strain-dependent rate processes.

These arguments suggest that the cross-bridge states populated in relaxed fibers are characterized by a rapid equilibrium between attachment and detachment but with more complex strain-dependent kinetics.

ESTIMATE OF THE FRACTION OF WEAK BINDING CROSS-BRIDGES AT-TACHED IN RELAXED AND ACTIVE FIBERS   Both stiffness and equatorial X-ray diffraction experiments are consistent with significant cross-bridge attachment at low ionic strength (0.02 M) and 5°C. In muscles in rigor there is evidence that nearly all of the cross-bridges are attached to actin (16, 17, 38). Assuming that stiffness per cross-bridge is the same in rigor and relaxation, the stiffness measurements indicate that at least 50% of the cross-bridges are attached in the relaxed fibers. This is only a lower limit since the speed dependence of relaxed fiber stiffness even at the fastest stretches indicates that detachment and reattachment occur during the length change, reducing the observed stiffness (Figure 1; 7).

At more physiological ionic strengths, both stiffness and X-ray diffraction data suggest less cross-bridge attachment. However, since fiber stiffness (7) depends on speed of stretch, it is not clear whether faster rates of cross-bridge detachment also contribute to the decrease in fiber stiffness when ionic strength is increased. Similarly, in X-ray diffraction experiments, the increasing disorder in the actin and myosin filaments at ionic strengths above 0.1–0.12 M decreases the accuracy of estimating the extent of cross-bridge attachment. Therefore, an indirect approach was used to get an estimate of the extent of cross-bridge attachment under these conditions (7). If changes in conditions such as the type of nucleotide, nucleotide concentration, temperature, and ionic strength affect cross-bridge attachment to actin in the same way they affect the binding of S-1 to actin, then the extent of cross-bridge attachment can be determined from S-1 binding to actin in solution using the relation between the fraction of attached cross-bridges in muscle (K_{mus}) and the binding of S-1 to actin in solution (K_{sol}). This relation is $K_{mus} = K_{sol} \times A_{eff}$, where A_{eff} is the *effective actin concentration*. This is the actin concentration required in solution to observe the same fraction of S-1 bound to actin as cross-bridges are attached to actin in muscle under the same conditions.

An effective actin concentration of 1.5–6.5 mM was determined experimentally from parallel measurements of S-1 binding to actin in the presence of 4 mM MgPP$_i$ and of cross-bridge attachment in muscle under the same conditions (11). On this basis, at low ionic strength and 5°C, about 90% of the cross-bridges are attached in relaxed fibers. This fraction decreases to about 10% at an ionic strength of 0.17 M. Using the values for HMM binding to regulated actin in the presence of ATP, which are probably more realistic, the calculated fraction of attached cross-bridges in relaxed muscle is 65% and 2% at low and high ionic strength, respectively. Since Ca^{2+} increases the binding of HMM to regulated actin about five-fold (15, 57, 58), about 10% of the cross-bridges in the weak binding state are expected to be attached to actin in active muscle at the more physiological ionic strength of 0.17 M.

SUMMARY   The results of stiffness and equatorial X-ray diffraction experiments suggest that the cross-bridge states in relaxed fibers have properties similar to those described for the weak binding states of the actomyosin ATPase in solution. However, attachment and detachment rate constants have a single value in solution but may have a spectrum of rate constants in muscle. At more physiological ionic strengths (~0.17 M), both in the presence and absence of Ca^{2+}, only a small fraction of the cross-bridges in the weak binding states are attached to actin. This finding implies that under physiological conditions weak binding cross-bridges can contribute little to the isometric force generated in active muscle. The general ability of cross-bridges to attach to actin in relaxed fibers appeared inconsistent with the idea that muscle contraction is regulated simply by blocking or unblocking of crossbridge attachment. Although under certain conditions regulation does exert a large measure of control over cross-bridge attachment (36a), the observed attachment without ATP hydrolysis or generation of active force or active shortening was interpreted to indicate control of a kinetic step subsequent to attachment (9, 13, 14). The exact details of regulation, however, are still controversial and may well include both control of the extent of cross-bridge attachment and of a kinetic step subsequent to attachment.

Evidence for Cross-Bridge States with Properties Similar to Those Described for the Strong Binding States in Solution

The strong binding states of the actomyosin ATPase in solution (see Figure 1 of the general introduction) are characterized by (a) a much higher actin affinity at comparable ionic strength (23, 29, 39, 43, 60); (b) an equilibrium between association with and dissociation from actin, but with much slower dissociation than observed for the weak binding states (41, 60); and (c) Ca^{2+} sensitive, cooperative binding to actin (24).

DETACHMENT KINETICS IN ACTIVE MUSCLE   To see whether cross-bridge states with properties similar to those of the strong binding states in solution can be found in active muscle, fiber stiffness was measured at various speeds of stretch (3, 6). The ionic strength in these experiments (0.17 M) was chosen such that any existing cross-bridge attachments equivalent to the weak binding states would not be detected by the stiffness measurements. The stiffness of fully Ca^{2+}-activated fibers was again found to depend on the speed of the applied length change (6, 21). The stiffness data obtained from active muscle are shifted toward lower speeds by more than an order of magnitude compared to the data from relaxed fibers. This finding is consistent with lower rate constants for detachment (6). In Ca^{2+}-activated fibers, however, a mixture of various cross-bridge states is present. Thus, the stiffness measurements may be influenced by the differences in elastic or kinetic properties of the various cross-bridge states and by transitions between these states taking place during the measurements.

BINDING STRENGTH AND DETACHMENT KINETICS IN THE PRESENCE OF $MgPP_i$ For less ambiguous characterization, nucleotide analogs were used to obtain pure populations of cross-bridge states with properties characteristic of the strong binding states. The fiber stiffness and equatorial X-ray diffraction patterns were recorded in the presence of $MgPP_i$ because in solution the binding of S-1 to actin in the presence of $MgPP_i$ has some of the properties of the strong binding states in the ATPase pathway (23, 24). In muscle, both stiffness and equatorial X-ray diffraction showed that, with $MgPP_i$, cross-bridge attachment to actin is stronger than in relaxed fibers. Greater increases in ionic strength are required to detach cross-bridges. In fact, a significant detachment can only be achieved by raising the ionic strength to above 0.12 M and lowering the temperature to at least 6°C (11). For comparison with measurements in relaxed fibers at low ionic strength, attachment and detachment kinetics in the presence of $MgPP_i$ were characterized using the speed dependence of fiber stiffness at an ionic strength of 0.12 M. Under this condition the binding of S-1 is about the same as in the presence of 5-mM Mg-ATP and low ionic strength (0.02 M). The rates of detachment and reattachment appeared to be about three orders of magnitude lower than those observed in relaxed fibers at low ionic strength (7). In addition, when the speed of applied length changes was increased from 10^{-2} to 5×10^3 nm half-sarcomere^{-1} s^{-1}, apparent fiber stiffness varied over the whole range of speeds (7). Although part of this effect may be due to incomplete saturation of cross-bridges with $MgPP_i$ (2, 51), the fact that the fiber stiffness varied over a greater range of speeds than the two decades that can be accounted for by a single rate constant suggests that the kinetics of detachment are determined by a spectrum of rate constants. The same conclusion was also drawn from measurements of the decay in force following step stretches under comparable conditions (51).

Ca^{2+}-SENSITIVE AND COOPERATIVE CROSS-BRIDGE ATTACHMENT IN THE PRESENCE OF $MgPP_i$ The other typical feature of the strong binding states in solution, the Ca^{2+}-sensitive and cooperative binding to actin (24), was also found in the skinned fiber preparation. When stiffness measurements and equatorial X-ray diffraction were used to probe for changes in cross-bridge attachment, the results were very similar to the data obtained in solution, especially when experiments done at the same temperature are compared (11).

SUMMARY   The experimental results obtained so far imply that there are cross-bridge states in muscle that show properties similar to those described for the strong binding states found in solution. However, as with the weak binding states, in muscle the kinetics of detachment are described by a spectrum of rate constants, whereas in solution the rate constants for detachment and reattachment have a single value.

EVIDENCE FOR STRUCTURAL DIFFERENCES BETWEEN THE WEAK AND STRONG BINDING CONFORMATIONS OF ATTACHED CROSS-BRIDGES

One of the major implications of findings from solution studies is that there should be a large-scale structural difference between the weak and the strong binding conformations of attached cross-bridges. The first evidence for structural differences between various cross-bridge states was presented by Reedy et al (47) and was based on observations of detached relaxed and attached rigor cross-bridges in insect flight muscle.

Electron microscopic (EM) studies revealed that myosin S-1 cross-linked to actin filaments has a different appearance in the presence or absence of ATP, i.e. in the weak binding versus in the rigor conformation (18). Similarly, in other EM studies, N,N'-p-phenylenedimaleimide- (pPDM)-modified S-1 (59a), presumably an analog of the S-1·ADP·P_i state (1), showed a structure similar to S-1 cross-linked to actin in the presence of ATP (1). Due to the potential for artifacts in EM studies, and because myosin fragments are used to decorate the actin filaments, it still remained uncertain whether cross-bridges attached to actin in the weak binding and strong binding states also show detectably different structures in muscle. This question became testable once experimental conditions were found under which cross-bridges in the weak binding states are mainly attached.

To answer this question, X-ray diffraction experiments on skinned muscle fibers from rabbit (12, 44) and frog (62) were used to compare the structure of the attached cross-bridges in relaxed muscle at low ionic strength with their structure in rigor or active muscle. To compare the structure of attached cross-bridges in relaxed and rigor fibers, equatorial diffraction patterns for these two conditions were recorded. As discussed above, lowering ionic strength leads to significant cross-bridge attachment in relaxed fibers. To account for possible effects from changes in ionic strength, relaxed and rigor patterns were recorded at the same ionic strengths. At 0.05 M the intensity of the *11* reflections in the two conditions is comparable and approximately three times the value observed in relaxed fibers at 0.17 M (Figure 2; 12). Thus, cross-bridge attachment in relaxed and rigor fibers at 0.05 M leads to nearly identical changes in the *11* reflections. In contrast, this same cross-bridge attachment does not lead to comparable changes in the *10* reflections. In relaxed fibers the *10* reflection stays almost unchanged, while in rigor fibers a large decrease is observed. The differential behavior of the *10* and *11* reflections cannot be explained by different numbers of attached cross-bridges. If the extent of attachment in rigor matched the *10* intensity, the *11* intensity would be less (10, 27, 35, 65). Thus it is impossible to match the intensities of both *10* and *11* reflections by merely changing the amount of cross-bridge attachment. This indicates that the configuration of attached cross-bridges in relaxed and rigor fibers must be different, leading to a different axial projection of the mass distribution between thick and thin filaments (12).

In preliminary experiments similar changes in equatorial patterns were found between relaxed and active fibers at an ionic strength of 0.05 M (B. Brenner & L. C. Yu, unpublished results). This observation indicates that not only rigor cross-bridges but also attached strong binding cross-bridges in active muscle have a configuration different from the weak binding cross-bridges attached in relaxed fibers.

Further details of the differences in the structure of the attached weak binding and rigor cross-bridges are revealed by reconstructions of two-dimensional electron-density maps from equatorial diffraction patterns, including the first five reflections (64). These reconstructions suggest that cross-bridges attached in rigor are confined to an area closer to the actin filament than those attached in relaxed fibers. This is consistent with the observed maintenance of the myosin-based layer lines from the myosin-based helical arrangement of the cross-bridge majority, and the lack of an increase in the actin-based layer lines from mass regularly disposed with the actin-based helical arrangement when cross-bridges attach in relaxed fibers (44, 62).

In summary, X-ray diffraction experiments indicate that in relaxed fibers the structure of attached weak binding cross-bridges is different from the structure of attached strong binding cross-bridges in active muscle or in rigor. This observation suggests that within the cross-bridge cycle the transitions

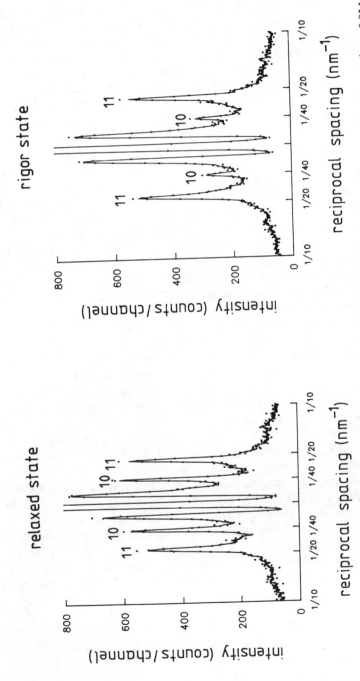

Figure 2 Equatorial diffraction patterns obtained from a single skinned rabbit psoas fiber in the relaxed and rigor states. The ionic strength was 0.05 M. Dots represent the original data; curves represent data smoothed using a three-point weighted average (B. Brenner & L. C. Yu, unpublished results).

between the weak binding states and the strong binding states are accompanied by significant changes in the structure of the attached cross-bridges.

PHYSIOLOGICAL SIGNIFICANCE OF THE RATE-LIMITING STEP OF THE ACTOMYOSIN ATPase IN SOLUTION

Assuming that cross-bridges in the weak binding states do not contribute much to isometric force compared to cross-bridges in the strong binding states, Eisenberg & Hill (20) postulated that the rate of force generation is mainly determined by the overall rate of the transition from the weak to the strong binding states. This same transition is the rate-limiting step of the actomyosin ATPase in solution (48, 54). Eisenberg & Hill (20) therefore predicted that the rate of the rate-limiting step in the ATPase cycle in solution should be equal to the rate of force development in muscle. Below we discuss experimental evidence for the postulated close correlation between the actomyosin ATPase in solution and the rate of force generation in muscle.

Experimental Protocol to Determine the Rate of Force Generation in Muscle

The simplest approach to measurement of the rate of force generation, i.e. following development of isometric force in skinned fibers after rapidly increasing the Ca^{2+} concentration, cannot be used because in this case the rate of force development is limited by slow steps in activation (26, 45). In a recently developed experimental approach (4, 5, 8) cross-bridges accumulate in the weak binding states during free or lightly loaded shortening while a fiber is continuously activated (3). The fiber is then quickly restretched back to the original length. The redevelopment of force and stiffness in the subsequent isometric period (Figure 3) can be used to follow the transition of cross-bridges from the weak to the strong binding states if conditions are adjusted so that only cross-bridges in the strong binding states contribute to force and stiffness (i.e. at an ionic strength of ≥ 0.12 M).

Correlation Between the Rate of Force Redevelopment and the Actomyosin ATPase in Solution

If we assume that the rate of force redevelopment is dominated by the transition of cross-bridges into the force-generating states, we can measure the rate of force redevelopment and test the prediction that the rate-limiting step for the actomyosin ATPase cycle in solution determines the rate of force generation in the cross-bridge cycle.

The rate constant of force redevelopment and the maximum rate of actin-activated actomyosin ATPase, measured with S-1 cross-linked to actin (46,

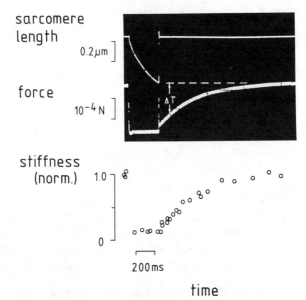

sarcomere
length

0.2 μm]

force

10^{-4} N]

ΔT

stiffness
(norm.)   1.0 ┐

0 ┘

┌─────┐
200 ms

time

Figure 3 Experimental protocol to measure the rate of force redevelopment. Following an approximately 300-ms period of isotonic shortening at near-zero load, fibers are restretched to their original sarcomere length and subsequent redevelopment of force is recorded *(upper panel)*. Measurements of fiber stiffness at 0.17 M ionic strength show that during the period of isotonic shortening the number of cross-bridges attached in the strong binding states decreases to less than 1/5 compared to the isometric steady state. Following the restretch, force and stiffness redevelop in parallel. This finding suggests that the redevelopment of force reflects the increase in the number of cross-bridges attached in the strong binding states. The time course of force redevelopment is well fit by a single exponential function (4, 5, 8). (Reproduced from Reference 5.)

55), were compared at different temperatures and at two different ionic strengths (8). In these experiments a rather close correlation between the magnitude of the two parameters was found. This finding is consistent with the postulated correlation between the rate-limiting mechanism in solution and the rate constant for force generation in the cross-bridge cycle in muscle.

The assumption that force redevelopment is mainly controlled by the transition of cross-bridges into the force-generating states was recently tested (6). In somewhat preliminary experiments it was found that this assumption holds at higher temperatures, while at 5°C the rate at which cross-bridges return to the non-force-generating states is almost half the rate at which cross-bridges enter the force-generating states. Since the rate of force redevelopment is the sum of the two rate constants, this observation explains the somewhat lower ATPase rate in solution at 5°C when compared to the rate of force redevelopment (8).

CONCLUSIONS

The results of mechanical and structural approaches reviewed here are consistent with the idea that there are two kinetically and structurally different groups of cross-bridge states in muscle and that these states are similar to the weak and strong binding states described in solution. The differences between the kinetic properties of cross-bridges in muscle and of actomyosin in solution can be accounted for by the expected strain dependence of cross-bridge kinetics (see the general introduction to this section; 31). Furthermore, the cross-bridges attached in the weak binding states have a different structure from that of cross-bridges attached in the strong binding states. This observation is consistent with the idea that a change in the configuration of attached cross-bridges, induced by the transition from the weak to the strong binding states, is the key element for force generation or filament sliding. Finally, the finding of cross-bridge attachment in relaxed fibers, i.e. in the absence of Ca^{2+}, supports the idea that muscle contraction is not regulated simply by blocking and unblocking of cross-bridge attachment. The exact mechanism of regulation, however, is still controversial. Experimental evidence has been provided that suggests Ca^{2+} exerts control over the extent of cross-bridge attachment (e.g. 15, 36a, 57, 58), but the idea that Ca^{2+} regulates a kinetic step subsequent to cross-bridge attachment has recently been given further support by analysis of the kinetics of cross-bridge cycling in muscle contracting at different degrees of Ca^{2+} activation (6). Thus, regulation appears to include control at several points within the cross-bridge cycle.

For future experiments, the described mechanical and structural approaches should provide a useful tool for more detailed kinetic studies of the cross-bridge cycle, including the rates of the various reaction steps and their regulation.

ACKNOWLEDGMENT

I thank my colleagues at NIH, especially Drs. E. Eisenberg and L. C. Yu, for many stimulating discussions and comments during the preparation of this article.

Literature Cited

1. Applegate, D., Flicker, P. 1986. Acto·pPDM·S-1: An analog of acto·S-1·ADP·P$_i$. *Biophys. J.* 49:445a (Abstr.)
2. Biosca, J. A., Greene, L. E., Eisenberg, E. 1986. Binding of ADP and ATP analogs to crosslinked and non-crosslinked acto·S-1. *J. Biol. Chem.* 261:9793–9800
3. Brenner, B. 1983. Cross-bridge attach-ment during isotonic shortening in single skinned rabbit psoas fibers. *Biophys. J.* 41:33a (Abstr.)
4. Brenner, B. 1984. The rate of force redevelopment in single skinned rabbit psoas fibers. *Biophys. J.* 45:155a (Abstr.)
5. Brenner, B. 1985. Correlation between

the cross-bridge cycle in muscle and the actomyosin ATPase cycle in solution. *J. Muscle Res. Cell Motil.* 6:659–64

6. Brenner, B. 1986. The cross-bridge cycle in muscle. Mechanical, biochemical and structural studies on single skinned rabbit psoas fibers to characterize cross-bridge kinetics in muscle for correlation with the actomyosin ATPase in solution. *Basic Res. Cardiol.* 81, Suppl. 1:1–15

7. Brenner, B., Chalovich, J., Greene, L. E., Eisenberg, E., Schoenberg, M. 1986. Stiffness of skinned rabbit psoas fibers in MgATP and MgPP$_i$ solution. *Biophys. J.* 50:685–91

8. Brenner, B., Eisenberg, E. 1986. The rate of force generation in muscle: Correlation with actomyosin ATPase in solution. *Proc. Natl. Acad. Sci. USA* 83:3542–46

9. Brenner, B., Schoenberg, M., Chalovich, J. M., Greene, L. E., Eisenberg, E. 1982. Evidence for cross-bridge attachment in relaxed muscle at low ionic strength. *Proc. Natl. Acad. Sci. USA* 79:7288–91

10. Brenner, B., Yu, L. C. 1985. Equatorial X-ray diffraction from single skinned rabbit psoas fibers at various degrees of activation. Changes in intensities and lattice spacing. *Biophys. J.* 48:829–34

11. Brenner, B., Yu, L. C., Greene, L. E., Eisenberg, E., Schoenberg, M. 1986. Ca^{2+}-sensitive cross-bridge dissociation in the presence of MgPP$_i$ in skinned rabbit psoas fibers. *Biophys. J.* In press

12. Brenner, B., Yu, L. C., Podolsky, R. J. 1984. X-ray diffraction evidence for cross-bridge formation in relaxed muscle fibers at various ionic strengths. *Biophys. J.* 46:299–306

13. Chalovich, J. M., Chock, P. B., Eisenberg, E. 1981. Mechanism of action of troponin-tropomyosin. *J. Biol. Chem.* 256:575–78

14. Chalovich, J. M., Eisenberg, E. 1982. Inhibition of actomyosin ATPase activity by troponin-tropomyosin without blocking the binding of myosin to actin. *J. Biol. Chem.* 257:2431–37

15. Chalovich, J. M., Eisenberg, E. 1986. The effect of troponin-tropomyosin on the binding of heavy meromyosin to actin in the presence of ATP. *J. Biol. Chem.* 261:5088–93

16. Cooke, R., Franks, K. 1980. All myosin heads form bonds with actin in rabbit rigor skeletal muscle. *Biochemistry* 19:2265–69

17. Cooke, R., Thomas, D. 1980. Spin label studies of the structure and dynamics of glycerinated muscle fibers: Applications. *Fed. Proc.* 39:1962

18. Craig, R., Greene, L. E., Eisenberg, E. 1985. Structure of the actin-myosin complex in the presence of ATP. *Proc. Natl. Acad. Sci. USA* 82:3247–51

19. Eisenberg, E., Greene, L. E. 1980. The relation of muscle biochemistry to muscle physiology. *Ann. Rev. Physiol.* 42:293–309

20. Eisenberg, E., Hill, T. L. 1985. Muscular contraction and free energy transduction in biological systems. *Science* 227:999–1006

21. Ford, L. E., Huxley, A. F., Simmons, R. M. 1977. Tension responses to sudden length change in stimulated frog muscle fibres near slack length. *J. Physiol. London* 269:441–515

22. Ford, L. E., Huxley, A. F., Simmons, R. M. 1981. The relation between stiffness and filament overlap in stimulated frog muscle fibres. *J. Physiol. London* 311:219–49

23. Greene, L. E., Eisenberg, E. 1980. Dissociation of the actin·subfragment 1 complex by adenyl-5'-yl imidodiphosphate, ADP, and PP$_i$. *J. Biol. Chem.* 255:543–48

24. Greene, L. E., Eisenberg, E. 1980. Cooperative binding of myosin subfragment-1 to the actin-troponin-tropomyosin complex. *Proc. Natl. Acad. Sci. USA* 77:2616–20

25. Greene, L. E., Sellers, J. R., Eisenberg, E., Adelstein, R. S. 1983. Binding of gizzard smooth muscle myosin subfragment-one to actin in the presence and absence of ATP. *Biochemistry* 22:530–35

26. Griffiths, P. J., Kuhn, H. J., Güth, K., Rüegg, J. C. 1979. Rate of isometric tension development in relation to calcium binding of skinned muscle fibres. *Pflüg. Arch.* 382:165–70

27. Haselgrove, J. C., Huxley, H. E. 1973. X-ray evidence for radial cross-bridge movement and for the sliding filament model in actively contracting skeletal muscle. *J. Mol. Biol.* 77:549–68

28. Hibberd, M. G., Trentham, D. R. 1986. Relationships between chemical and mechanical events during muscular contraction. *Ann. Rev. Biophys. Biophys. Chem.* 15:119–61

29. Highsmith, S. 1977. The effects of temperature and salts on myosin subfragment-1 and F-actin association. *Arch. Biochem. Biophys.* 180:404–8

30. Hill, D. K. 1968. Tension due to interaction between the sliding filaments in resting striated muscle. The effect of stimulation. *J. Physiol. London* 199:637–84

31. Hill, T. L. 1974. Theoretical formalism

for the sliding filament model of contraction of striated muscle. Part I. *Prog. Biophys. Mol. Biol.* 28:267–340

32. Huxley, A. F. 1974. Muscular contraction. *J. Physiol. London* 243:1–43
33. Huxley, A. F. 1980. *Reflections on Muscle. The Sherrington Lectures XIV.* Liverpool: Liverpool Univ. Press.
34. Huxley, A. F., Simmons, R. M. 1971. Porposed mechanism of force generation in striated muscle. *Nature* 233:533–20
35. Huxley, H. E. 1968. Structural differences between resting and rigor muscle. Evidence from intensity changes in the low-angle equatorial x-ray diagram. *J. Mol. Biol.* 37:507–20
36. Huxley, H. E., Faruqi, A. R. 1983. Time-resolved X-ray diffraction studies on vertebrate striated muscle. *Ann. Rev. Biophys. Bioeng.* 12:381–417
36a. Kress, M., Huxley, H. E., Faruqi, A. R., Hendrix, F. 1986. Structural changes during activation of frog muscle studied by time-resolved x-ray diffraction. *J. Mol. Biol.* 188:325–42
37. Kuhn, H. J. 1978. Crossbridge slippage induced by the ATP analogue AMP-PNP and stretch in glycerol-extracted fibrillar muscle fibers. *Biophys. Struct. Mech.* 4:159–68
38. Lovell, S. J., Harrington, W. F. 1981. Measurement of the fraction of myosin heads bound to actin in rabbit skeletal myofibrils in rigor. *J. Mol. Biol.* 149:659–74
39. Margossian, S. S., Lowey, S. 1978. Interaction of myosin subfragments with F-actin. *Biochemistry* 17:5431–39
40. Marston, S. B. 1973. The nucleotide complexes of myosin in glycerol-extracted muscle fibers. *Biochim. Biophys. Acta* 305:397–412
41. Marston, S. B. 1982. The rates of formation and dissociation of actin-myosin complexes. *Biochem. J.* 203: 453–60
42. Marston, S. B., Tregear, R. T. 1972. Evidence for a complex between myosin and ADP in relaxed muscle fibers. *Nature New Biol.* 235:23–24
43. Marston, S. B., Weber, A. 1975. The dissociation constant of the actin-heavy meromyosin subfragment-1 complex. *Biochemistry* 14:3868–73
44. Matsuda, T., Podolsky, R. J. 1984. X-ray evidence for two structural states of the actomyosin cross-bridge in muscle fibers. *Proc. Natl. Acad. Sci. USA* 81:2364–68
45. Moisescu, D. G. 1976. Kinetics of reaction in calcium-activated skinned muscle fibres. *Nature* 262:610–13
46. Mornet, D., Bertrand, R., Pantel, P.,

Audemard, E., Kassab, R. 1981. Structure of the actin-myosin interface. *Nature* 292:301–6
47. Reedy, M. K., Holmes, K. C., Tregear, R. T. 1965. Induced changes in orientation of the cross-bridges of glycerinated insect flight muscle. *Nature* 207:1276–80
48. Rosenfeld, S. S., Taylor, E. W. 1984. The ATPase mechanism of skeletal and smooth muscle acto-subfragment 1. *J. Biol. Chem.* 259:11908–19
49. Schoenberg, M. 1985. Equilibrium muscle cross-bridge behaviour: Theoretical considerations. *Biophys. J.* 48:467–75
50. Schoenberg, M., Brenner, B., Chalovich, J. M., Greene, L. E., Eisenberg, E. 1984. Cross-bridge attachment in relaxed muscle. In *Contractile Mechanism in Muscle,* ed. G. H. Pollack, H. Sugi, pp. 269–79. New York: Plenum
51. Schoenberg, M., Eisenberg, E. 1985. Muscle cross-bridge kinetics in rigor and in the presence of ATP analogues. *Biophys. J.* 48:863–71
52. Sleep, J. A., Smith, S. J. 1981. Actomyosin ATPase and muscle contraction. *Curr. Top. Bioenerg.* 11:239–86
53. Squire, J. 1981. *The Structural Basis of Muscular Contraction.* New York: Plenum
54. Stein, L. A., Chock, P. B., Eisenberg, E. 1984. The rate-limiting step in the actomyosin adenosinetriphosphatase cycle. *Biochemistry* 23:1555–63
55. Stein, L. A., Greene, L. E., Chock, P. B., Eisenberg, E. 1985. Rate-limiting step in the actomyosin adenosinetriphosphatase cycle: Studies with myosin subfragment 1 cross-linked to actin. *Biochemistry* 24:1357–63
56. Stein, L. A., Schwarz, R. P., Chock, P. B., Eisenberg, E. 1979. Mechanism of actomyosin adenosine triphosphatase. Evidence that adenosine 5'-triphosphate hydrolysis can occur without dissociation of the actomyosin complex. *Biochemistry* 18:3895–3909
57. Wagner, P. D. 1984. Effect of skeletal muscle myosin light chain 2 on the Ca^{2+}-sensitive interaction of myosin and heavy meromyosin with regulated actin. *Biochemistry* 23:5950–56
58. Wagner, P. D., Giniger, E. 1981. Calcium-sensitive binding of heavy meromyosin to regulated actin in the presence of ATP. *J. Biol. Chem.* 256:12647–50
59. Webb, M. R., Trentham, D. R. 1981. The mechanism of ATP hydrolysis catalyzed by myosin and actomyosin using rapid reaction techniques to study

oxygen exchange. *J. Biol. Chem.* 256: 10910–16

59a. Wells, J. A., Yount, R. G. 1979. Active site trapping of nucleotides by cross-linking two sulfhydryls in mysoin subfragment 1. *Proc. Natl. Acad. Sci. USA* 76:4966–70

60. White, H. D., Taylor, E. W. 1976. Energetics and mechanism of actomyosin adenosine triphosphatase. *Biochemistry* 15:5818–26

61. Wray, J. S., Holmes, K. C. 1981. X-ray diffraction studies of muscle. *Ann. Rev. Physiol.* 43:553–65

62. Xu, S. G., Kress, M., Huxley, H. E. 1986. X-ray diffraction studies of the structural state of cross-bridges in skinned frog sartorius muscle at low ionic strength. *J. Muscle Res. Cell Motil.* In press

63. Yanagida, T., Kuranaga, I., Inoue, A. 1982. Interaction of myosin with thin filaments during contraction and relaxation: Effect of ionic strength. *J. Biochem.* 92:407–12

64. Yu, L. C., Brenner, B. 1986. High resolution equatorial x-ray diffraction from single skinned rabbit psoas fibers. *Biophys. J.* 49:133–35

65. Yu, L. C., Hartt, J. E., Podolsky, R. J. 1979 Equatorial x-ray intensities and isometric force levels in frog sartorius muscle. *J. Mol. Biol.* 132:53–67

Ann. Rev. Physiol. 1987. 49:673–90

MUSCLE ENTHALPY PRODUCTION AND ITS RELATIONSHIP TO ACTOMYOSIN ATPase

Earl Homsher

Department of Physiology, School of Medicine, Center for Health Sciences, University of California, Los Angeles, California 90024

INTRODUCTION

The rate of energy liberation by contracting muscle is determined by mechanical conditions, and it has been assumed that differences in energy liberation rates reflect differences in the rate of ATP utilization. With the advance in understanding of the mechanism of ATP hydrolysis by purified muscle proteins (71), cross-bridge models have been devised (18, 43, 44), and their adequacy has been tested by comparing the ATPase rates predicted by the models with the rates of enthalpy liberation by contracting muscle. This comparison is based on the following assumptions: (*a*) that the only significant ATPase in the muscle is that associated with the cross-bridge; (*b*) that the only energetically significant reaction occurring in the muscle is ATP hydrolysis; and (*c*) that the heat measurements in Hill's work (32, 33) represent steady-state processes. Each of these assumptions is only approximately correct. Over the past decade, muscle energeticists have examined the extent to which the measured ATP hydrolysis accounts for muscles' enthalpy production. These studies have revealed two distinct instances in which there are significant discrepancies. In the process they have discovered heat-liberating reactions occurring in the muscle whose role is not yet understood. This essay describes which reactions in the muscle are energetically significant, the factors that alter muscular energy liberation rate, and the conditions under which muscle energy liberation and ATPase rates do not match.

673

0066-4278/87/0315-0673$02.00

SOURCES OF ENTHALPY PRODUCTION

Enthalpy production is related to ATP usage via the first law of thermodynamics in Equation 1:

$$h + w = \sum_{i=1}^{n} \xi_i \cdot \Delta H_i, \qquad\qquad 1.$$

where $h + w$ is the heat (h) and work (w), enthalpy, produced by the muscle (J/g); ξ_i is the extent of the ith chemical reaction (mol/g); and ΔH_i is the molar enthalpy change for the ith reaction (J/mol) (74). The accuracy of ATPase estimates from myothermal measurements depends on the accuracy of the molar enthalpy values and myothermal determinations. Measurements of the molar enthalpy changes are performed with a high degree of accuracy, but a 5% potential error remains because of uncertainty about the ionic contents of the cell (pH, magnesium content, buffers, etc) (10, 76). The accuracy of the heat measurements depends on characteristics of the thermopile, the time interval over which the measurements are made, and the type of contraction examined (see Reference 77, pp. 171–89). Given the current technology, myothermal measurements to 5% accuracy can be routinely obtained with whole muscle preparations, while those with single fibers (8) are somewhat less accurate.

If the only reaction in the cell were ATP hydrolysis, conversion of the enthalpy produced to moles of ATP hydrolyzed would be trivial using Equation 1. A major limitation of the myothermal technique is its lack of specificity: The observed enthalpy is the sum of all the enthalpy changes occurring in the muscle. There are additional reactions that can take place in the muscle and contribute to the measured enthalpy change. To assess the role various reactions play in muscle enthalpy production, *energy balance* experiments are performed. In these experiments, the enthalpy produced under a specified condition is measured *(observed enthalpy)*. Next the chemical changes occurring in muscles contracting under conditions identical to the enthalpy measurements are determined. Multiplication of the extent of each reaction by its molar enthalpy change and summation of all measured reactions yields the *explained enthalpy*. The explained enthalpy is then subtracted from the observed enthalpy. If the remainder is zero, then one may provisionally conclude that no other energetically significant reactions are occurring in the muscle. If the remainder is nonzero, then other reactions are occurring in the muscle, and additional experimentation is required to identify those reactions. Tables 1–3 contain information about the reactions known to take place in the muscle and the molar enthalpy change for each. Table 1 lists reactions related to high energy phosphate metabolism. Energy balance studies on frog muscle contracting at 0°C show that of these reactions the only net reaction occurring is creatine phosphate splitting (9, 11, 36, 52). ADP is rephosphorylated as rapidly as it is formed, so reactions 3–6 do not occur to any significant extent. If the tetanus is <20 sec, reactions 7 and 8 do not occur to a significant extent during the tetanus (13, 26, 52).

Besides the reactions shown in Table 1, enthalpy changes accompany calcium binding to troponin, parvalbumin, and proteins in the sarcoplasmic reticulum (49a). The role these reactions play in the muscle is only inferred from conventional energy balance studies. Knowledge of the amount of each calcium binding ligand in the muscle, the dissociation constants, and the enthalpy change for each binding reaction (see Table 2), along with measurements of the calcium contents of subcellular regions using microprobe analysis (69, 72), permits estimation of the contribution of calcium binding to the energy balance. The role calcium binding plays in the heat production in contracting muscle is considered in a subsequent section.

Yamada et al (79) were the first to show that there were significant enthalpy changes associated with the elementary steps of the myosin ATPase reaction mechanism. Since that time there have been a number of studies (see Reference 49 for a review) in which the enthalpy changes associated with the steps of the myosin and actomyosin ATPase mechanism have been examined. Table 3 lists the various steps of the myosin and actomyosin ATPase reaction mechanisms and, where available, the enthalpy change. There are large gaps in our knowledge of the enthalpy changes associated with actomyosin states, partly because of the difficulties of working at actin concentrations high enough to form significant amounts of actomyosin. This problem may be circumvented in studies using cross-linked acto-S-1 or cross-linked myofibrils

Table 1 Apparent enthalpy changes (H_{app}) associated with high-energy phosphate metabolism[a]

Reaction	H_{app} (kJ/mol)
1. $H^+ + B^- \rightarrow HB$	−31
2. $PCr \rightarrow Cr + P_i$	−32
3. $ATP \rightarrow ADP + P_i$	−47
4. $ADP + PCr \rightarrow ATP + Cr$	+15
5. $ADP \rightarrow 0.5\ ATP + 0.5\ AMP$	+5[b]
6. $AMP \rightarrow IMP + NH_3$	−25
7. glycogen unit + 3 Cr + 3$P_i \rightarrow$ 2 lactate + 3 PCr	−92[c]
8. 1/6 glycogen unit + O_2 + 6.5P_i + 6.5Cr → CO_2 + H_2O + 6.5 PCr	−269[d]

[a]Data based on Figure 8 and Table 3 of Reference 10. Reaction 1 refers to combined average for intracellular buffers, B. Values apply to 0° C, pH 6.8–7.2, ionic strength of 0.2 M, and pMg of 2.5. Apparent enthalpy values include proton buffering, partial reactions, and changes in cation binding.

[b,c,d]Values expressed per mole ADP, glycogen unit, and oxygen, respectively.

Table 2 Apparent enthalpy changes (H_{app}) associated with calcium binding in frog muscle[a]

Reaction	Calcium binding sites (μmol/g muscle)	K_{diss} (M)	H_{app} (kJ/mol Ca^{2+})
Calcium-specific Sites			
Ca^{2+} + TnC→CaTnC	0.18 (81)	3×10^{-7}[b]	−32 to −36 (28, 60)
Ca-Mg Sites			
Ca^{2+} + MgPA→CaPA + Mg^{2+}	0.80 (30, 55)	8×10^{-9} (31, 70)	−30 (67, 70)
Ca^{2+} + MgTNC→CaTNC + Mg^{2+}	0.18 (81)	—[c]	—[c]
Terminal Cistern Sites			
Ca^{2+} + SR→CaSR	0.7 (20)	—	+5 (49a)

[a]TnC = troponin C; PA = parvalbumin; SR = binding sites in terminal cisterns. The reference numbers for the data sources are indicated in parentheses.
[b]Value calculated from fit to force versus pCa curve in Reference 28 with the assumption that force is proportional to the fraction of troponin molecules whose calcium-specific sites are both occupied by calcium (59).
[c]Values assumed to be the same as those for parvalbumin because of their similar properties (31).

(56) in a stopped-flow microcalorimeter. The net production of enthalpy from reactions given in Table 3 depends on the distribution of cross-bridges before and after the measuring period. Such an enthalpy production may contribute to the enthalpy production in shortening contractions.

PROCESSES THAT CONSUME ATP IN SKELETAL MUSCLE

At least four processes consume ATP in contracting skeletal muscle.

1. *Na,K-ATPase*   The amount of ATP consumed by the Na-K pump during a tetanus has not been studied in skeletal muscle. From estimates of the Na^+ entry per action potential (73) and the heat produced during a tetanus (6) one can calculate that the ATP used by the Na-K pump is ~10% of the isometric hydrolysis rate. Experiments designed to isolate the energetics of the action potential in muscle by blocking excitation-contraction coupling with methoxyverapamil (19) could be informative.

2. *Calcium pump of the sarcoplasmic reticulum*   The energy usage associated with calcium release and sequestration (inclusive of the action potential energetics) has been estimated to be about 20–35% of the ATP consumed in maintained isometric tetanus (see Reference 35 for a review).

3. *Phosphorylation of myosin light chains*   Myosin light chain (LC2)

Table 3 Apparent enthalpy (H_{app}) changes associated with actomyosin intermediates[a]

Reaction		H_{app} (kJ/mol)
1d.	M + ATP→M·ATP	-65
3d.	MATP→M·ADP·P$_i$	$+58$
5d.	M·ADP·Pi→M'·ADP + Pi	-104
7d.	M'·ADP→M·ADP	?
9d.	M·ADP→M + ADP	$+63$
1a.	AM + ATP→AM·ATP	?
3a.	AM·ATP→AM·ADP·P$_i$	?
5a.	AM·ADP·P$_i$→AM'·ADP + P$_i$	?
7a.	AM'·ADP→AM·ADP	?
9a.	AM·ADP→AM + ADP	$+18$[b]
10.	M + A→AM	$+26$[b]
2.	MATP + A→AM·ATP	?
4.	M·ADP·P$_i$ + A→AM·ADP·P$_i$	?
6.	M'·ADP + A→AM'·ADP	?
8.	M·ADP + A→AM·ADP	$+75$[b]

[a]M=myosin S−1; A=actin. Values given for 100 mM KC1, 2.5–10 mM magnesium, pH = 7–8, and a temperature of 4–12°C. H_{app} includes proton release and reabsorption. Data is based on Table 4 of Reference 49.
[b]Data from Reference 67.

phosphorylation takes place during tetanic stimulation of frog skeletal muscle at 0°C (2, 3). About 50% of the myosin S-1 molecules are phosphorylated during the tetanus. The ATP consumed is equivalent to 5% of the energy used in a 5-sec tetanus at 0°C.

4. *Actomyosin ATPase* This accounts for 65–80% of the ATP consumed in an isometric tetanus and corresponds to an acto-S-1 ATPase reaction rate of 1 sec^{-1} in the isometric case (7, 35, 42).

ENTHALPY PRODUCTION IN CONTRACTING MUSCLES

The two main types of muscle contractions relevant to enthalpy measurements are isometric contractions and contractions involving muscle shortening.

Isometric Contractions

The energy produced during an isometric tetanus [$h(t)$] as a function of the duration of stimulation (t) is described empirically by Equation 2 (1):

$$h(t) = 20\text{--}45 \text{ mJ/g}(1-e^{-1t}) + (14 \text{ mW/g})t. \qquad 2.$$

Hill called $h(t)$ the maintenance heat, based on the assumption that it represented only reactions leading to a state of readiness to shorten and maintaining that state (32). These assumptions imply that $h(t)$ is ancillary to the reactions of the contractile proteins. The 20–45 mJ/g term of Equation 2 is called the labile maintenance heat, and it is produced only at the beginning of a tetanus. The 14 mW/g·t term is called the stable maintenance heat (SMH), and it is produced continuously during a tetanus (1, 9, 41, 58). Studies (39) of the variation of the isometric heat production with sarcomere length show that labile maintenance heat is produced by reactions independent of thick and thin filament overlap. Similar studies of SMH suggest that 70% of it (10 mW/g·t) is produced by the cross-bridges, and the remaining 4 mW/g·t is a consequence of calcium release and sequestration (9, 12, 39). Energy balance studies have shown that the time course of energy liberation $E(t)$ from high-energy phosphate hydrolysis during an isometric tetanus is given approximately by Equation 3 (11, 36):

$$E(t) = 15 \text{ mJ/g}(1-e^{-1t}) + 14 \text{ mW/g } (t). \qquad 3.$$

The difference between Equations 2 and 3 shows that during the tetanus, another unknown enthalpy-producing reaction is occurring besides ATP splitting. Studies of the isometric unexplained enthalpy (IUE) have led to the following conclusions: (*a*) IUE is produced during the first 3–5 sec of a tetanus. Thereafter all the enthalpy produced comes from high-energy phosphate splitting (11, 36). (*b*) IUE production is not strongly dependent on thick and thin filament overlap (12). (*c*) If a muscle is given a 6-sec *conditioning* tetanus followed at variable times (Δt) by a second 6-sec *test* tetanus, the IUE produced in the test tetanus is dependent on the time interval. If Δt is 6 sec, the amount of test IUE is 15–25% of that produced by the conditioning tetanus. However, if Δt is >30 sec, the amount of IUE in the test and conditioning tetanus is the same (9, 41). (*d*) Paul (57) was the first to show that IUE is reversed by ATP hydrolysis sometime during the recovery from a tetanus. Recently, we found that the reversal at 0°C occurs in the first 30 sec following a tetanus (41). (*e*) Somlyo et al (69), using microprobe analysis at 20°C in frog muscle, found that the sarcoplasmic calcium content remains elevated after the muscle has mechanically relaxed. Tormey & Homsher (72) extended these observations to muscles contracting at 0°C and found that the sarcoplasmic calcium content rises from 0.25 mM at rest to 1.0 mM during a tetanus [when free sarcoplasmic Ca^{2+} is 1×10^{-5}M (4)], falls to 0.8 mM by the end of mechanical relaxation, and over the next 30 sec returns to resting levels [about 5×10^{-8} M free sarcoplasmic Ca^{2+} (73a)]. These observations are consistent with the hypothesis that the isometric unexplained enthalpy is produced by calcium binding to the proteins troponin (60) and parvalbumin (68, 70), which could produce up to 37 mJ/g of enthalpy (see Table 2; for a discussion of this hypothesis see Reference 77, pp. 257–60). After the muscle has relaxed, this reaction is reversed by the removal of calcium from the sarcoplasm by the calcium pump. This hypothesis should be further tested by measuring the rate of Mg^{2+} and Ca^{2+} dissociation from frog parvalbumin at 0°C and by measuring the IUE production in muscles containing varying amounts of parvalbumin.

Although other energetically significant reactions occur early in a tetanus, the stable maintenance heat is produced by ATP hydrolysis. This steady rate of energy liberation corresponds to a cross-bridge turnover rate of 1–1.5 s^{-1} [assuming an S-1 content of 0.2–0.3 μmol/g (14, 82)] and an SR ATPase rate of 0.12 μmol/g sec. Measurements of the ATPase rate in single skinned muscle fibers agree with this turnover rate within a factor of two (54). A variety of factors affect the isometric ATPase rate.

1. *Muscle length*   The SMH is proportional to the filament overlap at sarcomere lengths greater than 2.25. At sarcomere lengths less than 2.0 the rate of energy liberation falls for reasons that are not understood (39, 64).

2. *Calcium concentration*   Available data indicate that the ATPase activity related to cross-bridge reactions is a linear function of the extent of calcium activation; i.e. force and ATPase rate rise in parallel as Ca^{2+} concentration is raised (14, 28, 51, 59). Unlike mammalian soleus fibers (51) calcium has a small effect on cross-bridge kinetics in frog muscle fibers (54).

3. *Fiber type*   Table 4.IV in Reference 77 lists the steady-state rate of energy liberation for muscles from different species. There is a correlation between the isometric energy liberation rate and the maximum velocity of active shortening.

4. *Temperature*   Studies of the steady-state energy liberation rate show that its Q_{10} is 4–5, and isometric force rises with a Q_{10} of 1.3 (1, 5, 34, 35). Stiffness measurements show little or no change between 0 and 10°C (23), so the force per cross-bridge rises with temperature. This latter behavior could be explained if there are two or more force-generating cross-bridge states (of differing intrinsic force) and the equilibrium constant between these states is temperature dependent.

Contractions in Which Muscles Shorten

Although an increased rate of energy liberation during shortening is easily observed in myothermal and mechanical recordings, quantitation of the records has been a source of confusion. Before we discuss energy liberation during shortening, we describe technical aspects of the measurements and their inherent problems.

The rate of a biochemical reaction is measured by determining the difference in the amount of reaction products before and after the measurement time interval. The rate of the reaction is this difference divided by the time interval. Myothermal measurements use the same principle. A muscle is tetanized, and after tension has fully developed, the muscle is allowed to shorten a distance (ΔS) at a fixed load or velocity over an interval of time (Δt). The total heat production (h_b) is noted when shortening begins and at the end of the shortening period (h_t). In principle, the amount of heat produced during shortening is $h_t - h_b$; the heat produced per unit shortening is $(h_t - h_b)/\Delta S$; the work done (w) is the integral of the product of muscle force and displacement. The rate of enthalpy production is $(h_t - h_b + w)/\Delta t$. In practice, however, corrections are required. The force at the end of shortening is less than that at the beginning, so that part of the measured heat is thermoelastic heat that should be subtracted from h_b. The value of w is overestimated by an amount equal to the work stored in the series elastic components during the development of tetanic tension. The distance shortened, ΔS, is also overestimated by an amount equivalent to the shortening of the series elastic component (27, 32, 33, 46, 75, 77).

The magnitude of these corrections relative to $(h_t - h_b + w)$ is proportional to the difference in tension between isometric and shortening conditions and is inversely proportional to the distance shortened. The corrections can be large. For example, the data from a muscle shortening 10% of its initial length at 0.6 V_{max} requires corrections equal to 60% of the energy liberated. As the corrections for both the thermoelastic heat and series elastic component can be in error by 25%, significant uncertainty is introduced.

Such corrections are unnecessary if the thermal measurement period includes tension redevelopment to the isometric level following shortening. The total heat produced to the end of tension redevelopment is h_e, and the heat produced during shortening and tension redevelopment is $(h_e - h_b)$. No corrections of $h_e - h_b$ are needed for thermoelastic heat, series elastic work, or ΔS because the forces at the beginning and end of the measurement period are equal. However, during force redevelopment, muscles produce heat unrelated to the shortening per se; this heat is assumed to be equal to the product of the isometric heat rate (h_i) at the shortened length and the time interval of tension redevelopment, (Δtr). Thus the heat (h_s) produced as a result of a muscle shortening a distance of ΔS is $(h_e - h_b) - (h_i \cdot \Delta tr)$. The heat produced per unit shortening (α_s) is $h_s/\Delta S$. The average rate of energy liberation during shortening is $(h_s+w)/\Delta t$. Hill (32) assumed that the maintenance heat rate was not associated with the contractile element. Therefore he subtracted from h_s the amount of heat ($h_i \cdot \Delta t$) the isometrically contracting muscle would have produced during the period of shortening; he called the remainder *shortening heat*. This subtraction does not change the fundamental concept because the total heat produced by the muscle during shortening is Hill's shortening heat plus the isometric heat.

The average rates of energy liberation plotted in Figure 1 are $(h_s+w)/\Delta t$. The following calculation illustrates how much energy is evolved during shortening. If a muscle shortens by 15% of its initial length at V_{max}, the heat produced during shortening is three times that produced during an isometric contraction over the same time interval. A muscle shortening 15% at $0.1 V_{max}$ produces 30% more heat than a muscle contracting isometrically. The amount of work produced is approximately equal to the isometric heat.

Three additional factors in experiments on shortening muscle should be noted. First, tetanic contractions, rather than twitches, should be used in such studies because experimental conditions are defined much more tightly than in

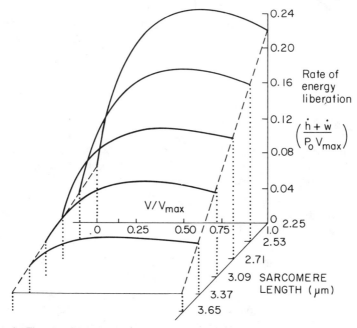

Figure 1 The rate of muscle energy liberation by frog skeletal muscle contracting at 0°C as a function of relative shortening velocity and muscle length. (See text for additional details.) Energy liberation rate is expressed relative to the maximal force (P_0) and maximum velocity of shortening (V_{max}).

twitches (61; see Reference 77, pp. 226–33). Second, muscle shortening should be confined to the plateau region of the length-tension curve where filament overlap is constant. At sarcomere spacing <1.8 μm, the extent of muscle activation is questionable (65). At sarcomere lengths >2.4 μm, parallel elastic heat absorption complicates corrections of myothermal recordings (38) and may produce sarcomere inhomogeneities that hamper data interpretation (38, 48). If shortening must begin from such lengths, uniformity of muscle shortening should be examined (38, 42, 46). Finally, measurement of the heat production over very short time intervals (<50 msec) is difficult: Signal to noise ratios are low, corrections for thermal diffusion are large and uncertain, and thermoelastic and parallel elastic heat components are large for rapid releases. These problems are reduced when measurements are made over longer time intervals.

THE EFFECT OF DISTANCE SHORTENED   Hill (32) found that the amount of heat liberated when a muscle shortens is linearly dependent on the distance shortened. This idea is supported by the *approximately* linear time course of the heat produced during shortening when plotted as a function of time (32, 33, 40, 75). However, shortening heat is not precisely linear with distance shortened. Irving & Woledge (47) reexamined this question in muscles allowed to shorten distances ranging from 0.016 to 0.52 μm/sarcomere at constant velocity near 0.5 V_{max}. They found that the shortening heat produced by a muscle per unit distance shortened (α) is greater for shorter distances. After the muscle has shortened a distance of ~0.13 μm/sarcomere, α is constant. Yamada & Homsher (78) confirmed these results and found that the effect is more pronounced at higher velocities. These results suggest that the muscle does not reach a steady state immediately when it is allowed to shorten. Irving & Woledge (47) hypothesized that at the start of shortening there is an exothermic redistribution of the cross-bridge population between two fairly long-lived cross-bridge states.

There is one caveat about the interpretation of these experiments. During the isovelocity releases in the experiments of Irving & Woledge (46), the first portion of shortening occurred against a force greater than the steady-state load; likewise, during tension redevelopment, sarcomere shortening took place against a progressively increasing force. If the heat produced during shortening is load dependent, the periods of higher load during the initial and late phases of the procedure would have contributed a disproportionate fraction of the heat production when the muscles shortened a small distance. This effect would yield spuriously large heat values. This point can be tested by measuring the linearity of heat production versus distance shortened using a step-ramp length protocol that early in the shortening period brings the force to a level near that at steady state. In such experiments (E. Homsher & T.

Yamada, unpublished data) we find that the curvilinear relationship between distance shortened and heat production during shortening is attenuated at 0.5 V_{max} but exists to a significant degree at velocities near V_{max}. Thus, the heat produced by muscles shortening against a constant load can be regarded as proportional to the distance shortened, except in the case of shortening at high velocities.

THE EFFECT OF LOAD   Hill (32) concluded that the amount of heat produced above the isometric heat per unit shortening (α) was independent of the load. However, linear regression of Hill's data (Table 4, Reference 32) yields a normalized shortening heat coefficient (which is the shortening heat produced per centimeter shortened divided by the tetanic tension, α/P_0) that exhibits load dependence (i.e. $\alpha/P_0 = 0.16 + 0.07P/P_0$, $r^2 = 0.84$). Hill (33) reexamined this question and concluded that shortening heat was force dependent, i.e. $\alpha/P = 0.16 + 0.18P/P_0$, a result confirmed by Homsher & Rall (40). Why did Hill not recognize the force dependence in 1938? First, at high loads shortening heat is only fractionally greater than the isometric heat rate, and the isometric controls must be carefully made. There is no evidence that he paid as close attention to this detail in 1938 as he did in 1964. Second, though he did observe a load dependence in 1938, he chose to ignore it on the basis of its unreliability. Had he not done so, he could not have argued for the myothermal and mechanical identity of the constants a and b, the thesis of the 1938 paper.

The consequence of the load dependence of shortening heat is that as V/V_{max} increases from 0.5 to 1.0, the rate of energy liberation declines (see Figure 1). Huxley (44) explained this behavior within the context of his cross-bridge model (43) by invoking a two-step cross-bridge attachment. This reduces the net ATPase by reducing the number of cross-bridges entering the hydrolytic cycle per unit time at high shortening velocities.

THE EFFECT OF OVERLAP   If the increased rate of heat liberation during shortening is produced by cross-bridges, the amount of shortening heat evolved per unit shortening must be proportional to the degree of filament overlap. Tests of this hypothesis over the sarcomere length range 2.25–3.75 μm in muscles shortening at velocities near V_{max} revealed that the shortening heat per unit shortening was proportional to the amount of filament overlap and fell to zero at a sarcomere spacing of 3.70 μm (38). Given that the force-velocity equation applies to lengths > 2.25 μm (15, 29) and using the length dependence of the shortening heat, the rate of energy liberation ($\dot{h} + \dot{w}$) was calculated as a function of sarcomere length and shortening velocity. The results are shown in Figure 1. The rate of energy liberation (and presumably ATP splitting) is constantly changing as the muscle shortens from any sarcomere length greater than 2.25μm. Although not shown in Figure 1, the energy liberation rate for a given shortening velocity is constant in the range from 2.25 to 2.05 μm. At sarcomere lengths less than 2.05 μm, the rate of energy liberation declines. However, quantitative values can not be given because no definitive studies of shortening heat production have been made at sarcomere lengths less than 2.05 μm. The following calculation shows that the constancy of energy liberation within only the narrow plateau region of the length-tension curve makes it difficult to obtain precise whole-muscle steady-state ATPase rates for comparison with heat measurements or ATPase rates from isolated muscle proteins. In frog skeletal muscle shortening at 0.5 V_{max} at 0°C, the transit through the plateau region lasts 135 msec. At V_{max}, it lasts only 67 msec. During these time intervals, the amount of ATP hydrolyzed by the muscle shortening at 0.5 V_{max} and V_{max} should be 0.038 and 0.017 μmol/g, respectively. These changes are too small to measure in whole muscles.

THE EFFECT OF TEMPERATURE   Hill published the only study of the effect of temperature on enthalpy production during shortening (32). He measured the amount of shortening heat produced in four experiments at temperatures of 8.9–19.8°C and found that the amount of shortening heat increases in proportion to the increase in isometric force. Thus α/P_0 does not change with temperature. The Q_{10} is 1.3 for P_0, 2.3 for V_{max} (see 77, p. 56), and 3.1 for the normalized steady-state isometric heat rate (34). The energy liberated by the SR was estimated to be about 30% of the isometric heat rate (39). From this information we can calculate the S-1 turnover rate at different temperatures and different shortening velocities. Thus at 0.5 and 1.0 V_{max} at 20°C the actomyosin ATPase should be 32 and 27 sec^{-1}, respectively, as compared to 3.5 sec^{-1} and 3.2 sec^{-1}, respectively, at 0°C.

THE EFFECT OF DIFFERENT FIBER TYPES   Although most studies of the energetics of shortening muscles have been done on anurans, Woledge (75) showed the value of comparative studies. In tortoise muscle he found that the amount of heat produced concurrent with shortening is only about 15% as much as in the frog sartorius. Thus tortoise muscles are more efficient than those of frogs. There is no marked change in the heat rate during shortening of chicken muscle (63) or rat soleus muscles (25). These results suggest that the rate of ATP hydrolysis during shortening does not increase beyond that needed to do the work.

ATP CONSUMPTION DURING SHORTENING AND ITS RELATIONSHIP TO ENTHALPY PRODUCTION   Measurements of the changes in high-energy phosphate content in whole muscles are temporally less precise, more time consuming, and more difficult to make than heat measurements. Consequently, characterization of the high-energy phosphate consumption during contraction is not as detailed as is the enthalpy production. Studies (7, 42, 50) have shown that during shortening the amount of high-energy phosphate used is enough to account for the work performed, i.e. enough free energy is produced by ATP splitting to perform the observed work. Kushmerick & Davies (50) showed that in muscles shortening at velocities less than $0.5 \, V_{max}$, the ATPase rate varies in a manner similar to that shown in Figure 1 (see Figure 4.35 in Reference 77 for a comparison of this rate with enthalpy production). Homsher et al (42) directly compared the enthalpy produced during shortening at $0.5 \, V_{max}$ to that liberated by the measured high-energy phosphate splitting. During neither the 350-msec period of shortening nor the 650-msec isometric interval following shortening was a significant amount of unexplained enthalpy produced; more than 93% of the energy liberated was accounted for by the splitting of phosphocreatine. In addition, Kushmerick & Davies (50) found that the rate of ATP hydrolysis during shortening at 0.7 and $1.0 \, V_{max}$ was less than expected. Energy balance studies (37, 62) showed that during shortening at V_{max} more enthalpy is liberated than can be explained by the concomitant high-energy phosphate usage. However, in the period immediately following shortening more ATP is hydrolyzed than is necessary to explain the heat production. These results suggest that *during* shortening a reaction other than high-energy phosphate hydrolysis produces heat, and immediately *after* shortening ATP is used to reverse this reaction. Thus the implication of Figure 1 is valid: Shortening does increase the ATPase reaction rate in muscle. At high shortening velocities, however, the increased rate of ATP splitting is not in phase with the increased rate of energy liberation. Therefore, the cross-bridge cycle during rapid shortening is not simply a faster version of that occurring in the isometric case. Other data suggest that rapid shortening alters the cross-bridge reaction mechanism: (*a*) Yanagida et al (80) found very little ATP hydrolysis during unloaded shortening in myofibrils; (*b*) the rate of force redevelopment is depressed after an episode of rapid shortening (16); and (*c*) the ability of the muscle to generate work and shortening heat is reduced after shortening long distances at high velocities (47, 77).

Two hypotheses to explain the energy imbalance seen during rapid shortening have been proposed. Irving & Woledge (47) proposed that the cross-bridge population is redistributed during shortening, leading to a lower enthalpy content. For example, if during the transition from an isometric tetanus to shortening at V_{max} 60% of the S-1 molecules (0.18 μmol/g) detach from the thin filaments, and if the transition from the attached to the detached state is accompanied by an enthalpy change of -50 kJ/mol, then shortening would be accompanied by the production of 9 mJ/g enthalpy beyond that due to ATP splitting. This is consistent with the decline in muscle stiffness during shortening (24) and the exothermic nature of the dissociation of certain acto-S-1 states (see Table 3). A second hypothesis postulates a branch point in the "normal" cross-bridge cycle such that during rapid shortening cross-bridges redistribute into a state not highly populated during isometric contraction. The rate at which the cross-bridges return to the "normal" cycle is dependent on the shortening velocity; i.e. there may be cross-bridge attachment-detachment cycles in which ATP is not hydrolyzed (45, 62). The isometric cross-bridge reaction mechanism might include reactions a–d, below:

$$\underset{a}{\rightarrow} \text{AM} \cdot \text{ADP} \cdot \text{Pi} \underset{b}{\rightarrow} \text{AM} \cdot \text{ADP} + \text{Pi} \underset{c}{\rightarrow} \text{AM} + \text{ADP} \underset{d}{\rightarrow}$$

$$e \updownarrow$$

$$\text{M} \cdot \text{ADP}$$

However, during rapid shortening attached cross-bridges might be torn from the thin filament after releasing Pi via path e, presumably liberating a large amount of enthalpy. Then M·ADP presumably rapidly reattaches to actin and then proceeds through steps c and d (17). However, near V_{max} a given g-actin spends so little time close to a given cross-bridge (2–4 msec within 2.5 nm) that the strongly attached state (AM·ADP) may not form before detachment is forced again. If this is the case, M·ADP will accumulate during rapid shortening, leading to more enthalpy production than can be accounted for by the measured ATP hydrolysis. Upon the cessation of shortening, there would be a sudden release of ADP, as M·ADP rapidly reattaches to the thin filaments, followed by a burst of ATP cleavage.

Can such hypotheses be experimentally tested? Measurements of the time course of ATP splitting in whole muscle are not useful because the standard deviation (0.3 μmol/g) and time resolution (30–80 msec) of these measurements are inadequate. Better temporal and chemical resolution is required. The "flash and smash" method developed by Ferenczi et al (22), which uses the photolytic release of radioactively labeled ATP from caged ATP in single, skinned muscle fibers, can resolve time intervals of less than 20 msec and amounts of nucleotide hydrolysis equivalent to 10–20% of the myosin heads. Using this technique, the time course of ATP hydrolysis can be studied before, during, and after shortening. Thus the characteristics of the first hypothesis (rapid approach to steady-state ATPase during shortening and gradual return to steady-state after cessation of shortening) may be distinguished from those of the second hypothesis (progressive approach to a steady-state during rapid shortening and a sudden release of ADP and burst of ATP hydrolysis following cessation of shortening). This approach also permits study of the energetics of different fiber types and examination of the effects of calcium, ionic strength, phosphate, etc on these ATPases. But most importantly, it allows one to examine the ATPase reaction rate in an isolated, controlled, but mechanically coupled, actomyosin system.

Thus the available data indicate that, except at high shortening velocity, changes in muscle energy liberation can be explained by changes in the rate of high-energy phosphate splitting. To further analyze the energy imbalance observed during shortening at velocities near V_{max}, new analytical techniques will be needed.

SUMMARY

During a maintained tetanus most of the energy liberated is produced by ATP hydrolysis at the cross-bridge. The energy produced by ATP hydrolysis by the sarcolplasmic reticulum is, however, a significant fraction (0.35) of the total. The energy liberation rate depends on a variety of factors (including the shortening velocity, sarcomere length, temperature, fiber type, and duration of contraction) and is, for the most part, consistent with current cross-bridge models. At the beginning of tetanic stimulation, a significant amount of heat ($\sim$30 mJ/g) is produced by calcium binding reactions in the sarcoplasm. In the transition from an isometric to a shortening contraction, the cross-bridge cycling rate increases, and as much as 6 mJ/g of unexplained heat is produced. This unexplained heat appears to involve enthalpy changes accompanying a redistribution of cross-bridge intermediates, and it is reversed by high-energy phosphate splitting after the cessation of shortening. The mechanistic significance of these enthalpy changes remains to be elucidated.

ACKNOWLEDGMENTS

The author gratefully acknowledges the assistance of Dianne Smith in the preparation of the manuscript and the research support of the National Institutes of Health through grant AM 30988.

Literature Cited

1. Aubert, X. 1956. *Le Couplage Energetique de la Contraction Musculaire*. Brussels: Arscia
2. Barany, K., Barany, M. 1977. Phosphorylation of the 18,000-dalton light chain of myosin during a single tetanus of frog muscle. *J. Biol. Chem.* 252:4752–54
3. Barany, K., Barany, M., Gillis, J. M., Kushmerick, M. J. 1979. Phorphorylation-dephosphorylation of the 18,000-dalton light chain of myosin during the contraction-relaxation cycle of frog muscle. *J. Biol. Chem.* 254:3617–23
4. Blinks, J. R., Wier, W. G., Hess, P., Prendergast, F. G. 1982. Measurement of Ca^{2+} concentrations in living cells. *Prog. Biophys.* 40:1–114
5. Burchfield, D. M., Rall, J. A. 1984. Effects of temperature on V_0, force, stiffness, and energy liberation in frog skeletal muscle. *Biophys. J.* 45:342a
6. Canfield, P., LeBacq, J., Marechal, G. 1973. Energy balance in frog sartorius

muscle during an isometric tetanus at 20°C. *J. Physiol.* 232:467–83

7. Curtin, N. A., Gilbert, C., Kretzchmar, K. M., Wilkie, D. R. 1974. The effect of the performance of work on total energy output and metabolism during muscular contraction. *J. Physiol.* 238:455–72

8. Curtin, N. A., Howarth, J. V., Woledge, R. C. 1983. Heat production by single fibres of frog muscle. *J. Muscle Res. Cell Motil.* 4:207–22

9. Curtin, N. A., Woledge, R. C. 1977. A comparison of the energy balance in two successive isometric tetani of frog muscle. *J. Physiol.* 270:455–71

10. Curtin, N. A., Woledge, R. C. 1978. Energy changes and muscular contraction. *Physiol. Rev.* 58:690–761

11. Curtin, N. A., Woledge, R. C. 1979. Chemical change and energy production during contraction in frog muscle: How are their time courses related? *J. Physiol.* 288:353–66

12. Curtin, N. A., Woledge, R. C. 1981. Effect of muscle length on energy balance in frog skeletal muscle. *J. Physiol.* 316:453–68

13. Dawson, M. J., Gadian, D. G., Wilkie, D. R. 1977. Contraction and recovery of living muscles studied by ^{31}P nuclear magnetic resonance. *J. Physiol.* 267:703–35

14. Ebashi, S., Endo, M., Ohtsuki, I. 1969. Control of muscle contraction. *Q. Rev. Biophys.* 2:351–84

15. Edman, K. A. P. 1979. The velocity of unloaded shortening and its relation to sarcomere length and isometric force in vertebrate muscle fibres. *J. Physiol.* 291:143–59

16. Edman, K. A. P. 1980. Depression of mechanical performance by active shortening during twitch and tetanus of vertebrate muscle fibres. *Acta Physiol. Scand.* 109:15–26

17. Eisenberg, E., Hill, T. 1985. Muscle contraction and free energy transduction in biological systems. *Science* 227:999

18. Eisenberg, E., Hill, T., Chen, Y. 1980. Cross-bridge model of muscle contraction. *Biophys. J.* 29:195–227

19. Eisenberg, R. S., McCarthy, R. T., Milton, R. L. 1983. Paralysis of frog skeletal muscle fibers by the calcium antagonist D-600. *J. Physiol.* 341:495–505

20. Endo, M. 1977. Calcium release from the sarcoplasmic reticulum. *Physiol. Rev.* 57:71–108

21. Ferenczi, M. A., Homsher, E., Simmons, R. M., Trentham, D. R. 1978. Reaction mechanism of the magnesium ion-dependent adenosine triphosphatase of frog muscle myosin and subfragment 1. *Biochem. J.* 171:165–75

22. Ferenczi, M. A., Homsher, E., Trentham, D. R. 1984. The kinetics of magnesium adenosine triphosphate cleavage in skinned muscle fibers of rabbit. *J. Physiol.* 352:575–99

23. Ford, L. E., Huxley, A. F., Simmons, R. M. 1977. Tension responses to sudden length change in stimulated frog muscle fibres near slack length. *J. Physiol.* 269:441–515

24. Ford, L. E., Huxley, A. F., Simmons, R. M. 1985. Tension transients during steady state shortening of frog muscle fibers. *J. Physiol.* 361:131–50

25. Gibbs, C. L., Gibson, W. R. 1972. Energy production of rat soleus muscle. *Am. J. Physiol.* 223:864–71

26. Gilbert, C., Kretzschmar, K. M., Wilkie, D. R., Woledge, R. C. 1971. Chemical change and energy output during muscular contraction. *J. Physiol.* 218:163–93

27. Gilbert, S. H., Ford, L. E. 1986. The thermoelastic effect in rigor muscle of the frog. *J. Muscle Res. Cell Motil.* 7:35–46

28. Godt, R. E., Lindley, B. D. 1982. Influence of temperature upon contractile activation and isometric force production in mechanically skinned muscle fibres of the frog. *J. Gen. Physiol.* 80:279–97

29. Gordon, A. M., Huxley, A. F., Julian, F. J. 1986. The variation in isometric tension with sarcomere length in vertebrate muscle fibres. *J. Physiol.* 184:170–92

30. Gosselin-Rey, C., Gerday, C. 1977. Parvalbumins from frog skeletal muscle. Isolation and characterisation. Structural modifications associated with calcium binding. *Biochim. Biophys. Acta* 492:53–63

31. Haiech, J., Derancourt, J., Pechere, J. F., Demaille, J. P. 1979. Magnesium and calcium binding to parvalbumins and an explanation of their relaxing function. *Biochemistry* 18:2752–58

32. Hill, A. V. 1938. The heat of shortening and the dynamic constants of muscle. *Proc. R. Soc. London Ser. B.* 126:136–95

33. Hill, A. V. 1964. The effect of load on the heat of shortening of muscle. *Proc. R. Soc. London Ser. B.* 159:297–318

34. Hill, A. V., Woledge, R. C. 1962. An examination of absolute values in myothermic measurement. *J. Physiol.* 162:311–33

35. Homsher, E., Kean, C. J. 1978. Skeletal muscle energetics and metabolism. *Ann. Rev. Physiol.* 40:93–131

36. Homsher, E., Kean, C. J., Wallner, A., Garibian-Sarian, V. 1979. The time course of energy balance in an isometric tetanus. *J. Gen. Physiol.* 73:553–67

37. Homsher, E., Irving, M., Wallner, A. 1981. High-energy phosphate metabolism and energy liberation associated with rapid shortening in frog skeletal muscle. *J. Physiol.* 321:423–36

38. Homsher, E., Irving, M., LeBacq, J. 1983. The variation in shortening heat with sarcomere length in frog muscle. *J. Physiol.* 345:107–21

39. Homsher, E., Mommaerts, W. F. H. M., Ricchiuti, N. V., Wallner, A. 1972. Activation heat, activation metabolism and tension-related heat in frog semitendinosus muscles. *J. Physiol.* 220:601–25

40. Homsher, E., Rall, J. A. 1973. Energetics of shortening muscles in twitches and tetanic contractions. I. A reinvestigation of Hill's concept of shortening heat. *J. Gen. Physiol.* 62:663–76

41. Homsher, E., Lacktis, J., Yamada, T., Zohman, G. 1986. Repriming and reversal of the isometric unexplained enthalpy in frog sartorius muscle at 0°C. *J. Physiol.* In press

42. Homsher, E., Yamada, T., Wallner, A., Tsai, J. 1984. Energy balance studies in frog skeletal muscles shortening at one-half maximal velocity. *J. Gen. Physiol.* 84:347–60

43. Huxley, A. F. 1957. Muscle structure and theories of contraction. *Prog. Biophys. Biophys. Chem.* 7:255–318

44. Huxley, A. F. 1973. A note suggesting that the cross-bridge attachment during muscle contraction may take place in two stages. *Proc. R. Soc. London Ser. B.* 183:83–86

45. Irving, M. 1985. Weak and strong cross-bridges. *Nature* 316:292–93

46. Irving, M., Woledge, R. C. 1981. The dependence on extent of shortening of the extra energy liberated by rapidly shortening frog skeletal muscle. *J. Physiol.* 321:411–22

47. Irving, M., Woledge, R. C. 1981. The energy liberation of frog skeletal muscle in tetanic contractions containing two periods of shortening. *J. Physiol.* 321:401–10

48. Julian, F. J., Morgan, D. L. 1979. The effect on tension of non-uniform distribution of length changes applied to frog muscle fibres. *J. Physiol.* 293:379–92

49. Kodama, T. 1985. Thermodynamic analysis of muscle ATPase mechanism. *Physiol. Rev.* 65:467–551

49a. Kodama, T., Kurebayashi, N., Ogawa, Y. 1980. Heat production and proton release during the ATP-driven Ca uptake by fragmented sarcoplasmic reticulum from bullfrog and rabbit skeletal muscle. *J. Biochem.* 88:1259–65

50. Kushmerick, M. J., Davies, R. E. 1969. The chemical energetics of muscle contraction. II. The chemistry, efficiency and power of maximally working sartorius muscles. *Proc. R. Soc. London Ser. B.* 174:315–53

51. Kushmerick, M. J., Krasner, B. 1982. Force and ATPase rate in skinned skeletal muscle fibers. *Fed. Proc.* 41:2232–37

52. Kushmerick, M. J., Paul, R. J. 1976. Aerobic recovery metabolism following a single isometric tetanus in frog sartorius at 0°C. *J. Physiol.* 254:693–709

53. Kushmerick, M. J., Paul, R. J. 1976. Relationship between initial chemical reactions and oxidative recovery metabolism for single isometric contractions of frog sartorius at 0°C. *J. Physiol.* 254:711–27

54. Levy, R. M., Umazume, Y., Kushmerick, M. J. 1976, Ca^{++} dependence of tension and ADP production in segments of chemically skinned muscle fibres. *Biochim. Biophys. Acta.* 430:325–65

55. Maughan, D., Lord, C., Guilian, G. 1986. Protein separation of cytosolic and cytomatrix fractions from skinned skeletal muscle fibers. *Biophys. J.* 49:251a

56. Mornet, D. R., Bertrand, R., Pantel, P., Audemard, E., Kassab, B. 1981. Structure of the actin-myosin interface. *Nature* 292:301–6

57. Paul, R. J. 1983. Physical and biochemical energy balance during an isometric tetanus and steady state recovery in frog sartorius at 0°C. *J. Gen. Physiol.* 81:337–54

58. Peckham, M., Woledge, R. C. 1986. Labile heat and changes in rate of relaxation of frog muscles. *J. Physiol.* 374:123–35

59. Potter, J. D., Gergely, J. 1975. The calcium and magnesium binding sites on troponin and their role in the regulation of myofibrillar adenosine triphosphatase. *J. Biol. Chem.* 250:4628–33

60. Potter, J. D., Hsu, F., Pownall, H. J. 1976. Thermodynamics of Ca^{+2} binding to troponin C. *J. Biol. Chem.* 252:2452–54

61. Rall, J. A. 1982. Sense and nonsense about the Fenn effect. *Am. J. Physiol.* 242:H1–H6

62. Rall, J. A., Homsher, E., Wallner, A., Mommaerts, W. F. H. M. 1976. A temporal dissociation of energy liberation and high energy phosphate splitting during shortening in frog skeletal muscle. *J. Gen. Physiol.* 68:13–27

63. Rall, J. A., Schottelius, B. A. 1973. Energetics of contraction in phasic and tonic skeletal muscles of the chicken. *J. Gen. Physiol.* 62:303–23

64. Sandberg, J. A., Carlson, F. D. 1966. The length dependence of phosphorylcreatine hydrolysis during an isometric tetanus. *Biochem. Z.* 345:212–31

65. Schoenberg, M., Podolsky, R. J. 1972. Length-force relation of calcium activated muscle fibers. *Science* 176:52–54

66. Smith, I. C. H. 1972. Energetics of activation in frog and toad muscle. *J. Physiol. London* 220:583–99

67. Smith, S. J., White, H. D., Woledge, R. C. 1984. Microcalorimetric measurement of the enthalpy of binding of rabbit skeletal myosin subfragment 1 and heavy meromyosin to F-actin. *J. Biol. Chem.* 259:10303–8

68. Smith, S. J., Woledge, R. C. 1985. Thermodynamic analysis of calcium binding to frog parvalbumin. *J. Muscle Res. Cell Motil.* 6:757–68

69. Somlyo, A. V., McClellan, G., Gonzales-Serratos, H., Somlyo, A. P. 1985. Electron probe x-ray microanalysis of post-tetanic Ca and Mg movements across the sarcoplasmic reticulum in situ. *J. Biol. Chem.* 260:6801–7

70. Tanokura, M., Yamada, K. 1985. A calorimetric study of calcium binding to two major isotypes of bullfrog parvalbumin. *FEBS Lett.* 185:165–69

71. Taylor, E. W. 1979. Mechanism of actomyosin ATPase and the problem of muscular contraction. *Crit. Rev. Biochem.* 6:103–64

72. Tormey, J. McD., Homsher, E. 1986. Calcium sequestration in frog sartorius muscle at 0°C correlated with unexplained enthalpy reversal. An electron probe microanalysis study. *Biophys. J.* 49:423a

73. Venosa, R. A. 1974. Inward movement of sodium ions in resting and stimulated frog's sartorius muscle. *J. Physiol.* 241:155–73

73a. Weingardt, R., Hess, P. 1984. Free calcium in sheep cardiac tissue and frog skeletal muscle measured with Ca^{+2} selective microelectrodes. *Pflüg. Arch. Gesamte Physiol. Menschen Tiere* 402:1–9

74. Wilkie, D. R. 1960. Thermodynamics and interpretations of biological heat measurements. *Prog. Biophys. Biophys. Chem.* 10:259–98

75. Woledge, R. C. 1968. The energetics of tortoise muscle. *J. Physiol.* 197:685–707

76. Woledge, R. C. 1973. In vitro calorimetric studies relating to the interpretation of muscle heat experiments. *Cold Spring Harbor Symp. Quant. Biol.* 37:629–34

77. Woledge, R. C., Curtin, N. A., Homsher, E. 1985. *Energetic Aspects of Muscle Contraction.* London: Academic

78. Yamada, T., Homsher, E. 1984. The dependence on the distance of shortening of the energy output from frog skeletal muscle shortening at velocities of V_{max}, $1/2V_{max}$, and $1/4V_{max}$. *Adv. Exp. Med. Biol.* 170:883–86

79. Yamada, T., Shimuzu, H., Suga, H. 1973. A kinetic study of the energy storing enzyme product complex in the hydrolysis of ATP by heavy meromyosin. *Biochim. Biophys. Acta.* 305:642–53

80. Yanagida, T., Arata, T., Oosawa, F. 1985. Sliding distance of actin filament induced by a myosin crossbridge during one ATP hydrolysis cycle. *Nature* 316:366–69

81. Yates, L. D., Greaser, M. L. 1983. Troponin subunit stoichiometry and content in rabbit skeletal muscle and myofibrils. *J. Biol. Chem.* 258:5770–74

82. Yates, L. D., Greaser, M. L. 1983. Quantitative determination of myosin and actin in rabbit skeletal muscle. *J. Mol. Biol.* 168:123–41

Ann. Rev. Physiol. 1987. 49:691–709

SPECTROSCOPIC PROBES OF MUSCLE CROSS-BRIDGE ROTATION

David D. Thomas

Department of Biochemistry, University of Minnesota Medical School, Minneapolis, Minnesota 55455

INTRODUCTION

Recent progress in the quantitative study of the mechanics, biochemistry, and molecular structure of muscle has resulted in the formulation of detailed models for the molecular mechanism of force production (reviewed in References 18 and 31). Most of these models involve the motions of myosin cross-bridges, which are coupled to the actin-activated ATPase cycle of myosin. Spectroscopic probes play an essential role in testing these models. In general, spectroscopic methods permit studies to be carried out under physiological or near-physiological conditions that are often inaccessible to more invasive analytical techniques such as electron microscopy or chemical analysis. The detection of site-specific signals, particularly from extrinsically introduced molecular probes attached to myosin heads, offers the kind of selectivity that is not usually possible with mechanical or x-ray diffraction studies. Most importantly, each spectroscopic technique is sensitive to its own specific physical properties, so a judicious choice of technique permits a relatively direct selection of physical parameters that are particularly relevant to contraction models. Techniques sensitive to orientation and rotational motion are particularly important, since cross-bridge rotations are the key events according to most models (18, 32).

The present review surveys the recent literature on spectroscopic studies of cross-bridge orientation and rotational motion. Emphasis is placed on applications to intact or skinned fibers, although studies on myofibrils or purified myosin are also included in cases where they are of particular relevance to fiber work or where extensions of the techniques to fibers are likely. The review is divided into two main sections, optical probes and spin probes.

Space does not permit a detailed discussion of instrumentation or theoretical principles, but key methodological aspects are discussed briefly in each section in order to compare the strengths and weaknesses and illustrate the complementary information obtainable with different techniques. These techniques differ not only in the types of probes and instruments used and the types of physical parameters measured, but also in their sensitivity and ability to resolve individual molecular states in a complex system. Although some relatively noninvasive techniques involving intrinsic spectroscopic signals are discussed briefly, more space is devoted to the discussion of extrinsic probes. These are more likely to perturb the system, but they offer the advantages of site-selectivity and choice of physical property measured, which are requirements for direct and unambiguous tests of specific molecular models. By providing these brief discussions of technical principles, I hope to help muscle physiologists who are not spectroscopists, in their attempts to assess the literature on muscle spectroscopy and to gain insight into possible spectroscopic applications related to their own work.

Several more comprehensive reviews on the application of particular spectroscopic methods to muscle have appeared recently, including a volume on optical techniques (7), and review articles on molecular dynamics (29), fluorescence (17), EPR (44), and NMR (43). Spectroscopic data are also discussed in a recent review of the molecular mechanism of muscle contraction (18). The reference list is not exhaustive; to minimize its length, these reviews are sometimes cited below instead of specific research articles.

OPTICAL ANISOTROPY

Methods and Principles

The intensities of transitions in the ultraviolet and visible regions of the spectrum, which reflect the extinction coefficient in absorption and the quantum yield (lifetime) in fluorescence emission, have provided information about the local environments of intrinsic and extrinsic chromophores in myosin. However, the interpretation of these effects in terms of specific physical changes (as opposed to vaguely defined "conformational changes") is usually not possible. An exception is the technique of fluorescence energy transfer, which can provide relatively specific information about interchromophore distances (17). However, the requirement of two specifically placed chromophores has so far prevented extensive applications to muscle fibers, and this technique is not very useful for studying chromophore orientation or rotation.

Techniques with sensitivity to molecular rotation require the use of polarized light. When the interaction of light with the sample depends on the polarization, the sample is said to be optically anisotropic, and information about orientation can be extracted. Some techniques, such as depolarized light scattering (28) and birefringence (59), involve light scattering (as opposed to absorptive or emissive electronic transitions). These techniques can complement those involving absorption or emission, since they do not require the introduction of probes and are sensitive only to large-scale motions. However, the assignment of these signals to particular molecular components (e.g. cross-bridges or myosin heads) in a complex system (e.g. a muscle fiber) is usually ambiguous, and the remainder of this section is restricted to a discussion of absorption or emission of polarized light by site-specific chromophores. More detailed reviews of some of these methods and their applications to muscle have appeared recently (10, 41).

PROBES   Intrinsic ultraviolet absorption and fluorescence, which presumably arises primarily from tryptophan residues, provided some of the earliest spectroscopic signals from myosin. However, the large number of tryptophan residues within myosin and other myofibrillar proteins effectively eliminates the possibility of detecting fluorescence from specific sites in fiber studies. Thus most recent studies of optical absorption and fluorescence have used organic dyes, with absorption and/or emission in the visible region of the spectrum, bound covalently or ionically to myosin. The most commonly used of these probes are iodoacetamide or maleimide derivatives, which react relatively specifically with SH_1 (Cys 510) on the myosin heavy chain or with Cys 177 on isolated alkali light chains. Probes that react covalently at other sites sometimes have sufficient specificity to be used in studies of isolated myosin but the specificity is usually not sufficient for use in fibers. The most specific noncovalent probes are nucleotide analogs, notably etheno-ATP and its derivatives, which bind with high affinity and specificity to myosin's active site.

Most optical experiments are performed on fluorescent probes, which have excited singlet states with lifetimes in the nanosecond range. Some of these probes are also phosphorescent; i.e. they have efficiently populated and stable triplet states (and are hence often called "triplet probes"), which result in long-wavelength emission with lifetimes on the order of a millisecond or longer. In principle, intrinsic tryptophan residues could serve as triplet probes, but their phosphorescence quantum yields are extremely low in solution at room temperature, and no applications have been reported for myosin. Therefore, extrinsic probes, usually derivatives of eosin or erythrosin, are used for most triplet probe studies. The derivatives used in myosin studies have the same functional groups—usually iodoacetamide or maleimide—used to label SH_1 with other probes (47).

TRANSIENT OPTICAL ANISOTROPY   Excitation with a pulse of polarized light, followed by time-resolved detection of the polarization anisotropy $r(t)$ of emitted light, is used to measure rotational motion. The time constant (rotational correlation time, τ_r) and amplitude of each resolved exponential decay component of $r(t)$ are determined by the time constants and angular amplitudes of probe motion, as well as by the mole fraction of each rotating species. Rotational motions can be detected only if they occur within the time scale of the excited-state lifetime. Thus for transient fluorescence anisotropy (TFA), if there are no nanosecond rotations, $r(t)$ is constant over the detectable time range, and slower motions can only be detected by transient phosphorescence anisotropy (TPA), which usually requires a different probe. Transient anisotropy is usually detected by emission (TFA or TPA) but can also be detected by absorption (transient absorption anisotropy, TAA), which is often used to study the rotational motion of phosphorescent probes. The rotational correlation times and amplitudes obtained from TFA, TPA, and TAA experiments can provide information about segmental flexibility and processes that limit it (e.g. steric constraints or binding). Macroscopic orientation of the sample (e.g. a muscle fiber) is not required for the detection of these motions. However, if the sample is macroscopically oriented, more detailed information can be obtained about anisotropic motions (13). The methods and principles of transient optical anisotropy were reviewed recently (47).

STEADY-STATE FLUORESCENCE POLARIZATION   If a labeled muscle fiber (or bundle of fibers) is irradiated with polarized light, in the absence of nanosecond rotational motion, the steady-state (time-averaged) polarization anisotropy is determined by the distribution of probe orientations relative to the fiber axis. Because of the inherent symmetry of the muscle fiber, only the axial orientations (not the azimuthal ones) are detectable. If both exciting and emitted light are passed through polarizers, the experiment is usually called *fluorescence polarization* (41). If the exciting light is polarized, but the fluorescence emission is detected with a wide-angle lens and no polarizer, the result is equivalent to that of absorption dichroism. This experiment, referred to below as *fluorescence dichroism* (10), maximizes the fluorescent signal detected, thus facilitating studies of single fibers. These two techniques can detect small changes in orientation, but the quality of information about the orientational distribution of probes is relatively low compared with that of the magnetic resonance techniques discussed in later sections. This results in considerable ambiguity in data interpretation, especially for the fluorescence dichroism measurement, which only reports the average orientation. Therefore, in fluorescence dichroism, there is not enough resolution to determine the number of different orientations, and a change in average orientation can not be distinguished from a change in the width (disorder) of the orientational distribution (10). Fluorescence polarization measurements can provide slightly more information, but many different orientational models are usually consistent with each measurement (41).

Purified Myosin

NANOSECOND MOTIONS   TFA experiments on myosin, labeled primarily at SH_1 with an iodoacetamide derivative of dansyl (1,5-IAEDANS), provided some of the earliest direct evidence for dynamic segmental flexibility within myosin (39). The motion of the probe in isolated subfragment 1 of myosin (S-1) was slow enough to suggest that the probe reported overall reorientation of the major axis of S-1 and that S-1 behaves as a rigid body. However, the motion was not much slower in heavy meromyosin (HMM) or myosin monomer, which suggested that the two heads of myosin rotate freely relative to each other and to the rest of myosin, with a rotational correlation time of several hundred nanoseconds at 20°C. The probe was found to be much less mobile in myosin filaments and actomyosin; very little rotational motion could be detected in the observed time window (1–100 nsec). The slight anisotropy decay that was observable in myosin filaments was not affected significantly by addition of calcium nor by removal of one of the two myosin heads (41). The increase in the anisotropy of 1,5-AEDANS on SH_1 has been used to measure binding constants of S-1 and HHM to actin in solution (41).

MICROSECOND MOTIONS   TPA and TAA experiments on an iodoacetamide derivative of eosin (EIA) provided sensitivity to motions on a time scale from ten nanoseconds to tens of microseconds (25, 36). This time range was short enough to confirm (and characterize more completely) the nanosecond motions observed previously for S-1 and myosin monomers by TFA (39), and it was long enough to quantitate slower motions. These measurements showed that considerable microsecond rotational mobility remains in myosin filaments, although the motions are restricted in both rate and amplitude, and even the microsecond head motions are prevented by actin. These results confirmed earlier findings from saturation transfer electron paramagnetic resonance (EPR) (discussed below) and also showed that two degrees of rotational freedom can be resolved in both myosin monomers and filaments. The two proposed "hinges" that separate S-1, S-2, and light meromyosin (LMM) probably account for this flexibility. The correlation times for these motions are about 0.7 and 5 microseconds at 4°C, and each has an amplitude of about ±30° or 40°, if a model is adopted in which the two cross-bridge segments (S-1 and S-2) wobble independently within cones. This finding of large-amplitude motions in synthetic myosin filaments is consistent with the low steady-state anisotropy observed with fluorescent probes bound to myosin heads in relaxed muscle fibers and with the large range of orientations reported for spin labels bound to myosin heads in relaxed or stretched muscle fibers (discussed below). The motions are inhibited by Mg^{2+}, H^+, and decreased ionic strength (36). These results are consistent with the proposal that such conditions promote the partial immobilization of the cross-bridge on the thick filament surface, but they indicate that the myosin heads are at least partially mobile a large fraction of the time. Evidence for microsecond myosin flexibility was also obtained in TPA and TAA experiments on myosin labeled with eosin-maleimide (35). The measurements were performed in 60% sucrose to increase the viscosity of the solution to slow the molecular motions, since the instrument used did not have sufficient time resolution to detect the motions at the normal viscosity. Nevertheless, when the decays were scaled to lower viscosity, they were in remarkably good agreement with the direct measurements reported in Reference 25.

Rigor and Relaxation

NANOSECOND MOTIONS   TFA measurements on IAEDANS-labeled myofibrils or muscle fibers show very little anisotropy decay, which indicates that most of the rotational motion that does exist must be in the microsecond range or slower (41). However, when the experiments were performed with exciting polarization perpendicular to the fiber axis (13), fibers in rigor showed faster probe mobility than in relaxation. This result suggests that some nanosecond rotation about the fiber axis occurs within the actomyosin complex that does not occur in free myosin.

MICROSECOND MOTIONS   Preliminary reports of TPA studies on eosin-labeled myofibrils (33, 38) indicate that the mobility of myosin heads in relaxation is similar to that in synthetic myosin filaments (moderately restricted microsecond motion) and that the mobility in rigor is similar to that in actomyosin (little or no microsecond motion). These findings are consistent with previous EPR results (discussed below).

ORIENTATION   Although the tryptophan fluorescence of a muscle fiber arises only partially from myosin, the change in tryptophan fluorescence polarization observed when fibers go from relaxation to rigor is probably due, at least in part, to changes in cross-bridge orientation (24, 30, 41). More site-selective fluorescence polarization studies, with extrinsic probes attached primarily to myosin heads, have also shown differences between relaxation and rigor states. For both fluorescence polarization, using IAEDANS (41), tryptophan (30), or fluorescent nucleotides (56–58), and fluorescence dichroism, using iodoacetamidotetramethylrhodamine (IATR) (9, 10, 41), the probes become much more disordered in relaxation or when myosin and actin filaments do not overlap. In at least some of these cases, the disorder in relaxation is high but not complete (i.e. the distribution of axial probe angles is not completely random), and the center of the broad orientational distribution may not be significantly different from that of the narrow distribution in rigor (10, 41, 55).

Contraction

NANOSECOND MOTIONS   TFA experiments showed that IAEDANS undergoes restricted nanosecond motions (which are probably azimuthal, i.e. involve rotation about the fiber axis) in active fibers at 4°C; this motion is closer to that seen in rigor than that occurring in relaxation (12). This data did not reveal two (or more) resolved components that could be used to quantitate directly the fractions of probes in different states. However, if the nanosecond motions of this probe in actin-attached myosin heads are assumed to be the same during contraction as in rigor, this result suggests that most heads (>80%) interact with actin in actively contracting fibers.

MICROSECOND MOTIONS   Preliminary phosphorescence studies using EIA indicate that, on the microsecond time scale, the motions of the probe in active fibers are closer to those in relaxation than those in rigor (38).

ORIENTATION   Early studies of tryptophan fluorescence polarization reported polarization values in bundles of activated fibers that were intermediate between those observed during relaxation and rigor (24, 41). However, a more recent study (30) concluded that the difference between the relaxation and activation values was greatly decreased if an ATP-regenerating system was provided to prevent the appearance of a rigor core in the fiber bundle (30). This finding indicates that the nanosecond rotations and orientational distribution of tryptophan residues, a substantial proportion of which are on myosin heads, are very similar in relaxation and activation.

More recent studies have used extrinsic probes. At low concentrations of etheno-ATP (56) or its aza derivative (58) in isometrically contracting glycerinated fibers, fluorescence polarization shows that the only oriented nucleotide population has an orientation similar to that of the ADP derivative in rigor. At saturating nucleotide concentrations, it was estimated that ~40% of the nucleotide molecules were oriented as in rigor with the remainder disoriented as in relaxation (58). Similar results were obtained with IAEDANS (57). In contrast to other fluorescent and spin probes, the fluorescence dichroism of IATR bound to SH_1 has a value during contraction that cannot be a linear combination of the signals seen in rigor and relaxation unless the ADP-rigor state is used. (The effects of ADP are discussed below.) Thus IATR has an orientation in attached heads that is distinct from that observed in the absence of nucleotides (14). This difference may be related to the fluctuations in fluorescence polarization observed in IATR-labeled fibers during contraction (11).

Intermediate States

A variety of chemical and mechanical perturbations have been applied in an attempt to resolve possible intermediate states that occur during the cross-bridge cycle in contraction. Since the cross-bridge cycle is accompanied by changes in the chemical state of the nucleotide bound to myosin, the physical properties of myosin heads have been studied after the addition of a number of nonhydrolyzable nucleotides and nucleotide analogs.

The physiological state of rigor can be achieved either in the presence or absence of Mg-ADP in glycerinated fibers, and ADP causes no changes in x-ray diffraction nor in the fluorescence polarization of intrinsic tryptophan residues in fibers (24). Similarly, the fluorescence dichroism of IAEDANS bound to SH_1 is unaffected by ADP (9). Nevertheless, two other fluorescent probes [IATR and iodoacetamido fluorescein (IAF)] bound to the same site show substantial fluorescence dichroism changes upon addition of ADP. This observation has prompted investigators to propose that the myosin head undergoes an internal conformational change in which one domain (of un-known size) rotates while another remains relatively stationary (9). Another interpretation is that ADP causes a large rotation of the whole myosin head but that some probes (including most tryptophans) have orientations within the head that make them insensitive to the rotation. However, this idea is difficult to reconcile with the negative x-ray diffraction results. In the pres-ence of 50% glycerol, lowering the temperature produces a change in IATR fluorescence polarization similar to that caused by ADP (1).

AMPPNP and pyrophosphate (PP_i) are nonhydrolyzable nucleotide analogs that have been proposed as candidates for power-stroke intermediates. They both increase the disorder of optical probes bound to SH_1 in fibers, as detected statically by fluorescence dichroism of IATR (9) and fluorescence polariza-tion of etheno-AMPPNP (56) or dynamically by TPA of EIA (38). This increase in disorder could correspond to the dissociation of some cross-bridges. Since other studies on unlabeled fibers have reported that similar conditions produce x-ray diffraction changes without changes in stiffness, another possibility is that probes (and possibly the cross-bridges to which they are attached) become disordered while the cross-bridges remain attached.

Neither strain in rigor (57) nor a transient length change during an isometric contraction (58) causes a significant change in the orientation of fluorescent nucleotides. These findings suggest that the reorientation of the active-site region of the cross-bridge is not coupled to force generation.

ELECTRON PARAMAGNETIC RESONANCE

Methods and Principles

Magnetic resonance spectroscopy offers uniquely high spectral resolution, which permits probes in different states (e.g. of orientation or motion) to be detected independently in the steady-state spectrum. Both nuclear magnetic resonance (NMR) and electron paramagnetic resonance (EPR) have been applied to the study of cross-bridges. NMR has the potential advantage of not requiring extrinsic probes, but its low sensitivity and low specificity (e.g. in assigning a particular proton resonance to a particular protein or peptide in a complex system) has so far limited most NMR studies to qualitative studies of poorly resolved ^1H or ^{13}C spectra in S-1 or purified myosin or to studies of phosphorus resonances from nucleotides (reviewed in 43). Once the problem of specific spin-labeling is solved, EPR offers the sensitivity and resolution to detect orientations and rotational motions in either purified myosin or muscle fiber bundles. More comprehensive technical discussions of nitroxide EPR have appeared recently (reviewed in 47), including a discussion of muscle applications (44).

SPIN LABELS   The probes used in EPR studies of muscle proteins are usually nitroxide spin labels, stable free radicals that absorb microwaves when they are placed in a dc magnetic field of the appropriate strength. Most myosin EPR studies have been performed on maleimide or iodoacetamide derivatives, which can be attached selectively to SH_1 in myosin or muscle fibers without significantly inhibiting the physiological ATPase activity, isometric tension, or velocity of contraction (21). Noncovalently attached spin-labeled nucleotide analogs have also been used (22, 23), as have paramagnetic metal ions such as Mn^{2+} (reviewed in 44). Spin labels are more compact than most optical probes, and they tend to bind more rigidly to proteins, which facilitates studies of overall protein motion (47). Another advantage of spin labels is their susceptibility to the destruction of the free radical (and hence the signal) following a treatment with a mild reducing or oxidizing agent. The latter has proven to be an effective means of selectively eliminating virtually all of the signals originating from sites other than SH_1, even in glycerinated fibers (50, 48), which results in better site-specificity than is possible with other probes.

CONVENTIONAL EPR: NANOSECOND ROTATIONAL MOTION   In a conventional EPR experiment, the derivative of the steady-state absorption is plotted against the magnetic field strength. If the sample has no macroscopic order (e.g. a solution of myosin or a suspension of myofibrils), the spectrum is determined almost exclusively by nanosecond rotational motions, which narrow the spectrum. Even in a steady-state EPR experiment, a motionally narrowed spectrum is easily resolved from a broad spectrum that corresponds to no motion. Thus the conventional EPR experiment is useful for measuring the same kind of rapid (usually intramolecular) rotational motions as the time-resolved fluorescence anisotropy experiment. If the conventional EPR spectrum shows that there is no nanosecond rotational motion (as is the case for the maleimide spin label, discussed below), information about slower motions can be obtained by two complementary approaches, as discussed below.

CONVENTIONAL EPR: ORIENTATIONAL RESOLUTION   If the sample is macroscopically oriented (e.g. by placing labeled fibers parallel to the magnetic field), the spectrum is sensitive to the orientational distribution of probes relative to the system symmetry axis (the fiber axis). This sensitivity is analogous to that of fluorescence polarization (described above), but the quality of information is much higher for EPR. First, different orientations are directly resolved in the spectrum, so populations of probes that differ in orientation by a few degrees can be detected independently (3, 20, 47, 48). Thus enough information is present to characterize the orientational distribution of the probes in detail, with virtually none of the ambiguity inherent in an optical polarization experiment (3, 15). For example, a change in average orientation is easily distinguishable from a change in order (48, 5, 3), and the presence of multiple peaks in an orientational distribution is easily detected (20). Second, the orientational dependence of the spin label spectrum depends on an asymmetric tensor, not a simple dipole, which means that rotations about *any* axis are detectable with high resolution (52).

SATURATION TRANSFER EPR: MICROSECOND ROTATIONAL MOTION   Even if the conventional EPR experiment shows evidence for a wide range of probe orientations, the conventional EPR experiment cannot tell whether the rotational motions giving rise to this disorder are in the microsecond time range (dynamic disorder) or much slower (static disorder). Saturation transfer EPR (ST-EPR), which uses more intense radiation than conventional EPR and uses a different detection scheme, is sensitive to microsecond rotational motions ($\tau_r < 10^{-3}$ sec) and can thus be used to determine whether disorder is dynamic on the microsecond time scale (45, 47). Conversely, if a ST-EPR spectrum shows that there is microsecond rotational motion, conventional EPR can be used on an oriented sample to determine the amplitude of this motion. Thus conventional EPR and ST-EPR are analogous to fluorescence and phosphorescence, respectively. The principal differences are that fluorescence provides better time resolution, EPR provides better orientational resolution, and all of the EPR experiments can be performed with the same probe.

Purified Myosin

NANOSECOND MOTIONS   Early conventional EPR experiments on an iodoacetamide spin label (IASL) bound to SH_1 on the myosin head showed that Mg-ATP induces nanosecond rotational motions during the steady state of ATPase activity (44). Similar EPR spectra can be induced by ADP plus vanadate (54, 6). Computer analysis shows that IASL myosin spectra, in the presence of a wide range of nucleotides and nucleotide analogs, can be resolved into two principal components, which probably correspond to two principal interconverting conformational states of myosin in the vicinity of the probe (6). These results support the proposal that the myosin head undergoes nucleotide-influenced conformational transitions. These probe movements may be related to those induced by nucleotides in IATR-labeled muscle fibers (9, 14).

MICROSECOND MOTIONS   In the absence of ATP, IASL remains rigidly bound to myosin, apparently reporting the "rigid-body" rotations of the head (51, 50). ST-EPR experiments on IASL-myosin confirmed the fluorescence result (39) that heads have submicrosecond rotational freedom relative to the rest of monomeric myosin. They showed further that this mobility is present in the microsecond time range in myosin filaments but is strongly inhibited by actin in the absence of ATP (51). Similar studies on scallop myosin yielded similar results, but they also showed evidence for head-head interactions that are not apparent in rabbit myosin (53). A maleimide spin label (MSL) was found to remain rigidly bound to the myosin head, even in the presence of nucleotides (51). In the absence of actin, myosin head mobility detected by this probe in filaments is independent of ATP (50) but is partially inhibited by 10-mM Mg^{2+} (36, 37). This result supports models in which Mg^{2+} stabilizes interactions between myosin heads and the thick filament backbone.

Rigor and Relaxation

NANOSECOND MOTIONS   Using IASL, studies of rapid (presumably local) nucleotide-influenced nanosecond motions within the head have been extended to myofibrils and fibers (2, 6). Actin influences the proportions of the resolved states, even in relaxation, which confirms that myosin and actin interact in relaxation (6).

ORIENTATION AND MICROSECOND MOTIONS   Conventional EPR on oriented fibers, labeled with IASL or MSL, was used to characterize the orientational distribution (5, 48, 49), and ST-EPR on disoriented myofibrils or minced fibers was used to determine whether the observed disorder was static or dynamic on the microsecond time scale (4, 5, 48, 49). The results showed that both MSL and IASL on myosin heads are uniformly and rigidly oriented in rigor; they have the same narrow (full width 10–15°) orientational distribution as observed for isolated heads (S-1) bound to actin in fibers. Therefore, the rigor bond between actin and the myosin head is quite rigid and stereospecific. Indirectly, these results also indicate that the rest of the attached cross-bridges must have considerable flexibility in order for all heads from the thick filament to attach at the same angle to actin subunits on the thin filament, despite the mismatch in helix geometry. The source of this flexibility must, however, be farther from actin than both the SH_1 and nucleotide-binding sites, which are known to be at least 6 nm from actin (17, 18). Similar results were obtained for insect flight muscle, although slightly more orientational disorder was observed in rigor, which is consistent with predictions that steric constraints in insect muscle might prevent uniform binding of cross-bridges (49).

In contrast to rigor, relaxation produces considerable orientational disorder (48) (over at least a 90° full axial range) that is dynamic on the microsecond time scale. [The effective correlation time was 10 μsec (50).] Since this motion is very similar to that observed for isolated myosin filaments (50, 51), these results indicate that essentially all cross-bridges are detached from actin in rigor, and that their steric constraints are no greater than in isolated myosin filaments. Although some of this axial disorder of the probes in relaxation could come from torsional disorder of the heads, the axial disorder of rigid heads is at least 50° (full width at half maximum) (40). Similar results were recently obtained for a spin-labeled ATP analog bound to myosin heads in glycerinated fibers (23).

Contraction

NANOSECOND MOTIONS   A correlation was noted between characteristics of IASL EPR spectra and isometric muscle fiber tension, as affected by ATP and Ca^{2+} (2). At 10-mM ATP, contracting fibers give spectra closer to relaxation than rigor. If the attached heads are assumed to yield the same signal in contraction as in rigor, about 30% of the heads are attached during contraction at 5°C and 125 mM ionic strength.

ORIENTATION AND MICROSECOND MOTIONS   The conventional EPR spectrum of MSL fibers in contraction clearly shows two resolved components (19, 20). One, which represents about 80% of the myosin heads, is indistinguishable from that in relaxation and thus corresponds to considerable orientational disorder. The other component, which represents about 20% of the heads, has a narrow line shape that is indistinguishable from the spectrum in rigor. For the latter component, neither the center nor the width of the narrow orientational distribution of the probe's principal axis differs from that of rigor by more than 2°. Similar results have been reported for MSL attached to another SH group on the myosin head (8). ST-EPR studies of contracting MSL-myofibrils (48) or MSL-fibers (4) show almost as much microsecond rotational mobility as in relaxation, which indicates that the disorder in contraction is dynamic. The simplest interpretation of these results is that about 20% of the heads are attached to actin, with the probed region of the head having the same orientation as in rigor, and the remainder are detached and dynamically disordered as in relaxation. Alternatively, more than 20% of the heads may be attached, but then at least some attached heads must be dynamically disordered on the microsecond time scale.

Intermediate States

Like most other probes, but unlike IATR and IAF, IASL and MSL both show little or no change of orientation or motion upon the addition of ADP to glycerinated muscle fibers in rigor (52). If these were all dipolar fluorescent probes, this might be explained if most probes happen to orient their principal axes parallel to the axis of cross-bridge rotation and thus fail to detect the rotation. However, since spin labels are sensitive to rotation about any axis, it is possible to conclude that if the spin labels all rotate as if attached to a rigid body, no axis changes its mean orientation by more than $10°$ (52), a value much less than the rotation observed for IATR. Very small changes are observed in the MSL EPR spectrum (P. Fajer, personal communication), which is consistent with a conformational change propagated from the nucleotide site when ADP binds. IASL, but not MSL, shows a slight increase in nanosecond motions upon ADP binding to purified myosin. This finding is consistent with the differential effects of ADP on probes at SH_1.

When AMPPNP and PP_i were added to MSL fibers, they produced conventional EPR spectra intermediate between those of rigor and relaxation (48). This result is qualitatively consistent with those of many other techniques, and it might seem to support the proposal that these ATP analogs produce an intermediate cross-bridge state that is analogous to an intermediate in the power stroke. However, the high resolution of EPR showed further that these spectra did not show a single orientation, but a mixture of two well-resolved spectral components similar to those of rigor and relaxation (48). Recent studies show that these spectra can be precisely simulated by a linear combination of spectra of rigor and relaxation (26). The fraction of the disordered component increases with nucleotide analog concentration, ionic strength, concentration of ethylene glycol or glycerol, and decreased temperature. In addition, the disordered component has as much microsecond rotational mobility as in relaxation (26, 34). Thus these results show no evidence for a significant population having a preferred orientation or mobility different from rigor and relaxation.

Simultaneous measurements were made of binding and orientation of labeled S-1 diffused into fibers, and the results indicated that the disorder produced by AMPPNP or PP_i corresponds to dissociation of S-1 from actin, not to disorder of attached heads (26, 34, 42). The simplest explanation for this finding is that in the presence of AMPPNP or PP_i a fraction of myosin heads are in an attached state similar to that of rigor and the rest are in a detached state similar to that of relaxation. In coordinated studies of EPR and stiffness, it was shown that under certain conditions nearly half of the myosin heads can become dynamically disordered (probably detached from actin) by either AMPPNP or PP_i without decreasing the stiffness below the rigor level (26, 42). This observation suggests that all of the cross-bridges are attached but that only one of the two heads of each myosin molecule is attached. Thus AMPPNP and PP_i do induce a cross-bridge state that is distinguishable from both rigor and relaxation, and it is possible that a similar state could be an intermediate in the force-generation process.

Another condition that may be relevant to intermediate cross-bridge states is that of relaxation at low ionic strength, in which substantial stiffness can be detected if the rate of stretch is extremely high. (The mechanical and structural properties of fibers under these conditions are discussed in the chapter by Brenner in this volume.) This condition produces EPR spectra of MSL fibers indicating that most of the heads are dynamically disordered, essentially as in relaxation, with a small fraction (15–25%) having a similar orientation to that in rigor (but slightly more disordered) (27). This behavior seems consistent with the proposal that "weakly attached" cross-bridges may be present as intermediates in the power stroke (32, 18).

Another technique for studying attached cross-bridge states directly is to covalently cross-link labeled S-1 to actin, thus presumably eliminating the detached phases of the cycle. ST-EPR has shown that ATP induces microsecond rotational mobility, similar to that observed in contracting fibers, in MSL-labeled S-1 that is covalently cross-linked to actin (46). This finding indicates that some of the dynamic disorder observed in contraction (50, 3) could correspond to attached myosin heads. Thus, the fraction of attached heads could be much greater than the 20% that are observed to be rigidly and uniformly oriented (48, 3).

A force applied to a muscle fiber in rigor should produce a mechanically intermediate cross-bridge state. When a force approximately equivalent to that developed in isometric contraction was applied to fibers in rigor, there was no detectable rotation of IASL attached to myosin heads (16); similar results have been obtained using a spin-labeled ADP analog (23) and using a fluorescent ADP analog (57). These observations provide further evidence that neither chemical nor mechanical means of reversing the power stroke causes a rotation of either the SH_1 region or the active site of the actin-attached myosin head.

CONCLUSIONS

Spectroscopic probes clearly provide essential information needed to test the proposed role of cross-bridge rotation in force generation. Because of the unavoidable uncertainties in interpreting probe results, it is important to ask what conclusions seem to be supported by a wide variety of probe experiments. One of the most consistent results is that cross-bridges have dynamic flexibility. This conclusion comes not only from the large-amplitude rotational motions detected by optical (9, 10, 30, 36, 41) and spin (5, 23, 48, 50, 51) probes for myosin heads not attached to actin, but also (ironically) from the remarkably uniform orientation of probes on myosin heads in rigor (48), which implies a rigid and stereospecific actomyosin bond. In light of the mismatch of actin and myosin helices, this uniform orientation could only be possible if the portion of the cross-bridge between the probe (at SH_1 or the active site) and the thick-filament core is quite flexible.

Another consistent result is that probes on myosin heads undergo rotational motions during contraction that are intermediate between those observed in relaxation and rigor (4, 12, 30, 38, 50). A problem in interpreting this result is that much of this motion could be due to the high mobility of heads in detached cross-bridges, which leaves open the possibility that cross-bridges do not rotate once they attach. However, a number of probe measurements have detected attached cross-bridge states whose probes are rotationally distinct from those in the rigor state: Nucleotide analogs induce single-headed binding and the accompanying mobility of detached heads in attached cross-bridges (56); ADP perturbs some probes much more than others (9, 52, 6); and weakly attached cross-bridges may be dynamically disordered during maximal actomyosin ATPase interaction (27, 46). It is more difficult to demonstrate that any of these motions is directly coupled to the force-generating event. The most highly resolved measurements of probes bound to myosin heads show that the only sharply defined and rigid orientations in steady-state contraction are very similar to those in rigor (19, 20). Neither spin labels nor optical probes bound to SH_1 or the nucleotide site have been found to rotate in response to strain in rigor (16, 57).

Taken together, the probe results do not seem to be consistent with a simple scheme in which each nucleotide state induces its own fixed cross-bridge angle and in which the cross-bridge (or myosin head) pivots as a rigid body on actin. A more plausible model must invoke a much more complex and dynamic cross-bridge than previously pictured, with flexibility within myosin heads and/or rods (18, 32). Myosin heads appear to have maximal rotational freedom in the detached phase of the cycle, probably facilitating attachment, and they may still be quite mobile upon initial attachment to actin. The power stroke that follows could involve the rigid rotation of the whole head only if (*a*) the orientation of the initial attachment can have a wide range of values, or (*b*) the initial orientation is so short-lived that it does not contribute to the detected spectroscopic signals and cannot be trapped by using mechanical or chemical perturbations. The probe data are more consistent with a power stroke in which at least a portion of the head remains rigidly fixed on actin, in essentially the same orientation as in rigor, with the distal portion of the cross-bridge changing its axial position. The latter movement could be most easily explained by a rotation within the head, but a change in the length of S-2 cannot be ruled out. Alternatively, the cross-bridge could translate from one actin site to another without much movement within either actin or myosin (57), but a plausible source for the driving force behind this vectorial movement has not been identified.

Some apparent discrepancies among probe results must be explained through further experimentation. Many apparent discrepancies are probably due to false assumptions, such as, myosin heads are always rigid bodies, all probes remain rigidly attached to myosin, probes do not alter the behavior of cross-bridges, actin is rigid and passive, and all preparations are quantitatively the same. For example, the wide range of values obtained for the fraction of myosin heads attached to actin during contraction (from less than 20% to at least 80%) probably arises from a number of these factors. The conditions used to produce contraction have varied widely in these studies, and most probe studies have not included enough mechanical and biochemical characterization to determine whether the preparations used with different probes are comparable. In estimating the fraction of attached heads, most of these probe techniques rely on the assumption that the signals from attached and detached heads are identical to those observed in rigor and relaxation, respectively; however, only the EPR technique (which has yielded values in the range of 20–30%) has actually resolved two signals during contraction and shown that they are essentially the same as those obtained in rigor and relaxation. Nevertheless, a possible explanation for the apparent discrepancy is that the larger values (more than 50% attached) are correct and that smaller values arise from probes that are mobile during part of the attached phase. Too much of our current information about cross-bridge rotation comes from probes at the SH_1 site, which has been shown to be a complex and probably flexible region itself. Much recent work is aimed at extending probe studies to other sites (the active site, light chains, S-2, actin, etc). There are some apparent discrepancies between conclusions drawn from probe studies and other studies, e.g. mechanical transients, x-ray diffraction, and electron microscopy. Thus one of the most important current trends is the collaboration of spectroscopists with other muscle biophysicists, who together can directly correlate the mechanical and structural properties of the probed preparations with the spectroscopic results. These studies will probably provide us with some surprises and challenges, but spectroscopic probes will continue to be essential tools for detecting cross-bridge rotation in muscle.

ACKNOWLEDGMENTS

I am grateful to Roger Cooke, Piotr Fajer, Richard Ludescher, Thomas Eads, and Vincent Barnett for helpful comments about this paper, and to many authors for sending me reprints and preprints. During the writing of this article, I was supported by grants from the National Institutes of Health (GM 27906, AM 32961), the American Heart Association, and the Muscular Dystrophy Association of America.

Literature Cited

1. Ajtai, K., Burghardt, T. P. 1986. Observation of two orientations from rigor cross-bridges in glycerinated muscle fibers. *Biophys. J.* 49:8a (Abstr.)
2. Arata, T., Shimizu, H. 1981. Spin label study of actin-myosin-nucleotide interactions in contracting glycerinated muscle fibers. *J. Mol. Biol.* 151:411–37
3. Barnett, V. A., Fajer, P., Polnaszek, C., Thomas, D. D. 1986. High-resolution detection of muscle cross-bridge orientation by electron paramagnetic resonance. *Biophys. J.* 49:144–46
4. Barnett, V. A., Thomas, D. D. 1983. Rotational motion of spin-labeled myosin heads during contraction: saturation transfer EPR. *Biophys. J.* 41:264a (Abstr.)
5. Barnett, V. A., Thomas, D. D. 1984. Saturation transfer EPR of spin-labeled muscle fibers: dependence on sarcomere length. *J. Mol. Biol.* 179:83–102
6. Barnett, V. A., Thomas, D. D. 1986. Resolution of the conformational states of spin-labeled myosin. *Biochemistry* In press
7. Baskin, R., Yeh, Y., eds. 1986. *Optical Studies of Muscle Cross-Bridges.* Boca Raton, Fla.: CRC. In press
8. Belagyi, J., Grof, P. 1984. Rotational dynamics of proteins in glycerinated muscle fibers. *Acta Biochim. Biophys. Acad. Sci. Hung.* 19:229–46
9. Borejdo, J., Assulin, O., Ando, T., Putnam, S. 1982. Cross-bridge orientation in skeletal muscle measured by linear dichroism of an extrinsic chromophore. *J. Mol. Biol.* 158:391–414
10. Borejdo, J., Burghardt, T. P. 1986. Cross-bridge order and orientation in resting and active muscle fibers studied by the linear dichroism of fluorescence. See Ref. 7
11. Borejdo, J., Putnam, S., Morales, M. F. 1979. Fluctuations in polarized fluorescence: Evidence that muscle cross-bridges rotate repetitively during contraction. *Proc. Natl. Acad. Sci. USA* 76:6346–50
12. Burghardt, T. P., Ajtai, K. 1985. Fraction of myosin cross-bridges bound to actin in active muscle fibers: Estimation by fluorescence anisotropy measure-

ments. *Proc. Natl. Acad. Sci. USA* 82:8478–82
13. Burghardt, T. P., Ajtai, K. 1986. Model-independent time-resolved fluorescence depolarization from ordered biological assemblies applied to restricted motion of myosin cross-bridges in muscle fibers. *Biochemistry* 25:3469–78
14. Burghardt, T. P., Ando, T., Borejdo, J. 1983. Evidence for cross-bridge order in contraction of glycerinated skeletal muscle. *Proc. Natl. Acad. Sci. USA* 80: 7515–19
15. Burghardt, T. P., Thompson, N. L. 1985. Model-independent ESR for measuring order of immobile components in a biological assembly. *Biophys. J.* 48:401–9
16. Cooke, R. 1981. Stress does not alter the conformation of a domain of the myosin cross-bridge in rigor muscle fibers. *Nature* 294:570–71
17. Cooke, R. 1982. Fluorescence as a probe of the contractile system. *Methods Enzymol.* 85B:574–93
18. Cooke, R. 1986. The mechanism of muscle contraction. *CRC Crit. Rev. Biochem.* 21:53–118
19. Cooke, R., Crowder, M. S., Thomas, D. D. 1982. Orientation of spin-labels attached to cross-bridges in contracting muscle fibers. *Nature* 300:776–78
20. Cooke, R., Crowder, M. S., Wendt, C. H., Barnett, V. A., Thomas, D. D. 1984. Muscle cross-bridges: Do they rotate? In *Contractile Mechanisms in Muscle*, ed. G. Pollack, H. Sugi, pp. 413–27. New York: Plenum
21. Crowder, M., Cooke, R. 1984. The effect of myosin sulphhydryl modification on the mechanics of fibre contraction. *J. Muscle Res. Cell Motil.* 5:131–46
22. Crowder, M., Cooke, R. 1986. The nucleotide site of myosin doesn't rotate during the power stroke. *Biophys. J.* 49:7a (Abstr.)
23. Crowder, M., Cooke, R. 1987. Orientation of spin-labeled nucleotides bound to myosin in glycerinated muscle fibers. *Biophys. J.* In press
24. dos Remedios, C. G., Yount, R. G., Morales, M. F. 1972. Individual states

in the cycle of muscle contraction. *Proc. Natl. Acad. Sci. USA* 69:2542–46

25. Eads, T. M., Austin, R. H., Thomas, D. D. 1984. Microsecond rotational motions of eosin-labeled myosin measured by time-resolved anisotropy of absorption and phosphorescence. *J. Mol. Biol.* 178:55–82

26. Fajer, P., Fajer, E., Brunsvold, N., Thomas, D. D. 1986. AMPPNP, glycol, and PP$_i$ effects on cross-bridge orientation and rotational motion. *Biophys. J.* 49:265a (Abstr.)

27. Fajer, P., Fajer, E., Svensson, E., Brunsvold, N., Wendt, C., Thomas, D. D. 1985. EPR studies of muscle contraction at low ionic strength. *Biophys. J.* 47:467a (Abstr.)

28. Fan, S., Chu, B., Dewey, M. 1986. Quasielastic light scattering, a new approach to the study of the contractile mechanism of striated muscle: The present status. See Ref. 7

29. Gergely, J., Seidel, J. C. 1983. Conformational changes and molecular dynamics of myosin. In *Handbook of Physiology, Section 10: Skeletal Muscle,* ed. L. Peachey, pp. 240–67. Bethesda: Am. Physiol. Soc.

30. Güth, K. 1980. Polarization of tryptophan fluorescence measurements in muscle. *Biophys. Struct. Mech.* 6:81–93

31. Highsmith, S., Cooke, R. 1983. Evidence for actomyosin conformational changes involved in tension generation. *Muscle Nonmuscle Motil.* 4:207–37

32. Huxley, H. E., Kress, M. 1985. Crossbridge behaviour during muscle contraction. *J. Muscle Res. Cell Motil.* 6:153–61

33. Ishiwata, S. I., Kinosita, K. Jr., Yoshimura, H., Ikegami, A. 1987. Rotational motions of myosin heads in myofibril studied by phosphorescence anisotropy decay measurements. *J. Biol. Chem.* Submitted

34. Ishiwata, S. I., Manuck, B. A., Seidel, J. C. 1986. ST-EPR study of the mobility of myosin heads in myofibrils under conditions of partial dissociation. *Biophys. J.* 49:821–28

35. Kinosita, K., Ishiwata, S., Yoshimura, H., Asai, H., Ikegami, A. 1984. Submicrosecond and microsecond rotational motions of myosin heads in solution and in myosin synthetic filaments as revealed by time-resolved optical anisotropy measurements. *Biochemistry* 23:5963–75

36. Ludescher, R. D., Eads, T. M., Thomas, D. D. 1986. Triplet anisotropy studies of restricted rotational motion in myosin monomers and filaments. See Ref. 7

37. Ludescher, R. D., Johnson, S., Eads, T. M., Thomas, D. D. 1985. Myosin crossbridge dynamics in filaments are influenced by Mg^{++}: A ST-EPR and transient absorption study. *Biophys. J.* 47:467a (Abstr.)

38. Ludescher, R. D., Nelson, W. B., Thomas, D. D. 1986. The rotational dynamics of myosin heads in myofibrils in the presence of ATP and ATP analogs determined by transient phosphorescence anisotropy. *Biophys. J.* 49:265a (Abstr.)

39. Mendelson, R. A., Morales, M., Botts, J. 1973. Segmental flexibility of the S-1 moiety of myosin. *Biochemistry* 12:2250–55

40. Mendelson, R. A., Wilson, M. G. 1982. Three-dimensional disorder of dipolar probes in a helical array. Application to muscle cross-bridges. *Biophys. J.* 39:221–27

41. Mendelson, R. A., Wilson, M. G. A. 1986. Fluorescence polarization studies of myosin and muscle cross-bridges. See Ref. 7

42. Pate, E., Cooke, R. 1986. The effects of pyrophosphate and glycerol on muscle fiber stiffness and on the spectra of spin probes attached to myosin heads. *Biophys. J.* 49:265a (Abstr.)

43. Ribeiro, A., Parello, J., Jardetzky, O. 1984. NMR studies of muscle proteins. *Prog. Biophys. Mol. Biol.* 43:95–160

44. Seidel, J. C. 1982. EPR of contractile systems. *Methods Enzymol.* 85:594–624

45. Squier, T. C., Thomas, D. D. 1986. Methodology for increased precision in saturation-transfer electron paramagnetic resonance studies of molecular dynamics. *Biophys. J.* 49:921–35

46. Svensson, E. C., Thomas, D. D. 1986. ATP induces microsecond rotational motions of myosin heads cross-linked to actin. *Biophys. J.* 50:999–1002

47. Thomas, D. D. 1986. Rotational diffusion of membrane proteins. In *Techniques for the Analysis of Membrane Proteins,* ed. C. I. Ragan, R. Cherry, Ch. 13, pp. 377–431. London/New York: Chapman and Hall. 440 pp.

48. Thomas, D. D., Cooke, R. 1980. Orientation of spin-labeled myosin heads in glycerinated muscle fibers. *Biophys. J.* 32:891–906

49. Thomas, D. D., Cooke, R., Barnett, V. A. 1983. Orientation and rotational mobility of spin-labeled myosin heads in insect flight muscle in rigor. *J. Muscle Res. Cell Motil.* 4:367–78

50. Thomas, D. D., Ishiwata, S., Seidel, J. C., Gergely, J. 1980. Submillisecond rotational dynamics of spin-labeled myosin heads in myofibrils. *Biophys. J.* 32:873–90

51. Thomas, D. D., Seidel, J. C., Hyde, J. S., Gergely, J. 1975. Motion of S-1 in myosin and its supramolecular complexes: ST-EPR. *Proc. Natl. Acad. Sci. USA* 72:1729–33

52. Thomas, D. D., Svensson, E. C., Polnaszek, C. F. 1985. ADP does not induce rigid axial rotation of myosin heads in rigor muscle fibers. *Biophys. J.* 47:380a (Abstr.)

53. Wells, C., Bagshaw, C. R. 1983. Segmental flexibility and head-head interaction in scallop myosin. A study using saturation transfer electron paramagnetic resonance spectroscopy. *J. Mol. Biol.* 164:137–57

54. Wells, C., Bagshaw, C. R. 1984. The characterization of vanadate-trapped nucleotide complexes with spin-labelled myosins. *J. Muscle Res. Cell Motil.* 5:97–112

55. Wilson, M. G. A., Mendelson, R. A.

1983. A comparison of order and orientation of cross-bridges in rigor and relaxed muscle fibers using fluorescence polarization. *J. Muscle Res. Cell Motil.* 4:671–93

56. Yanagida, T. 1981. Angles of nucleotides bound to cross-bridges in glycerinated muscle fiber at various concentrations of etheno derivatives of ATP, ADP, and AMPPNP detected by polarized fluorescence. *J. Mol. Biol.* 146:539–60

57. Yanagida, T. 1984. Angles of fluorescently labelled myosin heads and actin monomers in contracting and rigor strained muscle fibers. In *Contractile Mechanisms in Muscle,* ed. G. Pollack, H. Sugi, pp. 397–411. New York: Plenum. 520 pp.

58. Yanagida, T. 1985. Angle of active site of myosin heads in contracting muscle during sudden length changes. *J. Muscle Res. Cell Motil.* 6:43–52

59. Yeh, Y., Baskin, R. J. 1986. Optical ellipsometry studies on the diffracted orders of single fibers from skeletal muscles. See Ref. 7

SPECIAL TOPIC: PHOTOTRANSDUCTION IN VERTEBRATES

General Introduction

E. N. Pugh, Jr., Section Editor

Department of Psychology, University of Pennsylvania, 3813–15 Walnut Street, Philadelphia, Pennsylvania 19104

William H. Miller, Section Editor

Department of Ophthalmology and Visual Science, Yale Medical School, New Haven, Connecticut 06510–8061

Phototransduction is the process by which light energy is used by organisms to produce neural signals. In vertebrates this process is initiated with the absorption of a photon by a visual pigment protein in a rod or cone outer segment and leads, by a series of biochemical and electrophysiological steps, to a decrease in the rate of synaptic transmitter release at the photoreceptor/bipolar cell synapse.

The past 15 years witnessed an intense effort by many investigators around the globe to understand phototransduction, and this volume is devoted to reviewing that effort. Much of the research was focused by the early realization that an internal messenger was required to act as a signal between the site of photon capture in the rod disk membrane and the site of membrane conductance change in the plasma membrane: Ca^{2+} and cGMP were the leading candidates for the role of internal transmitter throughout the period. Research on the cyclic nucleotide hypothesis led to the discovery and detailed characterization of a light-activated enzyme cascade that results in cGMP hydrolysis and to the discovery of a number of other proteins that regulate this cascade and restore enzymic activity to baseline levels. Research on the Ca^{2+} hypothesis led to the development of new techniques for characterizing conductances, to novel insights into the problems of ionic specificity, and to important findings on the nature and role of Na^+-Ca^{2+} exchange in photoreceptors. Both hypotheses were extremely productive and led the field to ever-better science. But only one candidate transmitter could play the leading role. The selection made by nature was reported by a team of Soviet researchers, Fesenko, Lyubarsky, and Kolesnikov (1), who discovered that the outer segment plasma membrane contains a conductance directly gated by cGMP. Their work and subsequent work during the past two years leave little doubt that the light-sensitive conductance and the cGMP-gated conductance are one and the same. It has thus become possible to outline a standard "cGMP cascade theory of phototransduction," which is illustrated in Figure 1 and can serve as a backdrop for the reviews in this Special Topic section.

The article by Liebman et al reviews the initial events that occur in the disk membrane that lead to activation of G protein. The article by Hurley reviews the biochemistry of the proteins that participate in the cascade. The article by Pugh reviews the transmitter concept and the relationship between the cascade biochemistry and the gating of the light-sensitive conductance. The article by Owen reviews the conductances of the photoreceptor plasma membrane and in particular discusses the nature of $g_{h\nu}$, the light-sensitive conductance, and its identification with the cGMP-gated conductance.

The theory illustrated in Figure 1, we emphasize, is still just a theory, and most of its components remain to be fully tested. In this figure the filled arrows represent "excitatory" events that lead from photon capture to closure of $g_{h\nu}$; the open arrows represent events that lead to restoration of baseline activity. The analysis of each of the steps outlined in the figure can and will be much expanded before it can be said that phototransduction is fully understood. For example, how is the conformation of rhodopsin altered by photon absorption to transform it into a catalyst for GTP-GDP exchange on G_v, the outer segment G protein? What is the exact nature of the interaction of G_v with the cGMP phosphodiesterase (PDE) in the intact cell: Is the $G_{v,\alpha'}$ α-subunit released into the cytosol to find PDE by diffusion? How is the binding interaction altered by the hydrolysis of GTP, and is the hydrolysis of GTP bound to $G_{v,\alpha}$ the only mechanism of PDE inactivation? Similar questions arise about each step in the cascade.

In the theory outlined in Figure 1, the events that lead to restoration of the

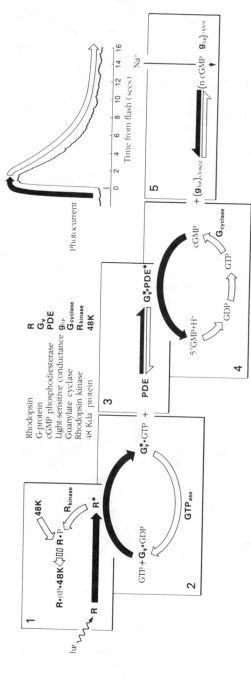

Figure 1 This schematic diagram shows a cGMP cascade theory of phototransduction derived from the work of many investigators. Each box represents a particular stage in the cascade. The filled arrows represent events leading to closure of g_{hv} the light-sensitive conductance channel; the open arrows represent events thought to restore the baseline condition after exposure to a flash of light, as suggested by the inset at upper right. In the upper right is shown a photocurrent response of a salamander rod to a just-saturating flash; the arrows suggest the way in which the events represented in the cascade govern this response. In reality, the molecular events represented by the filled and open arrows overlap in time.

cell's baseline enzymic activity after a light flash activation are indicated by open arrows. There is far more uncertainty about their identity than about the excitational events *(filled arrows)*, and the definitive version of the recovery side of the cascade is probably somewhat different from that shown in Figure 1. Nonetheless, our relative certainty about the excitational events will greatly speed discovery of the recovery mechanisms. Everything that goes up must come down!

A glaring omission in the theoretical sequence sketched in Figure 1 is the role of Ca^{2+}. Many experiments over the past 15 years have pointed to the importance of calcium regulation in photoreceptors. Recent experiments reviewed in the articles by Pugh and Owens support the conclusion that during a photoresponse, reduced inward flux of Ca^{2+} through $g_{h\nu}$ and continuing Na^+-Ca^{2+} exchange cause $[Ca^{2+}]_i$ in the photoreceptor to decline. These findings are consistent with the hypothesis that this dynamic regulation is part of a negative feedback loop that accelerates the restoration of the baseline condition and may provide a key to elucidation of the mechanism of photoreceptor light adaptation. The biochemical events regulated in the intact photoreceptor by Ca^{2+} remain the greatest unsolved mystery in the theory of phototransduction. Evidence is rapidly growing that Ca^{2+} interacts directly with one or more of the cascade steps. In short, even though Ca^{2+} does not play the leading role of excitational transmitter, it plays an essential and dynamic supporting role.

In summary, we present Figure 1 as a guide to the articles that follow. The current theory of vertebrate phototransduction is the foundation of a magnificent edifice erected by the efforts of many scientists, and we intend our reviews to be a tribute to all of them, and to the larger community that supports our work and is enriched by it.

Ann. Rev. Physiol. 1987. 49:715–41

THE NATURE AND IDENTITY OF THE INTERNAL EXCITATIONAL TRANSMITTER OF VERTEBRATE PHOTOTRANSDUCTION

E. N. Pugh, Jr.

Department of Psychology, University of Pennsylvania, 3813–15 Walnut Street, Philadelphia, Pennsylvania 19104

INTRODUCTION

Phototransduction: Modulation of Outer Segment Dark Current

Vertebrate rods and cones are cells marvelously differentiated, morphologically and physiologically, to transduce light into electrical signals. A fundamental physiological feature of these cells is a resting or "dark" current whose modulation constitutes the conversion of internal biochemical to transmembrane electrical events. Figure 1 shows a scanning electron micrograph of the receptor layer of the frog retina. Overlaid on the micrograph is a schematic diagram of the rod *dark current,* which was discovered by Hagins et al (52) with extracellular source/sink analysis. In the outer segment region the dark current is a uniformly distributed inward current, carried predominantly by Na^+; in the inner segment, the current is outward, with a sharp reversal occurring at the junction of the inner and outer segment (10, 52). Light suppresses the resting dark current, which gives rise to "photocurrents," in a fashion graded with intensity (10, 89). The photocurrent source is localized very near the site of photon absorption: Local outer segment illumination causes photocurrents within 1–2 μm of the site of photon absorption (52, 66, 74). The outer segment dark current is carried by the *light-sensitive conductance* ($g_{h\nu}$). Thus the first electrophysiological event in vision

715

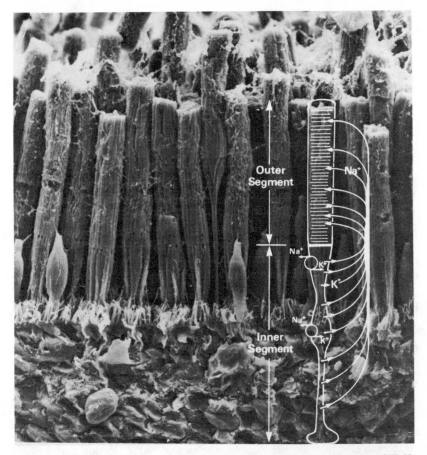

Figure 1   Scanning electron micrograph of photoreceptor layer of frog retina (courtesy of W. H. Miller). Superimposed on a rod at right is a schematic diagram of the dark, circulating current.

is the local closure of $g_{h\nu}$. (The nature of $g_{h\nu}$ is discussed in detail in the review by Owen in this section.)

Need for an Internal Transmitter

The possibility that light produces an "activator" whose concentration regulates a "light-sensitive channel" seems to have been proposed first by Fuortes & Hodgkin (44) in their investigation of *Limulus* photovoltages. Baylor & Fuortes (8) argued that the pattern of photovoltages they observed in recordings from turtle cones was consistent with the hypothesis that light produces a "substance which decreases the permeability of membrane channels acting as a shunt of the membrane in darkness." An absolute requirement for a substance to act as a transmitter or diffusible intermediary in phototransduction in vertebrate rods follows from two premises: first, the rhodopsin molecules that initiate the normal photoresponse are integral membrane proteins of the outer segment disk membranes; second, rod disk membranes (with the exception of a few basal disks) are not continuous with the outer segment plasma membrane. (See Reference 87 for a discussion of these premises.) The ability of the vertebrate rod to respond stereotypically to single photons (11) makes it likely that many hundreds or thousands of transmitters are "produced" per photon and diffuse up to 3 μm (in toad rod) to the plasma membrane. Furthermore, the fact that a single absorbed photon causes a 3–5% decrement in the outer segment light-sensitive membrane current (11, 52), which is uniformly distributed over the length of the outer segment (10, 52), means that the transmitters modulated by light must also diffuse longitudinally at least a few micrometers from the site of photon absorption in the disk.

Since the early 1970s the leading candidates for the role of the internal excitational transmitter of rod transduction have been Ca^{2+} and cGMP. Although cGMP has become generally accepted as the excitational transmitter (see General Introduction to this special section), it seems worthwhile to review the evidence that was put forward and the logic used to support each candidate over the past 15 years.

PROPERTIES OF THE INTERNAL TRANSMITTER OF RODS

Just as the existence of an internal transmitter in rod phototransduction can be deduced from structural features of the rod, so also can a number of general properties of the transmitter be inferred from consideration of structural and electrophysiological evidence. Among these properties are (a) hindered longitudinal diffusion of the transmitter in the outer segment; (b) kinetics of transmitter interaction with $g_{h\nu}$; (c) multiorder kinetics of transmitter modulation by light. Space limitations permit only a brief treatment here; a more extensive analysis can be found in Reference 90.

The longitudinal diffusion of small molecules in the outer segment can be expected to be up to 100 times slower than their unhindered diffusion in cytoplasm because the rod disks occupy 90% or more of the outer segment area cross-section, and the volume between the disks constitutes about 99% of the total volume (66). Thus molecules diffusing in the outer segment spend most of their time wandering between disks rather than moving longitudinally. Cytoplasmic binding sites can also constitute a major hindrance to longitudinal diffusion. For example, it has been estimated that negatively charged phospholipids retard Ca^{2+} diffusion in the outer segment (OS) by 7–31 fold

(77). The hindered longitudinal diffusion at low light intensities functionally compartmentalizes the effect of a single photon in a region of a few micrometers from the absorption site (66).

The rate of closure of $g_{h\nu}$ in response to brief, intense flashes (33, 89), combined with the power spectrum of outer segment light-sensitive membrane noise (19, 37, 50, 75), constrains the rate constants of transmitter binding and release. In brief, it can be shown that at 20°C in an amphibian rod the rate constant for binding of a "positive" transmitter (one whose concentration is increased by light) cannot be less than 60 sec^{-1}. Similarly, the rate constant for unbinding of a "negative" transmitter (one whose concentration is decreased by light) cannot be less than 300 sec^{-1} (90). The equilibrium rate constant for binding, which is the sum of the "on" and "off" rate constants, must always exceed whichever of these lower limits applies. As a result, the transmitter binding reaction comprises relatively little of the overall "delay" in the linear (dim-flash) photoresponse.

Recordings with extracellular electrodes in rat retina (89), voltage- and current-clamping microelectrodes in isolated salamander rods (5, 12, 14), and suction electrodes in toad (10, 13) and in monkey (15) have shown the linear (dim-flash) photocurrents of rods to have a rising phase that can be described as four stages of exponential delay with roughly equal time constants. For example, the linear photocurrents of toad rods at 20°C in HEPES-buffered Ringer's solution are well described with four stages of delay, each with a time constant of about 800 msec (13); in bicarbonate-buffered Ringer's solution they are described by four stages with time constants of about 300–400 msec (66). In principle, the observed photocurrent delay could be due to the compounding of rectangular photon quantal events distributed in time. However, it has been shown (11, 15, 94) that the single-photon response itself has a highly stereotypic form with a multiorder rising phase. It seems reasonable to conclude that several cascaded delay steps initiated by light must lead to the modulation of transmitter concentration.

CALCIUM ION AS INTERNAL TRANSMITTER

The hypothesis that calcium ion is the internal transmitter in rods was proposed by Yoshikami & Hagins (119). A solid rationale for proposing calcium existed at that time. Calcium was believed (a) to play a key role as an intracellular messenger in excitation-contraction coupling in muscle, (b) to be the signaling agent responsible for triggering synaptic vesicle fusion, and (c) to play a role as an internal messenger in a wide variety of other cellular processes, such as stimulus-related secretion. (For a general review of the roles of calcium in cellular regulation, see Reference 91.)

Experimental Evidence for the Calcium Hypothesis

The following facts have been taken to support the hypothesis that calcium acts as the internal transmitter in vertebrate rod transduction.

First, changes in external calcium and light have similar effects on the dark current. Elevated external calcium, like increased light, decreases this current (57, 120), whereas lowered external calcium rapidly increases it (53, 57, 114). Obviously, "negative light" cannot be produced, but the latter finding would be expected if lowered external calcium allowed the internal free calcium to drop below the level it would normally have in the dark, driving $g_{h\nu}$ toward the unbound, open state.

Second, the effects of altered external calcium on photoreceptor membrane potential and photovoltages are consistent with the notion that the immediate effect of altered external calcium is on $g_{h\nu}$ (7, 22). In very low external calcium the rod membrane depolarizes toward approximately $+10$ mV, the reversal potential of $g_{h\nu}$ (5, 14), as would be expected if this conductance became dominating. Photovoltages recorded during these large depolarizations drive the membrane potential to approximately the same hyperpolarized level to which it was driven by light prior to the exposure to low calcium. This finding indicates that little conductance besides $g_{h\nu}$ is altered by the short-term exposure to low Ca^{2+}. In elevated external calcium the membrane hyperpolarizes, and photovoltages become smaller.

Third, the effects of external calcium on the dark current, membrane potential, and photovoltages are greatly enhanced by calcium ionophores (7, 53). These enhancements are expected if the site of action of calcium in reducing the dark current is interior to the outer segment, where the transmitter must act.

Fourth, iontophoretic injection of calcium hyperpolarizes the rod membrane, as does light (21).

Fifth, ionotophoretic injection of calcium chelators into the outer segment causes a rapid depolarization toward the reversal potential of $g_{h\nu}$ (7, 21, 86) and increases the outer segment light-sensitive membrane current (76). These effects are expected if the rapid lowering of internal free calcium opens $g_{h\nu}$.

Sixth, infusion of calcium chelator by iontophoretic injection (21) or by vesicle fusion (54) decreases the light sensitivity of rods. Such decreased sensitivity is expected if some of the calcium hypothesized to be released internally by light is complexed with chelator rather than with $g_{h\nu}$.

Seventh, flashes of light cause an increase in extracellular calcium around rod outer segments; these increases in external calcium are graded with light intensity (47, 118) and closely follow the photocurrent kinetics (118). Such increases are expected if light causes a transient rise in internal calcium and if a mechanism exists to extrude this calcium against the large electrochemical gradient composed of the hyperpolarized membrane potential and the calcium concentration gradient.

Evidence Against the Calcium Hypothesis

In striking contrast to the findings just mentioned, several results reported during the past two years have cast serious doubt on the tenability of the calcium hypothesis and require the reassessment of the evidence cited in its support.

The first of these recent findings is that $g_{h\nu}$ is quite permeable to calcium and that large Ca^{2+} influxes through $g_{h\nu}$ do not immediately result in dark current suppression (57, 115). For example, (as shown in Figure 1 of Reference 115) a pure Ca^{2+} dark current of an initial magnitude of 300 pA ($\sim 10^9$ Ca^{2+}/sec) was suppressed after 1 sec by a step of light delivering 4500 isomerizations/sec. Since the suppression of $g_{h\nu}$ occurred in less than 0.2 sec, no more than 1000 isomerizations were delivered at the point of complete dark current suppression. Even if $10^4 Ca^{2+}$ per isomerization were instantaneously released inside the rod, the released Ca^{2+} would constitute only 1% of the total Ca^{2+} that entered the outer segment during the same period of time. Furthermore, any buffering or other process that could remove the Ca^{2+} as fast as it entered the outer segment would clearly buffer or remove the Ca^{2+} hypothesized to be released by light.

The second finding is that infusion of large amounts of calcium chelator into isolated salamander rods does not decrease their light sensitivity (65, 76). Lamb et al (65, 76) infused BAPTA or EGTA into rods through very low-resistance, tight-seal (patch) pipettes. Although large transient increases in the dark current were observed (as predicted by the calcium hypothesis), light sensitivity (the fraction of dark current suppression per isomerization) was found to *increase*. According to the calcium hypothesis, the observed increase in dark current requires that free calcium be lowered below its resting value (estimated to be ~ 1 μM) and that some BAPTA be free (otherwise the dark current would be expected to return to its normal magnitude). The free BAPTA should adsorb some of the calcium supposed to be released by light and thus decrease light sensitivity. These recent observations (65, 76) appear to conflict with earlier ones (53). Differences is preparation (suction current measurements of voltage-clamped, isolated salamander rods versus external current recording in strips of rat retina) or in technique of infusing chelator (infusion through gigaseal patch pipette versus vesicle fusion) may account for the discrepancy, but the new results seem incontrovertible.

A third line of recent evidence supports the conclusion that free calcium in the outer segment actually *decreases* during the light response. Yau & Nakatani (116) argue that a component of OS membrane current attributable to extrusion of calcium via Na^+-Ca^{2+} exchange results in the lowering of OS free calcium. Since $g_{h\nu}$ is permeable to calcium, the blockage by light of the inward leak of Ca^{2+} would allow the continued outward pumping by Na^+-Ca^{2+} exchange to lower internal free Ca^{2+}. Yau & Nakatani (116) also show that their results can provide a quantitative explanation of the apparent "extrusion" of calcium reported by Gold & Korenbrot (47). Because the latter investigation measured change in external free calcium, the decreased inward leak of calcium into outer segments during light exposure would be expected to cause a transient increase in external calcium. Gold (46) has reported that the rising phase of the photocurrent and the rise in external calcium have different light dependencies: The photocurrent rising phase (excitation) continues to increase its velocity as the light intensity increases, even when the rate of rise in external calcium is saturated. This latter saturation is expected if the increase in external calcium is due to a light-independent Na^+-Ca^{2+} exchange (116).

There have been several recent attempts to measure directly light-induced changes in the OS calcium concentration using, for example, rapid quenching after light exposure and x-ray microprobe (103) and laser micromass analysis (96). The results of these latter efforts disagree on the total calcium content of toad rods, and on the effect of light. The former found about 0.1 Ca^{2+}/ rhodopsin and no effect of light; the latter found about 1–2 Ca^{2+}/rhodopsin and a significant effect of light. Neither technique can readily distinguish between cytosolic and intradiskal calcium. It seems likely, however, that the bulk of OS calcium is not rapidly exchangeable (38, 103). A very important measurement of light-induced change in OS cytosolic calcium was made by Cervetto et al (28), who infused the calcium binding, luminescent protein aequorin into salamander rods through gigaseal pipettes. This work strongly corroborates the inferences from the exchange current measurements: During a saturated light response, free calcium in the OS was found to drop to a very low level.

Yet another line of evidence against the Ca^{2+} hypothesis is the failure of a number of investigations to find a conductance directly and exclusively gated by calcium in excised patches of OS membrane (39, 113, 121). Isolated patches of OS membrane do not become conductive when Ca^{2+} on the cytoplasmic face is lowered; thus some other intracellular cofactor must be responsible for opening the light-sensitive conductance, even if Ca^{2+} can close it.

In summary, the cumulative evidence against Ca^{2+} acting as the internal transmitter of rod transduction is very strong. Infusion of large amounts of calcium into rods under certain conditions does not rapidly close $g_{h\nu}$ as does a flash, which would be expected to release less Ca^{2+} from internal stores. Infusion of Ca^{2+} buffer into salamander rods does not decrease their sensitivity to light. During a saturated light response free calcium in the outer segment declines rather than rises. And finally, pulled patches of rod outer segment (ROS) membrane do not respond to alterations of $[Ca^{2+}]$ on the cytoplasmic face. Nonetheless, while the Ca^{2+} transmitter hypothesis can be rejected based on these and other observations, the profound and relatively rapid effects on rod transduction of manipulations that alter $[Ca^{2+}]_i$ must still be explained.

cGMP AS INTERNAL TRANSMITTER

Discovery of the cGMP Cascade

The hypothesis that a cyclic nucleotide might serve as the internal transmitter in rod transduction was proposed by W. H. Miller and M. Bitensky. After the initial demonstration that light decreased the amount of cAMP that could be extracted from rods (18), the story gradually unfolded that the ROS contains an interconnected set of enzymes that regulate cGMP. Light activates an amplifying enzymatic chain, the "cGMP cascade," whose final common path is destruction of outer segment cGMP. Inactivation reactions for each stage of the cascade have also been uncovered. Figure 1 of the general introduction to this section summarizes the molecular chain of cGMP regulation and will be used as a reference point in the remainder of this review. (Detailed discussions of the component molecules and events are provided in accompanying review articles in this Special Topic section.)

Electrophysiological Effects of cGMP

Although advances in photoreceptor biochemistry provided insight and incentive for the construction of models of transduction based upon the cGMP cascade, the means by which cGMP metabolism might be coupled to change in outer segment membrane current had to be determined by electrophysiology. Electrophysiological investigation of the cGMP transmitter hypothesis was initiated by Miller & Nicol (81, 84). In these investigations cGMP was injected iontophoretically into the outer segments of toad rods attached to the retina, and the membrane potential was recorded through the same micropipette.

Miller & Nicol found first that cGMP injection induces a very rapid, dose-dependent depolarization of the ROS membrane. Second, the duration of the cGMP-induced depolarization is dose-dependent in the dark. Third, the recovery from a given cGMP-induced depolarization is sped up by light, and the speed of recovery is increased with increasing light intensity. Fourth, in some cases there is a decided increase in the latency of the photovoltage after a cGMP injection. Fifth, photovoltages are typically prolonged by prior cGMP injection.

These basic findings were amplified and extended in a report (80) that also described the technique of using small ("puff") injections to probe the time course of phosphodiesterase (PDE) activity during a response to light. Since the microelectrode was penetrating the OS and longitudinal diffusion of molecules is relatively slow in the OS (see above), the rapidity of the cGMP-induced depolarization indicates that cGMP increases a depolarizing current in the OS and that the depolarization mechanism is sensitive to the concentration of cGMP. The second and third observations listed above make it likely that light-activated PDE speeds up the removal of excess, infused cGMP and that hydrolysis of cGMP is the mechanism by which the rod recovers its baseline membrane potential. The fourth effect, the latency increase, was interpreted to mean that the membrane potential could not return to baseline until the excess cGMP was removed and that the time to remove the excess depended on the amount injected. The fifth effect was not readily interpretable (see section on the negative feedback hypothesis). Related experiments have been reported by a number of investigators. It is generally agreed that cGMP injections cause OS membrane depolarizations (23, 60, 107), although there is some dispute about the latency phenomenon (107).

There have been two reports of the electrophysiological effects of injection into rods of activated proteins of the cGMP cascade. Clack et al (29) found that injections of both activated G protein and trypsin-activated PDE into toad rods caused reversible hyperpolarizations. Shimoda et al (98), however, reported that injection of trypsin-activated PDE into rods of the same species causes no immediate hyperpolarization but rather prolongs a subsequent light response.

An advance in understanding the effects of cGMP injection was made by MacLeish et al (73), who demonstrated in voltage-clamped, isolated salamander rods that iontophoretic injection of cGMP increased the light-sensitive membrane current by a least fivefold. This result strengthened the conclusion that the cGMP-induced depolarizations observed by Miller & Nicol and others were due to an increase in the light-sensitive membrane current. A further advance was made when OS membrane currents of isolated rods were measured with suction electrodes and rods infused with cGMP via a voltage-clamping tight-seal pipette penetrating the inner segment (31, 76). It was found that the infusion of cGMP rapidly increased the light-sensitive membrane current of the outer segment 10–20 fold.

These results strengthened the conclusions that increases in outer segment cGMP lead to opening of $g_{h\nu}$ and that the process that keeps $g_{h\nu}$ open under normal conditions requires cGMP; however, they did not establish *how* cGMP leads to opening of $g_{h\nu}$.

Discovery of a cGMP-Gated Conductance in the Outer Segment Membrane

A surprising and revolutionary mechanism for cGMP action was discovered by Fesenko and his coworkers (39). As shown in Figure 2, they demonstrated that cGMP could act directly on the cytoplasmic face of excised patches of ROS membrane to increase ionic permeability. In contrast, Ca^{2+} had no effect on the conductance of excised patches. The cGMP gating effect was operationally cooperative, i.e. the cGMP-dependence of each patch satisfied the Hill equation

$$I/I_{max} = S^N / [S^N + K_D^N], \qquad\qquad 1.$$

where $S = [cGMP]$, $K_D = 30 \ \mu M$ and $N \approx 2$. The unitary conductance was estimated by noise analysis to be 100 fS at an equivalent membrane potential of -30 mV.

The cGMP-gated conductance in the OS membrane has now been studied by a number of laboratories (55, 56, 117, 121), which have confirmed and extended the characterization of this conductance by Fesenko et al. The discovery of a cGMP-gated OS plasma membrane conductance was preceded by demonstrations that cGMP could stimulate release of cations from loaded rod disks (25–27; see also 24, 62). The cGMP dependence and ion selectivity of this stimulated cation release are consistent with the hypothesis that the cGMP-gated conductance found in the plasma membrane is present in the disks. Very recently, the cGMP-gated conductance of frog rods was successfully incorporated into artificial bilayers (104).

Is g_{cGMP} Identical to $g_{h\nu}$?

The fundamental question for the theory of transduction raised by the discovery of g_{cGMP} is this: Is g_{cGMP}, the cGMP-sensitive conductance, identical to $g_{h\nu}$, the light-sensitive conductance? Fesenko et al (39) presented several arguments in favor of making this identification, and recent work (75, 117), reviewed in the accompanying article by Owen, strongly supports this conclusion. In the remainder of this review, the identity of $g_{h\nu}$ and g_{cGMP} is assumed.

Photocurrent Rising Phase

Consider the photocurrent of an amphibian rod in response to a brief flash of light that causes ~ 1000 isomerizations, as shown in the inset in Figure 1 of the general introduction to this section. This response has two conspicuously distinct phases: a "rising phase" that lasts about 100 msec, which corresponds to the closure of $g_{h\nu}$, followed by a "falling phase", which corresponds to the reopening of $g_{h\nu}$. The discovery of g_{cGMP} seems to provide the missing

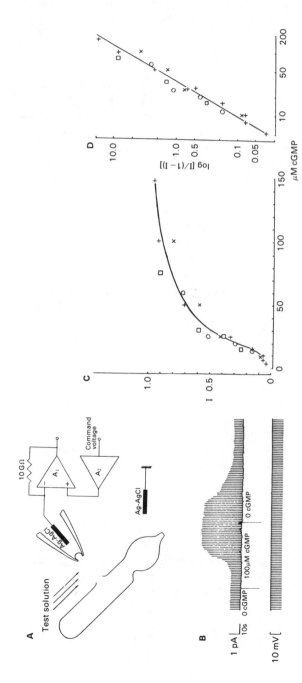

Figure 2 Experimental results of Fesenko et al (39) describing their discovery of cGMP-activated conductance of ROS plasma membranes. (A) Scheme used by Fesenko et al (39). A small patch of ROS membrane was excised from the OS with the tight-seal technique of Neher & Sakman. (B) Voltage pulses were applied across the membrane patch and voltage-clamp currents were measured under various perfusion conditions, one of which is illustrated. Addition of cGMP to the perfusate increased the current through the membrane patch. Ca^{2+} or calcium chelators applied to the patch had little effect. (C) The cGMP-concentration dependence of the membrane currents through patches as determined in (A). The smooth curve drawn through the data was generated with the Hill equation (equation 1) with $K_D = 30 \ \mu M$ and $N = 1.8$. (D) The same data as in (C) are plotted in the form $\log[I/(1-I)]$ versus $\log[cGMP]$, where I is clamp current normalized by the maximal current induced by cGMP perfusion. The slope gives N, the Hill coefficient.

link between the cGMP cascade and the closure of $g_{h\nu}$. Based on data for the activity of PDE induced per photon in amphibian rod membranes (e.g. 68, 110), one can calculate that light-activated PDE can hydrolyze OS cGMP with sufficient rapidity to a level sufficiently low to close $g_{h\nu}$.

However, a body of observations seems disturbingly inconsistent with this simple picture. A number of investigators have reported that the extractable cGMP content of rods is relatively little altered after exposure to light at a level that completely suppress the dark current (49, 61, 93). For example, Kilbride & Ebrey (61) found that after 1 sec of intense illumination that caused 7×10^7 isomerizations/sec there was no detectable drop in the cGMP content of the rapidly frozen bullfrog retina. [Microdissection observations show that greater than 50% of frog retina cGMP is in the outer segment layer (4).] The same failure of light to cause significant cGMP depletion was observed at all lower light intensities tested. Other investigations have measured rapid drops in cGMP content of isolated rods upon flash illumination at low to moderate flash levels (35, 110). For example, in their recent study, Cote et al (35) found that a step of 10^7 isomerizations/sec caused only a 15% drop in the extractable cGMP of a suspension of rods (outer and inner segments) in 200 msec. The closure of $g_{h\nu}$ measured by them in a subpopulation of the same rod suspension with a suction electrode was essentially complete in 180 msec. The consistent finding among all the reports of attempts to measure rod cGMP declines upon flash illumination is that light levels that completely suppress $g_{h\nu}$ do not cause much of a drop in the extractable cGMP.

The crucial issue is this: Does light cause the free [cGMP] in the normal, intact OS to drop? At present there are no direct measurements that settle this issue, because the techniques of recovering cGMP after rapid quenching do not distinguish cGMP that was bound from that which was free at the time of flash illumination—during extraction the bound cGMP becomes free. Despite the lack of crucial data distinguishing bound cGMP from free, it is clear that if the observations cited in the last paragraph are to be reconciled with a theory of transduction in which cGMP is the sole excitational transmitter to $g_{h\nu}$, then most of the cGMP in the rod must be inaccessible to light on the time scale of the photocurrent rising phase. One possibility is that it resides in an inaccessible compartment, perhaps the inner segment (IS). The experiments of Matthews et al (76) and Cobbs & Pugh (32) show that the inner segment is able to deliver cGMP to the outer segment in seconds to tens of seconds, which supports the idea that the inner segment constitutes such a compartment for cGMP. However, the recovery phase of the photocurrent appears to be too fast to be due entirely to diffusion from the IS, and the IS does not appear to have ten times or more the aqueous volume of the OS, which would be required to account for the low fraction of cGMP in the light-sensitive compartment. Furthermore, the results of Cote et al (35) show that the cGMP in isolated OS behaves in much the same way as the cGMP of the OS and IS when flash illuminated—only about 15% of the cGMP content seems to be accessible to light. Thus the hypothesis that cGMP is the sole transmitter of information to $g_{h\nu}$ can be consistent with the small fraction of total OS cGMP in a light-sensitive compartment only if most of the OS cGMP is bound during the rising phase and saturated phases of the photocurrent.

At present, postulation of such binding seems to be the most parsimonious account of the data. One bit of evidence consistent with such binding is that in the dark in normal Ringer's solution less than 10% of $g_{h\nu}$ is open relative to the maximal amount that can be opened when cGMP is elevated (31, 76, 117). From this it can be estimated with equation 1, if one assumes $N = 2$ and $K_D = 30\ \mu M$, that the free cGMP in the OS in a dark-adapted rod is 10 μM or less (31, 117). The value 10 μM corresponds to $\sim$10% of the total cGMP that can be extracted from the ROS (35), if the total cGMP is referred to cytoplasmic volume.

Some insight into the problem posed by the apparently small fraction of OS cGMP accessible to light can be had if one considers a simplified rate equation for the free cGMP in the outer segment:

$$\frac{dS}{dt} = -\frac{V(t)S}{S + k_m} + K_c. \qquad\qquad 2.$$

In this equation S = free [cGMP] in the OS, $V(t)$ is the time- and light-dependent PDE activity, k_m, has it usual meaning, and K_c is guanylate cyclase activity. (To make equation 2 stable, one has to assume that V is always greater than K_c.)

Now consider an idealized situation in which a very intense flash of light instantly activates all the PDE enzyme in a toad ROS to yield a step of PDE activity of 240 mM/sec. This activity is computed based on the assumptions that there is 1 PDE/50 rhodopsin molecules (which is equivalent to an aqueous PDE concentration of 120 μM) and that the turnover number of PDE is 2000/sec. The solution to equation 2 for such a step of maximal PDE activity can be readily obtained: S = free [cGMP] relaxes from its initial value, S_0, which we may assume to be approximately 5–10 μM, with a time constant k_m/V. Recent investigations estimate k_m for cGMP of PDE in disk membrane suspensions to be 0.5–1.4 mM (6, 99). If we assume the value of k_m is 0.5 mM in the toad ROS (6), we find that upon exposure to the most intense light, free cGMP relaxes from its initial value to its final value with a time constant of $\sim$2 msec. [0.5 mM/(240 mM/sec)]. Furthermore, the free [cGMP] relaxes to a new steady-state level, S_∞,

$$S_\infty = K_c\ (k_m/V), \qquad\qquad 3.$$

which may be obtained from equation 2 if dS/dt is set to zero and S is much smaller than k_m. Free cGMP does not fall to zero if there is ongoing guanylate cyclase activity. Importantly, because PDE hydrolytic velocity is proportional to free cGMP in equation 2, guanylate cyclase activity can eventually match even maximal PDE activity and thus stabilize the free cGMP at a nonzero value. The steady-state free cGMP level given by equation 3 may be very low (much too low to give rise to any measurable opening of the light-dependent conductance), but it may be high enough to keep a population of high-affinity cGMP binding sites populated.

Are there any specific candidates for the requisite cGMP binding sites? One such possible site is the presumed binding sites on g_{cGMP} itself. The number of g_{cGMP}'s (unitary conductances) in the rod plasma membrane has been estimated to be between 100 and 500 μm^{-2} (19, 121). If we assume that g_{cGMP}'s are in the disk membranes at the same surface density as in the plasma membrane (24, 62), i.e. 500 μm^{-2}, the number of such sites corresponds to an equivalent aqueous concentration of 100 μM, if we also assume that the water space is ~50% of the OS volume. Furthermore, each g_{cGMP} could have two or more cGMP binding sites (39, 55, 121). It seems unlikely, however, that the cGMP binding sites on g_{cGMP} are the sought-for sites.

The assumption that PDE-catalyzed hydrolysis of free cGMP is the sole excitational message to $g_{h\nu}$ permits one to use the maximal rate of rise of the photocurrent to estimate a lower limit to the rate of unbinding of at least one molecule of cGMP from $g_{h\nu}$, since the closure of $g_{h\nu}$ is presumably rate-limited by such an unbinding. Data on saturation of the photocurrent rate of rise (33, 89) can be used to estimate that the unbinding of at least one molecule of cGMP occurs in less than 1 msec in the rat rod at 37°C and in less than 3 msec in the voltage-clamped salamander rod at 21°C (33). The assumption that at least one molecule of cGMP can dissociate from a critical binding site on g_{cGMP} in 1–3 msec when the free cGMP drops to, say, 0.1 μM, means that this site cannot be one of those that constitutes an OS cGMP compartment inaccessible to light during the photocurrent rise. Neither are the other presumed binding sites on g_{cGMP} likely to constitute the missing sites: The cooperative dependence of g_{cGMP} on the free [cGMP] (equation 1; references 39, 55, 121) implicitly requires that at any given level of free cGMP the fraction of g_{cGMP} with fewer than N cGMP bound is negligible.

The sought-for cGMP binding sites could well be on the PDE itself. Yamazaki et al (112) using [^{3}H]cGMP and photoaffinity labelling, found that PDE apparently has two high-affinity (noncatalytic) binding sites with dissociation constants of 830 nM and 160 nM, respectively. Since PDE has an equivalent aqueous concentration of ~120 μM, clearly PDE could provide the 50 μM or more sought-for binding sites. One can readily calculate using equations 2 and 3, that even if all the PDE molecules in the ROS were instantly activated and remained activated, if the guanylate cyclase activity were 80 μM/sec, the free [cGMP] would only drop to about 160 nM. At this level of free cGMP, only 0.000028 of g_{cGMP} would be open (or ~0.0005 of the normal resting value), but the high-affinity cGMP binding site would be 50% titrated, which would be equivalent to more than 60 μM cGMP.

Analysis of equations 2 and 3 thus shows that one solution to the puzzle posed by the large fraction of OS cGMP apparently inaccessible to light can be formed from two hypotheses: (a) the existence of a population of high-affinity cGMP binding sites; and (b) a modest level of ongoing guanylate cyclase activity. The evidence for the former has been reviewed. Is there any evidence for the latter? Pannbacker et al (88) found a bovine ROS guanylate cyclase activity at 37°C of 1 nmol/min/mg protein, which corresponds to about 5–10 μM/sec in the intact ROS, depending on the assumptions made about the protein content of his preparation. Using their ^{18}O labelling technique, Goldberg et al (48) found a dark guanylate cyclase activity that corresponds to about 20 μM/sec in rabbit retina at 37°C. These values are about 4–8 fold lower than that necessary to maintain free cGMP at about 150–200 nM in the presence of complete activation of all OS PDE (V_{max} = 240 mM/sec) and thus keep the highest-affinity cGMP binding site on PDE titrated. However, even after maximal light exposure PDE may not maintain such activity, and guanylate cyclase activity may well be stimulated by the fall in free [cGMP] (e.g. by release of product inhibition or by some more direct effect of light).

In summary, data showing that most of the acid-extractable cGMP of the rod outer segment is inaccessible to light at any given instant can be reconciled with the hypothesis that cGMP is the sole excitational transmitter if there exist a population of high-affinity cGMP binding sites in the outer segment and a modest guanylate cyclase activity that continues or increases during the light response.

Photocurrent Falling Phase: Many Unresolved Issues

Although the cGMP cascade, coupled with the identification of $g_{h\nu}$ with g_{cGMP}, provides a reasonable account of the photocurrent rising phase, the cGMP theory currently faces a number of unresolved issues before it can be said to provide an account of the photocurrent "falling" or recovery phase of the flash response. The cGMP cascade theory diagrammed in Figure 1 of the general introduction to this section proposes that the effect of light is to sequentially activate rhodopsin (box 1, filled arrow), G protein (box 2, filled arrow), and PDE (box 3, filled arrow). If we assume that the photocurrent falling phase (inset, open arrow) represents complete recovery to the steady state that existed before the flash, then all of the light-activated proteins (rhodopsin, G protein, and PDE) must be rendered inactive and the free

[cGMP] restored to its baseline level by guanylate cyclase. In short, everything that goes up must come down.

An "ATP-dependent quenching" of PDE activity (69) seems the most likely mechanism by which rhodopsin could be inactivated with sufficient rapidity to account for the falling phase. However, published records of this quenching process suggest it could be up to ten times slower than the fall in the photocurrent in bovine membranes (if one assumes bovine rod photocurrents obey the same kinetics as those of rat and monkey) and 2–4 times slower in toad membranes (Figure 9 in Reference 68). The biochemical nature of the ATP-dependent quenching was hypothesized to be rhodopsin phosphorylation (69) on the basis of (a) the rough match between the k_m's for phosphorylation of rhodopsin by ATP and GTP (97) and the concentrations of ATP and GTP that give half-maximal quenching, and (b) the fact that phosphorylated rhodopsin is a very poor activator of PDE (102). It has been reported that phosphorylation of rhodopsin is rapid enough to cause the quenching (100) and that proteolytic removal of various lengths of rhodopsin's C-terminus, where most of the phosphorylation occurs, greatly diminishes the ATP-dependent quenching (79, 101). As would be expected from the findings just cited, phosphorylated rhodopsin has been demonstrated to be ineffective in activating G protein (1, 2). However, there is also evidence that the ATP-dependent quenching may depend on a 48-kd protein (48K) (109, 122). It has been shown that 48K binds to phosphorylated rhodopsin (64) and that this binding contributes considerably to further inactivation of photolyzed rhodopsin (R*), especially after flash illuminations that cause several isomerizations per disk (109). It remains to be established that under intracellular conditions these ATP-dependent reactions inactivate rhodopsin at least as rapidly as the photocurrent falling phase.

Since it was discovered that photolyzed rhodopsin catalyzes the binding of GTP to G protein (43), that the α-subunit of G protein complexed with GTP but not GDP is the activator of PDE (41, 42), and that G protein is a GTPase (108), it has been thought that the inactivation of G protein is via hydrolysis of bound GTP (Figure 1 in the general introduction, box 2, open arrow; Reference 42). Disturbingly, however, a number of investigations have reported GTPase rate constants of 1–2 min^{-1} (17, 45, 63, 67, 111). Even if rhodopsin were quenched in 0.5 sec or less, on the basis of these observations G protein would be expected to stay quite active for a minute or more! This would keep PDE active much longer than the normal photocurrent falling phase and thus would apparently rule out GTPase as the mechanism for inactivation of G protein in the cascade. At present, the low rate constant of GTPase stands as one of the major unresolved issues in the cGMP theory.

Although relatively little is known about the process of inactivation of PDE itself, it is clear that once G protein (α-subunit) is converted by GTPase to the form with GDP bound, further activation of PDE does not occur. One possibility, represented by the open arrow in box 3 of Figure 1 of the general introduction to this section, is that the G protein–PDE complex (G_v*·PDE*) has a relatively short mean life-time. Some evidence that supports this idea has been presented (70). If the life-time of each G_v*·PDE* were rather short, then the inactivation of PDE would simply track the time course of GTPase hydrolysis of GTP bound to G protein. Unfortunately, this mechanism of inactivating PDE is inadequate: the estimated rates of GTPase activity are much too slow to account for the photocurrent falling phase.

The final enzymatic step in the cGMP cascade explanation of the photocurrent falling phase is the restoration of the free [cGMP] by guanylate cyclase (88) (Figure 1 of the general introduction, box 4, initial open arrow). At present, relatively little is known about the regulation of guanylate cyclase. Guanylate cyclase in frog rods should be able to generate in excess of 10^7 cGMP/sec/rod, which is rapid enough to replenish the total OS cGMP content in 3–5 sec in the absence of PDE activity. It has been demonstrated that the guanylate cyclase associated with the rod axonemes is calcium-sensitive (40), but this calcium sensitivity is only significant (approximately twofold inhibition) at 1-mM Ca^{2+}. It seems extremely unlikely that the free Ca^{2+} in the normal photoreceptor ever approaches this level; its actual level is most likely 1 μM or less in the dark (28, 65, 78) and diminishes during the light response (see above). A number of studies have shown that in the presence of low calcium and PDE inhibitors, such as IBMX, the light-sensitive pool and/or extractable cGMP of rods rises very rapidly (e.g. Reference 34), reaching an equivalent ROS concentration (total extractable cGMP per aqueous volume) of several millimolar in tens of seconds. Such results have at times been interpreted to mean that a low calcium concentration stimulates guanylate cyclase activity (72). However, if the relatively weak effect of calcium on the axonemal guanylate cyclase (40) obtains in the intact rod, then cyclase stimulation is not likely to explain the rapid rise in cGMP in low calcium. Another interpretation of the rapid elevation of cGMP in low calcium Ringer's solution is that dark PDE activity is high initially and is inhibited by low calcium. The existence of a relatively high dark PDE activity is supported by a study of Goldberg et al (48).

A NEGATIVE FEEDBACK HYPOTHESIS FOR THE ROLE OF CALCIUM IN TRANSDUCTION

Not only must a complete theory of visual transduction account for the speed of the photocurrent rising and falling phases, but also it must explain the effects of calcium and calcium chelators discussed above. The foremost of these observations is that elevated calcium suppresses the dark current. The modulation of guanylate cyclase (G-cyclase) activity by calcium (40) has the correct sign to account for the first five electrophysiological effects of calcium outlined in the section above. If a rise in external $[Ca^{2+}]$ raises internal $[Ca^{2+}]$, and this inhibits G-cyclase, then free [cGMP] is expected to drop, and the dark current should diminish. Conversely, if a reduction in external $[Ca^{2+}]$ causes internal $[Ca^{2+}]$ to decrease, and this stimulates G-cyclase, free [cGMP] is expected to rise, which would increase the fraction of g_{cGMP} open and elevate the dark current. These effects on membrane potential would follow from general principles of membrane physiology. In short, all the calcium-dependent phenomena discussed above seem to be at least qualitatively explainable in terms of calcium modulation of G-cyclase activity.

One problem with the hypothesis that G-cyclase inhibition is the principal site of calcium's effect on rod cGMP, and thus the dark current, was pointed out above: The axonemal cyclase is only weakly inhibited by calcium, and the maximal inhibitory effect (at 1-mM Ca^{2+}) is only about twofold. Of course, some regulatory mechanism by which Ca^{2+} influences G-cyclase may not be included in the isolated axonemal preparation (40). The elevation of [cGMP] in dark-adapted rods by lowered $[Ca^{2+}]$ could equally well be explained by an inhibition of dark-active PDE, provided that such PDE activity is sufficiently high to begin with.

Bownds (20) proposed that Ca^{2+} might play a role in a negative feedback on light-activated PDE. Specifically, he hypothesized that a GTP-dependent Ca^{2+} pump lowers the internal $[Ca^{2+}]$ during the light response, which desensitizes light-activated PDE. It was shown that (a) elevation of $[Ca^{2+}]$ in the medium from 10^{-9} to 10^{-3} M caused a roughly 50% decrement in PDE V_{max} in response to steps of light (92), (b) an approximately tenfold increase in PDE light sensitivity occurred as $[Ca^{2+}]$ was elevated from 10^{-9} to 10^{-3} M, and (c) this second effect of $[Ca^{2+}]$ was dependent on the presence of ATP (59). Ca^{2+} "disinhibition" of ATP-dependent inhibition was studied by Del Priore & Lewis (36), who demonstrated that 1-mM Ca^{2+} blocks the ATP-dependent quenching of PDE activity. This finding raises the possibility that Ca^{2+} may block rhodopsin phosphorylation or interfere with the binding of 48K protein. At present, however, none of the reports of the effect of Ca^{2+} on PDE activity demonstrate that this effect occurs in the range of a_{Ca} in which one expects the free $[Ca^{2+}]$ in the rod to vary (roughly, from 1 μM down). Nor has it been demonstrated that the magnitude of the effects of $[Ca^{2+}]$ on enzyme activity are in any sense commensurate with the electrophysiological effects that seem to require interpretation in terms of changes in internal free $[Ca^{2+}]$.

Recent electrophysiological observations point toward an early step in inactivation of the cascade as a likely molecular site of the $[Ca^{2+}]$ effect. After an injection of cGMP the photovoltage response to a given flash of light is greatly prolonged (80). When the dark current is greatly increased by the infusion of cGMP, the duration of the saturated phase of the photocurrent and the time course of the dim flash are extended (30, 31, 76). Moreover, for a flash of a given intensity, the duration of the prolongation depends on how much dark current has flowed. Under these same conditions, the rising phase of the photocurrent is little altered (30, 31, 76). According to the hypothesis that cGMP is the sole transmitter, the prolongation of the photoresponse saturated phase cannot be due to a direct effect of cGMP—the prolongation occurs precisely when, according to theory, the free [cGMP] in the OS should be at its lowest level. An "integrating step" or memory of the prior dark current is needed to explain these photoresponse prolongation phenomena. Since increasing the dark current causes an excess of Ca^{2+} to leak into the cell (116), build-up of Ca^{2+} in the cytoplasm is an attractive candidate for the integrating step. In addition, immediately after the dark current is elevated by exposure of the cell to low external [Ca^{2+}], the responses are not prolonged (114); thus without normal external [Ca^{2+}], elevation of internal [cGMP] alone does not cause response prolongation. If photoresponse prolongation attendant on cGMP infusion is in fact due to Ca^{2+}, then it cannot be due to Ca^{2+} affecting G-cyclase, because in the experiments cited cGMP was supplied exogenously, not by native G-cyclase. Thus, electrophysiological data seem to point toward an effect of elevated [Ca^{2+}] on some component of the light-activated cascade. The fact that the rising phase of the response is little altered suggests that the effect of Ca^{2+} is to slow one or more of the inactivation steps in the PDE cascade before G-cyclase.

Recent electrophysiological observations suggest that regulation of internal calcium concentration exerts a dynamic influence in photocurrent kinetics. Recall that the evidence is now strong (see above) that free [Ca^{2+}] declines in the OS during a light response due to blockage of inward flow through g_{hv}, and continued extrusion via the Na^+-Ca^{2+} antiporter. An important observation demonstrating a dynamic influence of Ca^{2+} was reported by Matthews et al (76). These investigators infused the calcium chelator BAPTA into salamander rods through whole-cell patch pipettes. The saturated phase of photocurrent responses was prolonged, and the dark current showed very striking overshoots upon emergence from saturation that depended on the time spent in saturation. This striking observation could be explained in terms of the cGMP cascade in this way: During the saturated phase of the photocurrent, Na^+-Ca^{2+} exchange pumps the outer segment free [Ca^{2+}] to a low level. The longer the time spent in saturation, the lower the level that can be reached. If this level is low enough, some of the infused BAPTA which had Ca^{2+} bound becomes free. Lowered internal [Ca^{2+}] stimulates G-cyclase activity (or inhibits PDE activity). As [cGMP] rises, the dark current opens up again. The inward Ca^{2+} leak through g_{hv}—which would normally rapidly restore free [Ca^{2+}] to its resting state—does so more slowly than normal because it must first overcome the buffering effect of the Ca^{2+}-free BAPTA, which was depleted of Ca^{2+} by Na^{+}-Ca^{2+} exchange. In effect, the BAPTA infused into the cell acts as a "calcium capacitance;" it introduces a dramatic phase lag into a normally overdamped feedback loop. This feedback system uses OS free $[Ca^{2+}]$ as a signal to regulate an enzymatic step or steps that act to restore [cGMP] to its baseline (dark) level.

Torre et al (106) extended their earlier observations with BAPTA infusion in rods. They demonstrated that infused BAPTA greatly slows the component of OS membrane current attributable to Na^{+}-Ca^{2+} exchange (116). They showed that cells infused with BAPTA adapt to light much more slowly than cells with normal calcium-buffering capability. This finding suggests that the extrusion of Ca^{2+} can be a rate-limiting step in the process of light adaptation. Their work thus supports the hypothesis that the normal role of Ca^{2+} in the photoreceptor is as a negative feedback signal derived from the dark current. Thus higher internal $[Ca^{2+}]$ stimulates light-activated PDE activity, reduces cGMP, lowers dark current, and slows the inward leak of Ca^{2+}; lower internal $[Ca^{2+}]$ speeds up the inactivation of PDE and the return to normal free [cGMP] levels.

In summary, a "calcium negative feedback" hypothesis is emerging, both as an explanation of the well-known effects of $[Ca^{2+}]$ on the dark current and photocurrents (see section on experimental evidence for the calcium hypothesis, above) and as a generalization of the cGMP cascade theory that accomodates the new findings on the "leakiness" of $g_{h\nu}$ to Ca^{2+} and the powerful OS Na^{+}-Ca^{2+} exchange. According to this hypothesis, internal free $[Ca^{2+}]$ acts as a signal to one or more biochemical steps in the transduction cycle: Elevated $[Ca^{2+}]$ tends to cause free [cGMP] to drop, and lowered $[Ca^{2+}]$ tends to elevate [cGMP]. In effect, the Ca^{2+} "buffer space" of the photoreceptor acts as a capacitor that low-pass filters the signal, the inward leakage of Ca^{2+} through $g_{h\nu}$. The outward pumping of the Na^{+}-Ca^{2+} antiporter acts as a power source that maintains the feedback signal battery, the transmembrane $[Ca^{2+}]$ gradient. An elegant aspect of the BAPTA infusion experiments (65, 76, 106) is that infused BAPTA apparently changes the time constant of the feedback signal. The biochemical substrates regulated by internal free $[Ca^{2+}]$ have not been identified unequivocally. Evidence points to an inhibitory effect of Ca^{2+} on the ATP-dependent quenching mechanism. This effect suggests that Ca^{2+} could either block rhodopsin phosphorylation or the binding of 48K to phosphorylated rhodopsin, although other mechanisms are certainly not excluded. The effects of Ca^{2+} on the fully dark-adapted rod seem to require some other explanation, however, since in the dark there is presumably very little R* to quench. The "calcium negative feedback" hypothesis seems elegant and powerful: Not only does it provide a qualitative account of the major effects of altered calcium and infusion of calcium chelator, but it may also provide the basis for an explanation of photoreceptor light adaptation (106) and the faster photocurrent kinetics of cones.

THE ROLES OF cGMP AND Ca²⁺ IN CONE PHOTOTRANSDUCTION

Cones and rods clearly share many properties in their electrophysiological behavior, a fact noted early in microelectrode recordings of photovoltages from single cells (9, 105). More recently, suction and voltage-clamp electrode recordings from cones (3, 30, 85, 95) have provided evidence that cones have dark- and photocurrents of about the same magnitude as those of the rods of the same retina. Cones differ from rods in several dramatic ways, however. First, the intrinsic photoresponse gain (mV/hν or pA/hν) of cones is less than one tenth that of rods (16, 30). Secondly, the speed of the photocurrent response is typically much faster in cones than in rods of the same retina: The time-to-peak of dark-adapted, linear-flash response in an amphibian rod is typically 0.6–1.5 sec, whereas in cones of the same species it may be 150–200 msec. Third, cones adapt to light (i.e. change their gain and response speed) much more rapidly than rods.

Recent electrophysiological evidence supports the notion that rods and cones have similar transduction machinery. Haynes & Yau (56) showed that excised patches of catfish cone outer segments contain a cGMP-dependent conductance whose K_D and Hill coefficient (N in equation 1) are about the same as those of ROS membrane. There is physiological evidence for a light-activated cGMP enzyme cascade in cones (30, 82). Cones have been shown to contain a cGMP phosphodiesterase (58). Although the cone pigments (83), the phosphodiesterase (58), and the other protein components (51; J. B. Hurley, personal communication) of the cGMP cascade in cones differ somewhat from those in rods, it seems reasonable at present to think that the transduction mechanisms operate in essentially the same way in rods and cones and to hypothesize that [Ca²⁺] affects their respective cascades in a qualitatively similar fashion.

Quantitatively, an extension of the calcium feedback hypothesis might explain some of the differences in photocurrent kinetics between cones and rods. Because in some species the surface/volume ratio of cones is up to 200 times greater than that of rods, while their respective dark currents are roughly equal, the Na⁺-Ca²⁺ antiporter should be able to alter the internal free [Ca²⁺] much more rapidly in cones than in rods. Under voltage clamp, a light-insensitive component of OS membrane current can be measured in cones (32) that is similar to that attributed to the Na⁺-Ca²⁺ exchanger in rods (116). The time course of this component implies a larger and more rapid excursion of OS cytoplasmic Ca²⁺ in cones than in rods. In terms of the Ca²⁺ feedback hypothesis, cones may have a larger feedback gain (total Na⁺-Ca²⁺ exchange) and a much smaller "capacitor" (internal OS volume) in the feedback loop. It seems doubtful that all the differences in rod and cone photocurrents (e.g. much lower gain) are due solely to faster Na⁺-Ca²⁺ exchange, but the calcium feedback hypothesis does provide a unifying principle that may account for some differences in rod and cone physiology. The morphology of cones could be partly responsible for their faster photocurrent kinetics and ability to adapt to light more rapidly.

CONCLUSION

Perhaps a lesson or two can be drawn from the 15-year effort to identify the internal transmitter of rod transduction.

It proved extremely difficult to untangle the tightly intertwined roles of Ca^{2+} and cGMP in intact photoreceptors. The unequivocal proof that cGMP, not Ca^{2+}, acts upon a conductance in isolated patches of outer segment plasma membrane literally and figuratively broke open the loop.

A potent argument against cGMP as transmitter was based upon the relatively small fraction of cGMP in the outer segment that seemed to be light-sensitive. The resolution of this issue seems to be that most of the OS cGMP is bound and that basal guanylate cyclase is sufficient to prevent maximal PDE activity from reducing free [cGMP] below the K_D of the highest-affinity site. The inability of "quench and extract" procedures to distinguish bound from free components in intact cells limits the utility of such data for testing physiological hypotheses. Cyclic nucleotide–dependent protein kinases typically have submicromolar K_D's for their agonists, whereas total extractable cyclic nucleotides, if referred to cytoplasmic volume, are such as to keep the kinases saturated (71), which would mean that no regulation occurs. If, however, most of the nucleotide is bound to very high affinity sites, as is now believed to be the condition in rods, the free nucleotide concentration could vary in a way that regulates kinase activity.

Rods and cones both transduce light into neural signals, but apparently they have evolved to function effectively over different ranges of light intensity. The calcium negative feedback hypothesis provides a rational basis for explaining these functional difference in terms of cell structure. Thus in excitable cells, structure (e.g. surface-to-volume ratio) can be an important determinant of biochemical kinetics.

Literature Cited

1. Arshavsky, V. Yu., Dizhoor, A. M., Shestakova, I. I., Philippov, P. P. 1985. The effect of rhodopsin phosphorylation on the light-dependent activation of phosphodiesterase from bovine rod outer segments. *FEBS Lett.* 181:264–66
2. Aton, B., Litman, B. J. 1984. Activation of rod outer segment phosphodiesterase by enzymatically altered rhodop-
sin: A regulatory role for the carboxyl terminus of rhodopsin. *Exp. Eye Res.* 38:547–59
3. Attwell, D., Werblin, F. S., Wilson, M. 1982. The properties of single cones isolated from the tiger salamander retina. *J. Physiol.* 328:259–83
4. de Azeredo, F. A. M., Lust, W. D., Passoneau, J. V. 1981. Light-induced

changes in energy metabolites, guanine nucleotides and guanylate cyclase within frog retinal layers. *J. Biol. Chem.* 256:2731–35

5. Bader, C. R., MacLeish, P. R., Schwartz, E. A. 1979. A voltage-clamp study of the light response in solitary rods of the tiger salamander. *J. Physiol.* 296:1–26

6. Barkdoll, A. E. III, Sitaramayya, A., Pugh, E. N. Jr. 1986. Hydrolysis of 8-bromo-cGMP by light-sensitive phosphodiesterase of toad retinal rods. *Biophys. J.* 49:279a

7. Bastian, B. L., Fain, G. L. 1979. Light adaptation in toad rods: Requirement for an internal messenger which is not calcium. *J. Physiol.* 297:493–520

8. Baylor, D. A., Fuortes, M. G. F. 1970. Electrical responses of single cones in the retina of the turtle. *J. Physiol.* 207:77–92

9. Baylor, D. A., Hodgkin, A. L., Lamb, T. D. 1974. The electrical response of turtle cones to flashes and steps of light. *J. Physiol.* 242:685–727

10. Baylor, D. A., Lamb, T. D., Yau, K.-W. 1979. The membrane current of single rod outer segments. *J. Physiol.* 288:589–611

11. Baylor, D. A., Lamb, T. D., Yau, K.-W. 1979. Responses of retinal rods to single photons. *J. Physiol.* 288:613–34

12. Baylor, D. A., Matthews, G., Nunn, B. J. 1984. Location and function of voltage-sensitive conductances in retinal rods of the salamander, *Ambystoma tigrinum*. *J. Physiol.* 354:203–23

13. Baylor, D. A., Matthews, G., Yau, K.-W. 1980. Two components of electrical dark noise in toad retinal rod outer segments. *J. Physiol.* 309:591–621

14. Baylor, D. A., Nunn, B. J. 1986. Electrical properties of the light-sensitive conductance of salamander rods. *J. Physiol.* 371:115–45

15. Baylor, D. A., Nunn, B. J., Schnapf, J. L. 1984. The photocurrent, noise and spectral sensitivity of rods of the monkey, *Macaca fascicularis*. *J. Physiol.* 357:575–607

16. Baylor, D. A., Schnapf, J. L., Nunn, B. J. 1985. Transduction by cones in the retina of *Macaca fascicularis*. *Biophys. J.* 47:375a

17. Bennett, N. 1982. Light-induced interactions between rhodopsin and the GTP-binding protein: Relation with phosphodiesterase activation. *Eur. J. Biochem.* 123:133–39

18. Bitensky, M. W., Gorman, R. E., Miller, W. H. 1971. Adenyl cyclase as a link between photon capture and changes in membrane permeability of frog photoreceptors. *Proc. Natl. Acad. Sci. USA* 68:561–62

19. Bodoia, R. D., Detweiler, P. B. 1984. Patch-clamp recordings of the light-sensitive dark noise in retinal rods from the lizard and frog. *J. Physiol.* 367:183–216

20. Bownds, M. D. 1980. Biochemical steps in visual transduction: Roles for nucleotides and calcium ions. *Photochem. Photobiol.* 32:487–90

21. Brown, J. E., Coles, J. A., Pinto, L. H. 1977. Effects of injections of Ca^{++} and EGTA into the outer segment of the retinal rods of *Bufo marinus*. *J. Physiol.* 269:707–22

22. Brown, J. E., Pinto, L. H. 1974. Ionic mechanism for the photoreceptor potential of the retina of *Bufo marinus*. *J. Physiol.* 236:575–91

23. Brown, J. E., Waloga, G. 1981. Effects of cyclic nucleotides and calcium ions on *Bufo* rods. *Curr. Top. Membr. Transp.* 15:369–80

24. Caretta, A. 1985. Effect of cGMP and cations on the permeability of cattle retinal disks. *Eur. J. Biochem.* 148:599–606

25. Caretta, A., Cavaggioni, A. 1983. Fast ionic flux activated by cyclic GMP in the membrane of cattle rod outer segment. *Eur. J. Biochem.* 132:1–8

26. Caretta, A., Cavaggioni, A., Sorbi, R. T. 1979. Cyclic GMP and permeability of the disk membrane of photoreceptors. *J. Physiol.* 295:171–78

27. Cavaggioni, A., Sorbi, R. T. 1981. Cyclic-GMP releases calcium from disk membranes of vertebrate photoreceptors. *Proc. Natl. Acad. Sci. USA* 78:3964–68

28. Cervetto, L., McNaughton, P. A., Nunn, B. J. 1986. Aequorin signals from isolated salamander rods. *Biophys. J.* 49:281a

29. Clack, J. W., Oakley, B. II, Stein, P. J. 1983. Injection of GTP-binding protein of cyclic GMP phosphodiesterase hyperpolarizes retinal rods. *Nature* 305:50–53

30. Cobbs, W. H., Barkdoll, A. E. III, Pugh, E. N. Jr. 1985. Cyclic GMP increases photocurrent and light sensitivity of retinal cones. *Nature* 317:64–66

31. Cobbs, W. H., Pugh, E. N. Jr. 1985. Cyclic GMP can increase rod outer-segment light-sensitive current 10-fold without delay of excitation. *Nature* 313:585–87

32. Cobbs, W. H., Pugh, E. N. Jr. 1986. Two components of outer segment mem-

brane current in salamander rods and cones. *Biophys. J.* 49:280a

33. Cobbs, W. H., Pugh, E. N. Jr. 1986. Limiting rates of rise of flash photocurrent in isolated salamander rods and cones. *Invest. Ophthalmol.* 27:300a

34. Cohen, A. I., Hall, I. A., Ferendelli, J. A. 1978. Calcium and cyclic nucleotide regulation in incubated mouse retinas. *J. Gen. Physiol.* 71:595–612

35. Cote, R. H., Biernbaum, M. S., Nicol, G. D., Bownds, M. D. 1984. Light-induced decreases in cGMP concentration precede changes in membrane permeability in frog rod photoreceptors. *J. Biol. Chem.* 259:9635–41

36. Del Priore, L. V., Lewis, A. 1983. Calcium-dependent activation and deactivation of rods outer segment phosphodiesterase in calmodulin-independent. *Biochem. Biophys. Res. Commun.* 113: 317–24

37. Detweiler, P. B., Conner, J. D., Bodoia, R. D. 1982. Gigaseal patch clamp from outer segments of intact retinal rods. *Nature* 300:59–61

38. Fain, G. L., Schroeder, W. H. 1985. Calcium content and calcium exchange in dark-adapted toad rods. *J. Physiol.* 368:641–65

39. Fesenko, E. E., Kolesnikov, S. S., Lyubarsky, A. L. 1985. Induction by cyclic GMP of cationic conductance in plasma membrane of retinal rod outer segment. *Nature* 313:310–13

40. Fleischman, D., Denisevich, M. 1979. Guanylate cyclase of isolated bovine retinal rod axonemes. *Biochemistry* 18:5060–66

41. Fung, B. B.-K. 1983. Characterization of transducin from bovine retinal rod outer segments. Separation and reconstitution of the subunits. *J. Biol. Chem.* 258:10495–10502

42. Fung, B. B.-K., Hurley, J. B., Stryer, L. 1981. Flow of information in the light-triggered cyclic nucleotide cascade of vision. *Proc. Natl. Acad. Sci. USA* 78:152–56

43. Fung, B. B.-K., Stryer, L. 1980. Photolyzed rhodopsin catalyzes the exchange of GTP for bound GDP in retinal rod outer segments. *Proc. Natl. Acad. Sci. USA* 77:2500–4

44. Fuortes, M. G. F., Hodgkin, A. L. 1964. Changes in time scale and sensitivity in the ommatidia of *Limulus*. *J. Physiol.* 172:239–63

45. Godchaux, W. III, Zimmerman, W. F. 1979. Membrane-dependent guanine nucleotide binding and GTPase activities of soluble protein from bovine rod outer segments. *J. Biol. Chem.* 254:7874–84

46. Gold, G. H. 1986. Plasma membrane calcium fluxes in intact rods are inconsistent with the "calcium hypothesis." *Proc. Natl. Acad. Sci. USA* 83: 1150–54

47. Gold, G. H., Korenbrot, J. I. 1980. Light-induced calcium release by intact retinal rods. *Proc. Natl. Acad. Sci. USA* 77:5557–61

48. Goldberg, N. D., Ames, A. III, Gander, J. E., Walseth, T. F. 1983. Magnitude of increase in retinal cGMP metabolic flux determined by 18(0) incorporation into nucleotide alpha-phosphoryls corresponds with intensity of photic stimulation. *J. Biol. Chem.* 258:9213–19

49. Govardovskii, V. I., Berman, A. L. 1981. Light-induced changes of cyclic GMP content in frog retinal rod outer segments measured with rapid freezing and microdissection. *Biophys. Struct. Mech.* 7:125–30

50. Gray, P., Attwell, D. 1985. Kinetics of light-sensitive changes in vertebrate photoreceptors. *Proc. R. Soc. London Ser. B* 223:379–88

51. Grunwald, G. B., Gierschik, P., Nirenberg, M., Spiegel, A. 1986. Detection of a-transducin in retinal rods but not cones. *Science* 231:856–58

52. Hagins, W. A., Penn, R. D., Yoshikami, S. 1970. Dark current and photocurrent in retinal rods. *Biophys. J.* 10:380–412

53. Hagins, W. A., Yoshikami, S. 1974. A role for Ca^{++} in excitation of retinal rods and cones. *Exp. Eye Res.* 18:299–305

54. Hagins, W. A., Yoshikami, S. 1977. Intracellular transmission of visual excitation in photoreceptors: Electrical effects of chelating agents introduced into rods by vesicle fusion. In *Vertebrate Photoreception*, ed. H. B. Barlow, P. Fatt, pp. 97–138. New York: Academic

55. Haynes, L. W., Kay, A. R., Yau, K.-W. 1986. Single cGMP-activated channel activity in excised patches of rod outer segment membranes. *Nature* 321:66–70

56. Haynes, L. W., Yau, K.-W. 1985. Cyclic GMP-sensitive conductance in outer segment membranes of catfish cones. *Nature* 317:61–64

57. Hodgkin, A. L., McNaughton, P. A., Nunn, B. J. 1985. The ionic selectivity and calcium dependence of the light-sensitive pathway in toad rods. *J. Physiol.* 358:447–68

58. Hurwitz, R. L., Bunt-Milam, A. H., Chang, M. L., Beavo, J. A. 1985. cGMP phosphodiesterase in rod and

cone outer segments of the retina. *J. Biol. Chem.* 260:568–73

59. Kawamura, S., Bownds, M. D. 1981. Light adaptation of the cyclic GMP phosphodiesterase of frog photoreceptor membranes mediated by ATP and calcium ions. *J. Gen. Physiol.* 77:571–91

60. Kawamura, S., Murakami, M. 1983. Intracellular injection of cyclic-GMP increases sodium conductance in gecko photoreceptors. *Jpn. J. Physiol.* 33:789–800

61. Kilbride, P., Ebrey, T. G. 1979. Light-initiated changes of cyclic guanosine monophosphate levels in the frog retina measured with quick freezing techniques. *J. Gen. Physiol.* 74:415–26

62. Koch, K. W., Kaupp, U. B. 1985. Cyclic GMP directly regulates a cation conductance in membranes of bovine rods by a cooperative mechanism. *J. Biol. Chem.* 260:6788–6800

63. Kuhn, H. 1980. Light- and GTP-regulated interaction of GTPase and other proteins with bovine photoreceptor membranes. *Nature* 283:587–89

64. Kuhn, H., Hall, S. W., Wilden, U. 1984. Light-induced binding of 48KDa protein to photoreceptor membranes is highly enhanced by phosphorylation of rhodopsin. *FEBS Lett.* 176:473–78

65. Lamb, T. D., Matthews, H., Torre, V. 1986. Changes in the photocurrent of salamander retinal rods during incorporation of calcium buffers. *J. Physiol.* 372:315–49

66. Lamb, T. D., McNaughton, P. A., Yau, K.-W. 1981. Spatial spread of activation and background desensitization in toad rod outer segments. *J. Physiol.* 319:463–96

67. Lewis, J. W., Miller, J. L., Mendel-Hartvig, J., Schaechter, L. E., Kliger, D. S., Dratz, E. A. 1984. Sensitive light-scattering probe of enzymatic processes in retinal rod photoreceptor membranes. *Proc. Natl. Acad. Sci. USA* 81:743–47

68. Liebman, P. A., Mueller, P., Pugh, E. N. Jr. 1984. Protons suppress the dark current of frog retinal rods. *J. Physiol.* 347:85–110

69. Liebman, P. A., Pugh, E. N. Jr. 1980. ATP mediates rapid reversal of cGMP phosphodiesterase activation in visual receptor membranes. *Nature* 287:634–36

70. Liebman, P. A., Pugh, E. N. Jr. 1982. Gain, speed and sensitivity of GTP binding vs. PDE activation in visual excitation. *Vision Res.* 22:1475–80

71. Lincoln, T. M., Corbin, J. D. 1983. Characterization and biological role of

the cGMP-dependent protein kinase. *Adv. Cyclic Nucleotide Res.* 15:138–92

72. Lolley, R. N., Racz, E. 1982. Calcium modulation of cyclic GMP synthesis in rat visual cells. *Vision Res.* 22:1481–86

73. MacLeish, P. R., Schwartz, E. A., Tachibana, M. 1984. Control of the generator current in solitary rods of the *Ambystoma tigrinum* retina. *J. Physiol.* 348:645–64

74. Matthews, G. 1986. Spread of the light response along the rod outer segment: An estimate from patch-clamp recordings. *Vision Res.* 26:535–42

75. Matthews, G. 1986. Comparison of the light-sensitive and cyclic-GMP sensitive conductances of the rod photoreceptor: Noise characteristics. *Proc. Natl. Acad. Sci. USA* In press

76. Matthews, H. R., Torre, V., Lamb, T. 1985. Effects on the photoresponse of calcium buffers and cyclic GMP incorporated into the cytoplasm of retinal rods. *Nature* 313:582–85

77. McLaughlin, S., Brown, J. E. 1981. Diffusion of calcium ions in retinal rods. *J. Gen. Physiol.* 77:475–87

78. Miller, D. L., Korenbrot, J. 1986. The effects of the intracellular calcium buffer, Quin 2, on photocurrents and light-induced calcium release from individual rod cells. *Invest. Ophthalmol. Vis. Sci.* 26:168a

79. Miller, J. L., Dratz, E. A. 1984. Phosphorylation at sites near rhodopsin's carboxyl-terminus regulates light-initiated cGMP hydrolysis. *Vision Res.* 24:1509–21

80. Miller, W. H. 1982. Physiological evidence that light-mediated decrease in cyclic GMP is an intermediary process in retinal rod transduction. *J. Gen. Physiol.* 80:103–23

81. Miller, W. H., Nicol, G. D. 1979. Evidence that cGMP regulates membrane potential in rod photoreceptors. *Nature:* 280:64–66

82. Nakatani, K., Yau, K.-W. 1986. Light-suppressible, cyclic GMP-activated current recorded from a dialyzed cone preparation. *Invest. Ophthalmol. Vis. Sci.* 27:300a

83. Nathans, J., Thomas, D., Hogness, D. S. 1986. Molecular genetics of human color vision: The genes encoding blue, green and red pigments. *Science* 232:193–202

84. Nicol, G. D., Miller, W. H. 1978. cGMP injected into retinal rod outer segments increases latency and amplitude of response to illumination. *Proc. Natl. Acad. Sci. USA* 75:5217–20

85. Nunn, B. J., Schnapf, J. L., Baylor, D.

740   PUGH

A. 1985. Spectral sensitivity of single cones in the retina of *Macaca fascicularis*. *Nature* 309:264–66

86. Oakley, B. II, Pinto, L. H. 1983. Modulation of membrane conductance in rods of *Bufo marinus* by intracellular calcium ion. *J. Physiol.* 339:273–98

87. Olive, J. 1980. The structural organization of mammalian retinal disk membrane. *Int. Rev. Cytol.* 64:107–69

88. Pannbacker, R. G., Fleischman, D. E., Reed, D. W. 1972. Cyclic nucleotide phosphodiesterase: High activity in mammalian photoreceptor. *Science* 175:757–58

89. Penn, R. D., Hagins, W. A. 1972. Kinetics of the photocurrent of retinal rods. *Biophys. J.* 12:1073–94

90. Pugh, E. N. Jr., Cobbs, W. H. 1986. Properties of cytoplasmic transmitters of excitation in vertebrate rods and evaluation of candidate intermediary transmitters. In *The Molecular Mechanism of Vertebrate Photoreception*, ed. H. Stieve, pp. 127–58. Berlin: Springer

91. Rasmussen, H. 1981. *Calcium and cAMP as Synarchic Messengers*. New York: Wiley. 370 pp.

92. Robinson, P. R., Kawamura, S., Abramson, B., Bownds, M. D. 1980. Control of the cyclic GMP phosphodiesterase of frog photoreceptor membranes. *J. Gen. Physiol.* 76:631–45

93. Robinson, W. E., Hagins, W. A. 1979. GTP hydrolysis in intact rod outer segments and the transmitter cycle in visual excitation. *Nature* 280:398–400

94. Schnapf, J. L. 1983. Dependence of the single photon response on longitudinal position of absorption in toad rod outer segments. *J. Physiol.* 343:147–59

95. Schnapf, J. L., McBurney, R. N. 1980. Light-induced changes in membrane current in cone outer segments of tiger salamander and turtle. *Nature* 287:239–41

96. Schroeder, W. H., Fain, G. L. 1984. Light-dependent calcium release from photoreceptors measured by laser micromass analysis. *Nature* 309:268–70

97. Shichi, H., Somers, L. 1978. Light-dependent phosphorylation of rhodopsin. *J. Biol. Chem.* 253:7040–46

98. Shimoda, Y., Hurley, J. B., Miller, W. H. 1984. Rod light response augmented by active phosphodiesterase. *Proc. Natl. Acad. Sci. USA* 81:616–19

99. Sitaramayya, A., Harkness, J., Parkes, J., Gonzalez-Olivia, C., Liebman, P. A. 1986. Kinetic studies suggest that light-activated cyclic GMP phosphodiesterase is a complex with G-protein subunits. *Biochemistry* 25:651–56

100. Sitaramayya, A., Liebman, P. A. 1983. Mechanism of ATP quench of phosphodiesterase activation in rod disk membranes. *J. Biol. Chem.* 258:1205–9

101. Sitaramayya, A., Liebman, P. A. 1983. Phosphorylation of rhodopsin and quenching of cGMP phosphodiesterase activation by ATP at weak bleaches. *J. Biol. Chem.* 258:12106–9

102. Sitaramayya, A., Virmaux, N., Mandel, P. 1977. On the mechanism of light activation of retinal rod outer segments cyclic GMP phosphodiesterase. *Neurochem. Res.* 2:1–10

103. Somlyo, A. P., Walz, B. 1985. Elemental distribution in *Rana pipiens* retinal rods: Quantitative electron probe analysis. *J. Physiol.* 358:183–95

104. Tanaka, J. C., Furman, R. E., Cobbs, W. H., Mueller, P. 1986. Incorporation of retinal rod cGMP-dependent conductance into planar bilayers. *Proc. Natl. Acad. Sci. USA* In press

105. Tomita, T. 1970. Electrical activity of vertebrate photoreceptors. *Q. Rev. Biophys.* 3:179–222

106. Torre, V., Matthews, H. R., Lamb, T. D. 1986. The role of calcium in regulating the cyclic GMP cascade of phototransduction. *Proc. Natl. Acad. Sci. USA* 83:7109–13

107. Waloga, G. 1983. Effects of calcium and guanosine 3':5'-cyclic monophosphoric acid on receptor potentials of toad rods. *J. Physiol.* 341:341–57

108. Wheeler, G. L., Bitensky, M. W. 1977. A light-activated GTPase in vertebrate photoreceptors: Regulation of light-activated cyclic GMP phosphodiesterase. *Proc. Natl. Acad. Sci. USA* 74:4238–42

109. Wilden, U., Hall, S. W., Kuhn, H. 1986. Phosphodiesterase activation by photoexcited rhodopsin is quenched when rhodopsin is phosphorylated and binds the intrinsic 48KDa protein of rod outer segments. *Proc. Natl. Acad. Sci. USA* 83:1174–78

110. Woodruff, M. L., Bownds, M. D. 1979. Amplitude, kinetics and reversibility of a light-induced decrease in guanosine 3',5'-monophosphate in frog photoreceptor membranes. *J. Gen. Physiol.* 73:629–53

111. Yamanaka, G., Eckstein, F., Stryer, L. 1986. Stereochemistry of the guanyl nucleotide binding site of transducin probed by phosphorothioate analogues of GTP and GDP. *Biochemistry* 24:8094–8101

112. Yamazaki, A., Stein, P. J., Chernoff, N., Bitensky, M. W. 1983. Activation mechanism of rod outer segment cyclic

GMP phosphodiesterase. *J. Biol. Chem.* 258:8188–94

113. Yau, K.-W., Haynes, L. W., Nakatani, K. 1987. Roles of calcium and cyclic GMP in visual transduction. In *Membrane Control of Cellular Activity,* ed. H. C. Luttgau. Stuttgart: Fischer. In press

114. Yau, K.-W., McNaughton, P. A., Hodgkin, A. L. 1981. Effect of ions on the light-sensitive current in retinal rods. *Nature* 292:502–5

115. Yau, K.-W., Nakatani, K. 1984. Electrogenic Na-Ca exchange in retinal rod outer segment. *Nature* 311:661–63

116. Yau, K.-W., Nakatani, K. 1985. Light-induced reduction of cytoplasmic free calcium in retinal rod outer segment. *Nature* 313:579–81

117. Yau, K.-W., Nakatani, K. 1985. Light-suppressible, cyclic-GMP-sensitive conductance in the plasma membrane of a truncated rod outer segment. *Nature* 317:252–55

118. Yoshikami, S., George, S., Hagins, W. A. 1980. Light-induced calcium fluxes from the outer segment layer of vertebrate retina. *Nature* 286:395–98

119. Yoshikami, S., Hagins, W. A. 1970. Ionic basis of dark current and photocurrent of retinal rods. *Biophys. J.* 10:60a

120. Yoshikami, S., Hagins, W. A. 1973. Control of dark current in vertebrate rods and cones. In *Biochemistry and Physiology of Visual Pigments,* ed. H. Langer, pp. 245–55. New York: Springer

121. Zimmerman, A. L., Baylor, D. A. 1986. Single-channel currents from the cyclic GMP sensitive conductance of retinal rod outer segments. *Nature* 321:70–72

122. Zuckerman, R., Buzdygon, B., Philp, N., Liebman, P. A., Sitaramayya, A. 1985. Arrestin: An ATP/ADP exchange protein that regulates cGMP phosphodiesterase activity. *Biophys. J.* 47:37a

Ann. Rev. Physiol. 1987. 49:743–64
Copyright © 1987 by Annual Reviews Inc. All rights reserved

IONIC CONDUCTANCES IN ROD PHOTORECEPTORS

W. Geoffrey Owen

Department of Biophysics and Medical Physics, University of California, and Division of Biology and Medicine, Lawrence Berkeley Laboratory, Berkeley, California, 94720

INTRODUCTION

The vertebrate rod is structurally differentiated into an outer segment and an inner segment connected by a short ciliary stalk. In darkness, a positive ionic current flows out of the inner segment and reenters the rod across the plasma membrane of the outer segment (24). Illumination leads to a closure of ionic channels in that membrane and a consequent reduction in the dark current (6, 24). As a result the rod hyperpolarizes. This hyperpolarizing light response spreads through the inner segment to the synaptic terminal, from which it is transmitted to other cells.

This review focuses upon the ionic mechanisms known to exist in both the outer and inner segments of the rod. Briefly, the plasma membrane of the outer segment appears to contain but a single ionic conductance, the primary, "light-sensitive" conductance (5). It also contains a Na^+-Ca^{2+} exchanger whose action profoundly affects the light-sensitive conductance. The inner segment, on the other hand, contains a variety of ionic conductances, most of which are either directly or indirectly voltage dependent and vary over time and thus serve to shape the voltage response of the rod.

During the last five years or so, with the application of powerful new techniques, our understanding of phototransduction and of the nature and properties of ionic mechanisms in the rod outer segment has advanced dramatically. It is inevitable, therefore, that much of the discussion in this review centers upon outer segment mechanisms and emphasizes work carried out within that period. For comprehensive reviews of earlier work, the reader is referred to articles by Fain & Lisman (17) and Owen & Torre (42).

743

0066-4278/87/0315-0743$02.00

OUTER SEGMENT MECHANISMS

The Sodium-Calcium Exchange Mechanism

Before reviewing the properties of the light-sensitive channel, it is necessary to discuss the Na^+-Ca^{2+} exchange mechanism. Until the existence of this mechanism was recognized, many of the effects of external ion substitutions were misinterpreted (see 17, 42). Indeed, it was only recently that its properties were sufficiently well understood for reliable determinations of the ionic selectivity of the light-sensitive channel to be made.

The earliest indication that a photoreceptor membrane might include a Na^+-Ca^{2+} exchange mechanism came from studies of the *Limulus* lateral eye (30); this was subsequently confirmed with the aid of the metallochromic dye Arsenazo III (48). In later studies of vertebrate rods (21, 22, 58), it was found that light caused a rise in external $[Ca^{2+}]$, the magnitude of which was highly dependent upon external $[Na^+]$. At about the same time, Schnetkamp (43) found that the efflux of ^{45}Ca from preloaded rod outer segments was stimulated by external Na^+. These findings are consistent with the notion that external Na^+ activates a Na^+-Ca^{2+} exchange mechanism in the plasma membrane of the rod outer segment (ROS). This notion received additional support from experiments by Hodgkin et al (28), in which a suction pipette was used to monitor the current crossing that membrane. It was noted that many of the effects of changing external concentrations of Na^+ and Ca^{2+} upon the dark current and photocurrent were consistent with the action of a Na^+-Ca^{2+} exchanger that normally extrudes Ca^{2+} from the outer segment.

The properties of the Na^+-Ca^{2+} exchanger were revealed by two sets of suction pipette experiments (54, 55). In one of these (54), the light-sensitive conductance was first increased by perfusing a ROS with a Ringer's solution containing 55 mM Na^+ and 1 μM Ca^{2+}. A large, inward Ca^{2+} current was then induced by substituting an isotonic $CaCl_2$ solution. As illustrated in Figure 1, this Ca^{2+} current declined slowly in darkness but could be rapidly shut off by a bright flash of light, which indicates that Ca^{2+} enters the outer segment through the light-sensitive channels.

Upon cessation of the Ca^{2+} influx, a saturating light was turned on to close all the light-sensitive channels. External $[Na^+]$ was then raised to 110 mM and a transient inward current was seen. Because the light-sensitive channels were closed, it was argued that the transient inward current must have been generated by the Na^+-Ca^{2+} exchange mechanism. In support of this, (a) the current was not seen when Li^+ was substituted for external Na^+; (b) the magnitude of the current depended upon the electrochemical gradients of both Na^+ and Ca^{2+}; and (c) the total charge transfer depended only upon the amount of Ca^{2+} loaded. A stoichiometry of Na^+ to Ca^{2+} of 3:1 was inferred from these experiments.

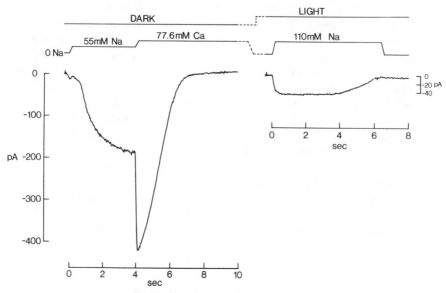

Figure 1 Isolation of a net inward current generated by the Na^+-Ca^{2+} exchange mechanism. Details are given in the text. (Reproduced from Reference 54 with permission.)

In a second set of experiments the net inward current generated by the Na^+-Ca^{2+} exchanger was studied under physiological conditions (55). Photocurrents were evoked by saturating flashes and steps of light. In all cases, during the initial phase of the response the dark current was rapidly reduced to a level of 1–1.5 pA. This residual current then declined exponentially to zero with a time constant of about 0.4 sec. The residual current was not seen when Li^+ was substituted for external Na^+, which indicates that it was generated by the Na^+-Ca^{2+} exchanger.

These findings indicate:

1. The ROS plasma membrane contains a Na^+-Ca^{2+} exchange mechanism that normally extrudes Ca^{2+} from the cytoplasm.
2. This exchanger transports three Na^+ into the ROS for each Ca^{2+} it extrudes; hence it is electrogenic, contributing a net current of 1–1.5 pA to the dark current.
3. The exchanger turns over the freely exchangeable Ca^{2+} in the cytosol with a time constant of about 0.4 sec.
4. In these and other experiments (27), it was shown that Sr^{2+} can be substituted for Ca^{2+} in the exchange but Li^+ and Cs^+ cannot substitute for Na^+. K^+ and Rb^+ appear to inhibit Na^+-Ca^{2+} exchange (27).

In darkness, the internal Ca^{2+} concentration must be set by the balance between the inward leakage of Ca^{2+} through the light-sensitive channels and its extrusion by the exchanger. The magnitude of the inward Ca^{2+} leakage can be inferred from the residual current (1–1.5 pA) measured immediately after exposure to a saturating light. From the stoichiometry, the Ca^{2+} efflux must carry 2–3 pA, and this must be balanced by an inward Ca^{2+} leakage of the same magnitude. Thus between 10 and 15% of the net current through the light-sensitive channels is normally carried by Ca^{2+} (55).

Since light has no direct effect upon the rate of exchange of Na^+ and Ca^{2+}, it follows that internal $[Ca^{2+}]$ should drop following illumination (55). In a recent study, this was confirmed directly by preloading rods with the luminescent Ca^{2+} indicator aequorin and monitoring the effect of light on the luminescence emitted from the outer segments (33). Almost certainly, therefore, the light-induced rise in external $[Ca^{2+}]$ reflects the reduced influx of Ca^{2+} through light-sensitive channels and not, as originally suggested, an extrusion of Ca^{2+} released into the cytosol from internal stores.

Ion Selectivity of the Light-Sensitive Channel

Cavaggioni et al first demonstrated that the light-sensitive channel is permeable to ions other than Na^+ (11). After preloading isolated rod outer segments with radioactive tracers, they observed a light-modulated efflux of K^+ and Rb^+, which suggested that the dark current might normally include an outward component carried by K^+. Similar experiments by Capovilla et al (10) showed that this efflux was significantly dependent upon external $[Ca^{2+}]$ and $[Mg^{2+}]$.

By applying radioactive tracers in the presence of 10^{-8} M external Ca^{2+}, Woodruff et al (50) found a significant light-modulated influx of Na^+, K^+, Rb^+, Cs^+, and Tl^+. Using a suction pipette to monitor transmembrane current, Yau et al (52) found that in a medium containing EGTA and no added Ca^{2+} the channel was permeable to Na^+, Li^+, K^+, Rb^+, and Cs^+ and the divalent ions Ca^{2+} and Mg^{2+}.

A similar conclusion was reached by Capovilla et al (10) on the basis of voltage recordings from rods bathed in media containing nanomolar concentrations of divalent ions. Moreover, when 0.5 mM IBMX was added to the bath (or higher concentrations of other phosphodiesterase inhibitors), they were able to show that divalent ions are permeable in the sequence $Mn^{2+} >$ $Ba^{2+} > (Ca^{2+}, Co^{2+}, Mg^{2+}, and Sr^{2+})$. Divalent ions appeared to be significantly more permeable than monovalent ions under these conditions.

These experiments were important because they demonstrated that the light-sensitive channel is permeable to a wide variety of monovalent and divalent cations. To determine the ratios of the permeabilities of the ions, however, a different experimental protocol is necessary. The substitution of another cation for some fraction of the external [Na^+] produces two effects: an instantaneous change in the current flowing through the light-sensitive channels and a slower change, owing to a reduction in the rate of Na^+-Ca^{2+} exchange, with consequent increase in [Ca^{2+}]$_i$ and reduction in the light-sensitive conductance (see below). Since the ionic selectivity is manifested in the instantaneous effect of the ion substitution, it is essential that the substitution be completed well before the secondary effects mediated by the Na^+-Ca^{2+} exchanger become significant.

This was achieved in recent studies by Yau & Nakatani (53) and Hodgkin et al (27). They drew the inner segment of a rod into a suction pipette and monitored the transmembrane current while rapidly changing the ionic milieu surrounding the outer segment. In the experiments of Hodgkin et al (27) the rod was held near the interface between two perfusion media streaming in laminar flow from a double-barrelled pipette made of theta tubing. By quickly translating the chamber, and therefore the laminar flow boundary, relative to the rod, the medium around the ROS could be changed within a few tens of milliseconds.

By this technique, it was found that with 1-μM Ca^{2+} in the external medium, the channel is permeable to monovalent ions in the sequence $Li^+ > Na^+ > K^+ > Rb^+ > Cs^+$, with relative permeabilities of $1.4:1:0.8:0.6:0.15$ (27). Similar values were obtained by Yau & Nakatani (53). The same sequence was found in 1-mM [Ca^{2+}]$_o$, though the relative permeabilities were less certain in that case (27). There is also good evidence (27) that Ca^{2+} may be considerably more permeable than Na^+ under these conditions, which is consistent with the notion that the light-sensitive channel may be more permeable to divalent ions than to monovalent ions (10). The relative permeabilities of divalent cations remain to be established.

The early finding that Na^+ was the principal ion carrying the normal dark current (24, 44) led to the commonly held belief that Na^+ flowed into the ROS through some form of Na^+ channel. This is clearly not the case. The light-sensitive channel is only slightly more permeable to Na^+ than to K^+ and is probably more permeable to divalent ions than to monovalent ones. It now seems possible that, under normal conditions, the dark current consists of four components. A small component ($\sim$5%) would be generated by the Na^+-Ca^{2+} exchanger. A further 10–15% would be due to the inward flux of Ca^{2+}. In addition, to the extent that Na^+ and K^+ move *independently* through the light-sensitive channels, the inward movement of Na^+ may be partially offset by an outward flux of K^+. If we take P_K/P_{Na} to be 0.8 (27), [Na^+]$_i$ to be about 12 mM (45, 46), and [K^+]$_i$ to be about 90 mM (40, 41), the estimated ratio of inward Na^+ flux to outward K^+ flux at the dark potential would be about $8:1$. These values would also be consistent with the finding (4, 9a) that the dark current reverses at a potential of about +7 mV.

Evidence That the Light-Sensitive Channel is a Pore

Until recently, it was not known whether the light-sensitive channel is a pore or an ion carrier. The evidence suggesting it is a pore comes from two classes of experiment: analyses of the noise in the light-modulated current recorded from intact rod outer segments and studies of the current that crosses excised patches of ROS plasma membrane.

MEASUREMENTS OF CURRENT NOISE IN INTACT RODS   Baylor et al carried out the first successful analysis of the noise in the current flowing across the ROS plasma membrane using the suction pipette technique (7). They identified two components of current noise, a continuous noise and randomly occurring discrete events that resembled quantal photocurrents in amplitude and waveform. By analyzing those records that contained no discrete events, the power spectrum of the continuous component was obtained. It could be described by the product of two Lorentzians. Subtracting this power spectrum from that obtained by analysis of all records yielded the power spectrum of the discrete component. It was identical to the Fourier transform of the quantal photocurrent and could be described by the product of four Lorentzians. The discrete component was thus ascribed to the random thermal bleaching of rhodopsin molecules, which each generate a current event by a four-stage process. The continuous component was believed to be due to random impulses propagated through the last two stages of this four-stage process. Therefore, both these components of noise reflect a variability in the internal biochemistry of the rod and not simply the random opening and closing of the light-sensitive channels.

A problem with the suction pipette technique is that the relatively low leakage resistance of the seal between the pipette and the plasma membrane acts as a significant source of Johnson noise, which masks low-power current noise at all frequencies. A gigaohm seal between a patch pipette and the plasma membrane generates much less Johnson noise. Recent studies of the light-sensitive noise using the patch-clamp technique in the whole-cell (9, 14, 23) and cell-attached modes (9, 32) revealed an additional component of noise, which is believed to be due to the random opening and closing of light-sensitive channels.

Figure 2 shows the power spectrum of the light-sensitive noise recorded under whole-cell patch-clamp conditions from the frog ROS (9). The low-frequency component can be described by the product of two Lorentzians and is identical with the continuous noise of Baylor et al (7). The high-frequency component is well described by a single Lorentzian with a half-power frequency of 212 Hz. The half-power frequency of the high-frequency component from similar experiments on lizard (9) and axolotl (23) rods were 62 and 100 Hz, respectively. A single Lorentzian would be expected if the noise were generated by channels fluctuating randomly between open and closed states having exponentially distributed lifetimes. The mean open lifetimes estimated from the half-power frequencies were 2.6 msec for lizard, 0.73 msec for frog, and 1.94 msec for axolotl.

The variance of the high-frequency component declined monotonically as the intensity of a steady background illumination was raised to a saturating level (9, 23) at which all channels were closed (5). The ratio of the change in variance ($\Delta\sigma^2$) to the change in mean transmembrane current (ΔI) was independent of the change in background illumination. For both these findings to be true, the probability of the channel being open in darkness must be small. For a simple two-state scheme:

$$\text{closed} \underset{\beta}{\overset{\alpha}{\rightleftharpoons}} \text{open}$$

this requires that the closing rate constant, β, must be considerably larger than the opening rate constant, α.

Bodoia & Detwiler (9) pointed out that if the effect of light were mediated by an increase in the concentration of blocking particles, β would be expected

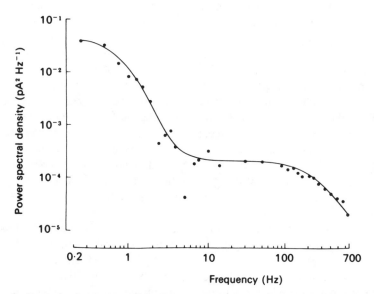

Figure 2 Power-density spectrum of the light-sensitive noise recorded from the outer segment of the frog rod under whole-cell patch-clamp conditions at the dark resting potential. (Reproduced from Reference 9 with permission.)

to increase, and this would reduce the mean open lifetime, $\tau_H = 1/(\alpha + \beta)$. If, however, the effect of light were mediated by a reduction in the concentration of an agonist, a reduction in α would occur and because β is much greater than α, this would have very little effect upon the mean open lifetime of the channel. Since the mean open lifetime of the channel did not change significantly as the background intensity was raised, it was concluded that the light response is mediated by an agonist rather than a blocker.

Given that the channel has a low probability of being open in darkness, the ratio $\Delta\sigma^2/\Delta I$ provides a measure of the single-channel current. Since neither this nor the mean open lifetime of the channel was significantly changed by steady illumination that desensitized the rods by up to five log units, it seems unlikely that the effects of adaptation are mediated by changes in the properties of the light-sensitive channel (23).

The single-channel current was found to depend upon the concentration of Ca^{2+} in the bath. In 0.1-mM $[Ca^{2+}]_o$, the single-channel current in the frog was found to be ~ 20 fA. On raising $[Ca^{2+}]_o$ to 0.5 mM the value dropped to 9 fA (9). Gray & Attwell (23) determined a value of 4.23 fA for the axolotl rod in 1-mM Ca^{2+}. A possible explanation for this dependence is that Ca^{2+} may partially block the channel by binding to a site near or within it. Earlier, it was proposed (28) that if channels could be blocked by Ca^{2+} and if the mean lifetime of the blocked state were too short to be resolved by the recording apparatus, then the single-channel current would appear to be reduced by the fraction of time that the channel was blocked. Such a fast, flickering block is reported to occur in other systems (29, 35). Using this argument, Bodoia & Detwiler (9) estimated that in the absence of external Ca^{2+} the current would be 50–75 fA, which at a resting potential of -40 mV corresponds to a single-channel conductance of 1.25–2.0 pS.

These studies of the current noise lead to several important conclusions. First, the channel is probably opened by an agonist, and the effect of light is mediated by a reduction in agonist concentration. Second, at physiological concentrations of Ca^{2+}, no more than 5% of the channels in the membrane are likely to be open at any instant. Third, the single-channel conductance is dependent upon external $[Ca^{2+}]$. Fourth, light adaptation does not appear to involve any significant change in channel properties.

MEASUREMENTS OF CURRENT NOISE IN EXCISED PATCHES OF PLASMA MEMBRANE   Excising a patch of the plasma membrane uncouples the channels in the patch from the internal chemistry of the rod, and the conductance of the membrane ceases to be measurably light-sensitive. To study the light-sensitive conductance using this technique, the investigator must recreate the internal environment of the outer segment as faithfully as possible, find an agent that will modulate the conductance of the patch, carry out experiments to determine if the modulated conductance is, in fact, the light-sensitive conductance and, if so, whether the experimental treatment has significantly affected its properties.

The first step in this difficult process was taken when Fesenko and his coworkers (20) reported that the conductance of an excised patch of frog ROS plasma membrane increased dramatically when low concentrations of cGMP were applied to the cytoplasmic side of the patch. In their experiments, the pipette was filled with a Ringer's solution containing 0.1-mM $[Ca^{2+}]$ and 2-mM $[Mg^{2+}]$. Adjusting $[Ca^{2+}]$ on the cytoplasmic face of the membrane had no effect upon the conductance of the patch in the absence of cGMP and only a small effect when cGMP was present. Neither ATP nor GTP was necessary for cGMP to exert its effect; from this fact it was concluded that cGMP acts directly upon the channel without the involvement of a protein kinase. This action was specific to cGMP, moreover, since cAMP, 2',3'-cGMP, and 5'-GMP were without effect. More recent work (32, 60a), has shown that 8-bromo-cGMP is also effective in evoking an increase in patch conductance. Since this derivative is resistant to hydrolysis by rod phospho-diesterase, channel activation is thought not to depend either upon cGMP hydrolysis or the products of its hydrolysis.

Single-channel events were not resolved in the experiments of Fesenko et al. Activation of the conductance was accompanied by an increase in noise whose power density spectrum could be described by a single Lorentzian with a half-power frequency of 316 Hz. The elementary event, estimated from the ratio of variance to mean current, was only 3.3 fA at -30 mV, which corresponds to a unitary conductance of 100 fS. These findings have been qualitatively confirmed in more recent studies (32, 34, 51, 59)

Analyses of the dose-response relation for cGMP are in agreement that the half-saturating concentration of cGMP, $(K_{1/2})$ is in the range 10–45 μM (20, 25, 60). The Hill plot of the cGMP-dependent current has a slope of nearly three (25, 60), which suggests that channel activation requires the cooperative binding of at least three cGMP molecules to sites on or near the channel. These sites are accessible only from the cytoplasmic side of the membrane, (32).

Matthews (32) recently recorded the cGMP-induced current noise using a pipette that contained divalent ions. Like Fesenko et al (20), he did not observe single-channel events. In analyzing the power-density spectrum, however, he was able to resolve two components, each of which could be fitted by a single Lorentzian. The low-frequency component had a half-power frequency of 70 Hz ($\tau = 2.3$ msec), while that of the high-frequency component was 1190 Hz ($\tau = 0.13$ msec). Of particular significance was his observation that the variance of the current increased steadily as the concentration of cGMP was raised to a saturating level. This would not be expected if the probability of the channel being open approaches unity with increasing [cGMP]. It would be expected, however, if the open state of the channel is accompanied by a rapid gating similar to that which occurs in other systems (12, 29, 35–37, 57), since each channel, as it is activated, will then contribute additional variance to the macroscopic current. In consequence, as the cGMP concentration is raised, both the mean current and its variance will rise until saturation occurs. The high-frequency component of the noise was interpreted as arising from such a gating process having a time-constant of 0.13 msec.

ANALYSIS OF SINGLE-CHANNEL CURRENTS IN EXCISED PATCHES   In view of the earlier findings of Hodgkin et al (28) and Bodoia & Detwiler (9), which suggested that the small size of the unitary conductance estimated from analyses of current noise might be due to a partial block of the channel by divalent ions, it was reasonable to suppose that removing the divalents from the bathing solutions would induce a large increase in the single-channel current, allowing single-channel events to be resolved. Figure 3, taken from

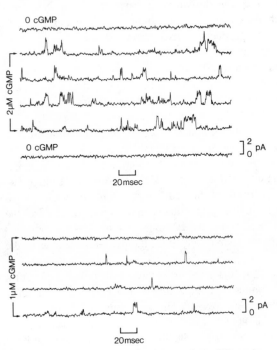

Figure 3   Single-channel currents elicited by application of two different low concentrations of cGMP and recorded from an inside-out patch of toad rod outer segment. Holding potential was −60 mV. The patch was bathed on both sides with an isotonic NaCl solution containing 118-mM NaCl, 0.1-mM EGTA, and 0.1-mM EDTA and buffered with HEPES to pH 7.6. All records filtered at 2 kHz. (Reproduced from Reference 25 with permission.)

Haynes et al (25), shows that, with isotonic NaCl on both sides of the patch and divalent cations buffered to nanomolar levels, micromolar concentrations of cGMP evoke noisy single-channel events of ~1.5 pA in amplitude, occurring singly and in bursts. Amplitude histograms reveal the existence of two populations of events (25, 60). The larger of the two populations is consistent with a single-channel conductance of about 25 pS (25, 60), the smaller with a conductance of 8 pS (60). It is not yet clear whether the two populations represent two different types of channels or two different conductance states of a single channel type. Of particular significance is the fact that both these values are too large to be accounted for by any known ion carrier (26). There can be little doubt, therefore, that the cGMP-activated channel is a pore.

Haynes et al (25) analyzed the noise in single-channel currents evoked by a low concentration of cGMP (see Figure 3). Their spectra were well-fitted by the sum of two Lorentzians having half-power frequencies of 20 and 150 Hz. The time-constant of the higher-frequency component (1 msec) agreed well with the mean duration of the large current events. The low-frequency component was thought to be related to the bursting behavior of the channels in the patch.

Evidence That the cGMP-Activated Channel is the Light-Sensitive Channel

Two sets of results argue strongly that the cGMP-activated channel is the light-sensitive channel. Yau & Nakatani (56) drew a rod outer segment into a suction pipette and, after checking to see that it responded normally to light, broke off the inner segment and the basal part of the outer segment, leaving an open-ended outer segment envelope whose interior could be dialyzed with a pseudointracellular solution. This technique is diagrammed in Figure 4A. The membrane potential was clamped to 0 mV. Adding cGMP to the dialyzing medium induced a large inward current; the current density was essentially uniform along the length of the outer segment. The dose-response relation of this cGMP-induced current closely resembled that measured with excised patches. A Hill plot of the data had a slope of ~2.5, and the $K_{1/2}$ was near 45 μM. The properties of this conductance were thus similar to those of the cGMP-activated conductance observed in excised patches.

With GTP in the dialyzing medium, the cGMP-induced current could be suppressed by light (Figure 4B). Without GTP, light had no effect (Figure 4C), which is consistent with the known requirement of GTP for the light-mediated activation of cGMP hydrolysis. These findings are consistent with the hypothesis that reduction in free cGMP by light-activated phosphodiesterase is required to terminate the cGMP-induced current, and that the cGMP-sensitive and light-sensitive conductances are one and the same.

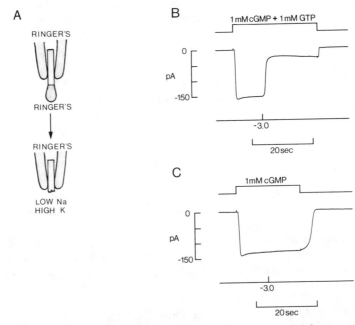

Figure 4 Effects of GTP and light on the cGMP-evoked current recorded from a truncated, dialyzed rod outer segment. (A) Diagram to illustrate the recording technique. (B) Effect of light on cGMP-evoked current in the presence of GTP. (C) Light is ineffective in the absence of GTP. (Modified from Reference 56.)

The hypothesis that the cGMP-sensitive and light-sensitive conductances are identical has received strong support from a recent experiment by Matthews (personal communication). Using patch pipettes filled with a modified Ringer's solution containing no divalent ions, he recorded the currents crossing patches of the plasma membranes of intact, dark-adapted frog rod outer segments. In darkness, brief inward currents were observed that resembled the single-channel events recorded from excised patches (see Figure 5A). A narrow slit of light centered upon the patch reduced the frequency of these events in a manner that was graded with light intensity over the rod's normal response range. When the light was displaced more than a few micrometers from the patch, however, it had no effect upon the event frequency. Hyperpolarizing the patch from its resting potential also had no effect upon the frequency of events. Thus, the light-induced change in event frequency did not result from a change of voltage across the patch.

The patch was then excised from the rod and the cytoplasmic face exposed to a low-sodium, high-potassium medium containing cGMP. The cGMP-induced current recorded under these conditions (Figure 5B) closely resembled the light-sensitive current recorded with the patch in situ. When the

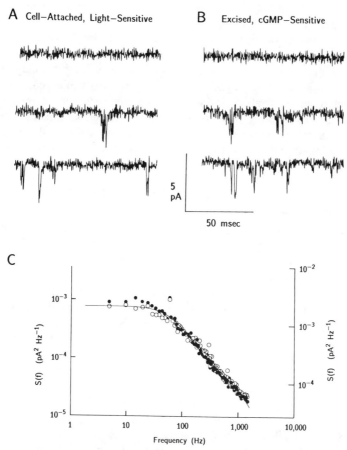

A Cell—Attached, Light—Sensitive

B Excised, cGMP—Sensitive

5 pA

50 msec

C

Figure 5 Light-sensitive and cGMP-sensitive currents recorded from the same patch of outer segment membrane before and after excising the patch. Patch electrodes filled with a Ringer's solution nominally free of Ca^{2+} and Mg^{2+}. (A) Recordings made with the cell attached and the patch hyperpolarized by 100 mV. Top trace recorded in bright light, others in darkness. (B) Recordings from same patch after excision, clamped to -87 mV. Inner face perfused with high KCl Ringer's solution nominally free of Ca^{2+} and Mg^{2+}. Top trace recorded in absence of cGMP, others during exposure to cGMP. (C) Power-density spectra calculated from these two sets of recordings fitted with the sum of two Lorentzians with corner frequencies of 80 and 960 Hz. (Reproduced with permission of G. Matthews.)

power spectra of the light-sensitive current noise and the cGMP-evoked current noise were compared, they were found to be indistinguishable (Figure 5C), as would be expected if they shared a common origin.

Taken together, these findings leave little doubt that the cGMP-activated channel and the light-sensitive channel are identical. This channel appears to be a pore of high conductance that undergoes some form of rapid gating in its open state and that can be partially blocked by divalent ions. The mechanism of this partial block is still uncertain. The most promising hypothesis is that the pore contains binding sites with a high affinity for divalent cations. If other ions are unable to pass through the pore while it is occupied by a divalent, the relatively long transit time of divalents will significantly reduce the time-averaged current. The extent of this reduction will depend upon the concentrations of divalents in the media on either side of the membrane. While the rapid gating may simply reflect an inherent instability of the channel protein in its open state, it is an attractive possibility that it results from the rapid blocking and unblocking of the pore as divalent ions pass through it.

Electrical Rectification of the Light-Sensitive Channel

The earliest determination of the current-voltage (I-V) relation of the light-sensitive channel was made by taking the difference between the I-V relations of solitary rods measured in darkness and in sufficiently bright light (4). Generally similar results were obtained in subsequent studies using this (31) and other, more direct techniques (8, 9, 9a). At potentials more negative than about -20 mV, the light-sensitive current was only weakly dependent upon voltage; at more positive potentials, a steep outward rectification was observed. The current reversed between 0 and 10 mV, and the rectification developed within the 3–6 msec time resolution of the recording apparatus.

ORIGIN OF THE ELECTRICAL RECTIFICATION   Instantaneous outward rectification would be imparted to the channel if the rate of ion permeation were limited by an energy barrier located within the channel, towards the outer face of the membrane. The I-V relation is extremely steep at positive potentials, however. Baylor & Nunn (9a) found the current changed e-fold for a change of only 11–14 mV. To explain this in terms of a barrier model would require the barrier to be located almost at the outer surface of the membrane and the effective charge on the current carrier to be 2. This would imply that monovalent ions cross in pairs and bind to sites of equal affinity (9a). A consequence of this would be that at very negative potentials the inward current should depend upon the square of the external [Na]; but the available evidence does not bear this out (27). An alternative explanation is that the rectification might reflect a voltage-dependent gating or partial blocking of the channel by a doubly charged particle (9).

Recent studies of the cGMP-activated channel in the excised patch (32, 51; A. L. Zimmerman & D. A. Baylor, personal communication) reveal that the direction of the rectification is determined by the concentration gradient of divalent cations. With normal concentrations of divalent ions on either side of the patch, the I-V relation was instantaneously ohmic. A marked outward rectification, similar to that measured in intact rods, developed within 2 msec of the voltage step, however (A. L. Zimmerman & D. A. Baylor, personal communication). When divalent ions were reduced to nanomolar levels on both sides of the patch, the conductance increased and the rectification disappeared (51). When the concentration gradient of divalent ions across the patch was reversed, so too was the direction of rectification (Figure 6), though the two *I-V* relations were not quite mirror images of each other (32). As an explanation of the rectification, therefore, a simple voltage-dependent gating of the channel seems to be ruled out since in that case one would not expect the rectification to reverse direction upon reversal of the divalent ion concentration gradient.

These initially surprising results are qualitatively consistent with the idea that the light-sensitive channel contains one or more binding sites with high affinity for divalent cations and that, when bound, the divalent ion(s) limits the movement of other ions through the channel. The rate at which divalents enter and block the channel would depend primarily upon the electrochemical potential gradient that moves them. Under normal conditions, at the resting potential, the strong inward gradient would cause divalents to enter the channel rapidly, keeping it blocked for a significant fraction of the time. Depolarizing the membrane would reduce the rate at which divalents enter the channel, and the channel would be less frequently blocked. The result would be an outward rectification. It is easy to see, too, that removing divalents

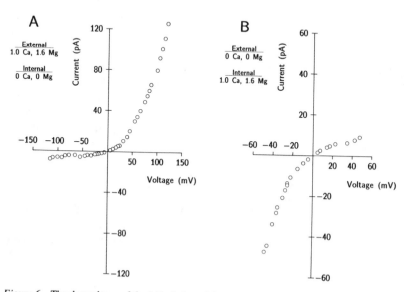

Figure 6 The dependence of the *I-V* relation of the light-sensitive channel upon the concentration gradient of divalent ions. (Reproduced from Reference 32 with permission.)

altogether from the system should cause the channel to behave ohmically, provided either that it contains no significant energy barriers to the permeation of monovalent ions or that such barriers are located symmetrically within the channel. Reversal of the concentration gradient of divalents should simply reverse the direction of the rectification, given that the binding site(s) is equally accessible from both sides of the membrane. It remains to be seen how this idea might be extended to account also for the extreme steepness of the rectification.

The Light-Sensitive Channel: A Summary

The light-sensitive channel appears to be a pore of very high conductance ($\sim$25 pS), that is maintained in its open configuration by the cooperative binding of at least three cGMP molecules to sites accessible from the cytoplasmic side of the membrane. The mean lifetime of the open state is less than 2 msec. The open state appears to undergo some form of rapid gating, the origin of which remains to be established. The channel is only weakly selective among monovalent cations, and there is reason to believe that some divalent cations may be more permeable than monovalents. Divalent cations, notably Ca^{2+} and Mg^{2+}, produce a partial block of the channel, reducing the single-channel conductance. The observed rectification of the channel depends upon the concentration gradient of divalent cations.

Many details have yet to be clarified, of course. The mechanisms by which divalent ions limit the single-channel conductance and produce the observed rectification have yet to be established. The finding of two different single-channel conductances in measurements on excised patches suggests that the channel may exist in more than one conductance state. If so, it would be interesting to know whether the ionic selectivity is the same or different in the two states. While the permeability ratios of the permeant monovalent cations were reliably determined under conditions of low external $[Ca^{2+}]$ using the suction pipette technique, the ratios in the presence of normal $[Ca^{2+}]$ or with phosphodiesterase inhibitors in the bath are less certain. Little is known about the ionic selectivity of the cGMP-activated channels in excised patches.

INNER SEGMENT MECHANISMS

The time course of the rod's voltage response differs significantly from that of the photocurrent at all stimulus intensities. At low stimulus intensities, the voltage peaks earlier and decays more rapidly than the photocurrent. This high-pass filtering of the photocurrent is known to be affected by a voltage-dependent, time-varying conductance that mimics the behavior of an electrical inductance (15, 16, 41, 47). At high stimulus intensities, the voltage response exhibits an initial peak followed by a relaxation to a plateau potential 10–15 mV more negative than the dark potential, at which it may remain for several seconds before finally decaying to resting values. There is no comparable relaxation in the photocurrent.

Owen & Torre showed the high-pass filtering of small signals to be mediated by a K^+ conductance (41), but one which could not be blocked by external application of Cs^+ or tetraethylammonium ions (TEA). By contrast, the peak-to-plateau relaxation in the voltage response to intense stimuli is blocked by externally applied Cs^+, which indicates that it is generated by a different mechanism (18, 41, 47).

Other mechanisms are also known to have profound effects upon the voltage response under certain circumstances. For example, application of either TEA, Ba^{2+}, or Sr^{2+} leads to the appearance of oscillations and/or action potentials that can be blocked by Co^{2+} (19, 42), which indicates the presence of a regenerative Ca^{2+} conductance.

In addition to ionic channels, the inner segment is known to contain a Na^+-K^+ ATPase that maintains the ionic gradients and drives the dark current (44, 46, 61).

The Sodium-Potassium Exchange Mechanism

Torre (46) used the cardioactive steroid strophanthidin to study the properties of the Na^+-K^+ ATPase and found it to be significantly electrogenic, transferring 6 Na^+ out of the rod for every 5 K^+ taken in. Since the dark current is normally about 30 pA, the *net* outward current generated by the exchange is about 5 pA at the dark potential—enough to hyperpolarize the rod by 5 mV. The effect of strophanthidin on rod responses elicited by bright light flashes indicated that the electrogenic current contributes about 15 mV to the peak voltage.

Ionic Conductances

Attwell & Wilson (1) and Bader et al (3) made systematic studies of the ionic conductances in the rod inner segment. In the latter study, solitary rod inner segments, obtained by enzymatic dissociation of the salamander retina, were

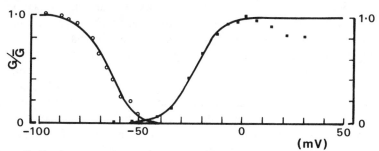

Figure 7 Steady-state activation curves of principal voltage-dependent, time-varying conductances of the rod inner segment. (I_h = *open circles;* I_{Ca} = *filled squares.*) (Redrawn from References 2, 3.)

voltage clamped, and the various ionic currents were isolated with the aid of known channel blockers. Five different ionic currents were identified. They are described below.

1. An inward current, activated by hyperpolarization beyond -50 mV, was isolated by perfusing with TEA and Co^{2+}. Its reversal potential was -32 mV, and it could be blocked by external application of Cs^+. It is this current, designated I_h, that causes the peak-to-plateau relaxation in the rod's voltage response to bright stimuli. Its activation curve is shown in Figure 7.

I_h was studied in greater detail by Bader & Bertrand (2) using patch electrodes to voltage-clamp solitary inner segments. Its reversal potential was found to be -32 mV. Though far from the equilibrium potentials of either Na^+ or K^+, the reversal potential was found to be sensitive to changes in the external concentrations of both those ions. Removal of Na^+ from the medium inside the patch electrode and from the medium bathing the inner segment caused the reversal potential to approach E_K. In view of these and other findings, it was concluded that I_h is carried by both Na^+ and K^+. Moreover, since these two components could not be separated, either pharmacologically or kinetically, it seems most likely that the current flows through a single type of channel.

A rather different conclusion was reached by Attwell & Wilson (1). They identified a current, which they called I_A, that appeared to consist of two components. An outward component was activated by depolarization over the range -80 to -40 mV, had a reversal potential of -106 mV, and was blocked by TEA. An inward component was activated by hyperpolarization over the range -40 to -80 mV, had a reversal potential of -33 mV, and was blocked by Cs^+. The two components had similar kinetics. In most respects, the inward component resembles the current I_h described above. However, the TEA-sensitive outward component of I_A does not resemble any of the currents described by Bader et al (3). The reasons for this discrepancy remain unclear.

2. Bader et al (3) found a fast, gated, outward current, designated I_K, that was activated by depolarization above -70 mV. Because its reversal potential, normally -72 mV, was acutely sensitive to external $[K^+]$ and it could be blocked by TEA, it was identified as a K^+ current. Over the physiological voltage range, this current is relatively small but becomes quite large at potentials more positive than -20 mV. Thus it may contribute to the marked outward rectification seen in intact rods. It is a long-standing observation that TEA applied to intact rods significantly reduces the outward rectification (19, 49). I_K is probably unrelated to the outward component of I_A described by Attwell & Wilson (1), since its activation range is quite different and it is much less steeply voltage dependent.

3. An inward calcium current, I_{Ca}, activated by depolarization over the range -45 to 0 mV (Figure 7) was observed in the presence of external Cs^+

and TEA after EGTA had been injected to eliminate Ca^{2+}-activated currents. It could be blocked by Co^{2+}. A region of negative slope was seen in the $I\text{-}V$ relation between -40 and -20 mV. A Ca^{2+} current having almost exactly these properties was predicted by Owen & Torre (42) to explain the oscillatory potentials and spikes recorded from toad rods in the presence of TEA.

As the only identified Ca^{2+} current, I_{Ca} might be expected to play an important role in synaptic transmission and therefore to be localized to the synaptic terminal. Bader et al (3) examined the distribution of I_{Ca} by comparing its magnitude in intact inner segments with that measured in inner segments whose terminals had been lost during dissociation. Only minor differences were found, which suggests that a significant fraction of the Ca^{2+} conductance is distributed over the whole of the inner segment.

4. Two Ca^{2+}-activated currents were detected. One of these, an outward current, could be blocked by external application of Co^{2+} or by injection of EGTA or Cs^{2+}. It was identified as a Ca^{2+}-activated K^{+} current and designated $I_{K(Ca)}$. In addition, a Ca^{2+}-activated anion current was detected following injection of Cs^{+}. This current reversed near -17 mV and could be blocked by external application of Co^{2+} or internally applied EGTA. The reversal potential was found to be sensitive to external $[Cl^{-}]$, which indicates that Cl^{-} carries a significant fraction of the current. Accordingly, it was designated I_{Cl}.

In addition to these voltage-dependent conductances, the inner segment may also contain a transmitter-activated conductance. Rods are known to contact other photoreceptors via chemical synapses in the turtle (38) and may do so in other species, too. In the turtle, the postsynaptic sites are located on long telodendria extending from the rod synaptic terminals and are likely to be disrupted by the usual dissociation procedures.

Inner Segment Mechanisms: A Summary

Because the current flowing through the light-sensitive channels of the outer segment is almost independent of voltage over the physiological range, it follows that it must be similarly independent of the resistive load presented by the inner segment. The rod can thus be conceptualized as a source of current (the photocurrent) in series with a variable load. The time-varying, voltage-dependent properties of the conductances that make up that load are responsible for shaping the voltage response of the rod. Since it is the voltage response that controls the release of transmitter from the rod's synaptic terminal, the ionic conductances of the inner segment can be thought of as comprising the first stage of signal processing in the retina.

Of the five ionic currents so far identified in rod inner segments, only I_h has been reliably correlated with some feature of the voltage response (specifically, the peak-to-plateau relaxation in the response to a bright stimulus). Since I_K is activated at potentials more positive than -70 mV, it must also contribute to rod responses, though its relatively weak voltage dependence implies a correspondingly small effect upon the shape of the response.

The three remaining currents are only activated at potentials more positive than -50 mV. Since the rod's dark potential is probably near -45 mV, these currents are likely to be small in darkness and to be modulated only by the initial 5 mV of any light response. This is particularly surprising in the case of I_{Ca}, which is presumably involved in the control of transmitter release from the synaptic terminal, since it implies that transmitter release is not modulated at potentials more negative than -50 mV. The results of recent experiments on horizontal cells and bipolar cells in the toad, however, are consistent with this notion (J. Belgum & D. R. Copenhagen, personal communication). The rod-generated components of the responses of these second-order cells appear to saturate at about one tenth of the rod's saturating intensity, an intensity that elicits responses of only 5 mV in the rods. Thus, it may be necessary to redefine the "physiological range" of the rod response.

CONCLUSION

The rod photoreceptor is a beautiful and complex device comprised of two highly specialized parts, the inner and outer segments, that each house a myriad of components precisely fitted to its function. The extent to which the two segments are functionally specialized and the complexity of the mechanisms they contain are only now becoming apparent as new and more precise techniques of measurement are applied. The basic properties of many of these mechanisms have been established. Five years ago, the properties of the light-sensitive conductance were poorly understood, and a review such as this would have concentrated upon the inner segment conductances. The reverse is true today. Undoubtedly, there is still much to be learned. But given the present rate of progress, characterization of the *essential* elements in the generation of the voltage response may not be very far away.

ACKNOWLEDGMENTS

I wish to thank Dr. King-Wai Yau for his patient reading of the manuscript and his many helpful criticisms and suggestions.

Literature Cited

1. Attwell, D., Wilson, M. 1980. Behaviour of the rod network in the tiger salamander retina mediated by membrane properties of individual rods. *J. Physiol.* 309:287–315
2. Bader, C. R., Bertrand, D. 1984. Effect of changes in intra- and extracellular sodium on the inward (anomalous) rectification in salamander photoreceptors. *J. Physiol.* 347:611–31
3. Bader, C. R., Bertrand, D., Schwartz, E. A. 1982. Voltage-activated and calcium-activated currents studied in solitary rod inner segments from the salamander retina. *J. Physiol.* 331:253–84
4. Bader, C. R., MacLeish, P. R., Schwartz, E. A. 1979. A voltage-clamp study of the light response of solitary rods of the tiger salamander. *J. Physiol.* 296:1–26

5. Baylor, D. A., Lamb, T. D. 1982. Local effects of bleaching in retinal rods of the toad. *J. Physiol.* 328:49–71

6. Baylor, D. A., Lamb, T. D., Yau, K.-W. 1979. The membrane current of single rod outer segments. *J. Physiol.* 288:589–611

7. Baylor, D. A., Matthews, G., Yau, K.-W. 1980. Two components of electrical dark noise in toad retinal rod outer segments. *J. Physiol.* 309:591–621

8. Baylor, D. A., Nunn, B. J. 1983. Voltage-dependence of the light-sensitive conductance of salamander retinal rods. *Biophys. J.* 41:125a

9. Bodoia, R. D., Detwiler, P. B. 1985. Patch-clamp recordings of the light-sensitive dark noise in retinal rods from lizard and frog. *J. Physiol.* 367:183–216

9a. Baylor, D. A., Nunn, B. J. 1986. Electrical properties of the light-sensitive conductance of rods of the salamander, *Ambystoma tigrinum. J. Physiol.* 371:115–45

10. Capovilla, M., Caretta, A., Cervetto, L., Torre, V. 1983. Ionic movements through light-sensitive channels of toad rods. *J. Physiol.* 343:295–310

11. Cavaggioni, A., Sorbi, R. T., Turini, S. 1973. Efflux of potassium from isolated rod outer segments: A photic effect. *J. Physiol.* 232:609–20

12. Colquhoun, D., Sheridan, R. E. 1981. The modes of action of gallamine. *Proc. R. Soc. Lond. Ser. B* 211:181–203

13. Deleted in proof

14. Detwiler, P. B., Connor, J. D., Bodoia, R. D. 1982. Gigaseal patch clamp recording from outer segments of intact retinal rods. *Nature* 300:59–61

15. Detwiler, P. B., Hodgkin, A. L., McNaughton, P. A. 1978. A surprising property of electrical spread in the network of rods in the turtle's retina. *Nature* 274:562–65

16. Detwiler, P. B., Hodgkin, A. L., McNaughton, P. A. 1980. Temporal and spatial characteristics of the voltage response of rods in the retina of the snapping turtle. *J. Physiol.* 300:213–50

17. Fain, G. L., Lisman, J. E. 1981. Membrane conductances of photoreceptors. *Prog. Biophys. Mol. Biol.* 37:91–147

18. Fain, G. L., Quandt, F. N., Bastian, B. L., Gerschenfeld, H. M. 1978. Contribution of a caesium-sensitive conductance increase to the rod photoresponse. *Nature* 272:467–69

19. Fain, G. L., Quandt, F. N., Gerschenfeld, H. M. 1977. Calcium-dependent regenerative responses in rods. *Nature* 269:707–10

20. Fesenko, E. E., Kolesnikov, S. S., Lyubarsky, A. L. 1985. Induction by cyclic GMP of cationic conductance in plasma membrane of retinal rod outer segment. *Nature* 313:310–13

21. Gold, G. H., Korenbrot, J. I. 1980. Light-induced calcium release by intact retinal rods. *Proc. Natl. Acad. Sci. USA* 77:5557–61

22. Gold, G. H., Korenbrot, J. I. 1981. The regulation of calcium in the intact retinal rod: A study of light-induced calcium release by the outer segment. *Curr. Top. Membr. Transp.* 15:307–30

23. Gray, P., Attwell, D. 1985. Kinetics of light-sensitive channels in vertebrate photoreceptors. *Proc. R. Soc. Land. Ser. B* 223:379–88

24. Hagins, W. A., Penn, R. D., Yoshikami, S. 1970. Dark current and photocurrent in retinal rods. *Biophys. J.* 10:380–412

25. Haynes, L. W., Kay, A. R., Yau, K.-W. 1986. Single cGMP-activated channel activity in excised patches of rod outer segment membrane. *Nature* 321:66–70

26. Hille, B. 1985. *Ionic Channels of Excitable Membranes,* pp. 201–3. Sunderland, Mass.: Sinauer. 426 pp.

27. Hodgkin, A. L., McNaughton, P. A., Nunn, B. J. 1985. The ionic selectivity and calcium dependence of the light-sensitive pathway in toad rods. *J. Physiol.* 358:447–68

28. Hodgkin, A. L., McNaughton, P. A., Nunn, B. J., Yau, K.-W. 1984. Effect of ions on retinal rods from *Bufo marinus. J. Physiol.* 350:649–80

29. Lansman, J. B., Hess, P., Tsien, R. W. 1985. Direct measurement of entry and exit rates for calcium ions in single calcium channels. *Biophys. J.* 47:67a

30. Lisman, J. E., Brown, J. E. 1972. The effects of intracellular iontophoretic injection of calcium and sodium ions on the light response of *Limulus* photoreceptors. *J. Gen. Physiol.* 59:701–19

31. MacLeish, P. R., Schwartz, E. A., Tachibana, M. 1984. Control of the generator current in solitary rods of the *Ambystoma tigrinum* retina. *J. Physiol.* 348:645–64

32. Matthews, G. 1986. Comparison of the light-sensitive and cyclic-GMP-sensitive conductances of the rod photoreceptor: Noise characteristics. *J. Neurosci.* 6:2521–26

33. McNaughton, P. A., Cervetto, L., Nunn, B. J. 1986. Measurement of intracellular free calcium concentration in salamander rods. *Nature* 322:261–63

34. Nakatani, K., Yau, K.-W. 1985. cGMP opens the light-sensitive conductance in retinal rods. *Biophys. J.* 47:356a

35. Nowak, L., Bregestovski, P., Ascher,

P., Herbert, A., Prochiantz, A. 1984. Magnesium gates glutamate-activated channels in mouse central neurones. *Nature* 397:462–65

36. Ogden, D. C., Colquhoun, D. 1985. Ion channel block by acetylcholine, carbachol and suberyldicholine at the frog neuromuscular junction. *Proc. R. Soc. Lond. Ser. B* 225:329–55

37. Ogden, D. C., Siegelbaum, S. A., Colquhoun, D. 1981. Block of acetylcholine-activated channels by an uncharged local anaesthetic. *Nature* 289:596–98

38. Owen, W. G. 1985. Chemical and electrical synapses between photoreceptors in the retina of the turtle, *Chelydra serpentina. J. Comp. Neurol.* 240:423–33

39. Owen, W. G., Torre, V. 1981. Ionic basis of high-pass filtering of small signals by the network of retinal rods in the toad. *Proc. R. Soc. Lond. Ser. B* 212:253–261

40. Owen, W. G., Torre, V. 1981. Ionic studies of vertebrate rods. *Curr. Top. Membr. Trans.* 15:33–57

41. Owen, W. G., Torre, V. 1983. High-pass filtering of small signals by retinal rods: Ionic studies. *Biophys. J.* 41:325–39

42. Owen, W. G., Torre, V. 1984. Regenerative photoresponses in toad rods. In *Photoreceptors*, ed. A. Borsellino, L. Cervetto, pp. 201–20. New York/London: Plenum

43. Schnetkamp, P. P. M. 1980. Ion selectivity of the cation transport system of isolated intact cattle rod outer segments: Evidence for a direct communication between the rod plasma membrane and the rod disk membranes. *Biochim. Biophys. Acta.* 598:66–90

44. Sillman, A. J., Ito, H., Tomita, T. 1969. Studies on the mass receptor potential of the isolated frog retina. II. On the basis of the ionic mechanism. *Vision Res.* 9:1443–51

45. Somlyo, A. P., Walz, B. 1985. Elemental distribution in *Rana pipiens* retinal rods: Quantitative electron probe analysis. *J. Physiol.* 358:183–95

46. Torre, V. 1982. The contribution of the electrogenic sodium-potassium pump to the electrical activity of toad rods. *J. Physiol.* 333:315–41

47. Torre, V., Owen, W. G. 1983. High-pass filtering of small signals by the rod network in the retina of the toad, *Bufo marinus. Biophys. J.* 41:305–24

48. Waloga, G., Brown, J. E., Pinto, L. H. 1975. Detection of changes in Ca_{in} from

Limulus photoreceptors using arsenazo III. *Biol. Bull.* 149:449

49. Werblin, F. S. 1979. Time- and voltage-dependent ionic components of the rod response. *J. Physiol.* 294:613–26

50. Woodruff, M. L., Fain, G. L., Bastian, B. 1982. Light-dependent ion influx into toad photoreceptors. *J. Gen. Physiol.* 80:517–36

51. Yau, K.-W., Haynes, L. W., Nakatani, K. 1986. Roles of calcium and cyclic GMP in visual transduction. *Progr. Zool.* Vol. 33

52. Yau, K.-W., McNaughton, P. A., Hodgkin, A. L. 1981. Effect of ions on the light-sensitive current in retinal rods. *Nature* 292:502–5

53. Yau, K.-W., Nakatani, K. 1984. Cation selectivity of the light-sensitive conductance in retinal rods. *Nature* 309:352–54

54. Yau, K.-W., Nakatani, K. 1984. Electrogenic Na-Ca exchange in retinal rod outer segment. *Nature* 311:661–63

55. Yau, K.-W., Nakatani, K. 1985. Light-induced reduction of cytoplasmic free calcium in retinal rod outer segment. *Nature* 313:579–82

56. Yau, K.-W., Nakatani, K. 1985. Light-suppressible, cGMP-sensitive conductance in the plasma membrane of a truncated rod outer segment. *Nature* 317:252–55

57. Yellen, G. 1984. Ionic permeation and blockade in Ca^{2+}-activated K^+ channels of bovine chromaffin cells. *J. Gen. Physiol.* 84:157–86

58. Yoshikami, S., George, J. S., Hagins, W. A. 1980. Light-induced calcium fluxes from the outer segment layer of vertebrate retinas. *Nature* 286:395–98

59. Zimmerman, A. L., Baylor, D. A. 1985. Electrical properties of the light-sensitive conductance of salamander retinal rods. *Biophys. J.* 47:357a

60. Zimmerman, A. L., Baylor, D. A. 1986. Cyclic GMP-sensitive conductance of retinal rods consists of aqueous pores. *Nature* 321:70–72

60a. Zimmerman, A. L., Yamanaka, G., Eckstein, F., Baylor, D. A., Stryer, L. 1986. Interaction of hydrolysis-resistant analogs of cyclic GMP with the phosphodiesterase- and light-sensitive channel of retinal rod outer segments. *Proc. Natl. Acad. Sci. USA* 82:8813–17

61. Zuckerman, R. 1973. Ionic analysis of photoreceptor membrane currents. *J. Physiol.* 235:333–54

Ann. Rev. Physiol. 1987. 49:765–91

THE MOLECULAR MECHANISM OF VISUAL EXCITATION AND ITS RELATION TO THE STRUCTURE AND COMPOSITION OF THE ROD OUTER SEGMENT

Paul A. Liebman

Department of Anatomy, University of Pennsylvania, Philadelphia, Pennsylvania 19104

Kenton R. Parker and Edward A. Dratz

Department of Chemistry, Montana State University, Bozeman, Montana 59717

Introduction

The idea that "structure mediates function" is a conceptual thread that has woven through biological research for decades. The molecules in biological superstructures such as membranes are vectorially oriented in both space and time. As with the code provided by the Rosetta Stone, if we could learn to recognize the meaning of the vectorial arrows and follow them through their causally interconnected junctions, we would indeed understand how function is mediated through the dynamic structure of the component molecules.

Few processes have as many structural signposts suggesting causal interpretation as does vertebrate vision. Rod and cone outer segments are so structurally specialized for the translation of optical into ionic events that even their enormous concentration of mitochondria (that are essential for driving the large light-modulated current in photoreceptors) are relocated in an adjacent chamber. The rod disk and cytoplasmic transduction apparatus of the receptor outer segment is axially repeated a thousand times with great precision. At the level of a single axial unit, which consists of a disk membrane

0066-4278/87/0315-0765$02.00

pair and its surrounding cytoplasm, the radial uniformity is impressive. We are left with the idea that we need only understand a region of less than a few cubic micrometers to comprehend the whole.

This review deals largely with such a reduced view of the rod. We focus on the molecules immediately surrounding the photoreceptor protein rhodopsin and the events that occur near the site of a single photon absorption.

The Cyclic GMP Cascade Hypothesis for Visual Excitation

A scheme describing the relationships between components of the cyclic GMP (cGMP) cascade of visual excitation is given in Figure 1. Figure 1a shows the light activation reactions, and Figure 1b shows the deactivation phase. This general scheme is now widely accepted in its major outlines by most workers in the field (19, 65, 119). The phosphatidyl inositol pathway (not shown) is known to be quite important in invertebrate photoreceptors (15, 32–34), but the role of this pathway in vertebrate vision is still poorly understood.

Table 1 shows the density of the several proteins known to be involved in the cGMP cascade of rod transduction, their (oligomeric) molecular weights, and their spherical-equivalent molecular diameters. All of these proteins are associated with the rod disk membrane (RDM).

Organization and Motion of Rhodopsin in the Rod Disk Membrane

Approximately half of rhodopsin's molecular mass is embedded within the RDM (29, 110, 111) in seven transmembrane helices and about 25% is found at both the outer and inner disk surfaces (4, 27). The seven transmembrane helix model predicts a rhodopsin globular mass with a diameter of ~2.8 nm at the outer or cytoplasmic disk surface, where all peripheral proteins are bound. If they were hexagonally arranged at a density of 25,000 rhodopsin molecules per μm^2 (62–64), the rhodopsins would be only 18 Å apart. In the disk membrane, monomeric rhodopsins (17) are more randomly arranged in a two-dimensional fluid state (14, 66, 104).

If one considers the measured lateral diffusion constant of rhodopsin in the membrane plane (5×10^{-9} cm^2s^{-1}) (66, 104) and the average separation, collision theory shows that a rhodopsin must collide every 5–10 μs with a neighboring rhodopsin. Indeed, like the cushions in a pinball machine, rhodopsin molecules impede the lateral diffusion of other rhodopsins through molecular crowding; this impediment is in addition to that imposed by the viscosity of the surrounding lipid molecules. Only 15% of the membrane surface area (and 20% of the membrane core) is occupied by rhodopsin. The RDM could accommodate a sixfold higher concentration of rhodopsin if it were tightly packed. However, such an "improvement" in light-catching

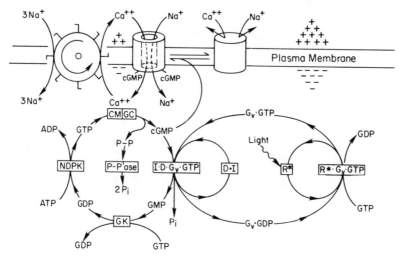

b

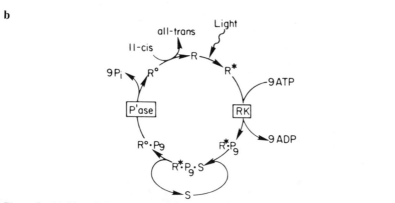

Figure 1 (a) The cGMP cascade model for the activation of the electrical response of the vertebrate rod. Light converts rhodopsin to R*, which forms a transient complex with the GTP binding protein (G_V) and catalyzes the exchange of GTP for GDP. The G_V-GTP complexes the inhibited phosphodiesterase (D·I) to activate the hydrolysis of cGMP. The reduced level of cGMP closes the Na^+-Ca^{2+} channels on the plasma membrane, which hyperpolarizes the cell and stops the entry of Ca^{2+}. A Na^+-Ca^{2+} exchanger in the plasma membrane reduces the Ca^{2+} concentration in the cytoplasm, which accelerates the production of cGMP, presumably by activating the guanylate cyclase–calmodulin complex (CM-GC). Other activities required to maintain the cGMP and GTP levels are guanylate kinase (GK), nucleotide diphosphokinase (NDPK), and pyrophosphatase (P-Pase). G_V-GTP is spontaneously inactivated by an endogenous GTPase activity to form G_V-GDP plus P_i. (b) The inactivation of the excited receptor (R*). R* is rapidly phosphorylated by ATP and rhodopsin kinase (RK) with up to 9 phosphates/R* (R*-P_9). R*-P_9 is fully inactivated by binding the S-antigen (48K or arrestin). The detailed pathway is poorly known after this point but probably involves first the spontaneous inactivation of R*-P_9 to R°-P_9, loss of S-antigen, loss of phosphate by phosphatase (Pase) and replacement of all-*trans* retinal by 11-*cis* retinal.

Table 1 Major protein content of 1 μm^2 of rod disk membrane

Membrane component[a]	Mol. wt.	No./μm^2	Ratio to rhodopsin	Diameter[b] (nm)	Projected molecule area (nm²)	Total area (nm²)	Percent area
Lipid	800	1.6×10^6	65		0.5	8.0×10^5	80.0
Rhodopsin (in membrane)	24,000	25,000	1	3.2	7.5	2.0×10^5	20.0
Na$^+$ channel	39,000	415	1/60	?	?	?	?
Rhodopsin head	9,000	25,000	1	2.8	6.2	15.5×10^4	15.5
G protein	80,000	2,500	1/10	5.8 (10)[c]	26.0 (78.5)[c]	6.5×10^4	6.5 (19.5)[c]
Phosphodiesterase	190,000	415	1/60	7.8	46.7	1.9×10^4	1.9
% Membrane Area Covered With Surface Bound Proteins:							23.9 (36.9)[c]

[a] The first three components are embedded in the oily membrane interior, whereas the last three components are located on the membrane surface.
[b] Spherical-equivalent diameter based on molecular weight.
[c] Numbers in parentheses are calculated for 5:1 axial ratio oblate ellipsoid as per text discussion.

ability was probably selected against in the course of evolution because it would have resulted in a membrane like that of the halobacterium (117), in which bacteriorhodopsin is so densely packed that it is not free to move. Why is lateral movement of rhodopsin so important, even at the expense of light-gathering capacity? One hypothesis is that this motion is necessary to permit light-activated rhodopsin to amplify its activation by interacting rapidly with many G-protein molecules, which are bound to the RDM surface under physiological salt conditions.

Interaction of G Protein with Excited Rhodopsin

Evidence suggests that G protein may bind directly to protein-free egg-lecithin vesicle surfaces (92), while a more recent report proposes that divalent cations and high ionic strength aid binding of G protein to the phosphatidylserine-rich cytoplasmic surface of rod disk membranes (87). Studies of G-protein binding to protein-stripped RDM show saturation at 1 G protein per 3–4 rhodopsin molecules (5, 73), with an association constant of 5 $\times$ 10^6 M^{-1} (73). There is little evidence to suggest that rhodopsin aids G-protein binding to the membrane in the dark, though at low ionic strength rhodopsin photolysis clearly does increase the strength of G-protein binding (54). GTP or GTP analogue binding to G protein reverses this affinity and causes G protein to be released into solution at low ionic strength. The $\beta\gamma$ oligomer of G protein appears to be the element most essential to the binding of G protein to the RDM (38). The α subunit of G protein binds GTP (39) and may under some circumstances separate from both the membrane and the β and γ subunits (41, 56).

Evidence has been presented that G protein is not spherical (5) and may be an oblate ellipsoid (5, 109). If so, its surface area would increase twofold for a 5:1 diameter-to-height ratio, which would provide a steric explanation for its saturation binding ratio of one G protein per 3–4 rhodopsins on the RDM. The natural RDM population of G protein is not well established but is no greater than one sixth that of rhodopsin and is probably closer to one tenth that amount (5, 73). Higher G-protein concentrations would sterically interfere with efficient rhodopsin-G-protein interaction via lateral diffusion. Presumably, the natural ratio of rhodopsin to G protein optimizes the amplification of activation and minimizes the loss of speed that could result from "overpacking" of the membrane with G protein.

Though the binding of G protein to the RDM may serve merely to keep this protein in the outer segment, it may also increase the rate at which G protein can be found and activated by photolyzed rhodopsin. The membrane-bound state accelerates bimolecular interaction rates through "reduction of dimensionality" (3, 11) and through an effective increase in molecular concentration compared to diffusion in three dimensions.

For a collision radius of 5 nm (which is a realistic value for protein-protein interactions) the diffusional separation time (i.e. the lifetime of a diffusional collision complex) is on the order of 100 ns in water and 10 μs within the more viscous membrane, and rotations have relaxation times comparable to those of translation in the two phases. Thus in water, molecules are in contact for only a short time and have little time to interact, whereas in the more viscous membrane phase, the critical reaction time is 100 times greater. However, membrane viscosity slows the frequency of collision as well as the rate of separation. To overcome the former, collision frequency may be increased by an increase in the number of molecules within the membrane phase (mass action). Thus membrane binding of reacting components may lead to rapid reactions with good yield.

Both the R*-G-protein bimolecular complex formation rate constants and binding constants are only properly specified in two-dimensional terms, which makes comparison with commonly used three-dimensional constants troublesome. Interactions known to occur on RDM would require extrinsic protein concentrations of 7–30 mM if they were in the aqueous phase rather than bound to the membrane (99). This value can be compared to the 10–30 μM concentrations of common cytoplasmic or blood enzymes that react (more slowly) in water. In the low viscosity of water, specific bonds may not form quickly enough after collision of two molecules to prevent diffusional separation, which results in a very large fraction of "missed opportunities" for bimolecular interactions. Enzyme-substrate bimolecular reaction rate constants are always less than 2×10^8 M^{-1}s^{-1}, i.e. at least ten times slower than their diffusional collision limit. In contrast, protein-protein interaction rate constants in water rarely exceed 10^5 M^{-1}s^{-1}, which is a factor of 10^4 lower than maximum enzyme-substrate interactions. This calculation implies that the efficiency of protein-protein collisions is 0.001–0.0001, which suggests that it is relatively improbable that the small active sites on two proteins will simultaneously rotate into the precise position required for effective interaction. The favorable mutual orientation made possible by membrane binding can overcome much of this kinetic limitation in the rate of effective protein-protein interactions.

The above considerations may be significant for visual transduction since it is known that thousands of G proteins and hundreds of phosphodiesterase (PDE) molecules are activated within seconds by a single photolyzed rhodopsin through serial catalysis of GTP binding (39, 69, 72, 132). Since G protein is not an integral membrane protein, it may encounter activated rhodopsin by diffusing through the cytoplasm after dissociating from the membrane or, alternatively, it may react directly on the RDM surface without using an aqueous route.

Aqueous Route for Interaction of G Protein with R* and PDE Is Too Slow

Keirns et al (52) made the interesting observation that an admixture of strongly bleached RDM could fully activate the PDE on a hundredfold excess of dark RDM. This result implies that aqueous transmission of activation can occur. A probable route for this transmission is via dissociation of inactive G protein from the dark membranes, followed by its diffusion through the cytoplasm to the active rhodopsins on the bleached membranes and return of the GTP-activated G protein to the dark membranes, where PDE is then activated. The originally active G protein could also move from the light-activated membranes to the dark ones, but the total amount of G protein available to be transferred from the light membranes would be totally inadequate to substantially activate a hundredfold excess of dark membranes.

To further examine the significance of aqueous transfer of G protein under the bright-light conditions used above (in which a high fraction of the rhodopsin was excited), Liebman & Sitaramayya (73) mixed equal amounts of just-bleached disk membranes containing PDE but no G protein with dark disk membranes containing G protein but no PDE. They characterized the kinetics and equilibrium factors in activation of PDE by photoexcited rhodopsin (R*) using membrane-to-membrane transfer rates and the measured G-protein binding constants. Table 2 presents rate constants for G protein (G_v) binding to (k_1) and dissociation from (k_{-1}) R*. These constants are based on experimentally determined rates of PDE activation by forced aqueous transfer of G_v (in the presence of GTP) and the calculated maximum $G_v^*\cdot GTP$ formation rate per R* if G_v binding is assumed to be rate limiting. The initial $G_v^*\cdot GTP$ formation rate is simply $d(R^*\cdot G_v)/dt = k_1(R^*)(G_v)$, where R* is one rhodopsin molecule in the single-photon activation limit. It is assumed that all the G protein is free (its concentration was 1 μM in these experiments) in order to calculate an upper limit for the aqueous transfer rate.

The "forced" aqueous activation proceeds with a second-order rate constant of 4×10^5 $M^{-1}s^{-1}$ for R*-G-protein interaction, slow activation (9-s delay), off-rate of about 1 per 2.5 s (73), and weak activity transfer (7.5% of PDE saturation velocity). Transfer of G protein from dark RDM (with normal protein complement) to bleached, enzyme-stripped RDM (sRDM) with bound PDE showed a similar second-order interaction constant (2.5×10^5 $M^{-1}s^{-1}$) but a slower off-rate (1 per 40 s) and an even weaker activity transfer (73). This bimolecular interaction rate constant for "forced" aqueous G-protein-PDE activation is close to that of other protein-protein interactions described

Table 2 Binding of G_v to membranes

Preparation	Forced aqueous G-protein transfer			Native activation
	$k_1(M^{-1}s^{-1})$	$k_{-1}(s^{-1})$	$G_v*/R*$ (s^{-1})	$G_v*/R*$ (s^{-1})
sRDM[a]	4×10^5	0.4	0.4	—
RDM	2.5×10^5	0.025	0.25	>1000[b]

[a]sRDM denotes rod disk membranes that were stripped of extrinsic proteins and selectively reconstituted with G protein on PDE as explained in the text.
[b]From Reference 72

above, and it is 1000 times smaller than the aqueous diffusion-limited rate constant $(2 \times 10^8 \ M^{-1}s^{-1})$ realized by enzyme reactions with small substrate molecules. More importantly, the maximum possible rate of aqueous transfer of G protein is more than 1000-fold slower than the experimentally determined rate of G-protein activations $(1000 \ s^{-1}R*^{-1})$ in native RDM using weak light activation, as shown in Table 2. Thus, aqueous transfers are slow and of low activity yield, especially for the natural RDM in vitro, and diffusion of G protein through water would offer no advantage theoretically or experimentally.

G Protein and PDE Activation Occur by Lateral Diffusion on the Membrane Surface

If an aqueous route for G-protein amplification is unlikely, interaction with rhodopsin and PDE must occur on the RDM surface, as first proposed by Yee & Liebman in 1978 (132). Arguments for this mechanism were further developed by Liebman & Pugh (69), who concluded that restriction of light-activated G protein and PDE to the native RDM surface would result in a light titration curve with a Poisson saturation function rather than the common hyperbolic saturation function that might result if an aqueous diffusible component were released by light (112). Careful light titration of PDE activity always saturates like a Poisson sum, whose shape is easily distinguishable from the hyperbolic form for bimolecular titrations (69, 71, 72). The compartment size given by the Poisson parameter ($1/e$ point of the light titration curve) showed that (in the presence of GTP and cGMP nucleotides alone) a compartment is fully activated by photoexcitation of about 1 rhodopsin in 20,000 for bovine and about 1 in 80,000 for toad RDM. At these and weaker levels of rhodopsin activation, PDE velocity increases only gradually to maximum with an exponential delay of 0.8 and 2.4 s in bovine and toad, respectively (69, 71).

What is the nature of such light-sensitive "compartments"? A 1.5-μm diameter bovine disk contains about 50,000 rhodopsins per side, and a 6-μm toad disk has about 750,000. These values are both larger than the light-sensitive "compartments" indicated by their respective Poisson parameters. These compartments are apparently not due to anatomical subdivisions set by disk incisures, since toad disks have about 19 incisures per disk and contain 40,000 rhodopsins per lobe, whereas the smaller disk of the bovine has only 1 deeply penetrating incisure that would not alone cause significant compartmentation.

Use of the poorly hydrolyzable GTP analogues (GMPPNP or GTPγS) instead of GTP causes the light-sensitive compartment size to increase up to about 50,000 and 250,000 rhodopsins, respectively, for bovine and toad. Mild sonication or extrusion of the membranes through polycarbonate filters with pores of 0.8, 0.6, or 0.4 μm reduces the compartment size (i.e. increases the fraction of rhodopsin that must be bleached to reach maximum activity) without affecting the total activity in bright light (P. A. Liebman & E. N. Pugh, Jr., unpublished work). A hypothesis consistent with each of these findings is that a light-sensitive compartment consists of a spatiotemporal region in which a single R* during its lifetime [here limited by metarhodopsin II (MII) decay] can activate G proteins with which it collides on the disk membrane surface. In turn, G protein can only activate PDE molecules on the same disk membrane surface. These PDE and G proteins subsequently undergo spontaneous deactivation, which appears to be rate-limited by the light-sensitive GTPase activity. Kinetic competition between the rate of activation by R* and of deactivation by GTPase would limit the build up of activated G protein and PDE in a compartment. If G proteins could transfer through water from one disk to another within the lifetime of R* activation, GMPPNP or GTPγS (which are not sensitive to GTPase inactivation) would permit infinite light sensitivity in the absence of either deactivation or compartmentation limits. If this were the case, one bleached rhodopsin would be able to activate all the molecules in an entire cuvette! In reality, the light sensitivity of bovine RDM in GTPγS reaches a finite limit at a compartment size equal to one side of a disk, and PDE velocity increases to its final value over a period of about 2 s. Toad light sensitivity reaches its limit in nonhydrolyzable GMPPNP at a compartment size of about one third of one side of a disk after about 8 s at 22°C (71). It is not certain why light sensitivity in toad is limited to one third the side of a disk. An adequate hypothesis may require both R* decay and gradual activity loss of GMPPNP-activated G protein on a time scale of 30–90 s.

The fact that the compartment size does not enlarge to include both sides of a bovine disk (about 100,000 rhodopsins) when GMPPNP or GTPγS is used suggests that an activated rhodopsin can neither diffuse beyond the disk rim nor can it convey activation to another disk. This finding gains further significance in view of the fact that the number of activated G proteins is at least five times that of PDEs (114); thus other disks could indeed be activated if activated G protein were able to leave its disk of origin.

Lateral diffusion carries a molecule of rhodopsin through an RDM at ~ 0.5 $\mu m^2 s^{-1}$. If G proteins, and the bleached rhodopsin with which they collide, move on the membrane surface at a similar speed, the lateral diffusion–limited mutual interaction rate would be 1.0 $\mu m^2 s^{-1}$. This rate would cause activation of all the G proteins in a 1 μm^2 RDM "compartment" in 1 s or of all the G proteins on one side of a bovine disk within 2–2.5 s. The lateral diffusion–activation hypothesis predicts that (*a*) activation must terminate when all the G protein in a compartment is activated, (*b*) the rate of activation cannot exceed 3000 G protein per second (3000 G protein/μm^2 times the diffusion rate of 1 $\mu m^2 s^{-1}$), and (*c*) decay of R* or activated G protein on a time scale close to that of full diffusional coverage of a compartment will shorten the apparent time to maximum activation and reduce the amount of activation. From this hypothesis it also follows that (*d*) dilution of the preparation should have no effect on the activation of the system (except to proportionately reduce the probability of light absorption), since the nature of the surface compartments will be unchanged. Experiments show all four of these predictions to be confirmed (69, 71, 72).

Trypsin activation of PDE was introduced by Miki et al (85) and exploited as a tool for the study of PDE-inhibitor interaction. It is puzzling that trypsin-activated RDM PDE always yields a higher maximum cGMP hydrolytic velocity than can be attained by maximal light activation. This is the more surprising in view of the large molar excess of G protein relative to PDE and the absence of evidence for anything other than a 1:1 G-protein/PDE interaction stoichiometry for activation. However, quantitative studies show that addition of higher than natural amounts of G protein (114) or its nucleotide-bearing subunit (39) can elicit the full trypsin-equivalent velocity. This finding indicates there is a weak interaction constant between G protein and PDE on the RDM surface (114).

Weak interaction between activated G protein and PDE on the membrane is advantageous to optimize the speed of visual excitation. If this binding were strong and there were only a single G protein activated for each PDE, there would be a lateral diffusion delay for each activated G protein to find its target PDE molecule, just as there is for an R* to find each G protein. Lateral diffusion delays for R* to activate PDE would thus be doubled. Instead, there are five or six activated G proteins for each PDE, and this "excess" results in a forward reaction rate six times faster than would exist if there were only a single activated G protein per PDE molecule. The excess of activated G protein allows the R*-G-protein diffusion-limited activation to be the single rate-limiting step of the visual excitation pathway.

It is of particular relevance that the PDE activity of toad RDM is more light sensitive than that of bovine RDM since their maximal bright-light and trypsin-activated PDE activities are identical. Rhodopsin, G-protein, and PDE content per unit area are also identical for the two species. A plausible explanation for the light-sensitivity difference is a simple structural one: The surface area of toad RDM is 30 times greater than that of bovine RDM. A single photolyzed rhodopsin can continue to activate G protein and PDE for a longer period on toad RDM than on bovine RDM before the G protein and PDE remaining to be activated on a single disk are depleted, as must occur on the bovine RDM within one second of exposure to a single photon. In fact, in the first 1–2 s after a 10^{-5} fractional photolysis, the increase in PDE activity as a function of time (no ATP present) is identical in toad and bovine RDM suspensions. However, after this initial period of congruence the PDE velocity in toad RDM continues to increase up to 8 s before it achieves its maximum, whereas in bovine RDM maximum PDE velocity is reached in 2.5 s (69, 71). If lateral diffusion occurs at the same speed in toad and bovine RDM at 22°C, the rate of G-protein collision with PDE and consequent PDE activation is expected to be the same in the two systems, which would explain the identical velocity-time profiles at early times. Their differences at later times can be explained by the smaller size of the disks in bovines, which are more rapidly depleted of activatable G protein.

It could be argued that these differences in the kinetic properties of toad and bovine preparations may be due to different rates of access of substrate molecules from the surrounding solution to the remaining interdisk spaces of the RDM particles; however, this notion is not supported by experimental evidence. On the contrary, addition of nucleotides and proteins has a nearly instantaneous effect in both systems. We thus conclude that disk size and lateral diffusion are principal factors controlling differences in light sensitivity (apparent compartment size) between toad and bovine membranes under the above conditions.

Release of Activated G Protein α-Subunit from Membrane May Be Nonphysiological

Several lines of experimental evidence have been used to argue that lateral diffusion–activation of G protein by rhodopsin is followed by release of the activated α-subunit of G protein from the disk, which diffuses through cytoplasm to activate PDE on any disk membrane. Godchaux & Zimmerman (41), and later Kuhn (54), showed that G protein can be eluted from bleached membranes by GTP. Low ionic strength and GTP are used to elute nearly pure G protein from illuminated disks, while an enriched G-protein α-subunit can be eluted by GTP even at normal ionic strength (55). However, although the membrane binding constant of GTP-complexed G protein may be less than that of unactivated G protein in physiological salt, the quantitative loss of G protein or α-subunit from RDM is very low at near-normal ionic strength, even though the elution conditions include 100–1000 fold dilution over the native volume of the intact rod. Thus, it appears that at physiological ionic strength the G protein α-subunit would still be more than 99% membrane bound upon activation in vivo, in spite of "weakened" membrane binding. Since the time scale of the weakened binding seen in in vitro preparation experiments is minutes, such effects may have nothing to do with mechanisms of activation on the 1-s or faster time scale of visual transduction.

All of the direct measurements of the G-GTP release from rod outer segment (ROS) membranes into the aqueous medium have been obtained with very low time resolution techniques, so this data cannot settle crucial questions regarding the kinetics of the response. Light-scattering signals have been attributed to the release of G-GTP or G-GMPPNP, and have been used to estimate a rapid release rate (125). The difficulty with the interpretation of these latter measurements is that the results may be due to other processes in this complex system. For example, the so-called G-protein dissociation signals (56) have a very different angular distribution of light-scattering intensity than do the well-documented binding signals (124), which are clearly due to the binding of G-GDP to R* (56). Thus the two processes are not the reverse of each other.

Although reasonable doubt remains, the strongest evidence favors lateral diffusion–mediated interaction both between rhodopsin and G protein and between G protein and PDE, with no components (other than nucleotides) leaving the disk membrane of origin over the lifetime of a visual excitation-recovery cycle. It seems, therefore, that the activation delay seen in the electrophysiological response to weak light flashes (7, 79, 100)) is explained by the time course of lateral diffusion as an R* linearly activates its quota of disk membrane G proteins and PDE (71). The time integral effect of the latter on cytoplasmic cGMP increases parabolically over part of a second until R* activity is quenched.

Quenching of Light Activation

Recovery from light activation must begin with inactivation of the receptor, as illustrated in Figure 1b. The activated form of the receptor, metarhodopsin II, is both a catalyst of G-protein activation and a target for rhodopsin kinase. Experimental evidence (86, 115, 116, 127) supports the hypothesis of Liebman & Pugh (70) that rhodopsin phosphorylation is essential to the termination (quenching) of PDE activation. The phosphorylation sites have been shown in at least four of the visual pigment sequences to be clustered in the C-terminal end on five of eleven contiguous serine and threonine residues. Phosphorylation of these sites in R* by rhodopsin kinase would be expected to increase significantly the negative charge density in this region. Models of the structure of rhodopsin in the membrane (e.g. 4, 27), as shown in Figure 2, suggest that the region of high charge density produced by the patch of phosphorylated sites may be complementary to a positively charged patch on the loop between helices I and II (Figure 2) on the aqueous protein surface. Lys66, Leu68, and Arg69 are conserved in all visual pigments studied and Lys67 is also present in four of seven pigments. The highly phosphorylated C-terminal peptide may change its conformation and cover up a portion of the surface of R* that normally excites the GTP binding protein.

It now appears that phosphorylation alone may only partially reduce the activity of MII, and the phosphorylated sites themselves may become a target for binding of the 48-kd protein (127) [also called S-antigen (102) or arrestin (133)]. Though insufficient detail is known, the binding of the 48-kd protein to the phosphorylated region of R* may completely block G-protein access to the surface loop(s) of R* that cause excitation (127). Interestingly, both kinase and arrestin originate in the cytoplasm and become dynamically associated with the membrane upon a conformational change of the photolyzed rhodopsin. Arrestin is not likely to be a rhodopsin phosphatase since its target appears to be MII-phosphate, and removal of phosphate before decay of MII would reactivate the receptor, which would not be in keeping with the apparent function of arrestin (127).

Though there is no further investigation on this topic, it appears reasonable that decay of MII would just precede arrestin release and that the consequent unblocking of rhodopsin would permit access to the receptor by phosphatase. Final regeneration of the original light-sensitive rhodopsin configuration requires delivery of a new prosthetic molecule, 11-*cis* retinal. This quench cycle is shown in Figure 1*b*.

An especially interesting aspect of this complicated design, which requires many phosphorylations and an auxiliary protein to reduce activated receptor function, is that the natural lifetime of MII is very long (minutes) compared to the required lifetime of single-photon visual responses (a second or less). Why is the receptor not shut off by a single phosphorylation? Perhaps such a single-phosphorylation mechanism would be unstable both energetically (75) and kinetically. Kinetically, phosphorylation as a pseudo-first-order process would generate a broad Lorentzian variation in the number of activated G proteins (standard error equal to the mean) in the lifetime of the activated receptor, which would conflict with the nature of vision, which is a high-precision, Gaussian process (7). Rather, receptor activity will be smoothly reduced by a series of phosphorylations, as was observed in vitro by Miller & Dratz (86). Each successive phosphorylation might have a higher binding affinity for arrestin, and the final site would bind arrestin to the exclusion of kinase, so that dephosphorylation is not catalyzed by the kinase.

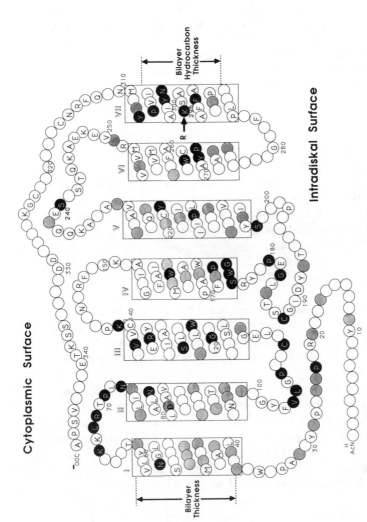

Figure 2   Model for the transmembrane arrangement of amino acids in vertebrate pigments in which each amino acid is represented by a circle (modified from Reference 4). The structure is composed of seven transmembrane helices (I–VII) with connecting aqueous loops and N- and C-terminal "tails." The degree of shading of the different residues represents the extent of conservation of the amino acids in seven sequences, including two fly pigments, bovine rhodopsin, human rhodopsin, and three human cone pigments. Black residues are identical in all seven sequences, open residues labeled with a letter are identical in at least four sequences, and shaded residues are very similar in chemical properties in at least four sequences. The one letter code is: A = alanine, C = cystine, D = aspartic acid, E = glutamic acid, F = phenylalanine, G = glycine, H = histidine, I = isoleucine, K = lysine, L = leucine, M = methionine, N = asparagine, P = proline, Q = glutamine, R = arginine, S = serine, T = threonine, V = valine, W = tryptophan, Y = tyrosine. **R** at Lys296 denotes retinal.

Recovery of cGMP Levels After a Flash of Light

Receptor quenching may be the fastest biochemical event in the cyclic nucleotide cycle (116). What then limits the rate of recovery from light-induced cGMP depletion? The rod membrane potential returns to dark levels within a second or so of a dim flash, which suggests that activated G protein must destroy its GTP in comparable time; however, several studies have shown that membrane potential recovery is faster than the reduction of PDE activity in "normal" rods (88, 91). This finding can only mean that an anabolic pathway (guanylate cyclase) accelerates formation of cGMP while the catabolic pathway (PDE) is still strongly activated, which results in a recovery-phase steady state with a normal cGMP concentration but greatly accelerated cGMP flux. Goldberg et al found such an effect of illumination (42). Goldberg's conclusion that a single photon causes an integrated flux through the hydrolytic cycle of PDE of about 10^4 cGMP molecules agrees within a twofold margin with the results of the open-cuvette RDM assay of Liebman & Pugh (68).

Yau & Nakatani (131) found, and it was recently confirmed (82), that cytoplasmic $[Ca^{2+}]$ falls upon illumination, due to rapid extrusion of Ca^{2+} by the plasma membrane Na^+-Ca^{2+} exchanger and the halt of Ca^{2+} influx through the Na^+ channel. Guanylate cyclase is sensitive to changes in Ca^{2+} concentration (36), which might couple the cGMP recovery cycle to the termination of light activation. The recovery current overshoots seen by Lamb et al (59) upon internal BAPTA perfusion of toad rods during a series of weak light flashes are consistent with this hypothesis. Critical damping of the recovery downswing is also compromised in these experiments, as would be expected of such a mechanism. It is not yet known if effects of Ca^{2+} on guanylate cyclase are mediated by calmodulin, as proposed in Figure 1a.

The cGMP-sensitive Na^+-Ca^{2+} channel located in the plasma membrane (shown schematically in Figure 1a) has also been found in RDM (78) and appears to be responsible for the observed cGMP-stimulated release of Ca^{2+} from isolated disk membranes (16, 53). Thus it may be involved in the fine-tuning of intracellular Ca^{2+} levels, which influence other aspects of the enzyme cascade through feedback mechanisms (122). Detailed discussion of the properties of this channel is presented in other chapters in this section (94, 107).

The proposed model for Ca^{2+} control of the recovery phase of the membrane potential suggests an explanation for the faster recovery kinetics of the cone relative to that of the rod photoreceptor. The cone has about a five times greater surface-to-volume ratio than does the rod, due to the continuity of the infolded cone disk and plasma membranes. If it is assumed that the density of Na^+-Ca^{2+} exchanger molecules is the same in the rod and cone plasma membranes and that this density limits the rate of change of cytoplasmic calcium ion concentration, then a fivefold faster recovery rate in the cone photoreceptor is expected. The recovery phase of the cone photoreceptor is in fact about five times faster than that of the rod (6).

Diffusible Control Factors may Help to Shut Off Visual Excitation

Recently, Dratz and coworkers (28) found evidence for a diffusible activator of the bovine ROS light-sensitive GTPase. Evidence for such an activator comes from observations of a strong dependence of the GTPase rate on the concentration of the bovine ROS membranes. If a rate is found to depend on ROS concentration, it implies that some non–membrane bound or weakly membrane bound factor modulates the rate. In typical dilute assays (<50-μM rhodopsin) the GTPase rates were 1–4 min^{-1}. However, when assays were performed at increasing concentrations (25–625 μM rhodopsin), extrapolation of the concentration-dependent GTPase rate to in vivo levels (3.5 mM rhodopsin) predicts a rate of 60–120 min^{-1} (28). This rate increase is of interest since it would allow the activated G protein to shut off 0.5–1 s after deactivation of R*. In the above experiments the plasma membrane was disrupted by a gentle dialysis procedure designed to retain the maximum amount of weakly bound accessory protein. As noted above, the excitation compartments in toad rods are smaller for GTP than GMPPNP, which implies that the GTPase in toad rods is rather fast even in more dilute form (12, 108). It may be that a GTPase control factor is retained in toad preparations but partially lost in bovine preparations or that the binding constants differ in the two cases.

The rate of R* deactivation was also found to depend on the concentration of the preparation (28). Earlier reports suggested that PDE might be shut off by a diffusible inhibitor (50). Thus all the deactivation steps (i.e. of R*, GTPase, and PDE) may involve water-soluble factors. As discussed above in some detail, excitation does not appear to involve proteins traveling through the aqueous medium. We argued that this may optimize the response of the excitation mechanism. Perhaps some or even all of the water-soluble factors involved in deactivation may act in light and/or dark adaptation.

Why Is Rhodopsin a Transmembrane Protein?

The general features of the transmembrane structure proposed for bovine rhodopsin (27) were recently found to be consistent with the amino acid sequences of other photoreceptor proteins (Figure 2) from fruit fly, sheep, horse, and man (including rod and cone pigments) (4, 90, 93, 134). A similar structure also appears to be present in *Chlamydomonas* (37), and additional retinal proteins with other functions are present in archaebacteria (117). The recent proposal that the structures of rhodopsin and the β-adrenergic receptor are structurally (25) and functionally (9, 10, 25) related further develops the conviction that rhodopsin is an adaptation of a widely used basic receptor structure. The transmembrane helices of rhodopsin are presumably bent by several conserved proline and glycine residues, and it has been proposed that these bends form a tight-fitting "basket" around the retinal chromophore (27). It is of great interest, as shown in Figure 2, that invarient proline and glycine residues are present in five helices (helix III: Gly121; IV: Pro171; V: Pro215; VI: Pro267; and VII: Pro or Gly291 and Pro303). In addition, Pro53 is present in helix I in all the rod pigments and the blue cone and is substituted by a Gly at a similar position in the fly pigments.

Since the only effect of light on rhodopsin is to isomerize retinal (49) deep in the membrane, this change must somehow be transmitted through the protein structure to the binding site for G protein on the cytoplasmic surface. The bundle of relatively rigid transmembrane helices may be well suited to act as lever arms to amplify the movement caused by retinal pushing the helices apart when it isomerizes from the shorter *cis*- to the longer *trans*-retinal. Efficient transmission of such motion requires that the bundle of helices be bound together and pivoted at the intradiskal side of the membrane (4). In fact, a substantial fraction of the rhodopsin sequence on the intradiskal side is rather highly conserved (Figure 2) across species as diverse as fly, herbivore and human, and these conserved sequences may include the proposed "hinge."

Evidence for Conformational Changes in Rhodopsin upon Excitation

There has been evidence for tertiary-structure anisotropy in rhodopsin for many years. Infrared amide I and amide II band linear dichroism measurements on oriented rods show a net orientation of both the $-C=O$ and $-NH$ groups that is consistent with helix orientation perpendicular to the disk membrane plane (84). Rods align parallel to a magnetic field of 5 kG (21) or more (18) due to helix diamagnetic anisotropy. The axial birefringence of rods must also be due to helix orientation superimposed on the membrane lipid orientation (64). Light excitation of rhodopsin causes a reduction in axial birefringence that has a time course and temperature dependence identical to those of metarhodopsin II formation (67). Both diamagnetic anisotropy and ultraviolet dichroism are reduced upon formation of metarhodopsin II (18, 84). The latter changes have both been ascribed to disorientation of a single tryptophan ring; however, an interpretation that also accounts for the birefringence loss on bleaching is that a moderate reduction in net helix orientation occurs, such as might be caused by a splaying of the seven-helix cluster away from axial orientation during formation of meta II (97).

The water-soluble reagents hydroxylamine and sodium borohydride are unable to reach rhodopsin's chromophoric site in the dark, but they easily gain access to the chromophoric Schiff base linkage after the formation of metarhodopsion II. This observation indicates an opening of the structure at meta II since the chromophoric site is buried in the middle of the hydrophobic core of the disk membrane (27, 121). It has been shown that the retinylidene moeity is oriented in the membrane plane perpendicular to the transmembrane helices in rhodopsin, meta I, meta II, and meta III (20, 27, 46, 62).

Flash photolysis kinetic studies show an entropy of activation of +50 to +90 eu for decay of meta I to meta II (1, 30, 44, 97, 105, 128), a figure larger than that for denaturation of many proteins. Similarly, large positive entropy values are obtained for meta II formation (80). Such values are much larger than those for formation of any of the preceding intermediates of bleaching, and this fact has been used for many years to argue that the critical step of light activation must be the formation of metarhodopsin II (2). Meta II is the last of the bleaching intermediates that forms faster (1 msec or less) than visual excitation. Meta II is stable for minutes before decaying further to metarhodopsin III or retinal/opsin, neither of which appears capable of mediating the changes associated with visual transduction (103).

Pressure jump studies show that formation of meta II is accompanied by a significant volume increase (60). This result is consistent with the interpretation of the previously described changes in optical anisotropy as splaying of the transmembrane α-helices. We do not yet understand what triggers this rapid helix reorientation, but the large enthalpy of activation and the disappearance of a proton into rhodopsin from the medium upon meta I decay suggests the existence of an energetic, charge-driven mechanism within the low dielectric constant membrane interior. This mechanism is expected to be secondary to chromophore isomerization and to lead to rearrangement of the protein binding site in the chromophoric pocket (48, 49).

There can now be little doubt that meta II mediates the proximal effects of light activation (8, 31, 74, 96, 98, 99). Alkaline titration of the MI-MII equilibrium towards MI reduces the light sensitivity of PDE activation by dim flashes (96). The speed of PDE activation by bright flashes as a function of temperature follows the speed of MII formation (8, 98). Decay of MII to MIII is accompanied by loss of PDE activation (72). PDE activation is quenched by phosphorylation of bleached rhodopsin (86, 115, 116), and MII appears to be the substrate for this phosphorylation (103). Rapid removal of MII by hydroxylamine is accompanied by rapid quenching of PDE activation (72) and unbinding of the R*-G-protein complex (47). G protein binds specifically to MII (31), which increases the net yield of MII from the MI-MII equilibrium, and GTP-mediated release of G protein from this binding complex reduces the amount of MII and increases that of MI. Retinylidene analogues that form rhodopsinlike pigments but do not permit MII analogue formation do not activate G protein, PDE (77), nor visual excitation (22), whereas analogues that do have MII intermediates do cause such activation (23, 101).

Expansion of the transmembrane helices of rhodopsin upon formation of MII is consistent with the pressure effects on the MI⇌MII equilibrium discussed above (60). We suppose that the helices may "hinge" open upon formation of MII with greater motion on the cytoplasmic surface and less on the intradiskal surface, thus small motions near the retinal binding site may be mechanically amplified. Interestingly, Deese et al (24) have obtained new evidence from reconstitution studies with rhodopsin and defined lipids that the 22:6 fatty acids can accommodate lateral expansion of rhodopsin in the membrane plane upon formation of MII rhodopsin, whereas lipids with single double bonds are much less accommodating. This finding may explain the predominance of C22:6 fatty acids in the photoreceptors (26, 118) and further demonstrates the importance of rhodopsin's ability to laterally expand upon excitation.

Possible Sites on Rhodopsin for G-Protein Binding

Comparison of the recently deduced amino acid sequences of seven different visual pigments has revealed a highly conserved region on the cytoplasmic surface that may be a principal site of interaction of R* with the G protein. A model for the transmembrane arrangement of amino acids in visual pigments that highlights the conserved amino acids is shown in Figure 2. The cytoplasmic loop connecting helices I and II is strongly conserved: 5 of 8 sequential residues are identical in all visual pigments examined, all 8 of these residues are identical in at least four of the visual pigments examined.

The cytoplasmic loop connecting helices III and IV is significantly homologous among vertebrate pigments but shows little homology when invertebrates are also considered. The cytoplasmic loop connecting helices V and VI has one amino acid, Ser240, that is conserved in all known sequences, and it has been found to be phosphorylated by rhodopsin kinase (81). Seventeen of twenty-seven residues in this loop are identical in at least four of the visual pigment sequences. However, the invertebrate visual pigments have a much larger V-VI loop. There is recent evidence that the bovine G protein can be activated by invertebrate rhodopsins (123). Therefore, the differences between the length of the V-VI loop in the vertebrate and invertebrate suggest that this loop may not play an essential part in G-protein activation.

Kuhn et al (58), however, have presented evidence that the accessibility of the V-VI loop to proteolysis is altered in MII and that the cleavage of the V-VI loop reduces the specific GTP release of the R*-G-protein complex when assayed at low ionic strength (57). Proteolysis may be a rather large perturbation in this context, but this evidence does suggest that the V-VI loop must have some involvement in the G-protein binding site. A closer look at the

sequences on this loop supports this notion. Two photoreceptor G proteins
have been sequenced: GI, which may be the rod G protein (83, 120, 130), and
GII (76), which is expressed in cones (61). There is strong homology between
an N-terminal sequence of the G-protein α-subunit of both G-I and G-II and a
portion of the sequence of the V-VI loop, as shown in Figure 3. The
homology is longest and most striking between the G proteins and the two fly
rhodopsin sequences (93, 134), but the homology with the vertebrates seems
quite significant. The N-terminal sequence of the G-protein α-subunit is
essential for GTP binding, GTPase activity, and for binding the $\beta\gamma$ subunits
of G protein (83). We hypothesized above that rhodopsin's cytoplasmic
surface opens up upon formation of R*, and presumably the I-II and the V-VI
loops are then exposed and able to interact with the G protein. It has been
hypothesized that the V-VI loop exposed in R* binds the $\beta\gamma$-subunits to
release the α-subunit of G protein (4). Alternatively, perhaps R* binding to a
region of G-$\beta\gamma$ leaves G-$\alpha\beta\gamma$ bound together in an altered conformation that
allows GTP-GDP exchange.

Rhodopsin Homology with the β-Adrenergic Receptor

The β-adrenergic receptor appears to have seven oily helices and connecting
loops similar to those of the opsins (25). The β-adrenergic receptor homology
is more striking in the cone and invertebrate opsins than in the rod pigments.
The light-activated rhodopsin system is functionally analogous to the hormone-activated adenylate cyclase system (113, 129). The action of both types
of receptors are mediated by G proteins, and the G proteins cross-react to
some degree (13).

Some of the conserved structural features of the opsins also appear in the
β-adrenergic receptor. In addition to the seven transmembrane helices, Asp83
is present (and may act as a counter ion to the catacholamine ligand), an
Asp-Arg pair at positions 134 and 135 on helix III is present in all of the
sequences, as are Cys110 and Cys187. The β-adrenergic receptor is also
phosphorylated by an endogenous kinase (10) and the β-adrenergic receptor
kinase carries out light-dependent phosphorylation of rhodopsin (9), although
not with great efficiency. The β-adrenergic receptor has significant structural
homology with opsin surface loops, where they both may activate G protein
(4).

Figure 3   Amino acid sequence homologies in opsin loops V–VI of three different pigments and the
N-termini of the α-subunit of G protein from rods (GI) and cones (GII). Boxed areas denote amino
acids that have been conserved or have similar properties. (The one letter code is as described in
Figure 2.)

Concluding Remarks

Light-induced isomerization of 11-*cis*-retinal in the hydrophobic pocket of rhodopsin triggers an elaborate chain of events that transduces photons into electrical signals useful to the organism's neural system. It has been found repeatedly that insights into molecular events in vision may be derived from comparisons of different visual systems.

The similarities in the amino acid sequences of rhodopsins from a variety of organisms have directed attention to conserved regions that are likely to be important for the function of the light-receptor protein. Comparison of the kinetics of the light responses of bovine and toad disks, combined with the large differences in the surface area of the membranes, has provided insight into the functional localizations of the interactions between many of the proteins of the enzyme cascade that triggers transduction in vertebrates.

An explanation has been proposed for the differences in the recovery phase of rods and cones, and as more is learned of the biochemistry of cone phototransduction, it should be possible to relate the hundredfold greater light sensitivity of the rod to structural and biochemical differences between these black-and-white and color vision receptors.

Comparison of the light response mechanisms of the vertebrate and invertebrate visual systems should also prove valuable. At the superstructural level, the highly fluid vertebrate disks (66, 104) seem quite different from the semicrystalline microvilli in invertebrate photoreceptors (43), even though the visual pigments are practically identical (4). At the same time that patch clamp studies were suggesting that cGMP is the primary messenger in the vertebrate visual system (35, 89), electrophysiological studies were demonstrating that invertebrate light responses are mediated by inositol trisphosphate (IP3) (15, 32–34). Does this apparent difference reflect variations in basic biochemical mechanisms, or does it simply reflect the different experimental techniques that are suitable for the structure of each photoreceptor cell type? For example, the ease with which the ROS can be isolated in the vertebrate system lends itself to biochemical studies, whereas the larger size of the invertebrate photoreceptor cells makes them highly suitable for intracellular injection experiments. The above concern is particularly relevant in light of recent evidence that cGMP is also involved in the invertebrate light response (51) and that IP3 may be involved in the vertebrate visual system (40, 95, 126).

The Rosetta Stone had tremendous value because the same text was presented in three different scripts, which could then be painstakingly compared and deciphered. The "text" we are seeking to understand in vision research describes how the stringent engineering requirements of a single-photon detector are met. Comparison of the variations in biochemical scripts presented to us by diverse organisms in nature is providing information necessary to reveal the secrets of visual transduction.

ACKNOWLEDGMENTS

This work was supported by grants to PAL and EAD from the National Eye Institute.

Literature Cited

1. Abrahamson, E. W., Marquisee, J., Gavizzi, P., Roubie, J. 1960. Flash photolysis of visual pigments. *J. Electrochem.* 64:177–80
2. Abrahamson, E. W., Wiesenfeld, J. R. 1972. The structure, spectra and reactivity of visual pigments. In *Handbook of Sensory Physiology,* ed. H. J. A. Dartnall, VII/1:69–116. Berlin: Springer Verlag
3. Adam, G., Delbruck, M. 1968. Reduction of dimensionality in biological diffusion processes. In *Structural Chemistry and Molecular Biology,* ed. A. Rich, N. Davidson, pp. 198–215. San Francisco, Calif.: Freeman
4. Applebury, M., Hargrave, P. A. 1986. Molecular biology of the visual pigments. *Vision Res.* 26: In press
5. Baehr, W., Morita, E., Swanson, R., Applebury, M. 1982. Characterization of bovine rod outer segment G-proteins. *J. Biol. Chem.* 257:6452–60
6. Baylor, D. A., Hodgkin, A. L., Lamb, T. D. 1974. The electrical response of turtle cones to flashes and steps of light. *J. Physiol.* 242:685–727
7. Baylor, D. A., Lamb, T. D., Yau, K.-W. 1979. Responses of retinal rods to single photons. *J. Physiol.* 288:613–34
8. Bennett, N., Michel-Villaz, M., Kuhn, H. 1982. Light induced interaction between rhodopsin and GTP-binding protein. *Eur. J. Biochem.* 127:97–103
9. Benovic, J. L., Mayor, F. Jr., Somers, R. L., Caron, M. G., Lefkowitz, J. 1986. Light-dependent phosphorylation of rhodopsin by β-adrenergic receptor kinase. *Nature* 321:869–72
10. Benovic, J. L., Strasser, R. H., Caron, M. G., Lefkowitz, R. J. 1986. β-Andrenergic receptor kinase: Identification of a novel protein kinase that phosphorylates the agonist-occupied form of the receptor. *Proc. Natl. Acad. Sci. USA* 83:2797–2801
11. Berg, H. C., Purcell, E. M. 1977. Physics of chemoreception. *Biophys. J.* 20:193–219
12. Biernbaum, M. S., Bownds, M. D. 1979. Influence of light and calcium on guanosine 5'-trisphosphate in isolated frog rod outer segments. *J. Gen. Physiol.* 74:649–69
13. Bitensky, M. W., Wheeler, M. A., Rasenick, M. M., Yamazaki, A., Stein, P. J., et al. 1982. Functional exchange of components between light activated photoreceptor phosphodiesterase and hormone-activated adenylate cyclase systems. *Proc. Natl. Acad. Sci. USA* 79:3408–12
14. Blasie, J. K., Worthington, C. R. 1969. Planar liquid-like arrangement of photopigment molecules in the frog retinal receptor disk membranes. *J. Mol. Biol.* 39:417–39
15. Brown, J. E., Rubin, L. J., Ghalayini, A. J., Tarvar, A. P., Irvine, R. F., et al. 1984. Myo-inositol polyphosphate may be a messenger for visual excitation in *Limulus* photoreceptors. *Nature* 311: 160–63
16. Cavaggioni, A., Sorbi, R. T. 1981. Cyclic-GMP releases calcium from disk membranes of vertebrate photoreceptors. *Proc. Natl. Acad. Sci. USA* 78:3964–68
17. Chabre, M. 1975. X-ray diffraction studies of retinal rods: I. Structure of the disk membrane, effect of illumination. *Biochim. Biophys. Acta* 382:322–35
18. Chabre, M. 1978. Diamagnetic anisotropy and orientation of an helix in frog rhodopsin and meta II intermediate. *Proc. Natl. Acad. Sci. USA* 75:5471–74
19. Chabre, M. 1985. Trigger and amplification mechanisms in visual phototransduction. *Ann. Rev. Biophys. Biophys. Chem.,* 14:331–60
20. Chabre, M., Breton, J. 1979. The orientation of the chromophore of vertebrate rhodopsin in the meta intermediate states and the reversibility of the meta II–meta III transition. *Vision Res.* 19:1005–19
21. Chalzonitis, N., Chagneux, R., Arvanitaki, A. 1970. Rotation des segments externes des photorecepteurs dans le champ magnetique constant. *C. R. Acad. Sci. Ser. D* 271:130
22. Crouch, R., Nodes, B. R., Perlman, J. I., Pepperberg, D. R., Akita, H., et al. 1984. Cycloheptatrieneylidene analog of II-*cis* retinal. *Invest. Ophthalmol. Visual Sci.* 25:419–28
23. Crouch, R., Pepperberg, D. R. 1978. Sensitizing activity of 9,13-*dicis* retinal

in bleached photoreceptors of the skate. *Invest. Ophthalmol. Visual Sci.* 17: 1024–29

24. Deese, A. J., Ryba, N., Watts, A., Dratz, E. A. 1986. New evidence for the role of highly unsaturated fatty acids in membranes. Submitted for publication

25. Dixon, R. A. F., Kobilka, B. K., Strader, P. J., Benovic, J. L., Dohlman, H. G., et al. 1986. Cloning of the gene and cDNA for mammalian β-adrenergic receptor and homology with rhodopsin. *Nature* 321:75–79

26. Dratz, E. A., Deese, A. J. 1986. The role of docosahexaenoic acid (22:6w3) in biological membranes: Examples from photoreceptors and model membrane bilayers. In *Health Effects of Polyunsaturated Fatty Acids in Seafoods,* ed. A. Simopolous, R. Kifer, pp. 319–51. New York: Academic

27. Dratz, E. A., Hargrave, P. A. 1983. The structure of rhodopsin and the rod outer segment disk membrane. *Trends Biochem. Sci.* 8:128–31

28. Dratz, E. A., Lewis, J. W., Schaechter, L. E., Parker, K. R., Kliger, D. S. 1986. The retinal rod GTPase turnover rate increases with concentration: A key to the mechanism of visual excitation? Submitted for publication

29. Dratz, E. A., Miljanich, G. P., Nemes, P. P., Gaw, J. E., Schwartz, S. 1979. The structure of rhodopsin and its disposition in the rod outer segment disk membrane. *Photochem. Photobiol.* 29:661–71

30. Ebrey, T. 1968. The thermal decay of the intermediates of rhodopsin in situ. *Vision Res.* 8:965–82

31. Emeis, D., Kuhn, H., Reichert, J., Hofmann, K. P. 1982. Complex formation between metarhodopsin II and GTP-binding protein in bovine photoreceptor membranes leads to a shift of the photoproduct equilibrium. *FEBS Lett.* 143: 29–34

32. Fein, A. 1986. Blockade of visual excitation and adaptation in *Limulus* photoreceptors by GDP-γ-S. *Science* 232: 1543–45

33. Fein, A. 1986. Excitation and adaptation of *Limulus* photoreceptors by light and inositol, 1,4,5-trisphosphate. *Trends Neurosci.* 9:110–14

34. Fein, A., Payne, R., Corson, D. W., Berridge, M. J., Irvine, R. F. 1984. Photoreceptor excitation and adaptation by inositol 1,4,5-trisphosphate. *Nature* 311:157–60

35. Fesenko, E. E., Kolesnikov, S. S., Lyubarsky, A. L. 1985. Induction by cyclic GMP of cationic conductance in

plasma membrane of retinal rod outer segment. *Nature* 313:310–13

36. Fleischman, D., Denisevich, M. 1979. Guanylate cyclase of isolated bovine retinal rod axonemes. *Biochem.* 18: 5060–66

37. Foster, K. W., Saranak, J., Patel, N., Zarilli, G., Okabe, M., et al. 1984. A rhodopsin is the functional photoreceptor for phototaxis in the unicellular eukaryote *Chlamydomonas. Nature* 311: 756–59

38. Fung, B. K.-K. 1985. The light-activated cyclic GMP phosphodiesterase system in retinal rods. In *Molecular Mechanisms of Transmembrane Signalling,* ed. P. Cohen, M. D. Houslay, 4:183–214. New York/Amsterdam: Elsevier

39. Fung, B. B.-K., Stryer, L. 1980. Photolyzed rhodopsin catalyzes the exchange of GTP for bound GDP in retinal rod outer segments. *Proc. Natl. Acad. Sci. USA* 77:2500–4

40. Ghalayini, A., Anderson, R. E. 1984. Phosphatidylinositol 4, 5-bisphosphate: Light-mediated breakdown in the vertebrate retina. *Biochem. Biophys. Res. Commun.* 124:503–6

41. Godchaux, W. III, Zimmerman, W. F. 1979. Membrane-dependent guanine nucleotide binding and GTPase activities of soluble protein from bovine rod outer segments. *J. Biol. Chem.* 254:7874–84

42. Goldberg, N. D., Ames, A. III, Gander, J. E., Walseth, T. F. 1983. Magnitude of increase in retinal cGMP metabolic flux determined by [18]O incorporation into nucleotide α-phosphoryls corresponds with intensity of photic stimulation. *J. Biol. Chem.* 258:9213–19

43. Goldsmith, T. H., Wehner, R. 1977. Restrictions on rotational and translational diffusion of pigment in the membranes of a rhabdomeric photoreceptor. *J. Gen. Physiol.* 70:453–90

44. Hagins, W. A. 1957. Rhodopsin in the mammalian retina. PhD thesis. Univ. Cambridge.

45. Hargrave, P. A., McDowell, J. H., Curtis, D. R., Wang, J. K., Juszczak, E., et al. 1983. The structure of bovine rhodopsin. *Biophys. Struct. Mech.* 9:235–44

46. Harosi, F. I. 1975. Absorption spectra and linear dichroism of some amphibian photoreceptors. *J. Gen. Physiol.* 66: 357–82

47. Hofmann, K. P., Emeis, D., Schnetkamp, P. P. M. 1983. Interplay between hydroxylamine, meta II and G-protein in photoreceptor membranes. *Biochim. Biophys. Acta* 725:60–70

48. Honig, B., Dinur, U., Nakanishi, K., Balogh-Nair, V., Gawinowicz, M. A., et al. 1979. The external point-charge model for wavelength regulation in visual pigments. *J. Am. Chem. Soc.* 101: 7084–86

49. Honig, B., Ebrey, T., Callender, R. H., Dinur, U., Ottolenghi, M. 1979. Photoisomerization, energy storage, and charge separation: A model for light energy transduction in visual pigments and bacteriorhodopsin. *Proc. Natl. Acad. Sci. USA* 76:2503–7

50. Hurley, J. B., Stryer, L. 1982. Purification and characterization of the gamma regulatory subunit of the cyclic GMP phosphodiesterase from retinal rod outer segments. *J. Biol. Chem.* 257:11094–99

51. Johnson, E. C., Robinson, P. R., Lisman, J. E. 1986. Cyclic GMP is involved in the excitation of invertebrate photoreceptors. *Nature* 324:468–70

52. Keirns, J. J., Miki, N., Bitensky, M. W., Keirns, M. 1975. A link between rhodopsin and disc membrane cyclic nucleotide phosphodiesterase: Action spectrum and sensitivity to illumination. *Biochem.* 14:2760–66

53. Koch, K.-W., Kaupp, U. B. 1985. Cyclic GMP directly regulates a cation conductance in membranes of bovine rods by a cooperative mechanism. *J. Biol. Chem.* 260:6788–6800

54. Kuhn, H. 1980. Light- and GTP-regulated interaction of GTPase and other proteins with bovine photoreceptor membranes. *Nature* 283:587–89

55. Kuhn, H. 1981. Interactions of rod cell proteins with the disk membrane: Influence of light, ionic strength, and nucleotides. *Curr. Top. Membr. Transp.* 15:171–201

56. Kuhn, H., Bennett, N., Michel-Villaz, M., Chabre, M. 1981. Interactions between photoexcited rhodopsin and GTP-binding protein: Kinetic and stoichiometric analyses from light-scattering changes. *Proc. Natl. Acad. Sci. USA* 78:6873–77

57. Kuhn, H., Hargrave, P. A. 1981. Light-induced binding of guanosine-triphosphatase to bovine photoreceptor membranes: Effect of limited proteolysis of the membranes. *Biochemistry* 20:2410–17

58. Kuhn, H., Mommertz, O., Hargrave, P. A. 1982. Light dependent conformational change at rhodopsin's cytoplasmic surface detected by increased susceptibility to proteolysis. *Biochim. Biophys. Acta.* 679:95–100

59. Lamb, T. D., Matthews, H., Torre, V. 1986. Changes in the photocurrent of salamander retinal rods during incorporation of calcium buffers. *J. Physiol.* 372:315–49

60. Lamola, A. A., Yamane, T., Zipp, A. 1974. Effects of detergents and high pressures upon the metarhodopsin I to metarhodopsin II equilibrium. *Biochemistry* 15:738–45

61. Lerea, C. L., Somers, D. E., Klock, I. B., Bunt-Milam, A. H., Hurley, J. G. 1986. Identification of a transducin (Tc) specifically expressed in bovine cone outer segments. *Science* 234:77–80

62. Liebman, P. A. 1962. In situ microspectrophotometric studies on the pigments of single retinal rods. *Biophys. J.* 2:161–78

63. Liebman, P. A. 1972. Microspectrophotometry of photoreceptors. In *Handbook of Sensory Physiology*, ed. J. J. A. Dartnall, pp. 481–528. New York: Springer-Verlag.

64. Liebman, P. A. 1975. Birefringence, dichroism and rod outer segment structure. In *Photoreceptor Optics*, ed. A. W. Snyder, R. Menzel, pp. 199–214. Berlin: Springer-Verlag.

65. Liebman, P. A. 1986. Visual receptor transduction. *Ann. NY Acad. Sci.* In press

66. Liebman, P. A., Entine, G. 1974. Lateral diffusion of visual pigment in photoreceptor disk membranes. *Science* 185: 457–59

67. Liebman, P. A., Kaplan, M. W., Jagger, W. S., Bargoot, F. G. 1974. Membrane structure changes in rod outer segments associated with rhodopsin bleaching. *Nature* 251:31–36

68. Liebman, P. A., Mueller, P., Pugh, E. N. Jr. 1984. Protons suppress the dark current of frog retinal rods. *J. Physiol.* 347:85–110

69. Liebman, P. A., Pugh, E. N. Jr. 1979. The control of phosphodiesterase in rod disk membranes: Kinetics, possible mechanisms and significance for vision. *Vision Res.* 19:375–80

70. Liebman, P. A., Pugh, E. N. Jr. 1980. ATP mediates rapid reversal of cGMP phosphodiesterase activation in visual receptor membranes. *Nature* 287:734–36

71. Liebman, P. A., Pugh, E. N. Jr. 1981. Control of rod disk membrane phosphodiesterase and a model for visual transduction. *Curr. Top. Membr. Transp.* 15:157–60

72. Liebman, P. A., Pugh, E. N. Jr. 1982. Gain, speed and sensitivity of GTP binding vs. PDE activation in visual excitation. *Vision Res.* 22:1475–80

73. Liebman, P. A., Sitaramayya, A. 1984.

Receptor interaction in amplified phosphodiesterase activation of retinal rods. In *Adv. Cyclic Nucleotide Protein Phosphorylation Res.* 17:215–25

74. Liebman, P. A., Sitaramayya, A., Parkes, J. H., Buzdygon, B. 1984. Mechanism of cGMP control in retinal rod outer segments. *Trends Pharmacol. Sci.* 5:293–96

75. Lisman, J. 1985. The role of metarhodopsin in the generation of spontaneous quantum bumps in ultraviolet receptors of *Limulus* median eye. *J. Gen. Physiol.* 85:171–87

76. Lochrie, M. A., Hurley, J. B., Simon, M. I. 1985. Sequence of the alpha subunit of photoreceptor G protein: Homologies between transducin, *ras*, and elongation factors. *Science* 228:96–99

77. Longstaff, C., Calhoon, R. D., Rando, R. R. 1986. Deprotonation of the Schiff base of rhodopsin is obligate in the activation of the G protein. *Proc. Natl. Acad. Sci. USA* 83:4209–13

78. Matesic, D., Liebman, P. A. 1986. 39 KD protein from bovine ROS mediates cGMP-dependent cation flux. *Invest. Ophthalmol. Visual Res.* 27:218 (Suppl.)

79. Matthews, G., Baylor, D. A. 1981. The photocurrent and dark current of retinal rods. *Curr. Top. Membr. Transp.* 15:3–18

80. Matthews, R. G., Hubbard, R., Brown, P. K., Wald, G. 1963. Tautomeric forms of metarhodopsin. *J. Gen. Physiol.* 47:215–40

81. McDowell, J. H., Curtis, D. R., Baker, V. A. 1985. Phosphorylation of rhodopsin: Localization of phosphorylated residues in the helix-V-helix-VI connecting loop. *Invest. Ophthalmol. Visual Sci.* 26:291

82. McNaughton, P. A., Nunn, B. J., Cervetto, L. 1986. Measurement of intracellular free Ca^{++} concentration in salamander rod outer segments. *Nature* 322:261–63

83. Medynski, D. C., Sullivan, K., Smith, P., Van Dop, C., Chang, F. H. et al. 1985. Amino acid sequence of the γ subunit of transducin deduced from the cDNA sequence. *Proc. Natl. Acad. Sci. USA* 82:4311–15

84. Michel-Villaz, M., Saibil, H. R., Chabre, M. 1979. Orientation of rhodopsin α-helices in retinal rod outer segment membranes studied by infrared linear dichroism. *Proc. Natl. Acad. Sci. USA* 76:4405–8

85. Miki, N., Baraban, J. M., Keirns, J. J., Boyce, J. J., Bitensky, M. W. 1975. Purification and properties of the light-activated cyclic nucleotide phosphodiesterase of rod outer segments. *J. Biol. Chem.* 250:6320–27

86. Miller, J. L., Dratz, E. A. 1984. Phosphorylation at sites near rhodopsin's carboxyl-terminus regulates light initiated cGMP hydrolysis. *Vision Res.* 24:1509–21

87. Miller, J. L., Litman, B. J. 1986. Phosphatidylserine and divalent cations facilitate PDE activation in rhodopsin containing reconstituted vesicles. *Invest. Ophthalmol. Visual Sci.* 27:216 Suppl.

88. Miller, W. H. 1982. Physiological evidence that light-mediated decrease in cyclic GMP is an intermediary process in retinal rod transduction. *J. Gen. Phys.* 80:103–23

89. Nakatani, K., Yau, K.-W. 1985. cGMP opens the light-sensitive conductance in retinal rods. *Biophys. J.* 47:356a

90. Nathans, J., Thomas, D., Hogness, D. S. 1986. Molecular genetics of human color vision: The genes of inherited variation in human color vision. *Science* 232:193–202

91. Oakley, B. II, Bert, R. J., Proenza-Mueller, C. 1985. Electrophysiological assessment of phosphodiesterase activity in rod photoreceptors. *Invest. Ophthalmol. Visual Sci.* 26:333

92. O'Brien, D. F. 1982. The chemistry of vision. *Science* 218:961–66

93. O'Tousa, J. E., Baehr, W., Martin, R. L., Hirsh, I., Pak, W. L., et al. 1985. The *Drosophila* nina E gene encodes an opsin. *Cell* 40:839–50

94. Owen, W. G. 1986. Ionic conductances in rod photoreceptors. *Ann. Rev. Physiol.* 49:743–64

95. Parker, K. R., Briggs, J. A., Dratz, E. A. 1986. Inositol trisphosphate stimulates Ca^{2+} release from toad retinal rod outer segment preparations. *Biophys. J.* 49:31a

96. Parkes, J. H., Liebman, P. A. 1982. pH dependence of light sensitive PDE activation matches fraction of bleached rhodopsin converted to metarhodopsin II. *Invest. Ophthalmol. Visual Sci.* 22:44 Suppl.

97. Parkes, J. H., Liebman, P. A. 1984. Temperature and pH dependence of the metarhodopsin I-metarhodopsin II kinetics and equilibria in bovine rod disk membrane suspensions. *Biochemistry* 23:5054–61

98. Parkes, J. H., Liebman, P. A., Pugh, E. N. Jr. 1979. Comparison of delay in hydrolysis of cGMP in ROS suspensions with rate of formation of metarhodopsin II. *Invest. Ophthalmol. Visual Sci.* 20:22 Suppl.

99. Parkes, J. H., Sitaramayya, A., Harkness, J., Liebman, P. A. 1985. Mechanism of light activation of PDE in rod disk membranes. *Invest. Ophthalmol. Visual Sci.* 26:45

100. Penn, R. D., Hagins, W. A. 1972. Kinetics of the photocurrent of retinal rods. *Biophys. J.* 12:1073–94

101. Pepperberg, D. R., Lurie, M., Brown, P. K., Dowling, J. E. 1976. Visual adaptation: Effects of externally applied retinal on the light-adapted, isolated skate retina. *Science* 191:394–96

102. Pfister, C., Dovey, C., Vadot, E., Mirshahi, M., Deterre, P., et al. 1984. Identification of the "48K" protein that interacts with illuminated rhodopsin in vertebrate rods with the "retinal S antigen" inducing experimental autoimmune uveoretinitis. *C. R. Acad. Sci.* 299:261–65

103. Pfister, C., Kuhn, H., Chabre, M. 1983. Interaction between photoexcited rhodopsin and peripheral enzymes in frog retinal rods. *Eur. J. Biochem.* 136:489–99

104. Poo, M., Cone, R. A. 1974. Lateral diffusion of rhodopsin in the photoreceptor membrane. *Nature* 247:438–42

105. Pratt, D. C., Livingston, R., Grellman, K. H. 1964. Flash photolysis of rod particle suspensions. *Photochem. Photobiol.* 3:121–27

106. Deleted in proof

107. Pugh, E. N. Jr. 1986. The nature and identity of the internal excitational transmitter of vertebrate phototransduction. *Ann. Rev. Physiol.* 49:715–41

108. Robinson, W. E., Hagins, W. A. 1979. GTP hydrolysis in intact rod outer segments and the transmitter cycle in visual excitation. *Nature* 280:398–400

109. Roof, D. J., Korenbrot, J. I., Heuser, J. E. 1982. Surfaces of rod photoreceptor disk membranes: Light-activated enzymes. *J. Cell Biol.* 95:501–9

110. Saibil, H., Chabre, M., Worcester, D. 1976. Neutron diffraction studies of retinal rod outer segment membranes. *Nature* 262:266–70

111. Schwartz, S., Cain, J. E., Dratz, E. A., Blasie, J. K. 1975. An analysis of lamellar x-ray diffraction from disordered membrane multilayers with application to data from retinal rod outer segments. *Biophys. J.* 15:1201–33

112. Setlow, R. B., Pollard, E. C. 1962. *Molecular Biophysics.* Reading, Mass.: Addison-Wesley. 545 pp.

113. Shinozawa, T., Sen, I., Wheeler, G., Bitensky, M. W. 1979. Predictive value of the analogy between hormone-sensitive adenylate cyclase and light-sensitive photoreceptor cyclic GMP phosphodiesterase: A specific role for light sensitive GTPase as a component in the activation sequence. *J. Supramol. Struct.* 10:185–90

114. Sitaramayya, A., Harkness, J., Parkes, J. H., Gonzales-Oliva, C., Liebman, P. A. 1986. Kinetic studies suggest that light-activated cyclic GMP phosphodiesterase is a complex with G-protein subunits. *Biochemistry* 25:651–56

115. Sitaramayya, A., Liebman, P. A. 1983. Mechanism of ATP quench of phosphodiesterase activation in rod disk membranes. *J. Biol. Chem.* 258:1205–9

116. Sitaramayya, A., Liebman, P. A. 1983. Phosphorylation of rhodopsin and quenching of cGMP phosphodiesterase activation by ATP at weak bleaches. *J. Biol. Chem.* 258:12106–9

117. Stoeckenius, W., Bogomolni, R. A. 1982. Bacteriorhodopsin and related pigments of halobacteria. *Ann. Rev. Biochem.* 52:587–616

118. Stone, W. L., Farnsworth, C. C., Dratz, E. A. 1979. A reinvestigation of the fatty acid content of bovine, rat and frog rod outer segments. *Exp. Eye Res.* 28:387–97

119. Stryer, L. 1986. Cyclic GMP cascade of vision. *Ann. Rev. Neurosci.* 9:87–119

120. Tanabe, T., Nu, T., Nishikawa, Y., Sugimoto, K., Suzuki, H., et al. 1985. Primary structure of the α-subunit of transducin and its relationship to ras proteins. *Nature* 315:242–45

121. Thomas, D. D., Stryer, L. 1982. The transverse location of the retinal chromophore of rhodopsin in the rod outer segment disk membranes. *J. Mol. Biol.* 154:145–57

122. Torre, V., Matthews, H. R., Lamb, T. D. 1986. The role of calcium in regulating the cyclic GMP cascade of photo-transduction. *Proc. Natl. Acad. Sci. USA* 83:7109–13

123. Tsuda, M., Tsuda, T., Terayama, Y., Fukada, Y., Akino, T., et al. 1986. Kinship of cephalopod photoreceptor G-protein with vertebrate transducin. *FEBS Lett.* 198:5–10

124. Uhl, R., Desel, H., Wagner, R. 1985. Separation and characterization of light scattering transients from rod outer segments of vertebrate photoreceptors: Design and performance of a multi-angle flash photolysis apparatus. *J. Biochem. Biophys. Methods* 11:31–44

125. Vuong, T. M., Chabre, M., Stryer, L. 1984. Millisecond activation of transducin in the cyclic nucleotide cascade of vision. *Nature* 311:659–61

126. Waloga, G., Anderson, R. E. 1985.

Effects of inositol 1-4,5-trisphosphate injections into salamander rods. *Biochem. Biophys. Res. Commun.* 126:59–62

127. Wilden, U., Hall, S. W., Kuhn, H. 1986. Phosphodiesterase activation by photoexcited rhodopsin is quenched when rhodopsin is phosphorylated and binds the intrinsic 48-kDa protein of rod outer segments. *Proc. Natl. Acad. Sci. USA* 83:1174–78

128. Wulff, V. J., Adams, R. G., Linschitz, H., Abrahamson, E. W. 1958. Effect of flash illumination on rhodopsin in solution. *Ann. N.Y. Acad. Sci.* 74:290–91

129. Yamazaki, A., Halliday, K. R., George, J. S., Nagao, S., Kuo, C.-H., et al. 1985. Homology between light-activated photoreceptor phosphodiesterase and hormone-activated adenylate cyclase systems. *Adv. Cyclic Nucleotide Protein Phosphorylation Res.* 19:113–24

130. Yatsunami, K., Khorana, H. G. 1985.

GTPase of bovine rod outer segments: The amino acid sequence of the α subunit as derived from the cDNA sequence. *Proc. Natl. Acad. Sci USA* 82:4312–15

131. Yau, K.-W., Nakatani, K. 1985. Light-induced reduction of cytoplasmic free calcium in retinal rod outer segment. *Nature* 313:579–81

132. Yee, R., Liebman, P. A. 1978. Light-activated phosphodiesterase of the rod outer segment. Kinetics and parameters of activation and deactivation. *J. Biol. Chem.* 253:8902–9

133. Zuckerman, R., Buzdygon, B., Philp, N., Liebman, P. A., Sitaramayya, A. 1985. Arrestin: An ATP/ADP exchange protein that regulates cGMP phosphodiesterase activity. *Biophys. J.* 47:37a

134. Zuker, C. S., Cowman, A. F., Rubin, G. M. 1985. Isolation and structure of a rhodopsin gene from *D. melanogaster*. *Cell* 40:851–58

Ann. Rev. Physiol. 1987. 49:793–812

MOLECULAR PROPERTIES OF THE cGMP CASCADE OF VERTEBRATE PHOTORECEPTORS

James B. Hurley

Howard Hughes Medical Institute, SL-15, University of Washington, Seattle, Washington 98195

INTRODUCTION

Vertebrate photoreceptors are among the most differentiated eukaryotic cells. These cells rapidly hyperpolarize when exposed to light, and the speed and sensitivity of this response has been optimized by the evolution of a unique cellular structure and enzymatic cascade. The photoresponse is made up of unique electrical and metabolic changes that are initiated by rhodopsin photolysis.

Perhaps the best understood metabolic photoresponse, a rapid light-induced hydrolysis of cGMP appears to be an essential intermediate in phototransduction. Other chapters in this volume cover the molecular properties of rhodopsin (17), the electrical properties of photoreceptor plasma membranes (75), and the coupling between the light-induced metabolic changes and the plasma membrane (79). This review details several biochemical processes that are unique to photoreceptor cells. Only the enzymatic hardware that couples rhodopsin photolysis to cGMP hydrolysis will be described in detail here.

GENERAL MECHANISM OF LIGHT-STIMULATED cGMP HYDROLYSIS IN ROD OUTER SEGMENTS

The pioneering work of Bitensky and Miller and colleagues (9, 10) demonstrated a metabolic activity unique to photoreceptor cells: light stimulates cGMP hydrolysis. The enzyme responsible for this activity is a phosphodiesterase (PDE) that specifically hydrolyzes cGMP to 5'-GMP (67). Light

0066-4278/87/0315-0793$02.00

activation of this enzyme is mediated by rhodopsin photolysis. The first evidence for this was a demonstration that the action spectrum for PDE activation matches the percent absorption spectrum for rhodopsin (48).

Further major advances toward understanding this phenomenon were made when Yee & Liebman demonstrated that PDE activation by photolyzed rhodopsin (R*) is a catalytic process (108). PDE activity had been measured in previous experiments with fixed time assays utilizing ion exchange or thin layer analysis (TLC) analysis of the products of 8-[^{3}H]cGMP hydrolysis. Yee & Liebman adapted a simpler, continuous assay for rapid measurement of PDE activity in photoreceptor homogenates (108). This assay measures protons released when cGMP is hydrolyzed to 5'-GMP. Each R* molecule stimulated hydrolysis of 4×10^5 cGMP molecules per second in their experiments (108). However, each cGMP PDE molecule in their preparation hydrolyzed only 800 cGMP molecules per second (67). Therefore, they concluded that in the steady state each R* molecule keeps 500 PDE molecules activated.

The next major step towards understanding cGMP regulation in photoreceptors was the realization that R* does not activate the cGMP PDE directly. Instead, the immediate effect of rhodopsin photolysis is to stimulate a GDP-GTP exchange reaction (32) on transducin, a heterotrimeric guanyl nucleotide binding protein (27, 50). (Transducin from rod outer segments is also referred to as G protein, but it is actually only one member of a family of related guanyl nucleotide binding proteins (31) that as a class are referred to as G proteins.) It is the GTP complex of transducin that activates the cGMP-specific PDE (27). A single photolyzed rhodopsin molecule can catalyze GTP binding to several hundred transducin molecules (29). This activation persists as long as GTP is bound, but transducin slowly hydrolyzes its bound GTP to GDP (turnover rate of 0.5–2 min^{-1}) (4, 5, 32, 50, 102). The resulting T-GDP complex does not activate PDE (27). However, if R* and GTP are available after transducin hydrolyzes its bound GTP, transducin will again be stimulated to bind GTP and activate PDE. A schematic diagram of a current view of this cascade is shown in Figure 1.

This PDE activation cycle will continue indefinitely until R* is inactivated. The mechanisms by which the cGMP cascade is regulated are currently under investigation in many laboratories. Liebman & Pugh demonstrated that an ATP-dependent quenching of PDE activation occurs within seconds after rhodopsin photolysis (57). At least part of this inactivation mechanism may involve rhodopsin phosphorylation. A photoreceptor kinase (53) specifically phosphorylates several serines and threonines at the carboxyl terminus (C-terminus) of rhodopsin (99). R* phosphorylated by this kinase activates transducin less efficiently than unphosphorylated R* (69, 98). In addition, a 48-kd protein referred to as "48K," "S-antigen," or "arrestin" is also present

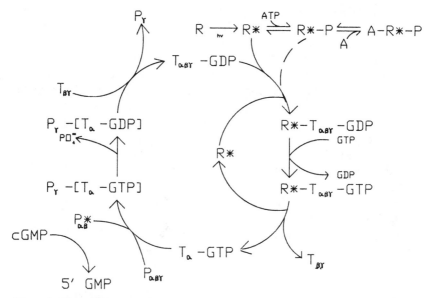

Figure 1 The cGMP cascade of vertebrate photoreceptors.

in photoreceptor outer segments, and this protein binds tightly to phosphory-lated R* (49, 54, 98). Arrestin may compete with transducin for binding sites on phosphorylated R* and therefore further reduce the efficiency of PDE activation (98).

Many of the proteins involved in this process (PDE, transducin, rhodopsin kinase, and arrestin) have been characterized in detail at the molecular level. The following sections describe molecular and enzymatic properties of these proteins. This short review emphasizes only recent, especially significant findings that have not yet been reviewed. References 26 and 88 and the accompanying chapters in this volume should be consulted for more complete background information and for more detailed discussions of the significance of the cGMP cascade in phototransduction.

BIOCHEMICAL CHARACTERIZATION OF PHOTORECEPTOR-SPECIFIC ENZYMES

cGMP PDE

Photoreceptor PDEs in species from goldfish to man (39, 45, 50, 67) are ~170-kd heterotrimeric proteins exclusively expressed in photoreceptor cells. Estimates indicate that there are 0.6–2.5 PDE molecules per 100 rhodopsin molecules in bovine rod outer segments (ROS) (3, 84). This enzyme has been purified to homogeneity by several different methods (3, 39, 45, 50, 67) and shown to be a complex of two 85–90 kd subunits associated with at least one 11-kd γ subunit. Two types of 85–90 kd subunit, α and β, are found in purified PDE preparations. The α and β subunits appear to be related to each other. Partial proteolysis of the α subunit yields several polypeptides that are similar in size to peptides derived from the β subunit (3). The relative stoichiometry of the α, β, and γ subunits in the holoenzyme is uncertain.

INHIBITOR SUBUNIT   The 11-kd γ subunit (P_γ) is an inhibitory subunit of the photoreceptor PDE. It can be purified from the pure photoreceptor PDE holoenzyme by heating the holoenzyme to 100°C under conditions that precipitate the α and β subunits but leave the γ subunit in solution (18, 40, 43). Alternatively, P_γ can be purified from the holoenzyme by gel filtration chromatography under denaturing conditions (43).

P_γ is very sensitive to proteolysis by trypsin under conditions where the α and β subunits remain nearly intact. As the γ subunit is degraded, the cGMP hydrolytic activity of the α and β subunits increases dramatically (43, 67). Subsequent addition of a trypsin inhibitor results in a stable preparation of very high specific activity phosphodiesterase (40). The activated catalytic subunit preparation can still be regulated by P_γ. Added P_γ inhibits as much as 99% of the PDE activity. Wensel & Stryer recently demonstrated (95) that activation by trypsin modifies the α and β PDE subunits in a way that affects kinetic properties of the PDE. This is apparently due to minor structural modification because it has not been detected by standard SDS polyacrylamide gel electrophoresis (95).

Other methods have been used to characterize inhibitors of photoreceptor PDE. Dumler & Etingof reported a purification of PDE inhibitor activity from heat-denatured PDE (18). The protein responsible for this activity eluted from a gel filtration column at an apparent size of 60 kd. Similar results were reported by Yamazaki et al (103). In addition, Baehr et al reported partial purification of a heat-stable inhibitory protein that appears to copurify with transducin (3). The relationship between these different inhibitor preparations and the 11-kd P_γ subunit was not established. A monoclonal antibody that specifically recognizes the bovine rod outer segment PDE γ subunit has been reported (19).

The complete amino acid sequence of P_γ was recently determined, and a cDNA clone encoding it was isolated and characterized (73). P_γ is an 86–amino acid polypeptide with a short, hydrophilic, and very basic domain near the middle of the polypeptide chain. This basic domain may be part of the molecule that is sensitive to trypsin proteolysis, and it may play a direct role in inhibiting PDE activity. Polycations such as histones or protamine activate PDE holoenzyme (67), perhaps by electrostatically displacing P_γ from its binding site on the catalytic subunits.

BINDING CONSTANTS AND KINETICS   The affinity of P_γ for the PDE α and β catalytic subunits varies greatly depending on the method of preparation and analysis. The dissociation constant for P_γ binding to trypsin-activated PDE has been reported to be 0.005 (95) and 0.13 nM (43) when determined with the radioisotope PDE assay (40) and 15 nM (84) when determined with the proton-release PDE assay (108). The reason for the more than 1000-fold discrepancy of these independent determinations is unresolved. The dissociation constant for P_γ binding to intact, purified PDE was reported to be 0.01 nM (95). Association of P_γ with light-activated PDE was reported to be much weaker ($K_d = 440$ nM) (84) when determined with the proton-release PDE assay.

Removal of P_γ from the PDE holoenzyme by trypsin proteolysis increases the turnover rate for cGMP from ~45 mol cGMP s^{-1} mol^{-1} (depending on the source, method of preparation, and assay conditions) to 800–3700 mol cGMP s^{-1} mol^{-1} with little or no K_m change (3, 43, 67). The K_m of purified PDE has been reported to be 0.04–0.15 nM (3, 43, 84). However, Sitar-amayya et al recently demonstrated that the K_m of photoreceptor PDE, determined by the pH assay of rod outer segment homogenates performed in the dark after a light flash, can be as high as 1.4 mM (84).

HIGH-AFFINITY cGMP BINDING SITES   Frog photoreceptor PDE binds cGMP at two high-affinity sites (104). The dissociation constants for cGMP at these sites were reported to be 160 and 830 nM (104). Trypsin degradation of the inhibitor subunit not only activates the photoreceptor PDE but also abolishes this high-affinity cGMP binding activity (103). The high-affinity cGMP binding sites have not yet been reported in mammalian photoreceptors. In addition, the mechanism of regulation of these sites by P_γ, the effects of transducin-induced activation of PDE on these sites, and the physiological function of these sites remain uncertain (79).

ANTIBODIES   Antibodies that recognize photoreceptor PDE have been re-ported. Two monoclonal antibodies, ROS-1 and ROS-2, specifically recog-nize photoreceptor PDE from retinas of a variety of species (44, 45). These two antibodies recognize different determinants on the PDE molecule. For example, only one of them inhibits cGMP hydrolytic activity.

PDE from standard preparations of bovine rod outer segments fractionates into two peaks by anion exchange chromatography (44, 45). The first peak contains a 92-kd subunit, whereas the second peak contains the 85–90 kd α and β subunits. The immunoreactivity of monoclonal antibodies ROS-1 and ROS-2 with PDE from these peaks was tested. ROS-1 antibody recognizes PDE in both peaks, whereas ROS-2 antibody only reacts with the second peak. Immunocytochemical analyses of bovine retina sections with ROS-1 and ROS-2 demonstrate that ROS-2 binds only to rod outer segments and that ROS-1 binds to both rod and cone outer segments (44, 45). Therefore, the 85–90 kd subunits that react with both antibodies appear to be subunits of a rod-specific PDE, whereas the 92-kd protein may be a cone-specific PDE. Recently, a polyclonal antibody prepared against purified bovine ROS PDE was described (20). Like ROS-2, this antibody recognizes rod PDE but not cone PDE in bovine retinas.

OTHER PHOSPHODIESTERASES   Photoreceptor PDEs are part of a multigene family of PDEs (14). This family includes several well-characterized PDEs such as calmodulin-regulated PDE, cGMP-stimulated PDE, and cGMP-inhibited PDE. PDEs have been characterized from a variety of organisms including *Drosophila,* in which a defect in learning is associated with defective cAMP PDE (12). There is significant amino acid sequence homology among members of this family. However, only one PDE, the photoreceptor PDE, is known to be regulated by a G protein (transducin). The photoreceptor PDE apparently interacts with transducin through P_γ. The relationship between P_γ and subunits or domains of adenylate cyclase and phospholipase C and other enzymes that are regulated by G proteins promises to be particularly interesting.

Transducin

Transducin has been identified in several vertebrate species as a heterotrimeric guanyl nucleotide binding protein unique to photoreceptors. Its physiological role is to convert signals generated by rhodopsin photolysis into PDE activation, cGMP hydrolytic activity, and ultimately hyperpolarization of the photoreceptor. Estimates indicate that there are 7–10 transducin molecules per 100 rhodopsin molecules in the bovine rod outer segment (4, 5, 32, 50, 52).

SUBUNIT STRUCTURE AND FUNCTION   The transducin holoenzyme consists of a 39-kd α subunit, T_α, weakly associated with a complex of β and γ subunits, $T_{\beta\gamma}$. T_α can be separated from the $T_{\beta\gamma}$ complex by gel filtration (27) or other methods (23, 25). The 36-kd β subunit and the 8-kd γ subunit form a tight complex that can only be dissociated with denaturants. Guanyl nucleotides and analogues bind to a site on the α subunit (27). Nonhydrolyzable GTP analogues bound to the α subunit enhance chromatographic separation of T_α from $T_{\beta\gamma}$ (25, 27), presumably by dissociating the subunits. However, the physiological significance of this nucleotide-induced dissociation is not clear because the state of association of transducin subunits at physiological concentrations and the effects of nucleotides under such conditions have not been determined.

The $T_{\alpha\beta\gamma}$ complex has only a weak affinity for unphotolyzed rhodopsin, but it binds tightly to R* (50). This binding causes a measurable change in the light-scattering properties of a suspension of rod outer segment membranes when rhodopsin is photolyzed in the presence of transducin (16, 52). The high-affinity binding of transducin to R* allows guanyl nucleotide exchange on T_α (32), but GTP or GTP analogue binding to T_α reduces the affinity of transducin for R* (50, 51). Time-resolved light-scattering measurements show that this binding and GTP-induced release occur efficiently and rapidly (within a msec) (94). In fact, transducin can be purified by a method based on its nucleotide-dependent affinity for R* (27, 50, 51).

Purified T_α with bound GTP or a nonhydrolyzable GTP analogue (such as GppNHp or GTP-γ-S) stimulates cGMP PDE activity in ROS homogenates (27). Saturating amounts of T_α-GppNHp activate PDE to the same level as when the inhibitory subunit P_γ is removed by proteolysis as described in the previous section (27). Apparently, T_α-GTP relieves inhibitory constraints imposed on the PDE catalytic subunits by the PDE inhibitor subunit. The mechanism by which T_α-GppNHp removes the inhibitory effects of P_γ is being investigated, but the most recent results suggest that T_α-GTP dissociates P_γ from the catalytic PDE subunits by forming a P_γ-T_α-GTP complex (15, 95, 105).

The role of the $T_{\beta\gamma}$ complex appears to be to present T_α to R* on the membrane surface (25), but the roles of the individual T_β and T_γ polypeptides are uncertain. T_α alone neither binds to R* nor catalyzes GTP hydrolysis. However, only substoichiometric (catalytic) amounts of $T_{\beta\gamma}$ are required to maximally stimulate T_α. A similar role for the $T_{\beta\gamma}$ complex of other guanyl nucleotide binding proteins has also been reported (87).

TRANSDUCIN AND G PROTEINS   Transducin is a member of a family of guanyl nucleotide binding proteins most often referred to as G proteins (Table 1). These are heterotrimeric signal-transducing proteins that have 39–52 kd α subunits, 35–36 kd β subunits, and 8–10 kd γ subunits. Besides transducin, the three best-characterized classes of G proteins are G_s and G_i, which respectively stimulate and inhibit adenylate cyclase, and G_o, a G protein with uncertain function that is abundant in bovine brain. In addition, G proteins appear to be part of the regulatory mechanisms of phospholipase C (66) and certain ion channels (76). At least four other types of G proteins have recently been identified by biochemical and recombinant DNA techniques (11).

Each class of G protein has a characteristic α subunit with a unique peptide map and amino acid composition (61). A detailed comparison of the primary structures of G-protein subunits is possible now that cDNA clones corresponding to the α subunits of G_s, G_i, G_o, several G_i-related polypeptides, and two forms of transducin have been isolated and characterized (Figure 2) (37, 46, 60, 65, 71, 72, 80, 90, 106). The amino acid sequence encoded by one of these clones (65, 90, 106), labeled rod T_α in Figure 2, corresponds exactly to amino acid sequence determined from proteolytic fragments of purified rod outer segment T_α (42, 59, 90). The amino acid sequences of $G_{o\alpha}$, $G_{i\alpha}$, and $G_{s\alpha}$ are 60%, 58%, and 38% identical to the rod T_α sequence.

T_α is a G-protein α subunit that is expressed only in rod outer segments (56). It is also unique in its structure and in its solubility properties. Transducin is the only G protein that can be solubilized as a holoenzyme without detergents. A low ionic strength buffer alone is sufficient to extract T_α from ROS membranes (4, 39, 50, 51). This unusual property of T_α may be localized at its N-terminus or in the $\beta\gamma$ subunit with which it associates. In most G proteins, the N-terminus seems to either anchor the α subunit to the membrane or to the $\beta\gamma$ subunit, which subsequently associates with the membrane. Proteolytic removal of 15–20 N-terminal amino acids is sufficient to release many G-protein α subunits from the membrane (38a, unpublished observation).

Like the α subunits of other characterized G proteins, T_α is a substrate for ADP-ribosylation catalyzed by bacterial toxins. Each of the biochemically characterized G-protein α subunits has a site that can be ADP-ribosylated by either cholera toxin or pertussis toxin (31), but only T_α has both sites. The locations of the amino acids of transducin that become ADP-ribosylated and the corresponding sites in other G proteins are identified in Figures 2 and 3 (62, 93, 96). ADP-ribosylation either by cholera toxin (1, 62, 92) or by

Table 1 Summary of properties of the best-characterized G proteins

G protein	Target enzyme	Receptor	Subunit molecular weight (kd)	Toxin sites
G_s	activates adenylate cyclase	β-adrenergic	$\alpha = 42$–52 $\beta = 35$ $\gamma \approx 5$	cholera
G_i (family)	inhibits adenylate cyclase	α-adrenergic muscarinic opiate dopamine	$\alpha = 41$ $\beta = 35$ $\gamma \approx 5$	pertussis
G_o	unknown	muscarinic	$\alpha = 39$ $\beta = 35$ $\gamma \approx 5$	pertussis
Transducin	activates cGMP phosphodiesterase	rhodopsin	$\alpha = 39$ $\beta = 36$ $\gamma \approx 8$	cholera, pertussis

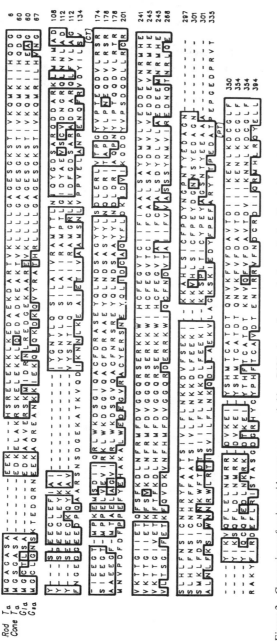

Figure 2 Comparison of amino acid sequences encoded by cDNA clones for transducins and other G proteins and α subunits (60, 65, 71, 72, 80, 90, 106).

pertussis toxin (62, 93, 96) occurs at specific sites in T_α, and modification at each site has specific biochemical effects. Cholera toxin catalyzes ADP-ribosylation of arginine 174 (92) and inhibits transducin GTPase activity but not its ability to bind GTP or activate PDE (1). ADP-ribosylation catalyzed by pertussis toxin modifies cysteine 347 and prevents T_α from interacting with R* (93, 96). Optimal conditions for ADP-ribosylation by each toxin are also quite different. Cholera toxin catalyzed ADP-ribosylation of T_α is most effective when R* and GppNHp are included in the reaction (1), i.e. under conditions that favor dissociation of T_α from $T_{\beta\gamma}$. Pertussis toxin, on the other hand, is most effective under conditions that favor association of T_α and $T_{\beta\gamma}$ (62, 93).

The transducin β subunit appears to be identical to β subunits of other G proteins. cDNA clones encoding T_β have been characterized, and the amino acid sequence of T_β has been reported (23, 89). mRNA transcripts that encode T_β are found in many different tissues, but transcripts from retina appear to be spliced differently than those from other tissues (89). However, the alternate splicing occurs outside the coding region and therefore does not affect the structure of the protein product. After T_β is synthesized, the N-terminal methionine of T_β is cleaved off and the new N-terminus is acetylated (59; V. Lipkin, personal communication). Two forms of β subunit are often resolved into a 36-kd, 35-kd doublet on SDS polyacrylamide gel electrophoretic analyses of G proteins from tissues other than ROS (70). However, only the 36-kd form is associated with transducin. The nature of the two types of β subunit is not understood.

Although the γ subunits of G_s, G_i, and G_o appear to be identical on the

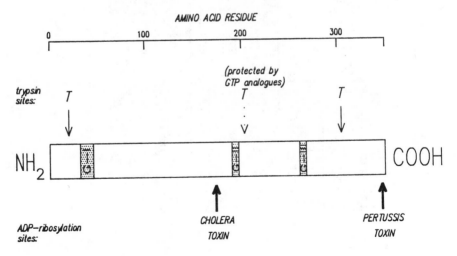

Figure 3 Primary structure of the transducin α subunit.

basis of peptide maps and immunoreactivity, the transducin γ subunit is quite different. Two laboratories independently determined the complete amino acid sequence of T_γ by Edman degradation of the purified subunit (63, 74). The results reveal a 69–amino acid polypeptide that is acidic and quite hydrophilic. Two other laboratories have also characterized cDNA clones that encode the complete T_γ coding region (41, 107). Both cDNA clones encode a 73–amino acid polypeptide with an amino acid sequence that is identical to T_γ except that the cDNAs encode four extra amino acids, C-V-I-S, at the C-terminus. Posttranslational processing mechanisms that might account for this discrepancy need to be investigated. A potential model for another type of processing that might account for this anomolous result is the GTP binding RAS protein that has a cysteine in a homologous C-terminal sequence (41). This cysteine has been found to be acylated and essential for the function of RAS (82, 100).

STRUCTURE/FUNCTION RELATIONSHIPS   A complete understanding of the three-dimensional structure of transducin awaits crystallization and x-ray diffraction analysis. However, recent studies provide a glimpse of the structure-function relationships of T_α such an analysis might be expected to reveal.

Limited digestion of T_α with trypsin under nondenaturing conditions suggests that T_α is made up of as many as four domains. Trypsin first cleaves 18 amino acids from the N-terminus and then cleaves 40 amino acids from the C-terminus (28, 35, 42). Further exposure to trypsin cleaves the remaining 32-kd fragment into 23- and 9-kd fragments in a nucleotide-dependent manner (Figure 3). Interestingly, this cleavage site is not accessible to trypsin when a nonhydrolyzable GTP analogue is bound to T_α. The N- and C-termini of T_α are essential for transducin activity. Removal of 18 amino acids from the T_α N-terminus prevents interaction between T_α and R* as well as recognition of T_α by pertussis toxin (28, 65). The effect of this modification on the interaction of T_α with $T_{\beta\gamma}$ has not been investigated. Removal of both termini with trypsin does not release bound nucleotides but prevents T_α from efficiently activating PDE (28).

The guanyl nucleotide binding sites of G proteins and other guanyl nucleotide binding proteins such as elongation factors and *ras* oncogene products appear to be made up of three short, highly conserved polypeptide chains, labelled G-I to G-III in Figure 3. Halliday first identified these conserved sequences in elongation factors and *ras* (34). Homologous sequences are also present in T_α and other G-protein α subunits (42, 60, 64, 65, 90, 106). Bacterial elongation factor EF-Tu has been crystallized in a modified form, and recently three-dimensional structures of EF-Tu were proposed (47, 55). In these structures, the conserved regions identified by Halliday (34) combine to form a guanyl nucleotide binding pocket. McCormick has proposed a model for a similar nucleotide binding site in RAS based on the EF-Tu structure (64). An analogous model for the structure of transducin and other G proteins has also been proposed (11). The nucleotide binding site on T_α binds many types of nucleotide analogues. Like many other G proteins, transducin can be activated by aluminum fluoride salts (AlF$_4$). Recently, Bigay et al proposed that AlF$_4$, which requires GDP bound to T_α for activation, has a role analogous to that of the γ-phosphate of GTP in the nucleotide binding site (8).

Little is known about the secondary and tertiary structure of T_β. However, the primary structure of T_β is made up of several repeated units each 43 amino acids long whose function is unknown (23). Trypsin very rapidly cleaves the nondenatured β subunit into a 14-kd N-terminal fragment and a 26-kd C-terminal fragment, each of which is resistant to further proteolysis (28, 35). This result suggests that the β subunit may be made up of two major domains linked by a hydrophilic, trypsin-labile chain.

ANTIBODIES   Many monoclonal (36) and polyclonal (24, 33, 65, 77, 81) antibodies have been raised against intact transducin subunits, and polyclonal antibodies have been raised against synthetic peptides derived from transducin subunit sequences (56, 70). Many of the anti-T_α antibodies raised against purified protein cross-react with α subunits of other G proteins (77, 81). In general, the antibodies against the transducin β subunit consistently cross-react with the 36-kd form of the β subunits of other G proteins, and antibodies against the transducin γ subunit do not cross-react with γ subunits from other G proteins (30, 91).

Rods and cones express different transducin α subunits. A cDNA clone that was isolated from a bovine retinal cDNA library (60) encodes a form of transducin that is specifically expressed in cones and is 78% identical to rod outer segment transducin. This polypeptide is labeled cone T_α in Figure 2. Cone T_α ($T_{C\alpha}$) is more homologous to rod outer segment transducin $T_{r\alpha}$) than to any other characterized G protein (Figure 2). An antibody against a polypeptide with a sequence found only in rod transducin ($T_{r\alpha}$) localizes $T_{r\alpha}$ to rod outer segments in bovine retina as expected (Figure 4), whereas $T_{C\alpha}$ specific antibodies localize $T_{C\alpha}$ to cone outer segments (56). Further characterizations of purified cone transducin and cone PDE are necessary to determine whether biochemical differences account for the physiological differences between rods and cones.

Rhodopsin Kinase and Arrestin

RHODOPSIN KINASE   A unique photoreceptor kinase, rhodopsin kinase, phosphorylates as many as 9 serines and threonines on the hydrophilic

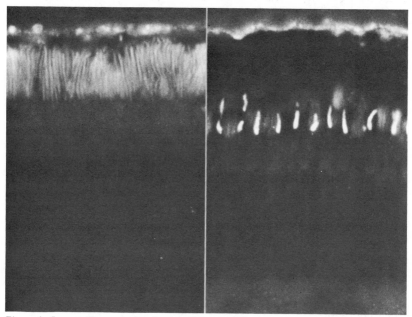

Figure 4   Immunofluorescent localization of the two different types of photoreceptor transducin α subunits using antibodies that specifically recognize rod *(left)* and cone *(right)* transducins (56).

C-terminal tail of R* (99). Rhodopsin kinase is a 68-kd soluble protein that, like transducin, binds specifically to R* (26, 49, 51). The kinase appears to be active only when it is bound to R*. There is ~0.1 rhodopsin kinase for every ~100 rhodopsin molecules in a rod outer segment (51).

The significance of rhodopsin phosphorylation is uncertain. Rhodopsin phosphorylation catalyzed by rhodopsin kinase might turn off an excitation signal generated by rhodopsin photolysis, or it might adapt the photoreceptor cell to background illumination. Other roles for rhodopsin phosphorylation are also possible. The effect of rhodopsin kinase activity on transducin and PDE activation has been difficult to assay in crude systems. Experiments with ROS homogenates demonstrated that some reaction in which ATP is hydrolyzed quenches PDE activation by R* (57). Light-stimulated PDE remains active in ROS homogenates for ~30 sec without ATP, but when ATP is included in the reaction PDE deactivates within 4 sec (57). Nonhydrolyzable ATP analogues do not substitute for ATP, therefore hydrolysis or phosphorylation must be involved in the quench reaction. However, many ATP hydrolysis reactions occur in crude photoreceptor homogenates, and many proteins become phosphorylated. ATP-dependent quenching alone therefore does not directly identify the role of rhodopsin phosphorylation.

At least two experimental results suggest that the ATP-dependent PDE deactivation may involve phosphorylation of R* by rhodopsin kinase. Miller & Dratz (68) proteolytically removed portions of the rhodopsin C-terminus, the domain of the rhodopsin molecule that becomes heavily phosphorylated by rhodopsin kinase. The modified rhodopsins were reconstituted into vesicles and recombined with transducin. ATP-dependent quenching is reduced by removal of the rhodopsin C-terminus. In a separate experiment, Sitaramayya & Liebman demonstrated that kinase-depleted membranes are less susceptible to ATP-dependent PDE quenching. ATP-dependent quenching can be restored to these membranes by addition of rhodopsin kinase (85).

Further evidence that phosphorylation of R* regulates cGMP hydrolysis comes from recent findings (69, 83, 98) that show that rhodopsin phosphorylation inhibits transducin and PDE activation. For example, phosphorylation states of photolyzed bovine rhodopsin from 0 to ≥ 4 phosphates per rhodopsin were separated from each other by chromatofocusing, regenerated, reconstituted into phospholipid vesicles, and then recombined with transducin and PDE (69). The photosensitivity of each preparation for activating PDE activity was determined. Activation of PDE by the most phosphorylated rhodopsin preparation required photolysis of significantly more rhodopsin than did activation of PDE reconstituted with unphosphorylated preparations.

The mechanism by which rhodopsin phosphorylation inhibits transducin activation is currently being investigated. Light-scattering measurements indicate that transducin binds to phosphorylated R* as well as it binds to unphosphorylated R* (2). However, whereas GTP normally dissociates T_α from R*, GTP apparently does not dissociate T_α from phosphorylated R* (2).

Like rhodopsin, PDE, and transducin, rhodopsin kinase is part of a family of structurally and functionally related proteins (6, 7, 86). β-adrenergic receptor kinase (β-ARK) phosphorylates agonist-occupied β-adrenergic receptors but not agonist-free receptors. β-ARK seems to phosphorylate the receptor at multiple C-terminal sites (6). This kinase appears to be essential for homologous desensitization adaptation that affects only stimulated receptors. The phosphorylated receptor is a much less efficient activator of G_s and adenylate cyclase than the unphosphorylated receptor (6). The receptor kinases, like the G proteins, are not absolutely specific for one type of receptor. Rhodopsin kinase, like β-ARK, phosphorylates agonist-occupied β-adrenergic receptor but not the agonist-free receptor. Likewise, β-ARK phosphorylates R*, but not unphotolyzed rhodopsin (6).

Arrestin

ARRESTIN   Arrestin is a 48-kd protein unique to photoreceptors that binds phosphorylated R* with high affinity (51, 54). Tightly bound arrestin reduces the effectiveness of phosphorylated R* for transducin and PDE activation by competing with transducin for binding sites on R* (98). Arrestin may be essential for light adaptation of the cGMP response or PDE deactivation under intense illumination conditions.

The C-terminal amino acid sequence of arrestin has been deduced from an arrestin cDNA clone, and it is somewhat homologous to the C-terminus of the T_α subunit (101). Perhaps this domain has an important rhodopsin binding function in both of these proteins.

Other Phosphorylation Reactions

The rapid, ATP-dependent quenching of PDE activation reported by Liebman & Pugh (57) occurs within 4 sec, markedly faster than the deactivation of transducin by hydrolysis of bound GTP (4, 5, 50, 102). If deactivation of photolyzed rhodopsin by phosphorylation were the only effect of ATP, activated transducin would persist for the lifetime of the bound GTP, >30 sec. Since the ATP-dependent deactivation occurs much more rapidly than this, other mechanisms besides rhodopsin phosphorylation reducing the efficiency of PDE activation must be responsible for the rapid ATP-dependent quench.

Phosphorylated R* might rapidly quench PDE activation by binding transducin in a way that dissociates GTP or that prevents the nucleotide-induced release of activated transducin from R* (2, 16). Alternatively, the rapid ATP-dependent quenching might result from modification of any of several other photoreceptor proteins reported to be phosphorylated in a light-dependent manner (21, 38, 78). Phosphorylation of many of these proteins is dependent on cGMP and Ca^{2+}. In addition, a preliminary report indicates that arrestin and ATP may significantly reduce the direct activation of PDE by activated transducin (109). Regulation of cGMP hydrolysis and other metabolic pathways via a variety of feedback mechanisms is therefore possible. At this time, the basic mechanism by which cGMP hydrolysis is activated is relatively well understood. Identification of mechanisms that regulate this pathway is one of the major challenges currently faced by photoreceptor biochemists.

CONCLUSION

Photoreceptors are highly specialized neurons in which many of the features of signal transduction mechanisms have become exaggerated to the point where nearly half of the cell is dedicated to signal transduction. For this reason, many of the enzymes involved in phototransduction have been relatively easy to isolate and characterize, and photoreceptors have been a useful model for the study of signal transduction mechanisms in other types of cells. Much of the biochemical machinery that couples rhodopsin photolysis through cGMP to ion channels in the photoreceptor plasma membrane (22, 75) are now understood. However, phototransducers as adaptable as vertebrate rod and cone cells certainly require other, more intricate mechanisms to recover, adapt, and fine-tune their responses. Protein phosphorylation, phosphoinositides, and Ca^{2+} may contribute to these types of regulation (66, 79). Similar types of regulation are essential for signal transduction in a variety of other cells, particularly neurons. Hopefully, further understanding of the regulation of phototransduction will continue to provide insights into homologous types of regulation of signal transduction mechanisms in other types of cells.

ACKNOWLEDGMENTS

I wish to thank Joe Beavo, Connie Lerea, and Carol Raport for carefully reading and criticizing this manuscript. This review was supported in part by the Howard Hughes Medical Institute and by grant EYO6641-01 from the National Institutes of Health.

Literature Cited

1. Abood, M. E., Hurley, J. B., Pappone, M. C., Bourne, H. R., Stryer, L. 1982. Functional homology between signal-coupling proteins: Cholera toxin inactivates the GTPase activity of transducin. *J. Biol. Chem.* 257:10540–43

2. Arshavskii, V. Y., Dizhur, A. M., Kaulen, A. D., Shestakova, I. K., Filipov, P. P. 1985. The effect of phosphorylation of rhodopsin on its interaction with transducin studied by the technique of light-scattering. *Biol. Membr.* 2:1–11

3. Baehr, W., Devlin, M. J., Applebury, M. L. 1979. Isolation and characterization of cGMP phosphodiesterase from bovine rod outer segments. *J. Biol. Chem.* 254:11669–77

4. Baehr, W., Morita, E. A., Swanson, R. J., Applebury, M. L. 1982. Characterization of rod outer segment G-protein. *J. Biol. Chem.* 253:6452–60

5. Bennett, N. 1982. Light-induced interactions between rhodopsin and the GTP-binding protein: Relation with phosphodiesterase activation. *Eur. J. Biochem.* 123:133–39

6. Benovic, J. L., Mayo, F. Jr., Somers, R. L., Caron, M. G., Lefkowitz, R. J. 1986. Light-dependent phosphorylation of rhodopsin by β-adrenergic receptor kinase. *Nature* 321:869–72

7. Benovic, J. L., Strasser, R. H., Caron, M. G., Lefkowitz, R. J. 1986. β-adrenergic receptor kinase: Identification of a novel protein kinase that phos-

phorylates the agonist-occupied form of the receptor. *Proc. Natl. Acad. Sci. USA* 83:2797–2801

8. Bigay, J., Deterre, P., Pfister, C., Charbre, M. 1986. Fluoraluminates activate transducin-GTP by mimicking the γ-phosphate of GTP in its binding site. *FEBS Lett.* 191:181–85

9. Bitensky, M. W., Gorman, R. E., Miller, W. H. 1971. Adenyl cyclase as a link between photon capture and changes in membrane permeability of frog photoreceptors. *Proc. Natl. Acad. Sci. USA* 68:561–62

10. Bitensky, M. W., Wheeler, G., Rasenick, M. M., Yamazaki, A., Stein, P. J. 1981. Cyclic nucleotide metabolism in vertebrate photoreceptors: A remarkable analogy and an unraveling enigma. *Curr. Top. Membr. Transp.* 15:237–71

11. Bourne, H. R. 1986. One molecular machine can transduce diverse signals. *Nature* 321:814–81

12. Byers, D., Davis, R. L., Kiger, J. A. Jr. 1981. Defect in cyclic AMP phosphodiesterase due to dunce mutation of learning in *Drosophila melanogaster*. *Nature* 289:79–81

13. Deleted in proof

14. Charbonneau, H., Beier, N., Walsh, K. A., Beavo, J. A. 1986. Identification of a conserved domain among cyclic nucleotide phosphodiesterases from diverse species. *Proc. Natl. Acad. Sci. USA* In press

15. Deterre, P., Bigay, J., Robert, M., Pfis-

ter, C., Kuhn, H., Charbre, M. 1986. Characterization of the complex formed by phosphodiesterase inhibitor and transducin α subunit. In press

16. Dizhur, A. M., Arshavskii, V. Y., Rybin, V. O., Filipov, P. P. 1986. Effect of membranes on transducin-dependent activation of cyclic nucleotide phosphodiesterase from the rod outer segments of bovine retina. *Biol. Membr.* 2:529–39

17. Liebman, P. A., Parker, K. R., Dratz, E. A. 1987. The molecular mechanism of visual excitation and its relation to the structure and composition of the rod outer segment. *Ann. Rev. Physiol.* 49:765–91

18. Dumler, I. L., Etingof, R. N. 1976. Protein inhibitor of cyclic adenosine 3′:5′monophosphate phosphodiesterase in retina. *Biochim. Biophys. Acta* 429:474–84

19. Dumler, I. L., Etingof, R. N. 1984. Immunochemical study of retina photoreceptor membranes: Antibodies to cGMP phosphodiesterase and to protein inhibitors of the enzyme. *Biol. Membr.* 1:565–72

20. Farber, D. B., Bok, D. 1985. Light-activated cGMP phosphodiesterase is absent from cone photoreceptors. *Invest. Ophthalmol. Vision Sci.* 26:334

21. Farber, D. B., Brown, B. M., Lolley, R. N. 1979. Cyclic nucleotide dependent protein kinase and the phosphorylation of endogenous proteins of retinal rod outer segments. *Biochemistry* 18:370–78

22. Fesenko, E. E., Kolesnikov, S. S., Lyubarsky, A. L. 1985. Induction by cyclic GMP of cationic conductance in plasma membrane of retinal rod outer segment. *Nature* 313:310–13

23. Fong, H. K. W., Hurley, J. B., Hopkins, R., Miake-Lye, R., Johnson, M. S., et al. 1986. Repetitive segmental structure of the transducin β subunit: Homology with the CDC4 gene and identification of related mRNAs. *Proc. Natl. Acad. Sci. USA* 83:2162–66

24. Fukada, Y., Akino, T. 1986. Immunohistochemical studies on localization of GTP-binding protein in vertebrate retina. *Photochem. Photobiol.* 11:269–79

25. Fung, B. K.-K. 1983. Characterization of transducin from bovine rod retinal rod outer segments: Separation and reconstitution of the subunits. *J. Biol. Chem.* 258:10495–10502

26. Fung, B. K.-K. 1985. *Molecular Mechanisms of Transmembrane Signalling,* ed. Cohen, Houslay, pp. 183–214. New York: Elsevier Science, Biomed. Div.

27. Fung, B. K.-K., Hurley, J. B., Stryer, L. 1981. Flow of information in the light-triggered cyclic nucleotide cascade of vision. *Proc. Natl. Acad. Sci. USA* 78:152–56

28. Fung, B. K.-K., Nash, C. R. 1983. Characterization of transducin from bovine retinal rod outer segments: Evidence for distinct binding sites and conformational changes by limited proteolysis with trypsin. *J. Biol. Chem.* 258:10503–10

29. Fung, B. K.-K., Stryer, L. 1980. Photolyzed rhodopsin catalyzes the exchange of GTP for GDP in retinal rod outer segment membranes. *Proc. Natl. Acad. Sci. USA* 77:2500–4

30. Gierschik, P., Codina, J., Simons, C., Birnbaumer, L., Spiegel, A. M. Antisera against a guanine-nucleotide binding-protein from retina cross-react with the β subunit of the adenyl cyclase associated guanine nucleotide binding proteins. *Proc. Natl. Acad. Sci. USA* 82:727–31

31. Gilman, A. G. 1984. G proteins and dual control of adenylate cyclase. *Cell* 36:577–79

32. Godchaux, W. III, Zimmerman, W. F. 1979. Membrane-dependent guanine nucleotide binding and GTPase activities of soluble proteins from bovine rod outer segments. *J. Biol. Chem.* 254:7874–84

33. Grunwald, G. B., Gierschik, M., Nirenberg, A., Spiegel, A. 1986. Detection of α-transducin in retinal rods but not cones. *Science* 231:856–59

34. Halliday, K. R. 1984. Regional homology in GTP-binding proto-oncogene products and elongation factors. *J. Cyclic Nucleotide Prot. Phosphorylation Res.* 9:435–48

35. Halliday, K. R., Stein, P. J., Chernoff, N., Wheeler, G., Bitensky, M. W. 1984. Limited trypsin proteolysis of photoreceptor GTP-binding protein: Light- and GTP-induced conformational changes. *J. Biol. Chem.* 259:516–25

36. Hamm, H. E., Bownds, M. D. 1984. A monoclonal antibody to guanine nucleotide binding protein inhibits the light activated cyclic GMP pathway in frog rod outer segments. *J. Gen. Physiol.* 84:265–80

37. Harris, B. A., Robishaw, J. D., Mumby, S. M., Gilman, A. G. 1985. Molecular cloning of complementary DNA for the α subunit of the G protein that stimulates adenylate cyclase. *Science* 229:1274–77

38. Hermolin, J., Karell, M. A., Hamm, H. E., Bownds, M. D. 1982. Calcium and cyclic GMP regulation of light-sensitive protein phosphorylation in frog photore-

ceptor membranes. *J. Gen. Physiol.* 79:633–55

38a. Hudson, T. H., Roeber, J. F., Johnson, G. L. 1981. Conformational changes of adenylate cyclase regulatory proteins mediated by guanine nucleotides. *J. Biol. Chem.* 256:1459–65

39. Hurley, J. B. 1980. Isolation and recombination of bovine rod outer segment cGMP phosphodiesterase and its regulators. *Biochim. Biophys. Res. Commun.* 92:505–10

40. Hurley, J. B. 1982. Isolation and assay of a phosphodiesterase inhibitor from retinal rod outer segments. *Methods Enzymol.* 81:542–47

41. Hurley, J. B., Fong, H. K. W., Teplow, D. B., Dreyer, W. J., Simon, M. I. 1984. Isolation and characterization of a cDNA clone for the γ subunit of bovine retinal transducin. *Proc. Natl. Acad. Sci. USA* 81:6948–52

42. Hurley, J. B., Simon, M. I., Teplow, D. B., Robishaw, J. D., Gilman, A. G. 1984. Homologies between signal transducing G proteins and *ras* gene products. *Science* 226:860–62

43. Hurley, J. B., Stryer, L. 1982. Purification and characterization of the γ subunit of the cyclic GMP phosphodiesterase from retinal rod outer segments. *J. Biol. Chem.* 257:11094–99

44. Hurwitz, R. L., Bunt-Milam, A. H., Beavo, J. A. 1984. Immunologic characterization of the photoreceptor outer segment cyclic GMP phosphodiesterase. *J. Biol. Chem.* 259:8612–18

45. Hurwitz, R. L., Bunt-Milam, A. H., Chang, M. L., Beavo, J. A. 1985. cGMP phosphodiesterase in rod and cone outer segments of the retina. *J. Biol. Chem.* 260:568–73

46. Itoh, H., Kozasa, T., Nagata, S., Nakamura, S., Katada, T., et al. 1986. Molecular cloning and sequence determination of cDNAs for α subunits of the guanine nucleotide-binding proteins G_s, G_i, and G_o from rat brain. *Proc. Natl. Acad. Sci. USA* 83:3776–80

47. Jurnak, F. 1985. Structure of the GDP domain of EF-Tu and location of the amino acids homologous to *ras* oncogene proteins. *Science* 230:32–36

48. Keirns, J. J., Miki, N., Bitensky, M. W., Keirns, M. 1975. A link between rhodopsin and disk membrane cyclic nucleotide phosphodiesterase action spectrum and sensitivity to illumination. *Biochemistry* 14:2760–65

49. Kuhn, H. 1978. Light-regulated binding of rhodopsin kinase and other proteins to cattle photoreceptor membranes. *Biochemistry* 17:4389–95

50. Kuhn, H. 1980. Light- and GTP-regulated interaction of GTPase and other proteins with bovine photoreceptor membranes. *Nature* 283:587–89

51. Kuhn, H. 1981. Interactions of rod cell proteins with the disk membranes: Influence of light, ionic strength and nucleotides. *Curr. Top. Membr. Transp.* 15:174–201

52. Kuhn, H., Bennett, N., Michel-Villaz, M., Charbre, M. 1981. Interactions between photoexcited rhodopsin and GTP binding protein: Kinetics and stoichiometric analyses from light-scattering changes. *Proc. Natl. Acad. Sci. USA* 78:6873–77

53. Kuhn, H., Dreyer, W. J. 1972. Light dependent phosphorylation of rhodopsin by ATP. *FEBS Lett.* 20:1–6

54. Kuhn, H., Hall, S. W., Wilden, U. 1984. Light regulated binding of 48 kD protein to photoreceptor membranes is highly enhanced by phosphorylation of rhodopsin. *FEBS Lett.* 176:473–78

55. La Cour, T. F. M., Nyborg, J., Thirup, S., Clark, B. F. C. 1985. Structural details of the binding of guanosine diphosphate to elongation factor Tu of *E. coli* studied by X-ray crystallography. *EMBO J.* 4:2385–88

56. Lerea, C. L., Somers, D. E., Hurley, J. B., Klock, I. B., Bunt-Milam, A. H. 1986. Identification of specific transducin α subunits in retinal rod and cone photoreceptors. *Science* 234:77–80

57. Liebman, P. A., Pugh, E. N. Jr. 1980. ATP mediates rapid reversal of cyclic GMP phosphodiesterase activation in visual receptor membranes. *Nature* 287:734–36

58. Liebman, P. A., Pugh, E. N. Jr. 1982. Gain, speed and sensitivity of GTP binding vs. PDE activation in visual excitation. *Vision Res.* 22:1475–80

59. Lipkin, V. M., Gubanov, V. V., Obukov, A. N., Ischenko, K. A., Ovchinnikov, Y. A. 1986. *Abstr. Int. Conf. Retinal Proteins, Lake Baikal, USSR*, p. 7

60. Lochrie, M. L., Hurley, J. B., Simon, M. I. 1985. Sequence of the α-subunit of photoreceptor G protein: Homologies between transducin, *ras* and elongation factors. *Science* 228:96–99

61. Manning, D. R., Gilman, A. G. 1983. The regulatory components of adenylate cyclase and transducin. A family of structurally homologous guanine nucleotide-binding proteins. *J. Biol. Chem.* 258:7059–63

62. Manning, D. R., Fraser, B. A., Kahn, R. A., Gilman, A. G. 1984. ADP-ribosylation of transducin by islet activating protein. Identification of

asparagine as the site of ADP-ribosylation. *J. Biol. Chem.* 259:749–56

63. McConnell, D. G., Kohnken, R. E., Smith, A. T. 1984. Tentative identification of complete amino acid sequence for smallest subunit of GTP binding protein of bovine retinal rod outer segment. *Fed. Proc.* 43:1585

64. McCormick, F., Clark, B. F. C., LaCour, T. F. M., Kjeldgaard, M., Norskov-Lauritsen, L., Nyborg, J. 1985. A model for the tertiary structure of p21, the product of the *ras* oncogene. *Science* 233:78–82

65. Medynski, D. C., Sullivan, K., Smith, D., Van Dop, C., Chang, F. H., et al. 1985. Amino acid sequence of the α subunit of transducin deduced from the cDNA sequence. *Proc. Natl. Acad. Sci. USA* 82:4311–15

66. Michell, B. 1986. Profusion and confusion. *Nature* 319:176–77

67. Miki, N., Baraban, J. M., Keirns, J. J., Boyce, J. J., Bitensky, M. W. 1975. Purification and properties of the light-activated cyclic nucleotide phosphodiesterases of rod outer segments. *J. Biol. Chem.* 150:6320–27

68. Miller, J. L., Dratz, E. A. 1984. Phosphorylation at sites near rhodopsin's carboxyl terminus regulates light initiated cGMP hydrolysis. *Vision Res.* 24:1509–21

69. Miller, J. L., Fox, D. A., Litman, B. J. 1986. The amplification of phosphodiesterase activation is greatly reduced by rhodopsin phosphorylation. *Biochemistry* 25:4983–88

70. Mumby, S. M., Kahn, R. A., Manning, D. R., Gilman, A. G. 1986. Antisera of designed specificity for subunits of guanine nucleotide-binding regulatory proteins. *Proc. Natl. Acad. Sci. USA* 83:265–69

71. Nukada, T., Tanabe, T., Takahashi, H., Noda, M., Haga, K., et al. 1986. Primary structure of the α subunit of bovine adenylate cyclase inhibitory G protein deduced from the cDNA sequence. *FEBS Lett.* 187:305–9

72. Nukada, T., Tanabe, T., Takahashi, H., Noda, M., Hirose, T., et al. 1986. Primary structure of the α subunit of bovine adenylate cyclase–stimulatory G-protein deduced from the cDNA sequence. *FEBS Lett.* 195:220–24

73. Ovchinnikov, Y. A., Lipkin, V. M., Kumarev, V. P., Gubanov, V. V., Khramstov, N. V., et al. 1986. Cyclic GMP phosphodiesterase from cattle retina. Amino acid sequence of the γ-subunit and nucleotide sequence of the corresponding cDNA. *FEBS Lett.* 204:288–92

74. Ovchinnikov, Y. A., Lipkin, V. M., Shuvaeva, T. M., Bogachuk, A. P., Shemyakin, V. V. 1984. Complete amino acid sequence of γ subunit of the GTP-binding protein from cattle retina. *FEBS Lett.* 179:107–10

75. Owen, W. G. 1986. Ionic conductances in rod photoreceptors. *Ann. Rev. Physiol.* 49:743–64

76. Pfaffinger, P. J., Martin, J. M., Hunter, D. D., Nathanson, N. M., Hille, B. 1985. GTP-binding proteins couple muscarinic receptors to a K channel. *Nature* 317:536–38

77. Pines, M., Gierschik, P., Milligan, G., Klee, W., Spiegel, A. 1986. Antibodies against the carboxyl-terminal 5-kD peptide of the α subunit of transducin cross-react with the 40-kD but not the 39-kD guanine nucleotide binding protein from brain. *Proc. Natl. Acad. Sci. USA* 82:4095–99

78. Polans, A. S., Hermolin, J., Bownds, M. D. 1979. Light-induced dephosphorylation of two proteins in frog rod outer segments: Influence of cyclic nucleotides and calcium. *J. Gen. Physiol.* 74:595–613

79. Pugh, E. N. Jr. 1986. The nature and identity of the internal excitational transmitter of vertebrate phototransduction. *Ann. Rev. Physiol.* 49:715–41

80. Robishaw, J. D., Russell, D. W., Harris, B., Smigel, M. D., Gilman, A. G. 1986. Deduced primary structure of the α subunit of the GTP binding stimulatory protein of adenylate cyclase. *Proc. Natl. Acad. Sci. USA* 83:1251–55

81. Roof, D. J., Applebury, M. L., Sternweis, P. C. 1985. Relationships within the family of GTP-binding proteins isolated from bovine central nervous system. *J. Biol. Chem.* 260:16242–49

82. Sefton, B., Trowbridge, I. S., Cooper, J. A., Scolnick, E. M. 1982. The transforming proteins of rous sarcoma virus, Harvey sarcoma virus and Abelson virus contain tightly bound lipid. *Cell* 31:465–74

83. Shichi, H., Yamamoto, K., Somers, R. L. 1984. GTP binding protein properties and lack of activation by phosphorylated rhodopsin. *Vision Res.* 24:1523–31

84. Sitaramayya, A., Harkness, J., Parkes, J. H., Gonzalez-Olivia, C., Liebman, P. A. 1986. Kinetic studies suggest that light-activated cyclic GMP phosphodiesterase is a complex with G-protein subunits. *Biochemistry* 25:651–56

85. Sitaramayya, A., Liebman, P. A. 1983. Mechanism of ATP quench of phospho-

diesterase activation in rod disc membranes. *J. Biol. Chem.* 258:1205–9

86. Somers, R. L., Klein, D. C. 1984. Rhodopsin kinase activity in the mammalian pineal gland and other tissues. *Science* 226:182–84

87. Sternweis, P. 1986. The purified α subunits of G_o, and G_i from bovine brain require βγ for association with phospholipid vesicles. *J. Biol. Chem.* 261:631–37

88. Stryer, L. 1986. Cyclic GMP cascade of vision. *Ann. Rev. Neurosci.* 9:87–119

89. Sugimoto, K., Nukada, T., Tanabe, T., Takahashi, H., Noda, M., et al. 1985. Primary structure of the β subunit of bovine transducin deduced from the cDNA sequence. *FEBS Lett.* 191:235–40

90. Tanabe, T., Nukada, T., Nishikawa, Y., Sugimoto, K., Suzuki, H., et al. 1985. Primary structure of the α subunit of transducin and its relationship to *ras* proteins. *Nature* 315:242–45

91. Van Dop, C., Medynski, D., Sullivan, K., Wu, A. M., Fung, B. K.-K., Bourne, H. R. 1984. Partial cDNA sequence of the γ subunit of transducin. *Biochem. Biophys. Res. Commun.* 124:250–55

92. Van Dop, C., Tsubokawa, M., Bourne, H. R., Ramachandran, J. 1984. Amino acid sequence of retinal transducin at the site ADP-ribosylated by cholera toxin. *J. Biol. Chem.* 259:696–98

93. Van Dop, C., Yamanaka, G., Steinberg, F., Sekura, R. D., Manclark, C. R., et al. 1984. ADP-ribosylation of transducin by pertussis toxin blocks the light-stimulated hydrolysis of GTP and cGMP in retinal photoreceptors. *J. Biol. Chem.* 259:23–26

94. Vuong, T. M., Charbre, M., Stryer, L. 1984. Millisecond activation of transducin in the cyclic nucleotide cascade of vision. *Nature* 311:659–61

95. Wensel, T. G., Stryer, L. 1986. Reciprocal control of retinal rod cyclic GMP phosphodiesterase by its γ subunit and transducin. In press

96. West, R. E. Jr., Moss, J., Vaugh, M., Liu, T. 1985. Pertussis toxin–catalyzed ADP-ribosylation of transducin: Cysteine 347 is the ADP-ribose acceptor site. *J. Biol. Chem.* 260:14425–30

97. Wheeler, G. L., Matuo, Y., Bitensky, M. W. 1977. Light-activated GTPase in vertebrate photoreceptors. *Nature* 269:822–24

98. Wilden, U., Hall, S. W., Kuhn, H. 1986. Phosphodiesterase activation by photoexcited rhodopsin is quenched when rhodopsin is phosphoryated and

binds the intrinsic 48 kD protein of rod outer segments. *Proc. Natl. Acad. Sci. USA* 83:1174–78

99. Wilden, U., Kuhn, H. 1982. Light-dependent phosphorylation of rhodopsin: Number of phosphorylation sites. *Biochemistry* 21:3014–22

100. Willumsen, B. M., Norris, K., Papageorge, A. G., Hubbert, N. L., Lowy, D. R. 1984. Harvey murine sarcoma virus p21 *ras* protein: Biological and biochemical significance of the cysteine nearest the carboxy terminus. *EMBO J.* 3:2581–85

101. Winstow, G. V., Katial, A., Craft, C., Shinohara, T. 1986. Sequence analysis of bovine retinal S-antigen: Relationships with α transducin and G-proteins. *FEBS Lett.* 196:23–28

102. Yamanaka, G., Eckstein, F., Stryer, L. 1985. Stereochemistry of the guanyl nucleotide binding site of transducin probed by phosphorothionate analogues of GTP and GDP. *Biochemistry* 24:8094–8101

103. Yamazaki, A., Bartucca, F., Ting, A., Bitensky, M. W. 1982. Reciprocal effects of an inhibitory factor on catalytic activity and non-catalytic cGMP binding sites of rod phosphodiesterase. *Proc. Natl. Acad. Sci. USA* 79:3702–6

104. Yamazaki, A., Sen, I., Bitensky, M. W. 1980. Cyclic GMP-specific, high affinity, non-catalytic binding sites in light-activated phosphodiesterase. *J. Biol. Chem.* 255:11619–24

105. Yamazaki, A., Stein, P. J., Chernoff, N., Bitensky, M. W. 1983. Activation mechanism of rod outer segment cyclic GMP phosphodiesterase. Release of inhibitor by the GTP/GDP-binding protein. *J. Biol. Chem.* 258:8188–94

106. Yatsunami, K., Khorana, G. K. 1985. GTPase of bovine rod outer segments: The amino acid sequence of the α subunit as derived from the cDNA sequence. *Proc. Natl. Acad. Sci. USA* 82:4316–20

107. Yatsunami, K., Pandya, B. V., Oprian, D. P., Khorana, H. G. 1985. cDNA-derived amino acid sequence of the γ subunit of GTPase from bovine rod outer segments. *Proc. Natl. Acad. Sci. USA* 82:1936–40

108. Yee, R., Liebman, P. A. 1978. Light-activated phosphodiesterase of the rod outer segment. Kinetics and parameters of activation and deactivation. *J. Biol. Chem.* 253:8902–9

109. Zuckerman, R., Cheasty, J. E. 1986. Mechanisms of rapid quench of cGMP phosphodiesterase activation in rod disk membranes (RDM). *Invest. Ophthalmol. Vision Sci.* 27:217 (suppl.)

SUBJECT INDEX

A

Acanthamoeba palestinesis
phospholipid transport in, 194
Acclimation, 465
Acclimatization, 465
Acetate
pancreatic fluid secretion and, 92
Acetazolamide
bicarbonate secretion and, 55
hepatocyte ion exchange and, 79
intracellular gastric mucosa pH and, 20
pancreatic fluid secretion and, 94
salt absorption and, 55, 61
Acetic acid
pancreatic fluid secretion and, 92
Acetylcholine
acinar cell enzyme secretion and, 89, 99
airway smooth muscle and, 557
blood pressure and, 417
cation channels and, 229
paratracheal ganglia and, 578
rapidly adapting receptors and, 618
receptors for
heparan surface proteoglycan and, 169
thirst and, 416
Acid-base balance
intestinal electrolyte transport and, 56
Acidosis
metabolic, 56
respiratory, 56
Acid phosphatase
in juxtaglomerular cells, 267
Acinar cells, 87-88
enzyme secretion by, 99
ion transport in, 98-99
Actin
erythrocyte membrane and, 167, 238-40
isolation of, 633
muscle contraction and, 520
muscular force generation and, 136-37
myosin ATPase and, 630
Actinomycin D
DNA transcription and, 261
Action potentials
cardiac muscle and, 522-24

Actomyosin
ATP hydrolysis and, 642
force generation and, 643-44
inorganic phosphate and, 646-47
muscle contraction and, 520
Actomyosin ATPase
ATP consumption and, 677
cross-bridge cycle and, 655-69
muscle enthalpy and, 673-87
muscle fibers and, 637-50
muscular force generation and, 136-37
in solution, 630-32, 667-68
Adenosine
tubuloglomerular feedback mechanism and, 286-87
Adenosine diphosphate
muscle fibers and, 647-48
Adenosine triphosphate
anaerobic glycolysis and, 136
caged, 638-39
chloride ion uptake and, 74
consumption in skeletal muscle, 676-77
cross-bridge detachment and, 639-41
echinocytes and, 185
enthalpy production and, 674-76
hepatocyte organelles and, 71
hydrolysis in muscle fibers, 641-43
muscular force generation and, 136-38
Adenylate cyclase
vasoactive intestinal polypeptide and, 559
Adipocytes
lipolysis in, 199
Adipose tissue
fatty acid transport in, 198
Adipsia
anteroventral third ventricle lesions and, 417
Adrenal gland
angiotensin receptors in, 429
β-Adrenergic receptor
rhodopsin and, 784
Adrenocortical steroids
brain and, 397-409
Adrenocorticotropin hormone
aldosterone secretion and, 399
angiotensin II and, 424-25
secretion of, 398
Airway
receptors of, 611-23

Airway ganglia
peripheral, 573-80
characteristics of, 575-77
circuitry in, 579-80
neurotransmission in, 577
Airway smooth muscle
gap junctions in, 590
innervation of, 583-91
motor control of, 595-98
neural inputs to, 573-75
neuromuscular junctions in, 589-90
neuropeptides in, 557-67
Airway tone
respiration and, 607
Albumin
monensin and, 77
Aldosterone
angiotensin II and, 425
antinatriuresis and, 422
binding in brain, 402-3
binding sites for, 401
macula densa cytosolic calcium concentration and, 283
secretion of, 399
selectivity of, 405-8
sodium appetite and, 421-22
specificity of, 399
uptake of, 404-5
Alkaline phosphatase
lateral diffusion of, 170
small intestine and, 61
Alkaline-phosphatasedipeptidyl-peptidase-IV reaction, 444
Alkalosis
metabolic, 56
chloridorrhea and, 51
respiratory, 56
Allometry
interspecific, 110-16
intraspecific, 114-16
metabolic, 109-10
Amiloride
canalicular bile formation and, 80
hepatic regeneration and, 80
hepatocyte pH and, 79
intracellular gastric gland pH and, 22
intracellular sodium ion activity and, 40-41, 43
intracellular surface cell pH and, 27
ouabain-induced cell swelling and, 39
pancreatic fluid secretion and, 94

Amino acid uptake
  insulin and, 342
Amino acid transport systems
  lipid modulation of, 230
6-Aminonicotinamide
  renin and, 263
Amygdala
  thyroid hormone receptors in,
    323
Anaerobic glycolysis
  ATP and, 136
Anaerobic metabolism
  neovascular growth and, 461-
    62
Androgens
  brain responses to, 350-52
Anemia
  hemolytic, 242
  left ventricular hypertrophy
    and, 483-84
Angiogenesis, 453-63
Angiotensin
  blood-brain barrier and, 413-
    14
  central nervous system and,
    413-30
  juxtaglomerular cells and, 267
  tubuloglomerular feedback
    and, 260-61
Angiotensin I
  in juxtaglomerular cells, 267
Angiotensin II
  adrenocorticotropin hormone
    and, 424-25
  aldosterone and, 425
  atrial natriuretic factor and,
    423-24
  baroreflex and, 419-20
  blood pressure and, 416-20
  catecholamines and, 426-28
  corticotropin-releasing factor
    and, 424-25
  glomerular filtration rate and,
    260
  hypovolemia and, 414-15
  juxtaglomerular cells and, 267
  kidney function and, 422-23
  mineralocorticoid secretion
    and, 398-99
  neurotransmitter function and,
    426-29
  opioid interactions of, 428-29
  plasma renin and, 423
  reproductive hormones and,
    425-26
  serotonin and, 428
  sodium appetite and, 421-22
  thirst and, 415-16
  vasopressin release and, 420-
    21
Angiotensin-converting enzyme
  tubuloglomerular feedback
    mechanism and, 313

Ankyrin
  erythrocyte membrane and,
    167, 238-39
Antibodies
  photoreceptor phosphodiester-
    ase and, 797-98
  transducin and, 804
Antidiuretic hormone
  angiotensin II and, 420-21
  glomerular filtration rate and,
    257-58
Aorta
  coarctation of, 493-95
  normal development of, 490-
    93
Apical membrane
  ion exchange at, 39-42
  cyclic AMP and, 46-47
  rates of, 42-43
  salt transport at, 37-39
Aplysia neurons
  cholesterol and, 229
Aprotinin
  tubuloglomerular feedback
    mechanism and, 313
Arachidonic acid
  tubuloglomerular feedback
    mechanism and, 287-
    90
Arginine vasopressin
  angiotensin II and, 414
Arrestin
  metarhodopsin II and, 777
  photoreceptors and, 806-7
Arterial-venous grafts, 495
Arterioles
  regenerated skeletal muscle
    and, 447-48
Artificial heart
  forerunner of, 4
Asialoglycoproteins
  uptake by hepatocytes, 76
Astrocytes
  glutamine synthetase in
    triiodothyronine and, 328
Atherosclerosis
  left ventricular hypertrophy
    and, 478
ATP
  See Adenosine triphosphate
ATPase
  actomyosin
    ATP consumption and, 677
    cross-bridge cycle and,
      655-69
    muscle enthalpy and, 673-
      87
    in muscle fibers, 637-50
    muscular force generation
      and, 136-137
    in solution, 630-32, 667-68
  hepatocellular
    inhibition of, 71, 74-75

intestinal brush border membrane and, 61
  myofibrillar, 527-28
  myosin
    actin and, 630
    thyroxine-induced cardiac
      hypertrophy and, 483
Atrial natriuretic factor
  angiotensin II and, 423-24
  tubuloglomerular feedback
    mechanism and, 312
Atrial septal defect, 505
Atropine
  thirst and, 416
Autonomic ganglia
  neuropeptide Y in, 387
Autoradiography
  insulin receptors and, 339-40

B

Bacteriorhodopsin
  lateral diffusion of, 166
Band 3 protein
  lipid modulation of, 223-27
Barbiturates
  brain sexual differentiation
    and, 356-58
Baroreflex
  angiotensin II and, 419-20
Basal metabolism
  theory of elastic similarity
    and, 127-28
Benzodiazepine receptors
  in kidney, 265-66
Benzyl alcohol
  erythrocyte deformability and,
    184
Bicarbonate ion
  absorption by jejunum, 54
    sodium ion dependency of,
      58
  intestinal electrolyte transport
    and, 56
  pancreatic fluid secretion and,
    92-93
  secretion by colon, 55
  secretion by duodenum, 53-54
Bicarbonate ion exchange
  in hepatocytes, 80-81
Bicarbonate ion transport
  at basolateral plasma mem-
    brane, 61-62
  in intestine, 51-62
  pancreatic, 90-99
Bile
  hepatic formation of, 77-78
Biochemistry
  brain insulin and, 336
Bladder
  angiotensin receptors in, 429
Blood
  carbamino hemoglobin in, 3

material exchange between
CSF and, 11
pH of
intestinal electrolyte transport and, 56
viscosity of
factors determining, 177
Blood-brain barrier
angiotensin and, 413-14
insulin and, 338, 341
Blood flow
chronic hypoxia and, 470
erythrocyte deformability and,
177-89
regenerated skeletal muscle
and, 447-48
Blood pressure
angiotensin II and, 416-20,
427
Blood vessels
angiogenesis and, 455-59
neuropeptide Y and, 387
skeletal muscle transplantation
and, 439-48
Body fluid volume
angiotensin II and, 414-15
Body mass
body surface area vs., 124-26
Body surface area
body mass vs., 124-26
Body weight
insulin and, 342-43
pancreatic polypeptide and,
387
Bohr effect, 2
Bombesin
acinar cell enzyme secretion
and, 89, 99
central nervous system and,
386-87
Bone
erythrocyte trapping in, 188
Bradykinin
airway neurons and, 566
C-fiber receptors and, 621-22
rapidly adapting receptors
and, 618
Brain
adrenocortical steroids and,
397-409
aldosterone binding in, 401-3
development of
thyroid hormones and, 321-
31
insulin in, 335-44
functions of, 341-43
receptors for, 338-41
neuropeptide Y in, 387
renin-angiotensin system in,
413
sexual differentiation in, 349-
61
somatostatin in, 389

Brain stem
airway smooth muscle and,
595-601
thyroid hormone receptors in,
323
Breathing
chemical regulation of, 10-
11
See also Respiration
Bronchi
C-fiber receptors in, 619-22
innervation of, 597, 599-601
nerve fibers in, 583
rapidly adapting receptors in,
616
Bronchioles
rapidly adapting receptors in,
616
Bronchoconstriction
bradykinin and, 566
clonidine and, 567
induction of, 564-65
nicotine and, 566
Bronchodilation
vasoactive intestinal
polypeptide and, 558
Bronchomotor tone
respiration and, 606-7
Brown fat thermogenesis
bombesin and, 386-87
Brush border membrane
ATPase activity in, 61
ion exchange mechanisms in,
55
ion transport at, 57-61
salt transport at
acetazolamide and, 59-60
Bumetanide
chloride-bicarbonate ion exchange and, 81
hepatocyte ion exchange and,
79
ouabain-induced cell swelling
and, 39
pancreatic fluid secretion and,
94-95
transepithelial fluid transport
and, 39
Butyl hydroperoxide
erythrocyte deformability and,
184
Butyrate
pancreatic fluid secretion and,
92
Butyric acid
pancreatic fluid secretion and,
92

C

Calcitonin gene-related peptide
airway neurons and, 560-62

Calcium
erythrocyte deformability and,
182
tubuloglomerular feedback
mechanism and, 279-83
Calcium ion
ATP-induced cross-bridge detachment and, 640
cone phototransduction and,
735-36
phototransduction and, 712,
718-22
Calcium ion channels
sarcoplasmic reticulum and,
525-26
Calcium ion pump
ATP consumption and, 676
erythrocytes and, 227-28
sarcoplasmic reticulum and,
228
Calcium metabolism
hypertrophied myocardium
and, 506
Calmidazolium
calmodulin inhibition and,
284
Calmodulin
erythrocyte membrane and,
238
smooth muscle contraction
and, 284
tubuloglomerular feedback
mechanism and, 283-85
Capillaries
angiogenesis and, 454-55
osmotic pressure and, 9
peripheral gas exchange and,
148-50
See also Microcirculation
Capsaicin
peptide-containing sensory
nerves and, 562
tracheobronchial afferent
neurons and, 565-67
Captopril
enkephalins and, 429
plasma aldosterone and, 425
plasma renin activity and, 423
renin-angiotensin system and,
307
Carbachol
cardiac myosin heavy chain
genes and, 548
thirst and, 416
Carbon dioxide
airway stretch receptors and,
614-15
rapidly adapting receptors
and, 619
Carbonic anhydrase
intestinal acidification and,
59-60
in intestine, 51

intracellular oxyntic cell pH
and, 21
in kidney, 266
Carbon monoxide poisoning, 6
Carbonyl cyanide phenylhydrazones
intestinal chloride ion transport and, 58
Cardiac hypertrophy, 477-78
anemia-induced, 483-84
animal models of, 535
biochemical mechanisms of,
533-41
cardiac load regulation and,
509-15
cardiac overloading and, 502-
8
cardiac underloading and,
508-9
coronary vasculature and,
479-80
mechanical factors in, 539-40
pathological manifestations of,
478
protein degradation in, 538-39
protein synthesis in, 535-38
systemic hypertension and,
480-82
thyroxine-induced, 482-83
volume-overload, 484-85
Cardiac load regulation, 509-15
Cardiac muscle
ATPase activity in, 527-28
chronic hypoxia and, 471
excitation-activation-
contraction model for,
519-21
inotropic agents and, 528-29
myosin heavy chain genes in,
546
sarcoplasmic reticulum in,
525-26
senescence and, 521-30
stiffness in, 526-27
Cardiac output
chronic hypoxia and, 468-70
metabolic scaling and, 110
Cardiac overloading, 502-8
Cardiac underloading, 508-9
Cardiocytes
cardiac load regulation and,
511-15
hypertrophied myocardium
and, 506-7
Cardiolipid
transport proteins and, 222
Cardiovascular system
chronic hypoxia and, 467
Catecholamines
angiotensin II and, 414, 426-
28
cardiac hypertrophy and, 510
cardiac muscle and, 528

hypertrophied myocardium
and, 507
neuropeptide Y and, 388
turnover of
insulin and, 343
ventricular cardiocytes and,
513
Cathepsin B
juxtaglomerular cells and,
267
Caudate nucleus
cholecystokinin receptors in,
384
Ceftizoxime, 112
Cells
acinar, 87-88
enzyme secretion by, 99
ion transport in, 98-99
brain
insulin receptors in, 339
chief
buffer capacity of, 26
intracellular pH of, 19, 26
transmembrane pH gra-
dients and, 29-30
endocrine
somatostatin in, 389
endothelial
angiogenesis and, 453-63
Goormaghtigh
biochemical characteristics
of, 266-67
granular
biochemical characteristics
of, 267
hypothalamic
differentiation of, 353
juxtaglomerular
angiotensins in, 267
Leydig
angiotensin receptors in,
429
oxyntic
basolateral membrane of,
25-26
buffer capacity of, 26
intracellular pH in, 19-21
parietal
intracellular pH in, 23-26
Purkinje
hypothyroidism and, 325
retinoblastoma
insulin receptors in, 339
satellite
muscle grafts and, 440
stomach
intracellular pH in, 19-31
Central nervous system
adrenocortical steroids and,
397-409
angiotensin and, 413-30
bombesin and, 386-87
cholecystokinin and, 384-86

gastrin-releasing peptide and,
386-87
gastroenteropancreatic peptides and, 383-91
glucagon and, 389-90
insulin and, 335-44
pancreatic polypeptide and,
387-88
sexual differentiation in, 349-
61
somatostatin and, 389
thyroid hormones and, 321-
31
Cerebellum
thyroid hormone receptors in,
323-24
thyroid hormones and, 325
Cerebral cortex
cholecystokinin receptors in,
384
thyroid hormone receptors in,
323
Cerebrospinal fluid
material exchange between
blood and, 11
sleep-inducing properties of
sleep deprivation and, 12-
13
Cerebrum
thyroid hormone receptors in,
324
Ceruloplasmin
angiogenesis and, 457
C-fiber receptors, 619-22
Chemoreceptors
tracheal, 584
Chief cells
buffer capacity of, 26
intracellular pH in, 19, 26
transmembrane pH gradients
and, 29-30
Chloride ion
brush border membrane and,
58
pancreatic fluid secretion and,
93-94
uptake by multivesicular bodies, 74
Chloride ion exchange
apical membrane and, 41-42
hepatocytes and, 80-81
Chloridorrhea
colon and, 55
metabolic alkalosis and, 51
p-Chlorophenylalanine
brain sexual differentiation
and, 358
Chloroquine
endocytic organelles and, 76
Chlorpromazine
sexual behavior and, 357-
58
stomatocytes and, 184-85

Cholecystokinin
  acinar cell enzyme secretion
    and, 89, 99
  central nervous system and,
    384-86
  dopamine and, 384-85
  feeding behavior and, 343
Cholera toxin
  ADP-ribosylation and, 800-2
Cholesterol
  amino acid transport systems
    and, 230
  Aplysia neurons and, 229
  band 3 protein and, 223
  erythrocyte anion transport
    and, 227
  erythrocyte cation transport
    and, 229
  intermembrane transport of,
    196-97
  mitochondrial membrane and,
    227
  monosaccharide transport and,
    230
  Na,K-ATPase activity and,
    228-29
Choline chloride
  pancreatic fluid secretion and,
    90
Chondroitin sulfate glycosami-
    noglycan
  murine fibroblasts and, 169
Chromaffin granules
  acidification of, 77
Chromatin
  mineralocorticoid receptors
    and, 406-7
Chyme
  alkalinization of, 53
  pH of
    regulation of, 51
Circumventricular organs
  angiotensin and, 414
  thirst and, 415-16
  vasopressin release and,
    421
Cisternae
  acidic organelles in, 75
Clonidine
  bronchoconstriction and,
    567
Coarctation
  aortic, 493-95
Cold stress
  chronic hypoxia and, 468
  metabolic scaling and, 109
Collagen
  angiogenesis and, 456-57
Collateral vessels
  angiogenesis and, 459-63
Colon
  electrolyte transport in, 55
  peptide YY in, 388

Complement
  erythrocyte deformability and,
    183-84
Cones
  phototransduction and, 735-36
Contractile proteins
  genetic control of, 545-52
  RNA processing and, 549-51
Copper
  angiogenesis and, 457
Coronary occlusion
  left ventricular hypertrophy
    and, 478
Corticosteroids, 397-400
  receptors for, 400-3
Corticosterone
  hippocampus and, 401-2
  mineralocorticoid receptors
    and, 401
Corticotropin-releasing factor
  angiotensin II and, 424-25
Cortisone
  specificity of, 400
Cretinism, 321, 329
Cyclic AMP
  apical membrane ion transport
    and, 46-47
  cardiac muscle and, 528-29
  cardiac myosin heavy chain
    genes and, 548
  cardiocyte growth regulation
    and, 514-15
  estrogens and, 359
  tubuloglomerular feedback
    mechanism and, 285-87
  vasoactive intestinal
    polypeptide and, 559
Cyclic GMP
  cone phototransduction and,
    735-36
  electrophysiological effects of,
    722-23
  hydrolysis in rod outer seg-
    ment, 793-95
  light-sensitive channel and,
    753-56
  outer segment membrane and,
    724
  phosphodiesterase and, 795-98
  phototransduction and, 722-31
  receptor quenching and, 779-
    80
  visual excitation and, 766
Cyclic GMP cascade
  photoreceptors and, 793-808
Cycloheximide
  proteolysis and, 538-39
Cyclooxygenase inhibitors
  tubuloglomerular feedback
    mechanism and, 288
Cytoplasm
  acidic organelles in, 75
  pH in, 21

D

DCCD
  hepatocellular ATPases and,
    75
Dehydration
  tubuloglomerular feedback
    mechanism and, 302-3,
    310-11
Deoxycorticosterone
  salt appetite and, 422
2-Deoxyglucose uptake
  insulin and, 341
Dexamethasone
  mineralocorticoid receptors
    and, 401
  specificity of, 400
Dextran
  endocytic organelles and, 76
Diabetes mellitus
  erythrocyte deformability and,
    187
Diacylglycerol
  hepatic regeneration and, 80
  macula densa cytosolic cal-
    cium concentration and,
    283
Diamides
  erythrocyte deformability and,
    184
  erythrocyte membranes and,
    245
sn-1,2-Dibutyrolphosphatidylcho-
    line
  transmembrane movement of,
    201
Dictyostelium discoideum
  phospholipid synthesis in, 194
Dicyclohexylcarbodiimide
  hepatocellular ATPases and,
    71
DIDS
  bicarbonate secretion and, 55
  chloride-bicarbonate ion ex-
    change and, 81
  hepatocyte ion exchange and,
    79
  hepatocyte organelles and, 74
  intestinal chloride ion trans-
    port and, 58
Diet
  high-protein
    glomerular filtration rate
      and, 256-57
    tubuloglomerular feedback
      mechanism and, 304-5
Diffusion
  hydrodynamic flow and, 9
  molecular sieving and, 9
2,3-Diphosphoglycerate
  echinocytes and, 185
Dipole potential
  lipid bilayers and, 221

Dipyridamole
    tubuloglomerular feedback
        mechanism and, 287
DNA sequencing
    myosin heavy chain genes
        and, 548-49
DNA synthesis
    angiogenesis and, 456
    cardiocyte growth regulation
        and, 514
    insulin and, 342
DNA transcription
    actinomycin D and, 261
Dopamine
    blood pressure and, 419
    cholecystokinin and, 384-85
    renin and, 427
Duchenne muscular dystrophy,
    212
Duodenum
    bicarbonate secretion in, 53-
        54

E

Ear oximeter, 5, 6
Echinocytes
    ATP and, 185
    deformability of, 184-85
EGTA
    tubuloglomerular feedback
        and, 282
Ektacytometry
    erythrocyte deformability and,
        181
Elastic similarity
    theory of, 127-28
Electrodiffusion
    cyclic AMP and, 46-47
    salt transport and, 37
Electrolyte transport
    in colon, 55
    in ileum, 55
    intestinal, 52-53, 55
        acid-base balance and, 56
Electron microscopy
    erythrocyte membrane and,
        238
Electron paramagnetic resonance
    muscle cross-bridge rotation
        and, 698-704
Electron spin resonance
    lipid motion and, 222
Eledoisin
    airway neurons and, 560
Elliptocytosis, 243
    hereditary, 241-43
Endocrine cells
    somatostatin in, 389
Endocytosis
    receptor-mediated
        hepatocytes and, 76

Endoplasmic reticulum
    acidification of, 71
    hepatic cholesterol biosynthe-
        sis and, 196
    lipid synthesis in, 193
    membrane continuities and,
        198-99
    phospholipid transport across,
        201
Endorphins
    angiotensin II and, 428
Endosomes
    acidic organelles in, 75
    acidification of, 71
    endocytic pathway and, 76
Endothelial cells
    angiogenesis and, 453-63
Enkephalinase, 429
Enkephalins
    angiotensin II and, 428-29
Enthalpy
    muscle
        actomyosin ATPase and,
            673-87
Epidermal growth factor
    hepatic regeneration and, 80
Epinephrine
    bombesin and, 386
    cardiac hypertrophy and, 510
    renin and, 427
Epithelia
    protein localization in, 170
Erythrocytes
    anion transport system in, 227
    calcium ion pumps in, 227-28
    deformability of
        alterations in, 181-87
        blood flow and, 177-89
        determinants of, 178-79
        disease states and, 186-87
        measurement of, 179-81
    geometry of, 178
    leucine transport in, 230
    membrane of
        actin in, 238-40
        band 3 protein of, 223-27
        deformability of, 240-41,
            245
        elasticity of, 210-14
        lateral diffusion in, 167
        properties of, 178-79, 237-
            46
        protein 4.1 in, 239-40, 244
        spectrin in, 238-45
        stability of, 241-44
        structure of, 238-40
        viscosity of, 214-17
    monosaccharide transporters
        in, 230
    Na,K-ATPase of, 228-29
    passive cation transport in,
        229

Erythropoietin
    chronic hypoxia and, 467-68
Estradiol
    brain neonatal neurons and,
        355
    gonadotropin-releasing hor-
        mone and, 367-73
    luteinizing hormone and, 368-
        73
Estrogens
    angiotensin II and, 425-26
    brain electrical activity and,
        355
    brain responses to, 350-52
    cyclic AMP and, 359
    receptors for, 406
Estrus
    angiotensin II and, 425-26
N-Ethylmaleimide
    erythrocyte membranes and,
        244
    hepatocellular ATPases and,
        71, 75
Eukaryotes
    lipid transport in, 193-202
Excitatory postsynaptic poten-
    tial, 576, 578-79
Exocytosis
    hepatocytes and, 76-77
Extracellular fluid volume
    tubuloglomerular feedback
        mechanism and, 299-304
Extracellular matrix
    angiogenesis and, 456-57
    membrane glycoproteins and,
        169
Extrathoracic trachea
    innervation of, 597-99

F

Fatty acid binding proteins, 198
Fatty acids
    intermembrane transport of,
        198-200
    ion channels and, 229
    lateral diffusion of, 198-200
Feeding behavior
    bombesin and, 386
    cholecystokinin and, 384-385
    glucagon and, 390
    insulin and, 342-43
    neuropeptide Y and, 388
    pancreatic polypeptide and,
        387
    peptide YY and, 388
    somatostatin and, 389
Fibroblasts
    chondroitin sulfate glycosami-
        noglycan and, 169
    monosaccharide transporters
        in, 230

Thy-1 diffusion in, 164
Fibronectin
  angiogenesis and, 456
  plasma membrane receptors
    for, 169
Fluorescence dichroism, 694
Fluorescence polarization, 694
Follicle-stimulating hormone
    secretion
  ovarian steroids and, 365
Forebrain
  thyroid hormones and, 324-25
Formate
  pancreatic fluid secretion and,
    92
Formic acid
  pancreatic fluid secretion and,
    92
Forskolin
  tubuloglomerular feedback
    mechanism and, 286
Furosemide
  bicarbonate secretion and, 55
  chloride-bicarbonate ion ex-
    change and, 81
  hepatocyte ion exchange and,
    79
  intestinal chloride ion trans-
    port and, 58
  intestinal salt transport and,
    59
  pancreatic fluid secretion and,
    94-95
  renin and, 263
  salt transport and, 55
  tubuloglomerular feedback
    mechanism and, 302-4

G

N-acetyl-Galactosamine
  macula densa and, 264
Gallbladder epithelium
  salt transport in, 35-46
  transport functions of, 35-37
Ganglia
  autonomic
    neuropeptide Y in, 387
  peripheral airway, 573-80
    characteristics of, 575-77
    circuitry in, 579-80
    neurotransmission in, 577
Gap junctions
  airway smooth muscle and,
    590
Gas exchange
  peripheral, 148-50
  pulmonary, 150-56
Gastric emptying
  cholecystokinin and, 384
Gastric glands
  intracellular pH in, 21-22

Gastric mucosa
  intracellular pH in, 20-21
Gastric ulcers
  hydrogen ion permeability
    and, 30
  transmembrane pH gradients
    and, 29-30
Gastrin-releasing peptide
  central nervous system and,
    386-87
Gastroenteropancreatic peptides
  central nervous system and,
    383-91
Glomerular filtration rate
  antidiuretic hormone and,
    257-58
  high-protein diets and, 256-57
  loop of Henle flow rate and,
    254-55
  metabolic scaling and, 110
  salt concentration and, 251-52
  tubuloglomerular feedback
    mechanism and, 276-77,
    295-99, 308
Glucagon
  cardiac myosin heavy chain
    genes and, 548
  central nervous system and,
    389-90
  hepatic regeneration and, 80
Glucocorticoids
  circulating levels of, 399
  specificity of, 399-400
N-acetyl-Glucosamine
  macula densa and, 264
Glucose-6-phosphate de-
    hydrogenase
  macula densa and, 262-63
Glucose uptake
  insulin and, 341
Glutamine synthetase
  triiodothyronine and, 328
Glyceraldehyde-3-phosphate
  hexose monophosphate shunt
    and, 263
Glycodiazine
  pancreatic fluid secretion and,
    92
Glycolipids
  intermembrane transport of,
    200
  transbilayer movement of,
    201-2
Glycolysis
  anaerobic
    ATP and, 136
Glycophorin A
  erythrocyte deformability and,
    183
  skeletal proteins and, 245
Glycophorin C
  protein 4.1 and, 239, 244

Glycoproteins
  diffusion in cell membranes,
    164
  macula densa and, 264-65
  membrane
    extracellular matrix and,
      169
Glycosphingolipids
  hydrolysis of
    activator proteins and, 200
Goiter, 321
Golgi complex
  acidic organelles in, 75
  acidification of, 71
  phospholipid transport and,
    194
Gonadotropin-releasing hormone
  estradiol and, 368-73
  secretion of
    ovarian steroids and, 365-
      67
Goormaghtigh cells
  biochemical characteristics of,
    266-67
G protein
  guanyl nucleotide binding
    sites of, 803-4
  metarhodopsin II and, 776-77
  phosphodiesterase and, 771-75
  rhodopsin and, 769-71, 783-
    84
  transducin and, 799-803
Granular cells
  biochemical characteristics of,
    267
Growth factors
  angiogenesis and, 457-59

H

Harmaline
  hepatocyte ion exchange and,
    79
Heart
  artificial
    forerunner of, 4
Heavy meromyosin
  binding of, 657-59
Hematocrit
  blood viscosity and, 177
  chronic hypoxia and, 467-68
Heme proteins
  erythrocyte deformability and,
    184
Hemoglobin
  carbamino, 3
  chronic hypoxia and, 467-68
  erythrocyte intercellular fluid
    and, 178
Hemoglobin S
  sickle cell anemia and, 186
Hemolytic anemia, 242

Hemorrhage
  tubuloglomerular feedback
    mechanism and, 302
Heparan surface proteoglycan
  acetylcholine receptors and,
    169
Heparin
  angiogenesis and, 457
Heparin-binding growth factors
  angiogenesis and, 458-59
Hepatocytes
  bicarbonate ion exchange in,
    80-81
  canalicular bile formation in,
    77-78
  chloride ion exchange in, 80-
    81
  exocytosis in, 76-77
  hydrogen ion exchange in,
    79-80
  intracellular pH of, 78
  membrane continuities in,
    198-99
  proton transport in, 69-82
  receptor-mediated endocytosis
    in, 76
  sodium ion exchange in, 79-
    80
Hereditary elliptocytosis, 241-
  43
Hereditary pyropoikilocytosis,
  241-43
Hereditary spherocytosis, 212
Hexose monophosphate shunt
  macula densa and, 263
Hindbrain
  cholecystokinin receptors in,
    384
Hippocampus
  cholecystokinin receptors in,
    384
  corticosterone-preferring sites
    in, 401-2
  neuronal firing in
    insulin and, 341
  thyroid hormone receptors in,
    323
Histamine
  C-fiber receptors and, 621-22
  intracellular oxyntic cell pH
    and, 20
  rapidly adapting receptors
    and, 618
Histocompatibility antigens
  lateral confinement of, 170
Homomorphism
  metabolic power function and,
    128-31
Hydrocortisone
  specificity of, 400
Hydrodynamic flow
  molecular sieving and, 9
  restricted diffusion and, 9

Hydrogen ion exchange
  apical membrane and, 39-41
  basolateral plasma membrane
    and, 61-62
  brush border membrane and,
    57-58
  hepatocyte organelles and, 71
  hepatocytes and, 79-80
Hydrogen ion transport
  pancreatic, 90-99
Hydroxycholesterol
  sterol carrier protein and, 197
6-Hydroxydopamine
  cardiac hypertrophy and, 509-
    10
5-Hydroxytryptamine
  rapidly adapting receptors
    and, 618
Hypercapnia
  airway stretch receptors and,
    616
Hypernatremia
  anteroventral third ventricle
    lesions and, 417
Hypertension
  erythrocyte deformability and,
    187
  systemic
    cardiac hypertrophy and,
      480-82
    left ventricular hypertrophy
      and, 478
    tubuloglomerular feedback
      mechanism and, 306-8
Hyperventilation
  acidic ventricular perfusion
    and, 10
Hypoglycemia
  insulin and, 343
Hypothalamic cells
  differentiation of, 353
Hypothalamo-hypophyseal axis
  estradiol and, 372
Hypothalamo-pituitary axis
  angiotensin II and, 425
Hypothalamus
  cholecystokinin receptors in,
    384
  estradiol feedback mechanism
    and, 373
  glucagon in, 389
  gonadotropin-releasing hor-
    mone and, 365-67
  insulin receptors in, 339, 343
  neuronal firing in
    insulin and, 341
Hypothalamus-preoptic area
  pharmacological deafferenta-
    tion of, 356-60
Hypothyroidism, 321, 324-25
  behavioral effects of, 329-30
  electrophysiological effects of,
    328-29

Hypovolemia
  angiotensin II and, 414-15
Hypoxia
  airway stretch receptors and,
    615
  chronic
    blood flow and, 470
    body growth and, 467
    cardiac output and, 468-70
    cardiovascular responses to,
      465-74
    cardiovascular system and,
      467
    hematological effects of,
      467-68
    mechanism of, 466
    mitochondria and, 473-74
    muscle capillarity and, 470-
      73
    oxygen consumption and,
      468-70

I

Ileum
  electrolyte transport in, 55
Immunocytochemistry
  brain insulin and, 336-37
Immunoglobulin
  surface
    lymphocyte plasma mem-
      brane and, 169
Indomethacin
  airway smooth muscle and,
    558
  tubuloglomerular feedback
    mechanism and, 288-89
Inhibitory postsynaptic potential,
  576
Inorganic phosphate
  muscle fibers and, 645-47
  nucleotide analogs and, 648-
    49
Inositol trisphosphate
  macula densa cytosolic cal-
    cium concentration and,
    282-83
Inotropic agents
  cardiac muscle and, 528-29
Insulin
  blood-brain barrier and, 338,
    341
  brain, 335-44
    functions of, 341-43
    receptors for, 338-41
  hepatic regeneration and, 80
Insulin secretory granules
  acidification of, 77
Interspecific allometry, 110-16
Interstitial pressure
  tubuloglomerular feedback
    mechanism and, 309-12

Intestine
  acidification of
    carbonic anhydrase and,
      59-60
  bicarbonate transport mech-
    anisms in, 51-62
  crypt epithelium of
    salt and fluid secretion and,
      56
  electrolyte transport in, 52-53
  peptide YY in, 388
  proton transport mechanisms
    in, 51-62
  small
    salt entry mechanism in,
      60-61
Intracellular fluid
  erythrocyte
    properties of, 178
Intraspecific allometry, 114-16
Intrathoracic trachea
  innervation of, 599
Inulin
  endocytic organelles and, 76
Ion channels
  lipid modulation of, 229
Ion exchange
  apical membrane and, 39-43
  basolateral plasma membrane
    and, 61-62
  brush border membrane and,
    57-61
Isethionate
  pancreatic fluid secretion and,
    93
Isometric tetanus
  energy produced during, 678-
    79
Isoproterenol
  cardiac myosin heavy chain
    genes and, 548
  rapidly adapting receptors
    and, 618
  renin and, 263

J

Jejunum
  bicarbonate absorption by, 54
    sodium ion dependency of,
      58
Juxtaglomerular apparatus
  biochemical characteristics of,
    261-66, 261-67
Juxtaglomerular cells
  angiotensin in, 267

K

Kallikrein-kinin system
  tubuloglomerular feedback
    mechanism and, 313
Kidney

angiotensin II and, 422-23
angiotensin receptors in, 429
benzodiazepine receptors in,
  265-66
carbonic anhydrase in, 266
extravascular transcortin in,
  404
mineralocorticoid receptors in,
  400-1
tubuloglomerular feedback in,
  251-68
  characteristics of, 275-79
Kinins
  tubuloglomerular feedback
    mechanism and, 313
Krebs cycle
  mitochondria and, 138

L

Laminin
  angiogenesis and, 457
  plasma membrane receptors
    for, 169
Lanosterol
  sterol carrier protein and, 197
Lecithin
  amino acid transport systems
    and, 230
  phospholipase A$_2$ and, 227
Lectins
  erythrocyte deformability and,
    183
  lateral diffusion of, 170-71
Leucine
  transport in erythrocytes, 230
Leucine aminopeptidase
  lateral diffusion of, 170
Leydig cells
  angiotensin receptors in, 429
Life-support systems
  forerunner of, 4
Ligands
  uptake by hepatocytes, 76
Lipid bilayers
  bulk properties of, 221
  erythrocyte membrane and,
    238
  fluidity of, 221-22
  membrane proteins and, 222
  protein diffusion in, 163-70
Lipids
  amino acid transport systems
    and, 230
  intermembrane transport of,
    200-1
  ion channels and, 229
  membrane
    erythrocyte deformability
      and, 184
  membrane proteins and, 221-
    31

modification in membranes,
  223
monosaccharides and, 230
transport of
  eukaryotic, 193-202
  See also Phospholipids
Lipoproteins
  uptake by hepatocytes, 76
Lithium chloride
  pancreatic fluid secretion and,
    90
Liver
  erythrocyte trapping in, 188
  regeneration of, 80
Luminal factor
  tubuloglomerular feedback
    mechanism and, 313-14
Lung
  aldosterone binding sites in,
    401
  C-fiber receptors in, 619-22
  erythrocyte trapping in, 188
  oxygen consumption in, 150-
    56
  rapidly adapting receptors in,
    616
Luteinizing hormone
  estradiol and, 368-73
  progesterone and, 373-76
  secretion of
    feedback regulation of,
      365-76
Luteinizing hormone releasing
  hormone
  angiotensin II and, 426
Lymphocytes
  membrane of
    surface immunoglobulin
      and, 169
glycyl-L-histidyl-L-Lysine
  angiogenesis and, 457
Lysolecithin
  echinocytes and, 185
Lysosomes
  acidic organelles in, 75
  acidification of, 71
  ATP and, 71
  endocytic pathway and, 76

M

Macula densa
  benzodiazepine receptors in,
    265-66
  biochemical characteristics of,
    261-66
  carbonic anhydrase in, 266
  glycoproteins and, 264-65
  Na,K-ATPase and, 263-64
  pentose phosphate shunt in,
    262-63
  RNA synthesis in, 261-62
  salt concentration and, 251-52

tubuloglomerular feedback
mechanism and, 275-79
Malonyldialdehyde
erythrocyte deformability and,
184
erythrocyte membranes and,
245
Mammals
oxygen consumption in, 135-
36
Mammary gland
aldosterone binding sites in,
401
Mechanoreceptors
tracheal, 584
Membrane lipids
erythrocyte deformability and,
184
Membrane proteins
erythrocyte deformability and,
183-184
Membranes
apical
ion exchange at, 39-47
salt transport at, 37-39
basolateral plasma
ion transport in, 61-62
brush border
ATPase activity in, 61
ion exchange mechanisms
in, 55
ion transport in, 57-61
salt transport at, 59-60
erythrocyte
elasticity of, 210-14
lateral diffusion in, 167
properties of, 178-79
viscosity of, 214-17
glycoprotein diffusion in,
164
lipid modification in, 223
plasma
cholesterol biosynthesis in,
196
H+-ATPase in, 75-76
membrane continuities and,
198-99
phospholipid transport and,
194
protein diffusion in, 163-73
transport proteins in
α-helix of, 222
lipid bilayers and, 222
lipid modulation of, 221-31
Membrane transport
irreversible thermodynamics
and, 9
Meromyosin
binding of, 657-59
Metabolic acidosis, 56
Metabolic alkalosis, 56
chloridorrhea and, 51
Metabolic allometry, 109-10

Metabolic scaling, 107-18
taxonomy and, 113-17
Metabolism
anaerobic
neovascular growth and,
461-62
basal
theory of elastic similarity
and, 127-28
oxidative, 135-45
Metarhodopsin II
G-protein activation and, 776-
77
Methylsergide
serotonin synthesis and, 428
3-isobutyl-1-Methylxanthine
tubuloglomerular feedback
mechanism and, 285-
86
Metrazol
brain sexual differentiation
and, 356
Microcirculation
resting muscle and, 5
See also Capillaries
Microspectrofluorimetry
intracellular oxyntic cell pH
and, 25
Microspherocytosis, 242
Midbrain
cholecystokinin receptors in,
384
Mineralocorticoids
circulating levels of, 399
Na,K-ATPase and, 262
receptors for, 400-1, 405-8
secretion of, 398-99
specificity of, 399-400
specificity-conferring mechanisms of, 404-8
Minimal brain damage syn-
drome, 328
Mitochondria
chronic hypoxia and, 473-74
membrane of
ADP-ATP carrier in, 227
oxygen consumption in, 138-
44
peripheral gas exchange and,
148-50
pH in, 21
Mitral regurgitation, 506
Molecular sieving
hydrodynamic flow and, 9
restricted diffusion and, 9
Monensin
chloride ion uptake and, 74
protein transport and, 77
Monoamine uptake
insulin and, 342
Monocarboxylates
transport in erythrocytes,
227

Monoclonal antibodies
photoreceptor phosphodiesterase and, 797-98
transducin and, 804
Monosaccharides
lipid modulation of, 230
Morphine
angiotensin II and, 428
Multivesicular bodies
acidic organelles in, 75
anionic permeability of, 74
chloride ion uptake by, 74
endocytic pathway and, 76
Muramyl peptides
sleep induction and, 12-
13
Muscle
cross-bridge rotation in, 691-
706
cross-bridge states in
kinetic properties of, 657-
64
force generation by
ATP and, 136-38
microcirculation in
sympathetic nervous system
and, 5
Muscle capillarity
chronic hypoxia and, 470-
73
Muscle cells
acetylcholine receptors in
heparan surface pro-
teoglycan and, 169
Muscle contraction
enthalpy production and, 677-
87
molecular mechanism of, 629-
35
Muscle fibers
actomyosin ATPase in, 637-
50
ADP and, 647-48
ATP cleavage in, 641-43
inorganic phosphate and, 645-
47
Muscle grafts
mature
blood vessels in, 444-47
modes of, 440-42
revascularization of, 442-44
Myocardial hypertrophy
cardiac overloading and, 502-
8
cardiac underloading and,
508-9
vascular adaptations to, 477-
85
Myocardial infarction
erythrocyte deformability and,
186-87
left ventricular hypertrophy
and, 478

Myocardial ischemia
  neovascular growth and, 461-
    62
Myocardium
  load regulation in, 509-11
Myofilaments
  muscle contraction and, 520-
    21
Myosin
  ATP hydrolysis and, 642
  electron paramagnetic reso-
    nance and, 700-1
  isolation of, 632-33
  muscle contraction and, 520
  muscular force generation
    and, 136-37
  optical anisotropy and, 695-96
Myosin ATPase
  actin and, 630
  thyroxine-induced cardiac
    hypertrophy and, 483
Myosin heavy-chain gene ex-
    pression
  regulation of, 546-49
Myosin light chains
  alternative RNA processing
    and, 551
  ATP consumption and, 676-
    77

N

Na,K-ATPase
  ATP consumption and, 676
  erythrocyte, 228-29
  macula densa and, 263-64
  mineralocorticoids and, 262
  pancreatic fluid secretion and,
    91
Naloxone
  angiotensin II and, 429
  bronchoconstriction and, 567
Naltrexone
  angiotensin II and, 429
Necturus maculosus
  gallbladder epithelium of, 35
    ionic transport in, 36-47
    salt transport in, 38
Neurokinin A
  airway neurons and, 560
Neuromuscular junctions
  airway smooth muscle and,
    590
Neurons
  Aplysia
    cholesterol and, 229
  brain neonatal
    estradiol and, 355
  insulin receptors in, 339
  parasympathetic
    peptides in, 557-60
  sensory
    peptides in, 560-67

sodium channels in
  differential lateral mobility
    of, 170
  somatostatin in, 389
  sympathetic
    insulin and, 341
Neuropeptide K
  airway neurons and, 560
Neuropeptides
  airway smooth muscle and,
    557-67
Neuropeptide Y
  catecholamines and, 388
  central nervous system and,
    387-88
Neurosecretory granules
  acidification of, 77
Neurotransmission
  glucagon and, 389-90
  insulin and, 341-42
  peripheral airway ganglia and,
    577
Neurotransmitters
  angiotensin II and, 426-29
Nicotine
  bronchoconstriction and, 566
Norepinephrine
  airway smooth muscle and,
    557
  angiotensin II and, 427-28
  bombesin and, 386
  cardiac hypertrophy and, 510
  cardiac myosin heavy chain
    genes and, 548
  cholecystokinin and, 385
  paratracheal ganglia and, 578
Normoxia, 469
Nuclear magnetic resonance
  muscle cross-bridge rotation
    and, 698-99
Nucleotide analogs
  inorganic phosphate and, 648-
    49
Nucleus ambiguus, 598
Nucleus dorsomedialis, 598
Nucleus retroambigualis, 598
Nucleus tractus solitarius
  airway afferents and, 598
  angiotensin II and, 419-20

O

Obesity
  cholecystokinin and, 385
  insulin and, 342
Olfactory bulb
  cholecystokinin receptors in,
    384
  insulin receptors in, 339, 342
Oligomycin
  hepatocellular ATPases and,
    71
Opioids

angiotensin II and, 428-29
Optical anisotropy
  muscle cross-bridge rotation
    and, 692-98
Organelles
  fatty acid transport in, 199-
    200
  hepatocyte
    H$^+$-ATPase in, 75
    proton transport by, 71-75
    phospholipid transport in,
      194-95
Orthovanadate
  inorganic phosphate and, 649
Osmotic pressure
  capillary walls and, 9
Ouabain
  basolateral salt transport and,
    39, 45
  cardiac muscle and, 528
  duodenal bicarbonate secretion
    and, 54
  hepatic regeneration and, 80
  hepatocellular ATPases and,
    71
  hepatocyte pH and, 79
  intracellular gastric gland pH
    and, 22
  pancreatic fluid secretion and,
    91
  transmembrane chief cell pH
    gradients and, 30
Ovarian steroids
  luteinizing hormone regulation
    and, 365-76
Oxidative metabolism, 135-45
Oxygen consumption
  chronic hypoxia and, 468-70
  in lung, 150-56
  upper limit to, 135-36
Oxyntic cells
  basolateral membrane of
    conductance in, 25-26
  buffer capacity of, 26
  intracellular pH in, 26
    carbonic anhydrase and, 21
    histamine and, 20
Oxytocin
  angiotensin II and, 426
Oyxgen consumption
  mitochondrial, 138-44

P

Pancreas
  fluid and electrolyte secretion
    by, 88
  control of, 89-90
  morphology of, 87-88
Pancreatic polypeptide
  central nervous system and,
    387-88

Parachlorophenylalanine
serotonin synthesis and, 428
Parietal cells
intracellular pH in
regulation of, 23-26
Parvalbumin
calcium binding to
enthalpy and, 675
Pentobarbital
brain sexual differentiation
and, 356-57
Pentose phosphate shunt
in macula densa, 262-63
Peptide histidine isoleucine
airway smooth muscle and,
559-60
Peptides
angiotensin II and, 414
calcitonin gene-related
airway neurons and, 560-62
gastrin-releasing
central nervous system and,
386-87
gastroenteropancreatic
central nervous system and,
383-91
in parasympathetic neurons,
557-60
in sensory neurons, 560-67
Peptide YY
central nervous system and,
388
Pericytes
angiogenesis and, 455
Pertussis toxin
ADP-ribosylation and, 800-2
pH
of blood
intestinal electrolyte transport and, 56
of chyme
regulation of, 51
of hepatocytes, 78
of stomach cells, 19-31
Phenobarbital
brain sexual differentiation
and, 356
Phenoxybenzamine
brain sexual differentiation
and, 358
Phentolamine
feeding behavior and, 388
tissue perfusion and, 187
Phenylalanine
proteolysis and, 538-39
Phenyldiguanide
C-fiber receptors and, 621
Phenylhydrazine
erythrocytes and, 184
Phosphate
inorganic
muscle fibers and, 645-47

nucleotide analogs and,
648-49
pancreatic fluid secretion and,
93
Phosphatidylcholine
cholesterol distribution and,
197
vesicular transport of, 194
Phosphatidylethanolamine
cholesterol distribution and,
197
mitochondrial ADP-ATP carrier and, 227
Phosphatidylinositol
cardiocyte growth regulation
and, 514
Phosphatidylinositol-4,5-
bisphosphate
macula densa cytosolic calcium concentration and,
283
Phosphatidylserine
transport proteins and, 222
Phosphodiesterase
activation cycle of, 794-95
cyclic GMP and, 795-98
G protein and, 771-75
trypsin activation of, 774
Phospholipase A2
ion channels and, 229
lecithin and, 227
Phospholipase C
macula densa cytosolic calcium concentration and,
282
Phospholipid exchange proteins,
195-96
Phospholipids
anionic
ion channels and, 229
mitochondrial ADP-ATP
carrier and, 227
Na,K-ATPase and, 228
transport proteins and, 222
band 3 protein and, 227
calcium diffusion in outer
segment and, 717
erythrocyte calcium ion pump
and, 227-28
intermembrane transport of,
194-96
lateral diffusion of, 196
transbilayer movement of,
201
tubuloglomerular feedback
mechanism and, 289-90
See also Lipids
Photoreceptors
arrestin and, 806-7
cyclic GMP and, 795-98
rhodopsin kinase and, 804-6
transducin and, 798-804

Phototransduction, 711-14
calcium ions and, 718-22
cyclic GMP and, 722-31
internal transmitter in, 716-36
outer segment dark current
and, 715-16
Piretanide
pancreatic fluid secretion and,
94
Pituitary gland
aldosterone binding sites in,
401
estradiol feedback mechanism
and, 373
Plasma membrane
basolateral
ion transport in, 61-62
erythrocyte
lateral diffusion in, 167
hepatic
cholesterol biosynthesis in,
196
hepatocyte
H+-ATPase in, 75-76
lymphocyte
surface immunoglobulin
and, 169
membrane continuities and,
198-99
phospholipid transport in,
194
Plasma proteins
capillary walls and, 9
Plasma viscosity
blood viscosity and, 177
Platelet-derived growth factor
hepatic regeneration and, 80
Platelet granules
acidification of, 77
Platelets
cytoplasmic calcium concentration of
cyclic AMP and, 285
Poikilocytosis, 242
Polycythemia
high-altitude, 470
normovolemic, 469
Potassium
pancreatic fluid secretion and,
91-92
Potassium chloride
pancreatic fluid secretion and,
90
Power function, 121-31
biological, 124-26
geometric similitude and,
122-24
metabolic
homomorphism and, 128-31
Pregnanes
brain sexual differentiation
and, 356-58

Pregnenolone
  sterol carrier protein and,
    197
Probenecid
  chloride-bicarbonate ion ex-
    change and, 81
Progesterone
  brain electrical activity and,
    355
  brain sexual differentiation
    and, 356-57
  luteinizing hormone and, 373-
    76
Progestins
  brain responses to, 350-52
  brain sexual differentiation
    and, 356
Prolactin
  secretion of
    ovarian steroids and, 365
Propionate
  pancreatic fluid secretion and,
    92
Prostaglandins
  C-fiber receptors and, 621-22
  duodenal bicarbonate secretion
    and, 54
  glomerular filtration rate and,
    260
  intracellular cyclic AMP and,
    46
  rapidly adapting receptors
    and, 618
  tubuloglomerular feedback
    mechanism and, 288
Protein 4.1
  erythrocyte membrane and,
    239-40, 244
  glycophorin C and, 239, 244
Protein kinase C
  cardiocyte growth regulation
    and, 514
  hepatic regeneration and, 80
  macula densa cytosolic cal-
    cium concentration and,
    283
Proteins
  allosteric reactions of, 2
  band 3
    lipid modulation of, 223-27
  contractile
    genetic control of, 545-52
    RNA processing and, 549-
      51
  lateral confinement of, 170-71
  lateral diffusion of, 163-73
  membrane
    erythrocyte deformability
      and, 183-84
    α-helix of, 222
    lipid bilayers and, 222
    lipid modulation of, 221-31

phospholipid exchange, 195-
    96
  skeletal
    glycophorin A and, 245
    triacylglycerol transfer, 200-1
Protein synthesis
  cardiac hypertrophy and, 535-
    38
  insulin and, 342
Protein transport
  monensin and, 77
Proteolysis
  cardiac hypertrophy and, 538-
    39
Proton transport
  in intestine, 51-62
  primary, 69-78
Purkinje cells
  hypothyroidism and, 325
Pyridostigmine
  sexual behavior and, 359
Pyropoikilocytosis
  hereditary, 241-43

R

Radioimmunoassay
  brain insulin and, 336
Recombinant DNA
  G protein and, 799
Rectum
  peptide YY in, 388
Red blood cells
  See Erythrocytes
Renal plasma flow
  metabolic scaling and, 110
Renin
  angiotensin II and, 423
  dopamine turnover and, 427
  epinephrine turnover and, 427
  macula densa and, 261
  pentose phosphate shunt and,
    262-63
  tubuloglomerular feedback
    and, 260-61
Renin-angiotensin system
  in brain, 413
  tubuloglomerular feedback
    mechanism and, 307
Reproductive hormones
  angiotensin II and, 425-26
Reserpine
  sexual behavior and, 357-59
Respiration
  airway tone and, 607
  bronchomotor tone and, 606-7
Respiratory acidosis, 56
Respiratory alkalosis, 56
Respiratory structures
  scaling of, 147-57
Retinoblastoma cells
  insulin receptors in, 339

Rheoscopy
  erythrocyte deformability and,
    180-81
Rhodopsin
  β-adrenergic receptor and,
    784
  conformational changes in
    visual excitation and, 781-
      83
  diffusion in disc membrane,
    164
  G protein and, 769-71, 783-
    84
  rod disk membrane and, 766-
    69
  transmembrane structure of,
    780-81
Rhodopsin kinase
  metarhodopsin II and, 776
  photoreceptors and, 804-6
RNA processing
  contractile proteins and, 549-
    51
  mechanisms of, 551
RNA synthesis
  cardiac hypertrophy and, 534,
    536-38
  cardiocyte growth regulation
    and, 514
  insulin and, 342
  in macula densa, 261-62
Rod disk membrane
  rhodopsin and, 766-69
Rod inner segment, 758-62
  ionic conductances in, 759-61
  sodium-potassium exchange
    in, 759
Rod outer segment
  cyclic GMP hydrolysis in,
    793-95
  sodium-calcium exchange in,
    744-46
  visual excitation and, 765-85
Rods
  internal transmitter of, 717-18
  ionic conductances in, 743-62
  light-sensitive channel in,
    746-58

S

Salt absorption
  acetazolamide and, 61
Salt appetite
  brain angiotensin and, 421-22
Salt transport
  at apical membrane, 37-39
  at brush border membrane
    acetazolamide and, 59-60
  furosemide and, 55, 59
  in gallbladder epithelium, 35-
    46

in macula densa, 263-64
stilbene disulfonates and, 55
water absorption and, 36
Saralasin
plasma aldosterone and, 425
renin-angiotensin system and,
307
thirst and, 416
vasopressin release and, 421
Sarcomeres
muscle contraction and, 520-
21
Sarcoplasmic reticulum
ATP consumption and, 676
calcium binding in
enthalpy and, 675
calcium channels in, 525-26
calcium ion pump of, 228
ion channels in, 229
membrane continuities and,
199
muscular force generation
and, 137
Satellite cells
muscle grafts and, 440
Secretin
acinar cell enzyme secretion
and, 89, 99
intracellular cyclic AMP and,
46
Secretory granules
acidification of, 77
Semliki Forest virus
monensin and, 77
Senescence
cardiac muscle and, 521-30
Sensory neurons
peptides in, 560-67
Serotonin
angiotensin II and, 414, 428
blood pressure and, 417
bronchoconstriction and, 558-
59
C-fiber receptors and, 621-22
Sex steroids
brain sexual differentiation
and, 349-61
Sexual behavior
demasculinization of, 357-58
Sickle cell anemia
erythrocyte deformability and,
186
SITS
bicarbonate secretion and, 55
chloride-bicarbonate ion exchange and, 81
hepatocyte ion exchange and,
79
hepatocyte organelles and, 74
intestinal chloride ion transport and, 58
ouabain-induced cell swelling
and, 39

pancreatic fluid secretion and,
95
Skeletal muscle
ATP consumption in, 676-77
chronic hypoxia and, 471-73
mitochondrial volume in
allometry of, 140
myosin heavy chain genes in,
546
oxygen consumption in, 138-
44
transplantation of
blood vessels in, 439-48
modes of, 440-42
Sleep deprivation
cerebrospinal fluid and
sleep-inducing properties
of, 12-13
Small intestine
salt entry mechanism in, 60-
61
Smooth muscle
airway
gap junctions in, 590
innervation of, 583-91
motor control of, 595-98
neural inputs to, 573-75
neuromuscular junctions in,
589-90
neuropeptides in, 557-67
aldosterone binding sites in,
401
contraction of
calmodulin and, 284
neuropeptide Y and, 387
vascular
adaptations to load, 489-97
Sodium
pancreatic fluid secretion and,
90-91
Sodium appetite
angiotensin II and, 421-22
Sodium-calcium exchange
rod outer segment and, 744-
46
Sodium ion channels
differential lateral mobility of,
170
Sodium ion exchange
at apical membrane, 39-41
at brush border membrane,
57-58
in hepatocytes, 79-80
Sodium ionophores
hepatic regeneration and, 80
Sodium-potassium-chloride cotransport system, 229
Sodium-potassium exchange
rod inner segment and, 759
Sodium-potassium pump
erythrocytes and, 228-29
Sodium salicylate
echinocytes and, 185

Somatostatin
central nervous system and,
389
Spectrin
erythrocyte membrane and,
167, 238-45
Spectrophotometry
intracellular gastric mucosa
pH and, 20
Spectroscopy
intracellular gastric mucosa
pH and, 25
Sperm
glycoprotein antigen in
lateral confinement of, 170
Spherocytosis
hereditary, 212
Sphingomyelin
band 3 protein and, 227
cholesterol distribution and,
197
vesicular transport of, 194
Sphingomyelinase
erythrocyte calcium ion pump
and, 227-28
Spinal cord
neuropeptide Y in, 387
Spleen
erythrocyte trapping in, 188
Squalene
sterol carrier protein and,
197
Steroids
adrenocortical
central nervous system and,
397-409
ovarian
luteinizing hormone regulation and, 365-76
sex
brain sexual differentiation
and, 349-61
Sterol carrier protein, 197
Stilbene disulfonates
bicarbonate transport and, 61-
62
intestinal chloride ion transport and, 58
salt transport and, 55
Stomach
intracellular pH in
regulation of, 19-31
transmembrane pH gradients
and, 29-30
Stomatocytes
deformability of, 184-85
Stretch receptors
airway, 584, 601-6, 611-16
Substance P
acinar cell enzyme secretion
and, 89
airway neurons and, 560
Sucrose

pancreatic fluid secretion and, 90
Sulfamerazine
pancreatic fluid secretion and, 92-93
Sulfonamides
pancreatic fluid secretion and, 92
Surface epithelial cells
intracellular pH in, 19, 26-27
Surface potential
lipid bilayers and, 221
Symmorphosis, 147-48, 156-57
Sympathetic nervous system
resting muscle microcirculation and, 5
Synapses
insulin and, 341
sexual differentiation in, 352-53
Systemic hypertension
cardiac hypertrophy and, 480-82
left ventricular hypertrophy and, 478

T

Tachycardia
cold-induced
bombesin and, 386
Tachykinins
airway neurons and, 560-62
sensory neurons and, 563-65
Taxonomy
metabolic scaling and, 113-17
Temperature
erythrocyte deformability and, 183
Tetanus
energy produced during, 678-79
Tetrachlorosalicylanide
gastric gland membrane conductance and, 26
Thalamus
cholecystokinin receptors in, 384
Theophylline
tubuloglomerular feedback mechanism and, 285
Theory of elastic similarity, 127-28
Thermogenesis
brown fat
bombesin and, 386-87
Thirst
angiotensin II and, 415-16
Thromboxane
tubuloglomerular feedback mechanism and, 307
Thyroid hormones
behavioral effects of, 329-30

biochemical effects of, 326-28
brain development and, 321-31
cardiac hypertrophy and, 540
coronary vasodilator reserve and, 483
electrophysiological effects of, 328-29
myosin heavy chain genes and, 547-48
receptors for, 322-24
Thyrotoxicosis
cardiac hypertrophy and, 482-83
Thyroxine
cardiac hypertrophy and, 482-83, 538
Trachea
extrathoracic
innervation of, 597-99
intrathoracic
innervation of, 599
nerve fibers in, 583
distribution of, 585-86
Tracheobronchial tree
receptors of, 611-23
Transcortin
kidney and, 404
Transducin
G protein and, 799-803
photoreceptors and, 798-804
Transferrin
monensin and, 77
uptake by hepatocytes, 76
Trees
power function and, 126
Triacylglycerol transfer proteins, 200-1
Trifluoperazine
tubuloglomerular feedback and, 284
Triiodothyronine
glutamine synthetase and, 328
receptors for, 324
8-(N,N-diethylamino)-octyl-3,4,5-Trimethoxybenzoate
tubuloglomerular feedback and, 282
Tropomyosin
alternative RNA processing and, 551
muscle contraction and, 520
Troponin
alternative RNA processing and, 549-50
calcium binding to
enthalpy and, 675
muscle contraction and, 520
Trypsin
phosphodiesterase and, 774
Tryptophan hydroxylase
angiotensin II and, 428
Tubuloglomerular feedback

mechanism, 251-68
arachidonic acid and, 287-90
atrial natriuretic factor and, 312
calcium and, 279-83
calmodulin and, 283-85
characteristics of, 275-79
cyclic AMP and, 285-87
extracellular fluid volume and, 299-304
genetic hypertension and, 306-8
glomerular filtration rate and, 276-77, 295-99, 308
growth and maturation and, 305-6
high-protein diet and, 304-5
interstitial pressure and volume and, 309-12
kallikrein-kinin system and, 313
luminal factor and, 313-14
quantitation of, 296-99
Tubulovesicles
pH in, 21
Tyrosine
proteolysis and, 538-39
Tyrosine kinase
neural insulin receptor and, 341

U

Urine production
metabolic scaling and, 110
Ursodeoxycholic acid
basolateral ion exchange and, 80
Uterus
angiotensin receptors in, 429

V

Vagus nerve
dorsal motor nucleus of, 597-98
Valinomycin
gastric gland membrane conductance and, 26
Vanadate
hepatocellular ATPases and, 71
Vascular smooth muscle
adaptations to load, 489-97
Vasoactive intestinal peptide
acinar cell enzyme secretion and, 89, 99
airway smooth muscle and, 557-59
intracellular cyclic AMP and, 46
postganglionic inhibitory motor neurons and, 574

Vasopressin
  angiotensin II and, 420-21
Venous-arterial grafts, 495
Verapamil
  tubuloglomerular feedback
    and, 282
Vertebrates
  body mass vs. body surface
    area in, 124-26
  metabolic scaling of, 107-18
  power function and, 124-26
Vesicles
  clathrin-coated
    acidification of, 71

anionic permeability of, 74
  endocytic pathway and, 76
  phospholipid transport and,
    194-95
Vesicular stomatitis virus
  G glycoproteins of, 168-69
Viscometry
  erythrocyte deformability and,
    181
Visual excitation
  control factors and, 780
  cyclic GMP and, 766
  rod outer segment and, 765-
    85

W

Water absorption
  salt transport and, 36
Wheat germ agglutinin
  erythrocyte deformability and,
    183
  erythrocyte membranes and,
    245

Z

Zymogen granules
  acidification of, 77

CUMULATIVE INDEXES

CONTRIBUTING AUTHORS, VOLUMES 45–49

A

Agnew, W. S., 46:517–30
Aickin, C. C., 48:349–61
Al-Awqati, Q., 48:153–61
Andersen, O. S., 46:531–48
Anderson, D. E., 46:143–53
Andrews, W. V., 48:495–514
Arendshorst, W. J., 49:295–317
Aronin, N., 48:537–50
Aronson, P. S., 47:545–60
Atkinson, M. M., 47:337–54

B

Banchero, N., 49:465–76
Barde, Y.-A., 45:601–12
Bardin, C. W., 46:107–18
Barger, A. C., 46:291–308
Baskin, D. G., 49:335–47
Bassingthwaighte, J. B., 48:321–34
Bastian, J., 46:561–83
Beaugé, L., 45:313–24
Bell, P. D., 49:275–93
Bennett, M. V. L., 47:281–304
Bergeron, J. J. M., 47:383–404
Berglindh, T., 46:377–92
Betz, A. L., 48:241–50
Beyer, C., 49:349–64
Biagi, B. A., 45:497–517
Bisgaier, C., 45:625–36
Björklund, A. B., 48:447–59
Bliss, C., 45:651–77
Blomqvist, C. G., 45:169–89
Boron, W., 45:483–96; 48:377–88
Boulant, J. A., 48:639–54
Boveris, A., 48:703–20
Brengelmann, G. L., 45:191–212
Brenner, B., 49:655–72
Briggs, J. P., 49:251–73
Brownstein, M. J., 45:129–35
Buckalew, V. M., 46:343–58
Budzik, G. P., 46:53–65
Bukoski, R. D., 47:645–64
Burg, M., 45:533–47
Burri, P. H., 46:617–28

Burton, H. W., 49:439–51
Busa, W. B., 48:389–402
Butler, T. M., 47:629–44
Bye, P. T. P., 45:439–51

C

Cadenas, E., 48:703–20
Calder, W. A., 49:107–20
Campbell, E. J. M., 45:465–79
Campbell, G. R., 48:295–306
Campbell, J. H., 48:295–306
Carey, M., 45:651–77
Carlson, B. M., 49:439–51
Caveney, S., 47:319–36
Chan, L., 45:615–23
Chance, B., 48:703–20
Chander, A., 47:789–802
Chasis, J. A., 49:237–48
Chatterjee, B., 45:37–50
Cheng, K., 47:405–24
Chien, S., 49:177–92
Chilian, W. M., 49:477–87
Christensen, N. J., 45:139–53
Chua, B. H. L., 49:533–43
Clark, W. G., 48:613–24
Coburn, R. F., 49:573–82
Cohen, D. H., 46:187–97
Cohen, F. S., 48:163–74
Conn, P. M., 48:495–514
Connor, J. A., 47:17–28
Cooper, G., 49:501–18
Coronado, R., 46:485–95
Coslovsky, R., 48:537–50
Crapo, J. D., 48:721–31
Cross, N. L., 48:191–200
Cruz, J., 47:383–404
Currie, M. G., 46:327–41
Czech, M. P., 47:357–82

D

Dahmer, M. K., 46:67–81
D'Amore, P. A., 49:453–64
Davenport, H. W., 47:1–14
Davies, A., 46:119–30
Dean, J. B., 48:639–54
De Pont, J. J. H. H. M., 49:87–103
Deuticke, B., 49:221–35
DeVries, A. L., 45:245–60

DiPolo, R., 45:313–24
Donahoe, P. K., 46:53–65
Donowitz, M., 48:135–50
Dorsa, D. M., 49:335–47
Dratz, E. A., 49:765–91
Duman, J., 45:261–70
Dunham, B., 48:335–45
Dussault, J. H., 49:321–34
Dzau, V. J., 46:291–308

E

Edelman, G. M., 48:417–30
Edén, S., 47:483–500
Edgar, D., 45:601–12
Engle, B. T., 46:199–210
Engle, M. J., 47:803–22
Evans, R. M., 48:431–46

F

Fallat, M. E., 46:53–65
Farhi, E. R., 46:291–308
Farkas, G. A., 45:439–51
Farner, D. S., 47:65–82
Farrell, P. M., 47:803–22
Faulkner, J. A., 49:439–51
Feder, H. H., 49:349–64
Fevold, H. R., 45:19–36
Figlewicz, D. P., 49:335–47; 49:383–95
Finkelstein, A., 48:163–74
Fisher, A. B., 47:789–802
Fishman, J., 45:61–72
Flenley, D. C., 45:415–26
Forman, H. J., 48:669–80
Forte, T. M., 46:403–15
Franco, M., 49:275–93
Frawley, L. S., 45:109–27
Freeman, B., 48:693–702
Fridovich, I., 48:693–702
Friesen, H. G., 47:469–82
Froesch, E. R., 47:443–68
Frohman, L. A., 45:95–107
Fullmer, C. S., 45:375–90
Funder, J. W., 49:397–411

G

Gabella, G., 49:583–94
Gage, F. H., 48:447–59

Galbo, H., 45:139–53
Ganong, W. F., 46:17–31
Gardner, J. D., 48:103–17
Gelato, M. C., 48:569–92
Gershengorn, M. C., 48:515–26
Gibbons, G. H., 46:291–308
Gibert, A. J., 46:393–402
Giebisch, G., 45:497–517
Gil, J., 47:753–74
Glickman, R., 45:625–36
Goldman, Y. E., 49:637–54
Goldstein, G. W., 48:241–50
Good, D., 45:533–47
Gordon, C. J., 48:595–612
Gordon, E. E., 49:533–43
Gordon, J. L., 47:617–28
Gorospe, W. C., 48:495–514
Gould, J. L., 46:585–98
Greenberg, M. J., 45:271–88
Griffith, L., 45:427–37
Gruber, K. A., 46:343–58
Gustafsson, J. A., 45:51–60

H

Haddad, G. G., 46:629–43
Haest, C. W. M., 49:221–35
Hansen, J., 48:495–514
Harding, R., 46:645–59
Harris, C., 48:495–514
Hasselbach, W., 45:325–39
Havel, R. J., 48:119–34
Heath, J. E., 44:133–43; 48:595–612
Heiligenberg, W., 46:561–83
Henderson-Smart, D. J., 46:675–86
Henning, S. J., 47:231–46
Herd, A. H., 46:177–85
Hersey, S., 46:393–402
Hertzberg, E. L., 47:305–18
Heusner, A. A., 49:121–33
Hinkle, P. C., 47:503–18
Hochmuth, R. M., 49:209–19
Hodgkin, A. L., 45:1–16
Holmes, E. W., 47:691–706
Holmsen, H., 47:677–90
Holz, R. W., 48:175–89
Homsher, E., 49:673–90
Hopfer, U., 49:51–67
Horwath, K., 45:261–70
Housley, P. R., 46:67–81
Houston, D. S., 48:307–20
Howlett, T. A., 48:527–36
Hsueh, A. J. W., 45:83–94
Huckle, W. R., 48:495–514
Hughes, J. P., 47:469–82
Hurley, J. B., 49:793–812
Hutson, J. M., 46:53–65

I

Imig, T. J., 46:275–87
Inesi, G., 47:573–602

Ingram, R. H. Jr., 45:453–63
Inman, R., 49:163–75
Isaksson, O. G. P., 47:483–500
Ishihara, A., 49:163–75
Ito, S., 47:217–30
Iwamoto, G. A., 45:229–42

J

Jänne, O. A., 46:107–18
Jacobson, K., 49:163–75
Jacobus, W. E., 47:707–26
Jaffe, L. A., 48:191–200
Jamieson, D., 48:703–20
Jansson, J.-O., 47:483–500
Jennings, M. L., 47:519–34
Jennings, R. B., 47:727–50
Jensen, R. T., 48:103–17
Johnson, L. R., 47:199–216
Jones, D. P., 48:33–50
Jones, N. L., 45:427–37
Jones, P. B. C., 45:83–94

K

Kalia, M. P., 49:595–609
Kamagata, S., 46:53–65
Kane, J. P., 45:637–50
Kaplan, J. H., 47:535–44
Karsch, F. J., 49:365–82
Kaufman, M. P., 45:229–42
Kaunitz, J. D., 46:417–33
Kemnitz, J. W., 47:803–22
Khan, M. N., 47:383–404
Kick, S. A., 46:599–614
Killian, K. J., 45:465–79
King, R, J., 47:775–88
Kira, Y., 49:533–43
Koeppen, B. M., 45:497–517
Kreisberg, J. I., 48:51–71
Kuijpers, G. A. J., 49:87–103

L

Lacour, F., 49:383–95
Lakatta, E. G., 49:519–31
Landis, S., 45:567–80
LaNoue, K. F., 47:143–72
Larner, J., 47:404–24
LaTorre, R., 46:485–95
Leeman, S. E., 48:537–50
Lefkowitz, R., 44:475–84; 46:119–30
Leong, D. A., 45:109–27
Lewis, U. J., 46:33–42
Lictman, J., 45:553–65
Liebman, P. A., 49:765–91
Liedtke, C. M., 49:51–67
Lindemann, B., 46:497–515
Lipkin, M., 47:175–98
Lipton, J. M., 48:613–24
Lown, B., 46:155–76

Ludbrook, J., 45:155–68
Lundberg, J. M., 49:557–72

M

Machen, T. E., 49:19–33
Mandel, L. J., 47:85–102
Manfredi, J. P., 47:691–706
Marcus, M. L., 49:477–87
Margolius, H. S., 46:309–26
Masterton, R. B., 46:275–87
Mayo, K. E., 48:431–46
McArdle, C. A., 48:495–514
McDermott, P. J., 49:533–43
McFadden, E. R., 45:453–63
Mela-Riker, L. M., 47:645–64
Mellins, R. B., 46:629–43
Merriam, G. R., 48:569–92
Miller, C., 46:549–58
Miller, V. M., 48:307–20
Mitchell, J. H., 45:229–42
Mode, A., 45:51–60
Moolenaar, W. H., 48:363–76
Morgan, H. E., 49:533–43
Morkin, E., 49:545–54
Moulins, M., 47:29–48
Murphy, D. J., 45:289–99

N

Navar, L. G., 49:275–93
Needleman, P., 46:327–41
Neher, E., 46:455–72
Neill, J. D., 45:109–27
Nicholson, B. J., 47:263–80
Nissley, S. P., 47:425–42
Norris, S. H., 46:393–402
Norstedt, G., 45:51–60
Oetliker, H., 45:325–39
Owen, W. G., 49:743–64

P

Pappenheimer, J. R., 49:1–15
Paradiso, A. M., 49:19–33
Pardridge, W. M., 45:73–82
Parker, K. R., 49:765–91
Parsegian, V. A., 48:201–12
Passow, H., 45:359–74
Patel, Y. C., 48:551–68
Pearson, J. D., 47:617–28
Perelman, R. H., 47:803–22
Peterson, D. J., 49:533–43
Philipson, K. D., 47:561–72
Phillips, M. I., 49:413–35
Plotsky, P. M., 48:475–94
Porte, D., 49:335–47; 49:383–95
Posner, B. I., 47:383–404
Pratt, W. B., 46:67–81
Price, D. A., 45:271–88
Prosser, C. L., 48:1–6
Pryor, W. A., 48:657–68

Pugh, C. E., 45:427–37
Pugh, E. N., 49:715–41
Purves, D., 45:553–65
Putney, J. W. Jr., 48:75–88

R

Rand, R. P., 48:201–12
Randall, D. C., 46:187–97
Read, D. J. C., 46:675–86
Rechler, M. M., 47:425–42
Rees, L. H., 48:527–36
Reuss, L., 49:35–49
Reuter, H., 46:473–84
Revel, J.-P., 47:263–80
Rhode, W. S., 46:231–46
Rigatto, H., 46:661–74
Rivier, C. L., 48:475–94
Rosenfeld, G. M., 48:431–46
Roussos, Ch., 45:439–51
Rovetto, M. J., 47:605–16
Roy, A. K., 45:37–50
Rubanyi, G. M., 48:307–20
Rubel, E. W, 46:213–29
Rudnick, G., 48:403–13
Ruel, J., 49:321–34
Russo, L. A., 49:533–43
Ryan, U. S., 44:223–39;
    48:263–77

S

Sachs, M. B., 46:261–73
Sackin, H., 45:483–96
Sakmann, B., 46:455–72
Salen, G., 45:679–85
Saltin, B., 45:169–89
Sanders, M. J., 48:89–101
Sanes, J., 45:581–600
Sant'Ambrogio, G., 49:611–27
Saria, A., 49:557–72
Schafer, J. A., 47:103–26
Scharschmidt, B. F., 49:69–85
Schatzmann, H. J., 45:303–12
Schildmeyer, L. A., 49:489–99
Schmid, Ch., 47:443–68
Schneiderman, N., 46:199–210
Schnermann, J., 49:251–73
Schoolwerth, A. C., 47:143–72

Schultz, S. G., 46:435–51
Schwander, J., 47:443–68
Schwartz, G. J., 48:153–61
Schwarz, W., 45:359–74
Schwertz, D. W., 48:51–71
Seidel, C. L., 49:489–99
Selverston, A. I., 47:29–48
Shefer, S., 45:679–85
Sheppard, K., 49:397–411
Shepro, D., 48:335–45
Sheridan, J. D., 47:337–54
Sherman, M. R., 46:83–105
Shohet, S. B., 49:237–48
Siegman, M. J., 47:629–44
Silen, W., 47:217–30
Simionescu, M., 48:279–93
Simionescu, N., 48:279–93
Simmons, J. A., 46:599–614
Sipols, A., 49:383–95
Skett, P., 45:51–60
Sleight, R. G., 49:193–208
Small, D., 45:651–77
Smith, L. L., 48:681–92
Smith, M. W., 47:247–60
Smith, W. L., 48:251–62
Snyder, S. H., 48:461–71
Soll, A. H., 48:89–101
Soltoff, S. P., 48:9–31
Sparks, H. V. Jr., 48:321–34
Spray, D. C., 47:281–304;
    48:625–38
Srikant, C. B., 48:551–68
Staley, D., 48:495–514
Steenbergen, C. Jr., 47:727–50
Stephenson, R. B., 46:133–42
Stevens, B. R., 46:417–33
Stevens, J., 46:83–105
Stoddard, J. S., 49:35–49
Stone, H. L., 45:213–27
Su, C., 47:665–76
Sutton, J. R., 45:427–37

T

Taylor, A., 45:519–32
Taylor, C. R., 49:135–46
Thoenen, H., 45:601–12
Thomas, D. D., 49:691–709
Thomas, M. J., 48:669–80

Thompson, R. W., 49:453–64
Troyer, D. A., 48:51–71
Tsien, R. W., 45:341–58
Turek, F. W., 47:49–64

V

Van Dyke, R. W., 49:69–85
van Golde, L. M. G., 47:765–74
Vanhoutte, P. M., 48:307–20
Venkatachalam, M. A., 48:51–71
Vergara, C., 46:485–95
Verrier, R. L., 46:155–76
von Muralt, A., 46:1–13

W

Wade, J. B., 48:213–23
Walker, D., 46:687–703
Warren, P. M., 45:415–26
Wasserman, R. H., 45:375–90
Watson, P. A., 49:533–43
Waugh, R. E., 49:209–19
Weibel, E. R., 49:147–59
Weiss, G., 46:43–52
Weiss, T. F., 46:247–59
Welsh, M. J., 48:135–50
Wheeler, T. J., 47:503–18
Whipp, B. J., 45:393–413
Williams, J. A., 46:361–75;
    48:225–38
Williams, J. C. Jr., 47:103–26
Windhager, E., 45:519–32
Wolfe, L. S., 41:669–84
Woods, S. C., 49:335–47;
    49:383–95
Wright, E. M., 46:417–33;
    47:127–42

Y

Yancey, S. B., 47:263–80

Z

Zapf, J., 47:443–68
Zimmerberg, J., 48:163–74

CHAPTER TITLES, VOLUMES 45–49

ACID-BASE REGULATION

Intracellular pH Regulation by Vertebrate
  Muscle   C. C. Aickin   48:349–61
Effects of Growth Factors on Intracellular pH
  Regulation   W. H. Moolenaar   48:363–76
Intracellular pH Regulation in Epithelial Cells   W. F. Boron   48:377–88
Mechanisms and Consequences of
  pH-Mediated Cell Regulation   W. B. Busa   48:389–402
ATP-Driven H^+ Pumping into Intracellular
  Organelles   G. Rudnick   48:403–13

CARDIOVASCULAR PHYSIOLOGY

Sympathetic Nervous Activity During
  Exercise   N. J. Christensen and H. Galbo   45:139–53
Reflex Control of Blood Pressure During
  Exercise   J. Ludbrook   45:155–68
Cardiovascular Adaptations to Physical
  Training   C. Gunnar Blomqvist and Bengt
                                      Saltin   45:169–89
Circulatory Adjustments to Exercise and Heat
  Stress   G. L. Brengelmann   45:191–212
Control of the Coronary Circulation During
  Exercise   H. Lowell Stone   45:213–27
The Exercise Pressor Reflex: Its
  Cardiovascular Effects, Afferent
  Mechanisms, and Control Pathways   Jere H. Mitchell, Marc P. Kaufman,
                                      and Gary A. Iwamoto   45:229–42
Modification of Reflex Regulation of Blood
  Pressure by Behavior   R. B. Stephenson   46:133–42
Interactions of Stress, Salt, and Blood
  Pressure   D. E. Anderson   46:143–53
Behavioral Stress and Cardiac Arrhythmias   R. L. Verrier, B. Lown   46:155–76
Cardiovascular Response to Stress in Man   J. A. Herd   46:177–85
Classical Conditioning of Cardiovascular
  Responses   D. H. Cohen, D. C. Randall   46:187–97
Operant Conditioning and the Modulation of
  Cardiovascular Function   B. T. Engel, N. Schneiderman 46:199–210
Myocardial Nucleotide Transport   M. J. Rovetto   47:605–16
Nucleotide Metabolism by Endothelium   J. D. Pearson, J. L. Gordon   47:617–28
High-Energy Phosphate Metabolism in
  Vascular Smooth Muscle   T. M. Butler, M. J. Siegman   47:629–44
Regulation of Mitochondrial Activity in
  Cardiac Cells   L. M. Mela-Riker, R. D. Bukoski 47:645–64
Extracellular Functions of Nucleotides in
  Heart and Blood Vessels   C. Su   47:665–76
Nucleotide Metabolism of Platelets   H. Holmsen   47:677–90
Purine Salvage Pathways in Myocardium   J. P. Manfredi, E. W. Holmes   47:691-706
Respiratory Control and the Integration of
  Heart High-Energy Phosphate Metabolism
  by Mitochondrial Creatine Kinase   W. E. Jacobus   47:707–726
Nucleotide Metabolism and Cellular Damage
  in Myocardial Ischemia   R. B. Jennings, C. Steenbergen, Jr. 47:727–49
Specialized Properties and Solute Transport in
  Brain Capillaries   A. L. Betz, G. W. Goldstein   48:241–50

Prostaglandin Biosynthesis and Its
  Compartmentation in Vascular Smooth
  Muscle and Endothelial Cells W. L. Smith 48:251–62
Metabolic Activity of Pulmonary Endothelium U. S. Ryan 48:263–77
Functions of the Endothelial Cell Surface M. Simionescu, N. Simionescu 48:279–93
Endothelial Cell Influences on Vascular
  Smooth Muscle Phenotype J. H. Campbell, G. R. Campbell 48:295–306
Modulation of Vascular Smooth Muscle
  Contraction by the Endothelium P. M. Vanhoutte, G. M. Rubanyi,
 V. M. Miller, D. S. Houston 48:307–20
Indicator Dilution Estimation of Capillary
  Endothelial Transport J. B. Bassingthwaighte, H. V.
 Sparks, Jr. 48:321–34
Endothelial Cell Metabolism of Biogenic
  Amines D. Shepro, B. Dunham 48:335–45
Microcirculatory Adaptation to Skeletal
  Muscle Transplantation H. W. Burton, B. M. Carlson, J.
 A. Faulkner 49:439–51
Mechanisms of Angiogenesis P. A. D'Amore, R. W. Thompson 49:453–64
Cardiovascular Responses to Chronic Hypoxia N. Banchero 49:465–76
Coronary Vascular Adaptations to Myocardial
  Hypertrophy W. M. Chilian, M. L. Marcus 49:477–87
Vascular Smooth Muscle Adaptation to
  Increased Load C. L. Seidel, L. A. Schildmeyer 49:489–99
Cardiocyte Adaptation to Chronically Altered
  Load G. Cooper, IV 49:501–18
Cardiac Muscle Changes in Senescence E. G. Lakatta 49:519–31
Biochemical Mechanisms of Cardiac
  Hypertrophy H. E. Morgan, E. E. Gordon, Y.
 Kira, B. H. L. Chua, L. A.
 Russo, C. J. Peterson, P. J.
 McDermott, P. A. Watson 49:533–43
Chronic Adaptations in Contractile Proteins:
  Genetic Regulation E. Morkin 49:545–54

CELL AND MOLECULAR PHYSIOLOGY
  The Red Cell Calcium Pump H. J. Schatzmann 45:303–12
  The Calcium Pump and Sodium-Calcium
    Exchange in Squid Axons R. DiPolo and L. Beaugé 45:313–24
  Energetics and Electrogenicity of the
    Sarcoplasmic Reticulum Calcium Pump W. Hasselbach and H. Oetliker 45:325–39
  Calcium Channels in Excitable Cell
    Membranes R. W. Tsien 45:341–58
  Ca^{2+}-Activated K^+ Channels in Erythrocytes
    and Excitable Cells Wolfgang Schwartz and Hermann
 Passow 45:359–74
  Calcium Transport Proteins, Calcium
    Absorption and Vitamin D R. H. Wasserman and C. S.
 Fullmer 45:375–90
  Patch Clamp Techniques for Studying Ionic
    Channels in Excitable Membranes B. Sakmann, E. Neher 46:455–72
  Ion Channels in Cardiac Cell Membranes H. Reuter 46:473–84
  K^+Channels Gated by Voltage and Ions R. Latorre, R. Coronado, C.
 Vergara 46:485–95
  Fluctuation Analysis of Sodium Channels in
    Epithelia B. Lindemann 46:497–515
  Voltage-Regulated Sodium Channel Molecules W. S. Agnew 46:517–30
  Gramacidin Channels O. S. Andersen 46:531–48
  Ion Channels in Liposomes C. Miller 46:549–58
  The Glucose Transporter of Mammalian Cells T. J. Wheeler, P. C. Hinkle 47:503–18
  Kinetics and Mechanism of Anion Transport
    in Red Blood Cells M. L. Jennings 47:519–34

Ion Movements Through the Sodium Pump — J. H. Kaplan — 47:535–44

Kinetic Properties of the Plasma Membrane Na$^+$-H$^+$ Exchanger — P. S. Aronson — 47:545–60

Sodium-Calcium Exchange in Plasma Membrane Vesicles — K. D. Philipson — 47:561–72

Mechanism of Calcium Transport — G. Inesi — 47:573–602

Regulation of Transepithelial H$^+$ Transport by Exocytosis and Endocytosis — G. J. Schwartz, Q. Al-Awqati — 48:153–61

Osmotic Swelling of Vesicles — A. Finkelstein, J. Zimmerberg, F. S. Cohen — 48:163–74

The Role of Osmotic Forces in Exocytosis from Adrenal Chromaffin Cells — R. W. Holz — 48:175–89

Electrical Regulation of Sperm-Egg Fusion — L. A. Jaffe, N. L. Cross — 48:191–200

Mimicry and Mechanism in Phospholipid Models of Membrane Fusion — R. P. Rand, V. A. Parsegian — 48:201–12

Role of Membrane Fusion in Hormonal Regulation of Epithelial Transport — J. B. Wade — 48:213–23

Regulation of Membrane Fusion in Secretory Exocytosis — R. C. De Lisle, J. A. Williams — 48:225–38

Lateral Diffusion of Proteins in Membranes — K. Jacobson, A. Ishihara, R. Inman — 49:163-75

Red Cell Deformability and Its Relevance to Blood Flow — S. Chien — 49:177–92

Intracellular Lipid Transport in Eukaryotes — R. G. Sleight — 49:193–208

Erythrocyte Membrane Elasticity and Viscosity — R. M. Hochmuth, R. E. Waugh — 49:209–19

Lipid Modulation of Transport Proteins in Vertebrate Cell Membranes — B. Deuticke, C. W. M. Haest — 49:221–35

Red Cell Biochemical Anatomy and Membrane Properties — J. A. Chasis, S. B. Shohet — 49:237–48

CELL BIOLOGICAL APPROACHES TO BRAIN FUNCTION

Cell Adhesion Molecules in Neural Histogenesis — G. M. Edelman — 48:417–30

Genes Encoding Mammalian Neuroendocrine Peptides: Strategies — K. E. Mayo, R. M. Evans, G. M. Rosenfeld — 48:431–46

Neural Grafting in the Aged Rat Brain — F. H. Gage, A. Björklund — 48:447–59

Neuronal Receptors — S. H. Snyder — 48:461–71

CNS

Specific Connections Between Nerve Cells — D. Purves and J. W. Lichtman — 45:553–65

Neuronal Growth Cones — S. C. Landis — 45:567–80

Roles of Extracellular Matrix in Neural Development — Joshua R. Sanes — 45:581–600

New Neurotrophic Factors — Y.-A. Barde, D. Edgar and H. Thoenen — 45:601–12

COMPARATIVE PHYSIOLOGY

Antifreeze Peptides and Glycopeptides in Cold-Water Fishes — A. L. DeVries — 45:245–60

The Role of Hemolymph Proteins in the Cold Tolerance of Insects — J. Duman and K. Horwath — 45:261–70

Invertebrate Neuropeptides: Native and Naturalized — M. J. Greenberg and D. A. Price — 45:271–88

Freezing Resistance in Intertidal Invertebrates — D. J. Murphy — 45:289–99

The Electric Sense of Weakly Electric Fish — W. Heiligenberg, J. Bastian — 46:561–83

Magnetic Field Sensitivity in Animals — J. L. Gould — 46:585–98

Physiological Mechanisms for Spatial Filtering and Image Enhancement in the Sonar of Bats — J. A. Simmons, S. A. Kick — 46:599–614

Neural Pacemakers and Rhythmicity — J. A. Connor — 47:17–28

Oscillatory Neural Networks — A. I. Selverston, M. Moulins — 47:29–48

Circadian Neural Rhythms in Mammals | F. W. Turek | 47:49–64
Annual Rhythms | D. S. Farner | 47:65–82
Integration and Central Processing in
  Temperature Regulation | C. J. Gordon, J. E. Heath | 48:595–612
Neurotransmitters in Temperature Control | J. M. Lipton, W. G. Clark | 48:613–24
Cutaneous Temperature Receptors | D. C. Spray | 48:625–38
Temperature Receptors in the Central Nervous
  System | J. A. Boulant, J. B. Dean | 48:639–54
Scaling Energetics of Homeothermic
  Vertebrates: An Operational Allometry | W. A. Calder III | 49:107–20
What Does the Power Function Reveal About
  Structure and Function in Animals of
  Different Size? | A. A. Heusner | 49:121–33
Structural and Functional Limits to Oxidative
  Metabolism: Insights from Scaling | C. R. Taylor | 49:135–46
Scaling of Structural and Functional Variables
  in the Respiratory System | E. R. Weibel | 49:147–59

ENDOCRINOLOGY
Regulation of the Adrenal and Gonadal
  Microsomal Mixed Function Oxygenases of
  Steroid Hormone Biosynthesis | H. R. Fevold | 45:19–36
Sexual Dimorphism in the Liver | A. K. Roy and B. Chatterjee | 45:37–50
Sex Steroid Induced Changes in Hepatic
  Enzymes | J.-A. Gustafsson, A. Mode, G.
  Norstedt, and P. Skett | 45:51–60
Aromatic Hydroxylation of Estrogens | Jack Fishman | 45:61–72
Neuropeptides and the Blood-Brain Barrier | William M. Pardridge | 45:73–82
Gonadotropin Releasing Hormone:
  Extrapituitary Actions and Paracrine
  Control Mechanisms | Aaron J. W. Hsueh and Phillip B.
  C. Jones | 45:83–94
CNS Peptides and Glucoregulation | Lawrence A. Frohman | 45:95–107
Neuroendocrine Control of Prolactin Secretion | Denis A. Leong, L. Stephen
  Frawley, and Jimmy D. Neill | 45:109–27
Biosynthesis of Vasopressin and Oxytocin | Michael J. Brownstein | 45:129–35
The Brain Renin-Angiotensin System | W. F. Ganong | 46:17–31
Variants of Growth Hormone and Prolactin
  and Their Posttranslational Modifications | U. J. Lewis | 46:33–42
Relaxin | G. Weiss | 46:43–52
Mechanism of Action of Mullerian Inhibiting
  Substance | P. K. Donahoe, J. M. Hutson, M.
  E. Fallat, S. Kamagata, G. P.
  Budzik | 46:53–65
Effects of Molybdate and Endogenous
  Inhibitors on Steroid-Receptor Inactivation,
  Transformation, and Translocation | M. K. Dahmer, P. R. Housley, W.
  B. Pratt | 46:67–81
Structure of Mammalian Steroid Receptors:
  Evolving Concepts and Methodological
  Developments | M. R. Sherman, J. Stevens | 46:83–105
Androgen and Antiandrogen Receptor
  Binding | O. A. Jänne, C. W. Bardin | 46:107–18
Regulation of Beta-Adrenergic Receptors by
  Steroid Hormones | A. O. Davies, R. J. Lefkowitz | 46:119–30
The Nature and Regulation of the Insulin
  Receptor: Structure and Function | M. P. Czech | 47:357–82
Uptake of Insulin and Other Ligands into
  Receptor-Rich Endocytic Components of
  Target Cells: The Endosomal Apparatus | J. J. M. Bergeron, J. Cruz, M. N.
  Khan, B. I. Posner | 47:383–404
Intracellular Mediators of Insulin Action | K. Cheng, J. Larner | 47:405–24

The Nature and Regulation of the Receptors
  for Insulin-Like Growth Factors | M. M. Rechler, S. P. Nissley | 47:425–42
Actions of Insulin-Like Growth Factors | E. R. Froesch, Chr. Schmid, J.
  | Schwander, J. Zapf | 47:443–68
The Nature and Regulation of the Receptors
  for Pituitary Growth Hormone | J. P. Hughes, H. G. Friesen | 47:469–82
Mode of Action of Pituitary Growth Hormone
  on Target Cells | O. G. P. Isaksson, S. Edén, J.-O.
  | Jansson | 47:483–500

Mediation by Corticotropin Releasing Factor
  (CRF) of Adenohypophysial Hormone
  Secretion | C. L. Rivier, P. M. Plotsky | 48:475–94
Mechanism of Action of Gonadotropin
  Releasing Hormone | P. M. Conn, D. Staley, C. Harris,
  | W. V. Andrews, W. C. Gorospe,
  | C. A. McArdle, W. R. Huckle,
  | J. Hansen | 48:495–514

Mechanism of Thyrotropin Releasing
  Hormone Stimulation of Pituitary Hormone
  Secretion | M. C. Gershengorn | 48:515–26
Endogenous Opioid Peptides and
  Hypothalamo-Pituitary Function | T. A. Howlett, L. H. Rees | 48:527–36
Substance P and Neurotensin | N. Aronin, R. Coslovsky, S. E.
  | Leeman | 48:537–50

Somatostatin Mediation of Adenohypophysial
  Secretion | Y. C. Patel, C. B. Srikant | 48:551–68
Growth Hormone Releasing Hormone | M. C. Gelato, G. R. Merriam | 48:569–92
Thyroid Hormones and Brain Development | J. H. Dussault, J. Ruel | 49:321–34
Insulin in the Brain | D. G. Baskin, D. P. Figlewicz, S.
  | C. Woods, D. Porte, Jr., D. M.
  | Dorsa | 49:335–47

Sex Steroids and Afferent Input: Their Roles
  in Brain Sexual Differentiation | C. Beyer, H. H. Feder | 49:349–64
Central Actions of Ovarian Steroids in the
  Feedback Regulation of Pulsatile Secretion
  of Luteinizing Hormone | F. J. Karsch | 49:365–82
Gastroenteropancreatic Peptides and the
  Central Nervous System | D. P. Figlewicz, F. Lacour, A.
  | Sipols, D. Porte, Jr., S. C.
  | Woods | 49:383–95
Adrenocortical Steriods and the Brain | J. W. Funder, K. Sheppard | 49:397–411
Functions of Angiotensin in the Central
  Nervous System | M. I. Phillips | 49:413–38

GAP JUNCTIONS
  Chemistry of Gap Junctions | J.-P. Revel, B. J. Nicholson, S. B.
  | Yancey | 47:263–80
  Physiology and Pharmacology of Gap
    Junctions | D. C. Spray, M. V. L. Bennett | 47:281–304
  Antibody Probes in the Study of Gap
    Junctional Communication | E. L. Hertzberg | 47:305–18
  The Role of Gap Junctions in Development | S. Caveney | 47:319–36
  Physiological Roles of Permeable
    Junctions:Some Possibilities | J. D. Sheridan, M. M. Atkinson | 47:337-54

GASTROINTESTINAL PHYSIOLOGY
  Hormonal Control of Apolipoprotein Synthesis | L. Chan | 45:615–23
  Intestinal Synthesis, Secretion, and Transport
    of Lipoproteins | C. Bisgaier and R. M. Glickman | 45:625–36
  Apolipoprotein B: Structural and Metabolic
    Heterogeneity | J. P. Kane | 45:637–50
  Lipid Digestion and Absorption | M. C. Carey, D. M. Small and C.
  | M. Bliss | 45:651–77

Bile Acid Synthesis | G. Salen and S. Shefer | 45:679–85
Regulatory Mechanisms in Pancreas and
 Salivary Acini | J. A. Williams | 46:361–75
The Mammalian Gastric Parietal Cell in Vitro | T. Berglindh | 46:377–92
Cellular Control of Pepsinogen Secretion | S. J. Hersey, S. H. Norris, A. J.
 | Gibert | 46:393–402
Primary Hepatocytes in Monolayer Culture: A
 Model for Studies on Lipoprotein
 Metabolism | T. M. Forte | 46:403–15
Intestinal Transport of Amino Acids and
 Sugars: Advances Using Membrane
 Vesicles | B. R. Stevens, J. D. Kaunitz, E.
 | M. Wright | 46:417–33
A Cellular Model for Active Sodium
 Absorption by Mammalian Colon | S. G. Schultz | 46:435–51
Growth and Development of Gastrointestinal
 Cells | M. Lipkin | 47:175–98
Functional Development of the Stomach | L. R. Johnson | 47:199–216
Mechanisms for Rapid Re-Epithelialization of
 the Gastric Mucosal Surface | W. Silen, S. Ito | 47:217–30
Ontogeny of Enzymes in the Small Intestine | S. J. Henning | 47:231–46
Expression of Digestive and Absorptive
 Function in Differentiating Enterocytes | M. W. Smith | 47:247–60
Identification of Cellular Activation
 Mechanisms Associated with Salivary
 Secretion | J. W. Putney, Jr. | 48:75–88
Characterization of Receptors Regulating
 Secretory Function in the Fundic Mucosa | M. J. Sanders, A. H. Soll | 48:89–101
Receptors and Cell Activation Associated with
 Pancreatic Enzyme Secretion | J. D. Gardner, R. T. Jensen | 48:103–117
Functional Activities of Hepatic Lipoprotein
 Receptors | R. J. Havel | 48:119–34
Ca^{2+} and Cyclic AMP in Regulation of
 Intestinal Na, K, and Cl Transport | M. Donowitz, M. J. Welsh | 48:135–50
Regulation of Intracellular pH in the Stomach | T. E. Machen, A. M. Paradiso | 49:19–33
Role of H^+ and HCO_3^- in Salt Transport in
 Gallbladder Epithelium | L. Reuss, J. S. Stoddard | 49:35–49
Proton and Bicarbonate Transport Mechanisms
 in the Intestine | U. Hopfer, C. M. Liedtke | 49:51–67
Proton Transport by Hepatocyte Organelles
 and Isolated Membrane Vesicles | B. F. Scharschmidt, R. W. Van
 | Dyke | 49:69–85
Role of Proton and Bicarbonate Transport in
 Pancreatic Cell Function | G. A. J. Kuijpers, J. J. H. H. M.
 | De Pont | 49:87–103

HEARING
Ontogeny of Auditory System Function | E. W Rubel | 46:213–29
Cochlear Mechanics | W. S. Rhode | 46:231–46
Relation of Receptor Potentials of Cochlear
 Hair Cells to Spike Discharges of Cochlear
 Neurons | T. F. Weiss | 46:247–59
Neural Coding of Complex Sounds: Speech | M. B. Sachs | 46:261–73
Neural Mechanisms for Sound Localization | R. B. Masterton, T. J. Imig | 46:275–87

MOLECULAR MECHANISM OF MUSCLE CONTRACTION
Kinetics of the Actomyosin ATPase in
 Muscle Fibers | Y. E. Goldman | 49:637–54
Mechanical and Structural Approaches to
 Correlation of Cross-Bridge Action in
 Muscle with Actomyosin ATPase in
 Solution | B. Brenner | 49:655–72

Muscle Enthalpy Production and Its
Relationship to Actomyosin ATPase   E. Homsher   49:673–90
Spectroscopic Probes of Muscle Cross-Bridge
Rotation   D. D. Thomas   49:691–709

PHOTOTRANSDUCTION IN VERTEBRATES
The Nature and Identity of the Internal
Excitational Transmitter of Vertebrate
Phototransduction   E. N. Pugh, Jr.   49:715–41
Ionic Conductances in Rod Photoreceptors   W. G. Owen   49:743–64
The Molecular Mechanism of Visual
Excitation and Its Relation to the Structure
and Composition of the Rod Outer Segment   P. A. Liebman, K. R. Parker, E.
                                           A. Dratz   49:765–91
Molecular Properties of the cGMP Cascade of
Vertebrate Photoreceptors   J. B. Hurley   49:793–812

PREFATORY CHAPTERS
Beginning: Some Reminiscences of My Early
Life (1914–1947)   A. L. Hodgkin   45:1–17
A Life with Several Facets   A. von Muralt   46:1–13
The Apology of a Second-Class Man   H. W. Davenport   47:1–14
The Making of a Comparative Physiologist   C. L. Prosser   48:1–6
A Silver Spoon   J. R. Pappenheimer   49:1–15

RENAL AND ELECTROLYTE PHYSIOLOGY
Measurement of Intracellular Ionic
Composition and Activities in Renal
Tubules   W. F. Boron and H. Sackin   45:483–96
Electrophysiology of Mammalian Renal
Tubules: Inferences from Intracellular
Microelectrode Studies   B. M. Koeppen, B. A. Biagi, and
                                           G. Giebisch   45:497–517
Regulatory Role of Intracellular Calcium Ions
in Epithelial Na Transport   E. E. Windhager and A. Taylor   45:519–32
Sodium Chloride Coupled Transport in
Mammalian Nephrons   M. Burg and D. Good   45:533–47
Interaction of Signals Influencing Renin
Release   G. H. Gibbons, V. J. Dzau, E. R.
                                           Farhi, A. C. Barger   46:291–308
The Kallikrein-Kinin System and the Kidney H. S. Margolius   46:309–26
Renal Arachidonic Acid Metabolism   M. G. Currie, P. Needleman   46:327–41
Natriuretic Hormone   V. M. Buckalew, Jr., K. A. Gruber 46:343–58
Metabolic Substrates, Cellular Energy
Production, and the Regulation of Proximal
Tubular Transport   L. J. Mandel   47:85–102
Transport of Metabolic Substrates by the
Proximal Nephron   J. A. Schafer, J. C. Williams, Jr. 47:103–26
Transport of Carboxylic Acids by Renal
Membrane Vesicles   E. M. Wright   47:127–42
Transport of Metabolic Substrates in Renal
Mitochondria   A. C. Schoolwerth, K. F. LaNoue 47:143–72
ATP and the Regulation of Renal Cell
Function   S. P. Soltoff   48:9–31
Renal Metabolism During Normoxia,
Hypoxia, and Ischemic Injury   D. P. Jones   48:33–50
Inositol Phospholipid Metabolism in the
Kidney   D. A. Troyer, D. W. Schwertz, J.
                                           I. Kreisberg, M. A.
                                           Venkatachalam   48:51–71
The Tubuloglomerular Feedback Mechanism:
Functional and Biochemical Aspects   J. P. Briggs, J. Schnermann   49:251–73

Calcium as a Mediator of Tubuloglomerular
Feedback | P. D. Bell, M. Franco, L. G. Navar | 49:275–93
Altered Reactivity of Tubuloglomerular
Feedback | W. J. Arendshorst | 49:295–317

RESPIRATORY PHYSIOLOGY
Ventilatory Control During Exercise in
Humans | B. J. Whipp | 45:393–413
Ventilatory Responses to O_2 and CO_2 During
Exercise | D. C. Flenley and P. M. Warren | 45:415–26
Exercise at Altitude | J. R. Sutton, L. Griffith, C. E.
Pugh, N. L. Jones | 45:427–37
Respiratory Factors Limiting Exercise | P. T. P. Bye, G. A. Farkas, C.
Roussos | 45:439–51
Exercise-Induced Airway Obstruction | E. R. McFadden, Jr., R. H.
Ingram, Jr. | 45:453–63
Dyspnea and Exercise | K. J. Killian, E. J. M. Campbell | 45:465–79
Fetal and Postnatal Development of the Lung | P. H. Burri | 46:617–28
Hypoxia and Respiratory Control in Early
Life | G. G. Haddad, R. B. Mellins | 46:629–43
Function of the Larynx in the Fetus and
Newborn | R. Harding | 46:645–59
Control of Ventilation in the Newborn | H. Rigatto | 46:661–74
Regulation of Breathing in the Newborn
During Different Behavioral States | D. J. C. Read, D. J.
Henderson-Smart | 46:675–86
Peripheral and Central Chemoreceptors in the
Fetus and Newborn | D. Walker | 46:687–703
Histological Preservation and Ultrastructure of
Alveolar Surfactant | J. Gil | 47:753–64
Synthesis of Surfactant Lipids in the Adult
Lung | L. M. G. van Golde | 47:765–74
Composition and Metabolism of the
Apolipoproteins of Pulmonary Surfactant | R. J. King | 47:775–88
Intracellular Processing of Surfactant Lipids in
the Lung | A. B. Fisher, A. Chander | 47:789–802
Developmental Aspects of Lung Lipids | R. H. Perelman, P. M. Farrell, M.
J. Engle, J. W. Kemnitz | 47:803–22
Oxy-Radicals and Related Species | W. A. Pryor | 48:657–68
Oxidant Production and Bactericidal Activity
in Phagocytes | H. J. Forman, M. J. Thomas | 48:669–80
The Response of the Lung to Foreign
Compounds That Produce Free Radicals | L. L. Smith | 48:681–92
Antioxidant Defenses in the Lung | I. Fridovich, B. Freeman | 48:693–702
The Relation of Free Radical Production to
Hyperoxia | D. Jamieson, B. Chance, E.
Cadenas, A. Boveris | 48:703–20
Morphologic Changes in Pulmonary Oxygen
Toxicity | J. D. Crapo | 48:721–31
Polypeptide-Containing Neurons in Airway
Smooth Muscle | J. M. Lundberg, A. Saria | 49:557–72
Peripheral Airway Ganglia | R. F. Coburn | 49:573–82
Innervation of Airway Smooth Muscle: Fine
Structure | G. Gabella | 49:583–94
Organization of Central Control of Airways | M. P. Kalia | 49:595–609
Nervous Receptors of the Tracheobronchial
Tree | G. Sant'Ambrogio | 49:611–27

Annual Reviews Inc.

A NONPROFIT SCIENTIFIC PUBLISHER

4139 El Camino Way
P.O. Box 10139
Palo Alto, CA 94303-0897 • USA

Annual Reviews Inc. publications may be ordered directly from our office by mail or use our Toll Free Telephone line (for orders paid by credit card or purchase order, and customer service calls only); through booksellers and subscription agents, worldwide; and through participating professional societies. Prices subject to change without notice.   ARI Federal I.D. #94-1156476

- **Individuals:** Prepayment required on new accounts by check or money order (in U.S. dollars, check drawn on U.S. bank) or charge to credit card — American Express, VISA, MasterCard.
- **Institutional buyers:** Please include purchase order number.
- **Students:** $10.00 discount from retail price, per volume. Prepayment required. Proof of student status must be provided (photocopy of student I.D. or signature of department secretary is acceptable). Students must send orders direct to Annual Reviews. Orders received through bookstores and institutions requesting student rates will be returned.
- **Professional Society Members:** Members of professional societies that have a contractual arrangement with Annual Reviews may order books through their society at a reduced rate. Check with your society for information.
- **Toll Free Telephone orders:** Call 1-800-523-8635 (except from California) for orders paid by credit card or purchase order and customer service calls only. California customers and all other business calls use 415-493-4400 (not toll free). Hours: 8:00 AM to 4:00 PM, Monday-Friday, Pacific Time.

Regular orders: Please list the volumes you wish to order by volume number.
Standing orders: New volume in the series will be sent to you automatically each year upon publication. Cancellation may be made at any time. Please indicate volume number to begin standing order.
Prepublication orders: Volumes not yet published will be shipped in month and year indicated.
California orders: Add applicable sales tax.
Postage paid (4th class bookrate/surface mail) **by Annual Reviews Inc.** Airmail postage or UPS, extra.

ANNUAL REVIEWS SERIES		Prices Postpaid per volume USA/elsewhere	Regular Order Please send:	Standing Order Begin with:
			Vol. number	Vol. number
Annual Review of ANTHROPOLOGY				
Vols. 1-14	(1972-1985)	$27.00/$30.00		
Vol. 15	(1986)	$31.00/$34.00		
Vol. 16	(avail. Oct. 1987)	$31.00/$34.00	Vol(s). _____	Vol. _____
Annual Review of ASTRONOMY AND ASTROPHYSICS				
Vols. 1-2, 4-20	(1963-1964; 1966-1982)	$27.00/$30.00		
Vols. 21-24	(1983-1986)	$44.00/$47.00		
Vol. 25	(avail. Sept. 1987)	$44.00/$47.00	Vol(s). _____	Vol. _____
Annual Review of BIOCHEMISTRY				
Vols. 30-34, 36-54	(1961-1965; 1967-1985)	$29.00/$32.00		
Vol. 55	(1986)	$33.00/$36.00		
Vol. 56	(avail. July 1987)	$33.00/$36.00	Vol(s). _____	Vol. _____
Annual Review of BIOPHYSICS AND BIOPHYSICAL CHEMISTRY				
Vols. 1-11	(1972-1982)	$27.00/$30.00		
Vols. 12-15	(1983-1986)	$47.00/$50.00		
Vol. 16	(avail. June 1987)	$47.00/$50.00	Vol(s). _____	Vol. _____
Annual Review of CELL BIOLOGY				
Vol. 1	(1985)	$27.00/$30.00		
Vol. 2	(1986)	$31.00/$34.00		
Vol. 3	(avail. Nov. 1987)	$31.00/$34.00	Vol(s). _____	Vol. _____

ANNUAL REVIEWS SERIES		Prices Postpaid per volume USA/elsewhere	Regular Order Please send:	Standing Order Begin with:
			Vol. number	Vol. number
Annual Review of COMPUTER SCIENCE				
Vol. 1	(1986)	$39.00/$42.00		
Vol. 2	(avail. Nov. 1987)	$39.00/$42.00	Vol(s). _____	Vol. _____
Annual Review of EARTH AND PLANETARY SCIENCES				
Vols. 1-10	(1973-1982)	$27.00/$30.00		
Vols. 11-14	(1983-1986)	$44.00/$47.00		
Vol. 15	(avail. May 1987)	$44.00/$47.00	Vol(s). _____	Vol. _____
Annual Review of ECOLOGY AND SYSTEMATICS				
Vols. 1-16	(1970-1985)	$27.00/$30.00		
Vol. 17	(1986)	$31.00/$34.00		
Vol. 18	(avail. Nov. 1987)	$31.00/$34.00	Vol(s). _____	Vol. _____
Annual Review of ENERGY				
Vols. 1-7	(1976-1982)	$27.00/$30.00		
Vols. 8-11	(1983-1986)	$56.00/$59.00		
Vol. 12	(avail. Oct. 1987)	$56.00/$59.00	Vol(s). _____	Vol. _____
Annual Review of ENTOMOLOGY				
Vols. 10-16, 18-30	(1965-1971, 1973-1985)	$27.00/$30.00		
Vol. 31	(1986)	$31.00/$34.00		
Vol. 32	(avail. Jan. 1987)	$31.00/$34.00	Vol(s). _____	Vol. _____
Annual Review of FLUID MECHANICS				
Vols. 1-4, 7-17	(1969-1972, 1975-1985)	$28.00/$31.00		
Vol. 18	(1986)	$32.00/$35.00		
Vol. 19	(avail. Jan. 1987)	$32.00/$35.00	Vol(s). _____	Vol. _____
Annual Review of GENETICS				
Vols. 1-19	(1967-1985)	$27.00/$30.00		
Vol. 20	(1986)	$31.00/$34.00		
Vol. 21	(avail. Dec. 1987)	$31.00/$34.00	Vol(s). _____	Vol. _____
Annual Review of IMMUNOLOGY				
Vols. 1-3	(1983-1985)	$27.00/$30.00		
Vol. 4	(1986)	$31.00/$34.00		
Vol. 5	(avail. April 1987)	$31.00/$34.00	Vol(s). _____	Vol. _____
Annual Review of MATERIALS SCIENCE				
Vols. 1, 3-12	(1971, 1973-1982)	$27.00/$30.00		
Vols. 13-16	(1983-1986)	$64.00/$67.00		
Vol. 17	(avail. August 1987)	$64.00/$67.00	Vol(s). _____	Vol. _____
Annual Review of MEDICINE				
Vols. 1-3, 6, 8-9 11-15, 17-36	(1950-1952, 1955, 1957-1958) (1960-1964, 1966-1985)	$27.00/$30.00		
Vol. 37	(1986)	$31.00/$34.00		
Vol. 38	(avail. April 1987)	$31.00/$34.00	Vol(s). _____	Vol. _____
Annual Review of MICROBIOLOGY				
Vols. 18-39	(1964-1985)	$27.00/$30.00		
Vol. 40	(1986)	$31.00/$34.00		
Vol. 41	(avail. Oct. 1987)	$31.00/$34.00	Vol(s). _____	Vol. _____